THEORETICAL
NUCLEAR PHYSICS

THEORETICAL
NUCLEAR PHYSICS

JOHN M. BLATT

ASSOCIATE PROFESSOR OF PHYSICS
UNIVERSITY OF ILLINOIS

VICTOR F. WEISSKOPF

PROFESSOR OF PHYSICS
MASSACHUSETTS INSTITUTE
OF TECHNOLOGY

JOHN WILEY & SONS, NEW YORK
LONDON

Library of Congress Catalog Card Number: 52–6665

Printed in the United States of America

PREFACE

The last twenty years have witnessed an enormous development of nuclear physics. A large number of data have accumulated and many experimental facts are known. As the experimental techniques have achieved greater and greater perfection, the theoretical analysis and interpretation of these data have become correspondingly more accurate and detailed. The development of nuclear physics has depended on the development of physics as a whole. While there were interesting speculations about nuclear constitution as early as 1922, it was impossible to make any quantitative theory of even the simplest nucleus until the discovery of quantum mechanics on the one hand, and the development of experimental methods sufficiently sensitive to detect the presence of a neutral particle (the neutron) on the other hand. The further development of our understanding of the nucleus has depended, and still depends, on the development of ever more powerful experimental techniques for measuring nuclear properties and more powerful theoretical techniques for correlating these properties. Practically every "simple," "reasonable," and "plausible" assumption made in theoretical nuclear physics has turned out to be in need of refinement; and the numerous attempts to derive nuclear forces and the properties of nuclei from a more "fundamental" approach than the analysis of the data have proved unsuccessful so far. Nuclear physics is by no means a finished edifice. It is very much to be hoped that simple fundamental laws can be discovered which will account for all the known properties of nuclei, and will allow us to predict new, unknown properties successfully. At present we must restrict ourselves to the investigation and correlation of all known nuclear properties on a semi-empirical basis.

This book is devoted in its entirety to this task. Its subject matter is *theoretical nuclear physics*, by which we mean the theoretical concepts, methods, and considerations which have been devised in order to interpret the experimental material and to advance our ability to predict and control nuclear phenomena.

Obviously, this book does not pretend to cover all aspects of theoretical nuclear physics. We are forced to omit many details and special developments. The omissions are due partly to the lack of space and partly to the authors' lack of special knowledge. We hope that the study of this book will make it somewhat easier for the reader to understand the original literature containing the material which is not covered in this book.

We have restricted ourselves to phenomena involving energies below about 50 Mev, a region which is sometimes called classical nuclear physics. Thus we exclude the nuclear phenomena in cosmic rays as well as the phenomena associated with the production and absorption of mesons. The only exception to this rule is Chapter IV, which deals with nucleon-nucleon scattering experiments at energies up to 350 Mev and their interpretation in terms of nuclear forces.

In general, we have omitted theoretical considerations which are not concerned directly with the properties of the nucleus itself. Thus we exclude, for example, the theory of the stopping of charged particles in matter, the theory of the diffraction and slowing down of neutrons, the theory underlying molecular beam and magnetic resonance experiments, and the theory of atomic hyperfine structure. Although all these subjects are important from an experimental point of view, their inclusion would have lengthened the book too much. We have also excluded subjects generally referred to as nuclear engineering, such as the theory of nuclear reactors. In so far as the relevant material has been declassified, adequate textbooks are already available. Unfortunately, the theory of nuclear fission (which properly belongs in this book) could be treated only in a very cursory manner, since too many relevant facts are still unavailable.

We have completely omitted the discussion of the theories of nuclear forces based on the various meson field theories. The numerous attempts to predict nuclear forces on the basis of meson fields have led to brilliant insights and predictions regarding mesons, but they have failed so far to reproduce quantitatively the observed forces between nuclear particles. This subject seemed to us not yet sufficiently developed to warrant a systematic treatment in this book.

It was our constant aim throughout the book to keep it on a level which is understandable to the experimental physicist who works in the field of nuclear physics or to a graduate student who knows the essential concepts and problems of nuclear physics. A one-term course in quantum mechanics, based on a book such as Schiff (49) should suffice as a prerequisite. Some parts of the book may be hard reading for students unaccustomed to theoretical work. Sections which are difficult and can be omitted without loss of understanding of subsequent material are indicated by the symbol ▶.

We have concentrated our efforts on a better understanding and a critical analysis of the different subjects. This has led in some cases to new developments which are not yet published elsewhere. Since we are dealing with a growing and changing part of science, we must expect that many ideas which today are considered valid will turn out to be incorrect before long. Hence, many assumptions and statements found in this book should be regarded as preliminary. It contains a great deal of information of which we are far from sure, and which is included only because nothing better is available at present. A characteristic example is the information about nuclear level densities given in Chapter VIII. In some instances recent developments have changed the emphasis from one way of description to another more successful one. For example, nuclear spectroscopy today is being based to an increasing extent upon the shell theory of nuclear structure, as indicated in Chapter XIV. At the time this book was conceived the concepts of Wigner's supermultiplet theory were the main tools for the understanding of nuclear spectra; they are the basis of the discussions in Chapter VI.

We make no pretense of having a complete list of references. We have tried to include the basic theoretical papers in each field, such other theoretical papers as we happened to come across, and experimental papers only in so far as they illustrate some points made in the discussion or substantiate values of nuclear constants used in the text. We have not made a systematic search of the whole literature. This applies especially to papers which appeared in journals other than *The Physical Review*. If a relevant reference is missing, it is very probable that we did not know of its existence. The manuscript was revised for the last time in the spring of 1951; it contains only occasional references to later work.

We are quite aware of the possibility that this book contains errors, not all of which may be trivial or typographical in nature. We have tried to keep a reasonable balance between the effort to eliminate errors and the effort to understand the subject matter and to clarify its presentation.

At the end of every chapter is a list of symbols with a short explanation of the meaning of each symbol, and the number of the equation in which the symbol is introduced and defined. If the symbol in question is defined in the body of the text, the section number is given in the symbol list. We have made an effort to have these lists of symbols comprehensive, but some minor symbols, which occur only a few times in the chapter, have been omitted.

It would be impossible to acknowledge in detail the enormous amount of generous help and constructive criticism which we have received from friends and colleagues. We would like, however, to express our special gratitude to H. Bethe, M. Deutsch, H. Feshbach, and E. Wigner for their extensive advice.   We are greatly indebted to Miss Inge Reethof for her constant help and patience in the typing and retyping of the manuscript.

J. M. BLATT

V. F. WEISSKOPF

June, 1952

CONTENTS

Contents

Contents

Contents

CHAPTER I

General Properties of the Nucléus

1. INTRODUCTION

In spite of the tremendous amount of information now available about atomic nuclei, nuclear physics is a very young science. The existence of a nucleus in each atom was discovered by Rutherford (11)[1] in the year 1911. Some of the fundamental properties of nuclei were found at that time:

(1) They have radii very small compared to atomic dimensions; Rutherford showed that the nucleus acts like a point charge down to distances of the order of 10^{-11} cm, at least.

(2) They are charged. The charge on each nucleus turned out to be an integral multiple of the charge on the electron, i.e., nuclear charge $= Ze$, where $Z = 1, 2, 3, \cdots$ is called the atomic number.

(3) Nuclei are very heavy compared to electrons. Most of the mass in an atom resides in the nucleus.

Since atoms are neutral entities, it was necessary to assume that the charge on the nucleus is exactly neutralized by the charges of the surrounding electrons. The charge Z of the nucleus then determines the number of the electrons in the atom and is the only property of the nucleus of importance for atomic physics, and consequently for most of the properties of matter as we know it.

The next important quantity of the nucleus is its mass. J. J. Thomson (13) discovered that the mass of the nucleus is not determined by its charge. Rather, there exist nuclei of the same charge Z but of different masses. Such nuclei are called isotopes. The mass of each isotope is nearly (but not precisely) equal to an integral number of proton masses.[2] The nearest integer is called the "mass number" and is denoted by A.

---

[1] References are listed according to the name of the first author and the year of publication, i.e., a paper by Smith and Jones, published in 1939, is referred to as Smith (39). All references are collected at the end of the book.

[2] The unit of mass in mass-spectroscopic work is not the mass of the proton, but $\frac{1}{16}$ of the mass of the oxygen isotope with mass number $A = 16$.

The simplest hypothesis regarding nuclear constitution would be that all nuclei are made up of protons. This is contradicted by the fact that the mass number A is at least twice the atomic number Z in practically all nuclei. Thus other particles are needed in the nucleus besides protons.

The next hypothesis, which was current until 1932, postulated that nuclei are made up of protons and electrons. The nucleus N^{14} ($Z=7$, $A=14$), for example, was thought to consist of 14 protons (to give the correct mass) and 7 electrons (to give the correct charge). Ehrenfest and Oppenheimer (31) pointed out that this hypothesis leads to a serious contradiction with known properties of N^{14} (see Section 8).

The experimental discovery of the neutron (Curie-Joliot 32, Chadwick 32) led Heisenberg (32) to suggest the hypothesis that nuclei are made up of neutrons and protons and to explore the consequences of this assumption. Thus nuclear physics, as we know it today, dates back no farther than 1932.[1]

Under the assumption (which is very well confirmed by now) that nuclei are made up of neutrons and protons, the number of neutrons, N, in the nucleus is equal to $A-Z$. Neutrons and protons have nearly equal masses, and both will be referred to as "nucleons." Nuclei with equal mass number A but different atomic number Z are called isobars or isobaric nuclei. Nuclei with equal Z but different A are called isotopes or isotopic nuclei. Nuclei with equal $N=A-Z$ but different Z are called isotones. Isotopes are chemically equal and therefore hard to separate. From the point of view of nuclear physics, however, isotopes are nuclei with a different number of constituents. Isobars are chemically different because of their different atomic number Z. They are, however, more similar than isotopes from the nuclear point of view, since they consist of the same number of nucleons, and protons and neutrons have very similar properties within the nucleus.

The forces which hold a nucleus together cannot be ordinary electrostatic forces, since the (electrically neutral) neutrons are bound in the nucleus. The "nuclear forces," unlike the forces which hold an atom together, have no analogy in classical physics. The fundamental steps in the exploration of nuclear forces were taken by Wigner (33a, 33b), who showed that they must have a very short range of action but must be very strong (millions of times as strong as the electrostatic forces in an atom) within this range; and by Heisenberg (32) and

[1] There were some interesting speculations as early as 1922 (Harkins 22), but at that time no quantitative theory could be given.

Majorana (33), who showed that the nuclear forces must be "saturated," i.e., that not all pairs of nucleons within a nucleus can exert attractive forces upon each other. These matters will be discussed in Chapters II and III, respectively.

2. QUANTUM STATES, BINDING ENERGY, BINDING FRACTION

A nucleus is a system of A elementary particles held together by attractive forces. There is reason for the belief that the mechanics of such a system can be treated to a good approximation by the methods of non-relativistic quantum mechanics. A nucleus can be found in a series of quantum states of different energy (a property of any bound system in quantum mechanics). The state of lowest energy is called the ground state. Under normal conditions nuclei are always found in their ground states. If a nucleus is brought into a higher "excited" quantum state, it returns to the ground state with the emission of one or several light quanta.

Exact measurements of atomic weights (Aston 27) have shown that the weight of a nucleus is not equal to the sum of the weights of its constituents but is actually smaller by a few tenths of a percent. The mass M_{nucl} of the nucleus is given by

$$M_{\text{nucl}} = ZM_p + (A-Z)M_n - \Delta \qquad \qquad {}^{1}(2.1)$$

where M_p and M_n are the masses of the proton and the neutron, respectively, and Δ is the "mass defect" of the nucleus. In most experiments the magnitude measured is the atomic weight M_{at}, which differs from the nuclear weight by the weight of the electrons. Since the number of electrons in the atom is always equal to the number of protons in the nucleus, the atomic weight can also be written in the form

$$M_{\text{at}} = ZM_{\text{H}} + (A-Z)M_n - \Delta \qquad \qquad (2.2)$$

where M_{H} is the mass of the hydrogen atom:

$$M_{\text{H}} = M_p + m_e \qquad \qquad (2.3)$$

(m_e = electron mass). The binding energy of the electrons in the

---

[1] The formulas are numbered separately in each section. The formula reference (3.6), for example, refers to equation 6 in Section 3 of the chapter in which the reference is made. References to formulas in chapters other than the one in which the reference is made contain the number of the chapter in Roman numerals. For example, (III,2.8) refers to equation 8 in Section 2 of Chapter III. Figures and tables are also numbered separately in each section.

atom is negligible compared to nuclear binding energies and has been neglected in (2.2) and (2.3).

The mass defect can be explained by the Einstein mass-energy relation and constitutes the most obvious proof of the equivalence of energy and mass. We introduce the total energy U of the nucleus through

$$U = c^2 M_{\text{nucl}} \qquad (2.4)$$

It follows from (2.1) that there is a difference between the energy U of the actual nucleus and the energy $[ZM_pc^2 + (A-Z)M_nc^2]$ of its constituents when they are at rest but separated from each other. This difference is equal to the work necessary to tear the nucleus apart into its separated constituents. It represents, therefore, the total binding energy B of the nucleus:

$$B = ZM_pc^2 + (A-Z)M_nc^2 - U = c^2\Delta \qquad (2.5)$$

and can be obtained from the observed value of Δ. If not otherwise specified, the quantities U and B always refer to the nucleus in its ground state. The energy U^* of an excited state is higher, and the binding energy B^* lower, than the respective values for the ground state. The difference $U^* - U = B - B^*$ is equal to the excitation energy. It is useful to introduce another magnitude, the binding fraction,[1]

$$f = \frac{B}{A} \qquad (2.6)$$

which represents the total binding energy per nuclear particle. In Fig. 2.1, f is plotted as a function of the mass number A for stable nuclei. After some irregular smaller values at the beginning, f varies very little over the range of A. It increases slowly up to $A = 50$ and then stays around 8.5 Mev up to $A = 150$. For higher A it drops slightly and reaches 7.4 Mev for uranium.

It follows from this curve that the total binding energy of a nucleus is roughly proportional to the number A of its constituents. Every constituent of the nucleus is more or less equally strongly bound. This property shows a similarity between a nucleus and a liquid drop or a piece of a solid material; for either of the latter every added molecule increases the total binding energy by the same amount. The behavior of the electronic shell of an atom exhibits a contrasting property. The average binding energy of an electron is very much larger for a heavy atom than for a lighter one.

[1] This quantity is related to, but not identical with, the "packing fraction" used in mass spectroscopy (Bethe 36a).

The small decrease of f for high A and for low A can be accounted for qualitatively. The protons repel each other within a nucleus because of their electric charge. This repulsion is weak compared to the nuclear binding forces. It becomes, however, more and more important for nuclei of higher Z, since it increases with Z^2, the square of the number of protons, whereas the binding energy, as we saw above, is roughly proportional to the first power of the number of

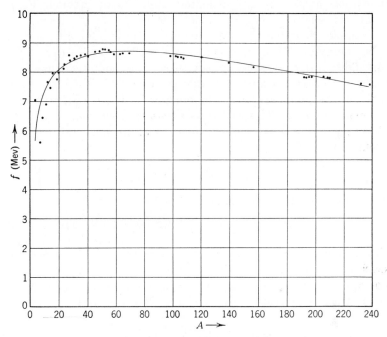

FIG. 2.1.   Binding fraction f of stable nuclei as a function of A.

constituents. The electrostatic repulsion is opposed to the binding effect of the nuclear forces and hence decreases the binding energy for high A. The decrease of f for small A is a surface effect. It is evident that the particles at the surface are less strongly bound than those in the interior. The smaller the nucleus, the larger is the percentage of constituents at the nuclear surface; this effect reduces the average binding energy per particle for low A (Chapter VI, Section 2).

Another useful concept is the "separation energy" S_a of a particle a from a given nucleus X. $S_a(\mathrm{X})$ is the energy necessary to remove to infinity the particle a from the nucleus X in its ground state, leaving the residual nucleus Y $(\mathrm{Y}+a=\mathrm{X})$ also in its ground state. $S_n(\mathrm{O}^{16})$, for example, is the energy necessary to remove a neutron from O^{16} to infinity and consequently to leave the nucleus O^{15} behind. The particle a need not be a nucleon; it can also be a nucleus itself, e.g., an alpha-particle.

The energy $S_a(X)$ can be computed from the difference between the mass of the nucleus X and the sum of the masses of a and the residual nucleus Y (Y+a=X). The values of S for nucleons are close to the value of the binding fraction $f \sim 8$ Mev. The energy necessary to remove *one* nucleon is approximately equal to the average binding energy per nucleon. Strong deviations are found in special cases; for example, $S_n = 16.8 \pm 0.4$ Mev in Si^{28} (McElhinney 49); the separation energy of a proton, $S_p = 1.95$ Mev in N^{13} (Tollestrup 50).

In addition to these special cases, there is a general tendency for the separation energy of a nucleon to deviate from the binding fraction in a region of mass numbers where the binding fraction varies appreciably with mass number. This can be seen from the following: The neutron separation energy S_n from the nucleus with Z protons and N neutrons is defined by

$$S_n = B(Z,N) - B(Z, N-1) \tag{2.7}$$

This expression can be rewritten in the form

$$S_n = f(Z,N) + (A-1) [f(Z,N) - f(Z, N-1)] \tag{2.8}$$

To a first approximation, we may assume that $f(Z,N)$ for the stable nuclei is a function of A only (see Fig. 2.1; this, however, is a very poor approximation in detail) and that it is a smooth enough function so that its derivative exists. Then (2.8) becomes

$$S_n(A) \cong f + (A-1) \frac{df}{dA} \tag{2.9}$$

Formula (2.9) shows that the separation energy is approximately equal to the binding fraction f only in the region of medium weight nuclei where f is nearly independent of A. For heavy nuclei the binding fraction decreases with increasing A so that the separation energies are systematically smaller than the binding fractions. For $A > 200$, the separation energies are of the order of 5.5 to 6 Mev, whereas f is of the order of 7.5 Mev. Formula (2.9) also predicts that the separation energies are systematically larger than the binding fractions for light nuclei, where f increases with A. However, the approximations used here are not applicable in this region: the binding fraction varies much too erratically with Z and N to be treated as a smooth function of the mass number only.

We can use the same approximation to estimate alpha separation energies. The result is

$$S_\alpha \cong 4f(A) - B(\alpha) + 4(A-4)\frac{df}{dA} \qquad (2.10)$$

where $B(\alpha) = 28.23$ Mev is the binding energy of the alpha-particle. It is interesting to compare this expression with (2.9). For heavy nuclei, the binding fraction f is of the order of 7.5 Mev. Thus the difference $4f - B(\alpha)$ is of the order of 2 Mev, which is much smaller than the corresponding term f in (2.9). Furthermore, the (negative) derivative df/dA is multiplied by a much larger factor in (2.10) than in (2.9). For both these reasons then, the alpha separation energies for heavy nuclei may be expected to be much lower than the neutron or proton separation energies:

$$S_\alpha \ll S_n \qquad \text{(for heavy nuclei)} \qquad (2.11)$$

Indeed, very many heavy nuclei are unstable against alpha-particle emission from their ground states, i.e., S_α is actually negative.

3. STABLE AND UNSTABLE NUCLEI, FISSION, ALPHA-DECAY, BETA-DECAY

An aggregation of nucleons can hold together and form a bound unit only if the number of one type of nucleon does not appreciably exceed the number of the other. There is, for example, no nucleus known to consist exclusively of neutrons or exclusively of protons. The probable reasons for this will be discussed in Chapter VI, but even among the combinations of neutrons and protons which form bound units only a relatively small fraction are stable. There are two forms of instability: (1) "dynamical" instability, which leads to the spontaneous breaking up of the nucleus into two or more parts (alpha-decay, fission, and similar phenomena); (2) "beta"-instability, which leads to the spontaneous change of charge by one unit with a simultaneous emission or absorption of an electron (beta-decay, electron capture).

A. "Dynamical" Instability

Some nuclei are unstable against a split into two (or more) parts. Such instability occurs if the binding energy of a nucleus A is smaller than the sum of the binding energies of the two separated parts B and C. Then arises the question how the two parts B and C can hold together, even temporarily, to form the nucleus A. In order to discuss the mechanism of splitting we consider the potential energy of this system as a function of the distance between the two parts B and C as plotted in Fig. 3.1. This plot is to be understood in a schematic way only, especially for small distances, since the potential energy of a many-body problem cannot be given exactly as a function of one

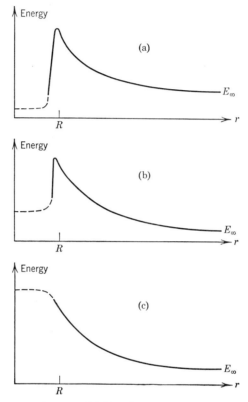

Fig. 3.1. The energy of two nuclei B and C as a function of their distance r. In case (a), the combined nucleus $A = B + C$ is stable against breakup into B and C; in case (b), A is metastable; in case (c), no combined nucleus A is formed. R is the distance wherein the two nuclei B and C merge.

coordinate. If the two constituents B and C are brought together from infinite distance, the potential energy increases, mainly because of the Coulomb repulsion between two positive charges. Finally, however, when the distance is of the order of the range of the attractive nuclear forces, the repulsion can be overcompensated and the potential energy may drop again. We distinguish three cases as illustrated in Fig. 3.1. If the energy of the system after complete assembly reaches a point lower than the value E_∞ at infinity, the nucleus A is stable against the split into B and C. If the energy reaches a point higher than E_∞, but lower than the highest point of the curve, the nucleus A is unstable with respect to the split into B and C; the two parts B and C are held together temporarily by a potential barrier and form an unstable nucleus A. If the energy does not drop at all for small values of r, B and C do not form a nucleus A.

The potential barrier in the second case does not hold the nucleus A together for an indefinite time. Because of the quantum-mechanical penetration effect (see Chapter VIII), there is a small but finite probability Π per unit time for the penetration, which leads to a splitting of the nucleus. If N specimens of the nucleus A are assembled at a given time, there will be a time interval $T = \Pi^{-1}$ after which on the average N/e are left, the rest having decayed. The probability Π decreases with an increase in the height of the barrier and with an increase in the masses of the penetrating parts.[1]

The most common result of dynamical instability is the splitting off of an alpha-particle, a partition against which a number of heavy nuclei are unstable (Becquerel 96, Rutherford 08). A detailed discussion of alpha-decay is found in Chapter XI. A split into two parts of comparable size is generally called fission. Because of the characteristic decrease of the packing fraction toward higher A, the sum of the binding energies of two nuclei with intermediate mass numbers A_1 and A_2 may become larger than the binding energy of the composite nucleus $A = A_1 + A_2$. Then the nucleus A would be unstable against fission into A_1 and A_2. The probability of spontaneous fission is extremely small because of the high mass of the fragments and the consequent small quantum-mechanical penetration of the barrier.

B. Beta-Radioactivity

A large number of nuclei have been found to emit positive or negative electrons, and in some kinds of atoms the nucleus has been observed to absorb one of the orbital electrons.

Since there are a number of reasons why electrons cannot be present in the nucleus (see Chapter XIII), we must conclude that the electron is created in the act of emission. A change of charge by one unit takes place in the nucleus, and the surplus charge leaves or enters the nucleus in the form of an electron. In this process the nucleus is transformed into a different one with one proton more and one neutron less, or one proton less and one neutron more. In the former case, a negative electron is emitted; in the latter case, a positron is emitted or an orbital electron absorbed.

[1] The importance of the barrier effect for nuclear physics was first recognized by Gamow (28) and Condon and Gurney (Condon 29).

Beta-radioactive decay is considered to originate from a fundamental property of nucleons, i.e., their ability to transform from one type to the other. A proton can change to a neutron, and a neutron to a proton. Because of the conservation of charge, these transformations are accompanied by the emission or absorption of an electron: the emission of a positive one or the absorption of a negative one if a proton changes to a neutron; the emission of a negative one if a neutron changes to a proton. As shown in Chapter XIII, conservation of angular momentum, as well as the continuous distribution-in-energy of the emitted electrons, requires that, together with the electron, a second particle be emitted which has no charge. This particle is called a neutrino. Its rest mass m_ν has been found to be very much smaller than the mass of an electron, and it is probable that m_ν is exactly zero.

The transformation processes can be written in the form of equations:

$$n \rightarrow p + e^- + \nu \qquad (3.1)$$

$$p \rightarrow n + e^+ + \nu \qquad (3.2)$$

where n, p, e^+, e^-, and ν stand for neutron, proton, positive and negative electron, and neutrino, respectively. The following transformation is also possible:

$$p + e^- \rightarrow n + \nu \qquad (3.3)$$

in which the proton absorbs a negative electron instead of emitting a positive one. This negative electron is taken from the electronic shell around the nucleus. The corresponding neutron process

$$n + e^+ \rightarrow p + \nu$$

should be theoretically possible, but no positive electron is available near the nucleus to make it occur.

The processes described in (3.1) and (3.2) are called negative and positive beta-decay, respectively; the process in (3.3) is called electron capture.

Naturally, these processes occur only if there is enough energy available. The creation of an electron-neutrino pair requires a minimum energy of 0.511 Mev, which is equivalent to the rest mass of the electron. The creation of a neutrino does not require any energy since its rest mass is zero. The mass difference between the neutron and the proton corresponds to an energy difference $\epsilon = (M_n - M_p)c^2 = 1.293$ Mev (Tollestrup 50). Thus in process (3.1) the difference between the energy of the initial state and that of the final state is 0.782 Mev. The corresponding differences are -1.804 Mev in process (3.2) and -0.782 Mev in process (3.3). Therefore only process (3.1) occurs spontaneously without energy supply from the outside. Hence the isolated neutron is beta-unstable,[1] whereas the isolated proton is beta-stable even if it is surrounded by an electron as in the hydrogen atom [neither process (3.2) nor (3.3) occurs spontaneously].

These rules no longer apply if the neutron or the proton is not isolated but forms part of a nucleus. Energy may then be supplied to or removed from the nucleon which undergoes the transformation by the rest of the nucleons in the nucleus. Consider a nucleus X with Z protons and N neutrons and a nucleus Y with $(Z+1)$ protons and $(N-1)$ neutrons. We study the following three processes:

$$_Z X = {}_{Z+1}Y + e^- + \nu \qquad (3.1')$$

$$_{Z+1}Y = {}_Z X + e^+ + \nu \qquad (3.2')$$

$$_{Z+1}Y + e^- = {}_Z X + \nu \qquad (3.3')$$

in which the elementary processes (3.1), (3.2) and (3.3), respectively, are occurring within a nucleus.

These processes can take place only if certain energy relations are fulfilled. Let us introduce the difference

$$\Delta_{Z,Z+1} = U(Z,N) - U(Z+1,N-1)$$

$$= B(Z+1,N-1) - B(Z,N) + (M_n c^2 - M_p c^2) \qquad (3.4)$$

between the energies $U(Z,N)$ of the nucleus X and $U(Z+1,N-1)$ of the nucleus Y as defined by (2.4). The following conditions must be fulfilled in order to provide enough energy for the three processes:

$$\Delta > 0.511 \text{ Mev} \qquad [\text{for } (3.1')] \qquad (3.5)$$

$$\Delta < -0.511 \text{ Mev} \qquad [\text{for } (3.2')] \qquad (3.6)$$

$$\Delta < 0.511 - \varepsilon \text{ Mev} \qquad [\text{for } (3.3')] \qquad (3.7)$$

where ε is the binding energy of the electron in the quantum state from which it is captured. Any energy available in excess of the minimum appears as kinetic energy of the created electron and neutrino in (3.1') and (3.2') and as kinetic energy of the neutrino in (3.3'). Hence a nucleus X with a charge Z is beta-stable only if two conditions are fulfilled:

(a) The difference $\Delta_{Z,Z+1}$ between its energy and the energy of the isobar with a charge $Z+1$ must be smaller than 0.511 Mev, i.e., $\Delta_{Z,Z+1} < m_e c^2$.

---

[1] The instability of the neutron has been confirmed experimentally by Robson (50) and Snell et al. (50).

(*b*) The difference $\Delta_{z,z-1}$ between its energy and the energy of the isobar with a charge $Z-1$ must be smaller than -0.511 Mev, i.e., $\Delta_{z,z-1} < -(m_e c^2 - \varepsilon)$. (Notice that $\Delta_{z,z-1} = -\Delta_{z-1,z}$.)

If $\Delta_{z,z+1} > m_e c^2$, the nucleus is unstable against negative beta-decay; if $\Delta_{z,z-1} > -(m_e c^2 - \varepsilon)$, it is unstable against electron capture; if $\Delta_{z,z-1} > m_e c^2$, it is unstable against positive beta-decay.

These stability relations can be expressed more succinctly in terms of the *atomic* mass M_{at}, (2.2). We have the relation

$$M_{at}(Z,N) = c^{-2} U(Z,N) + Z m_e \tag{3.8}$$

so that the difference Δ, (3.4), becomes

$$\Delta = c^2 [M_{at}(Z,N) - M_{at}(Z+1,N-1)] + m_e c^2 \tag{3.9}$$

When this form is substituted into the stability relations, (3.5), (3.6), and (3.7), they assume the very simple forms

$$M_{at}(Z,N) > M_{at}(Z+1,N-1) \qquad \text{(for } \beta^-\text{-decay)} \tag{3.5'}$$

$$M_{at}(Z,N) < M_{at}(Z+1,N-1) - 2m_e \qquad \text{(for } \beta^+\text{-decay)} \tag{3.6'}$$

$$M_{at}(Z,N) < M_{at}(Z+1,N-1) - \varepsilon \qquad \text{(for electron capture)} \tag{3.7'}$$

Since the tables of "nuclear" masses usually give the atomic masses (in units such that the atomic mass of O^{16} is 16.0000), stability relations (3.5') to (3.7') are more convenient to employ than the equivalent relations (3.5) to (3.7).

Most of the nuclei that can be formed of A nucleons (isobaric nuclei) are beta-unstable, and only one or two or, in some rare cases, three isobaric nuclei are known to be beta-stable. In almost all cases, two stable isobaric nuclei differ by more than one unit in Z. Two nuclei X and Y differing by only one unit in Z cannot both be stable, according to the energy rules given above, unless Δ is equal to 0.511 Mev.[1] This is very improbable, and in the few cases in which such apparently stable pairs have been found one nucleus is very probably unstable with an extremely long half-life.

The transformations discussed here take an extremely long time compared to any other nuclear processes except alpha-decay. The shortest observed lives of nuclei which are unstable against beta-decay are of the order of fractions of seconds.[2] These times should be compared with the lifetimes of excited nuclear states, which are of the

[1] A slight correction to this consideration is caused by the binding energy ε of the captured electron in the atom.

[2] The shortest half-life known is that of B^{12}: $t_{1/2} = 0.025$ sec (Seaborg 48).

order of 10^{-13} sec or less, except if transitions from these states are "highly forbidden."

For $A < 44$, there is only one stable isobar for each A. For odd A, $Z = \frac{1}{2}(A-1)$; for even A, Z is either $\frac{1}{2}A$ or $\frac{1}{2}A - 1$. For higher A, there may be more than one stable isobar but only if A is even. The Z for which the isobars are stable is consistently smaller than $\frac{1}{2}A$, and this difference increases with higher A. A critical discussion and explanation of nuclear stability is found in Chapter VI.

4. SIZE OF THE NUCLEI

All experimental evidence points to the fact that nuclei have a well-defined size, in contrast to the electronic shells of atoms. In an atom the probability of the presence of an electron gradually goes to zero with increasing distance from the center. The structure of nuclei is quite different. The surface of a nucleus is relatively well defined: the probability of the presence of nuclear constituents is high inside the surface and drops to zero outside in an interval which in heavy nuclei is small compared to the radius. This makes it possible to define a nuclear radius with some degree of accuracy. The concept of a nuclear surface is not applicable to very light nuclei ($A < 20$), however.

The size of nuclei is not too well known. All experiments from which the size can be deduced show that the volume is approximately proportional to the number A of constituents. The shape is, most probably, spherical. Small deviations from sphericity, however, have been observed in some nuclei in the form of electric quadrupole moments (see Section 7). The radius R of the nucleus is approximately proportional to $A^{1/3}$, and the relation that fits the experimental data best is

$$R = r_0 A^{1/3} \qquad (4.1)$$

where $r_0 \cong 1.5 \times 10^{-13}$ cm. The value of r_0 is probably subject to variations from element to element. There is some evidence that r_0 is smaller for high values of A, whereas the value given here is valid for medium-weight nuclei only. Since the surface of the nucleus is not accurately defined, the value of r_0 also depends on the way the nuclear radius was measured. Some measurements indicate an additional constant term in the expression (4.1).

There are several methods by means of which the nuclear radius can be measured. They are enumerated here, and the detailed discussion of each method is given wherever the process used in the measurement is treated.

A. Scattering of High-Energy Neutrons by Nuclei

The total cross section of very fast neutrons reaches the value $2\pi R^2$, which is just twice the target area which the nucleus offers to the beam. This limit should be reached when the wavelength of the neutron becomes much smaller than the radius. From the wave theory of neutron scattering the expected total cross section can be calculated more accurately as a function of the radius. The comparison of experiments and theory therefore provides a determination of the radius (see Chapter IX, Section 2).

B. The Yield of Nuclear Reactions Initiated by Protons or Alpha-Particles

When charged particles produce nuclear reactions, they must run against the electrostatic repulsion of the nucleus before they reach the nuclear surface. The electrostatic potential at the nuclear surface is inversely proportional to the nuclear radius, and the probability of reaching the surface is therefore a function of the radius. This function is very sensitive, especially for lower energies where the surface can be reached only because of the quantum-mechanical penetration effect. Hence the comparison of observed reaction yields with the expected ones can be used to determine nuclear radii.

C. Alpha-Decay Lifetimes

The spontaneous emission of an alpha-particle by some of the heavier nuclei is connected with a penetration by this alpha-particle through a region of very high potential energy near the nuclear surface; the region owes its existence to the repulsive potential between the nucleus and the alpha-particle and would act, in classical mechanics, as a barrier preventing emission. The penetration is a quantum-mechanical effect. Its probability depends very critically on the shape and the height of the potential energy barrier and on the kinetic energy of the alpha-particle after penetration. The height is given by the nuclear radius R, since the alpha-particle is under the influence of the Coulomb repulsion without any compensating nuclear attraction when its distance from the center is larger than R. The probability of penetration of the barrier is closely connected with the lifetime of the decaying nucleus. The theory (Chapter XI) allows a determination of the radius R from this lifetime and from the kinetic energy of the alpha-particle.

D. Maximum Energy of Some Beta-Rays

In some radioactive elements, it is reasonably certain that the nuclear structure of the radioactive nucleus and the product nucleus are

TABLE 4.1
NUCLEAR RADII

The nuclear radii are listed according to the four methods of determination. R is the nuclear radius in 10^{-13} cm. r_0 is the constant defined by (4.1), in 10^{-13} cm. Method A uses the scattering of high-energy neutrons (Feshbach 49a); method B, the yield of (p,n) reactions (Blaser 51, and private communication from same authors). These results are very inaccurate. Method C uses the lifetime-energy relation of alpha-decay (Devaney 50); method D uses the beta-ray energy of mirror nuclei. The effective radius of the alpha-particle was arbitrarily assumed to be 1.2×10^{-13} cm.

METHOD A						METHOD B		
Nucleus	R	r_0	Nucleus	R	r_0	Nucleus	R	r_0
Be	2.4	1.17	Zn	5.9	1.48	Ni^{61}	5	1.3
B	3.4	1.54	Se	6.3	1.46	Ni^{62}	6	1.5
C	3.8	1.65	Ag	6.8	1.44	Cu^{65}	6	1.6
O	4.3	1.71	Cd	7.2	1.48	Zn^{68}	7	1.6
Mg	4.5	1.57	Sn	7.4	1.52	Se^{80}	6	1.6
Al	4.6	1.53	Sb	7.3	1.46	Rb^{85}	7	1.6
S	4.1	1.30	Au	7.5	1.33	Zr^{92}	6	1.4
Cl	4.7	1.44	Hg	8.3	1.42	Zr^{96}	7	1.6
Fe	5.6	1.46	Pb	7.8	1.32	Sn^{120}	8	1.6
Cu	5.5	1.38	Bi	7.9	1.34	I^{127}	8	1.5

METHOD C						METHOD D		
Nucleus	R	r_0	Nucleus	R	r_0	Nucleus	R	r_0
Tl^{208}	6.5	1.10	Po^{218}	8.5	1.40	B^{11}	3.2	1.42
Tl^{210}	7.0	1.19	Em^{219}	8.5	1.40	C^{13}	3.4	1.46
Pb^{206}	7.2	1.21	Em^{220}	8.1	1.34	N^{15}	3.5	1.41
Pb^{208}	7.8	1.31	Em^{222}	8.7	1.44	O^{17}	3.6	1.39
Pb^{210}	8.1	1.35	Fr^{223}	8.4	1.39	F^{19}	3.9	1.47
Pb^{211}	8.3	1.40	Ra^{223}	7.6	1.26	Na^{23}	4.1	1.46
Pb^{212}	8.1	1.35	Ra^{224}	8.3	1.36	Al^{27}	4.2	1.39
Pb^{214}	8.4	1.39	Ra^{226}	8.3	1.36	Si^{29}	4.5	1.46
Bi^{211}	8.1	1.35	Ra^{228}	8.6	1.43	P^{29}	4.6	1.47
Po^{215}	8.4	1.39	Th^{230}	8.3	1.35	S^{33}	4.7	1.46
Po^{216}	8.5	1.40	Th^{234}	8.4	1.36	Cl^{35}	4.8	1.46
						Ca^{41}	5.2	1.50

very similar, so that the only reason for the difference in energy is the difference in electric charge. The energy difference can be computed from the maximum energy of the emitted beta-rays. The energy due to the electric charge is proportional to $1/R$; it is actually equal to $(\frac{9}{5})[Z(Z-1)e^2/R]$. The radius R can thus be deduced from the measured maximum energy of the beta-rays. Details can be found in Chapter VI.

The results obtained for nuclear radii by these various methods do not agree too well, as indicated in Table 4.1. They differ sometimes by as much as 2×10^{-13} cm. Better agreement should not be expected, however. The definition of the radius is necessarily inaccurate to within an interval of the order of the range of nuclear forces and of the average relative distance of nucleons in the nucleus. Both lengths are of the order of 2×10^{-13} cm. Actually the different methods measure different quantities. Methods A, B, and C measure the distance at which an incoming particle falls under the influence of the nuclear forces, whereas method D determines the radius of the actual charge distribution. The last method would be expected to give smaller radii.

5. THE COULOMB BARRIER

Let us consider the energy necessary to remove a proton or a neutron from a nucleus to infinity. We have called this energy S_p or S_n, the separation energy of a proton or a neutron. The neutron separation energy is the energy necessary to break the bonds of the nuclear forces which keep the neutron within the nucleus. The proton separation energy consists of two parts, $S_p = S_\nu - S_c$. The nuclear part S_ν is analogous to the neutron separation energy and is the energy necessary to break the nuclear bonds; the Coulomb part $-S_c$ is the additional effect of the electrostatic repulsion between the proton and the residual nucleus, after the bonds are broken.

Consider first the conditions in some light nuclei, i.e., those with $Z = N$ and $A < 40$. Because of the equality of neutron-neutron and proton-proton forces, the energy necessary to carry a proton from inside the nuclear surface to just outside the nuclear surface, S_ν, is not very different[1] from the energy necessary to do the same for a neutron:

$$S_\nu \cong S_n \qquad Z = N \qquad (5.1)$$

[1] A small systematic difference, making S_ν slightly less than S_n, is caused by the proton being repelled by the rest of the charge in the nucleus already *inside* the nuclear surface.

In the case of a neutron this is already the separation energy.   But a proton is repelled by the residual nucleus and hence gains energy as it goes farther away.   This is illustrated in Fig. 5.1.   The final separation energy for the proton is smaller than the neutron separation energy S_n approximately by the Coulomb effect:

$$S_c = \frac{(Z-1)e^2}{R} \qquad (5.2)$$

where $Z-1$ is the charge of the residual nucleus after the proton has been emitted, and R is the radius of the residual nucleus.

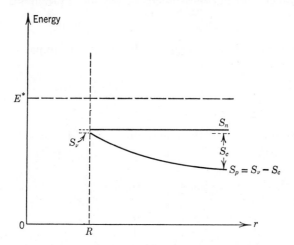

FIG. 5.1.   If $S_\nu \cong S_n$, the proton separation energy S_p is smaller than the neutron separation energy S_n by an amount $S_c = (Z-1)(e^2/R)$.   If the nucleus is excited to some energy $E^* > S_n$, it will emit protons more easily than neutrons.

The electrostatic potential energy of the proton outside the nuclear surface is usually called the "Coulomb barrier."   In the present case, however, it is rather artificial to speak of a Coulomb *barrier*.   For a certain amount of excitation energy E^* inside the nucleus, it is actually easier for a proton to emerge than for a neutron.   The Coulomb effect does act as a barrier, however, if a neutron and a proton are compared, not with the same excitation energy in the original nucleus, but rather with the same kinetic energy far away, after complete separation or before assembly.   Then the proton has to overcome a potential barrier before it can enter into the nucleus, whereas the neutron can enter without barrier.

For light nuclei other than those with $Z = N$, no such simple rule as (5.1) can be made.   For example, the neutron separation energy from

O^{17} is $S_n(O^{17}) = 4.155$ Mev, whereas the proton separation energy is $S_p(O^{17}) = 13.4$ Mev. The large difference is caused by the much weaker binding of N^{16} as compared to O^{16}. The emission of a proton from an excited O^{17} nucleus is impossible until the excitation energy is at least 13.4 Mev, whereas neutron emission occurs at much lower energies. This effect, however, can hardly be described as a barrier effect. In general, the light nuclei with $Z \neq N$ have to be treated as special cases.

We now turn to the heavier nuclei. We shall show that (5.1) fails to hold even approximately for nuclei in the beta-stable region of the periodic table. Rather these nuclei satisfy the approximate relation

$$S_p \cong S_n \qquad A > 40, \text{ beta-stable} \qquad (5.3)$$

This can be seen from the following: The neutron and proton separation energies are given by

$$S_n = B(Z,N) - B(Z, N-1)$$

$$S_p = B(Z,N) - B(Z-1, N)$$

Taking the difference of these equations, we obtain

$$S_p - S_n = B(Z, N-1) - B(Z-1, N) \qquad (5.4)$$

This energy is closely related to the energy of the beta-rays in the beta-decay $(Z, N-1) \rightarrow (Z-1, N)$ or vice versa, depending on the sign of the energy difference. In fact,

$$S_p - S_n = \Delta_{z,z-1} - (M_n c^2 - M_p c^2)$$

The beta-ray energies for heavier nuclei which differ by only one nucleon from a beta-stable nucleus are of the order of a few Mev, mostly even less than 1 Mev. Hence the difference $S_p - S_n$ does not exceed a few Mev. On the other hand, the Coulomb effect S_c as given by (5.2) becomes quite large. It is about 7 Mev for copper $(Z = 29)$ and larger for heavier elements. Hence (5.1) can no longer be fulfilled and (5.3) is valid within a few Mev. We get, instead of (5.1),

$$\left. \begin{array}{l} S_\nu > S_n \\ S_\nu - S_n \cong S_c \end{array} \right\} A > 40, \text{ beta-stable} \qquad (5.5)$$

This relation shows that it takes more energy to break the nuclear bond of a proton than to separate a neutron from a medium or heavy nucleus. The difference is roughly equal to S_c. The protons are more strongly bound by the nuclear forces in order to compensate for the electric repulsion energy. This situation is illustrated in Fig. 5.2.

The figure shows that we are now justified in talking of a Coulomb barrier.   Given the same excitation energy E^* in the original nucleus, a proton has to surmount a barrier of height:

$$\text{Barrier height} = S_p + S_c - E^* \tag{5.6}$$

whereas a neutron has no barrier to surmount and emerges at $r = R$ with an energy equal to its final energy far away:

$$\text{Neutron energy} = E^* - S_n \tag{5.7}$$

The final proton energy at $r \to \infty$,

$$\text{Proton energy} = E^* - S_p \tag{5.8}$$

is not very different from the final neutron energy, but the proton has

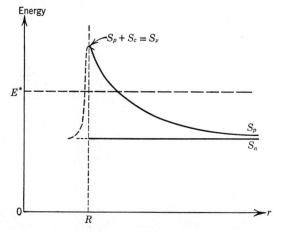

FIG. 5.2.   For heavy nuclei in the beta-stable region, $S_n \cong S_p$.   The Coulomb effect S_c then acts as a barrier against proton emission.   If the nucleus is excited to an energy E^*, neutrons emerge with $E_{\text{neut}} = E^* - S_n$; protons have to go through a barrier of maximum height $S_p + S_c - E^*$.   The surface separation energy S_ν for protons systematically exceeds the surface (= final) separation energy S_n for neutrons.

to penetrate the barrier in order to get outside.   Thus in the heavier nuclei proton emission (compared to neutron emission) is inhibited.

There is thus a rather complete reversal of the role of the Coulomb repulsion between light nuclei with $N = Z$ on the one hand, and heavy nuclei on the other hand.   In the first case (Fig. 5.1) the Coulomb repulsion makes it easier for a proton to leave the nucleus; in the second case the Coulomb repulsion, coupled with the need for beta-stability, produces a "barrier" which inhibits proton emission from an excited nucleus.   In either case, however, the Coulomb effect acts as a "barrier" to protons if we compare neutrons and protons with the same kinetic energy far away rather than with the same excitation energy in the compound nucleus.

The situation is similar for the case of alpha-particles. The separation energy S_α of an alpha-particle can be split into two parts,

$$S_\alpha = S_{\nu\alpha} - S_c(\alpha) \tag{5.9}$$

where $S_{\nu\alpha}$ is the energy necessary to remove the alpha-particle from

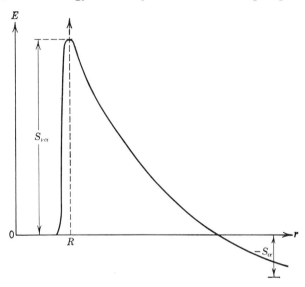

FIG. 5.3. Potential barrier in alpha-decay. Energy zero corresponds to the parent nucleus (Z,N), and energy $-S_\alpha$ to the daughter nucleus $(Z-2, N-2)$ plus the alpha-particle at rest.

the nucleus (Z,N) to a point just outside the nuclear surface. The Coulomb effect is given by

$$S_c(\alpha) = \frac{2\,(Z-2)\,e^2}{R'} \tag{5.10}$$

where R' is the radius of the residual nucleus $(Z-2,N-2)$.[1] In general $S_{\nu\alpha}$ is somewhat smaller than the corresponding magnitude S_ν for protons in light elements. In very heavy nuclei it often happens that S_α is negative, so that the nucleus even in its ground state is unstable against alpha-decay.

S_α can get as low as -8.95 Mev, corresponding to a nucleus

---

[1] Strictly speaking, R' is the sum of the radius of the residual nucleus and the radius of the alpha-particle. See Chapter XI for a discussion of this point.

which emits alpha-particles of 8.95 Mev (Po^{212}) (Perlman 50). $S_c(\alpha)$, however, for these very heavy nuclei is about 25 to 29 Mev, so that

$$S_{\nu\alpha} = S_\alpha + S_c(\alpha) \cong 16 \text{ to } 28 \text{ Mev} \qquad (5.11)$$

for alpha-unstable nuclei.[1]   The alpha-particle, before escaping from the nucleus, must overcome a potential barrier whose height at the nuclear surface is 16 to 28 Mev (see Fig. 5.3).   This high barrier is responsible for the long lifetimes of alpha-decaying nuclei, as will be shown in detail in Chapter XI.

6. ANGULAR MOMENTUM, SPIN

It has been found that the neutron and the proton possess an intrinsic angular momentum of magnitude $\frac{1}{2}\hbar$ just as the electron does.   This intrinsic angular momentum of the proton or of the neutron is commonly referred to as its "spin."   The quantum-mechanical properties of an angular momentum of magnitude $\frac{1}{2}\hbar$ are such that its orientation can be described by only two states, in which it is either "parallel" or "anti-parallel" to any given direction.   The component of the spin along a given direction, say the z axis, is either $+\frac{1}{2}\hbar$ or $-\frac{1}{2}\hbar$.

Since nuclei are built up of neutrons and protons, each possesses an angular momentum I which is the combined effect of the intrinsic spin of the constituents and of the angular momentum of the orbital motion within the nucleus.   The angular momentum of the orbital motion must be an integral multiple of $\hbar$.   The intrinsic spin of any nucleon can add or subtract $\frac{1}{2}\hbar$, depending on its orientation relative to the axis of reference (parallel or anti-parallel).   Thus the total angular momentum of a nucleus is an integral multiple of $\hbar$ for nuclei with an even number A of constituents, and it is an odd multiple of $\frac{1}{2}\hbar$ for nuclei with odd A.   This rule has been verified in all measurements.

This result is one of the reasons for assuming that nuclei consist of neutrons and protons, and not of electrons and protons.   It has been found, for example, that the nuclei H^2, Li^6, N^{14} all have spins equal to $\hbar$, an observation in accordance with our conclusions, since each of these nuclei consists of an even number of nucleons.   If these nuclei were built up of protons and electrons, the number of constituents would have to be odd in each case in order to account for the charge:

[1] Of course, not all alpha-unstable nuclei are observed to be alpha-radioactive. In practice, a nucleus with an alpha-decay energy ($= -S_\alpha$) of less than about 4 to 5 Mev has a half-life so long that the decay is never observed in the laboratory. Thus the upper limit in (5.11) ought to be reduced to about 24 Mev if we confine ourselves to nuclei which are not merely alpha-unstable but also have observable alpha-radioactivity.

2 protons and 1 electron in H^2; 6 protons and 3 electrons in Li^6; 14 protons and 7 electrons in N^{14}. The total spin would be a half-integral multiple of $\hbar$.

The total angular momentum of a nucleus is currently referred to as its "spin," even though the total angular momentum includes both orbital and intrinsic angular momenta whereas the term "spin" is usually reserved for intrinsic angular momenta of elementary particles. This unfortunate terminology for the angular momentum of nuclei was introduced at a time when their internal structure was not yet in the center of interest.

The angular momentum in an excited state of a nucleus can be different from the one in the ground state. The contribution of the orbital angular momenta and the relative orientation of the intrinsic spins of the constituents differ, in general, from state to state in one nucleus. Either effect changes the total angular momentum by an integral multiple of $\hbar$. Thus the spins of excited states may differ from the spin of the ground state by integral multiples of $\hbar$. The term "spin of the nucleus," without any specification, always refers to the state of lowest energy.

Most measurements of nuclear spins are based on the so-called "space quantization of angular momenta." Any angular momentum I can be oriented in space with respect to a given axis in only $(2I+1)$ directions. The component of the angular momentum along the axis of reference in any of these states has the magnitude $m\hbar$, where the integer or half-integer m, called the magnetic quantum number, is any member of the sequence $-I, -I+1, \cdots, +I$. Most observable effects of the spin are based on the magnetic moment (see Section 7) which invariably is connected with any angular momentum. The $2I+1$ orientations of this magnetic moment in a magnetic field give rise to $(2I+1)$ different energy values which can be observed in many ways.[1]

It has been found that all nuclei with even mass number A have no angular momentum $(I=0)$, with the exception of the so-called odd-odd nuclei in which Z and N are both odd. There are only four stable odd-odd nuclei, i.e., H^2, Li^6, B^{10}, and N^{14}.

The nuclear spins are relatively small; the largest measured value is $\frac{9}{2}$, and there is only one nucleus (Lu^{176}) with $I \geq 7$. These values are much less than the value $\frac{1}{2}A$ which could be expected if all intrinsic spins were parallel. This indicates that there is a tendency in nuclei for intrinsic spins to cancel, an effect which will be explained later in Chapter VI as a consequence of the nature of the nuclear forces.

[1] An exhaustive account of all methods and results is given by Kopferman (45).

7. ELECTRIC AND MAGNETIC MOMENTS

The electric moments of a nucleus are determined by the distribution of the electric charge within the nucleus, the magnetic moments by the distribution of the electric currents. These quantities are defined for a bare nucleus in a definite quantum state (usually its ground state). To the extent that external electric or magnetic fields do not perturb the internal distribution of charge and current in the nucleus, the electric and magnetic moments completely determine the interaction of the nucleus with these external fields. The external fields in question are usually caused by the electrons in the atom, or by the electrons and other nuclei in the molecule, of which the nucleus forms a part. The energies of interaction perturb the atomic or molecular energy levels and give rise to the "hyperfine structure" of spectral lines emitted by the atom or molecule. The explanation of the observed hyperfine structure in terms of nuclear properties was given by Pauli (24). The quantum theory of the interaction between nuclei and the electric and magnetic fields in atoms and molecules is summarized by Casimir (36).

A. Electric Moments

We first define the meaning of electric moments for a classical charge distribution $\rho(x,y,z)$, which is given as a function of position in space and confined within some small volume. We are interested in the energy E of this charge distribution in the electric field produced by the atom. Let us make a first approximation in which we neglect the variation of the field over the dimensions of the nucleus. We take the direction of the constant field E as our z direction. Then the electrostatic potential $\varphi(x,y,z)$ giving rise to this field can be written as

$$\varphi(x,y,z) = \varphi(0) - \mathsf{E}\,z \tag{7.1}$$

and the energy E of the charge distribution in this potential is

$$E = \int \varphi(x,y,z)\,\rho(x,y,z)\,dV = \varphi(0)\,\epsilon - \mathsf{E}\,D_z \tag{7.2}$$

where ϵ is the charge and D_z is the z component of the dipole moment, defined by

$$\epsilon = \int \rho(x,y,z)\,dV \tag{7.3}$$

$$D_z = \int z\,\rho(x,y,z)\,dV \tag{7.4}$$

z in (7.4) is measured from the center of *mass* of the distribution (the nucleus).

Unfortunately this simple approximation is not sufficient for our purposes. We shall now show that the electric dipole moment is necessarily zero for any quantum-mechanical system in a stationary state. We need the quantum-mechanical analogue of the classical definition (7.4). Let $\psi(\mathbf{r}_1,\mathbf{r}_2,\cdots,\mathbf{r}_Z; \mathbf{r}_{Z+1},\cdots,\mathbf{r}_A)$ be the wave function of our stationary state. The first Z coordinates are proton coordinates; the remaining ones are neutron coordinates. The probability of finding the ith nucleon in the volume element dV around the position $\mathbf{r}$ is given by $P_i\,dV$, where

$$P_i(\mathbf{r}) = \int |\psi(\mathbf{r}_1,\cdots,\mathbf{r}_A)|^2\,dV_1 \cdots dV_{i-1}\,dV_{i+1}\cdots dV_A \qquad (7.5)$$

The integration extends over the coordinates of all particles except the ith, and the coordinate $\mathbf{r}_i$ has to be given the value $\mathbf{r}$. The charge density $\rho(x,y,z)$ which has to be substituted into (7.4) is given by

$$\rho(x,y,z) = \sum_{i=1}^{Z} e\,P_i(x,y,z) \qquad (7.6)$$

This sum extends over the protons only, since the neutrons do not contribute to the density of electric charge in the nucleus. Through (7.4), (7.5), and (7.6), the quantum-mechanical value of the electric dipole moment (say the z component) is given by

$$D_z = \sum_{i=1}^{Z} \int ez_i\,|\psi(\mathbf{r}_1,\cdots,\mathbf{r}_A)|^2\,d\tau \qquad (7.7)$$

where $d\tau$ stands for an integration over the whole of configuration space (all the coordinates).

We shall now show that every term of the sum (7.7) vanishes in a stationary state ψ. A stationary state of a quantum-mechanical system has a definite parity,[1] i.e., a definite behavior under an inversion of the coordinate system. Either

$$\psi(-\mathbf{r}_1,-\mathbf{r}_2,\cdots,-\mathbf{r}_A) = +\psi(\mathbf{r}_1,\cdots,\mathbf{r}_A): \quad \text{Parity} = +1 \qquad (7.8)$$

or

$$\psi(-\mathbf{r}_1,-\mathbf{r}_2,\cdots,-\mathbf{r}_A) = -\psi(\mathbf{r}_1,\cdots,\mathbf{r}_A): \quad \text{Parity} = -1 \qquad (7.9)$$

In either case we have

$$|\psi(\mathbf{r}_1,\mathbf{r}_2,\cdots,\mathbf{r}_A)|^2 = |\psi(-\mathbf{r}_1,-\mathbf{r}_2,\cdots,-\mathbf{r}_A)|^2 \qquad (7.10)$$

Each integrand in (7.7) is therefore the product of an even function and

[1] This is, strictly speaking, true only for non-degenerate states. It is true for the ground states of nuclei provided that the center of gravity is at rest. See Wigner (27).

an odd function (z_i) under inversion, so that the integral vanishes. *Quantum-mechanical systems in stationary states do not have permanent electric dipole moments.*

In molecular physics, one often uses the concept of an electric dipole moment of a polar molecule such as NaCl. As long as the molecule is not subject to external forces, however, this electric dipole moment is effectively zero since it is "smeared out" over all directions. It becomes observable only in electric fields of such strength that the motion of the molecule is seriously affected (the dipole is lined up along the electric field). Although this effect is possible in principle for nuclei also, we do not have available electric fields of the requisite strength; even the field produced by the atomic electrons near the nucleus is not strong enough to perturb the internal nuclear motion appreciably. Some very small discrepancies have been observed in microwave spectroscopy which may be attributed to effects of this kind (Geschwind 51, Gunther-Mohr 51).

Since the electric dipole moment of the nucleus vanishes, the approximation, (7.1), (7.2), of a constant electric field over the nuclear volume gives no useful information. We must take the variation of the electric field over the nuclear volume into account explicitly. Let us assume for the sake of simplicity that the field is cylindrically symmetrical about the z direction. We can then write

$$\mathcal{E}_z = \left(\frac{\partial \mathcal{E}_z}{\partial z}\right)_0 z = K z \qquad (7.11)$$

(we put the electric field equal to zero at the origin since the effect of a constant electric field has already been investigated). The electric field (7.11) is produced by charges at some distance, and hence the divergence of $\mathcal{E}$ must vanish. Thus we must have

$$\mathcal{E}_x = -\tfrac{1}{2}Kx \qquad \mathcal{E}_y = -\tfrac{1}{2}Ky \qquad (7.12)$$

to give zero divergence as well as cylindrical symmetry. The potential $\varphi(x,y,z)$ associated with this field is

$$\varphi(x,y,z) = -\tfrac{1}{4} K (2z^2 - x^2 - y^2)$$
$$= -\tfrac{1}{4} K (3z^2 - r^2) \qquad (7.13)$$

The energy of a charge distribution $\rho(x,y,z)$ in this field is given by

$$E = \int \varphi(x,y,z)\, \rho(x,y,z)\, dV$$
$$= -\tfrac{1}{4} K \int (3z^2 - r^2)\, \rho(x,y,z)\, dV \qquad (7.14)$$

The integral which occurs in (7.14) is called the quadrupole moment of the charge distribution ρ. By use of the quantum-mechanical charge distribution, (7.5), (7.6), the quadrupole moment in the state ψ is defined by

$$Q(\psi) = \sum_{i=1}^{z} \int e\,(3z_i^2 - r_i^2)\,|\psi(\mathbf{r}_1,\cdots,\mathbf{r}_A)|^2\,d\tau \qquad (7.15)$$

The sum goes over all the protons. In terms of the quadrupole moment $Q(\psi)$, the additional energy produced by placing the nucleus in an inhomogeneous electric field, (7.11), (7.12), is given by

$$E = -\frac{1}{4}\left(\frac{\partial \mathcal{E}}{\partial z}\right)_0 Q(\psi) \qquad (7.16)$$

We note that a prolate (cigar-shaped) charge distribution with its axis parallel to the z axis will give rise to a positive quadrupole moment, and an oblate (pancake-shaped) distribution will give rise to a negative quadrupole moment. A spheroid with semi-axes c parallel to z and a perpendicular to z and uniform charge density everywhere inside produces the quadrupole moment

$$Q = \tfrac{2}{5}\,(c^2 - a^2)\,\epsilon = \tfrac{4}{5}\,\eta\,R^2\,\epsilon \qquad (7.17)$$

where ϵ is the total charge, $\eta \equiv (c^2 - a^2)/(c^2 + a^2)$, and $R^2 \equiv \tfrac{1}{2}(a^2 + c^2)$ is the mean square radius.

We will now show that *a nucleus can have a quadrupole moment only if its angular momentum I is equal to or larger than unity.* To prove this, consider the first term of the sum (7.15). We can write it in the form

$$\int \psi^*(\mathbf{r}_1,\cdots,\mathbf{r}_A)\,[e\,(3z_1^2 - r_1^2)\,\psi(\mathbf{r}_1,\cdots,\mathbf{r}_A)]\,d\tau$$
$$= \int \psi^*(\mathbf{r}_1,\cdots,\mathbf{r}_A)\,F(\mathbf{r}_1,\cdots,\mathbf{r}_A)\,d\tau \qquad (7.18)$$

where F denotes the quantity in the square brackets. ψ is a wave function with an angular momentum I. The quantity $(3z^2 - r^2)$ would have an angular momentum $l = 2$ if it were considered as a wave function. According to the combination rule of angular momenta the product F can be split into a sum

$$F = \sum_{J=|I-2|}^{I+2} F_J \qquad (7.19)$$

where each F_J is a wave function with angular momentum J. Since two wave functions with different total angular momenta are necessarily orthogonal to each other, the integral (7.18) vanishes unless one of the J values in the sum (7.19) is equal to I. This is impossible for $I = 0$ [the lowest J in (7.19), indeed the only J, is then equal to 2] and for $I = \frac{1}{2}$ [the lowest J in (7.19) is $\frac{3}{2}$ in that case], but it is possible for $I = 1$ or more. Hence quadrupole moments are necessarily zero in states whose angular momentum is zero or $\frac{1}{2}$.

Unlike the electric dipole moment, the quadrupole moment operator $e\,(3z^2 - r^2)$ is an even function under inversion of the coordinate system. Hence the parity rule does not prevent nuclei from having a permanent quadrupole moment.

The quadrupole moment $Q(\psi)$, (7.15), is a function of the state ψ of the nucleus. In practice we are interested in only one special case, where ψ is the ground state. This does not specify the wave function completely, however. A nucleus with angular momentum I can have this angular momentum oriented in any one of $2I+1$ different ways, corresponding to $I_z = m = I,\ I-1,\ I-2,\ \cdots,\ -I$. Thus there are $2I+1$ different "quadrupole moments" associated with a nucleus in its ground state. We shall show now that these $2I+1$ quantities are related to each other, so that all of them can be expressed in terms of any one of them.

Let us first consider a classical charge distribution with cylindrical symmetry, which is the closest classical analogue to the quantum-mechanical case. We shall study the dependence of the quadrupole moment

$$Q(\rho) = \int (3z^2 - r^2)\, \rho(x,y,z)\, dV \qquad (7.20)$$

upon the angle β between the z axis and the body axis (z') of the (cylindrically symmetric) charge distribution. We introduce polar coordinates, r, θ, φ centered around the z axis in space, as well as r, θ', φ' centered around the body axis z'. The quadrupole moment is

$$Q(\rho) = \int r^2\, (3\cos^2\theta - 1)\, \rho(x,y,z)\, dV \qquad (7.20')$$

Let the body axis point in the direction $\theta = \beta$, $\varphi = \phi$. Then we use the identity

$$\cos\theta = \cos\theta' \cos\beta + \sin\theta' \sin\beta \cos(\varphi - \phi) \qquad (7.21)$$

Substitution into (7.20') gives

$$Q(\rho) = \tfrac{1}{2}(3\cos^2\beta - 1)\, Q_0(\rho) \qquad (7.22)$$

where

$$Q_0(\rho) = \int r^2\, (3\cos^2\theta' - 1)\, \rho(x',y',z')\, dV'$$

is the quadrupole moment of the charge distribution ρ when the z direction is chosen along the body axis.

We now return to an actual nucleus in a quantum state with angular momentum I and study the dependence of the quadrupole moment $Q(\psi)$ on the magnetic quantum number m. The value of m specifies the orientation of the angular momentum I with respect to the z axis. The angle β between the z axis and I is a well-defined magnitude given by

$$\cos \beta = \frac{m}{\sqrt{I(I+1)}} \qquad (7.23)$$

Thus the quadrupole moments in the different substates m should have the same relation to one another as the values $Q(\rho)$ in (7.22) for the corresponding angles β. In particular, the ratio of two quadrupole moments $Q(m_1)$ and $Q(m_2)$ for the substates ψ, with $m = m_1$ and $m = m_2$, is, according to (7.22):

$$\frac{Q(m_1)}{Q(m_2)} = \frac{3\cos^2\beta_1 - 1}{3\cos^2\beta_2 - 1} = \frac{3m_1{}^2 - I(I+1)}{3m_2{}^2 - I(I+1)} \qquad (7.24)$$

The best alignment possible between I and the z axis is attained for $m = I$; therefore $Q(m = I)$ is the largest observable quadrupole moment, and it is the one that comes nearest to what we have called Q_0 in the classical case. The quadrupole moment $Q(m)$ in the state m is related to the quadrupole moment in the state $m_2 = I$ through

$$Q(m) = \frac{3m^2 - I(I+1)}{I(2I-1)} Q \qquad (7.25)$$

where Q, without any special notation, refers to the quadrupole moment $Q(\psi)$, (7.15), in the state ψ with $m = I$. Q is usually called "the quadrupole moment" of the nucleus.

Nuclear quadrupole moments are usually divided by the charge e of one proton and are then given in square centimeters. Table 7.1 (Feld 49) gives the values of Q for a number of nuclei. These values are often quite uncertain for the following reason: It is possible to measure the interaction energy (7.17), between the nucleus and the electric field produced by the surrounding electrons, with high accuracy; but the gradient of the electric field, $(\partial \mathcal{E}_z/\partial z)_0$, at the position of the nucleus is very hard to determine. It can be measured accurately in most atoms (Davis 48) but can only be estimated in most molecules (Townes 47). These estimates are not always reliable, and the quoted values of the quadrupole moments are doubtful in these cases (Sternheimer 50).

If we assume that the nuclear charge is distributed uniformly over the nucleus, we may use (7.17) to get an idea of the shape of the

TABLE 7.1

QUADRUPOLE MOMENTS Q AND ECCENTRICITIES

For the calculation of η, the nuclear radius R was determined from formula (4.1) using $r_0 = 1.5 \times 10^{-13}$ cm. This table is taken from Feld (49).

Nucleus	Z	Q $(10^{-26}$ cm$^2)$	η
N^{14}	7	2	0.028
Al^{27}	13	15.6	0.074
Cl^{35}	17	-7.92	-0.024
Cl^{37}	17	-6.19	-0.018
Cu^{63}	29	-10	-0.012
Cu^{65}	29	-10	-0.012
Ga^{69}	31	23.24	0.024
Ga^{71}	31	14.68	0.015
As^{75}	33	30	0.028
Br^{79}	35	28	0.024
Br^{81}	35	23	0.020
Kr^{83}	36	15	0.012
In^{115}	49	117	0.056
I^{127}	53	-46	-0.019
Eu^{151}	63	120	0.038
Eu^{153}	63	250	0.078
Yb^{173}	70	390	0.10
Lu^{175}	71	590	0.15
Lu^{176}	71	600–800	0.15–0.20
Ta^{181}	73	600	0.14
Re^{185}	75	280	0.064
Re^{187}	75	260	0.058
Hg^{201}	80	50	0.010
Bi^{209}	83	-40	-0.008

nucleus. We can infer that the deviations from the spherical shape are quite small. If we insert the nuclear radius for R in (7.17), we obtain very small values of the eccentricity parameter η. The largest quadrupole moment is observed in Lu^{176}, and it corresponds to a value of $\eta = 0.2$ only.

The concepts of electric dipole and quadrupole moments can be generalized by introducing the "electric multipole moments" Q_{lm} through[1]

$$Q_{lm} = \int r^l \, Y_{lm}^*(\theta,\varphi) \, \rho(x,y,z) \, dV \tag{7.26}$$

Here $Y_{lm}(\theta,\varphi)$ is the normalized spherical harmonic function defined in Appendix A. The quantum-mechanical equivalent of (7.26) is

$$Q_{lm}(\psi) = \sum_{i=1}^{Z} e \int r_i^l \, Y_{lm}^*(\theta_i,\varphi_i) \, |\psi(\mathbf{r}_1,\mathbf{r}_2,\cdots,\mathbf{r}_A)|^2 \, d\tau \tag{7.27}$$

We find the following relations

$$\epsilon = \sqrt{4\pi} \, Q_{0,0}$$

$$D_z = \sqrt{\frac{4\pi}{3}} \, Q_{1,0}$$

$$D_x \pm iD_y = \pm \sqrt{\frac{8\pi}{3}} \, Q_{1,\mp 1} \tag{7.28}$$

$$Q = \sqrt{\frac{16\pi}{5}} \, Q_{2,0}$$

The parity rule implies that all electric multipole moments with odd values of l vanish. The composition law of angular momenta implies that electric multipole moments of (even) order l vanish unless the angular momentum I of the wave function ψ is at least as large as $l/2$. The vanishing of the electric dipole moment and the fact that the electric quadrupole moment vanishes for $I = 0$ and $I = \frac{1}{2}$ are special cases of these two general rules. So far no effects of electric moments of an order higher than 2 have been found experimentally.

B. Magnetic Moments

The orbital motion of the charged particles within the nucleus produces a certain electric current density which gives rise to magnetic effects. The orbital motion is not the only source of magnetism, however. Each nucleon (proton or neutron) possesses an intrinsic magnetic moment which is parallel to its spin. It is probably caused by the rotation of the nucleon.[2]

There may be contributions to the magnetism of a nucleus from

---

[1] These "static" multipole moments refer to the charge distribution in one nuclear state and should not be confused with the multipole moments of Chapter XII, which determine transitions between two different states.

[2] It may seem surprising that an uncharged particle produces a magnetic moment upon rotation. However, the lack of charge means only that the integral of the charge density is zero. A sphere, for example, whose surface is negatively charged, and in whose center an equal but positive charge is concentrated, would appear uncharged, but it would produce a negative magnetic moment upon rotation. This picture serves as an illustration and is not meant as an actual model of the neutron.

sources besides those mentioned. It is possible that the intrinsic magnetism of a nucleon is different when it is in close proximity to another nucleon. It is also possible that the "field" which produces the nuclear forces carries a magnetic moment. Some evidence for such effects have been found in H^3 and He^3 (Lamb 38, Siegert 37, Sachs 48, Avery 48, Villars 47, Thellung 48). We shall not discuss them here.

According to the latest experiments (Poss 49, Gardner 49) the observed value of the magnetic moment of the proton is

$$\mu_p = (2.7934 \pm 0.0003)\,\frac{e\hbar}{2M_p c}$$

It is 2.79 times larger than would be expected from the analogy with the electron whose magnetic moment is $e\hbar/2m_e c$.

The magnetic moment of the neutron is (Bloch 48, Arnold 47, Rogers 49)

$$\mu_n = (-1.9135 \pm 0.0003)\,\frac{e\hbar}{2M_p c}$$

The negative sign indicates that it is directed opposite to the angular momentum of the neutron. It is useful to introduce the gyromagnetic factors g_p, g_n by expressing the proportionality of the magnetic moment vector $\mathbf{\mu}$ and the spin vector $\mathbf{S}$ in the form[1]

$$\mathbf{\mu} = g\,\frac{e\hbar}{2Mc}\,\mathbf{S} \tag{7.29}$$

Since the spin is $\frac{1}{2}$ for nucleons, we find

$$g_p = 5.59 \qquad g_n = -3.83 \tag{7.30}$$

for the proton and neutron gyromagnetic ratio, respectively.[2]

In the actual nucleus the magnetic moment is spread over the whole volume. We therefore introduce the magnetization density $\mathbf{M(r)}$, which is a vector depending on the space coordinates. We consider two sources of magnetization: the orbital motion of the charged particles (protons) and the magnetic moments associated with the spins of all the particles. The orbital motion of the protons gives rise

---

[1] We measure angular momenta in units of $\hbar$.

[2] It is easy to construct a charge distribution which would give a gyromagnetic ratio different from unity when rotated. If the charge density is proportional to the mass density everywhere, the ratio of magnetic to mechanical moment is $e/2Mc$; for proof, see (7.39). Any factor higher than $e/2Mc$ can be obtained by attributing more charge density to the surface layers.

to a (convection) current density $\mathbf{j}(\mathbf{r})$. The corresponding magnetic moment density $\mathbf{M}_c(\mathbf{r})$ is defined by

$$\mathbf{j}(\mathbf{r}) = c \text{ curl } \mathbf{M}_c(\mathbf{r}) \qquad (7.31)$$

For application to nuclei the quantum-mechanical form for the convection current density has to be used:

$$\mathbf{j}(\mathbf{r}) = \sum_{k=1}^{Z} \mathbf{j}_k(\mathbf{r})$$

$$\mathbf{j}_k(\mathbf{r}) = \int \psi^*(\mathbf{r}_1,\cdots,\mathbf{r}_A) \frac{e}{M} \mathbf{p}_k \, \psi(\mathbf{r}_1,\cdots,\mathbf{r}_A) \, d\tau_1 \cdots d\tau_{k-1} \, d\tau_{k+1} \cdots d\tau_A \quad (7.32)$$

The sum here is taken over all the protons, $k = 1,2,\cdots,Z$. The integration extends over all the coordinates except that of the proton in question, $\mathbf{r}_k$, which must be set equal to $\mathbf{r}$. The operator $\mathbf{p}_k = -i\hbar\nabla_k$ is the momentum operator for the kth proton.

We now turn to the spin contribution to the magnetic moment density $\mathbf{M}$. Let $\mathbf{S}_k(\mathbf{r})$ be the "spin density" of particle k. It is defined by an integral similar to (7.32) but with $(e/M)\mathbf{p}_k$ replaced by the spin operator $\mathbf{S}_k$ for the kth particle. Then the magnetic moment density $\mathbf{M}_s(\mathbf{r})$ due to the spins can be written as

$$\mathbf{M}_s(\mathbf{r}) = \frac{e\hbar}{2Mc} \left[g_p \sum_{k=1}^{Z} \mathbf{S}_k(\mathbf{r}) + g_n \sum_{k=Z+1}^{A} \mathbf{S}_k(\mathbf{r}) \right] \qquad (7.33)$$

The first sum extends over all the protons, the second sum over all the neutrons.

The entire magnetic moment density $\mathbf{M}(\mathbf{r})$ is made up of the two contributions, $\mathbf{M}_c(\mathbf{r})$ from the convection currents and $\mathbf{M}_s(\mathbf{r})$ from the spins:

$$\mathbf{M}(\mathbf{r}) = \mathbf{M}_c(\mathbf{r}) + \mathbf{M}_s(\mathbf{r}) \qquad (7.34)$$

Let $\mathcal{3C}(\mathbf{r})$ be an external magnetic field acting on the nucleus. The energy of the nucleus in this field is given by

$$E = -\int \mathbf{M}(\mathbf{r}) \cdot \mathcal{3C}(\mathbf{r}) \, dV \qquad (7.35)$$

since $\mathbf{M}(\mathbf{r})$ is a magnetic moment density. The most important case is a constant magnetic field $\mathcal{3C}(\mathbf{r}) = \mathcal{3C}$. The energy is then

$$E = -\mathbf{\mu} \cdot \mathcal{3C} \qquad (7.36)$$

where $\mathbf{\mu}$ is the "magnetic dipole moment" of the nucleus:

$$\mathbf{\mu} = \int \mathbf{M}(\mathbf{r}) \, dV \qquad (7.37)$$

Unlike the electric case, the parity rule does not force the magnetic dipole moment to vanish. The spin operators S_k which enter into the spin part of the magnetic moment are unchanged by an inversion of the coordinate system (parity), and we shall see right away that the convection current part of μ also can be written in terms of operators which are unchanged under inversion. The angular momentum rule implies that the magnetic dipole moment vanishes if the nucleus has an angular momentum $I = 0$, but not otherwise. The proof is completely analogous to the one given earlier for the electric quadrupole moment.

We decompose the magnetic moment μ into an orbital (convection) part and a spin part:

$$\mu = \mu_c + \mu_s$$

where $\mu_c = \int \mathbf{M}_c(\mathbf{r}) \, dV$ and $\mu_s = \int \mathbf{M}_s(\mathbf{r}) \, dV$. The orbital part can be written in a different form by means of the following identities (which can be proved by integration by parts):

$$\mu_c = \int \mathbf{M}_c(\mathbf{r}) \, dV = \frac{1}{2} \int \mathbf{r} \times \text{curl } \mathbf{M}_c \, dV = \frac{1}{2c} \int (\mathbf{r} \times \mathbf{j}) \, dV \quad (7.38)$$

If we recall the quantum-mechanical definition of $\mathbf{j}(\mathbf{r})$, (7.32), we see that the last integral is the expectation value in the state ψ of the following operator:

$$[\mu_c]_{\text{Op}} = \frac{e}{2Mc} \sum_{k=1}^{Z} \mathbf{r}_k \times \mathbf{p}_k$$

$$= \frac{e\hbar}{2Mc} \sum_{k=1}^{Z} \mathbf{L}_k \quad (7.39)$$

where $\mathbf{L}_k$ in the second sum is the orbital angular momentum operator (in units of $\hbar$) for the kth proton. The magnetic moment contributed by the convection current of each proton is proportional to its orbital angular momentum, the proportionality constant being $e\hbar/2Mc$. The form (7.39) for the orbital part of the magnetic moment μ_c shows that the operator does not change sign under inversion of the coordinate system: $\mathbf{r}$ goes into $-\mathbf{r}$, $\mathbf{p}$ goes into $-\mathbf{p}$; hence $\mathbf{L} = \mathbf{r} \times \mathbf{p}$ goes into $+\mathbf{L}$.

Similarly the spin part of the magnetic moment can be written as the expectation value of an operator $[\mu_s]_{\text{Op}}$ in the state ψ, where

$$[\mu_s]_{\text{Op}} = \frac{e\hbar}{2Mc} \left[g_p \sum_{k=1}^{Z} \mathbf{S}_k + g_n \sum_{k=Z+1}^{A} \mathbf{S}_k \right] \quad (7.40)$$

where S_k is the spin operator for the kth particle, and the first sum extends over the protons, the second over the neutrons, in the nucleus. The total magnetic moment μ is the expectation value in the state ψ:

$$\mu = \int \psi^* \mu_{Op} \, \psi \, d\tau \qquad (7.41)$$

of the operator:

$$\mu_{Op} = [\mu_c]_{Op} + [\mu_s]_{Op} \qquad (7.42)$$

We compare the magnetic moment operator (7.42) with the operator I of the total angular momentum:

$$I = \sum_{k=1}^{A} L_k + \sum_{k=1}^{A} S_k \qquad (7.43)$$

where the sums are extended over all the nucleons. The operators (7.43) and (7.42) are similar in form. However, L_k and S_k are multiplied with different factors in μ_{Op} and therefore the magnetic moment is not necessarily parallel to the angular momentum I. Since the vector I is a constant of motion, the magnetic moment is generally not constant in time and its significant value is its time average. Hence, as far as the expectation value (7.41) is concerned, we can replace the operator μ_{Op} by

$$\mu_{eff} = \frac{(\mu_{Op} \cdot I)}{I^2} I \qquad (7.44)$$

The "effective" magnetic moment μ_{eff} is parallel to I and has all properties of a vector in this direction. Only the z component, $(\mu_{eff})_z$, has a non-vanishing expectation value. Furthermore, there is a well-known relation between the expectation values of $(\mu_{eff})_z$ in the $2I+1$ substates of a given nuclear state of angular momentum I. The substates differ only by the orientation of I with respect to the z axis. The angle β between I and the z axis is given by (7.23), so that the expectation values μ_z in the different substates with magnetic quantum numbers m are proportional to m:

$$\mu_z = \text{const} \cos \beta = \text{const} \, \frac{m}{\sqrt{I(I+1)}}$$

Hence μ_z attains the maximum value in the substate $\psi(m)$ with $m = I$, and this maximum value is commonly called the magnetic moment μ of the nucleus:

$$\mu = \int \psi^*(I) \, (\mu_{Op})_z \, \psi(I) \, d\tau$$

Here $\psi(I)$ is the wave function of the substate $m = I$, and $(\mu_{Op})_z$ is the z component of the operator (7.42).

The gyromagnetic ratio g of the nucleus is defined by

$$\mu = g \frac{e\hbar}{2Mc} I \tag{7.45}$$

It is customary to measure magnetic moments in units of the Bohr magneton for a proton, where

$$1 \text{ Bohr magneton} = \mu_0 = \frac{e\hbar}{2M_pc} = 5.049 \times 10^{-24} \text{ erg/gauss} \tag{7.46}$$

The nuclear magnetic moment in these units is then given by

$$\text{Magnetic moment in Bohr magnetons} = \frac{\mu}{\mu_0} = gI \quad \cdot \tag{7.47}$$

The present precision methods of measuring magnetic moments were initiated by Rabi and his group (Kellogg 36, 46).   These methods provide a direct measurement of the gyromagnetic ratio g.   In order to obtain the magnetic moment μ itself, the nuclear angular momentum must be found separately.

The formula for the magnetic dipole moment of the magnetic moment distribution $\mathbf{M(r)}$ can be generalized as follows.   We use the "magnetic charge density"

$$\rho_m(\mathbf{r}) = -\text{div } \mathbf{M(r)} \tag{7.48}$$

to define the generalized magnetic multipole moment M_{lm} in analogy with the generalized electric multipole moment Q_{lm}, (7.26):

$$M_{lm} = \int r^l \, Y_{lm}^*(\theta, \varphi) \, \rho_m(x, y, z) \, dV \tag{7.49}$$

For the special case $l = 1$ we find the relations

$$M_{1,0} = \left(\frac{3}{4\pi}\right)^{\frac{1}{2}} \mu_z$$

$$M_{1,\pm 1} = \mp \left(\frac{3}{8\pi}\right)^{\frac{1}{2}} (\mu_x \mp i\,\mu_y) \tag{7.50}$$

The following rules hold for these generalized magnetic multipole moments: (1) they are zero for even values of l (because of the parity rule); (2) for odd l they vanish unless the angular momentum I of the nucleus is greater than or equal to $\frac{1}{2}l$ (because of the law of composition of angular momenta); (3) they vanish unless $m = 0$ (the vanishing of the components μ_x and μ_y of the magnetic dipole moment is a special case of this rule); (4) the non-vanishing component $M_{l,0}$ in the state ψ depends on the z-component m of the angular momentum of the nucleus; the values of $M_{l,0}$ for different m are related, however, so that there is only one independent value, which is commonly taken as $M_{l,0}$ in the state with $m = I$ and referred to as the magnetic multipole moment of order l.   (There are various conventional definitions of the higher moments which differ from each other by factors, however, so care should be taken to make sure which definition is used in any special case.)

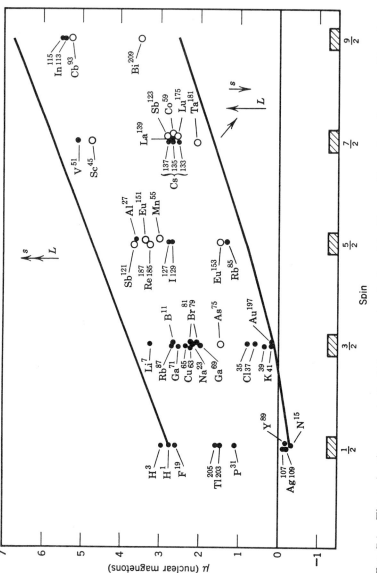

Fig. 7.1. The magnetic moments (in Bohr magnetons) of nuclei with an odd number of protons (Z) and an even number of neutrons (N), plotted against the nuclear angular momentum I. The upper solid line is computed from the Schmidt model assuming $l = I - \frac{1}{2}$ [formula (7.54) with $g_L = 1$]; the lower solid curve connects values of μ computed from the Schmidt model assuming $l = I + \frac{1}{2}$ [formula (7.55) with $g_L = 1$]. The measured magnetic moments cannot be fitted by either formula but lie between the two predictions of the Schmidt model. This figure is taken from Poss (49).

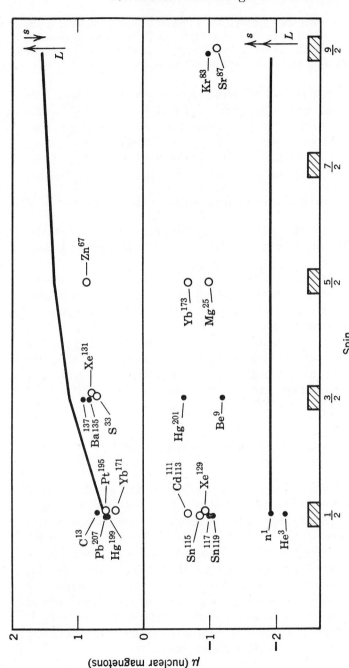

FIG. 7.2. The magnetic moments (in Bohr magnetons) of nuclei with an even number of protons (Z) and an odd number of neutrons (N), plotted against the nuclear angular momentum I. The lower (horizontal) straight line is computed from the Schmidt model assuming $l = I - \frac{1}{2}$ [formula (7.54) with $g_L = 0$]; the upper curve connects values of μ computed from the Schmidt model assuming $l = I + \frac{1}{2}$ [formula (7.55) with $g_L = 0$]. Again the measured magnetic moments lie mostly between the two curves of Schmidt. Notice that He³ has a magnetic moment more negative than that of the neutron; H³ (on Fig. 7.1) has a magnetic moment more positive than that of the proton. This is commonly interpreted as a cooperative effect which is beyond the simple theory given in this chapter. This figure is taken from Poss (49).

At present there exists some evidence for a magnetic octupole moment ($l=3$) in only one nucleus (iodine; see Tolansky 39). But the advances in precision measurements of magnetic moments should make it possible to find magnetic octupole moments of reasonable orders of magnitude before long.

It is impossible, in general, to find an expression for the gyromagnetic ratio g of the nucleus in analogy to the Landé factor used in atomic spectroscopy. The interactions between the nucleons in the nucleus depend significantly on their spin directions in contrast to the electron-electron interaction in atoms. Hence the individual spins of the nucleons are not constant, even to a first approximation. Neither the total proton orbital angular momentum $\sum\limits_{k=1}^{Z} \mathbf{L}_k$ nor the proton or neutron spin angular momenta are constants or even nearly constants. They can assume all values compatible with the total angular momentum I.

Hence any theoretical attempt to determine the gyromagnetic factor g must start from certain assumptions about the way the total magnetic moment μ is made up by the orbital and intrinsic angular momenta of the constituents.

Let us illustrate this point with a very simple assumption: We assume that the angular momentum I is due to the motion of *one* nucleon only and that the angular momenta (orbital and intrinsic) of all other nucleons add up to zero. This assumption is usually referred to as the "Schmidt model" (Schmidt 37). We get

$$\mathbf{I} = \mathbf{L}_k + \mathbf{S}_k \qquad \mathbf{\mu} = \frac{e\hbar}{2Mc}\,(g_L\mathbf{L}_k + g_S\mathbf{S}_k) \qquad (7.51)$$

where $g_L=1$, $g_S=g_p$ if the nucleon is a proton, and $g_L=0$, $g_S=g_n$ if the nucleon is a neutron. In general only $\mathbf{I}$ has a definite value, but neither $\mathbf{L}_k$ nor $\mathbf{S}_k$ has a sharp value. Since only one particle contributes to I, we have necessarily $S=\pm\frac{1}{2}$ and there are only two possibilities for L: $L=I+\frac{1}{2}$ or $L=I-\frac{1}{2}$, or perhaps linear combinations thereof. Since the state of the nucleus must have a well-defined parity (even or odd, but not both), the nucleon k cannot be in a state which is a mixture of the two possibilities. It therefore must have a well-defined orbital angular momentum given by the quantum number $l=I+\frac{1}{2}$ or $l=I-\frac{1}{2}$. The situation is then completely analogous to the conditions prevailing with electron orbits, and we get for the g factor

$$g = g_S a_S + g_L a_L \qquad (7.52)$$

where a_S and a_L are the quantum-mechanical values of $(\mathbf{S \cdot I})/I^2$ and $(\mathbf{L \cdot I})/I^2$, respectively:

$$a_S = \frac{I(I+1) + S(S+1) - l(l+1)}{2I(I+1)}$$

$$a_L = \frac{I(I+1) + l(l+1) - S(S+1)}{2I(I+1)}$$

$$(7.53)$$

In the case of the Schmidt model we must put $S=\frac{1}{2}$ and $l=I\pm\frac{1}{2}$. The expressions are particularly simple when the orbital and spin angular momenta of nucleon k line up: $I=l+\frac{1}{2}$. Then (7.53) gives $a_S = S/I$ and $a_L = l/I$, so that

$$g = \frac{\frac{1}{2}g_S + (I-\frac{1}{2})g_L}{I} \qquad \text{(Schmidt model, } l=I-\tfrac{1}{2}) \qquad (7.54)$$

The other possibility is that l and S are anti-parallel: $I=l-\frac{1}{2}$. We then get from (7.52) and (7.53)

$$g = \frac{-\frac{1}{2}g_S + (I+\frac{3}{2})g_L}{I+1} \qquad \text{(Schmidt model, } l=I+\tfrac{1}{2}) \qquad (7.55)$$

A study of the known magnetic moments of odd-mass-number nuclei (Poss 49, Goldsmith 48, Mack 50) shows that these moments cannot be fitted by either (7.53) or (7.54). It is true, however, that practically all the magnetic moments for a given I fall between the results of the two formulas above. Figures 7.1 and 7.2 (both taken from the report of Poss) show measured magnetic moments $\mu = gI$, plotted against the nuclear angular momentum I, for nuclei with an odd number of protons and neutrons, respectively. The solid lines connect the values given by the Schmidt model.

8. STATISTICS

The properties of quantum-mechanical systems composed of many particles are determined by the "statistics" of the constituents. There are two alternatives: Bose-Einstein statistics and Fermi-Dirac statistics. It is impossible to give a classical explanation of the significance of the choice of statistics. The consequences of this choice manifest themselves only in typical quantum phenomena, and they disappear in the classical limit.

Let us consider a system of A particles of which some are "equal" or indistinguishable, for instance a nucleus of A constituents of which the protons and the neutrons are both groups of "equal" particles.

The Schrödinger equation of this system has the form

$$H \psi(1,2,3,\cdots) = E \psi(1,2,3,\cdots) \qquad (8.1)$$

where H is the Hamiltonian operator and $\psi(1,2,3,\cdots)$ is the eigenfunction depending on the coordinates of the first, second, third, $\cdots$ particle, and we abbreviate our notation by writing the figures 1,2,3, $\cdots$ instead of the coordinates of these particles. Evidently the Hamiltonian operator H remains unchanged if the coordinates of any two equal particles are exchanged. It can be shown (Pauli 33) that the eigenfunctions ψ must be either symmetric or anti-symmetric with respect to the exchange of coordinates of any pair of equal particles.

If the wave function is symmetric under the exchange of the coordinates of any two equal particles, the particles are said to obey Bose-Einstein statistics. If the wave function is anti-symmetric (changes sign) under the exchange of the coordinates of two equal particles, the particles are said to obey Fermi-Dirac statistics. It has been established that protons and neutrons obey Fermi-Dirac statistics. All wave functions which describe states of a system of protons and neutrons must be such that they change sign if the coordinates of two protons are interchanged, or if the coordinates of two neutrons are interchanged. There is no special condition upon the behavior of the wave function under an interchange of the coordinates of a neutron and a proton, since these are not identical particles.[1] There are certain consequences of the Fermi-Dirac statistics which can be stated in less formal terms.

It follows directly from the anti-symmetry that the wave function vanishes if the coordinates of two equal particles assume the same value. This means physically that two equal particles can never be found exactly at the same place. It is also very improbable that they are found a small distance apart since the wave function is still small if the coordinates are almost equal. Actually they are found mostly at distances larger than a characteristic distance d which depends on their relative momentum p and is of the order $d \sim \hbar/p$. This can be shown as follows: Let us write the eigenfunction ψ as a function of the distance r_{12} between the two particles in the form

$$\psi \sim C \sin \frac{r_{12}}{\lambda(r_{12})} \qquad (8.2)$$

---

[1] In Chapter III we shall introduce a method of writing nuclear wave functions in which neutrons and protons appear formally as identical particles. We shall show, however, that this is merely a formal device, not an additional assumption about the nature of the particles.

where $\lambda(r_{12})$ is an even function of r_{12}, and C depends on all variables except r_{12}. Any function which is anti-symmetric in r_{12} can be written in this form. We now make the special assumption that $\lambda(r_{12})$ is a slowly varying function, i.e., that it does not change much over the distance $\lambda(0)$:

$$\lambda'(0) \ll 1 \qquad \lambda''(0) \cdot \lambda(0) \ll 1 \tag{8.3}$$

The significance of this assumption becomes evident when we apply the operator $-\hbar^2(\partial^2/\partial r_{12}{}^2)$ which corresponds to $p_{12}{}^2$, the square of the relative momentum. If (8.3) is valid, we get

$$p_{12}{}^2 \psi = \frac{\hbar^2}{(\lambda(0))^2} \psi \tag{8.4}$$

In this approximation, the operator $p_{12}{}^2$ is equivalent to multiplication by $\hbar^2/\lambda^2(0)$, and we can interpret $\hbar/\lambda(0)$ as the value of p_{12} in the neighborhood of $r_{12}=0$. Thus (8.3) gives the conditions under which it is possible to speak of a definite "value" of the relative momentum in the neighborhood of $r_{12}=0$. $\lambda = \hbar/p_{12}$ is the de Broglie wavelength corresponding to the momentum p_{12}. Equation (8.2) shows that the wave function is small as long as the distance r_{12} between two equal particles is small compared to λ. We thus conclude that identical particles are rarely found at distances small compared to the wavelength $\lambda = \hbar/p_{12}$, where p_{12} is of the order of their relative momentum. In order to bring two identical particles very close together, say within a distance d, their relative momentum must be at least of the order $\hbar/d$.

This effect of the Fermi statistics can also be derived from the more familiar formulation that not more than one particle of a given type can fill a "cell" in phase space. The phase space is a six-dimensional space whose coordinates are the three ordinary space coordinates and the three components of the momentum. One "cell" is a volume of the order of magnitude h^3. If the linear dimensions Δq of a cell are chosen of the order d, the momentum spread Δp must be of the order h/d so that $\Delta q^3 \cdot \Delta p^3 \sim h^3$. If the cell is filled with a particle, a second particle at a linear distance d must differ in momentum by at least Δp in order to be found in a different cell.

Another well-known consequence of the Fermi-Dirac statistics is found in systems of several equal particles of weak interaction. In this case, the particles can be considered almost independent and subject to the same potential V. They occupy energy levels which are the stationary levels of a single particle in the potential V, whose eigenfunctions we call ψ_i and whose eigenvalues are E_i. We shall call this way of describing a system of many particles the "independent-particle picture." It follows, then (Pauli 33), that not more than one particle can occupy the same level i if the particles obey Fermi statistics. This formulation is called the "Pauli exclusion principle."

It is necessary to take account of spin in the application of the Fermi-Dirac statistics to nucleons. The spin introduces into the description of a particle a new coordinate which can assume only two values, corresponding to the two possible orientations of the spin. The wave functions must be anti-symmetric with respect to the exchange of *all* coordinates of two equal particles, including the spin coordinates. Some of the consequences discussed above must be reformulated when the spin is taken into account. The rule that two identical particles are never found at a distance small compared to ƛ as defined above can be applied only if the particles are in the same spin state. Only then are all coordinates identical or almost identical. If the spins are opposite, the rule no longer holds since the spin coordinates do not coincide. The particles can approach one another just as if they were not identical.

In the independent-particle description, a level in the potential V is not completely defined by the eigenfunction ψ_i which depends only on the spatial variables. The levels are completely described only if the spin coordinate is included. This becomes particularly simple if the potential V does not depend on the spin. The form of ψ_i and the energy E_i are then independent of the spin. If we define a "level" by ψ_i and E_i only, without specification of the spin, the Pauli exclusion principle does not exclude *two* identical particles, provided that their spin orientations are different. Again, two identical particles of opposite spin must be considered "different."

The Fermi-Dirac statistics of nucleons has numerous and important consequences in the structure of nuclei which will be discussed especially in Chapter VI.

It is also interesting to determine the statistics which follow for entire nuclei, when they are considered entities (rigid bodies) themselves. This is of importance in the study of the interaction of nuclei with other nuclei in molecules. For this purpose the internal structure of the nucleus is irrelevant, because the energies in the molecule are very small compared with the excitation energies of nuclei. Consider two identical nuclei, each consisting of A nucleons. Let us assume that they are part of a dynamical system, say a diatomic molecule. An example is the oxygen molecule, both nuclei being O^{16}. Conversely, an oxygen molecule with one O^{16} nucleus and one O^{17} nucleus is not of the type under consideration (even though its chemical behavior is not very much different). The wave function of this molecule depends on the coordinates of the two nuclei as well as on the coordinates of all the electrons. Let us consider its behavior under an interchange of the coordinates of the two nuclei, leaving the electron coordinates unchanged. An interchange of the two nuclei is equivalent to A (the mass number) interchanges of individual nucleons. The exchange of each pair of identical nucleons multiplies the wave function by -1 (Fermi-Dirac statistics); hence A such exchanges give rise to multiplication by $(-1)^A$. We conclude that *nuclei with odd A obey Fermi-Dirac statistics and nuclei with even A obey Bose-Einstein statistics*. A rigorous proof of this theorem was given by Ehrenfest and Oppenheimer (Ehrenfest 31).

The statistics of nuclei have important consequences for the spectroscopy of molecules. Take the oxygen molecule as an example. Among the quantum states of the O^{16}-O^{17} molecule, there are some which are symmetric under an interchange of the nuclear coordinates and others which are anti-symmetric under this operation. Both kinds can be observed spectroscopically. In the O^{16}-O^{16} molecule only the symmetric states are allowed by the nuclear statistics, so that certain states are missing; in the O^{17}-O^{17} molecule, only the anti-symmetric states are allowed. It is apparent that a detailed study of the spectra of homonuclear diatomic molecules allows determination of the statistics of the nuclei of those molecules. For details, the reader is referred to the books by Herzberg (39), Fluegge (46), and Kopfermann (45).

Historically, the most important determination of the statistics of a nucleus was that of N^{14} (Heitler 29, Rasetti 30). N^{14} was found to obey Bose-Einstein statistics. This provided a crucial test against the proton-electron hypothesis of nuclear constitution: according to this hypothesis, N^{14} should consist of 14 protons and 7 electrons, i.e., 21 particles every one of which is known to obey Fermi-Dirac statistics. According to the theorem of Ehrenfest and Oppenheimer, the entire nucleus must then obey Fermi-Dirac statistics, in contradiction to experiment. On the other hand, the statistics of N^{14} is predicted correctly by the neutron-proton hypothesis of nuclear constitution, according to which N^{14} contains an even number (14) of Fermi-Dirac particles. Incidentally, the considerations of Ehrenfest and Oppenheimer also show that a neutron can *not* be considered a closely bound composite particle consisting of a proton and an electron: such a compound particle would have to obey Bose-Einstein statistics, whereas the neutrons are known to obey Fermi-Dirac statistics.

SYMBOLS

The numbers in parentheses ( ) are the numbers of the equations in which the symbol is first used or defined.

a	Semi-axis of a spheroid, perpendicular to its symmetry (z) axis (7.17)
a_L	Landé factor for the orbital motion (7.52), (7.53)
a_s	Landé factor for the spin motion (7.52), (7.53)
A	Mass number (Section 1)
B	Binding energy of a nucleus (2.5)
B^*	Binding energy of an excited nuclear state (Section 2)
$B(\alpha)$	Binding energy of an alpha-particle [$=28.2$ Mev] (2.10)
c	Semi-axis of a spheroid, parallel to the symmetry (z) axis (7.17)
c	Velocity of light [$=3\times10^{10}$ cm/sec] 7.15
D_z	Dipole moment of the charge distribution (z component) (7.4)
e	Electronic charge [$=4.8\times10^{-10}$ esu] (Section 1)
e^-	Negative electron (3.1)
e^+	Positive electron (positron) (3.2)
E	Energy associated with the charge distribution ρ in the external field with potential φ (Section 7)
E^*	Nuclear excitation energy before emission of a particle (5.6)
E_∞	Value of the potential energy $V(r)$ between two nuclei B and C at infinite separation (Section 3)
ε	Electric field vector (Section 7)
f	Binding fraction [$=B/A$] (Section 2)
g	Gyromagnetic ratio of a particle (7.29)
g	Gyromagnetic ratio of a nucleus (7.45)
g_L	Gyromagnetic ratio associated with the orbital motion (7.51)
g_n	Gyromagnetic ratio of a neutron [$=-3.83$] (7.30)
g_p	Gyromagnetic ratio of a proton [$=+5.58$] (7.30)
g_s	Gyromagnetic ratio associated with the spin motion (7.51)
$\hbar$	Planck's constant divided by 2π (Section 6)
H	Hamiltonian of the nucleus (8.1)
$\mathcal{H}$	$=\mathcal{H}(\mathbf{r})$ for a constant magnetic field (7.36)
$\mathcal{H}(\mathbf{r})$	Magnetic field vector at position $\mathbf{r}$ (7.35)
I	Total angular momentum ("spin") of a nucleus, usually in its ground state (Section 6)

I	Angular momentum operator for the nucleus as a whole (7.43)
$\mathbf{j(r)}$	Current density at position $\mathbf{r}$ (7.31)
$\mathbf{j}_k\mathbf{(r)}$	Current density associated with the motion of the kth proton (7.32)
K	Electric field gradient evaluated at the center of the nucleus $[=(\partial\mathsf{E}_z/\partial_z)]$ (7.11)
$\mathbf{L}_k$	Orbital angular momentum operator for the kth nucleon (7.39)
m	Magnetic quantum number (Section 6)
m_e	Mass of the electron (2.3)
m_ν	Mass of the neutrino $[=0?]$ (Section 3)
M	Mass of a nucleon, used when the difference between M_n and M_p is not important (Section 7)
M_{at}	Mass of an atom containing the nucleus (Z,N) and Z electrons (2.2)
M_{H}	Mass of the hydrogen atom (2.3)
M_{lm}	Generalized static magnetic multipole moment of order l,m (7.49)
M_n	Mass of the neutron (Section 2)
M_{nucl}	Mass of the nucleus (Z,N), without atomic electrons (2.1)
M_p	Mass of the proton (Section 2)
$\mathbf{M(r)}$	Magnetization density vector at position r (Section 7)
$\mathbf{M}_c\mathbf{(r)}$	Magnetization density associated with the convection current $\mathbf{j(r)}$ (7.31)
$\mathbf{M}_s\mathbf{(r)}$	Magnetization density associated with the intrinsic spins of the nucleons (7.33)
n	Neutron (3.1)
N	Number of neutrons in a nucleus $[=A-Z]$ (Section 1)
p	Proton (3.1)
$P_i\mathbf{(r)}\,dV$	Probability of finding the ith nucleon in the volume element dV at position $\mathbf{r}$ with respect to the center of gravity of the nucleus (7.5)
$\mathbf{p}_k$	Linear momentum operator for the kth nucleon $[=-i\hbar\boldsymbol{\nabla}_k]$ (7.32)
p_{12}	Relative momentum of particles 1 and 2 (Section 8)
Q	Electric quadrupole moment (7.17), (7.25)
Q_{lm}	Generalized electric multipole moment (static) of order l,m (7.26)
$Q(m)$	Electric quadrupole moment in the state ψ with angular

	momentum I and magnetic quantum number $I_z = m$ (7.24), (7.25)
$Q(\psi)$	Electric quadrupole moment in the quantum state ψ (7.15)
r_0	Nuclear radius parameter $[=R/\sqrt[3]{A}]$ (4.1)
$\mathbf{r}_k$	Position vector of the kth nucleon (Section 7)
R	Nuclear radius (Section 4)
R'	Radius of residual (daughter) nucleus after alpha-particle emission (5.10)
$\mathbf{s}$	Spin vector of a particle (7.29)
$S_a(X)$	Separation energy of a particle a from the nucleus X (Section 2)
S_α	Separation energy of an alpha-particle (2.10)
S_c	Coulomb part of the separation energy of a proton, equal to the "height of the Coulomb barrier" for a proton (5.2)
$S_c(\alpha)$	Coulomb part of the separation energy of an alpha-particle, equal to the "height of the Coulomb barrier" for an alpha-particle (5.9), (5.10)
$\mathbf{S}_k$	Spin vector for the kth particle (Section 7)
$\mathbf{S}_k(\mathbf{r})$	Spin density at position $\mathbf{r}$ associated with the kth particle (Section 7)
S_n	Separation energy of a neutron (Section 2)
S_ν	Nuclear part of the separation energy of a proton $[=S_p+S_c]$ (Section 5)
$S_{\nu\alpha}$	Nuclear part of the separation energy of an alpha-particle $[=S_\alpha+S_c(\alpha)]$ (5.9)
S_p	Separation energy of a proton (Section 2)
$t_{1/2}$	Half-life of a radioactive nucleus (footnote 2, page 12)
T	Mean life of an excited state $[=\Pi^{-1}]$ (Section 3)
U	Total energy of a nucleus (2.4)
U^*	Total energy of an excited state of a nucleus (Section 2)
$_Z X^A$	Symbol for a nucleus with mass number A, containing Z protons and $N=A-Z$ neutrons $[=_Z X = X^A]$ (3.1')
Y	Residual nucleus after separation of particle a from nucleus X (Section 2)
Y_{lm}	Normalized spherical harmonic of order l,m, as defined in Appendix A (7.26)
Z	Nuclear charge in units of e [= atomic number = number of protons in the nucleus] (Section 1)
β	Angle between the z axis and the body (z') axis of the charge distribution ρ (7.21), (7.22)

Δ — Mass defect (2.1)

Δ — $= \Delta_{z,z+1}$ (3.5) ff.

$\Delta_{z,z+1}$ — Total energy difference between isobaric nuclei (Z,N) and $(Z+1, N-1)$ (3.4)

ε — Atomic binding energy of an electron before capture (3.7)

ϵ — Total charge of the charge distribution ρ $[= \int \rho(x,y,z)\, dV]$ (7.4)

η — Eccentricity parameter of a spheroid $[= (c^2 - a^2)/(c^2 + a^2)]$ (7.17)

$\lambda(r_{12})$ — de Broglie wavelength associated with the relative motion of particles 1 and 2 (8.2)

μ — Magnetic moment of a nucleus (Section 7)

$\mathbf{\mu}$ — Magnetic moment vector (7.29), (7.37)

μ_0 — Bohr magneton for a proton (7.46)

μ_n — Magnetic moment of a neutron (Section 7)

μ_p — Magnetic moment of a proton (Section 7)

$[\mathbf{\mu}]_{Op}$ — Magnetic moment operator (7.40), (7.41), (7.42)

$[\mathbf{\mu}_c]_{Op}$ — Magnetic moment operator associated with the convection current (7.39)

$[\mathbf{\mu}_s]_{Op}$ — Magnetic moment operator associated with the intrinsic spins (7.40)

ν — Neutrino (3.1)

Π — Barrier penetration probability per unit time (Section 3)

ρ — A classical charge density (Section 7)

$\rho_m(\mathbf{r})$ — "Magnetic charge density" at point $\mathbf{r}$ (7.48)

φ — Electrostatic potential (Section 7)

ψ — Wave function of the nucleus (Section 7)

Two-Body Problems at Low Energies

1. INTRODUCTION

Compared to the rest of nuclear physics, the phenomena involving only two nucleons have received an extraordinary amount of attention in the literature and in textbooks. This appears to be due to two causes: (1) the mathematical simplicity of two-body problems, and (2) the expectation that the forces between nucleons are additive, so that (in principle at least) a complete knowledge of the two-nucleon systems would allow computation of all nuclear properties. Evidence that the nuclear forces are not additive seems to be accumulating: if more than two nucleons are close together, the forces between each pair are perhaps not equal to those acting between isolated pairs. Hence it appears that the knowledge gained from the study of two-body problems is not so fundamental for nuclear physics as a whole as anticipated. Still the two-nucleon problems are the basic problems of nuclear physics and are our best source of knowledge regarding the nature of nuclear forces.

This chapter will deal with two-body systems with relatively small energies on a nuclear scale (i.e., energies below 10 Mev). The recent high-energy results will be discussed in Chapter IV. Since we restrict ourselves to energies low compared to the rest energy of a nucleon, all relativistic effects can be neglected. Other uncertainties are much larger than the likely relativistic corrections (Feenberg 36, Share 37).

Since the nature of the force between two nucleons cannot yet be derived from a fundamental theory, the theory of the two-body systems must include certain heuristic assumptions regarding these forces. The correctness of these assumptions can be tested only by comparing the results with experiments.

Most treatments of the two-body systems assume that nuclear forces are conservative and can be described by a potential function $V(r)$, r being the internucleon distance. Although there is little doubt about the validity of the conservation laws, the description by means of a nuclear potential function assumes that internucleon forces are independent of the relative velocity of the particles.   It is entirely possible that future experiments may lead to the recognition of the existence of velocity-dependent forces.   However, it will turn out that the *low-energy* two-body problems are rather insensitive to the assumptions made about the laws of force.

The reason for this independence lies in the extremely short range and great strength (within the range) of the nuclear forces.   [This was first pointed out by Wigner (33a,b) in connection with the large binding energy of the alpha-particle compared to that of the deuteron]. For energies below 10 Mev, the range of the force is small compared to the de Broglie wavelength of the particles; hence the actual nuclear force is very nearly equivalent (in its action upon the wave function of the system) to an idealized force which has a zero range and an infinite strength.   The details of the law of force are correspondingly unimportant.   Of course, the finite range has some effects and the ensuing range corrections can be determined from experiment.   However, even very refined experiments at low energies do not suffice to determine more than an "effective range" and "depth" of the potential well, leaving the detailed shape completely indeterminate.

This chapter begins with a discussion of the ground state of a deuteron under the simplified assumption of spin-independent central forces.   There follows a discussion of neutron-proton scattering which leads to the necessity of a spin dependence of the nuclear potential. The scattering of neutrons by protons bound in molecules is treated in some detail.   The ensuing discussion of the nuclear interaction between two protons leads to the following remarkable result: while neither the proton-proton potential nor the neutron-proton potential is determined uniquely by the experimental data, it is possible to fit all the low-energy results by the assumption that the nuclear force between two protons is the same as that between a neutron and a proton.   The last section is devoted to the modifications of the nuclear potential which the discovery of the quadrupole moment of the deuteron has introduced (Kellogg 39, 40).   The force between two nucleons is no longer a central force but must contain a part which depends on the relative direction of the spins and the radius vector between the nucleons.

2. THE GROUND STATE OF THE DEUTERON; SIMPLIFIED DISCUSSION (CENTRAL FORCES ASSUMED)

The deuteron is a system of two particles of roughly equal mass M, held together by an attractive, short-range force.   In this section we shall assume that this force acts along the line joining the two particles, i.e., that it is a central force.   This assumption has turned out to be incorrect.   There is a spin-orbit coupling term in the actual force (the so-called tensor force) whose inclusion makes the wave equation considerably more complicated.   However, the simple central force problem exhibits many qualitative features of the actual case without the

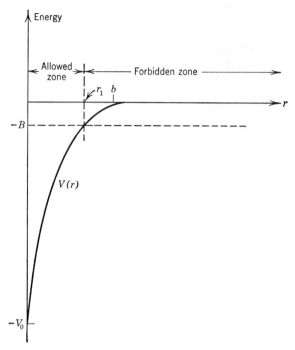

FIG. 2.1. The potential energy $V(r)$ caused by the attractive nuclear forces becomes negligible when the interparticle separation r exceeds the range b.   In the deuteron the region $E - V(r) > 0$ is the "allowed zone," $E - V(r) < 0$ the "forbidden zone."

complications introduced by the coupling between the spin and orbital motions.

The (assumed) central force can be derived from a potential $V(r)$. Since the force is attractive, $V(r)$ is negative and decreases with decreasing r.   It is assumed that it is different from zero only within a short range b of the order $b \sim 2 \times 10^{-13}$ cm, as indicated in Fig. 2.1. The wave equation for the relative motion in this system of two particles is

$$-\left(\frac{\hbar^2}{2\mu}\right) \nabla^2 \psi(\mathbf{r}) + V(r)\,\psi(\mathbf{r}) = E\,\psi(\mathbf{r}) \tag{2.1}$$

where μ is the reduced mass: $\mu = \frac{1}{2}M$ and E is the energy of the relative motion; $\mathbf{r}$ is the vector distance between the two particles. Since $V(r)$ is supposed to describe a central force, it depends only on the absolute value of the vector distance $r \equiv |\mathbf{r}|$.

We are interested in the ground state of this system whose energy E is equal to $-B$, where $B = 2.226 \pm 0.003$ Mev is the observed binding energy of the deuteron (Mobley 50, Tollestrup 50, Bell 48, Smith 48, Myers 42). We expect the ground state to be spherically symmetric (S state), so that $\psi(\mathbf{r})$ depends only on $r = |\mathbf{r}|$. We put $\psi = u(r)/r$. Then $u^2(r)\,dr$ is the probability of finding the two particles at a distance between r and $r+dr$. The equation for $u(r)$ becomes

$$-\left(\frac{\hbar^2}{M}\right)\left(\frac{d^2u}{dr^2}\right) + V(r)\,u(r) = E\,u(r) \tag{2.2}$$

with the boundary conditions

$$u(r) = 0 \quad \text{for} \quad r = 0 \quad \text{and for} \quad r \to \infty \tag{2.3}$$

It is useful to rewrite (2.2) in the form

$$\frac{d^2u}{dr^2} + \kappa^2(r)\,u(r) = 0 \tag{2.4}$$

where $\kappa(r)$ is the "local" wave number defined by

$$\kappa(r) = \pm \hbar^{-1}[M(E - V(r))]^{1/2} \tag{2.5}$$

The potential energy $V(r)$ is lower than the total energy E for small values of r (see Fig. 2.1). The function $V(r)$ increases with increasing r, so that there will be a distance r_1 of the order b for which

$$V(r_1) = E \tag{2.6}$$

$\kappa(r)$ is real for $r < r_1$ and imaginary for $r > r_1$. The region $r < r_1$ is the "allowed zone," the region where we would expect to find the distance r if the particles obeyed the laws of classical mechanics. $r > r_1$ is the "forbidden zone," the region where the system would never be found if it obeyed classical mechanics.

We shall now estimate the potential energy necessary to give the observed binding energy of the deuteron. For this purpose we study the shape of the eigenfunction $u(r)$ as given by (2.4). Going out from $r = 0$, $u(r)$ will behave roughly like $\sin Kr$ where K is some average value of $\kappa(r)$ in the allowed region. This general behavior persists within the range of the nuclear force until the forbidden zone is reached. In the forbidden zone $V(r)$ rapidly becomes negligible, the kinetic energy $T = E - V$ is negative, and the wave number is $k = \pm (i/\hbar)(2\mu B)^{1/2}$ according to (2.5). Then the wave function $u(r)$ behaves like $\exp(-r/R)$, with R given by

$$R = |k|^{-1} = \hbar(2\mu B)^{-1/2} = 4.31 \times 10^{-13} \text{ cm} \qquad (2.7)$$

The other solution, $\exp(+r/R)$, is excluded by the boundary condition at infinity.

A few radial wave functions $u(r)$ with this general behavior are shown in Fig. (2.2).[1] The inside region must contain slightly more than one-quarter wavelength (a), three-quarter wavelength (b), and so on, since it must join with an exponential whose tangent is directed toward the abscissa. The wave function is smoothest in case (a) and therefore corresponds to the lowest kinetic energy. Hence case (a) represents the ground state of the deuteron.

It is remarkable that the wave function $u(r)$ decays with increasing r exponentially with a decay length R which is considerably larger than the range b of the nuclear forces. The "size" of the deuteron exceeds the range, and there is a considerable probability of finding the two nucleons in the bound state at a distance larger than the range of the forces which hold them together. This is caused by the quantum-mechanical "tunnel effect" which is analogous to the diffraction of a light wave into a region where geometrical optics would predict a sharp shadow. The wave function leaks into the "forbidden" region; the distance of this "leakage" is given by (2.7). Since $R > b$, the "size" of the deuteron is determined by R rather than by b; by the wave-mechanical diffraction effect rather than by the range of the force. Therefore the deuteron is a rather weakly bound, extended structure. The nuclear force is effective only part (of the order of one-half) of the time, since the rest of the time the particles are outside the range of each other. In heavier nuclei the particles are pulled much closer together, so that better use is made of the full strength of the nuclear force. The binding energy per particle is therefore much larger (Wigner 33a).

We can get a *lower limit* for the depth of the potential necessary for a bound deuteron by assuming that the deuteron binding energy is very near zero. The decay length R in the outside region is then very large compared to the range of the nuclear forces, and $u(r)$ is essentially horizontal for $r \geq b$, b being the range. Figure 2.3 shows that we must then have one-quarter wavelength inside the well, i.e.,

---

[1] In nature only the first of these exists. The potential of the actual neutron-proton force is not deep enough to allow more than one bound state (Bethe 36a).

$$b \cong \frac{1}{4}\lambda = \frac{1}{4}\frac{(2\pi)}{K} = \frac{1}{4}(2\pi\hbar)(-M\bar{V})^{-1/2} \qquad (2.8)$$

where K, $\bar{V}$ are appropriate averages of the local wave number and the potential energy *inside* the well (it should be observed that the expectation value of the potential energy in the ground state is considerably

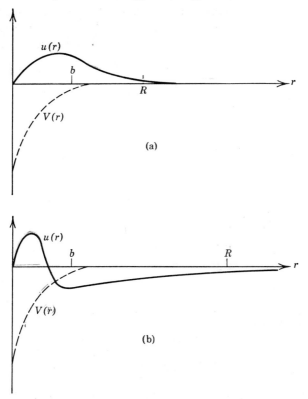

FIG. 2.2. Two stationary states in a short-range potential $v(r)$. The radial wave function $u(r)$ ($=r\psi$) behaves like $\exp\{=r/R\}$ in the "forbidden zone," where $R = (MB/\hbar^2)^{1/2}$, $B=$ binding energy. $u(r)$ has slightly more than one-quarter wavelength inside the well ($r<b$) for the ground state (a), slightly more than three-quarter wavelength for the next excited state (b). In the deuteron, state (b) does not exist as a bound state since the force is just barely strong enough to make state (a) a bound state.

less in absolute value than $|\bar{V}|$, since the particles are outside each other's range so much of the time). We have neglected the binding energy of the deuteron compared to $|\bar{V}|$ in (2.8), in accordance with our intention of getting a lower limit on the magnitude of $|\bar{V}|$. Equation (2.8) can be rewritten in the form

$$b^2|\bar{V}| \cong \left(\frac{\pi}{2}\right)^2 \frac{\hbar^2}{M} = 1.02 \times 10^{-24} \text{ Mev·cm}^2 \qquad (2.9)$$

Thus the potential energy inside the range of the forces has to be quite large to keep the deuteron together: for b of the order 2×10^{-13} cm, $|\bar{V}|$ must be at least of the order of 25 Mev.

To this approximation a knowledge of the binding energy of the deuteron allows us to find the product $b^2|\bar{V}|$ but not each factor separately. Thus we can get the same binding energy from a rela-

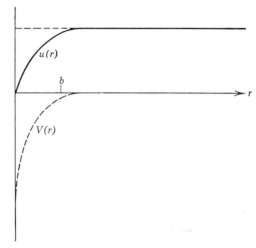

FIG. 2.3. In the limit, as the binding energy approaches zero, the radial wave function $u(r)$ has one-quarter wavelength inside the well $(r < b)$ and approaches a horizontal straight line outside the well.

tively weak force with a long range as from a strong force with a short range.

The relation (2.9) was based on the assumption that the binding energy of the deuteron is very small compared to the average potential energy inside the well. This is an excellent approximation for very short ranges b. However, for ranges b long enough so that $|\bar{V}|$ computed from (2.9) becomes comparable to the binding energy B, (2.9) needs correction. The corrections are two-fold: (1) the wave number $\kappa(r)$ inside the well, (2.5), is smaller than the approximation (2.8), hence the inside wavelength is longer, for the same strength of the potential; (2) the wave function inside the well has to join properly to the decreasing exponential solution outside, not to a horizontal straight line; hence we need slightly *more* than a quarter wavelength inside the well for proper joining. Both these corrections tend to increase the strength of potential necessary to give the observed binding, making the true $|\bar{V}|$ larger than the estimate (2.9).[1]

It will be useful to express this correction in terms of a parameter s, the "well depth parameter" which is defined as follows: s is the number by which the actual potential $V(r)$ must be divided in order to reduce the binding energy to zero. Thus the fictitious potential $V(r)/s$ gives rise to a binding energy $B=0$ and therefore satisfies (2.9) for all ranges b. The actual potential $V(r)$ in the deuteron has $s>1$, and the deviation of s from unity gives a measure of the inaccuracy of the approximation (2.9). It is plausible that s depends on the ratio b/R of the range of the well to the "size" of the deuteron, and is unity for $b/R=0$. The deviation of the well depth parameter s from unity is often called the "range correction" to the simple estimate (2.9).

The value of s for a given b/R depends on the shape of the potential. The variation of s with b/R is strongest for a shape which is sharply cut off like a rectangular well, and weakest for a force with a "tail." For conventional well shapes, the simple estimate (2.9) is too low by between 30 and 50 percent if a range $b \cong \frac{1}{2}R = 2.15 \times 10^{-13}$ cm is assumed. For details, see Table V in Blatt and Jackson (Blatt 49).

For purposes of calculation, it is necessary to assume some definite form for the radial dependence of the potential. The following forms have been used most widely in the literature (Bethe 36a, Rarita 37, 38, Sachs 38, Hulthén 42, Ramsey 48, Breit 36, 39, Feenberg 35, Hatcher 49, Hoisington 39, and many others):

Square well: $V(r) = -V_0 \qquad r < b$ (2.10)

$\qquad\qquad\qquad\qquad V(r) = 0 \qquad\quad r > b$

Gaussian well: $V(r) = -V_0 \exp\left(-\dfrac{r^2}{\beta^2}\right)$ (2.11)

Exponential well: $V(r) = -V_0 \exp\left(-\dfrac{2r}{\beta}\right)$ (2.12)

Yukawa well: $V(r) = -V_0 \dfrac{\exp(-r/\beta)}{(r/\beta)}$ (2.13)

In terms of these conventional well parameters, the well depth parameter s becomes

Square well: $s = \dfrac{4}{\pi^2}\dfrac{MV_0}{\hbar^2}b^2$ (2.14)

[1] An exact formula which is a generalization of (2.9) for finite ranges has been given by Low (48).

Gaussian well: $s = 0.37261 \dfrac{MV_0\beta^2}{\hbar^2}$ (2.15)

Exponential well: $s = 0.17291 \dfrac{MV_0\beta^2}{\hbar^2}$ (2.16)

Yukawa well: $s = 0.59531 \dfrac{MV_0\beta^2}{\hbar^2}$ (2.17)

The range parameters β are not really comparable. It is useful to introduce an "intrinsic range" parameter b instead of the conventional range parameter β (Blatt 49). The intrinsic range b for the wells quoted above is

Gaussian well: $b = 1.4354\,\beta$ (2.18)

Exponential well: $b = 1.7706\,\beta$ (2.19)

Yukawa well: $b = 2.1196\,\beta$ (2.20)

The precise significance of this intrinsic range appears in the next section.

3. NEUTRON-PROTON SCATTERING

A. Simple Theory

The scattering of neutrons on protons depends considerably on the energy of the neutrons. For energies below 10 Mev, the de Broglie wavelength (in the center-of-mass system) is long compared to the range of the nuclear forces; hence neutrons of orbital angular momenta larger than zero do not come close enough to the proton to be appreciably scattered. The scattering is due only to the $l=0$ neutrons ("S wave scattering") and is isotropic in the angle in the center-of-mass system as long as the proton can validly be treated as a free particle. The latter condition is satisfied if the energy of the neutron is large compared to the chemical binding energies which keep the proton in place in a molecule or in a crystal lattice, i.e., for neutron energies large compared to 1 ev. We shall treat neutron-proton scattering in the energy region 1 ev $< E <$ 10 Mev in detail; the modifications in the analysis for thermal and subthermal neutrons will be discussed in brief later; the discussion of scattering experiments at energies above 10 Mev is reserved for Chapter IV.

We shall treat neutron-proton scattering as if it were purely elastic scattering. This is not quite correct, since another, competing, process can occur: the capture of the neutron by the proton to form a deuteron, with the emission of a gamma-ray (Fermi 36).   This process will be discussed in Chapter XII; for our present purposes it suffices to observe that the radiative capture cross section is completely negligible compared to the cross section for elastic scattering as long as the energy of the neutrons is above 0.1 ev.

We recapitulate briefly the usual analysis of elastic scattering by central forces (Mott 33).   The wave function ψ is a solution of the Schrödinger equation for positive energy E, and we require that ψ describe a beam of incident particles plus a scattered wave of particles going away from the scattering center.   We shall carry on the analysis in the center-of-gravity system.   It must be emphasized that in most scattering experiments the center of gravity is not at rest.   Thus the energy E of the relative motion (with which we are concerned) is *half* the energy of the incident neutron beam in the laboratory system, and the angle of scattering θ in the center-of-gravity system is *twice* the angle through which the neutrons are scattered in the laboratory (these simple relations are due to the equal masses of neutron and proton).

At very large distances from the center, the wave function

$$\psi(\mathbf{r}) = \psi(x,y,z)$$

describing the relative motion ($\mathbf{r} = \mathbf{r}_n - \mathbf{r}_p$) has the form

$$\psi(\mathbf{r}) \cong \exp(ikz) + f(\theta)\, \frac{\exp(ikr)}{r} \qquad \text{(for } r \to \infty) \qquad (3.1)$$

where the first term corresponds to the incident beam (moving in the z direction) and the second term is the scattered wave. $f(\theta)$ is the amplitude of the scattered wave in the direction θ with respect to the incident beam.   The wave number k is the asymptotic value of (2.5) outside the range of the forces:

$$k = \left(\frac{ME}{\hbar^2} \right)^{1/2} \qquad (3.2)$$

where it must be remembered that E without subscript is the energy of the relative motion.   A useful numerical relation is:

$$k^2 \ (\text{in } 10^{24} \ \text{cm}^{-2}) = 1.206 \ E_{\text{lab}} \ (\text{in Mev}) \qquad (3.3)$$

where E_{lab} is the energy of the neutron in the laboratory system: $E_{\text{lab}} = 2E$.

The differential cross section for elastic scattering into the solid angle element $d\Omega$ in the direction θ is related to the scattering amplitude $f(\theta)$

through

$$d\sigma = |f(\theta)|^2 \, d\Omega \tag{3.4}$$

We decompose the wave function ψ, (3.1), into components of given orbital angular momentum l in the usual way:

$$\psi(\mathbf{r}) = \sum_{l=0}^{\infty} \psi_l(r) \, Y_{l,0}(\theta) \tag{3.5}$$

where $Y_{l,0}(\theta)$ is a normalized spherical harmonic. We shall restrict ourselves to energies low enough so that the scattering occurs predominantly in the S state, $l=0$. We are therefore interested only in the $l=0$ part of the expansion (3.5). This is found by multiplication of (3.1) by $Y_{0,0} = (4\pi)^{-1/2}$ and integration over angles:

$$\psi_0(r) = i\pi^{1/2}(kr)^{-1} \left[\exp\,(-ikr) - \exp\,(ikr) \right] $$
$$+ (4\pi)^{1/2} \bar{f} \, \frac{\exp\,(ikr)}{r} \qquad \text{(for } r \to \infty\text{)} \tag{3.6}$$

where $\bar{f}$ denotes the average of the scattering amplitude $f(\theta)$ over angles. For low energies $f(\theta)$ is independent of the angle and equal to the average value $\bar{f}$.

In order to find the scattering amplitude we notice that $r\psi_0(r) = u(r)$ must obey the radial wave equation, (2.2) or (2.4), with $E = \hbar^2 k^2/2\mu$, and the boundary condition $u(r) = 0$ for $r = 0$. In the present case E is positive and equal to the energy of the relative motion. As $r \to \infty$ the solution $u(r)$ assumes the form $C \sin\,(kr + \delta)$, where C is an arbitrary constant. The "phase shift" δ is determined uniquely by the boundary condition $u(0) = 0$ and the radial wave equation (2.2). Let us normalize the solution $u(r)$ such that

$$u(r) \to v(r) \equiv \frac{\sin\,(kr + \delta)}{\sin\,\delta} \qquad \text{(for } r \to \infty\text{)} \tag{3.7}$$

(This normalization[1] differs from the conventional one through the factor $\sin \delta$ in the denominator; it will be more convenient in later analysis.) A schematic plot of $u(r)$ against r is given in Fig. 3.1. Comparison of the ingoing wave part [proportional to $\exp\,(-ikr)$] of (3.6) and (3.7) shows that we must put

---

[1] As used here, the term "normalization" refers to any method used to fix an arbitrary multiplicative constant in a wave function. We here normalize the behavior of $u(r)$ as r approaches infinity. This is not related to the normalization of the ground state wave function by $\int_0^\infty u^2(r) \, dr = 1$.

$$\psi_0(r) = (4\pi)^{1/2} \exp(i\delta) \sin \delta \, \frac{u(r)}{kr} \tag{3.8}$$

and comparison of the outgoing wave parts [proportional to $\exp(ikr)$] then gives the following relation between the S wave scattering amplitude $\bar{f}$ and the S wave phase shift δ:

$$\bar{f} = k^{-1} \exp(i\delta) \sin \delta \tag{3.9}$$

To the extent that scattering in states of higher angular momentum can be neglected, (3.4) gives a differential scattering cross section in the center-of-gravity system independent of angle:

$$d\sigma = k^{-2} \sin^2 \delta \, d\Omega \tag{3.10}$$

The problem is therefore reduced to that of finding the S wave phase shift δ as a function of energy. In order to do this approxi-

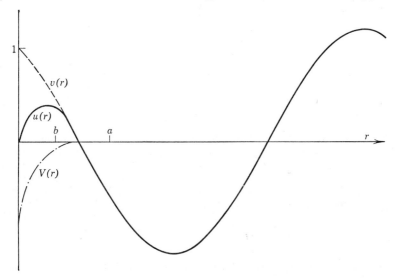

FIG. 3.1.   At positive energy E the radial wave function $u(r)$ becomes equal to its asymptotic form $v(r) = \sin(kr+\delta)/\sin\delta$ outside the range b of the nuclear force. $v(r)$ is normalized so that it becomes unity at $r = 0$.

mately, we shall start by discussing the behavior of the radial wave function $u(r)$ in the limit of zero energy, $E=0$. Let us call this wave function $u_0(r)$. We shall neglect the effect of chemical binding, however, so that, strictly speaking, we are concerned with the scattering above 1 ev, extrapolated down to zero energy, rather than with the actual scattering at zero energy. We shall refer to the extrapolated scattering as scattering at "zero" energy.

Beyond the range of the force, the radial wave equation (2.2) for "zero" energy, $E=0$, becomes $d^2u_0/dr^2=0$, i.e., $u_0(r)$ goes over asymptotically into a straight line. Since the solutions of (2.2) can be multiplied with an arbitrary factor C, the only significant feature of this straight line is the place $r \equiv a$, where it intersects the r axis.

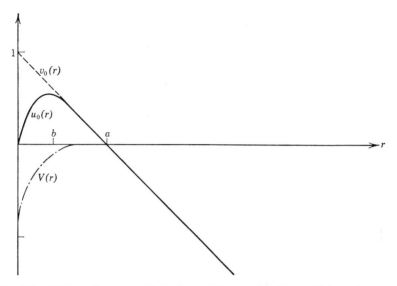

Fig. 3.2. At "zero" energy, $E=0$, the radial wave function $u_0(r)$ becomes equal to its asymptotic form $v_0(r) = 1 - (r/a)$ outside the range b of the nuclear force. Inside the range (for $r < b$), $u_0(r)$ is close to $u(r)$ (Fig. 3.1) and $v_0(r)$ is close to $v(r)$.

A schematic plot of $u_0(r)$ is shown in Fig. 3.2. We call[1] a the "scattering length" (Fermi 47a), and we can write

$$u_0(r) = C\,(r - a) \qquad \text{(for } E=0,\, r \to \infty \text{)} \tag{3.11}$$

If we use the special normalization (3.7) for $u_0(r)$, according to which the function is unity for $r = 0$, we obtain

$$u_0(r) \to v_0(r) = 1 - \frac{r}{a} \tag{3.12}$$

We compare this with (3.7) which, in the limit $k \to 0$, assumes the

[1] Sometimes the scattering length is defined more generally as the value of r for which the radial wave function $u(r)$ first becomes zero; it is then a function of energy, and our a is the scattering length in the limit of zero energy. We shall not make use of the general definition in this book, and, in what follows, a will be a constant, not an energy-dependent quantity.

form $v_0 = 1 + rk \cot \delta$, and we get

$$\tan \delta = -ka \qquad \text{(for } k \to 0) \qquad (3.13)$$

By inserting (3.13) into (3.10) we obtain the *total scattering cross section at "zero" energy:*

$$\sigma_0 = 4\pi a^2 \qquad (3.14)$$

This is identical with the scattering cross section (in the limit of zero energy) of an impenetrable sphere of radius a. Such a sphere would force the wave function $u(r)$ to vanish at $r=a$ and therefore would give rise also to the wave function (3.11). The measurement of the cross section at "zero" energy determines the absolute value of the scattering length, but not its sign.

The connection between a and the cross section can also be seen directly from the wave function (3.1). For zero energy, (3.1) becomes $\psi = 1 + (f/r)$ and the radial wave function $u(r) = r\psi$ becomes $r+f$. Comparing this with (3.11) gives $f = -a$, and (3.4) gives the differential cross section $d\sigma = a^2 \, d\Omega$, which leads immediately to (3.14).

We now find an expression for the phase shift and, consequently, the cross section at an arbitrary energy E.[1] We use the wave equation (2.2) for $u(r)$ at energy E and compare it with the wave equation

$$-\left(\frac{\hbar^2}{M}\right)\left(\frac{d^2 u_0}{dr^2}\right) + V(r)u_0(r) = 0 \qquad (3.15)$$

of the wave function $u_0(r)$ at energy $E=0$. We multiply (2.2) by $u_0(r)$ and (3.15) by $u(r)$ and subtract. The result is

$$\frac{d}{dr}(uu_0' - u_0u') = k^2 uu_0 \qquad (3.16)$$

A precisely similar relation holds for the asymptotic forms $v(r)$ of $u(r)$ as defined in (3.7) and $v_0(r)$ of $u_0(r)$ as given by (3.12):

$$\frac{d}{dr}(vv_0' - v_0v') = k^2 vv_0 \qquad (3.17)$$

---

[1] The essential step in the theory of neutron-proton scattering, i.e., the appreciation of the effect of the very short range and great strength of the nuclear force upon the scattering cross section, is due to Wigner (33b). The effective range theory was first derived by Schwinger (47), who used a variational method described in detail by Lippman and Schwinger (Lippman 50). The somewhat simpler derivation given here is due to Bethe (49). There is considerable literature on the theory of neutron-proton scattering, e.g., Bethe (35), Kittel (39), Hulthén (42,48), Landau (44), Smorodinski (44,47), Kohn (48), Ramsey (48), Barker (49), Blatt (49), Chew (49), Hatcher (49), Lax (50), Kato (50), Toraldo di Francia (50), Goldberger (51a), and many others.

since v and v_0 fulfill the wave equations (2.2) and (3.15), respectively, for $V=0$. We subtract (3.17) from (3.16) and integrate over r from zero to infinity. By using the relations $u(0)=0$, $v(0)=1$, $v'(0)=k\cot\delta$ and $v_0'(0)=-a^{-1}$ we get[1]

$$k \cot \delta = -a^{-1} + k^2 \int_0^\infty (vv_0 - uu_0)\, dr \qquad (3.18)$$

Equation (3.18) is exact. In order to use it as the basis of an approximation method, we observe that the significant contributions to the integral come from those regions of r where $u(r)$ and $u_0(r)$ differ appreciably from their asymptotic behavior $v(r)$ and $v_0(r)$, respectively. This is just the "inside" region where the nuclear force is effective. In this region the force is so strong that the behavior of the wave function [the local wave number $\kappa(r)$] is nearly independent of the value of the total energy E (cf. Figs. 3.1 and 3.2). The nuclear potential V inside the nuclear range is of the order of 10 Mev or larger, and the addition of E makes only little difference. Hence it is a very good approximation to replace $u(r)$ and $v(r)$ in the integral by their zero energy forms $u_0(r)$ and $v_0(r)$, respectively. We then obtain the so-called "shape-independent approximation" formula,

$$k \cot \delta = -a^{-1} + \tfrac{1}{2}r_0 k^2 \qquad (3.19)$$

where the length r_0 is defined by

$$r_0 = 2 \int_0^\infty (v_0^2 - u_0^2)\, dr \qquad (3.20)$$

The length r_0 depends only on the potential energy $V(r)$ and not on the energy k^2. The integrand of (3.20) is zero outside the range of the nuclear forces and is of the order of unity inside the range. Hence the integral represents a mean distance of interaction, and the factor 2 in front serves to make r_0 come out somewhere near the "edge" of the well. We therefore call r_0 the "effective range," and the term involving r_0 in (3.19) the "range correction." In using this terminology, it should be remembered that r_0 depends not only on the width but also on the depth of the potential well. It can be shown

[1] Some confusion may arise here because the integral $\int_0^\infty uu_0\, dr$ is zero according to the usual orthogonality relation for wave functions belonging to the same Hamiltonian but different values of the energy. However, this argument does not apply to the integral $\int_0^\infty vv_0\, dr$ because $v(r)$ satisfies an inhomogeneous boundary condition at $r=0$, i.e., $v(0)=1$. The integral $\int_0^\infty vv_0\, dr$ is different from zero, and can be shown to be precisely equal to $(k\cot\delta + a^{-1})/k^2$. Thus (3.18) reduces to an identity if use is made of the orthogonality of u and u_0.

3. Neutron-Proton Scattering

(Blatt 49) that the terms neglected in (3.19) are indeed negligible compared to the experimental inaccuracies for the energies in question.

The intrinsic range b introduced in Section 2 (Eqs. 2.18 to 2.20) is defined by

$$b \equiv \lim_{s \to 1} r_0 \qquad (3.21)$$

where s is the well depth parameter defined earlier. Since the nuclear forces in nature have values of s not very different from unity (this is true particularly for the force in the singlet spin state, see later), it follows that two wells of different shape but equal intrinsic range also have nearly equal effective ranges in scattering.

For values of s different from unity, the effective range differs from the intrinsic range. In Fig. 3.3 we give a plot of the ratio (r_0/b) as a function of the well depth parameter s. The figure shows that the effective range r_0 decreases as the well becomes deeper. The variation of r_0/b with well depth is strongest for the Yukawa well, weakest for the square well. This can be understood in terms of the well shape: the Yukawa well shape is "long-tailed," whereas the square well is sharply cut off beyond $r = b$. The order square, Gaussian, exponential, Yukawa, apparent in Fig. 3.3, is indeed the order of increasing "tail" of the well.

For higher numerical accuracy than can be obtained from Fig. 3.3, the reader is referred to Table I of Blatt and Jackson (Blatt 49).

The approximation (3.19) is called "shape-independent" because only two parameters enter: the scattering length a and the effective range r_0. Any potential shape (square well, Yukawa well, etc.) can be used to obtain these two experimental parameters by a proper choice of the range and depth of the well. Since (3.19) is actually a very good approximation, the *experimental data determine only the depth and range of the nuclear potential, not its detailed shape.*

We can also relate these scattering parameters to the properties of the ground state of the deuteron. Indeed, all we have to do is to replace the wave function $u(r)$ for positive energy E in the above derivation by the wave function of the ground state of the deuteron appropriate to the negative energy $E = -B$. The square of the outside wave number k^2 is now negative, $k^2 = -R^{-2}$, R being the "size of the deuteron" defined by (2.7). The asymptotic form of the ground state wave function is now $v(r) = \exp(-r/R)$. Hence $v'(0)$ is equal to R^{-1} instead of $k \cot \delta$. We then get, again in the shape-independent approximation,

$$R^{-1} = a^{-1} + \tfrac{1}{2} r_0 R^{-2} \qquad (3.22)$$

We see that *to the extent that the range of the nuclear forces can be neglected, the scattering length a is just equal to the "size" of the deuteron in its ground state.* In other words, neutron-proton scattering is

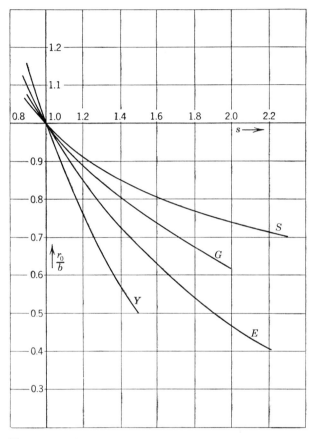

Fɪɢ. 3.3.   The ratio of the effective range r_0 to the intrinsic range b is shown as a function of the well depth parameter s for the four conventional well shapes (S = square well, G = Gaussian well, E = exponential well, Y = Yukawa well). By definition, $b = r_0$ ($r_0/b = 1$) when $s = 1$, i.e., when the force is just barely strong enough to produce a bound state. r_0 decreases as the well depth s increases, the amount of the change depending on the well shape.

(except for range corrections) equivalent to the scattering on an impenetrable sphere of radius R.

Putting together formulas (3.10), (3.19), and (3.22), we arrive at the following approximate formula for the neutron-proton scattering cross section as a function of energy [k is defined by (3.2) and (3.3)]:

$$\sigma = \frac{4\pi}{(k^2 + R^{-2})[1 - (r_0/R) + \frac{1}{4}r_0^2(k^2+R^{-2})]} \qquad (3.23)$$

This formula contains only one adjustable parameter: the effective range r_0 (R is determined by the known binding energy of the deuteron). In principle, a cross-section measurement at any one energy (e.g., at "zero" energy) suffices to determine the effective range of the nuclear force. Formula (3.23) also shows that to first order in r_0 the range correction to the scattering from an impenetrable sphere of radius R simply consists of multiplication of the cross section by the constant factor $[1-(r_0/R)]^{-1}$.[1]

This approximation for the cross section does not depend on any assumption about the nuclear potential $V(r)$ except its short range. It is true that we have used the fact that the shape of the wave function inside the well is nearly independent of the energy. This, however, is a necessary consequence of the short range of the nuclear forces and the experimental (small) binding energy of the deuteron (see Section 2). *Thus equation (3.23) is very well founded theoretically, and a disagreement with experiment must be interpreted as a fundamental oversight in our basic assumptions about the nuclear force.*

B. Comparison with Experiment; The Spin Dependence of Nuclear Forces

For "zero" energy neutrons, (3.23) gives

$$\sigma_0 = 4\pi R^2 \left[1 - \frac{r_0}{2R} \right]^{-2} \qquad (3.24)$$

If we neglect the range correction, the "zero" energy cross section is predicted to be 2.33×10^{-24} cm^2. We expect the effective range r_0 to be smaller than the size of the deuteron R; hence the range correction cannot be larger than its value 4 for $r_0 = R$. Higher-order corrections than the one included in (3.24) can be shown to be small for reasonable assumptions about the shape of the potential well. Thus we get a final theoretical estimate of $2.33 \times 10^{-24} \leq \sigma_0 \leq 9.32 \times 10^{-24}$ cm^2. The experimental value is $\sigma_0 = (20.36 \pm 0.10) \times 10^{-24}$ cm^2.[2] Such violent disagreement is a sign of some fundamental error in our assumptions.

[1] This result had been derived without the use of the effective range by Bethe and Peierls (Bethe 35).

[2] Early measurements of this cross section were made by Cohen (39, 40), Simons (39, 40), and Hanstein (40, 41). Recently some precision measurements have been performed by the use of neutron velocity selectors: Jones (48) and Melkonian (49). The value quoted in the text is taken from Melkonian's paper.

This point was cleared up by E. P. Wigner.[1] He called attention to the fact that there is a significant difference between the ground state of the deuteron and the scattering states of the neutron-proton system with which we are concerned here. The difference lies in the behavior of the spins.

Experimentally (Murphy 34, Farkas 34, Nafe 48) the total angular momentum of the deuteron nucleus is unity. Since we have good reason to believe that the deuteron ground state is predominantly a state of zero orbital angular momentum, the intrinsic spins of the neutron and proton must point in the same direction. The spins are therefore *correlated* in the ground state of the deuteron. The situation is different in a scattering experiment. A beam of neutrons is sent against an assembly of stationary protons. No attempt is made to control the spin directions of the neutrons in the incident beam, nor the spin directions of the protons in the scatterer. The spins are therefore *uncorrelated* in scattering experiments.[2]

A pair of uncorrelated spins of $\frac{1}{2}$ each are, on the average, lined up (triplet state) three-fourths of the time and opposite one another (singlet state) one-fourth of the time.[3] Our knowledge of the binding energy of the deuteron gives us information about the scattering provided that the two particles are scattered in a triplet state. But, if nuclear forces should depend on the relative orientations of the intrinsic spins of the nucleons, our knowledge of the binding energy of the (triplet) deuteron tells us nothing at all about the behavior of the neutron-proton system in the singlet state. This line of reasoning led Wigner to suggest spin dependence of the nuclear force as an explanation for the discrepancy between the simple theory and experiment.

Let σ_s and σ_t denote the scattering cross sections in the singlet and triplet states, respectively. We have just seen that (3.23) applies only to σ_t while σ_s is unknown. The experimentally measured cross section is the weighted average of the two, the weights being the a priori probabilities of finding the two uncorrelated spins in the triplet and singlet states with respect to each other, i.e., $\frac{3}{4}$ and $\frac{1}{4}$. Thus

$$\sigma = \tfrac{3}{4}\sigma_t + \tfrac{1}{4}\sigma_s \qquad (3.25)$$

[1] This important contribution of Wigner was never published by himself. The reference to his suggestion is contained on p. 117 of the review article by Bethe and Bacher (Bethe 36a).

[2] There has been some interest lately in experiments with polarized neutrons. The theory has been given by Wolfenstein (49). So far no experiments in this energy region are available.

[3] See Appendix A, Section 4.

We substitute the values for "zero" energy neutrons:

$$\sigma_0 = 20.4 \times 10^{-24} \text{ cm}^2 \text{ and } 2.33 \times 10^{-24} < (\sigma_t)_0 < 9.3 \times 10^{-24} \text{ cm}^2$$

This gives the following estimate for the scattering cross section in the singlet state: $74.6 \times 10^{-24} > (\sigma_s)_0 > 53.6 \times 10^{-24} \text{ cm}^2$. The singlet scattering cross section is therefore considerably larger than the triplet cross section for slow neutrons; in fact, it accounts for most of the observed scattering. The upper (zero range) limit on $(\sigma_s)_0$ gives for the singlet scattering length $a_s = \pm 2.43 \times 10^{-12}$ cm, according to (3.14).

In order to interpret the singlet scattering theoretically, we can use the whole development in Section 3A, up to and including equation (3.20). But we can *not* relate the scattering parameters $a = a_s$ and $r_0 = r_{0s}$ in the singlet state to the "size" of the deuteron because the deuteron is in a triplet state; i.e., (3.22) and (3.23) fail. Indeed, we do not even know, at this stage of the analysis, whether the nuclear potential $V_s(r)$ in the singlet state allows any bound state at all. We only know that, if it does allow one, the energy of this state must be higher than the deuteron ground state energy (because the deuteron is known to be in a triplet state). Experimentally, no bound singlet state has been observed directly. We shall see later that indirect, but nevertheless conclusive, evidence shows that no such bound singlet state exists.

Formula (3.14) shows that we can find the magnitude, but not the sign, of the singlet scattering length a_s from the "zero" energy singlet cross section. Since the singlet effective range is necessarily positive for a short-range attractive force, we could in principle decide the sign of the singlet scattering length by a study of the range correction to the scattering at energies different from zero. The experiments are not accurate enough for that, however. A much more clear-cut method is available, and it will be discussed later on in this section.

We can relate the sign of the scattering length to the existence or non-existence of a bound state of the system. Indeed, this can be read out of formula (3.22). A bound state of the system has a positive value of R; hence, neglecting the range correction, a is positive also. Conversely, a negative value of a implies a negative value of R, i.e., no bound state can exist. This is illustrated in terms of the behavior of the wave function in Figs. 3.4a and 3.4b, which show typical wave functions for zero energy giving positive and negative scattering lengths, respectively. The behavior of the wave function for $r < b$ is to a first approximation independent of the energy E; hence it is the same for a bound state with not too large binding energy. We see that Fig. 3.4a can lead to a bound state similar to that of Fig. 2.2a, as the energy is made negative; but a wave function with negative scattering length (Fig. 3.4b) just does not have enough curvature in the interior region to join on properly to a decreasing exponential in the exterior region, hence no bound state can exist. This correlation between the sign of the scattering length and the existence or non-existence of a bound state of the system depends on the assumption that the potential is not very different in strength from one which would give exactly zero binding (infinite scattering length), i.e., that the potential has a well depth parameter s not very much different from unity.

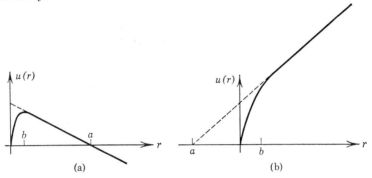

FIG. 3.4. (a) A positive scattering length a implies that a bound state exists (compare Fig. 2.2a). (b) A negative scattering length a implies that the system has no bound state close to zero energy.

The large value of the singlet cross section at "zero" energy implies that the singlet scattering length has a large absolute value, 2.43×10^{-12} cm. If a_s should be positive, the bound singlet state of the deuteron would have a correspondingly large value of R and hence a very low binding energy $B_s \cong 100$ kev. Actually, a_s is negative (see Section 3D), and there is no bound singlet state. It is nevertheless customary to define an energy $B_s{}^*$ in the following way: (3.22) is used to find R (which now turns out to be negative); the sign of R is reversed arbitrarily and substituted into (2.7) to find $B \equiv B_s{}^*$. Then there is said to be a "virtual state" at the (positive) energy $B_s{}^*$. The large absolute value of the singlet scattering length is interpreted to mean that the "virtual level" of the system is not very far above zero energy. It must be understood, however, that this is strictly a way of speaking. There is no distinction between the wave function at this particular energy $E = B_s{}^*$ and any other positive energy.

Combining (3.10) and (3.19) we get for the singlet scattering cross section

$$\sigma_s = 4\pi[(a_s{}^{-1} - \tfrac{1}{2}r_{0s}k^2)^2 + k^2]^{-1} \tag{3.26}$$

The corresponding expression for the triplet scattering cross section σ_t can be reduced to the form (3.23). We now set r_0 in (3.23) equal to r_{0t}, the effective range in the triplet state. The total cross section is then given by (3.25).

Three unknown parameters are involved in the cross section: the two effective ranges r_{0t}, r_{0s}, and the singlet state scattering length a_s. The scattering length in the triplet state, a_t, is determined by r_{0t} and the binding energy of the deuteron through (3.22). The most accurately known cross section is the one for "zero" energy neutrons (Jones 48, Melkonian 49). Its value is $\sigma_0 = (20.36 \pm 0.10) \times 10^{-24}$ cm^2. This value gives a relation between a_s and a_t through formulas (3.25) and (3.14). There then remain two independently variable parameters in the cross section at higher energies. We shall take these parameters to be the two effective ranges, r_{0t} and r_{0s}.

In principle it is possible to derive unique values of the two effective ranges from the measured cross sections. Unfortunately, the accuracy required for this determination is beyond present experimental technique. With cross sections known to an accuracy of a few percent, the situation is as follows. Values of r_{0s} and r_{0t} can be found which fit the data over the whole range of energies. These values, however, are not unique. It is possible to change one of the ranges (say r_{0t}) appreciably without destroying the fit to the data, provided only that a compensating change is made in the other effective range (r_{0s}) (Blatt 48).

We shall therefore restrict ourselves here to plotting the cross section for one definite value of the triplet effective range, $r_{0t} = 1.7 \times 10^{-13}$ cm (see Section 3D for the origin of this value). Figure 3.5 gives a plot of the triplet contribution to the scattering cross section ($\frac{3}{4}\sigma_t$) for this r_{0t}, and of the singlet contribution to the scattering cross section ($\frac{1}{4}\sigma_s$) for two different singlet effective ranges: $r_{0s} = 0$ and $r_{0s} = 3 \times 10^{-13}$ cm. The figure also shows the predicted experimental cross section which is the sum of these two contributions. The singlet contribution predominates at low energies. The two contributions are about equal at 1 Mev (laboratory energy). Thereafter the triplet scattering predominates. This is caused by the greater statistical weight of the triplet state.

Although the difference between the singlet cross sections for the two assumed ranges becomes quite appreciable at energies around 5 Mev, the net effect on the observed cross section stays uniformly small. The two total cross section curves in Fig. 3.5 are very nearly parallel (on a logarithmic scale); this implies that the sensitivity of the observed cross section to the singlet range is roughly constant

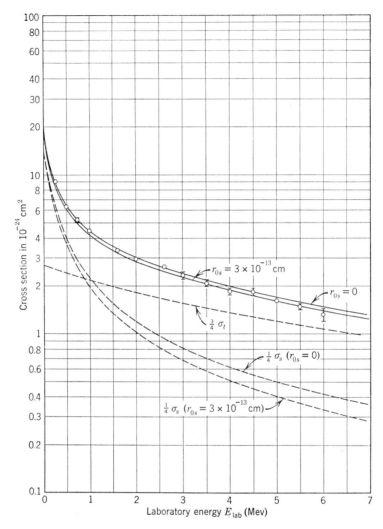

FIG. 3.5.   The neutron-proton scattering cross section σ_{np} is made up of two contributions: The singlet scattering $(\tfrac{1}{4}\sigma_s)$ and the triplet scattering $(\tfrac{3}{4}\sigma_t)$.   The two contributions as well as their sum are shown on the figure for the following values of the parameters: triplet state: $a_t = 5.37 \times 10^{-13}$ cm, $r_{0t} = 1.70 \times 10^{-13}$ cm; singlet state: $a_s = 2.37 \times 10^{-12}$ cm, $r_{0s} = 0$, and $r_{0s} = 3 \times 10^{-13}$ cm.   The experimental points in the figure were taken from Frisch (46) and Bailey (46).   These experimental values are not precise enough to allow determination of r_{0s}.

over the whole energy range between 1 and 6 Mev. The difference amounts to about 6 percent in the cross section for these two singlet ranges. Hence a cross-section measurement accurate to 1 percent (which is very difficult experimentally) does not define the singlet range to better than $\pm 0.5 \times 10^{-13}$ cm. The actual error in the singlet range would of course be much larger, since the triplet range is not precisely known, and any error in the triplet range implies a much larger (roughly 7 times) error in the singlet range. Some measured cross sections (Bailey 46, Frisch 46) are also shown on the figure. It is clear that more accurate values are needed to determine the singlet range r_{0s}.

Very fortunately more accurate values are now available (Lampi 50). If a triplet effective range $r_{0t} = 1.70 \times 10^{-13}$ cm (Section 3D), a triplet scattering length $a_t = 5.39 \times 10^{-13}$ cm, and a singlet scattering length $a_s = -23.7 \times 10^{-13}$ cm (Salpeter 51) are assumed, the new cross sections are consistent with a singlet effective range r_{0s} between 1.5 and 3.5×10^{-13} cm. We shall see in Section 4 that a value of r_{0s} around 2.6×10^{-13} cm would be very satisfactory from a theoretical point of view. The present experiments are in good agreement with such a value of r_{0s}, although they are by no means accurate enough to specify r_{0s} to two significant places.[1]

C. The Effect of Chemical Binding

Figure 3.6 shows the experimental values (Jones 48) of the neutron-proton scattering cross section in the region of very low energies. The "zero" energy value of 20.36×10^{-24} cm^2 is observed at energies between 1 and 100 ev. It seems surprising, therefore, that at very low energies (less than 1 ev) the cross section suddenly increases to about four times this value. Fermi (36) proved that this increase is an effect of the chemical binding forces which hold the proton in place in the molecule or crystal. The chemical binding forces influence the neutron-proton scattering only for very low neutron energies, energies of the order of the chemical binding energies (0.1 ev). At higher neutron energies the proton recoil is so large that the molecule is broken up during the impact, and the proton can be considered as if it were a completely free particle.

It can be seen very easily that the neutron-proton cross section is increased by a factor 4 if the proton is bound to a molecule whose weight is very high compared to the proton mass, and if the neutron

---

[1] An analysis of the earlier experimental material (Blatt 48) arrived at the erroneous conclusion that r_{0s} must be very close to 0.

energy is so low that its wavelength λ_n is large compared to the molecular dimensions. The center of mass of the scattering system is then located in the center of the molecule. Since λ_n is large, only S neutrons are scattered and the scattering must be spherically symmetric

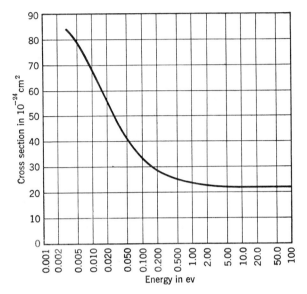

FIG. 3.6.   At energies below 1 ev the neutron-proton total cross section (measured in water) increases sharply above its "zero" energy value ($\sigma_0 = 20.36 \times 10^{-24}$ cm^2). At $E_{\text{lab}} = 0.004$ ev the cross section is about $4\sigma_0$ and still increasing.   This residual increase (not predicted by the simple theory of this chapter) has two causes: (1) the thermal motion of the water molecules (Doppler effect), (2) the neutron-proton capture cross section (which amounts to 10^{-24} cm^2 at the lowest energies in the figure).   The data are taken from Jones (48).

in the system in which the center of mass is at rest, which is the laboratory system.   Hence the differential cross section is given by

$$d\sigma = C \, d\Omega \qquad (3.27)$$

where C is a constant which has to be determined.   Now let us consider the scattering of "zero" energy neutrons by free protons. The angular distribution is spherically symmetric in the center-of-mass system of neutron and proton, which, in this case, is moving with half the velocity of the neutron.   The differential scattering cross section has the magnitude a^2, where a is the scattering length.   In the laboratory system this becomes

$$d\sigma_{\text{free}} = 4a^2 \cos \theta \, d\Omega \qquad (3.28)$$

We now observe that there can be no chemical binding effect of any importance in the elastic scattering of neutrons through very small angles θ, since then the recoil of the proton becomes negligible and it does not matter whether the proton is bound or not. Equating (3.27) and (3.28) for $\theta = 0$, we get $C = 4a^2$ and

$$d\sigma = 4a^2 \, d\Omega \qquad (3.29)$$

which gives for the total cross section $16\pi a^2$, four times as much as the cross section of the unbound case (3.14). This simple result is correct only in the limiting case of very slow neutrons and a very heavy molecule.

The effect of the molecular binding of the proton on the scattering cannot be treated by the usual methods for scattering problems: it is not possible to eliminate the center-of-gravity motion of the neutron and proton, since the proton is chemically bound to a molecule which can take up momentum. An essential simplification in this problem is due to the fact that the range of nuclear forces is extremely small compared to the relevant molecular dimensions (say the amplitudes of the vibration of the proton in the molecule, of the order of 10^{-9} cm), although the strength of this interaction is millions of times more than that of the chemical binding forces. Hence the neutron-proton interaction is to a very good approximation an interaction by *localized impacts*, i.e., it is zero when the neutron and proton are apart from each other and acts only when they are at the same place. We must therefore devise a method for treating localized impacts in quantum mechanics, just as special methods have had to be devised for the treatment of "instantaneous" (i.e., localized) impacts in classical mechanics.

Since we are dealing with very low energies, the range correction in (3.19) is completely negligible. The nuclear interaction can be described in its effect on the scattering by a single parameter, the scattering length a. Since the nuclear ranges are also very small compared to molecular dimensions, we conclude that *the observed scattering of slow neutrons from (chemically bound) protons can depend on the neutron-proton interaction only through the scattering length a.*

We now proceed to give the quantum-mechanical formulation of an interaction by localized impacts. The wave function for the motion of the neutron and proton will depend on the positions $\mathbf{r}_n$ and $\mathbf{r}_p$ of the two particles (and perhaps on other variables which we can ignore for our present purposes). As long as the neutron and proton are not at the same place (i.e., as long as $\mathbf{r}_n \neq \mathbf{r}_p$), the wave function Ψ obeys the

Schrödinger equation

$$H_0 \Psi = E\Psi \qquad \text{(for } \mathbf{r}_n \neq \mathbf{r}_p) \qquad (3.30)$$

where H_0 is the Hamiltonian of a free neutron and a bound proton:

$$H_0 = -\frac{\hbar^2}{2M_n} \nabla_n{}^2 - \frac{\hbar^2}{2M_p} \nabla_p{}^2 + U(\mathbf{r}_p) \qquad (3.31)$$

Here $\nabla_n{}^2$ and $\nabla_p{}^2$ are the Laplace operators for the neutron and proton coordinates, and $U(\mathbf{r}_p)$ is the potential energy of the proton which binds it to the molecule. Actually $U(\mathbf{r}_p)$ depends also on the positions of all the other atoms in the molecule. We simplify the problem by assuming that $U(\mathbf{r}_p)$ is a function of $\mathbf{r}_p$ only. The Hamiltonian H_0 does not contain any interaction between proton and neutron.

To discuss the behavior of the wave function at the points where $\mathbf{r}_n = \mathbf{r}_p$, we introduce the neutron-proton separation $\mathbf{r} = \mathbf{r}_n - \mathbf{r}_p$ and recall the form of the radial wave function near "zero" energy; see (3.11). The wave function Ψ must be proportional to $1 - (a/r)$, where a is the scattering length and $r = |\mathbf{r}| = |\mathbf{r}_n - \mathbf{r}_p|$. Thus the presence of an interaction by localized impacts implies a singularity in the wave function Ψ at $r = 0$.[1] The factor in front of the $[1 - (a/r)]$ depends on the position of the two particles in coincidence, say on $\mathbf{r}_p$. We therefore obtain the following *boundary condition on the wave function Ψ for $\mathbf{r}_n \rightarrow \mathbf{r}_p$*:

$$\Psi \rightarrow \left(1 - \frac{a}{r}\right) \varphi(\mathbf{r}_p) \qquad \text{(for } r \rightarrow 0) \qquad (3.32)$$

where $\varphi(\mathbf{r}_p)$ is some function which will be determined later on. Only the absolute value r of the neutron-proton separation occurs in (3.32), because we have assumed that the interaction by contact is spherically symmetric (an S state interaction).

Equations (3.30) for $\mathbf{r}_n \neq \mathbf{r}_p$ and (3.32) for $\mathbf{r}_n = \mathbf{r}_p$ determine the wave function completely. It is more convenient, however, to combine these two equations into one, which will be called the *fundamental equation for interaction by localized impacts*. It was first given by Breit (47a,b), by a somewhat different derivation.

The boundary condition (3.32) implies that for very small values of r

$$r^2 \frac{\partial \Psi}{\partial r} \rightarrow a \frac{\partial(r\Psi)}{\partial r} \qquad (3.33)$$

---

[1] Actually there is no singularity at $r = 0$. The form $1 - (a/r)$ is correct for values of r small compared to molecular dimensions but larger than the range b of nuclear forces.

We integrate both sides of this equation over the full solid angle. The left side becomes

$$\int \frac{\partial \Psi}{\partial r} r^2 \, d\Omega \; = \; \int (\nabla_r \Psi) \cdot \mathbf{n} \, dS \; = \; \int (\nabla_r^2 \Psi) \, dV$$

where the second integral is over the surface of the sphere of radius r, and the last integral is over the volume of that sphere. $\mathbf{n}$ is a unit vector normal to the surface of the sphere. The right side of (3.33) can also be written as a volume integral through introduction of the delta-function:

$$\int a \frac{\partial (r\Psi)}{\partial r} \, d\Omega \; = \; 4\pi a \, \varphi(\mathbf{r}_p) \int \delta(\mathbf{r}) \, dV$$

where we have made use of the fact that, for very small r,

$$\frac{\partial (r\Psi)}{\partial r} \; = \; \varphi(\mathbf{r}_p)$$

is finite and independent of the neutron-proton separation r. We can therefore rewrite the boundary condition (3.32) in a third form by identifying the integrands of the above two volume integrals in the limit as r approaches zero:

$$\nabla_r^2 \Psi \; = \; 4\pi a \, \delta(\mathbf{r}) \lim_{r \to 0} \frac{\partial (r\Psi)}{\partial r} \qquad \text{(for } r \to 0) \qquad (3.34)$$

Let us now rewrite H_0 as given in (3.31) in terms of the relative coordinate $\mathbf{r}$ and the center-of-gravity coordinate:

$$\mathbf{R} \; = \; \frac{M_n \mathbf{r}_n + M_p \mathbf{r}_p}{M_n + M_p}$$

We get, with the notation $\mu = M_n M_p / (M_n + M_p) \cong \frac{1}{2} M_n$,

$$H_0 \; = \; -\frac{\hbar^2}{2\mu} \nabla_r^2 \; - \; \frac{\hbar^2}{2(M_n + M_p)} \nabla_R^2 \; + \; U(\mathbf{r}_p)$$

We can therefore rewrite (3.30) in the form

$$\nabla_r^2 \Psi \; = \; -\frac{\mu}{M_n + M_p} \nabla_R^2 \Psi \; + \; \frac{2\mu}{\hbar^2} U(\mathbf{r}_p) \, \Psi \; - \; \frac{2\mu E}{\hbar^2} \, \Psi \qquad \text{(for } r \neq 0)$$

$$(3.35)$$

Equations (3.34) and (3.35) can be written in one single equation valid for all values of r by putting $\nabla_r^2 \Psi$ equal to the sum of the right sides of (3.34) and (3.35). This is possible since, for $r = 0$, the right side of (3.35) is negligible compared to the delta-function singularity on the right side of (3.34). We then get

$$(H_0 - E) \Psi = -V'(\mathbf{r}_n - \mathbf{r}_p) \lim_{r \to 0} \frac{\partial(r\Psi)}{\partial r} \qquad (3.36)$$

where

$$V'(\mathbf{r}_n - \mathbf{r}_p) \equiv 4\pi a \frac{\hbar^2}{2\mu} \delta(\mathbf{r}_n - \mathbf{r}_p) \qquad (3.37)$$

This equation is exact. In order to find a suitable approximation method for the solution of (3.36), we observe that the case of *no* neutron-proton interaction is obtained by setting V' (i.e., the scattering length a) equal to zero. Therefore, to the extent that V' can be treated as "small," we can hope to expand Ψ in a power series in increasing powers of V', the leading term of which is just the wave function for no neutron-proton scattering, Ψ_0. We put

$$\Psi = \Psi_0 + \Psi_1 + \Psi_2 + \cdots \qquad (3.38)$$

and equate terms of the same order in V' in equation (3.36). This gives

$$(H_0 - E) \Psi_n = -V' \lim_{r \to 0} \frac{\partial(r\Psi_{n-1})}{\partial r} \qquad (3.39)$$

The first of these equations is especially simple. Since the incident wave Ψ_0 has no singularity at the coincidence of neutron and proton, we have

$$\lim_{r \to 0} \frac{\partial(r\Psi_0)}{\partial r} = [\Psi_0(\mathbf{r}_n, \mathbf{r}_p)]_{\mathbf{r}_n = \mathbf{r}_p} \qquad (3.40)$$

In substituting this into (3.39) to get an equation for Ψ_1, we do not have to require explicitly that $\mathbf{r}_n = \mathbf{r}_p$ in Ψ_0, since Ψ_0 occurs multiplied by V' which contains a delta-function. The first of the equations (3.39) therefore assumes the form

$$(H_0 - E) \Psi_1 = -V'(\mathbf{r}_n - \mathbf{r}_p) \Psi_0 \qquad (3.41)$$

This equation is identical with what we would get in the first Born approximation for the scattering due to the potential V'. *We can therefore take over the whole theory of the calculation of cross sections in the Born approximation, provided that we use the "pseudopotential"* V', (3.37), *instead of the true neutron-proton interaction,* and provided that we restrict ourselves to the *first* Born approximation (i.e., to the calculation of Ψ_1). Our method of derivation shows that an exact solution of the Schrödinger equation with the pseudopotential would not yield the true scattering at all. Rather, any improvement over the first Born approximation must be based on (3.39) directly; the $\lim_{r\to 0} \partial(r\Psi_{n-1})/\partial r$ is not equal to Ψ_{n-1} for $n \geq 2$.

We still have to discuss the validity of the formal expansion (3.38) in increasing powers of V', i.e., in increasing powers of the scattering length a. This is justified if the neutron-proton interaction can be treated as a small perturbation in its effect on the wave function at points $r \neq 0$. One condition can be read off from the boundary condition (3.32): the $1 - (a/r)$ factor approaches unity for large r; to the extent that it can be replaced by unity when r varies over molecular dimensions, the perturbation introduced by the non-zero value of a is small in its effect on the *molecular* wave function. Furthermore, the perturbation on the wave function of the *neutron* is small provided that the scattering length a is much less than the wavelength of the relative motion of neutron and proton, λ. The two conditions for the validity of the Born approximation (3.41) therefore are

$$a \ll \text{molecular dimensions} \qquad (3.42)$$

$$a \ll \text{neutron wavelength} \qquad (3.43)$$

To this we have to add the condition that the whole treatment of the interaction as an interaction by direct contact is valid, i.e., the range b of the neutron-proton force must be small enough:

$$b \ll \text{molecular dimensions} \qquad (3.44)$$

Conditions (3.42) to (3.44) are very well satisfied in practice. For our purposes a typical molecular dimension is given by the amplitude of vibration of a proton in the molecule, which is of the order of 10^{-9} cm (it would be incorrect to take the bond distances for this purpose, since we are concerned with the scattering of neutrons from one nucleus in the molecule). The range of the nuclear forces is of the order of 10^{-13} cm, and the scattering length a is of the order of 10^{-12} cm even in the more unfavorable case (singlet state scattering). The neutron wavelengths employed in practice are always long compared to "molecular dimensions" as defined above, since the bonds in the molecule are ruptured by the impact, and the scattering is therefore essentially that from a free proton, for wavelengths of the order of 10^{-8} cm or smaller. Hence (3.43) is fulfilled at all energies for which the effects of chemical binding are important. Calculations of the next approximation Ψ_2 by Breit (47b) and Lippmann (50a) have shown that it contributes of the order of 0.3 percent to the scattering; this is just the order of the ratio of the scattering length a to the molecular dimensions, as expected. Breit did not calculate the correction for the finite range of the forces, but (3.44) shows that it is even smaller, since $b < a$ for neutron-proton scattering.

The derivation of (3.41) was carried out with a simple Hamiltonian H_0 which included the molecular binding of the proton only schematically as a potential energy $U(\mathbf{r}_p)$ binding the proton to a fixed center of force. However, the derivation depends only on the kinetic energy terms for the neutron and proton and is therefore also applicable to the actual case where the internal motion of the molecule must be treated in detail. Having established the validity of the Born approximation procedure in conjunction with the pseudopotential V', (3.37), for the simple case, we can therefore apply this procedure directly to the scattering of slow neutrons by protons bound to actual molecules. We assume that we know the wave functions for the various states of excitation of the molecule. The initial state of the system has the form

$$\Psi_0 = \exp[i\mathbf{k}_i \cdot (\mathbf{r}_n - \boldsymbol{\varrho})] \, u_i(\mathbf{r}_p, \cdots) \tag{3.45}$$

where $\mathbf{k}_i$ is the initial wave number of the relative motion of neutron and molecule (in the system where the center of gravity of neutron and *molecule* is at rest) $\boldsymbol{\varrho}$ is the center of gravity of the molecule, and u_i denotes the internal wave function of the molecule when struck; the dots after $\mathbf{r}_p$ are intended to denote the other coordinates in the molecular wave function. We now use standard Born approximation procedure to find the differential cross sections for the various (elastic and inelastic) scattering events which can take place. Let v_i and v_f be the speeds of the neutron relative to the molecule in the initial and final states; let $\mu' \equiv M_n M_{\text{mol}}/(M_n + M_{\text{mol}})$ be the reduced mass for the relative motion of neutron and molecule; and let $d\sigma_{if}$ be the differential cross section for scattering of the neutron into the solid angle element $d\Omega$ (in the system in which the center of gravity of the neutron and the molecule is at rest) with simultaneous excitation (or de-excitation) of the molecule to state u_f. Then the Born approximation gives

$$d\sigma_{if} = \frac{v_f}{v_i} \left(\frac{\mu'}{\mu}\right)^2 a^2 \, |I_{if}|^2 \, d\Omega \tag{3.46}$$

where the "form factor" integral I_{if} is defined

$$I_{if} \equiv \int \exp\left[i(\mathbf{k}_i - \mathbf{k}_f) \cdot \mathbf{r}_p\right] u_f^*(\mathbf{r}_p, \cdots) \, u_i(\mathbf{r}_p, \cdots) \, d\tau \tag{3.47}$$

the integration going over all the coordinates of the molecular wave functions.

The cross section becomes extremely simple in the limit of zero energy neutrons. We shall assume that the molecules are in their lowest state to begin with (i.e., that the scattering material is kept at an extremely low temperature). Then excitation or de-excitation of the molecule by the neutron impact is impossible and the scattering is purely elastic [i.e., $f = i$ in (3.46)]. Furthermore the wavelength of the neutron is so long compared to the size of the molecule that the exponential in (3.47) can be replaced by unity. The form factor for elastic scattering I_{ii} is unity in this approximation because of the normalization of the molecular wave function u_i. Equation (3.46) then reduces to

$$d\sigma_{ii} = \left(\frac{\mu'}{\mu}\right)^2 a^2 \, d\Omega \qquad (3.48)$$

We observe that the scattering is spherically symmetric in the center-of-gravity system of the neutron and molecule, rather than in the center-of-gravity system of the neutron and proton. The total cross section for elastic scattering can be found by integration over $d\Omega$ which gives a factor 4π. Substituting the values of μ and μ' and using the fact that the masses of neutron and proton are nearly equal, we get the total scattering cross section in the limit of zero neutron energy:

$$\sigma_{ii} = \frac{4}{[1 + (M_n/M_{\text{mol}})]^2} \, 4\pi a^2 \qquad (3.49)$$

This should be compared with the extrapolated value for "zero" energy neutrons, $4\pi a^2$. We see that for a heavy molecule the chemical binding has the effect of increasing the total cross section for scattering of extremely slow neutrons by almost a factor of 4 over the extrapolated value. Furthermore the scattering has a different angular distribution from the scattering by a free proton.

The scattering is in principle completely described by (3.46) and (3.47). As the energy of the neutrons is slowly increased from zero, the scattering is at first elastic (no excitation or de-excitation of the molecule) and spherically symmetric. At higher energies the integral I_{ii} leads to a non-uniform angular distribution of the scattering; I_{ii} is similar to the "form factor" for the scattering of x-rays or fast electrons. Increasing the neutron energy further makes inelastic scattering possible. The cross section has a rather complicated behavior in that region; it increases suddenly at each new threshold for inelastic scattering. Finally, at neutron energies high compared to the chemical binding energies, the proton is essentially free; the scattering is then practically elastic and spherically symmetric in the center-of-gravity system of the neutron and proton. A small fraction of the neutron energy is transferred from the neutron to the molecule to break the chemical bond of the proton.

This description is still very simplified. There are various effects which make the picture more complicated. The initial state of the molecule is not necessarily its ground state. Rather, the molecule may be in one of its excited states initially, with a probability depending on the temperature of the gas according to the usual Boltzmann factor. For molecules which are in excited states initially, inelastic scattering events in which the neutron *gains* energy are possible even for very slow neutrons. Furthermore the cross section for these events is inversely proportional to the initial neutron speed, according to (3.46), so that these events become important for low-energy neutrons. A second complication arises from the fact that we have tacitly assumed that there is only one proton in the molecule, and that the molecules scatter incoherently. In practice, there may be more than one proton in the molecule; there are always other neutron scatterers in the molecule; and, in the case of scattering by a solid substance, the various "molecules" (unit cells of the crystal lattice) scatter coherently. The latter kind of interference gives rise to phenomena analogous to the scattering of x-rays by crystals.

▶ D. Coherent Scattering of Neutrons by Protons

The scattering from single protons consists of two separate parts: singlet scattering and triplet scattering. It is very hard to separate these two parts as long as they add up *incoherently*, i.e., as long as there is no interference between the scattered amplitudes. Just as in optical interference experiments, appreciable interference effects can be expected from unpolarized neutrons only if the same neutron wave is allowed to strike more than one scattering center (proton) in close proximity, "close" meaning at distances of the order of, or smaller than, a neutron de Broglie wavelength. Since protons are naturally separated by distances of the order of 10^{-8} cm, we do not get appreciable interference effects for any but the very slowest neutrons (considerably below thermal energies).

The first experiment along these lines was suggested by Teller and Schwinger (Schwinger 37a) and involves the scattering of neutrons from hydrogen molecules. The protons in the molecule can have their spins aligned (orthohydrogen), or they can have their spins opposite (parahydrogen). The interference effect in the scattering of neutrons by such molecules is different for these two species. We might be tempted to think that the over-all interference effect vanishes if neutrons are scattered by an assembly containing orthohydrogen and parahydrogen molecules in the ratio $\frac{1}{4}:\frac{3}{4}$, for that is the ratio of the expectation values of the singlet and triplet states for two uncorrelated protons.[1] This reasoning is incorrect: the net interference effect is not zero even under these conditions. The reason is that we have a random assembly of *pairs* of protons, each pair being close together compared to the neutron de Broglie wavelength and having their spins correlated in some way (even though the average spin state of the assembly is just as it would be for uncorrelated proton spins). This differs essentially from a random assembly of separated protons of uncorrelated spins. Hence we should expect an interference effect in neutron-proton scattering even for this statistical mixture of ortho-hydrogen and parahydrogen. However, the interference effect is much sharper and much more pronounced if we have at our disposal hydrogen molecules of one kind only.

It is possible to separate orthohydrogen and parahydrogen at low temperature. Hydrogen is a diatomic homonuclear molecule, and the nuclear part of its wave function must obey the Pauli exclusion principle since the protons obey Fermi-Dirac statistics. The Pauli principle implies that the space behavior of the wave function for the nuclear motion in the molecule has the opposite symmetry from the spin part, e.g., in orthohydrogen where the spins are aligned and the spin wave function is symmetric, the space wave function for the nuclear motion in the molecule must be anti-symmetric under the exchange of the two protons; in parahydrogen the space wave function must be symmetric. Hence orthohydrogen and parahydrogen have space wave functions of opposite symmetry character and therefore entirely different energy levels. The two species of hydrogen can transform into each other, but the reaction rate is very slow unless a catalyst is present. Flipping of nuclear spins is required, and electromagnetic interactions with nuclear spins are notoriously weak. Experimentally, it is possible to prepare nearly pure parahydrogen gas at very low temperatures (of the order of 20°K). It is fortunate that the cross section of neutrons in parahydrogen is the interesting quantity from the nuclear point of view. The study of the neutron scattering from parahydrogen sup-

---

[1] Here the terms "singlet" and "triplet" are applied to the spin states of two protons, rather than to the spin states of the neutron and one of the protons. In this section we shall be interested in spin correlations between various pairs of nucleons. It will therefore be important to keep clear which pair is meant whenever the terms "singlet" and "triplet" are used.

plies a clear-cut decision as to the relative phase of the singlet and triplet state neutron-proton scattering.

For this purpose we introduce the spin dependence of the scattering in a formal way. The amplitude of the scattered wave is a_s if the neutron and proton are in the singlet spin state, a_t if they are in the triplet spin state. We introduce the "projection" operators π_s and π_t which have the following property:[1]

$$\pi_s = \tfrac{1}{4}\left[1 - (\mathbf{\delta}_n \cdot \mathbf{\delta}_p)\right] = 1 \quad \text{if } n \text{ and } p \text{ are in the singlet spin state}$$

$$= 0 \quad \text{if } n \text{ and } p \text{ are in the triplet spin state}$$

$$\pi_t = \tfrac{1}{4}\left[3 + (\mathbf{\delta}_n \cdot \mathbf{\delta}_p)\right] = 0 \quad \text{if } n \text{ and } p \text{ are in the singlet spin state} \tag{3.50}$$

$$= 1 \quad \text{if } n \text{ and } p \text{ are in the triplet spin state}$$

We can replace the scattering length a everywhere in Section 3C by the operator a_{eff} which has the value a_s in the singlet state and a_t in the triplet state of the neutron and the proton:

$$a_{\text{eff}} = a_s\pi_s + a_t\pi_t \tag{3.51}$$

The simplest case to discuss is the scattering of extremely slow neutrons by hydrogen molecules. We understand by "extremely slow" neutrons those whose wavelength (in the center-of-gravity system of the neutron and molecule) is much larger than the H-H distance in the molecule (0.74×10^{-8} cm). Under these conditions the scattered waves from the two protons interfere without appreciable retardation, i.e., as if they came from the *same* place. Furthermore the neutron impact does not change the internal motion of the molecule. (This is not true for the possible inelastic collisions in which the neutron gains energy, but we shall neglect this for the present.) The amplitude of the scattered wave is therefore the sum of the scattering amplitudes $a_{\text{eff},1}$, $a_{\text{eff},2}$ of the two protons as given by (3.51):

$$a_{\text{sc}} = a_{\text{eff},1} + a_{\text{eff},2} = 2\left(\tfrac{3}{4}a_t + \tfrac{1}{4}a_s\right) + 2\left(\tfrac{1}{4}a_t - \tfrac{1}{4}a_s\right)(\mathbf{\delta}_n \cdot \mathbf{S}) \tag{3.52}$$

The factor 2 comes from the two protons, and $\mathbf{S} = \tfrac{1}{2}(\mathbf{\delta}_{p1} + \mathbf{\delta}_{p2})$ is the spin vector operator of the hydrogen molecule in units of $\hbar$.

By observing the scattering by hydrogen molecules with $S = 0$ and with $S = 1$ we can separate the contributions of the first and second terms in (3.52). In particular we can measure the quantity

$$f = 2\left(\tfrac{3}{4}a_t + \tfrac{1}{4}a_s\right) \tag{3.53}$$

[1] Proof: $2(\mathbf{\delta}_n \cdot \mathbf{\delta}_p) = (\mathbf{\delta}_n + \mathbf{\delta}_p)^2 - (\mathbf{\delta}_n)^2 - (\mathbf{\delta}_p)^2 = 4s(s+1) - 6$, where $s = 0$ in the singlet spin state, $s = 1$ in the triplet spin state.

Indeed, the scattering from parahydrogen $(S=0)$ is proportional to f^2. We substitute the coherent scattering length f instead of a into (3.49) to get the scattering cross section per parahydrogen molecule:

$$\sigma_{\text{para}} = \frac{4}{(\frac{3}{2})^2} 4\pi f^2 = \tfrac{16}{9} 4\pi f^2 \tag{3.54}$$

It is instructive at this point to insert some numerical estimates. The triplet scattering length a_t is roughly equal to the "size" of the deuteron, $a_t \cong R = 4.31 \times 10^{-13}$ cm, if range corrections are neglected. The singlet scattering length can be estimated from the incoherent neutron-proton scattering cross section at "zero" energy [see (3.25) and the discussion thereafter]. We get $a_s = \pm 2.434 \times 10^{-12}$ cm, the plus sign applying in case of a bound singlet state. If we assume a bound singlet state, f turns out to be $f = 1.86 \times 10^{-12}$ cm, whereas for a virtual singlet state we obtain $f = -0.565 \times 10^{-12}$ cm. The corresponding scattering cross sections on parahydrogen are, according to (3.54),

$$\sigma_{\text{para}} = 77.6 \times 10^{-24} \text{ cm}^2 \quad \text{(bound singlet state)}$$
$$\sigma_{\text{para}} = 7.14 \times 10^{-24} \text{ cm}^2 \quad \text{(virtual singlet state)} \tag{3.55}$$

The tremendous difference between these two predictions is the result of a very fortunate accident: $3a_t$ is very nearly equal to a_s in absolute value, hence there is almost complete destructive interference between singlet and triplet scattering if the two scattering lengths have opposite signs.

The experimental value (Sutton 47) of the parahydrogen cross section is 3.9×10^{-24} cm^2. This shows, without any more refined analysis, that *the singlet scattering length has the opposite sign (negative) from the triplet scattering length, i.e., there exists no bound singlet state of the deuteron.*

The scattering of "zero" energy neutrons by *single* protons determines the quantity $\sigma_0 = \tfrac{3}{4}(4\pi a_t^2) + \tfrac{1}{4}(4\pi a_s^2)$; since we now also have a measurement of f^2, we can determine a_s and a_t separately, with much better accuracy. The value of a_t can then be used in conjunction with the known binding energy of the deuteron in order to determine the effective range $r_0 \equiv r_{0t}$ in the triplet state by equation (3.22).[1] This determination is quite sensitive, again because of the very fortunate, almost complete destructive interference in the parahydrogen

[1] The importance of the measurement of the parahydrogen cross section for nuclear physics has been stressed particularly by Schwinger (40).

scattering. The result is

$$r_{0t} = (1.6 \pm 0.2) \times 10^{-13} \text{ cm} \tag{3.56}$$

This range estimate proves the earlier statement that the "size" of the deuteron ($R = 4.31 \times 10^{-13}$ cm) greatly exceeds the range of the nuclear forces which hold it together.

We now enumerate the refinements necessary to make a detailed comparison between theory and experiment. A serious defect of our analysis so far has been the neglect of the inelastic collisions between the neutron and the hydrogen molecule. For neutrons of very low energy we need to include only those inelastic collisions in which the neutron *gains* energy. If the hydrogen molecules are in their ground states, there are no such collisions for parahydrogen (since its ground state lies below that of orthohydrogen). Thus the correction for inelastic scattering is unimportant for the scattering of very slow neutrons from very cold parahydrogen. On the other hand, a neutron colliding with an orthohydrogen molecule in its ground state can gain energy by a collision in which the molecule becomes parahydrogen in its ground state. We see from (3.46) that the cross section for this process is proportional to $(1/v_i)$ for low-energy neutrons (since v_f approaches a constant, non-zero value). Hence the correction for inelastic scattering of very slow neutrons from very cold orthohydrogen is important, indeed the more important the slower the neutrons.

Experimentally, the total (transmission) cross section for the neutron beam is measured. Hence, in addition to the (elastic and inelastic) scattering events, the experimental cross section includes a contribution from the neutron-proton radiative capture process in which a deuteron is formed (see Chapter XII). The correction for this is important at the energies used, especially for parahydrogen.

There are two more corrections to be applied on the theoretical side: (1) The form factor, (3.47), is not exactly equal to unity except for neutrons of exactly zero energy. (2) For very slow neutrons the Maxwell distribution of the velocities of the gas molecules must be taken into account. Indeed, for very slow neutrons the scattering is given to a first approximation by the impacts of moving molecules on stationary neutrons.

The result of the various theoretical corrections raises the scattering cross section (3.54) by about 16 percent for neutrons of energy $E = kT$ with $T = 20°$K impinging on parahydrogen at its boiling point (also 20°K). The additional correction for the neutron-proton capture cross section is large, indeed the capture cross-section is about equal to the scattering cross section at these very low energies. However, this correction can be made rather accurately, since the capture cross section is known at higher energies and there is every reason to believe that it follows a v^{-1} law.

There exists another, completely independent method for observing the coherent scattering of low-energy neutrons on protons. This method has become available only recently because the high neutron flux necessary can be obtained only from a pile. The method involves the scattering of neutrons on crystals containing hydrogen atoms in the lattice. The scattering of neutrons on crystals is a subject which we shall not treat here in any detail.[1] It is closely analogous to the scattering of x-rays on crystals. There are two types of scattering: diffuse (incoherent) and Bragg (coherent) scattering. The latter occurs only under certain very definite geometrical conditions (Bragg angles). It involves coherent effects from all the atoms in the lattice and can be used to determine the quantity f, (3.53), for hydrogen. The present result (Shull 48) is somewhat less accurate than the para-hydrogen value but is in excellent agreement with it. The crystal scattering method is inherently free of many of the systematic errors which can falsify the parahydrogen determination: it is not necessary to make a correction for neutron-proton capture, and there is no possibility of an admixture of orthohydrogen which can disturb the parahydrogen determination.

A very accurate method of determining the coherent scattering length f has been suggested by Hamermesh (50). It involves the total reflection of neutrons from a liquid "mirror" containing protons. Just as for x-rays, it may happen that the refractive index of a material, such as a liquid or a crystal, for neutrons is less than unity. Then neutrons impinging on the surface at glancing angles are totally reflected back into the air. The critical angle for total reflection is rather straightforward to measure. It depends on the refractive index. The refractive index in turn depends on the *coherent* scattering length of the material, since specular reflection is caused by a coherent superposition of scattered waves from very many scattering centers in the reflecting surface. The various incoherent effects (absorption, etc.) lead to a diminution of the reflected intensity but do not affect the critical angle for complete reflection. The experiment has been performed by Hughes, Burgy, and Ringo (Hughes 50, Ringo 51). Surprisingly enough, their very accurate result for f is outside the quoted error of the parahydrogen determination and just barely within the error of the crystal determination, showing that there were concealed systematic errors in both of them. We shall accept the measurement done with total reflection, which gives

$$f = -(3.78 \pm 0.02) \times 10^{-13} \text{ cm} \quad \text{(total reflection)} \quad (3.57)$$

The value of the triplet effective range r_{0t} is then

$$r_{0t} = (1.70 \pm 0.03) \times 10^{-13} \text{ cm} \quad (3.58)$$

---

[1] The reader is referred to Wick (37), Halpern (41), Seeger (42), Weinstock (44), Fermi (47b), Goldberger (47), especially the last of these, for the theory; and to Wollan (48) for some of the experimental work.

Schwinger (37b) has pointed out that the almost complete interference of singlet and triplet scattering in parahydrogen provides a very direct *proof that the spin of the neutron is* $\frac{1}{2}$. It is established experimentally that the spin of the deuteron is unity and the spin of the proton is $\frac{1}{2}$. Furthermore there is every reason to believe that the orbital angular momentum L of the deuteron is predominantly zero. Hence the spin of the neutron must have one of the two values: $\frac{1}{2}$, $\frac{3}{2}$. Let us assume the value $\frac{3}{2}$ for the moment. Then the possible spin states of the neutron-proton system are $S=2$ (quintet) and $S=1$ (triplet). The "zero" energy incoherent cross section becomes $\sigma_0 = \frac{5}{8}\sigma_q + \frac{3}{8}\sigma_t$ where $\frac{5}{8}$ and $\frac{3}{8}$ are the a priori statistical weights of the quintet and triplet spin states, and σ_q and σ_t are the corresponding cross sections. If we again neglect range corrections in the triplet scattering, we get $20.36 = \frac{5}{8}\sigma_q + \frac{3}{8}(2.36)$; $\sigma_q = 4\pi a_q^2 = 31.2$ (all cross sections in 10^{-24} cm^2). The coherent scattering amplitude analogous to f now becomes

$$f' = 2\left(\tfrac{5}{8}a_q + \tfrac{3}{8}a_t\right)$$

Putting in the numerical values of the two scattering lengths, we get

$$f' = 2.29 \times 10^{-12} \text{ cm} \qquad \text{(for a real quintet state)}$$

$$f' = -1.65 \times 10^{-12} \text{ cm} \qquad \text{(for a virtual quintet state)}$$

Thus, even under the assumption of a virtual quintet state, the parahydrogen cross section would be [see (3.54)] as high as 61×10^{-24} cm^2—in gross contradiction to experiment. We therefore conclude that the spin of the neutron cannot be $\frac{3}{2}$; since we have already narrowed it down to either $\frac{1}{2}$ or $\frac{3}{2}$, the spin must be $\frac{1}{2}$. This proof has the virtue that it does not depend on any detailed assumptions about the nuclear forces.

4. PROTON-PROTON SCATTERING

Since proton sources are not so readily available as neutron sources, protons must be accelerated artificially before scattering experiments can be done with them. The Coulomb force between two protons tends to keep them apart, outside the range of the nuclear interaction between them. At proton energies (in the laboratory system) of less than 100 kev the nuclear effects in the scattering are too small to be detectable. Thus the investigation of nuclear effects in proton-proton scattering had to wait until accelerators were built which could produce voltages of more than 100 kev. The first preliminary experiments, done around 1935, showed that the interaction between two protons at energies in the 500-kev region could not be a pure Coulomb interaction, but that nuclear effects were present. The theory of proton-proton scattering was then worked out by Breit, Condon, and Present (36). When more accurate experiments became available for analysis, the theory was compared with experiment, and conclusions could be drawn about the nuclear force between two protons (Breit 39). The post-war work in this field (both experimental and theoretical) has been summarized in a review article (Jackson 50) to which the reader is referred for details not included in this section.

There are two essential differences between proton-proton and neutron-proton scattering. First, the proton-proton scattering is caused not only by the nuclear forces but also by the Coulomb force. Second, the scattering and scattered particles are identical and obey the Pauli exclusion principle.

The Coulomb repulsion tends to keep the protons apart, but it is effective only at low energies. The wave-mechanical effect of "leaking" through a potential barrier makes it possible to find two protons very close to one another even if, classically, this is forbidden by the energy balance. Classically, the closest distance of approach is given by $d = e^2/E$, where E is the energy of the relative motion. In quantum theory the Coulomb field cannot effectively prevent them from coming close together if d is as small as the de Broglie wavelength $(\hbar^2/2\mu E)^{1/2}$ or smaller. The relative probability of finding two protons at the same point compared to the probability of finding two uncharged particles together (other things being equal) is given by the "Coulomb penetration factor" C^2:

$$C^2 = \frac{2\pi\eta}{\exp(2\pi\eta) - 1} \tag{4.1}$$

where $\eta = e^2/\hbar v$, and v is the relative velocity of the two particles. This penetration factor is $\frac{1}{2}$ at a relative energy $E \cong 0.4$Mev (a proton beam energy in the laboratory system of twice that, i.e., 0.8 Mev). For energies much lower than that (below 0.2 Mev in the laboratory system) the Coulomb field effectively prevents the protons from getting close enough for the nuclear forces to be effective. At higher energies the nuclear scattering plays an important role.

The identity of the two particles has two effects. First of all, the two collisions pictured in Fig. 4.1a and 4.1b can no longer be distinguished from each other. The differential cross section for identical particles determines the probability of finding *either one* of the two particles going at an angle θ to the direction of the incident one, after the collision. Classically, the scattering cross sections for the two cases in Fig. 4.1 should merely be added to get the cross section for identical particles. Quantum-mechanically, scattering amplitudes have to be added rather than the cross sections themselves, so that there are interference terms in the resulting cross section. In either case the differential scattering cross section in the center-of-gravity system is symmetrical around $\theta = 90°$ for identical particles.

The second effect of the identity of the two particles is a result of the

Pauli exclusion principle. The wave function for the two protons has to be antisymmetric under their exchange. Hence a symmetric space wave function (S, D, G states, etc.) can only be associated with an anti-symmetric (singlet) spin wave function, whereas an anti-symmetric space wave function (P, F states, etc.) requires a symmetric (triplet) spin wave function. At energies below about 10 Mev, only the S state interaction is of any importance in the scattering, since

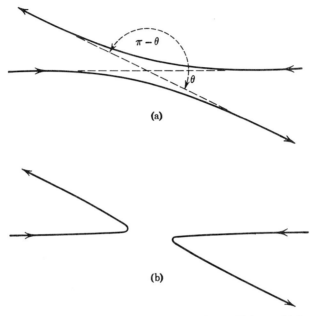

(a)

(b)

FIG. 4.1. Two seemingly different identical particle collisions which are experimentally indistinguishable.

protons in higher orbital angular momentum states stay apart from each other beyond the range of the nuclear force. Thus low-energy proton-proton scattering experiments give information about the nuclear interaction of protons with opposite spins only (singlet state).

Consider first the radial equation in the ^1S state for pure Coulomb scattering. The radial function, which we shall call $F(r)$, then satisfies (2.2) with $V(r) = e^2/r$:

$$-\frac{\hbar^2}{M}\frac{d^2F}{dr^2} + \frac{e^2}{r}F = E\,F(r) \tag{4.2}$$

$F(r)$ is subject to the boundary condition $F(0) = 0$. The solutions of (4.2) have been studied extensively (Yost 36, Beckerley 45) and have been tabulated for many values of energy E and distance r. We are particularly interested in the behavior of $F(r)$ at large distances. It is

$$F(r) \cong \sin [kr - \eta \ln (2kr) + \sigma_0] \qquad \text{(for large } r) \qquad (4.3)$$

where k is the wave number of the relative motion [see (3.2) and (3.3)] and η is as defined in (4.1). The quantity σ_0 is the Coulomb phase shift for the ^1S wave Coulomb scattering. The logarithmic term in (4.3) is due to the "infinite range" of the Coulomb force, i.e., the potential e^2/r affects the behavior of the wave function even at very large distances r. $F(r)$ is the analogue of $\sin (kr)$ in neutron-proton scattering.

We now assume that there is a nuclear potential $V(r)$ in addition to the Coulomb potential. The radial wave function $u(r)$ then satisfies the equation

$$-\frac{\hbar^2}{M} \frac{d^2 u}{dr^2} + \frac{e^2}{r} u(r) + V(r) u(r) = E u(r) \qquad (4.4)$$

Outside the range of the nuclear force, (4.4) becomes identical with (4.2), so that the asymptotic behavior of $u(r)$ is very similar to the asymptotic behavior of $F(r)$. The only change is a modification of the (pure Coulomb) phase shift σ_0. We set the modified phase shift equal to $\sigma_0 + \delta$, i.e.,

$$u(r) \cong \sin [kr - \eta \ln (2kr) + \sigma_0 + \delta] \qquad \text{(for large } r) \qquad (4.5)$$

The quantity δ is commonly called the "nuclear phase shift." It must be realized, however, that δ is by no means identical with the phase shift which would govern the purely nuclear scattering by the potential $V(r)$ in the absence of the Coulomb repulsion; we shall call this latter phase shift δ'.

Since the ^1S wave is the only part of the incoming wave which is appreciably changed by the nuclear effects at energies below 10 Mev, the phase shift δ in (4.5) is the only change from pure Coulomb scattering. All the other partial waves (^3P, ^1D, ^3F, $\cdots$) are effectively subject to the Coulomb force only, since the particles do not get close enough to each other to experience nuclear forces. This means that the observed scattering cross section at any one energy E is defined by only one parameter, δ. We should be able to fit the observed differential cross section at all scattering angles by the use of only one adjustable parameter. This is a rather stringent requirement, and the perfect agreement between theory and experiment is a non-trivial confirmation of the theory.[1]

The differential cross section is a complicated function of the energy E, the angle of scattering θ, and the phase shift δ. We shall confine ourselves to a qualitative description. At small scattering angles the scattering is essentially pure Coulomb (Rutherford) scattering. There

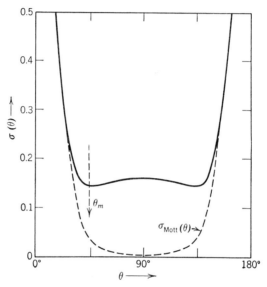

Fig. 4.2. Differential scattering cross section in the center-of-gravity system, plotted against the scattering angle θ. The dotted curve is for pure Coulomb scattering. The nuclear scattering predominates in the central region of angles. There is destructive interference between nuclear and Coulomb scattering around $\theta = \theta_m$ and $\theta = \pi - \theta_m$. The Coulomb scattering predominates for $\theta < \theta_m$ and $\theta > \pi - \theta_m$. The figure corresponds to the actual situation at an energy $E_{\text{lab}} = 2.4$ Mev.

then follows a region of angles in which the Coulomb scattering interferes appreciably with the nuclear scattering. Finally, at even larger scattering angles the nuclear scattering predominates. Because of the identity of the two protons, the scattering cross section at an angle $\pi - \theta$ is the same as at θ (in the center-of-gravity system). These points are illustrated in Fig. 4.2. The nuclear scattering predominates

[1] The situation in neutron-proton scattering is different for two reasons: (1) there are two phase shifts at our disposal, for the ^3S and ^1S scattering, respectively; (2) the differential cross section is expected to be spherically symmetrical in the center-of-gravity system. The more complicated angular dependence of the proton-proton scattering is caused by interference between Coulomb and nuclear scattering and therefore provides a much more sensitive test of the theory.

in the central region of angles. The cross section is approximately constant in this region, because the nuclear scattering is S wave scattering ($l=0$) only. The dip around $\theta = \theta_m$ on the figure is caused by interference between nuclear and Coulomb scattering. The interference is destructive because the Coulomb force is repulsive whereas the nuclear force is attractive. Finally, at angles $\theta < \theta_m$ (and correspondingly at $\theta > \pi - \theta_m$) the Coulomb scattering predominates.

We shall not go into the details of the analysis of the experiments here. Suffice it to say that an analysis very similar to the one for neutron-proton scattering can be made (Bethe 49, Jackson 50) to find the approximate energy dependence of the nuclear phase shift δ for proton-proton scattering. Again there exists a function of the observed phase shift and the relative velocity which should be approximately a straight line when plotted against energy (against k^2); only now that function is not just $k \cot \delta$ [see (3.19)] but the more complicated expression

$$K' \equiv C^2 \, k \cot \delta + D^{-1} \, h(\eta) \qquad (4.6)$$

where C^2 and η are as defined in (4.1). The distance

$$D = \frac{\hbar^2}{Me^2} = 2.88 \times 10^{-12} \text{ cm}$$

is characteristic for the Coulomb scattering. (It is the Bohr radius of a proton bound to a fixed center of charge e.) $h(\eta)$ is a slowly varying function of the energy, behaving logarithmically at high energies.[1] The first term of (4.6) allows a simple interpretation. It is just $k \cot \delta$, the relevant quantity in neutron-proton scattering, multiplied by the Coulomb penetration factor C^2. The second term is harder to understand. It owes its origin to the peculiarities of the Coulomb scattering, in particular to the fact that the Coulomb force has an infinite "range" of action, i.e., the wave function of the incident proton beam is deformed appreciably from a plane wave even at very large distances from the scattering center [see (4.3)].

The expansion of K' as a function of energy (k^2) can be written in the form

$$K' = -a^{-1} + \tfrac{1}{2} r_0 k^2 - P r_0^3 k^4 + \cdots \qquad (4.7)$$

[1] The definition of $h(\eta)$ is
$$h(\eta) = \operatorname{Re} \Psi(-i\eta) - \ln \eta$$
where $\Psi(z)$ is the logarithmic derivative of the factorial function (defined in Jahnke-Emde, *Tables of Functions*, Leipzig, 1938), ln denotes the natural logarithm, and Re denotes the real part of the expression in question.

II. Two-Body Problems at Low Energies

where a is called the (proton-proton) scattering length, r_0 is the (proton-proton) effective range, and P is a dimensionless parameter related to the detailed distance dependence ("shape") of the nuclear potential between two protons. The higher terms in (4.7) are presumably negligible. We have written down one more term of the series (4.7) than of the corresponding neutron-proton series (3.19),

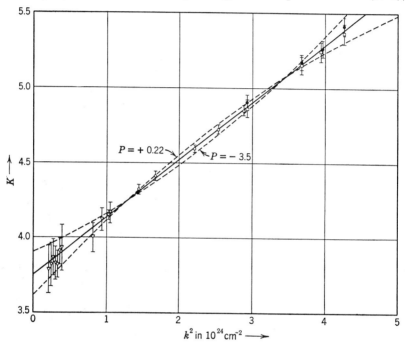

FIG. 4.3. Experimental values of $K = K'D$ plotted against energy, where K' is defined by (4.6) and D is a characteristic length for proton-proton scattering. The straight line corresponds to a shape parameter $P = 0$ in (4.7). It is an excellent fit. The two parabolas, corresponding to $P = +0.22$ and $P = -3.5$, respectively, are excluded by these data. The four conventional well shapes defined in Section 2 all lead to good fits to the data.

because the accuracy of the proton-proton scattering experiments is higher than that of the neutron-proton scattering experiments. Theoretically, P is expected to have rather small values. It is slightly negative (-0.033) for the sharply cut-off "square well," and slightly positive (0.055) for the "long-tailed" Yukawa well.

In Fig. 4.3 we have plotted the experimental values of the dimensionless quantity $K = K'D$ against k^2 for energies below 5 Mev in the laboratory system. It is seen that the straight line ($P = 0$) provides an excellent fit. The two parabolas which are also shown in the figure correspond to well shape parameters $P = +0.22$ and $P = -3.5$, respectively. They are both excluded by the data. Taking into account the preceding estimates of P for some conventional well shapes, we see that the present data do not suffice to discriminate between the commonly assumed well shapes. However, the accuracy needed to do so appears within the range of present techniques.

Of great interest is the value of the proton-proton scattering length a, determined by the intercept of the straight line on the graph. It turns out to be $a \cong -7.7 \times 10^{-13}$ cm (the precise value depends on the value assumed for P). The first significant fact about a is its sign: it is negative, and it can be shown (Landau 44) that this implies that the proton-proton system in its ^1S state does not allow a bound state. In other words, *the nucleus He^2 is dynamically unstable.* Just as for singlet neutron-proton scattering, a virtual level can be defined, and again the rather large value of the scattering length (compared to nuclear dimensions) implies that this virtual level lies not very far above zero energy; i.e., the di-proton (He^2) just barely misses being stable, in complete analogy to the singlet deuteron.

Within the range of the nuclear forces the Coulomb force can be treated as a small perturbation. In this way it is possible to derive an approximate relation between the scattering length a for proton-proton scattering and an "equivalent" scattering length a' for the case where the Coulomb field has been switched off. This relation involves the proton Bohr radius D and the proton-proton effective range r_0; it reads

$$(a')^{-1} \cong a^{-1} + D^{-1}\left[\ln \frac{D}{r_0} - 0.33\right] \qquad (4.8)$$

The constant 0.33 on the right side is an estimate which depends somewhat on the shape of the nuclear well (Jackson 50). If we substitute the experimental values of a and r_0 [the latter can be found from the slope of the straight line in figure (4.3), and it turns out to be $r_0 = 2.65 \times 10^{-13}$ cm], we find

$$a' \cong -1.7 \times 10^{-12} \text{ cm} \qquad (4.9)$$

This estimate should be compared with the observed value of the neutron-proton scattering length in the singlet spin state,

$$a_s = -2.43 \times 10^{-12} \text{ cm}$$

At first sight this comparison seems to imply that the nuclear force between two protons in the ^1S state is appreciably different from the nuclear force between a neutron and a proton in the ^1S state. It must be remembered, however, that both scattering lengths are very large, i.e., we are near resonance at zero energy for both neutron-proton and proton-proton scattering. Consequently the scattering lengths are very sensitive to slight changes in the potential, and the apparently large difference between a' and a_s can be attributed, for example, to a very small change in the well depth parameter s between the two cases (the value of the well depth parameter is larger for the singlet neutron-proton force by between one and three percent, depending on the well shape assumed). This small change may be attributed to non-nuclear effects (Schwinger 50).

We conclude that, *under the assumption that the distance dependence of the nuclear potential (in particular its range) is the same between two protons as between a neutron and a proton in the ^1S state, the strength of the force is very closely equal also* (the discrepancy being of the order of a few percent at most). The effective range for neutron-proton scattering in the singlet state is not in disagreement with the above assumption of equality of ranges.

The comparison between neutron-proton and proton-proton forces in the ^1S state gave rise to the *hypothesis of the charge independence of the nuclear forces* (Breit 36a, 37, 39a). This hypothesis states that the forces between two nucleons in the same spin and orbital angular momentum state are independent of the charge (neutron or proton) of the two nucleons. For example, the force between two neutrons in the ^3P state is the same, on this hypothesis, as the force between two protons or between a neutron and a proton. There is some evidence for equality of neutron-neutron and proton-proton forces from heavier nuclei (see Chapters V and VI). The equality of neutron-proton and proton-proton forces, however, is based mainly on the one piece of evidence given above, and that evidence is not conclusive because the range of the singlet neutron-proton force is not known well enough. The hypothesis of the charge independence of nuclear forces is not definitely established at the present time. Indeed, the scattering data in the high-energy region appear to be difficult to reconcile with charge-independent forces (see Chapter IV).

▶   **5. THE TENSOR FORCE**

A. Experimental Discovery of the Existence of Non-central Forces

In 1939 a serious discrepancy was discovered between theory and experiment (Kellogg 39, 40). A fine structure was predicted in the radiofrequency magnetic resonance spectrum of deuterium. The experimental results showed a fine structure, but it was different from the theoretical prediction. Its magnitude was much too large. Rabi and Nordsieck (Nordsieck 40) interpreted this phenomenon by ascribing to the deuteron a charge distribution which is not spherically symmetric. The quadrupole moment of this distribution (see Chapter I) gives rise to an additional energy of the deuteron in the inhomogeneous electric field of the molecule. This additional energy as given by (I,7.16) increases the energy difference between the different orientations of the deuteron. The discrepancies of the fine structure could be explained by assuming that the deuteron possesses a quadrupole moment (Newell 50, Kolsky 51):

$$Q = (2.74 \pm 0.02) \times 10^{-27} \text{ cm}^2 \qquad (5.1)$$

The existence of a quadrupole moment of the deuteron implies that *the nuclear force is not a purely central force.* As long as it is assumed that the nuclear force is a central force, the ground state of the deuteron must be an S state whose quadrupole moment is necessarily zero. It should be noted that the existence of quadrupole moments in heavier nuclei does not imply the presence of non-central forces. The ground state of heavier nuclei may have an orbital momentum higher than 0 (it may be a P state or D state, etc.). Such states can give rise to a quadrupole moment. The deuteron, however, is equivalent to a one-particle system after the coordinates have been separated into the relative coordinate $\mathbf{r}$ and the coordinate $\mathbf{R}$ of the center of gravity. The lowest state of a one-particle system in a central force is necessarily an S state.[1]

The rather small numerical value of Q shows that the wave function of the deuteron ground state is almost spherically symmetric. This can be seen by comparing Q with the mean square distance $\overline{r^2}$ between the particles in the deuteron; the latter quantity is of the order of the square of the "size" R of the deuteron, i.e., about 2×10^{-25} cm^2. Thus Q is two orders of magnitude smaller than $\overline{r^2}$. We conclude that the deuteron ground state is predominantly an S state, with only small admixtures of states of higher l.

From the small deviation of the deuteron wave function from spherical symmetry, there might be a temptation to conclude that the non-central part of the *force* is also very small compared to the central force part. This is not a valid conclusion, however. Even a very appreciable non-central part of the force will in general lead to a relatively small asymmetry of the wave function in the ground state.

---

[1] This statement is correct for ordinary potentials. It does not hold in general if the potential depends on the angular momentum as is the case for exchange forces. (See Chapter III.)

B. General Form of the Non-central Force

Even though the nuclear force has turned out to be non-central, we can still assume that it is conservative and independent of the relative velocities of the nucleons, i.e., that it is derivable from a potential function V. Of course, V can no longer be assumed to depend solely on the internucleon distance r.

The assumption that the nuclear force is derivable from a potential places severe restrictions on the possible forms which that force can take. The potential V must be invariant under rotations and reflections of the coordinate system which we use to describe the relative motion of the particles, i.e., in mathematical language it must be a scalar. The only quantities we can use to construct such scalars are their vector separation $\mathbf{r} = r\mathbf{e}$ ($\mathbf{e}$ = a unit vector in the direction of $\mathbf{r}$) and their spin vectors $\mathbf{s} = \frac{1}{2}\hbar\boldsymbol{\sigma}$, where $\boldsymbol{\sigma} = (\sigma_x, \sigma_y, \sigma_z)$ is the usual triple of Pauli matrices (see Appendix A). The gradient vector, for example, cannot be used because it would lead to velocity-dependent forces.

The simplest choice is the scalar $V(r)$ which would lead to a central force. Another possible combination is $(\boldsymbol{\sigma}_1 \cdot \boldsymbol{\sigma}_2)$ which, when multiplied by a scalar function $V(r)$, leads to a spin-dependent but central force. Spin-dependent central forces have already been used in this chapter. In order to construct a non-central force the vector $\mathbf{e}$ must enter into the potential. The bilinear combinations $(\boldsymbol{\sigma}_1 \cdot \mathbf{e})$ or $(\boldsymbol{\sigma}_2 \cdot \mathbf{e})$ as well as $(\boldsymbol{\sigma}_1 \times \boldsymbol{\sigma}_2 \cdot \mathbf{e})$ are not "scalars"; they change sign upon reflection of the coordinate system ($\mathbf{e}$ goes into $-\mathbf{e}$, $\boldsymbol{\sigma}$ into $+\boldsymbol{\sigma}$); in mathematical language, they are pseudoscalars.

Before we turn to combinations involving higher powers, we point out two simplifications: (1) since $\mathbf{e}$ is the only polar vector at our disposal, it must occur an even number of times in any acceptable product; (2) any polynomial in $\boldsymbol{\sigma}$ can be reduced to an expression linear in $\boldsymbol{\sigma}$ by means of spin identities. For instance, $(\boldsymbol{\sigma} \cdot \mathbf{e})^2 = 1$ and $(\boldsymbol{\sigma} \cdot \mathbf{e})^3 = (\boldsymbol{\sigma} \cdot \mathbf{e})$. The possibility of this reduction is the mathematical expression of the uncertainty relation between the angular momenta and angles for angular momenta of $\frac{1}{2}$. Hence an expression linear in $\boldsymbol{\sigma}_1$ and $\boldsymbol{\sigma}_2$ is the most general one we can use.

The only scalars bilinear in $\boldsymbol{\sigma}_1$ and $\boldsymbol{\sigma}_2$ and of even power in $\mathbf{e}$ are $(\boldsymbol{\sigma}_1 \cdot \mathbf{e})(\boldsymbol{\sigma}_2 \cdot \mathbf{e})$ and $(\boldsymbol{\sigma}_1 \times \mathbf{e}) \cdot (\boldsymbol{\sigma}_2 \times \mathbf{e})$. The second one is a linear combination of the first and $(\boldsymbol{\sigma}_1 \cdot \boldsymbol{\sigma}_2)$, by vector identities. Hence the combination $(\boldsymbol{\sigma}_1 \cdot \mathbf{e})(\boldsymbol{\sigma}_2 \cdot \mathbf{e})$ is essentially the only scalar leading to a non-central force. It is useful to define the potential of the non-central force in such a way that its average over directions of $\mathbf{e}$ vanishes. Since the average of $(\mathbf{A} \cdot \mathbf{e})(\mathbf{B} \cdot \mathbf{e})$ over directions is $\frac{1}{3}(\mathbf{A} \cdot \mathbf{B})$ for arbitrary constant vectors **A,B,** we define the *tensor operator* S_{12} by

$$S_{12} \equiv 3 \, (\mathbf{d}_1 \cdot \mathbf{e})(\mathbf{d}_2 \cdot \mathbf{e}) - (\mathbf{d}_1 \cdot \mathbf{d}_2) \tag{5.2}$$

The preceding argument has shown us that *a non-central force derivable from a potential function must have the form*

$$V = V_T(r) \, S_{12} \tag{5.3}$$

We emphasize again that there is no experimental reason for assuming that the nuclear forces can indeed be derived from a potential function; however, there is also no evidence against it, and it is by far the simplest assumption mathematically. Possible forms for central and non-central forces which do involve the velocities have been given by Wigner and Eisenbud (Eisenbud 41).

The most general potential for nuclear two-body forces depending only on the position of the particles and their spins is obtained by adding the possible central forces to (5.3):

$$V = V_d(r) + V_\sigma(r) \, (\mathbf{d}_1 \cdot \mathbf{d}_2) + V_T(r) \, S_{12} \tag{5.4}$$

A further generalization will prove advisable in the next chapter in the form of a dependence on the symmetry of the wave function. However, (5.4) with three arbitrary functions for the various $V(r)$ is sufficiently general for a discussion of the neutron-proton system at low energies.

C. Properties of the Tensor Force[1]

The tensor force potential (5.3) is a scalar; hence the total angular momentum **J** and the parity are constants of motion. Being a non-central force, (5.3) does not remain invariant under a rotation of the space coordinates or the spin coordinates separately. Hence the orbital angular momentum **L** and the spin angular momentum **S** are not constants of motion.

We shall now show, however, that the magnitude of the spin angular momentum, S^2, is still a constant of motion for the two-body systems, even though the individual components of the vector **S** do not commute with (5.3). To prove this, consider the behavior of (5.3) under an exchange of $\mathbf{d}_1$ and $\mathbf{d}_2$ (this is not the same as exchanging the neutron and the proton, which would involve the additional transformation $\mathbf{e} \rightarrow -\mathbf{e}$). Equation (5.3) is unchanged under this operation; hence the states of the system must be either symmetric or anti-symmetric

---

[1] This discussion is based primarily on the paper of Rarita and Schwinger (Rarita 41).

with respect to this spin exchange. However, there are only two spin states possible for particles of spin $\frac{1}{2}$, the symmetric triplet state and the anti-symmetric singlet state; hence our classification of the states of the system into states symmetric and anti-symmetric under the exchange of the spin coordinates of the two particles is equivalent to a classification into triplet and singlet spin states; this proves that S^2 is a constant of motion. We emphasize that this proof holds only because we have a two-body system of particles of spin $\frac{1}{2}$. In general, the behavior under spin exchange does not determine the total spin S^2 uniquely.

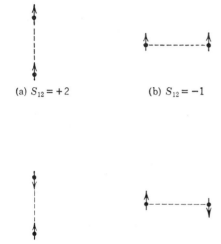

(a) $S_{12} = +2$ (b) $S_{12} = -1$

(c) $S_{12} = -2$ (d) $S_{12} = +1$

FIG. 5.1. Values of the tensor operator in special cases. The arrows indicate the spin directions of the two particles.

We have defined the tensor operator S_{12}, (5.2), in such a way that its average over all directions is zero. In the singlet spin state there is no preferred direction for the spin orientations; hence we expect S_{12} to be zero in singlet states. This is indeed the case: $\mathbf{S} = \frac{1}{2}(\mathbf{d}_1 + \mathbf{d}_2) = 0$ implies $\mathbf{d}_1 = -\mathbf{d}_2$; hence we get

$$S_{12} = -3(\mathbf{d}_1 \cdot \mathbf{e})^2 + (\mathbf{d}_1)^2$$
$$= -3 + 3 = 0$$

Since the tensor force is zero in the singlet state, all our previous results for singlet states (neutron-proton singlet scattering, proton-proton scattering) are entirely unaffected. *In singlet states the nuclear forces are central forces.*

Before going on to the analysis of the triplet states, it will help us to visualize the behavior of the tensor force if we put down the values of S_{12} for a few simple situations. This is done in Fig. 5.1. We observe that S_{12} is positive in the stretched-out configuration for parallel spins and negative in case (b) where the spin directions are perpendicular to the interparticle separation. We conclude that an attractive (negative) $V_T(r)$ in (5.3) favors the stretched-out configuration (a), i.e., it tends to deform the deuteron wave function from a sphere into a cigar shape, with a positive quadrupole moment. Since the observed quadrupole moment (5.1) is indeed positive, we see that $V_T(r)$ *is attractive (negative) in nature.*

Let us turn now to the consequences of these properties of the tensor force for the motion of a two-body system in the triplet spin state. A triplet state of given total angular momentum J can be written as a linear superposition of triplet states with orbital angular momenta $L=J, J-1, J+1$. The parity of a (two-body) wave function with orbital angular momentum L is $(-1)^L$. Hence the state with $L=J$ has opposite parity to the two states with $L=J-1$, $L=J+1$. For example, a triplet state with $J=1$ is a mixture of $^3S_1$, $^3P_1$, $^3D_1$ (in spectroscopic notation). $^3P_1$ has odd parity, and $^3S_1$ and $^3D_1$ have even parity. Hence the $J=1$ states of even parity are mixtures of $^3S_1$ and $^3D_1$; the $J=1$ states of odd parity are pure $^3P_1$. (The fact that L^2 is a constant of motion in the latter case does not contradict the non-central nature of the nuclear forces. Central forces would make L^2 a constant of motion always, not just sometimes.)

Proceeding this way, we can build up a classification of the triplet states of the neutron-proton system. The first few are given in Table 5.1.

TABLE 5.1

THE POSSIBLE TRIPLET STATES OF THE NEUTRON-PROTON SYSTEM WITH THE TENSOR FORCE

J	Even Parity	Odd Parity
0		$^3P_0$
1	$^3S_1$, $^3D_1$	$^3P_1$
2	$^3D_2$	$^3P_2$, $^3F_2$
3	$^3D_3$, $^3G_3$	$^3F_3$

D. The Ground State of the Deuteron: Dynamics

The observed angular momentum of the deuteron is $J=1$. It is expected that states of even parity have lower energy than the corresponding states of odd parity. Hence the deuteron ground state is expected to have $J=1$ and even parity, i.e., to be a mixture of $^3S_1$ and $^3D_1$.

We now investigate the dependence of the wave function on the angles. We use the normalized "spin angle" wave functions $\mathcal{Y}_{JlS}^M$ belonging to a state of total angular momentum J whose z component is M and which is a combination of an orbital angular momentum l with a spin S (see Appendix A, Section 5):

$$\mathcal{Y}_{JlS}^M = \sum_{m_l+m_s=M} C_{lS}(J,M;m_l,m_s)\, Y_{lm_l}(\theta,\varphi)\, \chi_{sm_s} \qquad (5.5)$$

The constants C_{lS} are given in Appendix A, Table 5.2, for the case of interest here $(S=1)$. For $J=M=S=1$ and $l=0,2$, respectively, we have

$$\mathcal{Y}^1_{101} = (4\pi)^{-1/2}\chi_{1,1} = Y_{0,0}\,\chi_{1,1} \tag{5.6}$$

$$\mathcal{Y}^1_{121} = (\tfrac{6}{10})^{1/2}Y_{2,2}\,\chi_{1,-1} - (\tfrac{3}{10})^{1/2}Y_{2,1}\,\chi_{1,0} + (\tfrac{1}{10})^{1/2}Y_{2,0}\,\chi_{1,1} \tag{5.7}$$

The wave function for a pure $^3S_1$ state, including its r dependence, can be written in the form

$$\phi_S = \frac{u(r)}{r}\,\mathcal{Y}^M_{101} \tag{5.8}$$

where $u^2(r)\,dr$ is the probability of finding two particles in this S state a distance between r and $r+dr$ apart. We shall omit the superscript for the z component M of the total angular momentum, since this does not matter in what follows. Similarly, the wave function for a pure $^3D_1$ state will be of the form

$$\phi_D = \frac{w(r)}{r}\,\mathcal{Y}^M_{121} \tag{5.9}$$

where $w^2(r)\,dr$ is the probability of finding the two particles in the D state a distance between r and $r+dr$ apart. The wave function for the composite state (the ground state of the deuteron) then is

$$\phi = \phi_S + \phi_L \tag{5.10}$$

Since the integration over angles and the sum over spin indices give unity, owing to the normalization of (5.5), the probability of finding the deuteron in the ^3S state is given by

$$p_S = (\phi_S,\phi_S) = \int_0^\infty u^2(r)\,dr \tag{5.11}$$

and the probability of finding the deuteron in the ^3D state is

$$p_D = (\phi_D,\phi_D) = \int_0^\infty w^2(r)\,dr \tag{5.12}$$

Since these two are the only states which can contribute to the ground state of the deuteron, the over-all normalization of the wave function ϕ, (5.10), is

$$(\phi,\phi) = p_S + p_D = \int_0^\infty [u^2(r) + w^2(r)]\,dr = 1 \tag{5.13}$$

We shall need to know the effect of the tensor force operator S_{12} on the spin angle wave functions $\mathcal{Y}$. We shall show below, in small print, that

$$S_{12} \, \mathcal{Y}_{101}^{M} = \sqrt{8} \, \mathcal{Y}_{121}^{M}$$

$$S_{12} \, \mathcal{Y}_{121}^{M} = \sqrt{8} \, \mathcal{Y}_{101}^{M} - 2 \, \mathcal{Y}_{121}^{M}$$

(5.14)

There are various ways of proving (5.14). The most straightforward one is simple calculation, using the definition (5.2) of the tensor operator and applying it to (5.6) and (5.7). We write

$$(\mathbf{\sigma} \cdot \mathbf{e}) = \sigma_x \sin \theta \cos \varphi + \sigma_y \sin \theta \sin \varphi + \sigma_z \cos \theta$$

and use the properties of the spherical harmonics to get the answer. However, as this procedure is quite tedious, we shall use a quicker method.

Table 5.1 shows that S_{12} acting on the $^3S_1$ wave function $\mathcal{Y}_{101}$ can only lead to a linear combination of the $^3S_1$ and $^3D_1$ wave functions:

$$S_{12} \, \mathcal{Y}_{101}^{M} = a \, \mathcal{Y}_{101}^{M} + b \, \mathcal{Y}_{121}^{M}$$

(5.15)

The operator S_{12} vanishes when averaged over the angles of orientation of **e**. In the operation (5.15) the operator S_{12} acts on a function, $\mathcal{Y}_{101}^{M}$, which is independent of the direction of **e** ($l=0$). The operation (5.15) therefore cannot result in a spherically symmetric state $l=0$. Hence we conclude that $a=0$.

In order to determine b in (5.15) we can pick a special case amenable to easy calculation. We shall choose $M=1$, and we shall pick the direction of the vector **e** as our z direction. Direct evaluation of the left side then gives

$$[3\sigma_{1z}\sigma_{2z} - (\mathbf{\sigma}_1 \cdot \mathbf{\sigma}_2)] \, (4\pi)^{-1/2} \, \alpha(1) \, \alpha(2) = 2 \, (4\pi)^{-1/2} \, \alpha(1) \, \alpha(2)$$

(5.16)

The right side of (5.15), with $a=0$, assumes a specially simple form in this case because $Y_{2,2} = Y_{2,1} = 0$ at the pole of the sphere, $\theta = 0$. The right side, according to (5.7), equals

$$b \, \mathcal{Y}_{121}^{1}(\theta=0) = b \, \sqrt{\tfrac{1}{10}} \, Y_{2,0}(\theta=0) \, \chi_{1,1}$$

$$= b \, (8\pi)^{-1/2} \, \alpha(1) \, \alpha(2)$$

(5.16')

Comparison of (5.16) and (5.16') gives the result $b = \sqrt{8}$, which proves the first equation of (5.14).

To prove the second equation of (5.14) we write

$$S_{12} \, \mathcal{Y}_{121}^{M} = b \, \mathcal{Y}_{101}^{M} + c \, \mathcal{Y}_{121}^{M}$$

where b must be the same as in (5.15) because the tensor operator S_{12} is Hermitean. We again evaluate both sides for the special case where **e** points in the z direction ($\theta=0$) and solve for the one unknown, c. The result is $c = -2$. This completes the proof of (5.14).

We are now in a position to write the wave equation for the ground state of the deuteron. It is

$$(T + V) \, \phi = E \, \phi$$

(5.17)

where E is the negative of the binding energy, $E = -B$. The kinetic energy operator T does not act on the spin variables; it can be written

$$T = \frac{\hbar^2}{M}\left(-\frac{1}{r}\frac{d^2}{dr^2}r + \frac{L^2}{r^2}\right) \tag{5.18}$$

where $L^2 = l(l+1) = 0$ in an S state and $L^2 = 2 \times 3 = 6$ in a D state. The potential energy V is given by (5.4). We shall introduce the notation

$$V_c(r) = V_d(r) + V_o(r) \tag{5.19}$$

for the potential of the central force in the triplet state. We combine (5.8), (5.9), (5.10), (5.14), (5.17), (5.18), and (5.19) to get

$$\left[-\frac{\hbar^2}{M}\frac{d^2u}{dr^2} + V_c u\right]\mathcal{Y}_{101} + \sqrt{8}V_T u\mathcal{Y}_{121}$$

$$+ \left[-\frac{\hbar^2}{M}\left(\frac{d^2w}{dr^2} - \frac{6w}{r^2}\right) + (V_c - 2V_T)w\right]\mathcal{Y}_{121} + \sqrt{8}V_T w\mathcal{Y}_{101}$$

$$= E\,(u\mathcal{Y}_{101} + w\mathcal{Y}_{121}) \tag{5.20}$$

We equate terms of the same spin angle wave function to get the following system of two coupled second-order differential equations for the determination of the radial wave functions u and w:

$$-\frac{\hbar^2}{M}\frac{d^2u}{dr^2} + V_c(r)\,u - E\,u = -\sqrt{8}\,V_T(r)\,w \tag{5.21a}$$

$$-\frac{\hbar^2}{M}\left(\frac{d^2w}{dr^2} - \frac{6w}{r^2}\right) + [V_c(r) - 2V_T(r)\,]\,w - E\,w$$

$$= -\sqrt{8}\,V_T(r)\,u \tag{5.21b}$$

For the ground state of the deuteron, E is negative and equal to $-B$. The discussion of these equations is difficult since no exact solutions exist in terms of tabulated functions, even for simple square well shapes. So far, there are complete numerical solutions for only two cases: (1) both potentials, V_c and V_T, have the square well shape (Padfield 49, Guindon 48, Biedenharn 50), (2) both potentials have the Yukawa well shape (Feshbach 49b); in each case the ranges and depths of the two wells have been varied over appreciable intervals.

The numerical calculations are lengthy, not only because of the nature of the system of coupled differential equations (5.21), but also because there are so many more variable parameters here than in the central force case. There are four parameters, the well depth and range of $V_c(r)$ and $V_T(r)$, respectively. The binding energy of the deuteron gives one relation between them. The quadrupole moment of the deuteron (see Section 5E) gives a second relation so that the number of free parameters is reduced to two. In principle, the remaining two parameters could be fixed by comparison with the experimental values of the magnetic moment of the deuteron and of the effective range for neutron-proton scattering in the triplet state (see Sections 5F and 5G, respectively). In practice, however, it is impossible to determine all four well parameters uniquely from the data. Rather, there are many sets of well parameters consistent with our present knowledge of the deuteron. For example, the strength of the tensor force can be increased if a compensating decrease is made in the strength of the central force, without contradicting the present experiments.

It is interesting to observe that, for long-tailed wells such as Yukawa wells, there exists one especially simple form of the potential which is consistent with all the known information. This potential has a central force which is equal to the force between a neutron and a proton in the *singlet* spin state, and a tensor force of somewhat longer range and somewhat weaker strength than the central force (Feshbach 49b):

$$V = -22.7 \frac{\exp{(-2.12r/b_c)}}{r/b_c} - 10.9 \frac{\exp{(-2.12r/b_T)}}{r/b_T} S_{12}$$

where $b_c = 2.47 \times 10^{-13}$ cm, $b_T = 3.68 \times 10^{-13}$ cm, and the strength of the potential is given in Mev. The ranges b_c and b_T are the intrinsic ranges and are therefore comparable to square well ranges. The well-depth parameters s corresponding to the central and tensor forces given above are: $s_c = 0.937$ and $s_T = 0.998$. This potential gives the correct binding energy and quadrupole moment of the deuteron; the D state probability would be about 3.3 percent and the effective range in the triplet state would be about 1.75×10^{-13} cm. Both of these are consistent with the present experimental information.

This potential would have the following interesting property: The central force between a neutron and a proton would be spin-independent [i.e., $V_\sigma(r) = 0$ in (5.4)]. Hence the actual spin dependence of the nuclear force would arise entirely from the tensor force which vanishes in the singlet spin state but is effective in the triplet spin state. In other words, the existence of a bound triplet state of the neutron-proton system would be entirely due to the tensor force. *We must emphasize, however, that the spin independence of the central force is by no means established by the present evidence.*

The behavior of $u(r)$ and $w(r)$ *outside* the range of the forces follows directly from the differential equations (5.21). The potentials V_c and V_T vanish, and the two equations (5.21a) and (5.21b) become independent. Their solutions are

$$u(r) = N \exp\left(-\frac{r}{R}\right) \tag{5.22a}$$

$$w(r) = N' \exp\left(-\frac{r}{R}\right)\left[3\left(\frac{R}{r}\right)^2 + 3\left(\frac{R}{r}\right) + 1\right] \tag{5.22b}$$

where R is the "size" of the deuteron, (2.7), and N, N' are normalization constants. A rough estimate of N can be obtained by neglecting the small D state probability compared to unity and by using the asymptotic form (5.22a) of $u(r)$ for all values of r (neglecting the range correction). We then put

$$\int_0^\infty u^2(r)\, dr \cong 1$$

and obtain

$$N \cong \left(\frac{2}{R}\right)^{1/2} \tag{5.22c}$$

The value of N' depends on the strength of the tensor force; it will be determined later.

It is interesting to determine the region of validity of these asymptotic forms in more detail, since there are two "ranges" in this problem, one for the central force and one for the tensor force. Equation (5.21a) determines the asymptotic behavior (5.22a) of u. It turns out that for physically reasonable force strengths the terms $V_c(r)u$ and $8^{1/2}V_T(r)w$ are not very different in magnitude; hence the "range" beyond which the asymptotic form (5.22a) is valid is the *larger* one of the two ranges in this problem.

The situation is different with the asymptotic form of w, (5.22b), as determined by (5.21b). In this equation the central force $V_c(r)$ enters in the same way as the centrifugal term $(\hbar^2/M)(6/r^2)$. For reasonable nuclear ranges and well depths this repulsive centrifugal term is very much larger than the nuclear potential $V_c(r)$ (this is indeed the reason why we do not expect any D state contribution to low-energy neutron-proton scattering with central forces, and why the ground state of the deuteron is not likely to be a predominantly D state). Hence the central force does not enter into (5.21b) in an important way, and the "range" beyond which the asymptotic form (5.22b) is valid is determined by the coupling term on the right side, i.e., is the *tensor force range*, which we shall call b_T from now on.

The behavior of $u(r)$ and $w(r)$ near $r=0$ is roughly[1] that for typical S state and D state functions, respectively. That is, u goes like r, w goes like r^3. Since the outside behavior (5.22b) of w is roughly proportional to r^{-2} (outside the range of the forces, but inside the size R of the deuteron), it follows that w has a rather sharp maximum just before the asymptotic form (5.22b) takes over, i.e., near $r \cong b_T$.

[1] The coupling terms in (5.21a) and (5.21b) lead to occurrence of logarithmic expressions like $r \log r$ in u, $r^3 \log r$ in w, so that, strictly speaking, neither u nor w is a pure power series in r.

This is illustrated schematically in Fig. 5.2. We see that the main contribution to the D state probability p_D, (5.12), comes from this

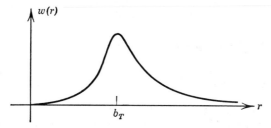

FIG. 5.2. A schematic drawing of the D state radial wave function $w(r)$ *versus* r. For small r, $w(r) \sim r^3$; for large r, $w(r) \sim 1/r^2$. There is a sharp maximum at $r \cong b_T$, where b_T is the range of the tensor force.

region of r. This is in contrast to the S state probability p_S, (5.11), which comes mostly from outside the range of the forces, i.e., from values of $r \cong R$, the size of the deuteron.

E. The Ground State of the Deuteron: Quadrupole Moment

In Chapter I the quadrupole moment Q was defined as the average value of $(3z^2 - r^2)$ in the state with $M = J$. In the deuteron only the proton contributes to the quadrupole moment, and its distance from the center of gravity is half of the neutron-proton separation r; hence the quadrupole moment operator for the deuteron is

$$Q = \tfrac{1}{4}(3z^2 - r^2) = \tfrac{1}{4}(3\cos^2\theta - 1)\, r^2 \qquad (5.23)$$

The expectation value of this operator is

$$(\phi, Q\phi) = (\phi_S, Q\phi_S) + (\phi_D, Q\phi_D) + 2\,(\phi_S, Q\phi_D) \qquad (5.24)$$

The first term is zero since the S state is spherically symmetric and cannot have a quadrupole moment. The second term is a pure D state term and is therefore smaller than the cross term $2(\phi_S, Q\phi_L)$. We shall show below, in small print, that

$$2\,(\phi_S, Q\phi_D) = (50)^{-1/2} \int_0^\infty r^2\, u(r)\, w(r)\, dr \qquad (5.25a)$$

$$(\phi_D, Q\phi_L) = -\tfrac{1}{20} \int_0^\infty r^2\, w^2(r)\, dr \qquad (5.25b)$$

The measured quadrupole moment is the sum of these two expressions:

$$Q \text{ of deuteron} = (\tfrac{1}{50})^{1/2} \int_0^\infty r^2 uw\, dr - \tfrac{1}{20} \int_0^\infty r^2 w^2\, dr \qquad (5.26)$$

We prove formula (5.25a) by direct substitution of (5.8) and (5.9). The quadrupole moment operator involves no spin quantities, and therefore the first two terms of the spin angle function (5.7) give zero in the scalar product with (5.6), since (5.6) contains the spin function $\chi_{1,1}$ only. We notice that

$$\frac{1}{4}(3\cos^2\theta - 1) = \left(\frac{\pi}{5}\right)^{1/2} Y_{2,0}(\theta)$$

and perform the sum over spin indices to get

$$2\,(\phi,Q\phi) = 2\int_0^\infty r^2\,dr\int d\Omega (4\pi)^{-1/2}\frac{u(r)}{r}\left(\frac{\pi}{5}\right)^{1/2} Y_{2,0}(\theta)\,r^2\,(10)^{-1/2}\frac{w(r)}{r}\,Y_{2,0}(\theta)$$

The normalization of $Y_{2,0}$ gives (5.25a) immediately.

In order to derive (5.25b) we use the following relation: the average value of $(3\cos^2\theta - 1)$ in a state of orbital angular momentum l with the z component m_l is given by (see Bethe 33)

$$(3\cos^2\theta - 1)_{\mathrm{av}} = 2\,\frac{l(l+1) - 3m_l^2}{(2l+3)(2l-1)}$$

Substitution of this result into the definition of $(\phi_D, Q\phi_D)$ gives (5.25b) immediately. We need only the average values of $(3\cos^2\theta - 1)$ since the cross terms between components of $\mathcal{Y}^1_{121}$ with different m_l drop out because of the orthogonality of the spin functions.

Since the ground state of the deuteron is predominantly an S state, the first term of (5.26), which contains $w(r)$ linearly, predominates over the second term, which involves $w^2(r)$. Furthermore, the factor r^2 in the integrand makes the quadrupole moment mostly an "outside" quantity, i.e., the main contribution to $\int_0^\infty r^2uw\,dr$ comes from outside the range of the forces; we shall therefore estimate the quadrupole moment by substituting expressions (5.22) into the first integral of (5.26). The result is

$$Q \cong 8^{-1/2}\,NN'R^3 \tag{5.27}$$

This relation can be used for a good estimate of N' if the relation (5.22c) for N is used:

$$N' \cong \frac{2Q}{R^{5/2}} \tag{5.27a}$$

Hence, *to a first approximation, the function $w(r)$ outside the range of the forces is determined completely by the value of the quadrupole moment.*

This result implies that the D state probability p_D depends strongly on the tensor force range b_T and increases rapidly as b_T is made shorter. Consider Fig. 5.3, in which the function $w^2(r)$ is drawn schematically for two different tensor force ranges b_T. The curves are the same for $r > b_T$, according to the preceding argument. Near the origin, $r = 0$, both curves are proportional to $(r^3)^2 = r^6$ but with different constants. Thus there is a very sharp maximum of $w^2(r)$ just inside the range of the tensor force, and most of the integral $\int_0^\infty w^2(r)\,dr$ comes from the neighborhood of this maximum. The figure shows that this maximum becomes rapidly higher as the tensor force range is shortened; hence the D state probability for a given quadrupole moment increases sharply with decreasing b_T.

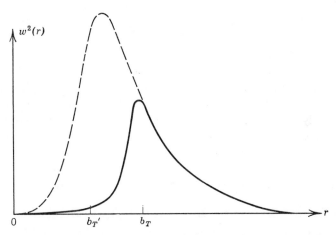

FIG. 5.3. The square of the D state radial wave function, $w^2(r)$, plotted schematically against r, for two different tensor force ranges b_T, b_T'. The behavior of $w^2(r)$ for $r > b_T$ is determined to a first approximation by the value of the quadrupole moment of the deuteron. For the same quadrupole moment Q, a shorter tensor force range $b_T' < b_T$ implies a much larger D state probability $p_D = \int_0^\infty w^2(r)\,dr$.

We shall now use these qualitative considerations to derive a rough approximation formula for the D state probability p_D, (5.12). Let the value of r for which $w^2(r)$ has its maximum be called r_m. We shall assume that $r_m \ll R$, the size of the deuteron. Then we can neglect all but the first term in the bracket of (5.22b) and set the exponential equal to unity. This gives for the "outside" contribution to p_D the estimate

$$\int_{r_m}^\infty w^2(r)\,dr \cong \int_{r_m}^\infty 9(N')^2 \left(\frac{R}{r}\right)^4 dr = 3(N')^2 \left(\frac{R}{r_m}\right)^3 R$$

$$\cong 12\left(\frac{Q}{R^2}\right)^2 \left(\frac{R}{r_m}\right)^3 \tag{5.28}$$

with the use of (5.27a).

From here on we shall use only very rough estimates: the function $w^2(r)$ has a very sharp maximum at $r = r_m$. Hence we can get the integral $\int_0^\infty w^2(r)\, dr$ from (5.28) roughly by multiplication by two. Furthermore the position r_m of the peak in $w^2(r)$ occurs right inside the range b_T of the tensor force (indeed, for tensor force well shapes without any clearly defined range, this could very easily be taken as a definition of the tensor force range). We therefore replace r_m in (5.28) by b_T and multiply by a factor of about 2 to get

$$p_D \cong C \left(\frac{Q}{R^2}\right)^2 \left(\frac{R}{b_T}\right)^3 \qquad (5.29)$$

where C is a numerical constant of the order of 20 to 30.

Equation (5.29) implies that *the tensor force cannot have an arbitrarily small range*,[1] otherwise the ground state would become a predominantly D state rather than a predominantly S state. Indeed, an experimental measurement of p_D, even with a rather large uncertainty, determines the tensor force range b_T within relatively narrow limits. In the next section we discuss the connection of $p_{\cdot}$ with the magnetic moment of the deuteron. This supplies a method for the measurement of $p_{\cdot}$.

F. The Ground State of the Deuteron : Magnetic Moment

As long as the nuclear forces were supposed to be central forces, the magnetic moment of the deuteron could be due only to the intrinsic magnetic moments of the component nucleons. The contribution of the *orbital motion* of the proton is zero in an S state. With non-central forces, however, there appears a contribution to the magnetic moment due to the orbital motion of the proton in the D state. This contribution is only a small correction to the spin contributions, but it lies within the accuracy of the present experimental methods.

The operator μ_{Op} describing the magnetic moment of the neutron-proton system is

$$\mathbf{\mu}_{Op} = \mu_n \mathbf{\delta}_n + \mu_p \mathbf{\delta}_p + \mathbf{L}_p \qquad (5.30)$$

where μ_n, μ_p are the magnetic moments of neutron and proton measured in nuclear Bohr magnetons, and $\mathbf{L}_p$ denotes the orbital angular momentum of the proton (the neutron, being uncharged, gives no orbital contribution to the magnetic moment). The factor of $\mathbf{L}_p$ is unity, since we are measuring the magnetic moment $\mathbf{\mu}_{Op}$ in Bohr magnetons.

---

[1] This argument was first given by Schwinger (41). It has been refined by Broyles and Kivel (50) and Foldy (50).

In the center-of-gravity system of neutron and proton the orbital angular momentum of the proton is half of the combined orbital angular momentum, $L_p = \frac{1}{2}L$. We rewrite (5.30) in the form

$$\mathbf{\mu}_{Op} = (\mu_n + \mu_P)\,\mathbf{S} + \tfrac{1}{2}\,(\mu_n - \mu_p)\,(\mathbf{\delta}_n - \mathbf{\delta}_p) + \tfrac{1}{2}\mathbf{L} \qquad (5.31)$$

where $\mathbf{S} = \frac{1}{2}(\mathbf{\delta}_n + \mathbf{\delta}_k)$ is the combined spin of the two particles. The operator $(\mathbf{\delta}_n - \mathbf{\delta}_p)$ in the second term has zero expectation value in triplet states; hence it does not contribute to the magnetic moment. We therefore omit this term in (5.31); furthermore we introduce the total angular momentum $\mathbf{J} = \mathbf{L} + \mathbf{S}$ and use it to eliminate $\mathbf{S}$ in (5.31), getting for the effective magnetic moment operator

$$\mathbf{\mu}_{\text{eff}} = (\mu_n + \mu_p)\,\mathbf{J} - (\mu_n + \mu_p - \tfrac{1}{2})\,\mathbf{L} \qquad (5.32)$$

The observed magnetic moment is the expectation value of this expression in the state with $J_z = J$ (see Chapter I). We therefore can replace $\mathbf{L}$ by L_z:

$$\mathbf{L} \to L_z = \frac{(\mathbf{L \cdot J})}{J^2}\,J_z = \frac{J(J+1) + L(L+1) - S(S+1)}{2J(J+1)}\,J_z$$

For the deuteron, $J(J+1) = S(S+1) = 2$, whereas $L(L+1)$ in a mixture of S and D states is

$$\langle L(L+1)\rangle_{\text{av}} = 0 \times p_S + 6 \times p_D = 6p_D$$

The value of J_z in the state with $J_z = J$ is unity for the deuteron ($J = 1$). Inserting these values into (5.32) gives for the magnetic moment of the deuteron

$$\mu \text{ of deuteron} = \mu_n + \mu_p - \tfrac{3}{2}\,(\mu_n + \mu_p - \tfrac{1}{2})\,p_D \qquad (5.33)$$

The deviation of the magnetic moment of the deuteron from a simple sum of the neutron and proton magnetic moments gives a direct measure of the D state probability. The experimental results (Bloch 48, Levinthal 50) imply a D state probability of about 4 percent.

Formula (5.33) cannot be expected to give high accuracy. The deviations we are concerned with are of the order of a few percent of the main term $\mu_n + \mu_p$. There are various other causes which can give corrections of this order of magnitude, especially relativistic effects. There is considerable literature (Margenau 40, Caldirola 46, Breit 47, 47c, Sachs 47, Primakoff 47) on the subject of relativistic corrections to the magnetic moment of the deuteron, but their precise magnitudes, even their signs, are unknown. All we can say is that the corrections are of the order of a few percent. Hence the measured magnetic moment gives only a rough estimate of the D state probability, and it is perhaps a reasonable *guess that p_D lies somewhere between 2 percent and 6 percent.*

In spite of this uncertainty in p_D the tensor force range b_T is defined rather closely through the estimate (5.29). Substituting the above value of p_D into (5.29), we get the estimate that *the tensor force range b_T is probably between 2 and 3×10^{-13} cm.* Exact numerical calculations (Biedenharn 50), using square well shapes and a D state probability of 4 percent, bear out these statements: the tensor force range is always of the order of 3×10^{-13} cm, almost independent of the range of the central force. The same result holds for Yukawa well shapes (Feshbach 49b) if one uses the intrinsic range (2.20) for b_T.

The large value of b_T/R implies that the approximations we used to derive the estimate (5.29) are not very good. It is hardly worth while, however, to attempt a more detailed estimate at this time, since the D state probability, being an "inside" effect, is likely to be quite well shape dependent.

G. Neutron-Proton Scattering below 10 Mev

Since it turns out that the existence of non-central forces has no noticable effect on the scattering in this energy region (Hepner 42, Rarita 41), we shall treat this subject rather summarily.

In principle, the analysis of the scattering is changed considerably by the presence of a non-central force. The orbital angular momentum is no longer an integral of motion; its value can change during the collision.

At energies below 10 Mev, it is advantageous to decompose the wave function into spherical harmonics by the use of the "spin angle" functions $\mathcal{Y}_{Jls}^M$, (5.5). The spin S can assume the values 0 and 1 corresponding to the singlet and triplet states. In such a decomposition we can restrict ourselves to the scattering in the S states ($l=0$), since states with higher orbital angular momentum than zero do not let the particles approach each other closely enough for the nuclear forces to become effective. The S scattering ($l=0$) in the singlet state, $S=0$, is unchanged by the presence of tensor forces since they do not act in that state. We therefore need to discuss only the triplet scattering in which the spins are parallel. In this case a pure ^3S state is impossible. Table 5.1 shows that the tensor force couples the $^3D_1$ state with the $^3S_1$ state, so that both states contribute to the scattering even at low energies.

An individual term in the spherical harmonic decomposition of the scattering wave function corresponds to a superposition of an ingoing [exp $(-ikr)$] and outgoing [exp (ikr)] spherical wave [see (3.6), for example]. If the ingoing wave is a pure $^3S_1$ wave, the outgoing wave is a mixture of S and D waves owing to the action of the tensor force during the impact. Similarly an ingoing pure $^3D_1$ wave emerges as a mixture outgoing wave.

It is more convenient to work with waves which have the same mixture ratio of S to D states before and after the scattering event; such waves are called "eigenstates" for the scattering.[1] There are two such eigenstates. One of them is predominantly an S wave with a very small D wave admixture; it will be called the α wave. The other is predominantly a D wave with a very small admixture of S wave; it will be called the β wave. It is physically plausible, and can also be shown mathematically, that the β wave behaves for all practical purposes like a D state in the scattering and can hence be ignored in the energy range considered here.

Since we are dealing with the same angular momentum state $(^3S_1 + {}^3D_1)$ as the ground state of the deuteron, the wave function can be written in the form (5.8) to (5.10), and the wave equation is given by the coupled differential equations (5.21).

The asymptotic form of $u(r)$ and $w(r)$ can be written in the form

$$u(r) \sim \mathsf{a} \sin (kr + \delta)$$
$$w(r) \sim \mathsf{b} \sin (kr - \pi + \delta) \qquad (r \to \infty) \qquad (5.34)$$

where the angle δ represents the phase shift compared to the asymptotic form of the unperturbed plane wave. The solution u, w of the wave equation is an *eigenstate of the scattering, in the sense discussed above, provided that the phase shift δ in (5.34) is the same for both $u(r)$ and $w(r)$.* There are two solutions, the α and β solutions, satisfying this condition, with two different phase shifts, δ_α and δ_β, and two different values of the ratio b/a which determine two different asymptotic ratios of w to u.

It can be shown that

$$\frac{\mathsf{b}_\alpha}{\mathsf{a}_\alpha} = - \frac{\mathsf{a}_\beta}{\mathsf{b}_\beta} \qquad (5.35)$$

Hence the condition that the α wave is predominantly an S wave, $\mathsf{b}_\alpha \ll \mathsf{a}_\alpha$, automatically implies that the β wave is predominantly a D wave.

If we neglect the phase shift δ_β, and the phase shifts of all the other waves except the α wave, the differential scattering cross section (in

[1] The use of the eigenstates was introduced by Schwinger (unpublished).

the center-of-gravity system) becomes (using $b_\alpha/a_\alpha \equiv \tan\epsilon$)

$$d\sigma = \frac{\sin^2 \delta_\alpha}{k^2}\left[1 + \left(1 + \frac{\tan\epsilon}{\sqrt{8}}\right)^2 \sin^2(2\epsilon)\, P_2(\cos\theta)\right] d\Omega \quad (5.36)$$

where $P_2(\cos\theta)$ is the second Legendre polynomial (see Appendix A, Section 2). The fact that the α wave is not a pure S wave is reflected in the differential cross section through the second term in the bracket, which shows the angular dependence expected for a D state-S state interference term. However, the coefficient of this second term involves the mixture angle ϵ and is small if ϵ is small.

We have seen before, (5.27), that the magnitude of the quadrupole moment determines the asymptotic behavior of the $w(r)$ function for the ground state of the deuteron. It is therefore not surprising that the quadrupole moment also can be used to estimate the asymptotic ratio of w to u, i.e., the angle ϵ, for the α solution at positive energies.[1] The result of this estimate is

$$\epsilon \cong \frac{b_\alpha}{a_\alpha} \cong \sqrt{2}\, Qk^2 \quad (5.37)$$

If we substitute the numerical value of the quadrupole moment into (5.37) and evaluate the angle-dependent term in (5.36) at, say, 10 Mev in the laboratory system, it turns out that the coefficient of $P_2(\cos\theta)$ is less than 0.01 even at that energy. At present the experimental errors for angular distribution measurements in this energy region are of the order of 10 percent. Hence this specifically tensor effect in the scattering is much too small in this energy range to be detected by present methods. We should remark, also, that P wave scattering can be expected to contribute terms with similar angle dependence of the same general order of magnitude.

Once it is accepted that the angular distribution due to the α wave scattering is so close to the complete spherical symmetry expected for a pure S wave that the difference is beyond experimental detection, it is then easy to show that the tensor force has no observable effect whatsoever in the scattering below 10 Mev. By methods completely analogous to those employed in Section 3A, (3.16) ff., we can show that the shape-independent approximation for the phase shift, (3.19), can be applied here also (Christian 49). The expression $k \cot \delta_\alpha$ is a

---

[1] The α solution is the one which can be made to continue into the ground state solution by analytic continuation; while the β solution, behaving like a D state, has a pole at the energy $E = 0$ as far as its analytic behavior is concerned. Thus the properties of the ground state, such as the quadrupole moment for example, can give information only about the α solution.

function of a scattering length a and an effective range r_0 just as in (3.19).

The scattering length a is defined in a manner similar to that in Section 3A, i.e., by the asymptotic behavior of the S state radial wave function $u(r)$ in the α wave at energy $E=0$, just as in (3.11). The effective range r_0 is a certain average of the central and tensor force ranges. It is given by the relation

$$r_0 = 2 \int_0^\infty \left[\left(1 - \frac{r}{a}\right)^2 - u_{0\alpha}{}^2(r) - w_{0\alpha}{}^2(r) \right] dr \qquad (5.38)$$

where $u_{0\alpha}(r)$ and $w_{0\alpha}(r)$ are the α wave solutions of (5.21) for zero energy $(E=0)$. The total cross section for the triplet state scattering can then be found from (5.36):

$$\sigma = \frac{4\pi \sin^2 \delta_\alpha}{k^2} \qquad (5.39)$$

This formula is the same as if the α wave were a pure S wave. The total cross section can therefore be used to find the values of the scattering length a and the effective range r_0 but cannot be used to find any specific tensor effects.

We have seen earlier that the tensor force range b_T cannot be chosen arbitrarily small; rather b_T is determined to a reasonable approximation by the quadrupole moment and magnetic moment of the deuteron. The scattering effective range r_0 lies in general somewhere between the ranges of the central and tensor forces. Hence r_0 stays finite even in the limit as the central force range is contracted to zero. Numerical calculations with square well shapes show that, in this limit, the effective range r_0 is still between 1 and 1.5×10^{-13} cm, depending on what is assumed for the D state probability in the ground state (Biedenharn 50). Needless to say, the experimental (finite) value of the triplet effective range cannot be interpreted as a tensor force effect since purely central forces in general also have a finite range.

SYMBOLS

$\mathrm{\partial}$	Asymptotic amplitude of $u(r)$ in neutron-proton scattering with tensor forces (5.34)
a	Scattering length (3.11)
a'	Scattering length in the (unchanged) nuclear potential after removal of the Coulomb force (4.8)
a_{eff}	Operator for the "effective" scattering length (3.51)
a_s	Scattering length in the singlet spin state (Section 3B)

a_t Scattering length in the triplet spin state   (Section 3B)

b Asymptotic amplitude of $w(r)$ in neutron-proton scattering with tensor forces   (5.34)

b Range of the nuclear force, more closely defined as the "intrinsic range parameter"   (2.18)–(2.20) and (3.21)

b_T Range of the tensor force   (Section 5D)

B Binding energy of the deuteron [$=2.226\pm0.003$ Mev] (Section 2)

$B_s{}^*$ Energy of the "virtual level" of the neutron-proton system in the singlet spin state   (Section 3B)

C^2 Coulomb penetration factor   (4.1)

d Classical distance of closest approach of two protons [$=e^2/E$]   (Section 4)

$d\sigma$ Differential scattering cross section   (3.4)

$d\sigma_{if}$ Differential cross section for a neutron-molecule collision in which the molecule is excited from state u_i to state u_f (3.46)

$d\Omega$ Element of solid angle   (3.4)

D Bohr radius of a proton [$=\hbar^2/Me^2=2.88\times10^{-12}$ cm] (4.6)

e Unit vector in the direction of the neutron-proton separation vector $\mathbf{r}$ (Section 5B)

E Energy of relative motion [$=\tfrac{1}{2}E_{\text{lab}}$]   (2.1)

E_{lab} Energy of the neutron in neutron-proton scattering, measured in the laboratory system [$=2E$]   (3.3)

f Coherent scattering length for neutron-proton collisions (3.53)

$\bar{f}$ Average value of $f(\theta)$ [$=S$ wave part of $f(\theta)$]   (3.6)

$f(\theta)$ Amplitude for scattering through the angle θ (3.1)

$F(r)$ Regular Coulomb wave function   (4.2), (4.3)

$h(\eta)$ A slowly varying function of η (Section 4)

H_0 Hamiltonian for a free neutron and a bound proton, excluding the neutron-proton interaction   (3.31)

I_{if} Form factor integral for scattering of neutrons by protons bound to a molecule   (3.46), (3.47)

J Total angular momentum quantum number of the neutron-proton system   (Section 5C)

$\mathbf{J}$ Total angular momentum operator for the neutron-proton system   (Section 5C)

k Wave number of the relative motion, at large separation [$=\lim_{r\to\infty}\kappa(r)$]   (3.2), (3.3)

$\mathbf{k}_f$	Relative wave vector of neutron and molecule after the collision (3.47)
$\mathbf{k}_i$	Relative wave vector of neutron and molecule before the collision (3.45)
K	An average wave number in the "allowed" region (inside the range of the forces) (Section 2)
K	$= K'D$ (Section 4 and Fig. 4.3)
K'	The proton-proton analogue of $k\cot\delta$ in neutron-proton scattering (4.6)
l	Orbital angular momentum quantum number (Section 3A)
L^2	Operator for the absolute square of the orbital angular momentum vector $\mathbf{L}$ (5.18)
$\mathbf{L}$	Orbital angular momentum operator of the neutron-proton system (Section 5C)
$\mathbf{L}_p$	Orbital angular momentum operator for the proton (5.30)
M	Magnetic quantum number for the total angular momentum $\mathbf{J}$ of the neutron-proton system (5.5)
M	Mass of a nucleon (Section 2)
M_{mol}	Mass of the molecule (Section 3C)
N	Normalization constant for the asymptotic behavior of $u(r)$ (5.22a)
N'	Normalization constant for the asymptotic behavior of $w(r)$ (5.22b)
p_D	Probability of finding the deuteron in the D state (5.12)
p_S	Probability of finding the deuteron in the S state (5.11)
P	Dimensionless shape parameter in the phenomenological description of proton-proton scattering (4.7)
Q	Quadrupole moment of the deuteron (5.1)
Q	Operator for the quadrupole moment of the deuteron (5.23)
r	Neutron-proton separation distance $[=|\mathbf{r}|]$ (Section 2)
r_0	Effective range for scattering (3.19), (3.20)
r_{0s}	Effective range in the singlet spin state (Section 3B)
r_{0t}	Effective range in the triplet spin state (Section 3B)
r_1	The classical distance of farthest separation in the deuteron (Section 2)
r_m	Value of the neutron-proton separation r for which $w(r)$ has its maximum value (Section 5E)
$\mathbf{r}$	Neutron-proton separation vector $[=\mathbf{r}_n-\mathbf{r}_p]$ (2.1)
$\mathbf{r}_n$	Position vector of the neutron (Section 3A)

$\mathbf{r}_p$ Position vector of the proton   (Section 3A)

R Decay length ("size") of the deuteron $[=4.31\times10^{-13}$ cm]   (2.7)

$\mathbf{R}$ Center-of-gravity coordinate for the neutron and proton (Section 3C)

s Well depth parameter [= ratio of actual well depth to that well depth which gives zero binding energy in the deuteron]   (Section 2)

$\mathbf{S}$ Spin operator for the hydrogen molecule $[=\frac{1}{2}(\mathbf{d}_{p1} + \mathbf{d}_{p2})]$ (3.52)

$\mathbf{S}$ Spin operator for the neutron-proton system   (Section 5C)

S_{12} Tensor operator for particles 1 and 2   (5.2)

T Kinetic energy of relative motion   (Section 2)

$u(r)$ Radial wave function in the S state $[=r\psi(r)]$; $u^2(r)\,dr$ is the probability of finding the particles a distance between r and $r+dr$ apart from each other   (2.2)

$u_0(r)$ Radial wave function $u(r)$ at "zero" energy   (Section 3A)

$u_f(\mathbf{r}_p,\cdots)$ Internal wave function of the molecule after the collision (3.47)

$u_i(\mathbf{r}_p,\cdots)$ Internal wave function of the molecule before the collision (3.45)

$U(\mathbf{r}_p)$ Potential energy of chemical binding of the proton at position $\mathbf{r}_p$ (3.31)

v Relative speed of two protons   (Section 4)

$v(r)$ Asymptotic form of $u(r)$ for large r (3.7)

$v_0(r)$ Asymptotic form of $u_0(r)$ for large r $[= v(r)$ at "zero" energy]   (3.12)

v_f Relative speed of neutron and molecule after collision (Section 3C)

v_i Relative speed of neutron and molecule before collision (Section 3C)

$\bar{V}$ Average value of the potential energy $V(r)$ inside the range (this is *not* the expectation value of V)   (2.8)

V Potential energy of two nucleons at separation r $[= V(r)]$ (Section 1)

V_0 Conventional well depth parameter, of dimension energy (2.10) to (2.13)

$V'(\mathbf{r}_n-\mathbf{r}_p)$ "Pseudopotential" for the scattering of neutrons by protons bound to molecules   (3.36), (3.37)

$V_c(r)$	Potential of the central force in the triplet spin state $[= V_d(r) + V_\sigma(r)]$ (5.19)
$V_d(r)$	Spin-independent part of the neutron-proton potential (5.4)
$V_\sigma(r)$	Radial behavior of the $(\boldsymbol{\sigma}_1 \cdot \boldsymbol{\sigma}_2)$ part of the neutron-proton potential (5.4)
$V_T(r)$	Radial behavior of the tensor force part of the neutron-proton potential (5.3)
$w(r)$	Radial wave function in the D state (5.9)
$Y_{lm}(\theta,\varphi)$	Normalized spherical harmonics (see Appendix A, Section 2) (3.5)
$\mathcal{Y}_{Jls}^M$	Normalized "spin angle" wave function (see Appendix A, Section 5) (5.5) to (5.7)
β	Conventional range parameter (2.11) to (2.13)
δ	Phase shift for S wave scattering (3.7)
δ	"Nuclear" phase shift in proton-proton scattering ($=$ the difference between the actual phase shift and the Coulomb phase shift σ_0) (Section 4)
δ_α	Phase shift of the α wave scattering with tensor forces (Section 5G)
ϵ	Parameter for the asymptotic ratio of $w(r)$ to $u(r)$ in the α wave neutron-proton scattering with tensor forces, $\tan\epsilon = b_\alpha / a_\alpha$ (5.36)
η	A parameter measuring the importance of Coulomb effects $[= e^2 / \hbar v]$ (4.1)
θ	Angle of scattering (3.1)
$\kappa(r)$	Local wave number at separation r (2.5)
μ	Reduced mass $[\cong \frac{1}{2} M]$ (2.1)
μ'	Reduced mass for the relative motion of neutron and molecule (Section 3C)
$\boldsymbol{\mu}_{\text{eff}}$	Effective magnetic moment operator for the ground state of the deuteron (5.32)
μ_n	Magnetic moment of the neutron $[= -1.914]$ (5.30)
$\boldsymbol{\mu}_{Op}$	Operator for the magnetic moment of the neutron-proton system (5.30)
μ_p	Magnetic moment of the proton $[= 2.793]$ (5.30)
π_s	Projection operator for the singlet spin state (3.50)
π_t	Projection operator for the triplet spin state (3.50)
$\boldsymbol{\varrho}$	Center-of-gravity coordinate of the molecule (3.45)
σ	Total scattering cross section (3.23), (3.25)

σ_0	Total scattering cross section at "zero" energy (3.14), (3.24)
σ_0	Coulomb phase shift for the S wave (4.3)
$\mathbf{d}_n$	Pauli spin vector for the neutron (3.50)
$\mathbf{d}_p$	Pauli spin vector for the proton (3.50)
σ_{para}	Total cross section for the scattering of neutrons by parahydrogen (3.54)
σ_s	Total scattering cross section in the singlet spin state (3.25)
σ_t	Total scattering cross section in the triplet spin state (3.25)
ϕ	Neutron-proton wave function in the state with $J = 1$ and even parity (5.10)
ϕ_D	D wave part of ϕ (5.9)
ϕ_S	S wave part of ϕ (5.8)
$\varphi(\mathbf{r}_p)$	$= \lim\limits_{r \to 0} \partial/\partial r[r\Psi]$ (3.32)
$\chi_{s m_s}$	Spin function for a spin S with z component m_s; the functions used in Section 5 are for $S = 1$ and are listed in Appendix A, Section 4 (5.5) to (5.7)
$\psi(\mathbf{r})$	Wave function for the relative motion in a two-body system (2.1)
$\psi_0(r)$	S wave part of $\psi(\mathbf{r})$ (3.5), (3.6)
Ψ	Wave function of a neutron interacting with a proton bound to a molecule (3.30)

CHAPTER III

Nuclear Forces

1. INTRODUCTION

The theoretical study of nuclear structure is appreciably more difficult than the study of the structure of atoms and molecules, because the basic law of force is not known. The difficulties encountered in atomic and molecular physics lie in the application of well-known force laws. The forces between electrons and atomic nuclei are entirely determined by the electromagnetic laws. Nuclear physics is beset not only by the difficulties of quantum mechanics applied to complicated systems, but also by the additional difficulty that we do not know the laws governing the nuclear forces. Thus, apart from the difficulty of handling the wave equation for a many-body system, we do not even know which wave equation to solve.

The problem in nuclear physics is therefore two-fold: first, to find the laws of the nuclear forces and, second, to calculate the nuclear properties resulting from those forces. Since at present there is no satisfactory fundamental theory of nuclear forces, their nature can be studied only by careful analysis of the properties of known nuclei. We must try to find the law of force which, when applied to the nuclei, will reproduce the observed properties. The difficulties of this attempt are obvious. One is experimental: our knowledge of nuclear properties is not very accurate, so there may be several laws of force whose implications are in agreement with the present experimental material. An example of this is provided by the insensitivity of low-energy neutron-proton and proton-proton scattering data to the detailed distance dependence of the nuclear potential in the S states of the two-nucleon systems. All we were able to determine was the scattering length and the effective range, i.e., only two parameters. The second difficulty is theoretical: the methods of calculating nuclear properties for all but the simplest nuclear processes are based on approximations whose accuracy is doubtful at best, and certainly very poor in all too many cases. Thus a reliable and unambiguous test of any given law of force is possible only in very few instances.

Since detailed tests of various possible force laws are so difficult, we usually try to work with the simplest force law which is not in obvious disagreement with known data. For example, it is assumed that nuclear forces act only between pairs of nucleons and do not depend on the relative velocity of the two nucleons in question. Both assumptions are very probably wrong, but it is a common hope that we can at least get a qualitative insight into nuclear structure by their use.

The criterion of "simplicity" is highly arbitrary and depends on the formalism used as well as on the particular choice of a method of approximating the solution of the wave equation. Furthermore the historical development of nuclear physics has not been such as to encourage the belief that the true force law is very simple. As more and more experimental material has accumulated, one after another of the simplifying assumptions has had to be dropped, often very reluctantly. The forces which are commonly assumed today are very different from the purely central, purely exchange (Majorana) forces acting only between unlike particles which were assumed in 1935.

This chapter deals with certain qualitative aspects of nuclear forces which become important when not only the two-body problem but also the properties of other nuclei are studied. There are two important facts: the density of nucleons is roughly equal for all nuclei ("saturation of density"), and the binding energy per nucleon is roughly equal for all nuclei ("saturation of binding energy"). The existence of these two saturation phenomena has decisive implications for the nature of nuclear forces and has led to the hypothesis of "exchange forces." This chapter contains the discussion of the arguments which prevent the assumption of a simple attractive nuclear force, and which have led to the introduction of exchange forces. The different types of exchange forces will be described, and some of the formalisms which are currently used in this connection will be developed.

It is by no means established that nuclear forces actually are of the "exchange" type. It is even less certain that the saturation properties of nuclei are caused by the exchange character of the forces. Recent results from high-energy scattering experiments between elementary nucleons seem to indicate that the potential between two nucleons has less exchange character than necessary in order to explain the saturation.

It is possible that the developments of this chapter will soon be obsolete in the light of future discoveries. The influence of the proximity of several nucleons on the nuclear forces (many-body forces) may turn out to be of greater importance to the saturation than the exchange character (Primakoff 39).

2. STABILITY OF A NUCLEUS AGAINST COLLAPSE. THE IMPOSSIBILITY OF ATTRACTIVE FORCES BETWEEN ALL PAIRS

The evidence from the study of nuclear two-body problems at low energies points to nuclear forces which are purely attractive. This is true of the force between two protons in the ^1S state, and between a neutron and a proton in either the ^1S or ^3S state. Furthermore all these forces are approximately equally strong and seem to have about the same range. More precisely, the following choice of a potential between any two nucleons in the S state would not contradict the data discussed in the preceding chapter (compare remarks on page 103):

$$V = V_c(r) + S_{12} V_T(r) \qquad (2.1)$$

where r is the distance between the two particles, S_{12} is the tensor operator (II,5.2), and $V_c(r)$ and $V_T(r)$ are two different functions of r which are not too well known but can be chosen to be Yukawa wells with different well parameters. The tensor force well has a longer range but is more shallow than the central force well.

It would be very inviting, from the point of view of simplicity, to assume that (2.1) is the basic law for nuclear forces, not merely between two isolated nucleons in S states, but between any two nucleons under all conditions. We could then represent the potential energy in a nucleus containing A particles by the sum

$$V = \sum_{i<j=1}^{A} V_{ij} \qquad (2.2)$$

where V_{ij} is the potential energy of two isolated nuclear particles a distance r_{ij} apart and is given by (2.1), i.e., the same for all pairs of nucleons within the nucleus.

We shall show now, however, that this simplest assumption of all is in direct contradiction to experimental evidence about heavier nuclei. Experiments have shown that the density of nuclear matter inside a heavy nucleus is nearly the same for all nuclei. In other words, the nuclear volume is to a good approximation proportional to the mass number A. Furthermore the separation energy of the last neutron (or proton) in a heavy nucleus is roughly independent of mass number also. We shall refer to the approximate proportionality of nuclear volume and mass number as "saturation of nuclear density," and to the approximate proportionality between total binding energy and mass number as "saturation of nuclear binding energies." We shall see that neither of these properties could be expected if the forces were between pairs of nucleons only, and attractive between all pairs.

To prove this let us study the behavior of the kinetic and potential energy as a function of the nuclear radius R. As long as the shape of the wave function is not changed greatly upon shrinking the nuclear radius, the kinetic energy is inversely proportional to the square of the nuclear radius: Let $\varphi_1(r_1, r_2, \cdots, r_A)$ be a normalized wave function. Then $\varphi_a = a^{3A/2} \varphi_1(ar_1, ar_2, ar_3, \cdots, ar_A)$ is also normalized (a = constant). Direct substitution of the kinetic energy operator

$$T = -\frac{\hbar^2}{2M} \sum_{i=1}^{A} \nabla_i^2 \qquad (2.3)$$

gives the result

$$(\varphi_a, T\varphi_a) = a^2 (\varphi_1, T\varphi_1) \qquad (2.4)$$

If the wave function φ_1 describes a nucleus of radius R, the wave function φ_a describes a "similar" nucleus of radius R/a. Hence (2.4) can be interpreted as saying that, other things being equal, the expectation value of the kinetic energy is inversely proportional to the square of the nuclear radius.

We now proceed to estimate the dependence of the potential energy on the nuclear radius R. We shall make the assumptions that the nucleus has a roughly spherical shape, and that there is sufficient averaging out of the directions of the spins and interparticle distances so that the tensor force does not contribute appreciably to the total potential energy in heavy nuclei; i.e., we shall assume that the average value of the tensor operator S_{ij} is close to zero for all nucleon pairs. As far as the central force part of the potential (2.1) is concerned, our argument will depend only on the short range, not on the detailed distance dependence of $V_c(r)$. We shall therefore make the simplifying assumption that $V_c(r)$ can be represented by a square well of range b and depth V_0.

The expectation value of the potential energy is then very close to zero for large separations between all the nucleons because of the short range of the nuclear forces. We can estimate the potential energy as follows:

$$\bar{V} \cong -\tfrac{1}{2}A(A-1)\, p\, V_0 \qquad (2.5)$$

where p is the average probability for a pair to be closer than the range b.

p can be estimated by assuming that the nucleons move independently of each other within a sphere of radius R. Let the function $e(x)$ be defined by

$$e(x) = 1 \quad \text{if} \quad x > 0$$
$$e(x) = 0 \quad \text{if} \quad x < 0 \tag{2.6}$$

Then the probability of finding two particles within a distance b of each other is

$$p = \left(\frac{4\pi R^3}{3}\right)^{-2} \int\int e(b - r_{12})\, dV_1\, dV_2 \tag{2.7}$$

where the integrations go over the interior of the sphere and r_{12} is the distance between the particles. The integral can be evaluated:

$$p = \left(\frac{b}{R}\right)^3 \left[1 - \frac{9}{16}\left(\frac{b}{R}\right) + \frac{1}{32}\left(\frac{b}{R}\right)^3\right] \quad \left(R > \frac{b}{2}\right)$$
$$p = 1 \quad \left(R < \frac{b}{2}\right) \tag{2.8}$$

We observe that this shows the right limiting behavior for large R and small R: for large R it is the ratio of a sphere of radius b to the nuclear volume (a sphere of radius R), i.e., $(b/R)^3$; for small R all the particles are within range, so the probability of interaction is unity.

Formulas (2.5) and (2.8) give an approximate expression for the potential energy of a nucleus as a function of its radius R and the range b of the forces. This is shown graphically in Fig. 2.1 as the curve labeled $\bar{V}$. Also shown on the figure is the estimate of the kinetic energy $\bar{T}$ (proportional to R^{-2}). The figure also exhibits the total energy $E = \bar{T} + \bar{V}$ as a function of the radius R. We see that E has a minimum for $R \sim b/2$, and a maximum for some value of $R = R_1 \gg b$.[1] If we start with an ensemble of nucleons within a sphere of radius $R > R_1$, it tends to fly apart. An ensemble of nucleons within a sphere of radius $R < R_1$ tends to collapse to the stable position, with a radius R of order $b/2$.

This predicted behavior is in complete disagreement with nature: the most stable position for an ensemble of nucleons must be the one realized in nature, and that is *not* the collapsed state at all. Rather,

---

[1] Since $\bar{V}$ and $\bar{T}$ depend on the mass number A in a different way, the positions of the minimum and maximum depend on the mass number.

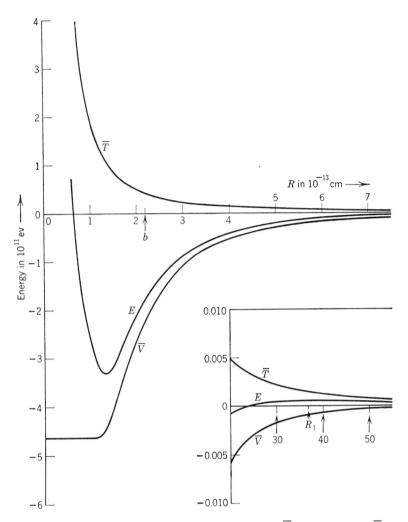

FIG. 2.1. A schematic picture of the potential energy $\overline{V}$, kinetic energy $\overline{T}$, and total energy $E = \overline{T} + \overline{V}$, as functions of the nuclear radius R, under the assumption of attractive forces between all pairs of nucleons. The numerical values were chosen to give an indication of the situation in a heavy nucleus $(A \cong 200)$, the energy scale is in units of 10^5 Mev, the abscissa in units of 10^{-13} cm. The total energy E has a very deep minimum for a radius R of order $b/2$, where b is the range of the nuclear force. E has a very shallow maximum for a very large radius R_1. An assembly of nucleons initially confined to a radius $R < R_1$ collapses to the stable radius corresponding to the minimum of E. This is in contradiction to observed nuclear radii. Also the minimum value of E corresponds to a binding energy of about 1600 Mev per nucleon, in contradiction to observed binding energies.

the nuclei tend to a state in which all the nucleons are kept apart by about the range of the nuclear forces. A similar contradiction is obtained by considering the binding energy. In the collapsed state every nucleon is close enough to every other nucleon so that the "bond" is effective and contributes to the total binding energy. The total binding energy in the collapsed state is therefore proportional to the number of pairs of nucleons, i.e., to A^2 for large values of A. In nature the binding energy of a nucleus of mass number A is roughly proportional to A, not to A^2. The binding energy (minimum value of E) for Fig. 2.1 is 3.3×10^5 Mev, or 1650 Mev per particle, compared to the experimental value of about 8 Mev per particle.

We are therefore forced to the conclusion that the very simplest assumption about nuclear forces, made before, is in contradiction to nature and does not correspond to reality. Let us now enumerate the essential assumptions which we have made before; one or more (or perhaps all) of these assumptions must be abandoned:

(1) The nuclear forces act between pairs of nucleons only. The presence of other nucleons nearby does not influence the force law between any given two nucleons.

(2) The force between two nucleons is conservative and velocity independent. It can therefore be written as the gradient of a potential function.

(3) The force between two nucleons is always attractive.

(4) The force between two nucleons is independent of the type (neutron or proton) of the nucleons.

(5) The force is the same for all relative orbital angular momenta.

(6) The force is predominantly a central force, i.e., the tensor force is not a main determinant of nuclear binding.

At first glance we are tempted to drop assumption 1. Such an assumption would certainly be invalid for the forces which are responsible for chemical binding; nevertheless, the historical development of nuclear theory has not been in this direction. Rather, most attempts to find the nuclear force law have maintained assumptions 1 and 2 but modified the other assumptions. The reason for this trend is not hard to find: in the absence of a fundamental theory of nuclear forces, it is practically hopeless to deduce, from empirical evidence only, a force law which violates assumption 1. Each time we added another particle to a nucleus, the basic force law would have to be modified. This gives so many arbitrary parameters that any set of data can be fitted; conversely, such a fit would mean very little. A similar statement holds for velocity-dependent forces: there are so many possible choices that agreement with experimental evidence would have to be considered accidental.

Why the assumption of velocity-independent forces was essential for our previous argument may not be obvious. It can be seen most easily by considering a counter example: suppose that the forces between any two nucleons are attractive and additive, but velocity dependent in such a way that the attraction becomes rapidly zero if the relative velocity increases beyond a certain limiting value. In the collapsed state all the nucleons are moving quite rapidly (since the wavelength is decreased). Hence our assumption would reduce the stability of the collapsed state appreciably, thereby invalidating the argument for its being the most stable state.

The next most obvious choice is to keep assumptions 1, 2, and 4 but to modify assumption 3 as follows:

(3′) The force between two nucleons is attractive for distances $r > d$, where d is of the order of the distance between nearest neighbors in actual nuclei. For distances $r < d$, the force becomes highly repulsive.

This force law would unquestionably lead to the observed constant density of nuclear matter and to the constant binding energy per particle. Indeed, a force law of this type is responsible for the fact that liquids and solids do not occur in a collapsed state: two atoms attract each other (mostly through van der Waals forces) only as long as there is no appreciable overlap of their electron clouds. For shorter distances the exclusion principle keeps the electrons apart and acts like a strong repulsive force.

There is relatively little evidence against this assumption as yet. Certainly the low-energy scattering experiments discussed in Chapter II are not sensitive enough to the details of the force law to allow the exclusion of assumption 3′. However, some scattering experiments have been performed at higher energies (10 Mev and above, the highest energy so far being 350 Mev), and their results seem to contradict this force law. In particular, there appears to be too little scattering in states of odd angular momentum to fit a force of type 3′. Other arguments against 3′ have been given by Feenberg (37). The arguments against assumption 3′ are not very strong at the present time. However, we shall discuss in the next sections the other explanations of the constant density and constant binding energy per particle, which are more commonly put forward.

3. EXCHANGE FORCES

A. Qualitative Considerations

The common trend in nuclear physics so far has been to avoid the contradiction discussed in the preceding section by modifying assumptions 3 and 5 but keeping the other assumptions. Assumption 3 is replaced by

(3″) The force, or part of the force, between two nucleons is sometimes attractive, sometimes repulsive, depending on the state of the two nucleons with respect to each other.

There are many ways of introducing a dependence of the force on the state of the two particles. The type of dependence which is most frequently used was first introduced by Heisenberg (32) and Majorana (33); it leads to the so-called "exchange forces."

The original argument of Heisenberg and Majorana goes like this: the force of chemical attraction between two hydrogen atoms depends on the state of the two electrons with respect to each other. There is attraction if the wave function is symmetric under an interchange of the positions of the electrons, repulsion if the wave function is anti-symmetric under this interchange.

In chemical binding the attraction or repulsion can be explained by the wave mechanics of the electron wave functions. Heisenberg and Majorana have taken over the formal dependence of the interaction on the symmetry without, however, trying to give a complete wave-mechanical explanation of this dependence. They introduce a type of nuclear force which is attractive for "symmetric" pairs and about equally strong but repulsive for "anti-symmetric" pairs. The symmetry of a pair depends on the wave function which describes the state. If the wave function is unchanged under the exchange of the coordinates of the two particles of the pair, the pair is symmetric. If the wave function changes its sign under this exchange of coordinates, the pair is anti-symmetric. A pair may be partially symmetric and partially anti-symmetric. Specification of the forces in purely symmetric and purely anti-symmetric states covers all possibilities, since any function of a pair of variables q_1, q_2 can be written as a linear combination of two functions, one being symmetric and the other anti-symmetric under an exchange of q_1 and q_2:

$$\varphi(q_1,q_2) = \tfrac{1}{2}[\varphi(q_1,q_2) + \varphi(q_2,q_1)] + \tfrac{1}{2}[\varphi(q_1,q_2) - \varphi(q_2,q_1)] \quad (3.1)$$

Before giving a quantitative formulation of the exchange forces we first show qualitatively that exchange forces can lead to saturation of both the binding energies and the nuclear densities. The Pauli exclusion principle provides the basis for this explanation. Because of the exclusion principle, it is impossible to have only symmetric pairs in a nuclear wave function. Rather, there are more anti-symmetric pairs than symmetric pairs in the collapsed state, and we shall show in Section 4 that the ratio is approximately $5:3$ in favor of the anti-symmetric pairs. Hence, if the repulsive forces for anti-symmetric pairs are about as strong as the attractive forces for symmetric pairs, there is a net repulsion in the collapsed state, i.e., the collapsed state is not bound at all. This must be compared with the result obtained by using ordinary forces, namely that the collapsed state gives the largest binding energy of all the nuclear states (Section 2).

We shall now show that (1) states of "normal" density (internucleon distances $\cong$ range of the forces) are stable against either an increase or a decrease of the nuclear radius, and (2) the binding energy is proportional to the mass number A rather than to its square. For this purpose we must find the expression for the potential energy $\bar{V}$ as a function of the nuclear radius when the nuclear forces are exchange forces; this expression will replace (2.5) and (2.8). The basic estimate (2.5) must be refined since there are two kinds of pairs. We call n_+ the total number of symmetric pairs, n_- the total number of anti-symmetric pairs in the nucleus; p_+ is the probability of finding a *symmetric* pair within the range b of the nuclear forces from each other, p_- is the probability of finding an *anti-symmetric* pair within the same distance. Then

$$\bar{V} \cong -(n_+p_+ - n_-p_-) \, V_0 \tag{3.2}$$

where V_0 is the well depth of the interaction potential (assumed to have equal magnitude for symmetric and anti-symmetric pairs). In the collapsed state all pairs interact, so that p_+ and p_- are both equal to unity, giving

$$\bar{V} \cong (n_- - n_+) \, V_0 = +\frac{1}{4}\frac{A(A-1)}{2} \, V_0 \qquad \text{(collapsed state)} \tag{3.3}$$

We have used the result of Section 4 for the ratio of n_+ to n_-:

$$\frac{n_+}{n_-} = \frac{3}{5}$$

It is essential for the subsequent argument that the probabilities p_+ and p_- do not depend in the same way on the nuclear radius R. Anti-symmetric pairs have to stay apart by a distance of order λ, the wavelength of the relative motion (see Chapter I, Section 8).

One can find the dependence of the average wavelength λ on the radius roughly as follows: Let us, in first approximation, consider the nucleus as A nucleons enclosed in a sphere of radius R, but without any mutual interaction. When the nucleons are all in the lowest possible states permitted by the Pauli exclusion principle, we can calculate the average wavelength $\bar{\lambda}$,[1] and we obtain for an equal number of neutrons and protons

$$\bar{\lambda} \cong \frac{0.85R}{A^{1/3}} \qquad (3.4)$$

This expression can be expected to be qualitatively correct in spite of the primitive approximations. The average wavelength $\bar{\lambda}$ is almost equal to the average distance d between nearest neighbors of A particles distributed uniformly throughout the interior of the sphere. It is possible to verify that

$$d = \frac{0.893R}{A^{1/3}} \qquad (3.5)$$

This distance can serve as a rough measure of the relative wavelength $\bar{\lambda}$.

We now write the probabilities p_+ and p_- as functions of the nuclear radius in the form

$$p_+ = g_+(R)\, p \qquad p_- = g_-(R)\, p \qquad (3.6)$$

where p is the same function which was defined in (2.8). The factor p gives the probability of finding a pair at a distance smaller than R if the partners are uniformly distributed over the nuclear volume. The functions g_+ and g_- express the deviation from this probability caused by the symmetry of the pair. It is expected that g_+ and g_- depend on the ratio of the relative wavelength $\bar{\lambda}$ to the range b of the nuclear forces; hence g_+ and g_- can be expressed as functions of d/b as shown in Fig. 3.1. As expected, the relative probability of finding an anti-symmetric pair within the range b is smaller than for a symmetric pair, and it approaches zero as the distance d becomes much larger than the range of the force.

The functions g can be found from the work of Wigner and Seitz (Wigner 33) on the theory of the solid state. The probability of finding two (free) electrons of

---

[1] This result corresponds actually to the average value of λ^{-2}. It can be derived from the total kinetic energy $\bar{T}$ of this system which is given by (4.16). One then uses the relation $\bar{T}/A = \hbar^2/2M\bar{\lambda}^2$ to get (3.4).

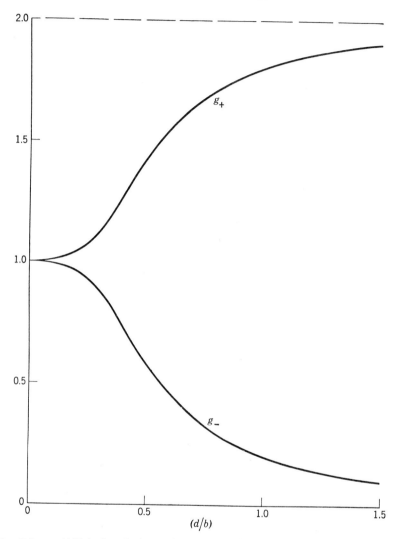

F<small>IG.</small> 3.1. $g_+(d/b)$ is the relative probability of finding a symmetric pair of nucleons within the nuclear range b if the distance between nearest neighbors in the nucleus is d; $g_-(d/b)$ is the corresponding quantity for anti-symmetric pairs.   The two probabilities are equal for a highly collapsed state $(d \ll b)$; but, in the normal density state $d \gtrsim b$, the probability of finding an anti-symmetric pair within range becomes very small compared to the probability for finding a symmetric pair within range.

parallel spin a distance between r and $r+dr$ apart is given by these authors as

$$\pi_a(r)\,dr = \left\{1 - 9\left[\frac{\sin x - x\cos x}{x^3}\right]^2\right\}\frac{3r^2}{R^3}\,dr \tag{3.7}$$

where

$$x \equiv \left(\frac{9\pi N}{4}\right)^{1/3}\frac{r}{R} \tag{3.8}$$

$N/2$ being the number of electrons with spins in a given direction. In order to apply this to nuclei we replace $N/2$ by $A/4$, since this is the number of identical particles (say neutrons with up spin) in the nucleus, and this number determines the average wavelength $\bar{\lambda}$ of the relative motion. The parameter x then becomes equal to

$$x = 1.36\,\frac{r}{d} \tag{3.9}$$

d is given by (3.5). Since electrons with parallel spin can form only anti-symmetric pairs, (3.7) refers to the probability of finding an anti-symmetric pair a distance between r and $r+dr$ apart. The probability of interaction p_- is[1]

$$p_- = \int_0^b \pi_a(r)\,dr \equiv g_-\left(\frac{b}{R}\right)^3 \tag{3.10}$$

The integral can be evaluated numerically. g_+ is determined from the conditions that the sum $g_+ + g_-$ is independent of the distance between nearest neighbors, and that g_+ approaches g_- for small values of d/b (collapsed state).

We now substitute (3.6) into (3.2) and use the fact that the ratio of n_+ to n_- is $3:5$. This gives the following estimate for the potential energy of a nucleus under the assumption of exchange forces:

$$\bar{V} \cong -\frac{1}{2}A(A-1)\left[\frac{3}{8}g_+ - \frac{5}{8}g_-\right]p\,V_0 \tag{3.11}$$

The function p is defined by (2.8) and g_+, g_- are given in Fig. 3.1. The dependence of (3.11) on the nuclear radius is shown in Fig. 3.2. The potential energy is positive (repulsive) for small radii. It then becomes negative (attractive) for radii such that d, the distance between nearest neighbors, is of order b, the range of the forces. The reason is that the repulsive part of $\bar{V}$ is proportional to g_-, which goes to zero if $d\gg b$. Thereafter the factor p becomes dominant, so that the potential energy approaches zero for large R like R^{-3}.

The potential energy $\bar{V}$ has a minimum at a nuclear radius R_0 which corresponds to $d\cong b$, i.e., the distance between nearest neighbors is of the same order of magnitude as the range of the nuclear force. Hence

[1] Since the whole calculation is consistent only if R is much larger than either d or b, we use the limiting form of p, (2.8), for large R. The error caused by this is insignificant for our purposes.

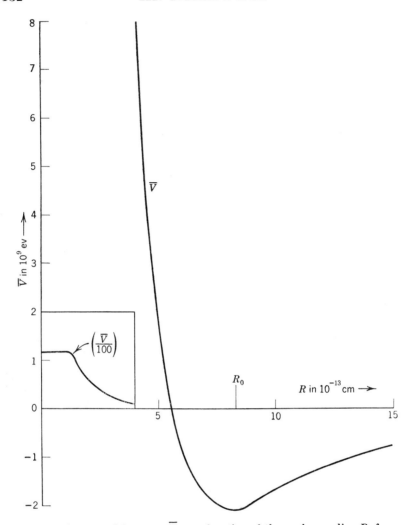

FIG. 3.2.   The potential energy $\overline{V}$ as a function of the nuclear radius R, for exchange forces, computed from the estimate (3.11) for a heavy nucleus ($A \cong 200$).
The ordinate is in Bev, the abscissa in 10^{-13} cm.   The collapsed state is now
unstable (the potential energy is positive).   The minimum in the potential energy
occurs for a nuclear radius R such that the distance between nearest neighbors,
(3.5), is of the same order of magnitude as the range of the nuclear forces.   This
corresponds to the observed normal density state of nuclei. The value of $\overline{V}$ at the
minimum is proportional to the mass number A, not to its square.

the stable nucleus has a radius $R \cong R_0$ (actually slightly larger because of the kinetic energy), i.e., a radius which corresponds to the normal density state.   There is now no tendency whatsoever toward collapse, since the potential energy is actually repulsive (positive) in the collapsed state.   *Exchange forces lead to saturation of nuclear densities.*

We now show that the binding energy in this normal density state is proportional to the mass number A rather than to its square.   The optimum radius is given by $d \cong b$.   Under the assumption that there are many particles in the nucleus (which assumption we have made all along), $d \cong b$ implies that the radius R is much larger than b, so that we can use the limiting form $(b/R)^3$ for p from (2.8).[1]   With $b \cong d$ we get $p \cong (b/R)^3 \sim A^{-1}$; consequently the potential energy $\bar{V}$, (3.11), is proportional to A rather than to A^2.   The kinetic energy will be treated in detail in the next section.   For identical particles distributed uniformly over a volume, the kinetic energy per particle depends only on the density of the particles.   In the normal density state this density is independent of the mass number, and so therefore is the kinetic energy per particle.   Thus the total kinetic energy $\bar{T}$ in the normal density state is proportional to A just as the potential energy is.   Hence the binding energy is proportional to A too.   *Exchange forces lead to saturation of nuclear binding energies.*

We run into difficulty when we try to use this estimate of the potential energy quantitatively to find the binding energy.   The kinetic energy (according to the estimate explained in Section 4) is always large enough so that $E = \bar{T} + \bar{V}$ is positive, i.e., the potential energy (3.11) is too weak to give binding.   This is a consequence of our crude approximations.   We have neglected completely the influence of the nuclear forces on the behavior of the wave function.   According to our assumptions symmetric pairs attract each other, anti-symmetric pairs repel each other.   These attractions and repulsions influence the wave function: the probability p_+ of finding a symmetric pair within range of each other is larger than we have estimated, the probability p_- of finding an anti-symmetric pair within range is smaller than our estimate.   The wave function exhibits a "dynamical correlation."   This dynamical correlation effect acts in the same direction as, and reinforces, the statistical correlation effect for symmetric as against anti-symmetric pairs.

We shall take the dynamical correlations into account by the artifice of replacing d in $g_+(d/b)$ and $g_-(d/b)$ by a larger value d'.   We shall take d' to be about 40 percent larger than d, (3.5).   Figure 3.1 shows that this gives a stronger correlation effect: $g_+(d/b)$ increases

---

[1] This provides the justification for our use of this same limiting form in (3.10).

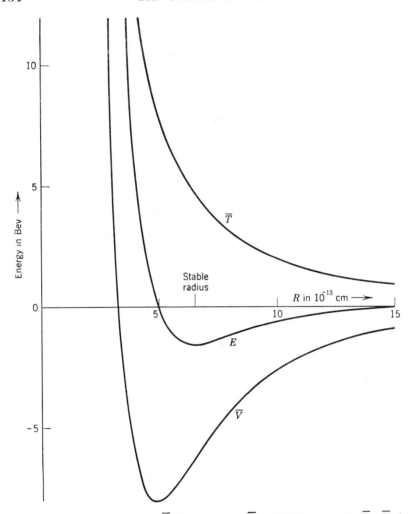

F<small>IG</small>. 3.3.   The potential energy $\overline{V}$, kinetic energy $\overline{T}$, and total energy $E = \overline{T} + \overline{V}$ of a heavy nucleus ($A \cong 200$) as a function of its radius R under the assumption of exchange forces.   The energy scale is in Bev, the radius scale in 10^{-13} cm.   There is now a stable radius $R \cong 6.5 \times 10^{-13}$ cm with a reasonable binding energy per particle of about 8 Mev.   Not much significance is attached to the precise numbers since the "dynamical correlations" in the wave functions were taken into account by a highly artificial procedure.

with increasing d; $g_-(d/b)$ decreases with increasing d. That is, the symmetric (and hence attractive) pairs are closer together than our previous estimate, the anti-symmetric (and hence repulsive) pairs are farther apart. This artifice therefore leads to the same result, qualitatively, as the actual (but so far neglected) dynamical correlations. Hence there is reason to believe that the calculation with an artificially increased value d' instead of d reproduces the main qualitative features of the correct solution.

The result is shown in Fig. 3.3. The total energy E has a minimum for a nuclear radius $R \cong 6.5 \times 10^{-13}$ cm, which is reasonable for the assumed mass number $A \cong 200$. This radius corresponds to a normal density state; the distance between nearest neighbors, $d \cong 1.8 \times 10^{-13}$ cm, is of the same order of magnitude as the assumed range of the force $b \cong 2.2 \times 10^{-13}$ cm. The behavior of E as a function of the nuclear radius implies that the nucleus is stable against either an increase or a decrease of the radius.

The minimum value of E in Fig. 3.3 corresponds to a binding energy of about 1600 Mev, or 8 Mev per particle. The fact that this is a reasonable result must not be taken too seriously, since we have used a highly artificial method of taking into account the dynamical correlations in the wave function. It is somewhat gratifying, nevertheless, that we were able to obtain reasonable values for the nuclear radius R and the binding energy with only one adjustable parameter (the d' in the correlation estimate). The well depth V_0 and the range b were taken from the two-body data discussed in Chapter II and were not used as adjustable parameters.

B. Formal Definition of Exchange Forces

We now construct the quantum-mechanical operator $V_x(r)$ which corresponds to the potential of an exchange force. We define the operator $V_x(r)$ by its action on a wave function φ depending on the coordinates $\mathbf{r}_1$ and $\mathbf{r}_2$ of two particles:

$$V_x(r) \, \varphi(\mathbf{r}_1, \mathbf{r}_2) = f(r) \, \varphi(\mathbf{r}_2, \mathbf{r}_1) \tag{3.12}$$

where $f(r)$ is some function of the distance r between the particles. The operator $V_x(r)$ "exchanges" the coordinates of the two particles in addition to multiplying φ by the function $f(r)$.

We now show that this formal exchange potential gives the desired properties provided that the sign of $f(r)$ is chosen properly (negative). In a symmetric state we have

$$\varphi(\mathbf{r}_1, \mathbf{r}_2) = \varphi(\mathbf{r}_2, \mathbf{r}_1) \qquad V_x \varphi = +f(r) \varphi \tag{3.13}$$

whereas in an anti-symmetric state

$$\varphi(\mathbf{r}_1, \mathbf{r}_2) = -\varphi(\mathbf{r}_2, \mathbf{r}_1) \qquad V_x \, \varphi = -f(r) \, \varphi \qquad (3.14)$$

If $f(r)$ is chosen as an attractive (negative) well, the operator V_x acts like an attractive potential in symmetric states, and like a repulsive potential in anti-symmetric states.

The operator form (3.12) does not involve any intrinsic spins. If the spins of the nucleons are taken into account, three types of "exchange" are possible. They are commonly denoted by the names of the investigators who first suggested them. Let $\mathbf{r}_1$ and ζ_1 stand for the space and spin coordinates of the first nucleon, respectively ($\zeta_1 = \pm 1$ only), and let $\psi(\mathbf{r}_1, \zeta_1; \mathbf{r}_2, \zeta_2)$ be the wave function for a given nucleon pair. Then the three possible exchange operators are as given in Table 3.1.

TABLE 3.1
POSSIBLE EXCHANGE OPERATORS

Name	Definition of Operator
Majorana (33)	$P^M \psi = \psi(\mathbf{r}_2, \zeta_1; \mathbf{r}_1, \zeta_2)$
Bartlett (36)	$P^B \psi = \psi(\mathbf{r}_1, \zeta_2; \mathbf{r}_2, \zeta_1)$
Heisenberg (32)	$P^H \psi = \psi(\mathbf{r}_2, \zeta_2; \mathbf{r}_1, \zeta_1)$

The Majorana exchange operator interchanges the positions of the particles, leaving their spin directions unaffected. This is the type of exchange force we have used in Section 3A. The Bartlett operator exchanges the spin directions of the two particles, leaving their positions unaffected, whereas the Heisenberg exchange operator interchanges both position and spin coordinates. Clearly

$$P^H = P^M P^B \qquad (3.15)$$

and

$$(P^M)^2 = (P^B)^2 = (P^H)^2 = 1 \qquad (3.16)$$

Equation (3.16) implies that each of the three exchange operators P has only two eigenvalues, $+1$ and -1.

It is interesting to investigate the effect of exchange forces on the two-particle systems. The exchange forces violate our earlier assumption 5 that the force should be independent of the relative angular momentum. The interchange of $\mathbf{r}_1$ and $\mathbf{r}_2$ (the Majorana exchange) is equivalent to reversing the sign of the relative coordinate $\mathbf{r} = \mathbf{r}_2 - \mathbf{r}_1$. In a two-particle system, but *only* in a two-particle system, this is the same as the parity operation. This operation gives $+1$ for the even values of the orbital angular momentum l, -1 for odd l. Thus a

Majorana force is attractive in states of even l (it must be chosen attractive to fit the known attractive force in the S state for two nucleons) but repulsive in states of odd l. The Bartlett exchange operator gives $+1$ in triplet states, -1 in singlet states, independently of the orbital angular momentum. We thus get the values shown in Table 3.2 for the exchange operators in the various states of the two-

TABLE 3.2

VALUES OF EXCHANGE OPERATORS IN STATES OF THE TWO-PARTICLE SYSTEMS

Operator	State			
	Even Parity (Even l)		Odd Parity (Odd l)	
	Triplet	Singlet	Triplet	Singlet
P^M	1	1	-1	-1
P^B	1	-1	1	-1
P^H	1	-1	-1	1

particle systems. The consequences of these changes of sign of the force in the various angular momentum states for neutron-proton and proton-proton scattering will be investigated in Chapter IV and compared with experiment.

The three types of exchange operators of Table 3.1 can be used to construct three types of exchange forces by multiplying by some function of the distance between the particles. In addition, there may still be present some ordinary force (although our previous arguments have shown that it must not be the predominant attractive force). An ordinary (non-exchange) force is often called a Wigner force.[1] Furthermore the tensor forces may or may not have an exchange character. In this connection it is useful to note that the tensor operator S_{12} commutes with the Bartlett spin exchange operator P^B: P^B gives $+1$ in triplet states, -1 in singlet states, whereas S_{12} gives zero in singlet states and transforms triplet states into triplet states. Thus

$$P^B S_{12} = S_{12} P^B = S_{12} \qquad (3.17)$$

[1] The important characteristic of a Wigner force, historically, is not its lack of exchange character but rather its short range. Wigner (33a,b) was the first to suggest forces of exceedingly short range as an explanation of the large binding energy of He[4] in comparison with the deuteron, as well as of the main features of neutron-proton scattering. Not until later was the name "Wigner force" applied exclusively to non-exchange forces.

and there are only two (not four) types of tensor forces: the ordinary tensor force, and the tensor force with a Majorana exchange character. The most general potential of the exchange type therefore has the form

$$V = V_W(r) + V_M(r)\,P^M + V_B(r)\,P^B + V_H(r)\,P^H + V_{TW}(r)\,S_{12} \\ + V_{TM}(r)\,S_{12}\,P^M \quad (3.18)$$

where the various $V(r)$ are functions of the distance r between the two particles; these functions may be different from each other in magnitude as well as in their distance dependence (range); some of them may vanish; they may also be different for neutron-neutron, proton-proton, and neutron-proton pairs. We shall assume, however, that charge independence of the nuclear forces (our assumption 4 in Section 2) is true in nature, i.e., the functions $V_W(r)$, etc., are the same for neutron-neutron, proton-proton, and neutron-proton pairs (Breit 36a, Schwinger 50). Formula (3.18) shows that even with this restrictive assumption we still have a large number of adjustable parameters at our disposal to fit the experimental data.

Not all conceivable combinations of arbitrary functions for the various $V(r)$ in (3.18) give agreement with experiment. For example, we have already ruled out a pure Wigner force because it fails to give saturation. We can rule out a pure Bartlett force or a pure Heisenberg force because either one has opposite sign in singlet and triplet states of the two-particle system, whereas we know that the neutron-proton force is attractive in both the ^1S and ^3S states. We shall be concerned in Section 4 with the restrictions (the "saturation conditions") on the choice of the $V(r)$ in (3.18) imposed by the observed saturation of nuclear binding energies. Since pure Heisenberg or Bartlett forces are already ruled out, we shall concentrate our attention mostly on mixtures of Wigner and Majorana forces.

The exchange forces should be considered as a first, crude approximation to a theory of the nuclear forces which takes the "structure" of the neutron and proton into account. Breit and Wigner (Breit 35, Plesset 36) have given an argument in favor of this point of view: if the neutron and proton really change places during their interaction, the center of gravity of the two particles also moves slightly because their masses are not quite equal. It would then be impossible to separate off the center-of-mass motion in neutron-proton scattering.

Wheeler (36) has pointed out that exchange forces may be considered a special case of a more general class of "velocity-dependent" forces (the name is slightly misleading when applied to exchange forces, however). We usually write the energy of interaction as an operator:

$$V\psi \equiv V(r)\,\psi(\mathbf{r}_1,\mathbf{r}_2)$$

There is nothing to prevent us, however, from using a more general operator of type

$$V\psi \equiv \iint K(\mathbf{r}_1,\mathbf{r}_2;\mathbf{r}_1',\mathbf{r}_2')\,\psi(\mathbf{r}_1',\mathbf{r}_2')\,dV_1'\,dV_2' \tag{3.19}$$

provided that it satisfies some simple conditions: It must be a Hermitean operator:

$$K(\mathbf{r}_1,\mathbf{r}_2;\mathbf{r}_1',\mathbf{r}_2') = K^*(\mathbf{r}_1',\mathbf{r}_2';\mathbf{r}_1,\mathbf{r}_2) \tag{3.20}$$

It must be invariant under translations of the coordinate system as a whole:

$$\left(\frac{\partial}{\partial x_1} + \frac{\partial}{\partial x_2} + \frac{\partial}{\partial x_{1'}} + \frac{\partial}{\partial x_{2'}}\right) K = 0, \qquad \text{same for } y,z \tag{3.21}$$

and it must be invariant under rotations of the coordinate system as a whole; the formal conditions for that are the same as (3.21) with $\partial/\partial x$ replaced by L_x, the component of the orbital angular momentum in the x direction, and similarly for y and z. Finally, K must be invariant under inversion of the coordinate system (the parity operation)

$$K(\mathbf{r}_1,\mathbf{r}_2;\mathbf{r}_1',\mathbf{r}_2') = K(-\mathbf{r}_1,-\mathbf{r}_2;-\mathbf{r}_1',-\mathbf{r}_2') \tag{3.22}$$

The ordinary non-exchange potential $V(r)$ is a special case of the more general operator (3.19) if we write

$$K(\mathbf{r}_1,\mathbf{r}_2;\mathbf{r}_1',\mathbf{r}_2') = V(|\mathbf{r}_1-\mathbf{r}_2|)\,\delta(\mathbf{r}_1-\mathbf{r}_1')\,\delta(\mathbf{r}_2-\mathbf{r}_2') \tag{3.23}$$

The Majorana exchange force $V_M(r)\,P^M$ can also be written as a special case of (3.19) with

$$K(\mathbf{r}_1,\mathbf{r}_2;\mathbf{r}_1',\mathbf{r}_2') = V_M(|\mathbf{r}_1-\mathbf{r}_2|)\,\delta(\mathbf{r}_1-\mathbf{r}_2')\,\delta(\mathbf{r}_2-\mathbf{r}_1') \tag{3.24}$$

Equations (3.23) and (3.24) are very special choices of K; a host of other choices is possible, giving rise to a large class of operators which might describe the energy of interaction between two nucleons. To mention just one possibility, consider the choice

$$K(\mathbf{r}_1,\mathbf{r}_2;\mathbf{r}_1',\mathbf{r}_2') = g(|\mathbf{r}_1-\mathbf{r}_2|)\,g(|\mathbf{r}_1'-\mathbf{r}_2'|) \tag{3.25}$$

where g is some arbitrary real function. This choice of K in (3.19) leads to interaction in S states only; the operator gives zero when applied to P, D, $\cdots$ states. It is possible to show that (3.25) leads to saturation of nuclear binding energies. This kind of force has been considered by Wigner (unpublished). Other possible choices of velocity-dependent forces have been discussed by Eisenbud and Wigner (Eisenbud 41), Way (36), Blanchard (51), and Breit (51).

This generalization of Wheeler is in the direction of abandoning our assumption 2 of Section 2, that the forces are velocity independent. Although it is true that exchange forces can be written formally as velocity-dependent forces [see (3.24)], they are a rather special, singular case. We shall continue to classify exchange forces as velocity-independent forces, which, however, depend on the relative angular momentum (both spin and orbital) of the two particles which interact. Exchange forces will therefore be considered as satisfying assumptions 1, 2, 4, and 6 but violating assumptions 3 and 5 quoted on p. 125.

4. THE SATURATION CONDITIONS

A. The Comparison Theorem

Some of the qualitative conclusions arrived at in Section 3 can be formulated in a more rigorous mathematical form. Instead of the dependence of the energy of a given nucleus on its radius, we shall now be interested in the dependence of the energy on the mass number. We shall show that the assumption of purely attractive, ordinary forces leads to a value of the energy of the ground state, $E_A(H)$, of the nucleus A, lower than the observed energy of this ground state, $E_A(\exp)$, for some range of values of A. We shall not attempt to calculate the precise value of $E_A(H)$ resulting from the assumed Hamiltonian. Rather we shall establish an upper bound for it, $\bar{H}_A$, with the properties

$$\bar{H}_A \geq E_A(H) \qquad \text{for all values of } A \tag{4.1}$$

Then we shall find that this upper bound is smaller than the experimental value for some values of A:

$$\bar{H}_A < E_A(\exp) \qquad \text{for some values of } A \tag{4.2}$$

The combination of (4.1) and (4.2) gives

$$E_A(H) < E_A(\exp) \qquad \text{for some values of } A \tag{4.3}$$

and can thus be used to exclude the assumed Hamiltonian H as being in contradiction to observation.

In order to find an upper bound, $\bar{H}_A$, for the theoretical energy of the ground state, $E_A(H)$, we shall use the *comparison theorem* of quantum mechanics. This theorem states that the expectation value of the energy in an arbitrary state Φ is larger than the energy of the actual ground state Ψ of the system. The proof of this theorem is given in any book on quantum mechanics.[1] We shall construct a simple comparison wave function Φ for which the expectation value of the Hamiltonian can be evaluated explicitly. This expectation value will serve as $\bar{H}_A$ in (4.1), and we shall show that it also fulfills (4.2).

The comparison state Φ need not be an eigenstate of H, and actually it will be rather far from being an eigenstate. We shall choose Φ such that it corresponds to the collapsed state with no correlations between particle motions other than those imposed by the exclusion principle. No nucleon can be farther away from the origin than half the range b of the forces:

[1] For example, Schiff (49), Chapter VII, Section 27.

$$\Phi(\mathbf{r}_1,\zeta_1,\mathbf{r}_2,\zeta_2,\cdots,\mathbf{r}_A,\zeta_A) = 0$$

$$\text{whenever } |\mathbf{r}_1| \geq \frac{b}{2} \text{ or } |\mathbf{r}_2| \geq \frac{b}{2} \text{ or } \cdots \text{ or } |\mathbf{r}_A| \geq \frac{b}{2} \tag{4.4}$$

We shall choose the comparison wave function Φ to describe a state in which the nucleons are moving independently of each other (even though this is certainly not true in nature). Mathematically this assumption takes the form

$$\Phi = \varphi_1(\mathbf{r}_1,\zeta_1)\,\varphi_2(\mathbf{r}_2,\zeta_2)\cdots\varphi_A(\mathbf{r}_A,\zeta_A) \tag{4.5}$$

where each factor in the product depends on the coordinates of one and only one nucleon. The φ_i will be chosen as eigenfunctions of a single free particle confined to move inside a sphere of radius $b/2$. Expression (4.5) is not an acceptable wave function in the sense of the Pauli principle. However, an acceptable wave function for identical particles can be constructed out of linear combinations of functions of type (4.5), provided that all the particles are put into different states (exclusion principle), i.e., no two functions φ can be equal to each other. Fortunately we shall *not* need to anti-symmetrize (4.5) for our purposes.[1]

In order to simplify the derivation, we shall use functions $\varphi(\mathbf{r},\zeta)$ of the form

$$\varphi(\mathbf{r},\zeta) = u(\mathbf{r})\,\chi(\zeta) \tag{4.6}$$

where $\chi(\zeta)$ defines the direction of the particle's spin: $\chi(\zeta)$ can be either $\alpha(\zeta)$ (for an up spin) or $\beta(\zeta)$ (for a down spin). The function $u(\mathbf{r})$ describes the motion of the particle inside the sphere. According to the Pauli principle, no more than four nucleons can occupy the same space state $u(\mathbf{r})$, and this only if no two of them are of equal spin or type. We shall therefore have to fill up at least $A/4$ different space states $u(\mathbf{r})$ to satisfy the Pauli principle. We shall label the different space states of a free particle inside a sphere of radius $b/2$ by the number m.

It will be assumed that the Hamiltonian has the form

$$H = T + V + C \tag{4.7}$$

where the kinetic energy operator T is

$$T = -\frac{\hbar^2}{2M}\sum_{i=1}^{A}\nabla_i^2 \tag{4.8}$$

[1] The terms introduced by the anti-symmetrization vanish in the collapsed state if the nuclear potentials have the square well shape.

the potential energy operator for the nuclear potential, V, is

$$V = \sum_{i<j=1}^{A} V_{ij} \qquad (4.9)$$

with V_{ij} in general of the form (3.18); and finally the Coulomb energy C is

$$C = \sum_{\text{proton pairs}} \frac{e^2}{r_{ij}} \qquad (4.10)$$

We first calculate the expectation value $\bar{T}_A$ of the kinetic energy T in the collapsed state Φ. Under assumptions (4.5) and (4.6) about Φ we find

$$\bar{T}_A = \sum_m s_m \, \epsilon_m \qquad (4.11)$$

where ϵ_m is the kinetic energy of a single particle in the mth space state $u_m(\mathbf{r})$, and s_m is the number of particles in this space state. According to the exclusion principle, s_m cannot be larger than 4. In order to get the lowest value of the kinetic energy for our comparison theorem, we shall assume that the nucleons occupy the lowest quantum states possible. We put $s_m=4$ for $m=1,2,\cdots,\tfrac{1}{4}A$ and $s_m=0$ from then on (we shall assume that A is divisible by 4). We then get

$$\bar{T}_A = 4 \sum_{m=1}^{A/4} \epsilon_m \qquad (4.12)$$

The sum in (4.12) can be approximated by an integral as follows: let $z(\epsilon)$ be the number of states $u_m(\mathbf{r})$ of a free particle of mass M inside a box of volume Ω, with energy $\epsilon_m \le \epsilon$. If there are very many particles inside the box, $z(\epsilon)$ is approximately independent of the shape of the box and can be replaced by a continuous and differentiable function [even though in actuality $z(\epsilon)$ increases by finite steps whenever ϵ sweeps over one of the eigenvalues ϵ_m and remains constant elsewhere]. Under these conditions the sum in (4.12) is approximated by

$$\sum_{m=1}^{A/4} \epsilon_m \cong \int_0^{\epsilon'} \epsilon \frac{dz}{d\epsilon} \, d\epsilon \qquad (4.13)$$

where the upper limit ϵ' of the integral is defined by

$$z(\epsilon') = \frac{A}{4} \qquad (4.14)$$

The function $z(\epsilon)$ is given by (Courant 31, p. 377):

$$z(\epsilon) = \frac{2^{1/2}}{3\pi^2} \Omega \left(\frac{M\epsilon}{\hbar^2}\right)^{3/2} \qquad (4.14a)$$

The integral (4.13) then gives for a spherical box with radius R the value

$$\frac{9\pi}{160} \left(\frac{3}{\pi}\right)^{1/3} \frac{\hbar^2}{MR^2} A^{5/3} \qquad (4.15)$$

Substitution of (4.15) into (4.12) provides us with the estimate of the kinetic energy of a nucleus of radius R:

$$\bar{T}_A = 0.695 \frac{\hbar^2}{MR^2} A^{5/3} \qquad (4.16)$$

For the collapsed state $(R = \tfrac{1}{2}b)$ we get

$$\bar{T}_A = 2.78 \frac{\hbar^2}{Mb^2} A^{5/3} \qquad (4.17)$$

The $A^{5/3}$ dependence of the kinetic energy on the mass number is a consequence of the Pauli exclusion principle. If the particles were not subject to the exclusion principle, we could put all of them into the lowest state, φ_1, of our box. $\bar{T}_A$ would then be equal to $\epsilon_1 A$, i.e., proportional to A rather than to $A^{5/3}$.

The $A^{5/3}$ law holds in the collapsed state but not in the actual state of nuclei. For the normal density state the kinetic energy is given by (4.16). Since the nuclear radius in the normal density state is proportional to $A^{1/3}$, the kinetic energy in this state is proportional to A, not to $A^{5/3}$. This completes the proof of Section 3 that the binding energy in the normal density state is proportional to the mass number.

Returning now to the comparison theorem, we proceed to estimate the Coulomb energy $\bar{C}_A$ in the collapsed state Φ. Under our assumptions about Φ the nucleons are distributed uniformly over a sphere of radius $b/2$. The electrostatic energy is then given by[1]

$$\bar{C}_A = \frac{6}{5} Z(Z-1) \frac{e^2}{b} \qquad (4.18)$$

We introduce $\hbar^2/Mb^2$ as the unit of energy, since this is of the order of the kinetic energy of a single particle confined to a box of dimensions

---

[1] The result (4.18) is, strictly speaking, correct only for the term of order Z^2. The correct, anti-symmetrized wave function gives additional contributions of order Z which are not included in (4.18) (the "Coulomb exchange energy," see Feenberg 46). These terms are unimportant for our present purposes.

b. Using

$$D \equiv \frac{\hbar^2}{Me^2} = 2.88 \times 10^{-12} \text{ cm,}$$

we get

$$\bar{C}_A = \frac{6}{5} \frac{b}{D} Z(Z-1) \frac{\hbar^2}{Mb^2} \tag{4.19}$$

The coefficient $\frac{6}{5}(b/D)$ is of the order of 0.1 for reasonable nuclear ranges b. Hence the leading term of $\bar{C}_A$ is quite small. In fact it is always much smaller than the potential energy. *We can therefore neglect the Coulomb energy as far as the saturation arguments are concerned.*

The expectation value for the potential energy must be calculated now. In order to emphasize the salient points in this consideration we simplify the calculation by assuming square well potentials in (3.18). We first consider Wigner forces and assume, therefore,

$$\begin{aligned} V_{ij} &= V_W \quad &\text{(for } r_{ij} \leq b) \\ &= 0 \quad &\text{(for } r_{ij} > b) \end{aligned} \tag{4.20}$$

In this case the expectation value $\bar{V}_A$ of (4.9) in the collapsed state Φ is very simple: every distance r_{ij} is necessarily smaller than b, hence every pair contributes an amount V_W to the potential energy:

$$\bar{V}_A = \tfrac{1}{2}A(A-1)\, V_W \tag{4.21}$$

According to our discussion in Chapter II (II, 2.9), V_W must be negative (attractive) and at least as large as

$$\left| V_W \right| \geq \left(\frac{\pi}{2}\right)^2 \frac{\hbar^2}{Mb^2} \tag{4.22}$$

We get the total energy $\bar{H}_A$ of the collapsed state by adding (4.21) to (4.17), neglecting (4.18). Using the estimate (4.22), we obtain

$$\bar{H}_A \leq (2.78A^{5/3} - 1.23A^2 + 1.23A) \frac{\hbar^2}{Mb^2} \tag{4.23}$$

The dependence of $\bar{H}_A$ on A is indicated in Fig. 4.1. For small A, $\bar{H}_A$ is nearly equal to $\bar{T}_A$ and positive. However, beyond a certain value of A the A^2 in the potential energy becomes dominant over the $A^{5/3}$ in the kinetic energy; thereafter $\bar{H}_A$ becomes negative and decreases very rapidly. It becomes lower than the experimental ground state energy $E_A(\exp)$ which is proportional to the first power of A only, and which is also shown in Fig. 4.1. We see that $\bar{H}_A$ becomes

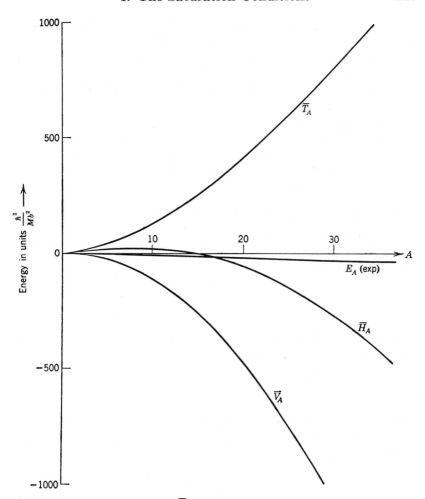

FIG. 4.1. The expectation value $\overline{V}_A$ of the potential energy in the collapsed state Φ is negative and proportional to A^2. The expectation value $\overline{T}_A$ of the kinetic energy is positive and proportional to $A^{5/3}$. Hence the expectation value of the total energy, $\overline{H}_A$, becomes negative for large mass numbers A, eventually becoming proportional to A^2. Very soon after $\overline{H}_A$ becomes negative, it falls below the experimental nuclear ground state energies $E_A(\text{exp})$. This is a contradiction which can be used to exclude the Hamiltonian H as a possibility. Figure 4.1 corresponds to attractive forces between all pairs of nucleons. The contradiction occurs even for quite low mass numbers $(A \geq 17)$ well within the range of known nuclei.

lower than $E_A(\exp)$ for values of A greater than 17. According to formulas (4.1) to (4.3) this constitutes a contradiction. *Purely attractive Wigner forces are excluded by the requirement of saturation of nuclear binding energies.*

It should be noted that the same calculation can also be made with a nuclear potential $V_W(r)$ which does not have the square well shape. The coefficient V_W in (4.21) is then replaced by an appropriate average of $V_W(r)$ in the collapsed state, and this average satisfies the inequality (4.22). Hence the essential points of the argument remain as before. The term of order A in the potential energy is changed, but this term is unimportant in our argument.

B. Saturation Conditions for Mixed Wigner and Majorana Forces

We now consider a potential in which both Wigner and Majorana forces are present, but which contains no Heisenberg or Bartlett forces. We assume instead of (4.20)[1]

$$V_{ij} = V_W + V_M P^M_{ij} \qquad \text{(for } r_{ij} < b)$$
$$= 0 \qquad \text{(for } r_{ij} > b) \qquad (4.24)$$

Here P^M_{ij} is the Majorana operator for the pair i, j as defined in Table 3.1. The kinetic energy in the collapsed state will be as before. The potential energy can be written in the form

$$\bar{V}_A = +\tfrac{1}{2}A(A-1)\, V_W + (n_+ - n_-)\, V_M \qquad (4.25)$$

where $n_+ - n_-$ is the difference between the number of symmetric and the number of anti-symmetric pairs in the collapsed state and is given by

$$n_+ - n_- = \sum_{i<j=1}^{A} \int \Phi^* P^M_{ij}\, \Phi\, d\tau \qquad (4.26)$$

This expression can be evaluated as follows:[2] When the exchange operator P^M_{ij} operates upon a pair i,j in the same space state m, the wave function remains unchanged; hence each such pair contributes $+1$ to (4.26). If the pair i,j consists of two identical particles (same spin and same type), the wave function must change its sign (Pauli principle) and these pairs contribute -1 each to (4.26). All other exchange operations are exchanges of two unequal particles in two

---

[1] The assumption of equal ranges for the two forces is not essential to the argument. If the ranges are different, the radius of the collapsed state is taken as half of the shorter of the two ranges.

[2] This argument is taken from the book by Gamow and Critchfield (Gamow 49)

different space states m and m'. Such exchanges create states which violate the Pauli principle (see Fig. 4.2). Hence the wave function $P^M{}_{ij}\Phi$ has essentially different symmetry properties from the wave function Φ and is therefore orthogonal to it. The integral in (4.26) vanishes for these pairs, and they contribute nothing.

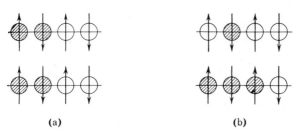

(a)   (b)

Fig. 4.2. Part (a) indicates a permissible occupation scheme for two levels; neutrons are indicated by shaded circles, protons by open circles, the spin directions are indicated by arrows. The state shown in part (b) violates the Pauli principle since there are two identical particles in each level (two up-spin protons in the upper level, two up-spin neutrons in the lower level). State (b) is obtained from state (a) by an exchange of the up-spin neutron in the top level with the up-spin proton in the bottom level. Since wave functions with different symmetry properties are orthogonal, state (b) is orthogonal to all states which are consistent with the Pauli principle.

There are six pairs of particles for each space state m, and $A/4$ different space states; there are four kinds of identical particles in the nucleus, and each kind contributes $\frac{1}{2}(\frac{1}{4}A)(\frac{1}{4}A-1)$ pairs. Hence

$$n_+ - n_- = 6\left(\frac{A}{4}\right) - 4\left(\frac{1}{2}\right)\left(\frac{A}{4}\right)\left(\frac{A}{4}-1\right) = -\frac{A^2}{8} + 2A \quad (4.27)$$

For heavy nuclei we can neglect the terms proportional to A; then (4.27) together with $n_+ + n_- = \frac{1}{2}A(A-1)$ gives

$$n_+ \cong \frac{3}{8}\left(\frac{A^2}{2}\right) \qquad n_- \cong \frac{5}{8}\left(\frac{A^2}{2}\right) \quad \text{provided } A \gg 1 \quad (4.28)$$

This provides the basis for our earlier statement (in Section 3) that there are more anti-symmetric pairs than symmetric pairs, in the ratio 5:3. We emphasize once more that this preponderance of anti-symmetric pairs (which is essential for saturation) is a consequence of the Pauli exclusion principle. If the exclusion principle did not apply, we could put all the nucleons into the lowest space state. Then all pairs would be symmetric, and we would not find any difference between Wigner and Majorana forces in the collapsed state.

Substitution of (4.27) into (4.25) gives the potential energy in the collapsed state:

$$\bar{V}_A = +\frac{A^2}{8}(4V_W - V_M) - \frac{A}{2}(V_W - 4V_M) \qquad (4.29)$$

Since the ground state of the deuteron is a symmetric (S) state, the potential in this state is $V_W(r) + V_M(r)$. Thus the sum $V_W + V_M$ must be negative and must satisfy the inequality (II,2.9)

$$|V_W + V_M| \geq \left(\frac{\pi}{2}\right)^2 \frac{\hbar^2}{Mb^2} \qquad (4.30)$$

Let us introduce the ratio

$$\rho = \frac{V_M}{V_W + V_M} \qquad (4.31)$$

which measures the relative contribution of the Majorana force in the ground state of the deuteron. Then (4.29) becomes

$$\bar{V}_A = +\frac{A^2}{8}(V_W + V_M)(4 - 5\rho) - \frac{A}{2}(V_W + V_M)(1 - 5\rho) \qquad (4.32)$$

We get the total energy $\bar{H}_A$ in the collapsed state by adding (4.32) to (4.17). The inequality (4.30) then gives

$$\bar{H}_A \leq \left[2.78A^{5/3} - \frac{\pi^2}{8}A^2\left(1 - \frac{5}{4}\rho\right) + \frac{\pi^2}{8}A(1 - 5\rho)\right]\frac{\hbar^2}{Mb^2} \qquad (4.33)$$

Expression (4.33) reduces to (4.23) for pure Wigner forces, $\rho = 0$. As long as the coefficient of A^2 in (4.33) is negative, this term eventually (for large enough A) overcompensates the kinetic energy term. $\bar{H}_A$ then becomes negative and lower than the value $E_A(\exp)$ (which is proportional to A only). Saturation of binding energies for all values of the mass number A therefore requires that the coefficient of A^2 in (4.33) be positive, i.e.,

$$\rho > \tfrac{4}{5} \qquad \text{or} \qquad V_M \leq 4V_W \qquad (4.34)$$

The Majorana force must contribute at least four-fifths of the attraction in the ground state of the deuteron. A Wigner force, if present, cannot contribute more than one-fifth of the attraction.

We could argue that the condition (4.34) is too stringent, since it assumes that the binding energy must not increase with mass number more strongly than proportional to A, for *all* values of A. Actually, there is no contradiction with experiment unless the value of A at which the potential energy term overcompensates the kinetic energy term is within the range of known nuclei, i.e., is smaller than about 250. Hypothetical nuclei with $A > 250$ may not be stable against collapse, but they have not yet been found nor could they be produced artificially because of the strong Coulomb repulsion between the parts with $A < 250$ which must be brought into contact. We can define "conditional saturation" as that property of a nuclear potential (Feenberg 46a) by which $E_A(H)$ is proportional to A for the observed mass numbers ($A < 250$) but becomes proportional to A^2 for (very much) higher mass numbers.

It is not easy to estimate when conditional saturation occurs. The condition

$$\bar{H}_A > E_A(\exp) \tag{4.35}$$

cannot be used since it is necessary but not sufficient. In view of the experimental results on high-energy scattering discussed in the next chapter, a more thorough-going investigation of conditional saturation is highly desirable. No such investigation has been made as yet.

In view of the fact that the condition $\bar{H}_A > E_A(\exp)$ is necessary but not sufficient, we may wonder whether the choice of a different comparison function would not lead to more stringent conditions upon the potential. Wigner (36) was able to prove, however, that the term proportional to A^2 in the exact $E_A(H)$ has the same *sign* as the corresponding term in (4.33) for a wide choice of well shapes. Thus, to the extent that we base our argument only on the *sign* of this term, neglecting its magnitude (and hence neglecting the possibility of conditional saturation), the necessary condition (4.34) is also a sufficient one.

▶ **C. The Complete Saturation Conditions for Central Forces**

So far we have considered mixtures of Wigner and Majorana forces only, since these are the most important from the practical point of view. The saturation condition (4.34) can be generalized for a potential V_{ij} between two nucleons which contains not only Wigner and Majorana forces but also the other two types of (central) exchange forces, the Heisenberg and Bartlett types. We shall not go through the proof here since it is closely analogous to the reasoning used already.[1] The comparison function Φ used so far leads to the condition

$$4V_W + 2V_B - 2V_H - V_M \geq 0 \tag{4.36}$$

[1] The reader is referred to the original papers: Feenberg (37a), Kemmer (37), and in particular the work of Breit and Wigner (Breit 38).

which reduces to (4.34) in the absence of Bartlett and Heisenberg forces. We can use other comparison wave functions which also correspond to collapsed states but with more restrictions on the spins and types of the nucleons (e.g., all the nucleons may be required to have spins pointing up). In this way we get four additional, linearly independent, saturation conditions:

$$2V_W + 2V_B - V_H - V_M \geq 0 \qquad (4.37)$$

$$2V_W + V_B + 2V_H - V_M \geq 0 \qquad (4.38)$$

$$2V_W + V_B - V_H - V_M \geq 0 \qquad (4.39)$$

$$V_W + V_B - V_H - V_M \geq 0 \qquad (4.40)$$

Breit and Wigner have proved that the five conditions (4.36) to (4.40) form a complete set of necessary conditions. Any other choice of the spins and types of nucleons in the collapsed (comparison) state leads to a condition already implied by conditions (4.36) to (4.40). Furthermore the sufficiency proof of Wigner (36) shows that these conditions are also sufficient for absolute (as distinguished from conditional) saturation.

Although these saturation arguments are rigorous from a strictly mathematical point of view, this should not be taken to imply that they are really unassailable. We have used the form (3.18) for the potential of the nuclear forces throughout the discussion. Wigner has emphasized that it is entirely conceivable that a potential of this type may be adequate to describe the normal density state of a nucleus but inadequate for the collapsed state. For example, velocity-dependent or many-body forces, or both, may be extremely important in the collapsed state and yet be unimportant in the normal density state. In that case an argument which depends on the assumption that the nuclear forces in the collapsed state are the same as in the normal density state gives incorrect conclusions, even though it is mathematically perfect.

▶ D. Saturation Conditions for Tensor Forces

The spherically symmetric comparison functions used so far do not lead to any conditions upon the tensor force part of the exchange potential (3.18), since the average value of the tensor operator S_{12} is zero for a sphere. In order to get conditions upon the tensor forces, comparison functions of lower symmetry (in practice, ellipsoids) are necessary.

The fact that the average of the tensor operator is zero over a sphere has the consequence that there is always a possible shape for the collapsed state in which the tensor force is on the average attractive, no matter whether the coefficient of S_{12} is positive or negative. In one case the oblate (doorknob) shape gives rise to an attractive tensor contribution to the energy; in the other case the prolate (football) ellipsoid is favored. Thus *tensor forces by themselves never lead to saturation*. In order to get saturation, the central forces must satisfy the saturation conditions, and *the tensor forces must be less strong than the central forces* (Volkoff 42, 42a).

Since the discussion of conditional saturation with tensor forces is quite involved,[1] we shall confine ourselves to the conditions for absolute saturation. We shall therefore investigate the expectation value of the potential energy $\bar{V}_A$ only, and we shall require that the term in $\bar{V}_A$ proportional to A^2 have a positive coefficient. This must be true for collapsed states of all (ellipsoidal) shapes. We put two particles[2] into each space state. For the sake of simplicity we shall assume that they are a neutron and a proton, both with spins pointing up. In that case, the operator S_{12} can be replaced by $(3 \cos^2 \omega - 1)$, where ω is the angle between the line joining the two particles and the (common) direction of their spins. Let $\bar{S}$ be the average value of this expression in the collapsed state. $\bar{S}$ is zero for a sphere, and it has its extreme values $+2$ for a needle-shaped ellipsoid, -1 for a disk-shaped ellipsoid.

In the collapsed state all pairs of nucleons interact. The contribution of the tensor terms in (3.18) to the potential energy is then

$$\bar{V}_{A,\text{tensor}} = (n_+ + n_-) \, V_{TW} \, \bar{S} + (n_+ - n_-) \, V_{TM} \, \bar{S} \qquad (4.41)$$

The quantity $n_+ - n_-$, i.e., the difference between the number of symmetric and anti-symmetric pairs, is no longer given by (4.27) since there are now only two particles in each space state. By the same counting method which yielded (4.27) we get for our case

$$n_+ - n_- = 1\frac{A}{2} - 2\frac{1}{2}\frac{A}{2}\left(\frac{A}{2} - 1\right) = -\frac{A^2}{4} + A \qquad (4.42)$$

---

[1] A start in that direction has been made by Volkoff, who computed $\bar{H}_A$ for ellipsoids of various sizes and eccentricities with two different assumptions about the strengths of central and tensor forces, both, however, having Wigner exchange character. In that case disagreement with experiment is found within the region of known nuclei.

[2] Filling each space state completely, with four nucleons, gives zero for the average of the tensor operator even if the shape of the nucleus is not spherical.

III. Nuclear Forces

Keeping the terms of order A^2 in (4.41), we obtain

$$\bar{V}_{A,\text{tensor}} = \frac{A^2}{4} (2V_{TW} - V_{TM}) \bar{S} + \text{terms of order } A \quad (4.43)$$

Equation (4.43) shows that the tensor forces by themselves never lead to saturation. $\bar{S}$ is positive for a needle-shaped ellipsoid, negative for a disk-shaped ellipsoid. Hence, no matter whether $2V_{TW} - V_{TM}$ is positive or negative, we can find a collapsed state in which the coefficient of A^2 in (4.43) is negative, contradicting absolute saturation.

In order to get saturation we must therefore assume that central forces are present also. Since $\bar{S} = 0$ for a spherical collapsed state, the central forces must obey the saturation conditions which were already derived, quite apart from the tensor forces. In order to simplify the discussion we shall again assume that the central forces consist of a mixture of Wigner and Majorana forces only. Then the contribution of the central forces to the potential energy of the collapsed state under consideration is

$$\bar{V}_{A,\text{central}} = (n_+ + n_-) V_W + (n_+ - n_-) V_M$$

$$= \frac{A^2}{4} (2V_W - V_M) + \text{terms of order } A \quad (4.44)$$

We now impose the condition that the sum of (4.43) and (4.44) must have a positive coefficient of A^2 for all possible values of $\bar{S}$: the largest possible value of $\bar{S}$ is $+2$ (for the needle), the smallest value is $\bar{S} = -1$ (for the disk). We therefore get *two* saturation conditions for the tensor forces:

$$2 (2V_{TW} - V_{TM}) + (2V_W - V_M) \geq 0 \quad (4.45)$$

$$-(2V_{TW} - V_{TM}) + (2V_W - V_M) \geq 0 \quad (4.46)$$

The combination of the central force parameters which enters here can be rewritten

$$2V_W - V_M = (V_W + V_M) (2 - 3\rho) \quad (4.47)$$

where the first factor has to be negative to give binding in the deuteron, and the second factor has to be negative to satisfy the saturation condition (4.34). Thus (4.47) is positive. We can combine (4.45) and (4.46) in the form

$$-\tfrac{1}{2}(2V_W - V_M) \leq 2V_{TW} - V_{TM} \leq 2V_W - V_M \quad (4.48)$$

This saturation condition has the expected form: the tensor force is limited in both directions. If positive, it must not be larger than the central forces; if negative, it must not be too negative.

We shall not write down the complete saturation conditions for the tensor forces [analogous to (4.36) to (4.40)] at this point, since they are rather involved and the essential results are already contained in (4.48). The conditions assume a simpler form in terms of the isotopic spin formalism and will be given explicitly in the next section.

Although there has not been any discussion of conditional saturation with exchange tensor forces in the literature, rough estimates seem to show that the condition (4.48) is probably considerably too stringent. As long as the central forces are saturated, it would take quite strong tensor forces to give contradiction with binding energies of observed nuclei. We emphasize once more, however, that tensor forces do not bring about saturation unless the central forces are already saturated. The tensor forces can only make saturation worse, not better.

▶   ## 5. THE ISOTOPIC SPIN FORMALISM

It is sometimes convenient to treat the neutron and proton not as two essentially different particles, but as two different states of one "particle," called the nucleon. There is some physical justification for this point of view in beta-decay, where a nucleon does change from a proton state to a neutron state (with emission of a positron and neutrino) and vice versa. This idea leads to a formalism which is used frequently in the literature: the isotopic spin formalism (Cassen 36). Although it will be used only rarely in this book, a short introduction to this method is presented in this section.

As long as we treat the neutron and proton as different particles, the wave function of a nucleus has the form

$$\phi = \phi(\mathbf{r}_1, \zeta_1, \mathbf{r}_2, \zeta_2, \cdots, \mathbf{r}_N, \zeta_N; \mathbf{r}_{N+1}, \zeta_{N+1}, \cdots, \mathbf{r}_A, \zeta_A) \qquad (5.1)$$

where $\mathbf{r}_1$ denotes the position of the first neutron, ζ_1 its spin direction ($\zeta = \pm 1$), the first N coordinates refer to neutrons, and the remaining ones refer to protons. The Pauli principle requires that the wave function change sign if any two neutrons are interchanged, or if any two protons are interchanged. There is no special requirement upon the behavior of ϕ under an interchange of a neutron and a proton.

We now introduce another coordinate η, which we shall call the "isotopic spin coordinate," and which can take only two values: $+1$ and -1. $\eta = +1$ means that the particle is a neutron, $\eta = -1$ means that the particle is a proton. (The sign is chosen in such a way that there is an excess of positive values of η in a heavy nucleus where there are more neutrons than protons.)

The wave function (5.1) could now be written in the form

$$\psi = \psi(\mathbf{r}_1,\zeta_1,\eta_1, \ \mathbf{r}_2,\zeta_2,\eta_2, \ \cdots, \ \mathbf{r}_A,\zeta_A,\eta_A) \qquad (5.2)$$

where ψ vanishes unless $\eta_1 = \eta_2 = \cdots = \eta_N = +1$ and $\eta_{N+1} = \cdots = \eta_A = -1$. We shall *not* do it this simply, however; rather we shall insist that all nucleons are identical particles which must obey the Pauli exclusion principle, and that the wave function (5.2) must therefore change its sign when *all* the coordinates (position, mechanical spin, and isotopic spin coordinates) of any two particles are interchanged. Our simple choice above satisfies this condition for interchanges within the first N coordinates, or within the last A-N coordinates, but it does not satisfy this condition for an interchange of $\mathbf{r}_1,\zeta_1,\eta_1$ with $\mathbf{r}_A,\zeta_A,\eta_A$, for example.

It might be thought that this requirement that the wave function must be anti-symmetric under the full interchange of any two particles imposes some additional conditions on the possible wave functions. We shall now show that this is not true: the requirement is merely a formal one; *any wave function which satisfies the exclusion principle if neutrons and protons are treated as different particles can be made into a properly anti-symmetric function in the isotopic spin language.* To avoid complications we shall do this explicitly for the case of only two particles.

If the two particles are both neutrons, the conventional wave function must be anti-symmetric under the exchange of their space and mechanical spin coordinates:

$$\phi(\mathbf{r}_1,\zeta_1;\mathbf{r}_2,\zeta_2) = -\phi(\mathbf{r}_2,\zeta_2;\mathbf{r}_1,\zeta_1) \qquad (5.3)$$

In order to write the corresponding wave function in the isotopic spin language, we introduce the isotopic spin function for a neutron, $\nu(\eta)$, which has the property

$$\begin{aligned} \nu(\eta) &= 1 \quad \text{if} \quad \eta = +1 \\ \nu(\eta) &= 0 \quad \text{if} \quad \eta = -1 \end{aligned} \qquad (5.4)$$

The wave function for two neutrons in the isotopic spin formalism is then given by

$$\psi(\mathbf{r}_1,\zeta_1,\eta_1; \mathbf{r}_2,\zeta_2,\eta_2) = \phi(\mathbf{r}_1,\zeta_1; \mathbf{r}_2,\zeta_2) \, \nu(\eta_1) \, \nu(\eta_2) \qquad (5.5)$$

This function is clearly anti-symmetric under the exchange of all the coordinates (position, mechanical spin, and isotopic spin) of the two particles, provided only that ϕ was anti-symmetric originally, as it had to be according to the Pauli principle.

The case of two protons is completely similar; we merely replace the isotopic spin function for a neutron, $\nu(\eta)$, by the isotopic spin function for a proton, $\pi(\eta)$, defined by

$$\pi(\eta) = 0 \quad \text{if} \quad \eta = +1$$
$$\pi(\eta) = 1 \quad \text{if} \quad \eta = -1 \tag{5.6}$$

In the case of a neutron-proton pair the conventional wave function $\phi(\mathbf{r}_1,\zeta_1; \mathbf{r}_2,\zeta_2)$ has no special properties under an interchange of the two particles. The most immediate choice of an isotopic spin analogue of this wave function would be

$$\psi_{\mathrm{I}} \equiv \phi(\mathbf{r}_1,\zeta_1; \mathbf{r}_2,\zeta_2)\, \nu(\eta_1)\, \pi(\eta_2) \tag{5.7}$$

However, this wave function is excluded by our requirement that the two nucleons are to be treated as identical particles: (5.7) implies that particle 1 is a neutron and particle 2 a proton, whereas we ought to be able to state merely that one of the two nucleons is in a neutron state, the other in a proton state. Indeed, we can form another wave function in which particle 2 is the neutron and particle 1 is the proton:

$$\psi_{\mathrm{II}} \equiv \phi(\mathbf{r}_2,\zeta_2; \mathbf{r}_1,\zeta_1)\, \nu(\eta_2)\, \pi(\eta_1) \tag{5.8}$$

The Pauli principle for two nucleons in the isotopic spin formalism requires that the isotopic spin wave function ψ which describes the same state of a neutron-proton pair as the conventional wave function, $\phi(\mathbf{r}_1,\zeta_1; \mathbf{r}_2,\zeta_2)$, be taken as the difference of (5.7) and (5.8), i.e.,

$$\psi(\mathbf{r}_1,\zeta_1,\eta_1; \mathbf{r}_2,\zeta_2,\eta_2) = 2^{-1/2}\, (\psi_{\mathrm{I}} - \psi_{\mathrm{II}}) \tag{5.9}$$

It is easily verified that this wave function is indeed anti-symmetric under the interchange of the two nucleons. Note that the wave function (5.9) does not allow us to say which of the two particles is the neutron, which the proton. All we can say is that one of the two nucleons is a neutron, the other (whichever it happens to be) is a proton.

This completes our proof that the requirement of anti-symmetry under the exchange of the coordinates of any two nucleons in the isotopic spin formalism is merely a formal requirement once the Pauli principle is assumed for neutrons and protons separately in the conventional way of writing wave functions: no matter whether we had a neutron-neutron pair, a proton-proton pair, or a neutron-proton pair, we were able to construct a properly anti-symmetric isotopic spin wave function ψ from the conventional wave function ϕ.

The general case can be treated as follows (Nordheim 37): We start with (5.1) and write the isotopic spin wave function

$$\psi_I \equiv \phi(\mathbf{r}_1,\zeta_1,\mathbf{r}_2,\zeta_2,\cdots,\mathbf{r}_N,\zeta_N; \mathbf{r}_{N+1},\zeta_{N+1},\cdots,\mathbf{r}_A,\zeta_A) \; \nu(\eta_1)\cdots\nu(\eta_N) \; \pi(\eta_{N+1})$$
$$\cdots\pi(\eta_A) \quad (5.10)$$

This function does not have the correct properties under an exchange of nucleon coordinates. There are many $(A!)$ functions of this type which differ from ψ_I merely by a relabeling of coordinates, i.e., by a permutation of the subscripts $1,2,\cdots,A$. The correct anti-symmetric isotopic spin wave function is then given by

$$\psi = \left[\frac{A!}{N!(A-N)!} \right]^{-1/2} \sum_P \delta_P \, P \, \psi_I \qquad (5.11)$$

where the sum is to be taken over all permutations P of the A subscripts (including the identity permutation, which does nothing to the subscripts); and δ_P is $+1$ for an even permutation, -1 for an odd permutation. It is easily verified that the two-particle wave functions discussed before are special cases of (5.11).

Although it is true that every conventional wave function can also be written in the isotopic spin notation, the converse does not hold. To take a simple example, consider the following wave function for a single nucleon:

$$\psi(\mathbf{r},\zeta,\eta) = \phi(\mathbf{r},\zeta) \, 2^{-1/2} \, [\nu(\eta) + \pi(\eta)]$$

This function corresponds to a nucleon in the ordinary state $\phi(\mathbf{r},\zeta)$, the nucleon, however, having equal probability of being a neutron or a proton at any one time. This state of affairs does not correspond to any conventional wave function for either a neutron or a proton. The isotopic spin formalism is therefore somewhat more general than the conventional method of writing wave functions. This generality, however, is not a help but merely a nuisance. We shall be interested only in those isotopic spin wave functions which do correspond to physical states of a system with a definite number of neutrons and protons.

It is of some interest to decompose the wave function (5.9) somewhat further, as follows:

$$\psi = \frac{1}{\sqrt{2}} (\psi_I - \psi_{II})$$
$$= \tfrac{1}{2} \left[\phi(\mathbf{r}_1,\zeta_1; \mathbf{r}_2,\zeta_2) + \phi(\mathbf{r}_2,\zeta_2; \mathbf{r}_1,\zeta_1) \right] X_0$$
$$+ \tfrac{1}{2} \left[\phi(\mathbf{r}_1,\zeta_1; \mathbf{r}_2,\zeta_2) - \phi(\mathbf{r}_2,\zeta_2; \mathbf{r}_1,\zeta_1) \right] X_{1,0} \qquad (5.12)$$

where the isotopic spin functions X are defined by

$$X_0 = \frac{1}{\sqrt{2}} \left[\nu(\eta_1)\, \pi(\eta_2) - \nu(\eta_2)\, \pi(\eta_1) \right] \tag{5.13}$$

and

$$X_{1,0} = \frac{1}{\sqrt{2}} \left[\nu(\eta_1)\, \pi(\eta_2) + \nu(\eta_2)\, \pi(\eta_1) \right] \tag{5.14}$$

The reason for the notation used for these two isotopic spin functions will become apparent later on.

X_0 is anti-symmetric under the exchange of the isotopic spin coordinates of the two particles; hence it occurs in (5.12) multiplied by a function of the space and mechanical spin variables which is symmetric under their interchange, making the product anti-symmetric. Correspondingly, $X_{1,0}$ occurs in (5.12) multiplied by an anti-symmetric function of the space and mechanical spin variables.

Equation (5.12) demonstrates clearly the equivalence of the old notation with the new one. In (5.12) ψ appears as a linear combination of two wave functions, one symmetric and the other anti-symmetric with respect to the exchange of the two nucleons, with the coefficients X_0 and $X_{1,0}$. Any arbitrary function $\phi(\mathbf{r}_1 \zeta_1; \mathbf{r}_2 \zeta_2)$ of a neutron-proton pair in the old notation can be represented in that form.

It is interesting to consider the two isotopic spin functions X_0 and $X_{1,0}$ defined in (5.13) and (5.14) together with the following ones which were used in connection with (5.5):

$$X_{1,1} = \nu(\eta_1)\, \nu(\eta_2) \tag{5.15}$$

$$X_{1,-1} = \pi(\eta_1)\, \pi(\eta_2) \tag{5.16}$$

X_0 is called "the isotopic spin singlet state"; the three functions $X_{1,1}$, $X_{1,0}$, $X_{1,-1}$ form the three substates of "the isotopic spin triplet state." These names are given on account of the analogy with the ordinary spin. The four possible combinations of the ordinary spin states of two particles are combined in the same way as in (5.13), (5.14), (5.15), and (5.16). The analogue of (5.13) represents a state with a total spin zero, whereas the analogues of the three other states represent the three substates of total spin 1. It must be emphasized that this analogy is purely formal. The isotopic spin is not an angular momentum, and all similarity existing between isotopic and ordinary spin variables is due to the fact that both can assume only two values, $+1$ and -1.

The main reason for introducing the isotopic spin method of describing nuclear states is the convenient way in which we can then describe the transformation of a neutron into a proton, and vice versa, and hence the exchange of a neutron and a proton. We introduce three operators which act on the isotopic spin variable η in the wave function. We shall define them by their effect on the neutron function $\nu(\eta)$ and the proton function $\pi(\eta)$; any isotopic spin function must be a linear combination of these two, hence the definitions are complete. The operator τ_+ transforms a proton into a neutron and gives zero when applied to a neutron:

$$\tau_+ \, \pi(\eta) \; = \; \nu(\eta) \qquad \tau_+ \, \nu(\eta) \; = \; 0 \tag{5.17}$$

The (Hermitean conjugate) operator τ_- transforms a neutron into a proton and gives zero when applied to a proton:

$$\tau_- \, \pi(\eta) \; = \; 0 \qquad \tau_- \, \nu(\eta) \; = \; \pi(\eta) \tag{5.18}$$

Finally, the operator τ_3 gives $+1$ when applied to a neutron, -1 when applied to a proton:

$$\tau_3 \, \nu(\eta) \; = \; +\nu(\eta) \qquad \tau_3 \, \pi(\eta) \; = \; -\pi(\eta) \tag{5.19}$$

These three operators bear a formal analogy to the Pauli spin matrices $\sigma_+ = \frac{1}{2}(\sigma_x + i\sigma_y)$, $\sigma_- = \frac{1}{2}(\sigma_x - i\sigma_y)$, and σ_z for the ordinary mechanical spin. The operators τ are therefore called isotopic spin operators. We emphasize again that this name is very misleading, since the isotopic "spin" has nothing whatsoever to do with rotations.

We now proceed to derive the expressions for the exchange operators P^M, P^B, P^H in terms of the mechanical and isotopic spin operators of the two nucleons. Let us start with the Bartlett exchange operator P^B. Two particles can be either in the singlet or the triplet (mechanical) spin state. The wave function for the singlet state is antisymmetric under the exchange of the two particles, hence the Barlett exchange operator gives -1; the three wave functions for the triplet states are symmetric under the interchange of the particles, hence the Bartlett operator gives $+1$. The singlet and triplet states are defined by

$$S^2 \, \psi \; = \; (\tfrac{1}{2}\mathfrak{d}_1 + \tfrac{1}{2}\mathfrak{d}_2)^2 \, \psi \; = \; s(s+1) \, \psi \tag{5.20}$$

where $s = 0$ in the singlet state, $s = 1$ in the triplet state. We therefore have the equality

$$P^B \; = \; S^2 - 1 \tag{5.21}$$

(the operators on the right and left sides of this equation give the same results for the two possible states of the system). We can evaluate the square of the operator

$$\mathbf{S} = \tfrac{1}{2}\mathbf{d}_1 + \tfrac{1}{2}\mathbf{d}_2$$

explicitly by using the fact that $(\mathbf{d}_1)^2 = (\mathbf{d}_2)^2 = 3$; this gives an alternative form for the Bartlett exchange operator:

$$P^B = \tfrac{1}{2}(1 + \mathbf{d}_1 \cdot \mathbf{d}_2) \qquad (5.22)$$

We proceed to the other two exchange operators. We define the "scalar product of the isotopic spins of two particles" by

$$\boldsymbol{\tau}_1 \cdot \boldsymbol{\tau}_2 \equiv 2\,[\tau_{+,1}\,\tau_{-,2} + \tau_{-,1}\,\tau_{+,2}] + \tau_{3,1}\,\tau_{3,2} \qquad (5.23)$$

in analogy to $\mathbf{d}_1 \cdot \mathbf{d}_2$ for the mechanical spin. Direct substitution of (5.23) [using definitions (5.17) to (5.19)] into (5.13), (5.14), (5.15), and (5.16) gives

$$(\boldsymbol{\tau}_1 \cdot \boldsymbol{\tau}_2)\, X_0 = -3\,X_0 \qquad (\boldsymbol{\tau}_1 \cdot \boldsymbol{\tau}_2)\, X_{1,0} = X_{1,0}$$
$$(\boldsymbol{\tau}_1 \cdot \boldsymbol{\tau}_2)\, X_{1,1} = X_{1,1} \qquad (\boldsymbol{\tau}_1 \cdot \boldsymbol{\tau}_2)\, X_{1,-1} = X_{1,-1} \qquad (5.24)$$

Thus the operator $\boldsymbol{\tau}_1 \cdot \boldsymbol{\tau}_2$ gives $+1$ when applied to isotopic spin triplet states, -3 when applied to isotopic spin singlet states (in complete analogy to $\mathbf{d}_1 \cdot \mathbf{d}_2$).

We can use $\boldsymbol{\tau}_1 \cdot \boldsymbol{\tau}_2$ to define an isotopic spin operator P^τ analogous to P^B:

$$P^\tau \equiv \tfrac{1}{2}(1 + \boldsymbol{\tau}_1 \cdot \boldsymbol{\tau}_2) \qquad (5.25)$$

This operator gives $+1$ when applied to the (symmetric) isotopic spin triplet states, -1 when applied to the (anti-symmetric) isotopic spin singlet states, and is therefore equivalent to a simple exchange of the isotopic spin coordinates η_1, η_2 of the two particles:

$$P^\tau\,\psi(\mathbf{r}_1,\zeta_1,\eta_1;\mathbf{r}_2,\zeta_2,\eta_2) = \psi(\mathbf{r}_1,\zeta_1,\eta_2;\mathbf{r}_2,\zeta_2,\eta_1) \qquad (5.26)$$

We have required complete anti-symmetry under the full exchange of all the coordinates (space, mechanical spin, and isotopic spin) of the two particles. Since the Heisenberg exchange operator exchanges position and mechanical spin and P^τ exchanges the isotopic spin coordinates, we can express this requirement in the form

$$P^H P^\tau\,\psi = -\psi \qquad \text{(for all permissible } \psi) \qquad (5.27)$$

This is a condition on ψ, not an operator identity: there exist wave functions ψ for which $P^H P^\tau$ is not equivalent to multiplication by -1; these wave functions are excluded by the Pauli principle, however.

We multiply (5.27) by P^τ on both sides. On the left side P^τ and P^H commute, and (5.26) shows that $(P^\tau)^2 = 1$; hence

$$P^H \psi = -P^\tau \psi \qquad \text{(for all permissible } \psi) \qquad (5.28)$$

Thus we can replace the Heisenberg exchange operator P^H by the isotopic spin operator $-P^\tau = -\frac{1}{2}(1 + \boldsymbol{\tau}_1 \cdot \boldsymbol{\tau}_2)$ in all applications as long as we restrict ourselves to isotopic spin wave functions which obey the Pauli principle.

Finally, the Majorana exchange operator is related to the two others through (3.15); multiplication on both sides by P^B gives

$$P^M = P^B P^H \qquad (5.29)$$

Thus we can replace the Majorana exchange operator by the combination

$$P^M \rightarrow -\frac{1}{4}(1 + \boldsymbol{d}_1 \cdot \boldsymbol{d}_2)(1 + \boldsymbol{\tau}_1 \cdot \boldsymbol{\tau}_2) \qquad (5.30)$$

Expressions (5.22), (5.28), and (5.30) are the expressions for the three linearly independent exchange operators P^B, P^H, P^M *in terms of the mechanical and isotopic spin operators.* From the point of view of the isotopic spin formalism it is more convenient to use three other linearly independent operators, i.e., $(\boldsymbol{d}_1 \cdot \boldsymbol{d}_2)$, $(\boldsymbol{\tau}_1 \cdot \boldsymbol{\tau}_2)$, and $(\boldsymbol{d}_1 \cdot \boldsymbol{d}_2)(\boldsymbol{\tau}_1 \cdot \boldsymbol{\tau}_2)$. We therefore write the most general potential of the exchange type, (3.18), in the form

$$V = V_d(r) + V_\sigma(r)(\boldsymbol{d}_1 \cdot \boldsymbol{d}_2) + V_\tau(r)(\boldsymbol{\tau}_1 \cdot \boldsymbol{\tau}_2) + V_{\sigma\tau}(r)(\boldsymbol{d}_1 \cdot \boldsymbol{d}_2)(\boldsymbol{\tau}_1 \cdot \boldsymbol{\tau}_2)$$
$$+ V_{Td}(r) S_{12} + V_{T\tau}(r) S_{12}(\boldsymbol{\tau}_1 \cdot \boldsymbol{\tau}_2) \qquad (5.31)$$

where

$$V_d = V_W + \tfrac{1}{2}V_B - \tfrac{1}{2}V_H - \tfrac{1}{4}V_M$$

$$V_\sigma = \tfrac{1}{2}V_B - \tfrac{1}{4}V_M$$

$$V_\tau = -\tfrac{1}{2}V_H - \tfrac{1}{4}V_M$$

$$V_{\sigma\tau} = -\tfrac{1}{4}V_M \qquad (5.32)$$

$$V_{Td} = V_{TW} - \tfrac{1}{2}V_{TM}$$

$$V_{T\tau} = -\tfrac{1}{2}V_{TM}$$

These relations follow by direct substitution; the subscript d denotes dependence on the distance only; the fact that V_d does not simply equal V_W has no special significance; indeed, if all the forces are of ordinary type (non-exchange), $V_W = V_d$.

It is useful to know the values of the spin and isotopic spin products in (5.31) for the various states of the two-particle systems. We therefore tabulate the values in Table 5.1; "triplet" and "singlet" in this table refer to the ordinary (mechanical) spin state.

TABLE 5.1

VALUES OF SPIN PRODUCTS IN STATES OF THE TWO-PARTICLE SYSTEM

Spin Product	State			
	Even Parity (Even l)		Odd Parity (Odd l)	
	Triplet	Singlet	Triplet	Singlet
$(\mathbf{d}_1 \cdot \mathbf{d}_2)$	1	-3	1	-3
$(\boldsymbol{\tau}_1 \cdot \boldsymbol{\tau}_2)$	-3	1	1	-3
$(\mathbf{d}_1 \cdot \mathbf{d}_2)(\boldsymbol{\tau}_1 \cdot \boldsymbol{\tau}_2)$	-3	-3	1	9

The line for $(\boldsymbol{\tau}_1 \cdot \boldsymbol{\tau}_2)$ is determined from the Pauli principle. For example, a triplet state with even l is symmetric under interchange of the space and spin coordinates of the two particles and must therefore be anti-symmetric under exchange of the isotopic spin coordinates η_1 and η_2. It must thus be a singlet isotopic spin state, with $(\boldsymbol{\tau}_1 \cdot \boldsymbol{\tau}_2) = -3$, and can occur only in the neutron-proton system, not for two protons or for two neutrons. The last line of the table is simply the product of the first two lines.

Rarita and Schwinger (Rarita 41a, b) have employed exchange forces of two types: the "symmetrical" theory,[1] in which the isotopic spin dependence of the potential is given by $(\boldsymbol{\tau}_1 \cdot \boldsymbol{\tau}_2)$, and the "charged" theory,[1] in which the isotopic spin dependence is given by $(\boldsymbol{\tau}_1 \cdot \boldsymbol{\tau}_2 - \tau_{3,1}\tau_{3,2})$. In the charged theory, there is no force between two protons or between two neutrons; the force acts only between a neutron and a proton. In terms of our notation, (5.31), these two exchange potentials are defined by

$$V_d(r) = V_\sigma(r) = V_{\tau d}(r) = 0 \qquad \text{(symmetrical theory)} \quad (5.33)$$

the other three functions $V(r)$ being arbitrary; and

$$V_d(r) = V_\tau(r) \qquad V_\sigma(r) = V_{\sigma\tau}(r)$$
$$V_{\tau d}(r) = V_{T\tau}(r) \qquad \text{(charged theory)} \quad (5.34)$$

We mention these particular choices of exchange dependence here because they have been used quite widely in the literature, in particular in connection with high-energy neutron-proton and proton-proton

---

[1] This terminology stems from the fact that the quoted isotopic spin dependence is the result of certain meson theories which introduce all three mesons (positive, negative, neutral) in a symmetric way or introduce only the charged ones.

scattering (see Chapter IV). Conditions (5.34) apply to the potential of interaction only between a neutron and a proton.

Perhaps the main advantage of the isotopic spin formalism is the simple way in which the saturation conditions can be formulated (Feenberg 37). The five saturation conditions, (4.36) to (4.40), assume the following form $[V_d \equiv$ value of $V_d(r)$ inside the range b, assumed constant, and similarly for the other potentials]:

$$V_d \geq 0 \qquad (4.36) = (5.35)$$

$$V_d + V_\sigma \geq 0 \qquad (4.37) = (5.36)$$

$$V_d + V_\tau \geq 0 \qquad (4.38) = (5.37)$$

$$V_d + V_{\sigma\tau} \geq 0 \qquad (4.39) = (5.38)$$

$$V_d + V_\sigma + V_\tau + V_{\sigma\tau} \geq 0 \qquad (4.40) = (5.39)$$

The (absolute) saturation conditions for the tensor forces take the form

$$-\tfrac{1}{2}\left(V_d + V_\tau\right) \leq \qquad V_{Td} \qquad \leq V_d + V_\sigma \qquad (5.40)$$

$$-\tfrac{1}{2}\left(V_d + V_{\sigma\tau}\right) \leq \qquad V_{T\tau} \qquad \leq V_d + V_{\sigma\tau} \qquad (5.41)$$

$$-\tfrac{1}{2}\left(V_d + V_\sigma + V_\tau + V_{\sigma\tau}\right) \leq V_{Td} + V_{T\tau} \leq V_d + V_\sigma + V_\tau + V_{\sigma\tau}$$
$$(5.42)$$

Condition (5.40) reduces to (4.48) in the absence of Bartlett and Heisenberg forces. Conditions (5.41) and (5.42) are two additional conditions on the tensor force which, however, are not very important from a practical point of view.

The isotopic spin formalism will not be used extensively in this book. It has been employed widely in the literature in order to describe the exchange character of nuclear forces. This section has shown that the isotopic spin formalism is completely equivalent to the description which uses Wigner, Majorana, Bartlett, and Heisenberg forces.

Some exchange potentials assume a simple form in one formalism; they are then not "simple" in the other formalism, and vice versa. The simplicity or compactness of a potential in either formalism cannot be used as a valid argument in favor of its choice.

SYMBOLS

b Range of the nuclear force; range of the square well approximation to $V_c(r)$ (Section 2)

B Binding energy of the nucleus   (Section 3B)

C Operator for the Coulomb energy of a nucleus with A nucleons   (4.7), (4.10)

$\bar{C}_A$ Expectation value of C in the collapsed state   (4.18)

d Distance at which the nuclear force becomes repulsive (Section 2)

d Distance between nearest neighbors in a nucleus (3.5)

d' Modified value of d to correct for dynamical correlations   (Section 3A)

D The Bohr radius of the proton $[= \hbar^2/Me^2 = 2.88 \times 10^{-12} \text{ cm}]$ (Section 4A)

$e(x)$ The unit step function   (2.6)

E Energy of the nucleus $[= \bar{T} + \bar{V}]$ (Section 2)

$E_A(\exp)$ Experimental ground state energy of a nucleus with mass number A (4.2)

$E_A(H)$ Ground state energy of an A-particle system with Hamiltonian H (4.1)

$f(r)$ Distance dependence of the exchange potential $V_x(r)$ (3.12)

$g_+(R)$ Relative probability of interaction for a symmetric pair in a nucleus of radius R $[= g_+(d/b)]$ (3.6)

$g_-(R)$ Relative probability of interaction for an anti-symmetric pair in a nucleus of radius R $[= g_-(d/b)]$ (3.6)

H Hamiltonian of the nucleus   (Section 4A)

$\bar{H}_A$ Expectation value of H in the comparison state Φ of the A-particle system $[=$ an upper bound for $E_A(H)]$ (4.1)

K Kernel for the integral operator of a velocity-dependent force $[= K(\mathbf{r}_1,\mathbf{r}_2; \mathbf{r}_1',\mathbf{r}_2')]$ (3.19)

l Orbital angular momentum quantum number in a two-particle system   (Section 3B)

m Running index for the different space wave functions $u(\mathbf{r})$ of a single particle in a spherical box   (Section 4A)

M Mass of a nucleon   (2.3)

n_+ Number of symmetric pairs   (Section 3A)

n_- Number of anti-symmetric pairs   (Section 3A)

p Probability of interaction between a pair of nucleons in a nucleus of radius R $[= p(b/R)]$ (2.5), (2.8)

p_+ Probability of interaction between a symmetric pair of nucleons   (Section 3A)

p_-	Probability of interaction between an anti-symmetric pair of nucleons (Section 3A)
P	A permutation of the subscripts $1,2,3,\cdots,A$ (5.11)
P	An exchange operator (Section 3B)
P^B	The Bartlett exchange operator (Table 3.1)
P^H	The Heisenberg exchange operator (Table 3.1)
P^M	The Majorana exchange operator (Table 3.1)
P^M_{ij}	The Majorana exchange operator for particles i and j (4.24)
P^r	Isotopic spin exchange operator (5.25), (5.26)
q	Coordinate of a nucleon, including the position and spin variables (3.1)
r	Distance between two nucleons (2.1)
r_1	Position vector of nucleon number 1 (3.12)
r_{12}	Distance between particles 1 and 2 (2.7)
R	Nuclear radius (Section 2)
R_0	Nuclear radius for which the potential energy $\bar{V}$ has its minimum value (Section 3A)
R_1	Nuclear radius for which the total energy E has its maximum value (Section 2)
s	Spin quantum number of a pair of nucleons (5.20)
s_m	Number of nucleons in the space state $u_m(\mathbf{r})$ (4.11)
$\bar{S}$	Average value of $3\cos^2\omega - 1$ [= expectation value of S_{12} if all spins are parallel] (4.41)
S^2	Absolute square of the spin of a pair of nucleons (5.20)
S_{12}	Tensor operator for particles 1 and 2 (2.1)
T	Operator for the kinetic energy (2.3)
$\bar{T}$	Expectation value of T (Section 2)
$\bar{T}_A$	Expectation value of T in the collapsed state of the nucleus with mass number A (4.11)
$u(\mathbf{r})$	Space wave function of a single nucleon in a spherical box (4.6)
V	Potential energy operator for two particles (2.1)
V	Potential energy operator for the nucleus as a whole (2.2)
$\bar{V}$	Expectation value of V (2.5)
V_0	Well depth of a square well approximation to $V_c(r)$ (Section 2)
$\bar{V}_A$	Expectation value of V in the collapsed state of a nucleus of mass number A (4.21)
$\bar{V}_{A,\,\text{central}}$	Contribution of the central forces to $\bar{V}_A$ (4.44)

$\bar{V}_{A,\text{tensor}}$	Contribution of the tensor forces to $\bar{V}_A$ (4.43)
V_B	Value of $V_B(r)$ inside the range b, in the square well approximation (4.36)
$V_B(r)$	Radial dependence of the Bartlett potential between two nucleons at separation r (3.18)
$V_c(r)$	Potential of the central force in the S state of two nucleons (2.1)
V_d	Value of $V_d(r)$ inside the range b, in the square well approximation (5.35)
$V_d(r)$	Spin- and isotopic spin-independent part of the two-nucleon potential (5.31)
V_H	Value of $V_H(r)$ inside the range b, in the square well approximation (4.36)
$V_H(r)$	Radial dependence of the Heisenberg potential between two nucleons at separation r (3.18)
$V_{ij}(r_{ij})$	Potential energy of two isolated nucleons i and j at separation r_{ij} (2.2)
V_M	Value of $V_M(r)$ inside the range b, in the square well approximation (4.24)
$V_M(r)$	Radial dependence of the Majorana potential between two nucleons at separation r (3.18)
$V_T(r)$	Radial dependence of the potential of the tensor force between two nucleons in the state with $J=1$ and even parity (2.1)
V_{Td}	Value of $V_{Td}(r)$ inside the range b, in the square well approximation (5.40)
$V_{Td}(r)$	Radial dependence of the isotopic spin-independent part of the tensor force potential between two nucleons (5.31)
V_{TM}	Value of $V_{TM}(r)$ inside the range b, in the square well approximation (4.41)
$V_{TM}(r)$	Radial dependence of the Majorana exchange part of the tensor force potential between two nucleons (3.18)
V_{TW}	Value of $V_{TW}(r)$ inside the range b, in the square well approximation (4.41)
$V_{TW}(r)$	Radial dependence of the non-exchange (Wigner) part of the tensor force potential between two nucleons (3.18)
$V_{T\tau}$	Value of $V_{T\tau}(r)$ inside the range b, in the square well approximation (5.41)

$V_{T\tau}(r)$ Radial dependence of the $(\boldsymbol{\tau}_1\cdot\boldsymbol{\tau}_2)S_{12}$ exchange tensor force part of the two-nucleon potential   (5.31)

V_W Value of $V_W(r)$ inside the range b, in the square well approximation   (4.20)

$V_W(r)$ Potential of the non-exchange (Wigner) force between two nucleons at separation r (3.18)

$V_x(r)$ Operator for the potential of an exchange force between two nucleons at separation r (3.12)

V_σ Value of $V_\sigma(r)$ inside the range b, in the square well approximation   (5.36)

$V_\sigma(r)$ Radial dependence of the $(\boldsymbol{\delta}_1\cdot\boldsymbol{\delta}_2)$ part of the two-nucleon potential   (5.31)

$V_{\sigma\tau}$ Value of $V_{\sigma\tau}(r)$ inside the range b, in the square well approximation   (5.38)

$V_{\sigma\tau}(r)$ Radial dependence of the $(\boldsymbol{\delta}_1\cdot\boldsymbol{\delta}_2)$ $(\boldsymbol{\tau}_1\cdot\boldsymbol{\tau}_2)$ part of the two-nucleon potential   (5.31)

V_τ Value of $V_\tau(r)$ inside the range b, in the square well approximation   (5.37)

$V_\tau(r)$ Radial dependence of the $(\boldsymbol{\tau}_1\cdot\boldsymbol{\tau}_2)$ part of the two-nucleon potential   (5.31)

X_0 Isotopic spin wave function for the singlet isotopic spin state of a neutron-proton pair   (5.13)

$X_{1,0}$ Isotopic spin wave function for the triplet isotopic spin state of a neutron-proton pair   (5.14)

$X_{1,1}$ Isotopic spin wave function for the (triplet) isotopic spin state of a neutron-neutron pair   (5.15)

$X_{1,-1}$ Isotopic spin wave function for the (triplet) isotopic spin state of a proton-proton pair   (5.16)

$z(\epsilon)$ Number of space states $u_m(\mathbf{r})$ with energy $\epsilon_m \leq \epsilon$ (4.14a)

$\alpha(\zeta)$ Spin wave function of a particle with spin pointing up (Section 4A)

$\beta(\zeta)$ Spin wave function of a particle with spin pointing down   (Section 4A)

δ_P The parity of the permutation P [$=+1$ for even permutations, $=-1$ for odd permutations]   (5.11)

$\delta(\mathbf{r}_1 - \mathbf{r}_1')$ Dirac delta function   (3.23)

ϵ' Highest energy ϵ_m occupied by nucleons [$=$ the Fermi energy]   (4.14)

ϵ_m Kinetic energy of a nucleon in the space state $u_m(\mathbf{r})$ (4.11)

ζ	Spin coordinate of a nucleon (Section 3B)
$\chi(\zeta)$	Spin wave function of a single nucleon (4.6)
η	Isotopic spin coordinate of a nucleon (Section 5)
$\bar{\lambda}$	Average de Broglie wavelength of the relative motion of two nucleons (3.4)
$\nu(\eta)$	Isotopic spin wave function of a neutron (5.4)
$\pi(\eta)$	Isotopic spin wave function of a proton (5.6)
ρ	Relative contribution of the Majorana force to the potential energy in the deuteron $[=V_M/(V_W+V_M)]$ (4.31)
$\boldsymbol{\sigma}$	Pauli spin vector with components σ_x, σ_y, and σ_z; see Appendix A, Section 4 (5.20)
σ_+	$=\frac{1}{2}(\sigma_x+i\sigma_y)$ (Section 5)
σ_-	$=\frac{1}{2}(\sigma_x-i\sigma_y)$ (Section 5)
τ_+	Isotopic spin operator transforming a proton into a neutron (5.17)
τ_-	Isotopic spin operator transforming a neutron into a proton (5.18)
τ_3	Isotopic spin operator $[=+1$ for a neutron, $=-1$ for a proton$]$ (5.19)
$\varphi(\mathbf{r},\zeta)$	Wave function of a single nucleon in a spherical box (4.5), (4.6)
$\varphi(\mathbf{r}_1,\mathbf{r}_2,\cdots,\mathbf{r}_A)$	Nuclear wave function (Section 2)
Φ	Comparison (collapsed state) wave function (Section 4A)
ψ	Wave function of a nucleus in the isotopic spin formalism (Section 5)
Ψ	Actual ground state wave function of an A-particle system with Hamiltonian H (Section 4A)
ω	Angle between the separation vector $\mathbf{r}_{12}$ of two particles and their common spin direction (Section 4D)
Ω	Volume of the box $[=\frac{4}{3}\pi R^3]$ (Section 4A)

CHAPTER IV

Two-Body Problems at High Energies

1. INTRODUCTION

The scattering of elementary nuclear particles at very high energies is an excellent tool for the detailed investigation of the forces between nucleons. The development of the high-energy accelerators has made it possible to extend the energy range of neutron-proton and proton-proton scattering to energies at which the de Broglie wavelength of the relative motion is considerably smaller than the range of nuclear forces. Hence, unlike the two-body problems at energies below about 10 Mev, the experiments at higher energies give results which are very sensitive to the details of the interaction, its dependence on the distance as well as its exchange properties.

In many respects the high-energy data available at present are strange and unexpected. They differ markedly from anything which could have been expected on the basis of an extrapolation of the low-energy experience. Especially two results must be emphasized in this connection:

(1) The high-energy evidence seems to indicate a force between a proton-proton pair *different* from the force between a proton-neutron pair. Hence the nuclear forces are probably *not charge independent* although the low-energy results strongly suggested charge-independent forces (see Chapter II). We recall that both the proton-proton scattering and the neutron-proton scattering results at low energies can be explained by assuming the same effective depth and range of the nuclear potential between like and unlike particles.

(2) The high-energy data apparently are *incompatible* with a nuclear force of an exchange character which is required to explain the *saturation properties* of nuclei (see Chapter III). The high-energy results do not indicate any repulsion between nucleons in anti-symmetric states; this repulsion was necessary for the explanation of the saturation on the basis of exchange forces.

On the whole, the theories developed on the basis of the low-energy data have failed badly when confronted with the new experiments at

* New Experimental material and recent more extensive theoretical study have cast considerable doubt on the validity of these statements. (Remark added in the second printing, 1954.)

168

high energy. This failure is an uncomfortable reminder that nuclear theory is still in a very early stage.

The high-energy data are considerably harder to interpret than the low-energy data because so many more parameters must be determined from the data. In low-energy neutron-proton scattering, for example, there are only two parameters (the phase shifts for the ^1S and ^3S states) to be determined by experiment. Furthermore the energy dependence of these two parameters can be predicted uniquely ($k \cot \delta$ = a linear function of the energy) by very general theoretical arguments. At higher energies, very many angular momentum states enter significantly into the scattering. At 100 Mev, for example, the S, P, D, and F states ($l=0,1,2,3$) presumably contribute appreciably to the scattering, and their phase shifts cannot be expected to show any simple energy variation. At high energies, when the de Broglie wavelength $\lambda = k^{-1}$ becomes smaller than the range of the forces, the details of the well shape have a strong influence on the energy dependence of the phase shifts. Finally, the presence of the tensor force (which has no appreciable effect in low-energy scattering) implies that there are four times as many independent parameters in the triplet spin state as there would be with central forces only.

On the experimental side, the interpretation of the data is complicated by the fact that the neutron beams used are not monoenergetic. They are obtained by "stripping" the neutron away from a fast-moving deuteron (Serber 47). The neutron energy spread in this process is of the order of 20 Mev at a mean energy of 100 Mev. The experimental cross section is therefore an average over a rather large energy region and may consequently fail to show rapid energy dependences, even if they exist.

The high-energy proton-proton scattering data are easier to interpret than the neutron-proton data for two reasons: (1) the Pauli exclusion principle cuts the number of phase shifts in half, and (2) the experimental cross sections were obtained with monoenergetic protons.

Because of the uncertainties in the interpretation of the present experiments, their precise implications are hard to determine. The usual procedure consists in substituting some definite assumptions about the nuclear forces (e.g., that they can be derived from a potential of a prescribed spin dependence and exchange character) and comparing the implications of this choice with the experimental data. If there is agreement within the experimental and theoretical errors, the assumed choice of the force law can be considered possible.

Because of uncertain relativistic corrections agreement to better than about 10 or 20 percent at energies in the 100 Mev region should not be expected. A potential $V(r)$ which depends on the distance r between the two nucleons is not a relativistically covariant quantity, since the distance r itself is not relativistically covariant. Furthermore the relativistic increase of mass with momentum gives rise to corrections of the order of 5 percent in the scattering at those energies. The correction for the mass increase is straightforward and consequently does not give rise to large uncertainties in the interpretation of the data. On the other hand, the dynamical corrections to be applied to the low-energy potential function $V(r)$ are quite uncertain (Breit 37a, 38a, Snyder 47, Siegel 51). Estimates on the basis of meson field theories (Snyder 47) indicate that the corrections can amount to 10 percent at 100 Mev, and to a factor of 2 at energies of several hundred Mev.

We shall concentrate our attention on the following kinds of exchange dependence for the assumed potential function between two nucleons:[1]

(1) Wigner force: $V = V(r)$ (1.1)

(2) Pure Majorana force: $V = P^M V(r)$ (1.2)

(3) Mixture of Wigner and Majorana force which obeys the saturation requirements:

$$V = (\alpha + \beta P^M) \, V(r) \qquad \left(\frac{\alpha}{\beta} < \frac{1}{4}\right) \qquad (1.3)$$

(4) Serber force: $V = \tfrac{1}{2} (1 + P^M) \, V(r)$ (1.4)

It is to be understood that $V(r)$ may be spin dependent: it can be different in the triplet and singlet spin states of the two particles. Furthermore there may be a tensor force present in the triplet state. We shall assume throughout that $V(r)$ is an attractive potential $[V(r) < 0]$ for all values of r. Although it has been suggested recently (Jastrow 50, 51) that $V(r)$ may become repulsive (positive) for small values of r, no detailed calculations with such potentials have yet been published. For the same reason we shall not consider the possibility of velocity-dependent forces (Wheeler 36, Case 50). To the

[1] Except for (1), which is often called the "neutral" theory, these are not the most widely used exchange forces. Very prevalent choices in the literature prior to 1950 were the "charged" and "symmetrical" exchange dependences introduced by Rarita and Schwinger (Rarita 41a,b). We shall not use the "charged" and "symmetrical" theories here, since neither of these exchange characters seems to fit the data and the discussion is much easier in terms of choices (1) to (4).

extent that these possibilities are neglected our discussion is necessarily incomplete, and the conclusions are subject to doubt.

Sections 2 and 3 contain a discussion of neutron-proton scattering, proceeding upwards in energy from the 12 to 15 Mev data to the 280 Mev measurements. Section 4 contains proton-proton scattering. The discussion will be based mostly on the work of Christian and collaborators at Berkeley (Christian 50, 50a). There is considerable additional theoretical literature on this subject (Camac 48, Chew 48, Eisenstein 48, Burhop 48, Massey 48, Wu 48, Ashkin 48, Rohrlich 49, Jean 50, and others) in which the methods of computation are discussed in more detail and results are given for particular assumptions about the nuclear forces.

The calculations for energies above 30 Mev are extremely tedious and complicated. There are no easy approximation methods below energies of the order of 300 Mev, where the Born approximation gives reasonably accurate results. In order to avoid needless complication, we shall give only very rough, qualitative arguments in Sections 3 and 4 and refer to the literature (especially Christian 50, 50a) for the results of the detailed calculations.

2. NEUTRON-PROTON SCATTERING AT ENERGIES BETWEEN 10 AND 30 MEV

Very little experimental material is available at the present time in the energy region between 10 and 30 Mev. We shall refer to this region as the "medium-energy range." Most of the measurements published so far have been made in the energy region between 12 and 13 Mev. The first relevant measurements were performed by Amaldi and collaborators (Amaldi 42). They showed a strong preference for scattering near the angle $\theta = \pi/2$ compared to scattering at $\theta = \pi$. Later measurements, however, have not confirmed this result (Powell 47; Laughlin 47, 48; Barschall 49). Within an accuracy of about 5 to 10 per cent the angular distribution is spherically symmetric in the center-of-gravity system at energies between 12 and 15 Mev. The total cross section was measured over a wider energy region (Salant 40, Sherr 45, Sleator 47), and its value is very close to $4\pi\lambda^2$ in the region between 10 and 24 Mev.

In order to get a qualitative insight into the theoretically expected behavior of the cross sections at energies above 10 Mev we shall employ the Born approximation in spite of the fact that this approximation is not sufficiently accurate for a quantitative determination of the cross sections. We consider first a central force of the ordinary type (1.1). The scattering amplitude as defined in (II,3.1) is given in the Born approximation by

$$f(\theta) = \int_0^\infty \frac{\sin (Kr)}{Kr} W(r) \, r^2 \, dr \tag{2.1}$$

where

$$W(r) = -\frac{2\mu}{\hbar^2} V(r) = -\frac{M}{\hbar^2} V(r) \tag{2.2}$$

and

$$K = |\mathbf{k}_{\text{final}} - \mathbf{k}_{\text{init}}| = 2k \sin (\tfrac{1}{2}\theta) \tag{2.3}$$

In the region where the scattering takes place $(r \lesssim b)$ the wave function is approximated by the incident wave $\exp (ikz)$. This is valid if the potential energy $V(r)$ is appreciably less than the kinetic energy in the center-of-gravity system, so that the incident wave is only slightly modified by the presence of the potential.

The form (2.1) is inapplicable to neutron-proton scattering except at extremely high energies (300 Mev or more). The largest error is made in the spherically symmetric (angle-independent) part of the scattering, i.e., the S wave scattering. We shall therefore write the scattering amplitude $f(\theta)$ in the form

$$f(\theta) = \bar{f} + g(\theta) \tag{2.4}$$

where $\bar{f}$ is the average of $f(\theta)$ over all directions:

$$\bar{f} = (4\pi)^{-1} \int f(\theta) \, d\omega \tag{2.5}$$

We shall use the exact expression (II,3.9) for $\bar{f}$ and use the Born approximation for $g(\theta)$. The Born approximation value of $g(\theta)$ can be determined from (2.1) as follows. We compute the average of the expression $\sin (Kr)/(Kr)$ over all directions:

$$(4\pi)^{-1} \int \frac{\sin (Kr)}{Kr} \, d\omega = \int_0^1 (kr)^{-1} \sin (2krx) \, dx = \left(\frac{\sin kr}{kr} \right)^2 \tag{2.6}$$

where we have put $x = \sin(\theta/2)$. We obtain the Born approximation for $g(\theta)$ by subtracting from the Born approximation $f(\theta)$, (2.1), its average over all directions, i.e.,

$$g(\theta) = \int_0^\infty \left\{ \frac{\sin (Kr)}{Kr} - \left[\frac{\sin (kr)}{kr} \right]^2 \right\} W(r) \, r^2 \, dr \tag{2.7}$$

The differential scattering cross section $d\sigma$ into the solid angle element $d\omega$ around the direction θ to the incident beam, in the center-of-gravity system, is given by

$$d\sigma = |f(\theta)|^2 \, d\omega = |\bar{f} + g(\theta)|^2 \, d\omega \tag{2.8}$$

The Born approximation value (2.7) for $g(\theta)$ is far from correct quantitatively. It is, however, sufficient for a qualitative understanding of the main features in the scattering, whereas (2.1) would have been qualitatively wrong. The reason is as follows: the effective potential energy in the state of orbital angular momentum l, at separation r, is given by the sum of the actual potential $V(r)$ and the potential of the "centrifugal force," $l(l+1)(\hbar^2/2\mu r^2)$. For a range b of the order of 2×10^{-13} cm, the centrifugal term is 20 Mev at the edge of the well in the P state, 60 Mev in the D state, and correspondingly more for higher values of l. Thus the nuclear potential is comparable to the centrifugal potential in the P state, and is considerably smaller than the centrifugal potential in all the higher states. It can therefore be treated approximately as a small perturbation. This argument fails completely for the S state, and this is our reason for treating the S wave scattering, $\bar{f}$, separately.

We first treat the medium-energy range (10 to 30 Mev in the laboratory system) where $kr \leq 1$ for values of r within the range of the force. We expand the brace in the integrand of (2.7) in a power series in kr. The first non-vanishing term in this expansion is equal to $\frac{1}{3}(kr)^2 \cos \theta$. We keep only this term in the medium-energy range, getting

$$g(\theta) \cong \tfrac{1}{3}\, k^2 \cos \theta \int_0^\infty W(r)\, r^4\, dr \qquad (2.9)$$

The angular dependence of $g(\theta)$ is characteristic of a P wave scattering amplitude. The energy dependence (k^2, proportional to the energy) and the power of r in the integral ($4 = 2l+2$) are characteristic of P wave scattering amplitudes in the Born approximation.

According to its definition, (2.2), $W(r)$ is positive for an attractive potential. Thus $g(\theta)$ is positive for forward scattering ($0 < \theta < \pi/2$) and negative for backward scattering ($\pi/2 < \theta < \pi$) in that case. (The fact that $g(\theta)$ is a real function of θ is a consequence of the Born approximation used here and is therefore only approximately true.) The effect of this term on the scattering cross section $d\sigma$, (2.8), depends on the S wave scattering amplitude $\bar{f}$. We shall denote the real and imaginary parts of $\bar{f}$ by $\bar{f}_r$ and $\bar{f}_i$, respectively. Comparison with (II,3.9) gives

$$\bar{f}_r = k^{-1} \sin \delta \cos \delta \qquad (2.10)$$

and

$$\bar{f}_i = k^{-1} \sin^2 \delta \qquad (2.11)$$

where δ is the S wave phase shift. Formulas (2.8) and (2.9) imply that we can write the differential scattering cross section in this energy region approximately in the form

$$d\sigma = (A_0 + A_1 \cos \theta + A_2 \cos^2 \theta)\, d\omega \qquad (2.12)$$

where

$$A_0 = (\bar{f}_r)^2 + (\bar{f}_i)^2 = k^{-2} \sin^2 \delta \qquad (2.13)$$

$$A_1 = \tfrac{2}{3} k^2 \bar{f}_r \int_0^\infty W(r)\, r^4\, dr \qquad (2.14)$$

$$A_2 = \tfrac{1}{9} k^4 \left[\int_0^\infty W(r)\, r^4\, dr \right] \qquad (2.15)$$

We observe that the sign of A_1 as well as its magnitude depends on the real part of the S wave scattering amplitude $\bar{f}$. In particular, $A_1 = 0$ when the S wave phase shift δ is equal to $\pi/2$, according to (2.10).

Expressions (2.10) to (2.15) must be computed separately in the triplet and singlet spin states. The observed cross section is then given by

$$d\sigma = \tfrac{3}{4}(d\sigma)_t + \tfrac{1}{4}(d\sigma)_s = (B_0 + B_1 \cos \theta + B_2 \cos^2 \theta)\, d\omega \qquad (2.16)$$

where $B_0 = \tfrac{3}{4}(A_0)_t + \tfrac{1}{4}(A_0)_s$, and so on.

We shall make a very rough estimate of the quantities of interest in the following way. We use the shape-independent approximation (II,3.19) for the S wave phase shift δ in the two spin states, and we use an exponential well shape potential to compute the integral

$$\int_0^\infty W(r)\, r^4\, dr$$

The result for the coefficients A_0, A_1, and A_2 in the two spin states is shown in Fig. 2.1. The solid curves refer to the triplet spin state, the dashed curves to the singlet state.[1] We call attention to the different behavior of A_1, the coefficient of $\cos \theta$, in the two spin states. A_1 is always positive in the singlet state but changes from negative (at low energies) to positive (at higher energies) in the triplet state.

This difference can be understood by reference to Fig. 2.2, in which we have plotted the real and imaginary parts of the S wave scattering amplitudes $\bar{f}$ in the two spin states. The numbers next to the curve are values of k^2 in 10^{24} cm^{-2} (k^2 in these units $= 1.2 E_{\text{lab}}$ in Mev). The difference between these two curves is related to the sign of the scattering length a in the two spin states. In the triplet state, $a = a_t$ is positive. Equation (II,3.13) then implies that the triplet phase shift δ_t approaches π as the energy approaches zero. δ_t then decreases,

---

[1] A warning is in order that these curves are meant for illustrative purposes only. The approximations used here are not sufficiently accurate to allow direct comparison with experiment.

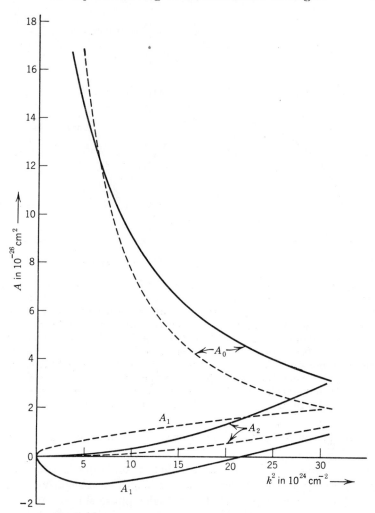

Fig. 2.1. The cross section for neutron-proton scattering is written as $d\sigma = (A_0 + A_1 \cos \theta + A_2 \cos^2 \theta)\, d\omega$. The coefficients A_0, A_1, and A_2 are shown as functions of k^2 (in 10^{24} cm^{-2} = 1.206 E_{lab} in Mev). The solid curves refer to the triplet, the dashed curves to the singlet, spin states. These coefficients are obtained by rough approximations and should not be used for detailed comparison with experiment. The curves refer to an ordinary (Wigner) force.

eventually goes through $\pi/2$, and approaches 0 for very high energies. Figure 2.2 shows that with our choice of constants ($a_t = 5.39 \times 10^{-13}$ cm, $r_{0t} = 1.73 \times 10^{-13}$ cm) the triplet phase shift δ_t becomes equal to $\pi/2$ for $k^2 \cong 22 \times 10^{24}$ cm^{-2}, i.e., at an energy $E_{\text{lab}} \cong 18$ Mev. At this energy the real part of $\bar{f}$ is zero, and consequently A_1, (2.14), also vanishes.

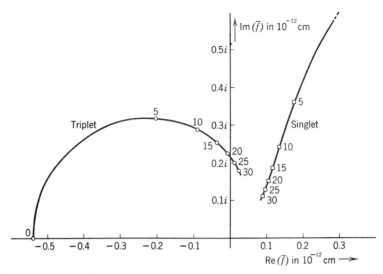

FIG. 2.2. The S wave scattering amplitude $\bar{f} = k^{-1} e^{i\delta} \sin \delta$ at various energies. The real part of $\bar{f}$ is plotted along the abscissa, the imaginary part along the ordinate. The curves connect values at different energies. Some particular values of k^2 (in 10^{24} cm^{-2}) are indicated along the curves. The real part of $\bar{f}$ in the triplet state is zero for $k^2 \cong 22 \times 10^{24}$ cm^{-2} ($E_{\text{lab}} \cong 18$ Mev). The real part of $\bar{f}$ in the singlet state is always positive. The curve for the singlet state is not shown for low energies because of limitations of space. If continued beyond the figure, the curve would bend over and approach the point $\bar{f} = +2.37 \times 10^{-12}$ cm (real) at zero energy. These curves are obtained from the shape-independent approximation (II,3.19) and are to be used only for qualitative purposes.

The real part of $\bar{f}$ and A_1 are both negative at lower energies, positive at high energies.

Now consider the singlet state. There is no bound singlet state of the deuteron, and the singlet scattering length a_s is negative. Equation (II,3.13) thus implies that the singlet phase shift δ_s approaches zero as the energy approaches zero.[1] Equation (II,3.19) shows that $k \cot \delta_s$ is always positive, i.e., the phase shift δ_s is always less than $\pi/2$. Hence the real part of $\bar{f}$ is also positive in the singlet state, and so is the coefficient A_1 in the singlet scattering cross section.

Since the measurements which give the angular distribution are commonly measurements of relative cross sections at various angles, rather than of absolute cross sections, we are interested primarily in the ratios B_1/B_0 and B_2/B_0 as defined in (2.16). These ratios are

---

[1] This is not shown on Fig. 2.2 because of limitations of size: if it were continued on, the singlet curve would bend over and approach the real axis vertically as E approaches zero, at the point $\text{Re}(\bar{f})_0 = -a_s = +2.37 \times 10^{-12}$ cm.

plotted as functions of the energy in Fig. 2.3.   At present the accuracy of angular distribution measurements is not better than 5 to 10 percent.   Thus a ratio B_1/B_0 or B_2/B_0 less than about 0.1 would probably escape detection.   Figure 2.3 shows that B_1/B_0 is of this

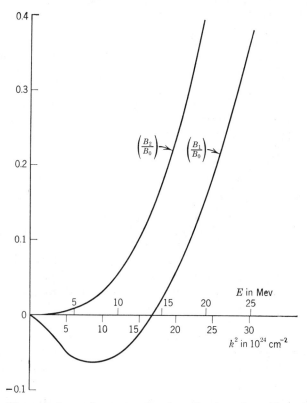

FIG. 2.3.   The experimental cross section is written as $d\sigma = (B_0 + B_1 \cos \theta + B_2 \cos^2 \theta) \, d\omega$.   The asymmetry parameters B_1/B_0 and B_2/B_0 are plotted as functions of energy in the figure.   These values are obtained by rough approximations and should not be used for detailed comparison with experiment.   The curves as shown are appropriate for an ordinary (Wigner) force.   If the force is a pure Majorana force, B_1/B_0 changes sign and B_2/B_0 stays unchanged.   A Serber force gives spherically symmetric scattering ($B_1 = B_2 = 0$) in the approximation underlying this figure.

order or smaller in the region between 12 and 15 Mev.   [The zero of B_1 is at a somewhat lower energy than that of the triplet coefficient $(A_1)_t$ because of the singlet state contribution.]   This is just the region where measurements of angular distribution were made.   *Thus we should not expect to find a strong* cos θ *term in the cross section at energies between* 12 *and* 15 *Mev. Rather the angular dependence should be of the type* $B_0 + B_2 \cos^2 \theta.$

There are in the literature theoretical estimates (Bethe 40a, Rarita 41a) which disagree with this conclusion. The reason for the disagreement is the choice of the effective range in the triplet state. Our choice, $r_{0t} = 1.73 \times 10^{-13}$ cm, is appreciably lower than the effective range implied by either the Rarita-Schwinger well or Bethe's neutral meson theory. A higher effective range would lower the energy at which $(B_1/B_0) = 0$. We would then expect an appreciable, positive term in $\cos \theta$ in the angular distribution at the energies under discussion. However, the recent measurements of coherent neutron-proton scattering (see Section 3D of Chapter II) are definitely in disagreement with such long triplet ranges.

We now consider the effect of an exchange force on the scattering in the medium-energy range. We first study the case of a pure Majorana force (1.2). Let us separate $g(\theta)$ into a symmetric and an anti-symmetric part around $\theta = \pi/2$:

$$g(\theta) = g_{\text{even}} + g_{\text{odd}} = \tfrac{1}{2}\,[g(\theta) + g(\pi - \theta)] + \tfrac{1}{2}\,[g(\theta) - g(\pi - \theta)] \quad (2.17)$$

Since the even spherical harmonics (l even) are even functions of θ in this sense and the odd spherical harmonics are odd functions, we conclude that scattering in states of even l contributes to g_{even} whereas scattering in states of odd l contributes to g_{odd}. The Majorana exchange operator P^M is equal to $+1$ for even l, -1 for odd l. Since the Born approximation value for $g(\theta)$, (2.7), depends linearly on the potential, we obtain the Born approximation to $g(\theta)$ for a pure Majorana force by reversing the sign of g_{odd} in (2.17). Thus

$$g_M(\theta) = g_W(\pi - \theta) \quad (2.18)$$

where the subscripts stand for Majorana and Wigner exchange character, respectively. Equation (2.18) is correct at all energies (to the extent that the Born approximation is valid, that is). In the medium-energy range under consideration the transformation (2.18) is equivalent to a reversal of the sign of the P wave $g(\theta)$, (2.9).

As the S wave scattering amplitude $\bar{f}$ is independent of the exchange character of the nuclear forces, we finally obtain the result: *for the same radial dependence (range, depth, and shape) of the force, and to the extent that the Born approximation for scattering in states of $l \neq 0$ is valid, a pure Majorana force gives the same scattering in the direction θ as a Wigner force does in the direction $\pi - \theta$.* In particular, if the Wigner force leads to a preference for scattering in the forward direction, a Majorana force leads to a preference for scattering in the backward direction.

This result has a very simple physical interpretation. Consider a collision between a neutron and a proton in which the neutron is deflected (in the center-of-gravity system) through an angle θ. The proton is observed emerging in the diagonally opposite direction. Now assume that the force which produced the deflection was an exchange force, but with otherwise identical dynamical properties (strength and range). The collision still looks the same as before, with one difference: the particles have exchanged their roles during the collision. Hence the particle emerging in the direction θ is now a proton, and the neutron appears in the direction $\pi - \theta$. This shows that observation in the direction $\pi - \theta$ with exchange forces is equivalent to observation in the direction θ with ordinary forces: the collisions observed are essentially the same, and the cross sections are equal. All these statements are only approximately true, of course. If the interaction is strong (so that the Born approximation is inapplicable), the neutron and proton could change places more than once during the collision, invalidating the above argument.

In the medium-energy range under consideration here a pure Majorana exchange force gives the cross section (2.16) with the sign of B_1 (the coefficient of cos θ) reversed. Thus, in particular, *there is no significant difference in the scattering by a pure Wigner and a pure Majorana force in the* 12 *to* 15 *Mev region*. The coefficient B_1 in the cross section is too small to be detected anyhow, so it does not matter whether its sign is reversed.[1]

Since there is little difference between Wigner and Majorana forces in the scattering around 12 to 15 Mev, we might think that the scattering cross section at that energy is independent of the exchange character of the force. This is by no means true, however. To demonstrate this point, consider the Serber force (1.4). This force acts only in states of even orbital angular momentum l. In states of odd l the Majorana exchange operator P^M equals -1, so the Serber force (1.4) is zero. We have proved already that the scattering in states of even l contributes only to g_{even} in (2.17), the scattering in states of odd l contributes only to g_{odd}.[2] We conclude that *the scattering amplitude* $f(\theta) = \bar{f} + g(\theta)$ *produced by a Serber force is an even function of* θ, *i.e.,*

---

[1] It is particularly unfortunate that the earlier calculations with longer triplet ranges gave a result opposite to this, since the experimenters were encouraged thereby to measure only the ratio of the cross section at $\theta = \pi$ and $\theta = \pi/2$ rather than the full angular distribution. This ratio is sufficient if the cos$^2 \theta$ term is negligible, but not otherwise. Furthermore, our estimates show that the 12 to 15 Mev region is just about the poorest region for distinguishing between Wigner and Majorana forces. Any other energy range (even lower energies) would be preferable for this purpose.

[2] Unlike (2.18), which depends on the use of the Born approximation for $g(\theta)$, the above statement is true even if the Born approximation is not valid.

$$f(\theta) = f(\pi - \theta) \qquad \text{(Serber force)} \qquad (2.19)$$

The scattering cross section (2.8) is then also an even function of θ in both spin states.

Let us investigate the effect of a Serber force in the medium-energy scattering. The approximate $g(\theta)$, (2.9), which we have employed so far is due to scattering in the P state. It is an odd function of $\cos \theta$ (proportional to $\cos \theta$) and is therefore not present if the force is a Serber force. Rather, we have to go to the next (D wave) term in the expansion of $g(\theta)$, (2.7). The even part of this term is

$$g(\theta) = \tfrac{1}{90} (3 \cos^2 \theta - 1) k^4 \int_0^\infty W(r) r^6 \, dr \qquad \text{(Serber force)} \qquad (2.20)$$

A simple calculation shows that this deviation from spherically symmetric scattering is much too small to be detected around 12 to 15 Mev.

We now determine the scattering due to the force (1.3) which obeys the saturation requirements. We can write (1.3) in the form

$$V = (\alpha + \beta) \frac{1 + P^M}{2} V(r) + (\alpha - \beta) \frac{1 - P^M}{2} V(r) \qquad (\beta > 4\alpha)$$

where the first term is a Serber force and the second term is an "anti-Serber" force which is zero in even states and acts in odd states only. Hence the P scattering is given exclusively by the second term and would be equal to the P scattering of a Wigner force of strength $(\alpha - \beta) V(r)$. The ratio B_2/B_0 in (2.16) is therefore equal to the one given in Fig. 2.3 multiplied by the factor $[(\alpha - \beta)/(\alpha + \beta)]^2$. This factor is $(\tfrac{3}{5})^2$ for $\beta = 4\alpha$. Hence the force (1.3) would give an angular variation in the cross section around 12 to 15 Mev which is $\tfrac{9}{25}$ times smaller than the angular variation due to a pure Wigner or a pure Majorana force (within the accuracy of the Born approximation).

Let us now compare the theoretical conclusions with the experimental results. As far as the total cross section is concerned, the theory is in agreement with the experiments. By far the main contribution to the total cross section comes from the S scattering in the medium-energy range. This part does not depend on the exchange character of the force. Since the triplet phase shift which is responsible for about 75 percent of the cross section is near 90° in this energy region, the total cross section is close to $4\pi\lambda^2$ within the limits of the experimental accuracy. This agrees with the observations. However, the predictions drawn from Fig. 2.3 for a pure Wigner force or a pure Majorana force are in disagreement with the experimental results between 12 and 15 Mev. While B_1/B_0 is negligible at these energies, the coefficient B_2/B_0 of the $\cos^2 \theta$ term is predicted to be of the order of 0.15 to 0.20. This would make the cross section at $\theta = \pi/2$ some 15 to 20 percent lower than the cross section at $\theta = \pi$, in definite disagreement with experiment[1] (quoted at the beginning of this section). The experimental result would be in agreement with a Serber force which gives almost complete spherical symmetry for these energies. It is also in fair agreement with a force of the type (1.3), since a variation which is about a third of the one predicted by Fig. 2.3 would not contradict the measurements.

It must be emphasized that the disagreement between experiment and the theoretical predictions of a pure Wigner or Majorana force could be removed by an assumption of a different well shape for the potential well. Figure 2.3 is based on the exponential well shape. A less "long-tailed" well, the square well for example, would give a much lower value for the integral $\int_0^\infty W(r)\, r^4\, dr$ because of the r^4 in the integrand. Since the coefficient of $\cos^2 \theta$, (2.15), is proportional to the square of this integral, the well shape effect is quite appreciable. (Under our shape-independent approximation for $\bar{f}$, on the other hand, there is no well shape effect at all on A_0 or B_0.) If we had chosen a square well rather than an exponential well shape, the ratio (B_2/B_0) would be only about a quarter of the values indicated in Fig. 2.3. The predictions would then be in agreement with experiment within the experimental errors even for pure Wigner or Majorana forces.

At this stage we encounter the difficulty of interpretation mentioned in the introduction. The theory can be made to agree with the present data in two entirely different ways: (1) we can choose a long-tailed potential shape with one of the mixed exchange characters, (1.3) or (1.4); or (2) we can use a pure exchange character (either Wigner or Majorana) provided the well shape is more compact (short-tailed). More specific information about the neutron-proton force will be acquired from measurements in the 20 to 30 Mev energy range. Figure 2.3 shows that, in that range, both the $\cos \theta$ and $\cos^2 \theta$ terms have large enough coefficients to be measurable with present experimental techniques; thus the measured angular dependence of the cross section would reveal more about the exchange character of the forces than similar measurements in the 12 to 15 Mev region. Some preliminary measurements (Brolley 50, 51) at 27 Mev show an appreciable angular variation of the cross section.

---

[1] We have warned the reader before against direct comparison of this figure with experiment. The comparison made here is permitted, however, because the disagreement is so large that it may be considered meaningful.

3. NEUTRON-PROTON SCATTERING AT ENERGIES LARGER THAN 30 MEV

In the limit of very high energy the scattering cross section as expected by theory is discussed most easily by considering the behavior of $g(\theta)$, (2.7). Let us assume that the de Broglie wavelength in the center-of-mass system, $\lambda = k^{-1}$, is small compared to the range b of the nuclear forces. The brace in the integrand of (2.7) contains two terms, one of which is an oscillating function of r $[\sin(Kr)/(Kr)]$, whereas the other always has the same sign. If the oscillations of the first term occur within the range b of the forces, the first term contributes very little compared to the second term. The oscillations of the first term occur for values of r larger than K^{-1}. Thus the first term in the brace of (2.7) makes a negligible contribution to the integral provided that

$$\frac{1}{b} < K = 2k \sin\left(\frac{\theta}{2}\right) \tag{3.1}$$

Under our assumption $kb \gg 1$ the maximum angle for which (3.1) is fulfilled is so small that we can replace the sine by its argument. Thus the first term in the brace of (2.7) makes a negligible contribution provided that the scattering angle θ exceeds a certain critical angle θ_c given by

$$\theta_c \cong (kb)^{-1} \tag{3.2}$$

Let us consider an attractive Wigner force for which $W(r)$ is positive. At angles $\theta > \theta_c$, $g(\theta)$ is negative and independent of θ. Since the average value of $g(\theta)$ over all directions is zero by construction, the variation of $g(\theta)$ with the angle θ is as indicated in Fig. 3.1. The S wave phase shifts δ are less than $\frac{1}{2}\pi$ in both spin states at these energies. The resulting cross section shows a sharp peak in the forward direction and drops to a roughly constant, lower value for angles $\theta > \theta_c$.

A pure Majorana force gives the opposite behavior according to (2.18): the cross section shows a sharp peak in the backward direction and drops to a roughly constant, lower value for angles $\theta < \pi - \theta_c$.

The experimental data (Brueckner 49, Hadley 49, Kelly 50, Wallace 51) were taken with neutron beams of "mean" energies around 40 Mev, 90 Mev, and 260 Mev. The energy spread in these beams is illustrated by Fig. 3.2, which is taken from Hadley *et al.* In Fig. 3.3, taken from the same source, there are plotted the experimental cross sections in the center-of-gravity system. The points in the upper part of the figure refer to the "40 Mev" data, the lower points to the "90

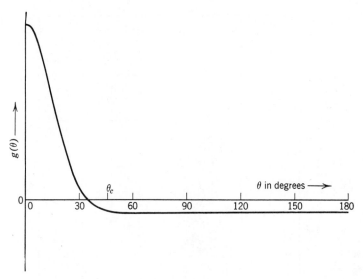

F IG . 3.1.   The non-*S*-wave scattering amplitude $g(\theta)$ is shown schematically as a function of θ, for very high energies, under the assumption of an ordinary (Wigner) force. $g(\theta)$ has a sharp maximum at $\theta = 0$, then drops to a constant, negative value at angles $\theta > \theta_c$, where $\theta_c \sim kb$ (k = relative wave number, b = range of the force). A Majorana force gives the same result with θ replaced by $\pi - \theta$.   A Serber force annihilates the odd part of $g(\theta)$, i.e., $g_{\text{Serber}} = \frac{1}{2}[g(\theta) + g(\pi - \theta)]$.

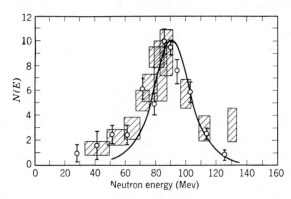

F IG . 3.2.   Energy distribution of the neutrons obtained by stripping 190-Mev deuterons on beryllium 1.27 cm thick.   The solid curve is from the theory of Serber (47).   The shaded rectangles and the vertical points (with errors) are experimental values obtained by different techniques of measurement.   There is a considerable spread of energies around the mean energy (90 Mev).   [This is Fig. 3 of Hadley (49).]

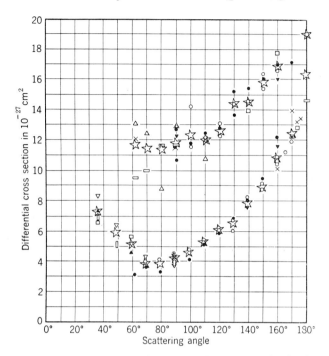

FIG. 3.3.   The differential neutron-proton scattering cross section in the center-of-gravity system in 10^{-27} cm²/steradian. The upper points were taken with "40 Mev" neutrons, the lower points with "90 Mev" neutrons. The various points for each angle were obtained in different runs with various experimental conditions. The stars represent the final best averages. [This is Fig. 10 of Hadley (49.)]

Mev" data. The stars in the figure represent the best averages available. It is apparent from Figs. 3.2 and 3.3 that any detailed fitting of these experiments by theory is out of the question. Only qualitative conclusions may be drawn from the data.

The total cross section

$$\sigma = \int d\sigma = \int |f(\theta)|^2 \, d\omega \qquad (3.3)$$

was also measured by the same authors and by De Juren (50) with the following results:

$$\sigma = (1.7 \pm 0.2) \times 10^{-25} \text{ cm}^2 \qquad (E_{\text{lab}} = \text{"40 Mev"}) \qquad (3.4)$$

$$\sigma = (7.6 \pm 1.0) \times 10^{-26} \text{ cm}^2 \qquad (E_{\text{lab}} = \text{"90 Mev"}) \qquad (3.5)$$

$$\sigma = (3.8 \pm 0.15) \times 10^{-26} \text{ cm}^2 \qquad (E_{\text{lab}} = \text{"280 Mev"}) \quad (3.5a)$$

We shall now show that both the angular distribution and the total cross section at 90 Mev favor the assumption of a Serber exchange force, (1.4). Consider first the angular distribution. If the force were a pure Wigner force, the cross section for angles $\theta > \theta_c$ ought to be roughly angle independent and low. At 90 Mev the critical angle θ_c is of the order of 0.5 radian. The experimental cross section shows a qualitatively different behavior: it rises sharply for angles $\theta > \frac{1}{2}\pi$. Thus pure Wigner forces are excluded by the data. Conversely, the rise in the cross section for $\theta < 70°$ can be used to exclude a pure Majorana force. On the other hand, (2.19) shows that a Serber force leads to a cross section which is symmetric around $\theta = \frac{1}{2}\pi$. Although the experimental cross section is not exactly symmetric around 90°, it is near enough to this behavior to show that the Serber exchange character gives a reasonable first approximation. The extensive calculations of Christian and Hart (50) bear out this qualitative conclusion.

The total cross sections, (3.5) at "90 Mev" and (3.5a) at "280 Mev," are quite low compared to most theoretical predictions. We shall now show that, given the potential $V(r)$ in the S state, the Serber exchange character gives the lowest possible cross section. The total cross section is given by (2.4) and (3.3). We again split $g(\theta)$ into an even and an odd part to get

$$\sigma = \int |\bar{f} + g_{\text{even}}|^2 \, d\omega + \int |g_{\text{odd}}|^2 \, d\omega \qquad (3.6)$$

The cross term vanishes because the integrand is an odd function of $\cos\theta$. Let us assume an arbitrary exchange character for the force:

$$V = (\alpha + \beta P^M) \, V(r) \qquad (\text{with} \quad \alpha + \beta = 1) \qquad (3.7)$$

Then the force in the states with even l is necessarily equal to the force in the S state, since $P^M = +1$ in states with even l. As the first integral in (3.6) contains the contributions of the states with even l, its value is determined by the force in the S state. It is now apparent that we get the minimum cross section if $g_{\text{odd}} = 0$, and this is the case for the Serber exchange force, $\alpha = \beta = \frac{1}{2}$. This theorem is true in the singlet and triplet spin states separately and is therefore also true for the observed cross section.

The Serber force is therefore a satisfactory exchange force to fit the neutron-proton scattering data at all energies at which they have been observed. On the other hand, the Serber force is completely unsatisfactory from the point of view of saturation. The Serber force is attractive for symmetric pairs, but zero (rather than repulsive) for anti-symmetric pairs. In the complete absence of repulsive forces the heavy nuclei are unstable against collapse.   There is no saturation with an attractive Serber force (Gerjuoy 50).

It is therefore of interest to determine whether the cross sections can also be fitted with a saturated force, i.e., with a mixture (3.7) for which $\beta/\alpha > 4$.   We come closest to the Serber force by choosing

$$\alpha = \tfrac{1}{5} \qquad \beta = \tfrac{4}{5} \qquad \text{(saturated)} \qquad\qquad (3.8)$$

According to Christian and Hart, such a force is in disagreement with the "90 Mev" data.   It does not give the rise in the differential cross section observed for $\theta > 70°$, and the predicted total cross section is considerably too large for reasonable well shapes and ranges.

The situation at present is rather disconcerting: we have introduced exchange forces in order to explain the saturation of nuclear binding energies and of nuclear densities.   Hence it is gratifying that the high-energy scattering data are in disagreement with a Wigner force and can be fitted with an exchange force.   But the exchange character which gives the best fit (the Serber force) does not lead to saturation!   Although there have been suggestions toward a solution of this contradiction (Jastrow 50, 51), no detailed calculations of neutron-proton scattering with forces other than those discussed here have been published as yet.

We add a few details resulting from the theoretical interpretation of the high-energy data in terms of a neutron-proton force derivable from a potential function (Christian 50):

(1) A long-tailed potential well shape (Yukawa or exponential well) gives an appreciably better fit to the data than a short-tailed (square or Gaussian) well shape.

(2) The shape of the angular distribution around 90° is evidence of a tensor force contribution to the scattering.   A purely central Serber force yields a flatter (more U-shaped) angular distribution than the experimental one (Figure 3.3), which is more nearly a V-shape.

(3) The triplet range needed for the high-energy data is in agreement with the triplet effective range from the low-energy data.   The singlet range must be larger than 2×10^{-13} cm to fit the high-energy data, and must be between 1.5 and 3×10^{-13} cm to fit the low-energy data.

(4) The shape and range of the tensor force are not uniquely determined.   In particular, the range of the tensor interaction may be *longer* than the central force range by as much as a factor of 2 without giving any disagreement.   On the other hand, a tensor range appreciably *shorter* than the central force range is in disagreement with the quadrupole moment and magnetic moment of the deuteron (see Section 5 of Chapter II).

4. PROTON-PROTON SCATTERING

The identity of the two protons in the proton-proton scattering reduces considerably the number of parameters necessary to describe the scattering.   States with even l have only singlet scattering, states with odd l have only triplet scattering.   If we ignore the tensor forces, we need to determine only one phase shift for each value of the orbital angular momentum l, whereas we had to determine two phase shifts for each l in neutron-proton scattering with central forces.

Measurements of proton-proton scattering have been performed at energies of 32 Mev (Cork 50, Panofsky 50) and 340 Mev (Chamberlain 50).   The data at 32 Mev are consistent with a nuclear interaction in the S state ($l=0$) only.   This is very surprising, since the P state and D state scattering should be expected to enter significantly at this energy.   It is possible that scattering in these states is present but the contributions add up in such a way as to simulate a pure S wave effect.   Experiments at different energies in the 20 to 60 Mev region would check this possibility since the cancellation of P wave and D wave angular dependences at 32 Mev could hardly be expected to maintain itself over a wide range of energies.

It is possible to construct a force which is effective only in the S state and is zero in all other states.   This force [given by (III,3.25)] is not an exchange force in the usual sense of the term, however.   Furthermore we shall see that the scattering at 340 Mev is in disagreement with this assumption.

Christian and Noyes (Christian 50a) have analyzed the 32-Mev data on the assumption of exchange forces which are purely attractive in the ^1S state.   They find that it is necessary to introduce appreciable tensor force effects in the ^3P state to explain the 32-Mev data on that basis.   (There are no tensor forces in the S, D, $\cdots$ states of the proton-proton system since states of even l are required by the Pauli exclusion principle to be singlet states.)   Alternative explanations of the data have been suggested, however (Jastrow 50, 51, Case 50).   More experimental material is necessary before there can be a definite decision between the various hypotheses.   The most important conclusion from the present results is this: it is likely that the proton-proton scattering cannot be described by the same force that reproduces the neutron-proton results.   The Serber force, which was a satisfactory possibility for the neutron-proton scattering, does not predict the observed proton-proton scattering at 32 Mev.   The charge independence of nuclear forces which seemed to be valid at low energies is probably invalid at higher energies.

Let us now turn to the 340-Mev data.   In the region of angles where the Coulomb scattering is unimportant, the experimental cross section is quite flat and has a value of (Chamberlain 51)

$$d\sigma = (4 \pm 0.4) \times 10^{-27} \text{ cm}^2/\text{steradian} \tag{4.1}$$

This cross section is too large to be explained on the basis of an interaction in the S state only. The largest possible S wave cross section is given by

$$d\sigma = \lambda^2 \, d\omega \qquad \text{(maximum } S \text{ wave)} \qquad (4.2)$$

where $\lambda = k^{-1}$ is the de Broglie wavelength in the center-of-mass system. At an energy of 340 Mev, we should expect the cross section to be appreciably smaller than this maximum (which corresponds to an S wave phase shift $\delta_0 = \frac{1}{2}\pi$). However, at 340 Mev in the laboratory system, the wavelength λ is about 5×10^{-14} cm. Hence *the experimental cross section is almost twice the maximum possible one for pure S wave scattering.* Thus the force (III,3.25) is excluded by the 340-Mev data, even though it is consistent with the 32-Mev data.

Christian and Noyes have tried to fit the 340-Mev data with an exchange force of the Serber type, and purely attractive (negative) $V(r)$. The usual potential well shapes lead to theoretical results in qualitative disagreement with the cross section at 340 Mev. The theoretical cross sections are approximately independent of angle in the central region of angles, but they are one order of magnitude too small in absolute value. This can be interpreted as more evidence against the charge independence of nuclear forces.

Several attempts were made to explain the abnormal behavior of the proton-proton scattering at high energies by means of new types of forces. Christian and Noyes (50a) used a highly singular tensor force to correlate the data. Jastrow (50, 51) has suggested that the large, spherically symmetric scattering found at 340 Mev may be due to strong repulsive forces when two protons approach each other closely. Case and Pais (50) have suggested a third explanation in terms of a force which cannot be derived from a potential function. It is a velocity-dependent force which includes spin orbit coupling. Only more experimental material can decide which of these choices, if any, is the correct one.

The only feature which appears to be common to all these attempts to explain the data is a very strong interaction of the proton-proton pair at distances of the order of 10^{-13} cm or less. It may be that this common feature of the otherwise completely disparate explanations is significant.

SYMBOLS

a	Scattering length (Section 2)	
a_s	Scattering length in the singlet spin state	(Section 2)
a_t	Scattering length in the triplet spin state	(Section 2)

A_0	Isotropic part of the differential scattering cross section $d\sigma$ $[=\|\bar{f}\|^2]$ (2.12), (2.13)
A_1	Coefficient of $\cos\theta$ in $d\sigma$ (2.12), (2.14)
A_2	Coefficient of $\cos^2\theta$ in $d\sigma$ (2.12), (2.15)
b	Range of the nuclear force (Section 2)
B_0	Isotropic part of the experimental differential scattering cross section (2.16)
B_1	Coefficient of $\cos\theta$ in the experimental differential scattering cross section (2.16)
B_2	Coefficient of $\cos^2\theta$ in the experimental differential scattering cross section (2.16)
$d\sigma$	Differential scattering cross section (2.8)
$(d\sigma)_s$	Differential scattering cross section in the singlet spin state (2.16)
$(d\sigma)_t$	Differential scattering cross section in the triplet spin state (2.16)
$d\omega$	Element of solid angle (2.5)
E	Energy of the relative motion (Section 2)
E_{lab}	Energy of the neutron in the laboratory system $[=2E]$ (Section 2)
$f(\theta)$	Scattering amplitude (2.1)
$\bar{f}$	Average value of $f(\theta)$ $[=S$ wave part of $f(\theta)]$ (2.4), (2.5)
$(\bar{f})_0$	Value of $\bar{f}$ at energy $E=0$ (Section 2)
$\bar{f}_i$	Imaginary part of $\bar{f}$ (2.11)
$\bar{f}_r$	Real part of $\bar{f}$ (2.10)
$g(\theta)$	The non-S-wave part of $f(\theta)$ $[=f(\theta)-\bar{f}]$ (2.4), (2.7)
g_{even}	$=\frac{1}{2}[g(\theta)+g(\pi-\theta)]$ (2.17)
$g_M(\theta)$	Value of $g(\theta)$ for a pure Majorana force (2.18)
g_{odd}	$=\frac{1}{2}[g(\theta)-g(\pi-\theta)]$ (2.17)
$g_W(\theta)$	Value of $g(\theta)$ for a pure Wigner force (2.18)
k	Wave number of the relative motion (Section 1)
$\mathbf{k}_{\text{final}}$	Wave vector of the relative motion after the collision (2.3)
$\mathbf{k}_{\text{init}}$	Wave vector of the relative motion before the collision (2.3)
K	$=\|\mathbf{k}_{\text{final}}-\mathbf{k}_{\text{init}}\|$ (2.1), (2.3)
l	Orbital angular momentum quantum number (Section 1)
M	Nucleon mass (2.2)
P^M	Majorana exchange operator (Section 1)
r	Distance between the two particles (Section 1)
r_{0t}	Effective range for scattering in the triplet spin state (Section 2)
V	Potential of the nuclear force (Section 1)
$W(r)$	$=-(M/\hbar^2)V(r)$ (2.1), (2.2)

z   Component of the interparticle separation vector along the direction of the incident beam   (Section 2)

α Coefficient of the Wigner part of the potential V (1.3)
β Coefficient of the Majorana part of the potential V (1.3)
δ Phase shift for S wave scattering   (2.10), (2.11)
δ_s S wave phase shift in the singlet spin state   (Section 2)
δ_t S wave phase shift in the triplet spin state   (Section 2)
θ Angle of scattering in the center-of-gravity system   (Section 2)
θ_c Critical scattering angle at high energies; for $\theta > \theta_c$, $d\sigma$ is roughly independent of θ (3.2)
λ de Broglie wavelength of the relative motion (divided by 2π) $[= k^{-1}]$ (Section 1)
μ Reduced mass $[\cong \tfrac{1}{2}M]$ (2.2)
σ Total scattering cross section   (3.3)

CHAPTER V

Three- and Four-Body Problems

1. INTRODUCTION

Historically, the study of the three- and four-body problems was of decisive importance for nuclear physics. The basic work of Wigner on the binding energy of the alpha-particle (Wigner 33a) showed that nuclear forces have a short range and are very strong inside that range. The range of the nuclear forces was estimated from the binding energies of the triton and the alpha-particle before the two-body scattering experiments were able to give any indication of a range of the force. In particular, L. H. Thomas (35) gave a proof that the nuclear forces cannot have zero range at a time when the neutron-proton scattering experiments were still completely consistent with a zero range interaction, and when no proton-proton scattering experiments were available at all. Thomas was able to show that a neutron-proton force of very small range, and of strength appropriate to give the correct binding energy of the deuteron, leads to a very large binding energy of the triton, even if the two neutrons in the triton do not attract each other at all. Indeed, the predicted binding energy of the triton can be made arbitrarily large by choosing the range of the force small enough.

The study of three- and four-body problems should allow us, in principle, to estimate the importance of many-body forces in nuclei.[1] If we knew the forces between two nucleons, we could solve the wave equation for the three- and four-body problems, assuming that there are no additional forces which come into play. If the results agree with the experimental data, there is no need to invoke many-body forces; if there is disagreement, many-body forces must be present.

Unfortunately, the situation is not nearly so clear cut. First of all, we do not know the forces between two nucleons well enough to delimit the three-body and four-body problems completely. Unlike the two-body problems at low energies, the three- and four-particle

[1] Estimates of the importance of three-body forces, based on field theory, have been given by Janossy (39) and by Primakoff and Holstein (Primakoff 39).

systems are sensitive to the finer details of the force law, such as the well shape and the ratio of tensor force to central force in the triplet spin state. There is one saving feature: the problems treated in this chapter are not very sensitive to the exchange character of the nuclear forces. The triton and the alpha-particle are tightly bound units in which the wave function is as symmetric as possible to take the most advantage of the short-range nuclear forces. Thus the effective nuclear interaction is the one in symmetric states, so that a Majorana force gives almost the same results as a Wigner force. Conversely, we cannot learn anything about the exchange nature of the nuclear forces from a study of the ground states of the triton and the alpha-particle.

Secondly, even if we did know the forces between two nucleons exactly, the mathematical treatment of the three- and four-body systems presents appreciable difficulties if the forces are central forces, and practically insurmountable difficulties if tensor forces are present. There is no simple approximation scheme which gives accurate results. Rather, we must have recourse to very complicated and tedious variational calculations similar to those used by Hylleraas (30) in his study of the atomic three-body problem, the helium atom. Although the problem is simple to set up in principle, carrying out the required operations for a sufficient number of choices of the force parameters would take a prohibitive amount of time by desk computing methods.

Thirdly, the theory of the scattering and reactions which can take place in three- and four-body systems has not even been developed schematically in a satisfactory form. Although there is considerable experimental information on the scattering of protons by deuterons, we do not as yet have any way of utilizing this information to infer something about nuclear forces. The calculations so far have used approximations of doubtful validity.

Fourthly, there is every reason to believe that relativistic corrections (Feenberg 36, Primakoff 47) are much more important here than in the study of the deuteron. The triton and the alpha-particle are much more tightly bound than the deuteron. The nucleons are closer together and have correspondingly larger kinetic energies. It is very difficult to estimate the relativistic corrections accurately; they may change the computed binding energy of the triton by 10 to 20 percent in either direction, and they have an even greater effect in the alpha-particle. Thus we should not hope for agreement between the non-relativistic theory and experiment to better than 10 percent accuracy.

The three- and four-body problems present a fascinating challenge to research. Presumably there is a great deal of information about nuclear forces contained in the experimental data, but we lack the means to get at that information.

2. THE GROUND STATE OF THE TRITON; CENTRAL FORCES

The wave function of the triton adjusts itself so as to take the greatest advantage of the short-range attractive forces between the three pairs of particles. This adjustment is best if there are no nodes in the wave function. Rather, the wave function has to be large whenever the two particles are close enough together to feel the nuclear forces, and it has to be as smooth as possible in order to minimize the kinetic energy.

We shall therefore assume that the wave function of the ground state is symmetric under the exchange of the space coordinates of any pair of particles. A state anti-symmetric under the exchange of the space coordinates of particle 1 and 2, say, would have $\Psi = 0$ wherever $r_1 = r_2$, and Ψ close to zero over a region of one (relative) de Broglie wavelength λ (see Chapter I, Section 8). Since λ in the triton is of the order of magnitude of the range of the nuclear forces, particles 1 and 2 would stay outside the nuclear range of each other most of the time. As this is very unfavorable energetically, it should be expected that such a wave function does not give the lowest (ground) state of the triton. In addition to this, the kinetic energy is also unfavorable in this state: the kinetic energy is increased by rapid variations in the wave function. An anti-symmetric wave function varies more rapidly near $r_1 = r_2$ than a symmetric wave function. Hence not only is the potential energy decreased in an anti-symmetric state but also the kinetic energy is increased as compared with a symmetric state.

The symmetry of the wave function of the ground state has two consequences: (1) the two neutrons must have opposite spin, according to the Pauli exclusion principle (see Chapter I, Section 8); (2) a Majorana exchange force cannot be distinguished from an ordinary (Wigner) force in this state, since the Majorana exchange operator gives the result $+1$ for every pair of particles.[1]

Since the intrinsic spins of the two neutrons cancel each other, the net intrinsic spin of the triton is contributed by the proton: $S = \frac{1}{2}$ (in spectroscopic notation the ground state of the triton is predominantly a doublet state). As far as the orbital angular momentum is con-

---

[1] Both of these statements are only approximately true, of course. The wave function of the ground state contains small admixtures of less symmetric states, unless the forces between all pairs of particles are precisely equal (and they are not). However, our arguments show that these admixtures are relatively unimportant, so that we are allowed to neglect them in a qualitative discussion.

cerned, the requirement that the wave function have as few nodes as possible restricts us to the state with $L = 0$. The total angular momentum I of the triton (the "nuclear spin") is then $\frac{1}{2}$, and it has its origin in the spin of the proton. The magnetic moment of the triton is predicted to be the same as the magnetic moment of an isolated proton (the two neutron magnetic moments cancel each other since the neutrons have opposite spins, and there is no orbital angular momentum to produce a convection-current magnetic moment). Experimentally, both these predictions check very well: $I = \frac{1}{2}$, and the magnetic moment is $\mu = 2.98$ nuclear (Bohr) magnetons (Dieke 49, Nelson 49, Bloch 47, Anderson 47). The small discrepancy between this magnetic moment and the proton magnetic moment, $\mu = 2.79$ magnetons, is commonly attributed to cooperative effects which do not concern us here (see Chapter VI).

We might think that the spin dependence of the nuclear forces should enter the calculation significantly. To a first approximation, however, the only quantity of significance for the triton problem is the *average* of the forces in the two spin states (singlet and triplet). To prove this, we assume that the wave function is completely symmetric under the exchange of the space coordinates of any two nucleons. We shall also assume that the nuclear force, although spin dependent, is charge independent, i.e., the neutron-neutron force is equal to the (singlet state) neutron-proton force. Under our assumptions about the wave function, the probability of finding two nucleons with parallel spins (triplet state) a given distance apart is the same as the probability of finding two nucleons with opposite spin (singlet state) the same distance apart. Furthermore, the potential energy as a function of distance depends only on the relative spin orientation, not on the type of pair (like or unlike particles).[1] Thus the contributions of the singlet and triplet pairs to the total potential energy are directly proportional to the number of each type of pair. Let us therefore count singlet and triplet pairs: the two neutrons form a singlet pair (Pauli); the up-spin neutron together with the up-spin proton forms a triplet pair; the remaining pair (down-spin neutron with up-spin proton) must be counted[2] as half triplet, half singlet; there are equal numbers

---

[1] A reminder is in place here, perhaps, that we are deliberately excluding tensor forces from the discussion in this section. The "spin-dependent" forces involved here are by assumption of type $(\mathbf{d}_1 \cdot \mathbf{d}_2)$ rather than tensor forces.

[2] Proof: The spin part of the wave function for an up-spin proton and a down-spin neutron is $\alpha(p)\beta(n)$, where α denotes an up spin, β a down spin. We write this as $\alpha(p)\beta(n) = \frac{1}{2}[\alpha(p)\beta(n) + \beta(p)\alpha(n)] + \frac{1}{2}[\alpha(p)\beta(n) - \beta(p)\alpha(n)]$. The first term corresponds to the triplet state; the second term to the singlet state. Since they occur with equal coefficients, the pair has to be counted as half singlet and half triplet.

($\frac{3}{2}$) of triplet pairs and singlet pairs in the triton. The effective potential energy between each pair of particles in the triton is, hence,

$$V_{\text{eff}}(r) = \tfrac{1}{2}\,[V_t(r) + V_s(r)] \tag{2.1}$$

Of course this is only a first approximation. The triplet force is stronger than the singlet force (see Chapter II), and the wave function tries to take advantage of this extra attraction. The probability of finding a triplet pair close together is somewhat larger than the probability of finding a singlet pair close together. The true wave function is not completely symmetrical under the space interchange of all pairs of particles. This is only a small correction, however, especially when compared with the effects of tensor forces. To the extent that the approximation (2.1) is justified, we cannot draw any conclusions about the spin dependence of the nuclear forces from a study of the ground state of the triton.

We now proceed to a discussion of the theoretical results for the triton binding energy under the assumption of central forces. This discussion is considerably simplified compared with earlier work. First of all, we now know that the tensor force exists and is important. We therefore do not need to strive for great accuracy in the calculations with purely central forces; rather, we can use rough approximation methods (which are easy to handle) provided that they do not yield qualitatively incorrect answers, since we are interested only in those qualitative conclusions which can be expected to remain valid when tensor forces are brought into the discussion. Secondly, the theory of the effective range (Chapter II, Section 3) has enabled us to define an intrinsic range b for each shape of the potential well in such a way that two wells with different well shape but the same intrinsic range are closely comparable in the two-body problems. This will allow us to study well shape effects in the triton ground state. Thirdly, Feshbach[1] has introduced a simple trial wave function which gives qualitatively correct results in the triton problem with very little effort.

We shall be concerned primarily with the exponential and Yukawa well shapes (see Section 2 of Chapter II for definitions and notation). Although there has been considerable theoretical work with the Gauss well shape (Feenberg 35, 36a, Fluegge 37, Margenau 37, 38, Svartholm 45, 48), it turns out to be impossible to fit the present data on the two-body problems by using Gauss wells of the same intrinsic range b in both the triplet and the singlet states. The use of two different intrinsic ranges complicates the calculations considerably. Since we

---

[1] Private communication.

are interested only in qualitative results anyhow, this complication will be avoided here by not using the Gaussian well shape at all.

The most useful method in the triton problem is the Ritz variational method. We calculate the expectation value of the energy with the following trial wave function (suggested by Feshbach):

$$\Psi = N \exp\left[-\tfrac{1}{2}\kappa(r_{12}+r_{13}+r_{23})\right] \tag{2.2}$$

where κ is an adjustable parameter which will be used to minimize the energy, r_{12} is the distance between particles 1 and 2, and so on. The normalization factor N is given by

$$N = \left(\tfrac{4}{7}\right)^{1/2}\kappa^3 \tag{2.3}$$

We do not need to write the wave function for the spins of the particles, provided that we use the "effective" potential (2.1) throughout.

The calculation of the expectation values of the kinetic and potential energies with this wave function is straightforward (Pease 50, 51). The result is

$$\text{Kinetic energy} = \frac{15}{14}\frac{\hbar^2\kappa^2}{M} \tag{2.4}$$

where M is the mass of a nucleon. Using the conventional forms (II,2.12, II,2.13) for the exponential and Yukawa wells, respectively, we obtain

$$\text{Potential energy} = -V_0\, f(\kappa\beta) \tag{2.5}$$

where β is the conventional range parameter, and

$$f(x) = \frac{3}{7}\left(\frac{x}{x+1}\right)^3\left[2 + 3\left(\frac{x}{x+1}\right) + 2\left(\frac{x}{x+1}\right)^2\right] \quad \text{(exponential)} \tag{2.6}$$

for the exponential well, and

$$f(x) = \frac{24}{7}\,x^3(2x+1)^{-2}\left[1 + 2\left(\frac{x}{2x+1}\right) + 2\left(\frac{x}{2x+1}\right)^2\right] \quad \text{(Yukawa)} \tag{2.7}$$

for the Yukawa well. We have to find the value of κ which minimizes the total energy [the sum of (2.4) and (2.5)] and insert this value into the expressions above. This can be done rather simply by numerical calculation. In order to be able to compare the two wells we introduce the intrinsic ranges b (see II,2.19 and II,2.20) and the well depth parameters s (see II,2.16 and II,2.17) instead of the conventional range parameters β and the conventional well depths V_0. The result can be written in the form

$$\text{Kinetic energy} = \frac{\hbar^2}{Mb^2}\, T(s) \tag{2.8}$$

$$\text{Potential energy} = -\frac{\hbar^2}{Mb^2}\, V(s) \tag{2.9}$$

$$\text{Binding energy} = \frac{\hbar^2}{Mb^2}\, B(s) = \frac{\hbar^2}{Mb^2}\,[V(s)-T(s)] \tag{2.10}$$

where $T(s)$, $V(s)$, and $B(s)$ are slowly varying functions of the well depth parameter s. These functions are shown in Fig. 2.1 for the two well shapes, and for reasonable values of the well depth parameter s. (We recall here that $s = 1$ corresponds to a force just barely strong enough to produce a bound state in the deuteron.)

Let us first consider the dependence of the binding energy B on the range b of the nuclear force. In the limit, as the range is made very short, the well depth parameters s necessary to fit the singlet neutron-proton scattering length a_s and the triplet binding energy of the deuteron approach unity both in the singlet and in the triplet states. Since $B(s)$ does not approach zero as s approaches unity, (2.10) shows that the binding energy of the triton is inversely proportional to the square of the range of the force. In other words, a force which gives the correct binding energy of the deuteron and the correct singlet state scattering length for neutron-proton scattering can give a very large binding energy for the triton if a very small range is chosen. In the limit of a zero range force, the predicted binding energy of the triton becomes infinite. We must assume that the force has a finite range of action. This argument is much less general than the one of Thomas for the following reasons: (1) we have restricted ourselves to some special well shapes, whereas Thomas' argument makes no assumption about the details of the force law; (2) we have assumed an attractive neutron-neutron force of the same strength as the (singlet state) neutron-proton force, whereas Thomas assumed that there was no attraction between the two neutrons. If we had assumed no attraction between the two neutrons, we would have had to multiply $V(s)$ by $\frac{2}{3}$. We would then get no binding at all [$B(s)$ negative] for $s = 1$.

Comparison of the results of Fig. 2.1 with the very accurate calculations of Rarita and Present (Rarita 37; exponential well, intrinsic range $b = 3.06 \times 10^{-13}$ cm) and of Brown and Plesset (Brown 39, 39a; Yukawa well, intrinsic range $b = 3.89 \times 10^{-13}$ cm) shows that the trial

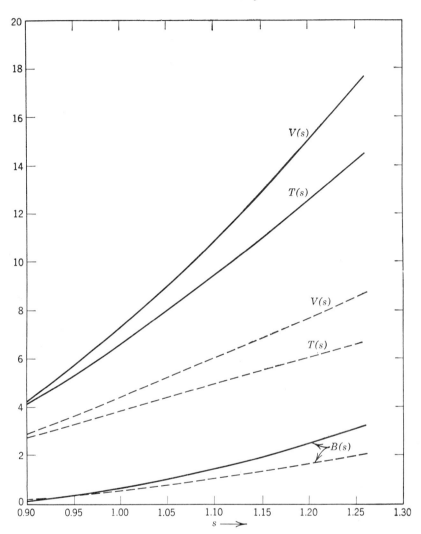

Fig. 2.1.   The potential energy $V(s)$, kinetic energy $T(s)$, and binding energy $B(s)$ of the triton (in units $\hbar^2/Mb^2$, where b is the intrinsic range of the force) as functions of the well depth parameter s for two well shapes: Yukawa well (solid curves) and exponential well (dashed curves).   The "deep hole" of the Yukawa well pulls the wave function toward the center, leading to large values of the kinetic and potential energies.

wave function (2.2) gives over 90 percent of the binding energy for these long ranges.[1] It is reasonable, therefore, to assume that the results obtained with (2.2) can be trusted for qualitative purposes also for ranges b more nearly in agreement with present data on the two-body problems ($b \cong 2.5 \times 10^{-13}$ cm).

Let us proceed to interpret the curves of Fig. 2.1. The figure shows that the binding energy is a small difference between two large quantities (the potential energy and the kinetic energy). This situation is very similar to the one in the deuteron ground state, except that the ratio of the potential energy to the binding energy is somewhat smaller here than in the (more weakly bound) deuteron.

There is a characteristic difference between the two well shapes, however. Both the kinetic and the potential energies are very much larger for a Yukawa well than for an exponential well of the same (intrinsic) range b (Irving 51). This result allows a simple interpretation: the Yukawa well, being more long-tailed, has a deeper hole near $r = 0$ than the exponential well. This is shown in Fig. 2.2, where we have drawn a Yukawa well and an exponential well of the same (intrinsic) range and the same well depth ($s = 1$). The triton wave function tries to take advantage of this region of strong attraction in the Yukawa well by "drawing in." For example, the value of κ which minimizes the energy for a well depth $s = 1$ is $\kappa = 1.90/b$ for the exponential well, $\kappa = 2.49/b$ for the Yukawa well. That is, the wave function is "drawn into" the Yukawa well some 30 percent more than into the exponential well for the same intrinsic range.

The results of calculations with a "deep hole" well (like the Yukawa well) are more questionable than the results with less singular well shapes for several reasons:

(1) The binding energy is a small difference between large quantities; hence high accuracy is needed in both the kinetic and the potential energies in order to get a good value for the binding energy.

(2) A less trivial source of error comes from the relativistic corrections; for reasonable well depths (s between 1 and 1.2) the ratio of kinetic energy to binding energy is between 6 and 10; thus a binding energy of 8.5 Mev implies kinetic energies of the order of 50 to 85 Mev for the Yukawa well. At such energies the relativistic corrections can become quite appreciable (10 to 20 percent in the binding energy).

[1] These very long ranges are a particularly regrettable choice since considerable theoretical work on light-weight nuclei has been based on these force parameters (Inglis 37, Margenau 38a, 38b, 39, Humblet 48, Nakabayasi 37). In view of the incorrect ranges employed, it is now impossible to interpret this work from a quantitative point of view.

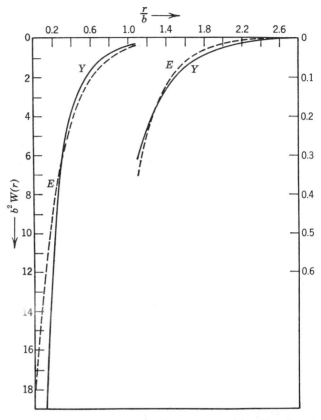

FIG. 2.2. Picture of a Yukawa well and an exponential well as functions of the interparticle distance r. The two wells shown here have the same intrinsic range b and the same well depth parameter s. The abscissa r is measured in units of the range b; the ordinate is in arbitrary units. Notice the "deep hole" of the Yukawa well for $r/b \lesssim 0.2$. The left-hand ordinate scale is to be used when $r/b < 1.1$, the right-hand one when $r/b > 1.1$.

(3) If the nuclear forces should turn out to be velocity dependent, this will give large corrections to the triton calculation with deep hole wells.

Let us now investigate the actual value of the predicted binding energy for nuclear forces adjusted to fit the two-body data approximately (there is no need to make an exact adjustment, since we are neglecting tensor forces). We shall choose the range so as to fit the proton-proton scattering data, and the well depths in the singlet and triplet states so as to fit the proton-proton scattering length and the binding energy of the deuteron, respectively. This adjustment gives an almost correct well depth for the singlet state neutron-proton force automatically (see the discussion of charge independence in Section 4 of Chapter II), and it gives a not unreasonable value for the effective range r_{0t} in the triplet state. The values for the exponential well are:

$$
\left.\begin{aligned}
b &= 2.51 \times 10^{-13} \text{ cm} \\
s_s &= 0.905 \text{ (singlet state)} \\
s_t &= 1.449 \text{ (triplet state)} \\
s &= 1.177 \text{ (average)}
\end{aligned}\right\} \quad \text{(exponential well)} \quad (2.11)
$$

The triplet well constants imply a triplet effective range $r_{0t} = 1.77 \times 10^{-13}$ cm, which is very close to the experimental value. Substitution into (2.10) and Fig. 2.1 gives a binding energy of

$$B = 9.79 \text{ Mev} \qquad \text{(exponential well)} \qquad (2.12)$$

This must be compared with the experimental value (Tollestrup 50) of $B_{\text{exp}} = 8.492$ Mev. If we recall that the figure in equation (2.12) was obtained from a variational calculation and gives therefore an underestimate of the theoretical binding energy, we can conclude that *an exponential well adjusted to the two-particle data gives too large a binding energy for the triton.*

The situation becomes even worse when we use a Yukawa well shape. The constants for a Yukawa well, adjusted as before, are

$$
\left.\begin{aligned}
b &= 2.47 \times 10^{-13} \text{ cm} \\
s_s &= 0.922 \text{ (singlet state)} \\
s_t &= 1.356 \text{ (triplet state)} \\
s &= 1.139 \text{ (average)}
\end{aligned}\right\} \quad \text{(Yukawa well)} \quad (2.13)
$$

The triplet effective range implied by these force constants is $r_{0t} = 1.51 \times 10^{-13}$ cm, which is somewhat low but not unreasonable. Equation (2.10) and Fig. 2.1 give

$$B = 12.3 \text{ Mev} \qquad \text{(Yukawa well)} \qquad (2.14)$$

The much larger theoretical value for the binding energy is a result of the "drawing" of the wave function into the deep hole of the Yukawa well. *A Yukawa well, adjusted to the two-particle data, gives even worse agreement with experiment in the triton (an even larger binding energy) than the exponential well.*

If we were restricted to the use of purely central forces, the conclusion of the argument would be that we must go to more concentrated well shapes (like the Gauss well or the square well) in order to fit experiment. However, we know from the deuteron analysis that there exists an appreciable tensor force which must also be present in the triton. We shall defer the discussion of the calculations with tensor forces until Section 5 of this chapter. Meanwhile, we conclude that

(1) The results for the triton ground state are highly well shape dependent.

(2) A "deep hole" well pulls the wave function toward the center and leads to a larger binding energy than a less singular potential.

(3) The theoretical results become more questionable (the likely corrections increase) as the well becomes more singular.

(4) Central force wells adjusted to the two-body data lead to excessive binding in the triton.

The first three conclusions remain correct when tensor forces are included in the discussion.

3. THE GROUND STATE OF THE ALPHA-PARTICLE; CENTRAL FORCES

The alpha-particle is the first completely saturated nucleus. The two protons have opposite spin, and so do the two neutrons. The space wave function is then symmetric under the interchange of the two protons, and also under the interchange of the two neutrons. To a good first approximation, it is also symmetric under the interchange of one of the neutrons with one of the protons. In spectroscopic notation, the alpha-particle ground state is a $^1S_0$ state. In the approximation that the space wave function is symmetric under the interchange of any pair of particles, we can again find the effective potential energy by counting singlet and triplet pairs. Of the six pairs, two are definitely singlet (neutron-neutron and proton-proton); two are definitely triplet (up-spin neutron with up-spin proton, and down-spin neutron with down-spin proton); and the remaining pairs are of mixed type and have to be counted as half singlet and half triplet. The result is again an equal number (3) of singlet and triplet pairs, so that the effective potential energy is still given by (2.1).

The result of Rarita and Present (Rarita 37) for the binding energy of the alpha-particle was larger than the experimental value. Since this was before the discovery of the quadrupole moment of the deuteron (and hence the tensor force), it was interpreted widely as a serious contradiction between theory and experiment. The contradiction becomes even worse when we use the adjusted exponential well (2.11) rather than the (longer-range) Rarita-Present well. The very simplest trial function of Rarita and Present (their formula 7) then gives a binding energy of 38.2 Mev for the alpha-particle—10 Mev too much. An improved trial function would make this disagreement much worse.

The relevant calculations for the Yukawa well shape were performed by Svartholm (45). He expresses his results in the form of the well depth necessary to fit the observed binding energy, rather than by giving the theoretical binding energy implied by a certain well depth. This makes little difference for our present purposes. Svartholm gives numerical results for the Breit (39) range which fits the proton-proton data ($b = 2.51 \times 10^{-13}$ cm, which is close to the best value at present): the well depth necessary to fit the alpha-particle is $V \leq 52.5$ Mev, which corresponds to $s = \frac{1}{2}(s_t + s_s) \leq 1.052$ compared to an "adjusted" value (2.13) of $s = 1.139$. The well depth necessary to fit the alpha-particle is appreciably smaller than the one from the two-body data. The adjusted well depth (2.13) (which is already too deep for the triton) would give an excessively large binding energy for the alpha-particle.[1]

Unlike the triton, the results for the alpha-particle are not extensive enough to allow interpretation, other than to say that the adjusted central forces give too much binding energy. In particular, we do not have enough information to draw conclusions regarding the effects of well shape in this problem. We expect, however, that the effects are very similar to those in the triton. There is reason to believe (Gerjuoy 42) that the tensor forces tend to reduce the theoretical binding energy of the alpha-particle (see Section 5).

4. H³ AND He³: THE EQUALITY OF NEUTRON-NEUTRON AND PROTON-PROTON FORCES

Although the two-body data give relatively good information about the forces between two protons and between a neutron and a proton, the information about neutron-neutron forces is very meager indeed. Our only piece of evidence is negative: the non-existence of a stable di-neutron. This puts an upper limit on the strength of an attractive neutron-neutron force. Neutron-neutron scattering experiments are out of the question from the practical point of view: the density of neutrons in the densest neutron beam available is many orders of magnitude too small to permit scattering experiments to be made.

The three-body systems are, therefore, most likely to give us

---

[1] The small differences in the well depth correspond to large differences in the binding energy, as a look at Fig. 2.1 will show for the triton; the statement is also true for the alpha-particle.

unambiguous information about neutron-neutron forces. There is only one like-particle pair in the triton (a neutron-neutron pair) and in He³ (a proton-proton pair). The remaining two pairs are neutron-proton pairs in each case. Thus these simplest "mirror nuclei" can be expected to give a more unambiguous test of various assumptions regarding the neutron-neutron force than any heavier nuclei.

The binding energies of H³ and He³ are rather close to each other (Tollestrup 50):

$$B(\mathrm{H}^3) = 8.492 \text{ Mev} \qquad B(\mathrm{He}^3) = 7.728 \text{ Mev} \qquad (4.1)$$

This near equality makes it reasonable to assume that the neutron-neutron force (in H³) is not very different from the proton-proton force (in He³). The small difference between the binding energies,

$$\Delta B = 0.764 \text{ Mev} \qquad (4.2)$$

is then attributed to the Coulomb repulsion between the two protons in He³ (which has no counterpart in H³). The effect is in the right direction to allow this interpretation, since He³ is less strongly bound than H³. ΔB is also of the right order of magnitude. We can see this by computing the Coulomb radius R_c of He³, which is defined through[1]

$$\text{Coulomb energy of He}^3 = \frac{6}{5}\frac{e^2}{R_c} \qquad (4.3)$$

If we attribute the entire difference of binding energies ΔB, (4.2), to the Coulomb effect, the Coulomb radius R_c of He³ turns out to be

$$R_c = 2.26 \times 10^{-13} \text{ cm} \qquad (4.4)$$

This is certainly a reasonable value for the "radius" of a light nucleus such as He³.

We conclude that the binding energies of H³ and He³ can be understood most simply under the assumption that *neutron-neutron forces are equal to proton-proton forces except for the Coulomb repulsion between two protons.*[2]

This assumption is in agreement with the lack of stability of the di-neutron. The proton-proton scattering experiments show that the di-proton is dynamically unstable (see Section 4 of Chapter II).

[1] The general definition of the Coulomb radius for arbitrary Z is given in Chapter VI.

[2] Three-body forces are not excluded by this argument. However, if present, the "neutron-neutron-proton" and "proton-proton-neutron" forces would have to equal each other.

Under the assumption of equal neutron-neutron and proton-proton forces, the neutron-neutron scattering length is just the a' of (II,4.9). Since a' is negative, we conclude that the removal of the Coulomb force is not enough to make the di-neutron stable.

Strong confirmation for equality of neutron-neutron and proton-proton forces comes also from the study of heavier mirror nuclei, which will be discussed in the next chapter.

Once we accept the hypothesis of equality of neutron-neutron and proton-proton forces, the observed binding energy difference ΔB provides an additional test of the theory, a test which is independent of the absolute amount of the binding energies. The Coulomb radius R_c depends on the "extent" of the wave function of the ground state. Since the Coulomb energy of He³ is equal to the expectation value of e^2/r_{12} in the ground state (where particles 1 and 2 are the two protons), we see from (4.3) that the Coulomb radius R_c can be found from the wave function of the ground state of He³ through the relation

$$R_c^{-1} = \frac{5}{6} \int \Psi^* \frac{1}{r_{12}} \Psi \, d\tau \qquad (4.5)$$

Since the Coulomb force is small compared to nuclear forces in the region which contributes most to this integral, we can approximate (4.5) by inserting for Ψ the wave function of H³, (2.2), with the best value of κ (adjusted to give the highest binding energy for H³). This gives

$$R_c = \frac{42}{25} \kappa \qquad (4.6)$$

According to the calculations of Brown and Plesset (39), equation (4.6) is within 10 percent of the correct value. If we substitute the force parameters for the "adjusted" wells, (2.11) and (2.13), we get

$$R_c = 1.81 \times 10^{-13} \text{ cm} \qquad \text{(exponential well)} \qquad (4.7)$$

$$R_c = 1.32 \times 10^{-13} \text{ cm} \qquad \text{(Yukawa well)} \qquad (4.8)$$

Comparison with the experimental value (4.4) shows that the Yukawa well shape gives considerably too low a value for the Coulomb radius (too high a Coulomb energy) and is probably excluded on this score. Preliminary calculations of Pease (50, 51) with tensor forces confirm this conclusion.

The two identical particles (two neutrons in H³, two protons in He³) have opposite spins in the ground state of the three-body system. Furthermore they have no relative orbital angular momentum to a first approximation. Thus the comparison of the binding energies of H^3 and He^3 gives information about neutron-neutron and proton-proton forces in one state only, the ^1S state. In principle there exists an excellent method of studying neutron-neutron forces in other states also: the analysis of neutron-deuteron and proton-deuteron impacts. Three events can happen when a neutron collides with a deuteron:

Elastic scattering: $n + d = n + d$ (4.9)

Deuteron disintegration: $n + d = p + n + n$ (4.10)

Radiative capture: $n + d = H^3 + \gamma$ (4.11)

The disintegration of the deuteron is less likely than elastic scattering at low energies (it is impossible energetically for neutron energies $E_{n,\text{lab}} \leq 3.34$ Mev, i.e., $\frac{3}{2}$ the binding energy of the deuteron) but should be observable.

The corresponding "mirror" reactions occur when a proton collides with a deuteron:

Elastic scattering: $p + d = p + d$ (4.9')

Deuteron disintegration: $p + d = p + p + n$ (4.10')

Radiative capture: $p + d = He^3 + \gamma$ (4.11')

Although there is considerable experimental material about these processes, especially about the elastic scattering (Barkas 39, Barschall 40, Taschek 42, Smith 48, Fermi 49, Mather 50, and many others), the theoretical interpretation of these results is still in a very preliminary state (Primakoff 37, Ochiai 37, Motz 40, Buckingham 41, Hoecker 42, Massey 48a, Burhop 48a, Critchfield 48).

▶ **5. GROUND STATE OF THE TRITON; TENSOR FORCES**

The presence of tensor forces has several effects on the ground state of the triton. First, it is no longer true that the ground state is a pure $^2S_{1/2}$ state. Various other states with the same $I = \frac{1}{2}$ and the same parity are admixed to the dominant $^2S_{1/2}$ part of the wave function. The main admixture is of type $^4D_{1/2}$ (Gerjuoy 42). This can be seen most simply by observing that the tensor operator S_{12}, (II,5.2), behaves like a wave function with $l = 2$ under rotations of the space coordinates. It therefore makes a D state out of an S state. In the deuteron the D state is the only possible admixture. In the triton other admixtures are possible (which can be obtained by applying the tensor operator S_{12} to the various D states which are admixed in first order), but they are less important than the D state admixture.

We can estimate the amount of admixture of other states from the measured magnetic moments of the triton and He[3] by their contribution to the magnetic moment. In order to distinguish between these contributions and the exchange magnetic moments, we must make the assumption that the exchange magnetic moment contributions are equal and opposite for these two nuclei (Sachs 48, Morrison 48, Spruch 50). This assumption is subject to some doubt, however, since we do not have a complete understanding of these cooperative effects in nuclear magnetism. The result of the estimate, interpreted in terms of a predominant D state admixture, is a D state probability of roughly 4 percent. This estimate is even less reliable than the similar one in the deuteron. The relativistic corrections to the magnetic moments of the triton and He[3] are much larger than for the deuteron, since the particles are, in general, moving much faster.

The most striking effect of the tensor forces in the triton is not their admixture of other states, but their effect in decreasing the predicted binding energy (which we have seen in Section 2 to be necessary for bringing theory and experiment into agreement). Equation (2.1) for the effective potential between two nucleons in the triton applies only to the central force part of the potential. Tensor forces must not be averaged in like this. The expectation value of the tensor operator is zero in a $^2S_{1/2}$ state (because the square of the wave function is spherically symmetric in such a state and the average of S_{12} over a spherically symmetric distribution is zero, by construction). Thus the tensor force contributes to the binding energy of the triton only indirectly, through coupling in other, less symmetric, states. This situation is entirely analogous to the one for the deuteron. However, the tensor force is considerably less effective in the triton than it is in the deuteron. First of all, only half of the pairs are triplet pairs. The other half are singlet pairs for which the tensor force is zero. Secondly, the states which are coupled in are much less favorable energetically in the triton than in the deuteron. The triton is a much more closely bound structure than the deuteron, so that a state with nodes in it (such as the admixed D state) is forced much farther out, comparatively, than in the deuteron. The binding energy contribution of the tensor force comes mostly from the cross term between the dominant S state and the various admixtures. This cross term is reduced in the triton because the wave functions for the admixed states overlap more poorly with the dominant wave function (the S state) than they do in the deuteron. The result is that a given strength of the tensor force has an appreciably smaller effect on the binding energy of the triton than on that of the deuteron.

This effect reduces the predicted binding energy of the triton compared to the value obtained with purely central forces. The potential energy is given by

$$\tfrac{1}{2}\int \Psi^*[V_t + V_s]\Psi\, d\tau$$

according to (2.1). If tensor forces are present, V_t contains a central and tensor part: $V_t = V_{tc} + V_{tr}$. The latter force contributes relatively less in the triton than in the deuteron. Since the force constants are adjusted to fit the deuteron, we expect that the binding energy of the triton is appreciably less with adjusted tensor forces than with adjusted central ones. This effect is even stronger in the alpha-particle.

The early computations (Gerjuoy 42, Feshbach 49) with the Rarita-Schwinger square well (Rarita 41) gave not enough binding energy for the triton, rather than too much binding energy as obtained from central forces. The situation is complicated by several factors. First, Clapp (49) has shown that the approximations used in the earlier calculations are not adequate to define the binding energy of the triton to sufficient accuracy. Secondly, the well constants used in these calculations (the Rarita-Schwinger well) are inconsistent with present data on the two-body problems (Biedenharn 50). Pease (50, 51), using Yukawa wells which fit the two-body data, gets close to the experimental value of the binding energy but gets too small a Coulomb radius for He^3.

In view of the tremendous labor of computation involved in finding the binding energy of the triton in the presence of tensor forces (and even more for the alpha-particle), it seems likely that a resolution of this problem requires large-scale computing machines. Until then, the situation is as follows: the introduction of the tensor force goes qualitatively in the right direction to explain the discrepancies between theoretical and experimental binding energies under the assumption of purely central forces. We cannot say at this time whether the discrepancies will actually disappear in the tensor force case, or whether introduction of explicit many-body forces will prove necessary. However, it seems likely that a fit will be possible using two-body forces only, because the two-body data permit a large range of choices of acceptable nuclear forces and the three- and four-body problems are sensitive to the details of the assumed force law.

SYMBOLS

a' Neutron-neutron scattering length, as deduced from proton-proton scattering data   (Section 4)

a_s Neutron-proton scattering length in the singlet spin state (Section 2)

b Intrinsic range of the nuclear force; for the definition see Chapter II, Sections 2 and 3   (Section 2)

B Nuclear binding energy   (Section 2)

$B(s)$ Parameter in the binding energy $[= V(s) - T(s)]$ (2.10)

I Total angular momentum of the nucleus   (Section 2)

L Quantum number for the orbital angular momentum of the nucleus   (Section 2)

M Nucleon mass   (2.4)

N Normalization constant for the trial wave function Ψ (2.2)

r Distance between two nucleons   (2.1)

$\mathbf{r}$ Position vector of a nucleon   (Section 2)

r_{0t} Effective range for neutron-proton scattering in the triplet spin state   (Section 2)

R_c Coulomb radius of He^3 (4.3)

s Non-dimensional well depth parameter for the nuclear force; for the definition of s see Chapter II, Section 2   (Section 2)

s_s Value of s for a neutron-proton pair in the singlet spin state (2.11)

s_t Value of s for a neutron-proton pair in the triplet spin state (assuming a purely central force in the triplet spin state) (2.11)

S Quantum number for the spin angular momentum of the nucleus   (Section 2)

S_{12} Tensor operator; for its definition see Chapter II, Section 5 (Section 5)

$T(s)$ The kinetic energy expressed in units $\hbar^2/Mb^2$, using the trial wave function Ψ (2.8)

V_0 Conventional well depth parameter of the nuclear potential; for its definition see Chapter II, Section 2   (2.5)

$V_{\mathrm{eff}}(r)$ The effective potential energy between each pair of nucleons in a completely symmetric state of the three- (or four-) body system   (2.1)

$V(s)$ The absolute value of the potential energy in units $\hbar^2/Mb^2$, using the trial wave function Ψ (2.9)

$V_s(r)$ Potential of the nuclear force in the singlet spin state   (2.1)

$V_t(r)$ Potential of the nuclear force in the triplet spin state   (2.1)

V_{tc} Potential of the central force in the triplet spin state   (Section 5)

V_{tT} Potential of the tensor force in the triplet spin state   (Section 5)

$\alpha(n)$ Spin wave function for a neutron with spin pointing up (Section 2)

$\alpha(p)$ Spin wave function for a proton with spin pointing up (Section 2)

β Conventional parameter for the range of the nuclear force; for the definition see Chapter II, Section 2   (2.5)

$\beta(n)$ Spin wave function for a neutron with spin pointing down (Section 2)

$\beta(p)$ Spin wave function for a proton with spin pointing down (Section 2)

ΔB Difference in binding energy of H^3 and He^3 (4.2)

κ Parameter in the trial wave function Ψ (2.2)

λ de Broglie wavelength of the relative motion of two particles (divided by 2π)   (Section 2)

μ Nuclear magnetic moment (in nuclear magnetons)   (Section 2)

$\mathbf{\sigma}$ Pauli spin vector of a nucleon   (Section 2)

Ψ Wave function for the triton   (Section 2); trial wave function for the triton   (2.2)

CHAPTER VI

Nuclear Spectroscopy
I. General Theory

1. THE SYSTEMATICS OF STABLE NUCLEI

A. Stability Conditions

It was observed quite early in the development of nuclear physics that, at least for light nuclei, the stable species contain approximately equal numbers of neutrons and protons (Harkins 22). This is illustrated in Fig. 1.1 where the quantity

$$T_\zeta = \frac{N - Z}{2} \tag{1.1}$$

is plotted against the mass number A. In Fig. 1.1 each stable nuclear species is indicated by a circle.

The fact that T_ζ is restricted to 0, $\frac{1}{2}$, and 1 for the light stable nuclei has led to the hypothesis that nuclear forces act between neutrons and protons but not between neutrons and neutrons or between protons and protons. Then the stability would be largest for the largest number of pairs of different types, and this would lead to a preference for T_ζ to be near zero. This drastic assumption of forces only between unlike particles is by no means necessary, however. Actually, the experiments on proton-proton scattering demonstrate conclusively the existence of nuclear forces between protons. Therefore the low values of T_ζ have to be accounted for by a more general argument.

We recall that there are two kinds of "stability" for a nuclear species:

(1) Dynamical stability: the breaking of the nuclear system into two or more parts is energetically impossible.

(2) Beta-stability: the transformation of a neutron into a proton (or vice versa) with the emission (capture) of an electron and a neutrino is energetically impossible.

211

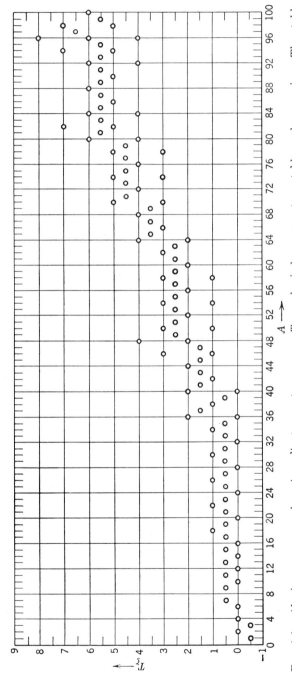

FIG. 1.1.   Abscissa: mass number A; ordinate: neutron excess T_ζ; each circle represents a stable nuclear species.   The stable light nuclei have approximately equal numbers of neutrons and protons ($T_\zeta \cong 0$), whereas heavier nuclei tend to have an excess of neutrons.

As the problems connected with dynamical stability are taken up in Chapter XI, we shall not be concerned here with that kind of stability. In this chapter we want to find out which is the stable nucleus of a group of isobaric nuclei with different neutron excess T_ζ. Since any nucleus can transform into any other one in this group by a series of beta-transformations, the stable nucleus is the one with the lowest energy.

Hence our problem can be formulated as follows: given a series of isobaric nuclei (same A), what are the decisive factors in the determination of the one or the ones with the lowest energy?

The stability conditions are based on two main factors which we enumerate in the order of their importance:

(1) The symmetry effect: the charge independence and the exchange character of nuclear forces, together with the Pauli exclusion principle, strongly depresses the energy of nuclei with equal or nearly equal numbers of neutrons and protons.

(2) The charge effect: the effect of the Coulomb repulsion of the protons favors nuclei with fewer protons than neutrons. The neutron-proton mass difference also enters the charge effect, but only as a small correction. The charge effect increases in importance with increasing nuclear charge.

(3) In a few special cases a third effect is important: the spin-dependence of nuclear forces favors parallel spin over anti-parallel spin of a pair of (extra) nucleons.

We discuss first the symmetry effect and the charge effect. The influence of the spin dependence of nuclear forces will be discussed in connection with the stability considerations for nuclei with mass numbers $A = 4n + 2$.

(1) **The Symmetry Effect.** The significance of the symmetry effect is easiest to see if applied to a very simple model of a nucleus, one which is far from reality: the independent-particle model. In this model we describe the nucleus by an assembly of independent nucleons moving inside a sphere of the nuclear radius R. This assumption is, of course, entirely unjustified; however, we shall use here only those properties of the independent-particle model which follow from symmetry considerations, and which, therefore, can be generalized as we shall indicate later on. Conclusions which make an essential use of this (or any other) special model will be deferred to the next chapter.

In the independent-particle picture, any one particle occupies one of the levels which are the stationary states in the common central field. We shall not use the specific properties of these levels in our

VI. Nuclear Spectroscopy I

present discussion.   We treat all nucleons as identical particles with two internal degrees of freedom: the spin and the charge, each with two possible values.   According to the exclusion principle, two identical particles cannot be in the same state.   Since we have four possible states corresponding to each "level" of the one-particle picture (neutron or proton, with spin up or down), each one-particle level

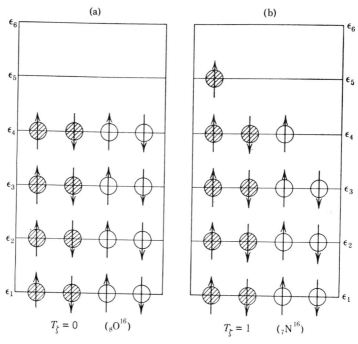

Fig. 1.2.   A schematic picture of two nuclei of mass number $A = 16$ on the independent-particle model.   Shaded circles represent neutrons, open circles represent protons; the spin directions (up or down) are indicated by arrows.   Each horizontal line represents a level of the independent-particle model; the levels are arranged in order of increasing energy, $\epsilon_1 \leq \epsilon_2 \leq \epsilon_3 \leq \cdots$.   Because of the Pauli exclusion principle, the state shown in part (a) for O^{16} ($T_\zeta = 0$) cannot occur in N^{16} ($T_\zeta = 1$).   In N^{16} one of the neutrons is forced into a higher level, thereby making the wave function less symmetric.

counts as four states in general and can accommodate four nucleons. This is illustrated in Fig. 1.2, where we have indicated the one-particle levels schematically by lines, a neutron by a shaded circle, a proton by an open circle, and the spin direction of either by an arrow.   The nucleus pictured in Fig. 1.2a consists of 8 neutrons and 8 protons, with zero net spin (i.e., O^{16}).   We see that the first four levels are filled and the levels of higher energy are empty.   Figure 1.2b also depicts a nucleus of 16 particles, but now made up of 9 neutrons and 7 protons (N^{16}), i.e., with $T_\zeta = 1$. We cannot put more than 2 neutrons in any one level; hence the extra neutron must go into the next level. There is a simple argument that the sum of all energies is smallest if the number of protons Z equals the number of neutrons N, for then the particles can be put into the lowest possible levels. If $N \neq Z$, higher levels must be used. In spite of its simplicity, this argument is not the main reason for the symmetry effect. In fact this argument breaks down when some of the levels are degenerate.

The main argument for the symmetry effect comes from the exchange character of nuclear forces. Exchange forces in nuclei[1] are attractive between two particles if the wave function is symmetric with respect to the space exchange of these particles; they are repulsive if the wave function is anti-symmetric. Thus exchange forces are attractive between particles in the same level, but less attractive or even repulsive between particles in different levels.[2] Hence we obtain the largest amount of attraction if the number of particles in equal levels is highest. This is the case for the smallest T_ζ among nuclei of equal A.

Thus the assumption of exchange forces provides a natural explanation for the increased stability of nuclei with equal numbers of neutrons and protons, for these are the nuclei which can have the largest number of symmetric pairs. Nuclei with an excess of either type of nucleon must have more anti-symmetric pairs, according to the Pauli principle. The anti-symmetric pairs do not contribute to the potential energy (in so far as they do make a contribution, it is of the wrong sign to give binding), so the stablest nuclei are the ones with the fewest anti-symmetric pairs, i.e., with T_ζ close to zero. This is the effect which we have called the *symmetry effect*.

So far it appears that we have made use of a specific model which is entirely unrealistic. This is not true, however. The independent-particle model merely provides us with a simple way of counting the number of symmetric pairs of the *true* wave function. We shall prove in Section 3 that the number of symmetric pairs is correctly given by the independent-particle model even if the wave function in its details differs considerably from an independent-particle wave function.

---

[1] In this chapter "exchange forces" will be understood to mean space exchange (Majorana) forces (see Chapter III) which involve an operator exchanging the positions of a pair of nucleons but not their spins.

[2] The wave function is evidently symmetric for a pair of particles in the same level. It is anti-symmetric on account of the Pauli principle for a pair of identical particles in two different levels. It is partially symmetric and anti-symmetric for a pair of non-identical particles in two different levels (see, footnote 2, p. 194).

The exchange nature of the nuclear forces is the main determinant of the symmetry effect. There are, however, two other reasons why nuclei with a large number of symmetric pairs are more stable than other nuclei of the same mass number. These two additional, subsidiary arguments are:

(a) The kinetic energy argument. A wave function anti-symmetric under the interchange of the space coordinates of two particles must be zero wherever the positions of these two particles coincide. It, therefore, oscillates more rapidly than a wave function symmetric under this interchange. Rapid oscillations in the wave function raise the kinetic energy. We conclude that a more symmetric wave function in general has lower (positive) kinetic energy.

(b) The overlap argument. It provides a reason why any interaction (also a non-exchange one) is more effective between symmetric pairs than between anti-symmetric ones. Two particles for which the wave function is symmetric are found more frequently near one another, and this enhances their interaction; anti-symmetric pairs stay apart from each other, and this reduces their interaction. Since the force between symmetric pairs is attractive, this effect favors again a state with a larger number of symmetric pairs.

(2) **The Charge Effect.** The effects of the electrostatic (Coulomb) energy of the protons and the difference in the rest energy between neutrons and protons ($M_n c^2 - M_p c^2 = 1.3$ Mev) can be investigated together.

The Coulomb force is repulsive; hence it favors stability of nuclei with fewer protons (positive T_ζ). The neutron is heavier than the proton; hence the rest mass contribution to the energy of the nucleus is lowered if neutrons are replaced by protons; the neutron-proton mass difference favors the stability of nuclei with few neutrons (negative T_ζ). Since two opposing tendencies are at work here, the stronger one determines the direction of the charge effect.

We proceed to estimate the order of magnitude of the charge effect. The electrostatic energy $\bar{C}$ can be used to define a "Coulomb radius" R of the nucleus by the equation

$$\bar{C} = \frac{1}{2} Z(Z-1) \frac{6}{5} \frac{e^2}{R} \qquad (1.2)$$

$\bar{C}$ would be the electrostatic energy of Z protons distributed uniformly over a sphere of radius R. This assumption is unjustified for two reasons: (1) the protons are not distributed uniformly over the nuclear volume, because the nuclear volume has no sharply defined boundaries, and because the Coulomb repulsion may increase the density of the protons near the boundary region (Feenberg 41); (2) the protons are correlated, i.e., the probability of finding two of them in two specified volume elements dV_1 and dV_2 is not simply the product of the probabilities of finding one of them in dV_1 and the other one in dV_2 (Feenberg 42, 46; Phillips 41). Since we do not know the magnitude of these two effects, we shall use (1.2) as a definition of R. For our present purposes it is sufficient to observe that R is of the order of magnitude of the nuclear radius determined by other means (scattering experiments).

In terms of A and T_ζ, Eq. (1.2) can be rewritten

$$\bar{C} = \frac{6}{10}\left[\left(\frac{A}{2}\right)^2 - \frac{A}{2} - T_\zeta(A-1-T_\zeta)\right]\frac{e^2}{R} \qquad (1.3)$$

The rest mass energy of the nucleons is

$$E_{\text{rest}} = ZM_pc^2 + NM_nc^2 \qquad (1.4)$$

or, in terms of A and T_ζ,

$$E_{\text{rest}} = A\frac{M_nc^2 + M_pc^2}{2} + T_\zeta(M_nc^2 - M_pc^2) \qquad (1.5)$$

The contribution of the charge effect to the total energy difference between two isobars with neutron excesses T_ζ and T_ζ' is therefore given by[1]

$$\Delta E_c = (T_\zeta - T_\zeta')$$
$$\times [(M_nc^2 - M_pc^2) - \tfrac{6}{10}(A-1-T_\zeta-T_\zeta')(e^2/R)] \quad (1.6)$$

B. Discussion of Stable Nuclei

We now study the stability conditions among isobars, using the two factors (symmetry and charge) discussed above. Let us first consider *nuclei with* $A = 4n$ (n integral). According to the symmetry effect, the most favored nucleus among isobars of given mass number $A = 4n$ is the one in which the number of protons and neutrons is equal, $T_\zeta = 0$. If $T_\zeta \neq 0$, one or several nucleons must be placed in higher levels, and the number of symmetric pairs is reduced. We therefore expect the stable nuclei to have $T_\zeta = 0$.

Figure 1.1 shows that this is true for the light nuclei of the sequence $A = 4n$. For nuclei of higher Z, the charge effect becomes strong enough to overcome the symmetry effect, and the stable species has a neutron excess (positive value of T_ζ). This takes place for $A \geq 36$.

---

[1] We assume that the nuclear radius R is independent of the neutron excess T_ζ.

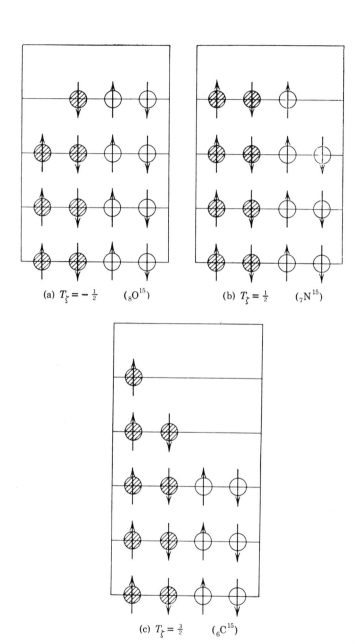

(a) $T_\zeta = -\tfrac{1}{2}$ ($_8O^{15}$)

(b) $T_\zeta = \tfrac{1}{2}$ ($_7N^{15}$)

(c) $T_\zeta = \tfrac{3}{2}$ ($_6C^{15}$)

Fig. 1.3.   A schematic picture of three nuclei of mass number $A = 15$ on the independent-particle model.   The nuclei O^{15} ($T_\zeta = -\tfrac{1}{2}$) and N^{15} ($T_\zeta = +\tfrac{1}{2}$) are mirror nuclei; they have the same kinetic energy and the same nuclear potential energy; the charge effect favors the stability of the one with the higher neutron excess, i.e., of N^{15}.   Nuclei with $|T_\zeta| > \tfrac{1}{2}$, such as the C^{15} ($T_\zeta = \tfrac{3}{2}$) shown in (c), are less stable because some of the particles are forced into higher levels, thereby making the wave function less symmetric.

218

Now consider *nuclei with odd mass numbers*. A typical case $(A = 15)$ is illustrated in Fig. 1.3. The symmetry effect favors the low values of T_ζ, $T_\zeta = -\frac{1}{2}$ and $T_\zeta = +\frac{1}{2}$, against higher values, such as $T_\zeta = \frac{3}{2}$. On the other hand, it does not decide between $T_\zeta = -\frac{1}{2}$ and $T_\zeta = +\frac{1}{2}$ (extra proton or extra neutron). Indeed, the kinetic energy and the nuclear part of the potential energy of two "mirror nuclei" (nuclei with equal A and opposite T_ζ) are exactly the same if it is assumed that the neutron-neutron forces equal the proton-proton forces.

In order to decide which of two mirror nuclei is stable we invoke the charge effect. The difference of the binding energies between the nuclei with $T_\zeta = +\frac{1}{2}$ and $T_\zeta = -\frac{1}{2}$ is given by ΔE_c only. We get from (1.6)

$$\Delta E_c = (M_n c^2 - M_p c^2) - \frac{6}{10}\frac{e^2}{R}(A-1) \tag{1.7}$$

The isobar with $T_\zeta = +\frac{1}{2}$ is the stable one if $\Delta E_c < mc^2$; then no electron can be emitted. If $\Delta E_c > mc^2$, the isobar with $T_\zeta = -\frac{1}{2}$ is stable (see I,3.5 and I,3.7). Thus we find that $T_\zeta = +\frac{1}{2}$ is stable if

$$R < (A-1) \times 1.05 \times 10^{-13} \text{ cm} \tag{1.8}$$

A good empirical formula for the nuclear radii observed in fast neutron scattering experiments is (see Chapter I)

$$R \cong 1.45 \times A^{\frac{1}{3}} \times 10^{-13} \text{ cm} \tag{1.9}$$

Equation (1.8) is certainly fulfilled for $A > 3$; therefore the isobar with less charge is the stable one in all mirror nuclei pairs except for $A = 3$ and 1. For $A = 3$, equation (1.9) gives $R = 2.02 \times 10^{-13}$ cm and equation (1.8) requires that R be less than 2.10×10^{-13} cm for stability. This is quite close, and actually (because of the unusually small binding energy per particle) the Coulomb radius of He^3 exceeds the limit (1.8): He^3 is stable, whereas H^3 decays by negative electron emission to He^3. The maximum kinetic energy of the electrons is only about 19 kev, and this fact shows how close our estimate is. Our rule is borne out by the data summarized in Fig. 1.1 up to $A = 35$. For larger values of A the charge effect is stronger than the symmetry effect and the stable nuclei have $T_\zeta > \frac{1}{2}$.

We now turn to light *nuclei with mass numbers $A = 4n + 2$ (n integral)*. A typical case $(A = 6)$ is illustrated in Fig. 1.4. The symmetry effect does not discriminate between the nuclei with $T_\zeta = -1, 0, +1$. Each of the three can have a set of filled levels with two extra particles in the top level. The symmetry effect tells us that nuclei with $|T_\zeta| \geq 2$ are much less stable, since one of the filled levels has to be broken up (Fig. 1.4d).

Of the three nuclei with $T_\zeta = -1, 0, +1$, those with $T_\zeta = -1$ and $T_\zeta = +1$ are mirror nuclei, and our previous argument applies, i.e., $T_\zeta = +1$ (He^6) is more stable than $T_\zeta = -1$ (Be^6). The choice therefore narrows down to the possibilities $T_\zeta = 0$ and $T_\zeta = 1$ (Li^6 and He^6, Figs. 1.4b and 1.4c).

We have seen that the charge effect favors the stability of the larger T_ζ. We are therefore tempted to conclude that $T_\zeta = +1$ is the stable nucleus. This, however, is an erroneous conclusion: Li^6 is stable whereas He^6 is unstable.

Our reasoning above was invalid because we cannot assume here (as we could for mirror nuclei) that the nuclear potential energy has the same value for the two nuclei in question. The two "extra" particles in Li^6 are a neutron and a proton, whereas the two "extra" particles in He^6 are both neutrons. The fact that Li^6 rather than He^6 is stable tells us that the effect of the neutron-proton force in Li^6 is stronger than the effect of the neutron-neutron force in He^6 by an amount sufficient to overcome the charge effect. This does not mean that we must give up the charge independence of nuclear forces. It is sufficient to give up the spin independence. Since the two extra particles in Li^6 are not identical they may have parallel spin without violating the Pauli principle, whereas the two extra neutrons in He^6 must have opposite spin. It is therefore sufficient to assume that two nucleons in the same level have a somewhat stronger attraction if their spins are parallel than if their spins are anti-parallel. This assumption of spin-dependent forces is justified on the basis of the experience in the deuteron, the simplest $4n+2$ nucleus. The fact that the spin of the neutron and that of the proton are parallel in the ground state of the deuteron is the most obvious realization of this rule.

We are therefore not required to drop the hypothesis of charge independence of nuclear forces to understand the stability of Li^6. If we maintain this hypothesis, we may draw some more conclusions about nuclear levels in the $4n+2$ nuclei. The charge-independence hypothesis implies that the wave function of that excited state of Li^6 in which the neutron and proton have *opposite* spin is identical with the wave function of He^6, except that the proton in Li^6 has been changed to a neutron in He^6. Let us call this excited state Li^{6*}. For the same reason this same wave function also describes the ground state of Be^6. The states of He^6, Li^{6*}, Be^6, all with the same wave function, form a simple example of a mass multiplet or *isotopic spin*

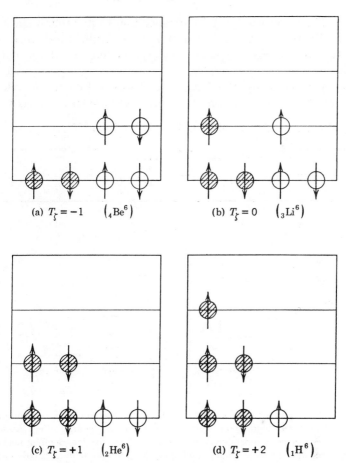

(a) $T_\zeta = -1$ $\left(_4\mathrm{Be}^6\right)$

(b) $T_\zeta = 0$ $\left(_3\mathrm{Li}^6\right)$

(c) $T_\zeta = +1$ $\left(_2\mathrm{He}^6\right)$

(d) $T_\zeta = +2$ $\left(_1\mathrm{H}^6\right)$

Fig. 1.4.   A schematic picture of four nuclei of mass number $A = 6$ on the independent-particle model.   The symmetry effect does not discriminate between the nuclei with $T_\zeta = -1$ (Be^6), $T_\zeta = 0$ (Li^6), and $T_\zeta = +1$ (He^6); but it does make the nuclei with $|T_\zeta| > 1$, such as H^6 ($T_\zeta = 2$), unstable.   The nuclei with $T_\zeta = \pm 1$ (He^6 and Be^6) are mirror nuclei; the charge effect favors the stability of He^6.   The nuclei He^6 ($T_\zeta = 1$) and Li^6 ($T_\zeta = 0$) are not mirror nuclei; the charge effect favors the stability of He^6, whereas the spin effect favors the stability of Li^6; the latter effect predominates so that Li^6 ($T_\zeta = 0$) is actually the stable nucleus, the others on the figure being unstable.

multiplet.   In this case we are dealing with an isotopic spin triplet; the three nuclei He^6, Li^{6*}, Be^6, with $T_\zeta = 1, 0, -1$, respectively, form the three components of this isotopic spin triplet.

To the extent that the charge effect can be neglected, the energy levels of the lowest states of He^6, Li^6, and Be^6 are as indicated in Fig. 1.5a.   The three levels of equal energy constitute the isotopic spin triplet. The lower level of Li^6 corresponding to its ground state contains the "extra" neutron and proton with parallel mechanical spin. This state is therefore a mechanical spin triplet and can suitably be called an isotopic spin singlet.

If we had given up the charge-independence hypothesis and had made only the (weaker) assumption that neutron-neutron forces equal

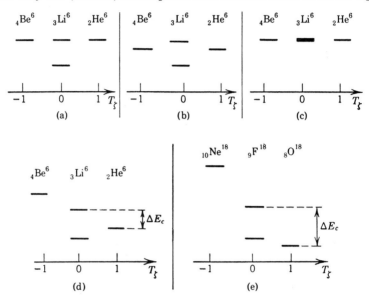

FIG. 1.5. Schematic level schemes of isobaric nuclei under various assumptions about nuclear forces and about the charge effect: (a) charge effect neglected, nuclear forces charge-independent but spin-dependent; (b) charge effect neglected, nuclear forces dependent on charge and spin, but neutron-neutron forces assumed equal to proton-proton forces; (c) charge effect neglected, nuclear forces spin- and charge-independent (this is the Wigner assumption of Sections 3 ff.); the nuclear states form a "supermultiplet"; (d) charge effect taken into account, nuclear forces charge-independent but spin-dependent; the energy difference ΔE_c between "corresponding" levels is due to the charge effect and can be estimated by (1.11); (e) same as (d) but for heavier nuclei for which the charge effect is more pronounced; the charge effect now dominates over the spin effect, making the nucleus with $T_\zeta = 1$ stable, the nucleus with $T_\zeta = 0$ unstable.

proton-proton forces, the level scheme (a) would look somewhat like (b); i.e., the two mirror nuclei He^6 and Be^6 would still have the same energy (except for the charge effect), but the anti-parallel spin level of $Li^6 (= Li^{6*})$ would no longer coincide in energy with the levels of Be^6 and He^6. On the other hand, the (stronger) assumption of charge- and spin-independent forces would make the level scheme (a) appear like (c); i.e., the parallel and anti-parallel spin levels of Li^6 would coincide in energy.   Hence such forces would make the isotopic spin triplet and isotopic spin singlet of Fig. 1.5a merge into the *super-multiplet* of Figure 1.5c.

Looking again at Fig. 1.1, we see that the $T_\zeta = 0$ nucleus is the stable one among the $A = 4n+2$ nuclei up to N^{14} inclusive.   From there on, however, the stable species has $T_\zeta = +1$ (e.g., O^{18}, Ne^{22}, etc.).   This can be understood as follows: the charge effect distorts the level scheme of Fig. 1.5a into that of Fig. 1.5d.   We can use our previous estimate (1.6) to determine the downward displacement of the ground state energy of the $T_\zeta = 1$ nucleus relative to the *corresponding* level in the $T_\zeta = 0$ nucleus.   It is

$$\Delta E_c = \frac{6}{10}\,(A-2)\,\frac{e^2}{R} - (M_n c^2 - M_p c^2) \tag{1.10}$$

Using the estimate (1.9) for the Coulomb radius R, we get

$$\Delta E_c = 0.41\,\frac{A-2}{A^{1/3}} - 1.29 \text{ Mev} \tag{1.11}$$

This shows that ΔE_c increases strongly with the mass number, as was of course to be expected, since the Coulomb energy is proportional to the number of *pairs* of protons; the slow increase of the nuclear radius R $(\sim A^{1/3})$ is not strong enough to stem this trend.   As the mass number increases, therefore, we eventually reach a point at which the $T_\zeta = 1$ member of the three states with opposite spin is below the $T_\zeta = 0$ nucleus with parallel spin.   This condition is illustrated in Fig. 1.5e.   From that point on, the stable isobar has $T_\zeta = 1$ rather than $T_\zeta = 0$.   As we have seen from Fig. 1.1, this happens between $A = 14$ and $A = 18$.

The considerations given so far account for the systematics of the stable light nuclei up to $A = 36$ inclusive.   From then on, Fig. 1.1 shows a trend toward higher values of T_ζ.   This relative increase of neutrons is the result of the electrostatic repulsion between the protons.   The Coulomb energy difference between adjacent isobars varies roughly like $A^{2/3}$ [see (1.6)] and is therefore the more effective the higher the mass number.

We shall consider separately the nuclear series $A = 4n$, $A = 4n+2$, and the odd nuclei $A = 4n+1$, $4n-1$ (n integral).

Starting with the *series* $A = 4n+2$ (Fig. 1.6a), the odd-odd nuclei with $T_\zeta = 0$ are stable until N^{14}; from O^{18} on, the stable species has a neutron excess $T_\zeta = 1$.   We have seen that this is due to the competition between the relatively weak spin effect and the charge effect.

224 VI. Nuclear Spectroscopy I

The charge effect increasingly favors larger values of T_ζ as A increases. Nevertheless, it takes until $A = 46$ before a nucleus with $T_\zeta > 1$ (Ca^{46}, $T_\zeta = 3$) becomes stable. This large value of A gives an indication of the decisive importance of the symmetry properties of the wave func-

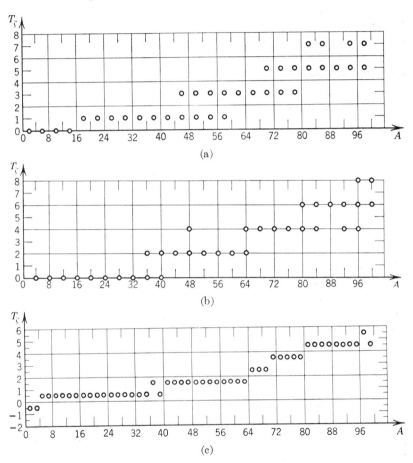

FIG. 1.6. Graph of the stable nuclei with $A \leq 100$, arranged in the same way as in Fig. 1.1, but with the different nuclear series shown separately: (a) nuclei with $A = 4n + 2$ (n integral); (b) nuclei with $A = 4n$; (c) nuclei with odd A, i.e., $A = 4n + 1$ and $A = 4n - 1$.

tion for nuclear stability: a nucleus with $T_\zeta = 3$ must necessarily have fewer symmetric pairs than the $T_\zeta = 1$ nucleus.

When the charge effect becomes comparable to the symmetry effect, the stable species has $T_\zeta = 3$ rather than $T_\zeta = 2$; i.e., the odd-odd nuclei with $T_\zeta = 2$ are never stable. Indeed, for $A = 46$, Ti^{46} ($T_\zeta = 1$) and

Ca^{46} ($T_\zeta = 3$) are both stable; they are separated by the radioactive (both β^- and electron capture) Sc^{46} with $T_\zeta = 2$. We shall see later that symmetry arguments can be used to assist us in understanding this fact.

A similar trend toward higher values of T_ζ can be observed for nuclei with *mass numbers* $A = 4n$ (Fig. 1.6b). The saturated nuclei with $T_\zeta = 0$ (integral number of alpha-particles) are the only stable ones until $A = 32$ inclusive. For each of $A = 36$ and 40, there are two stable species, $T_\zeta = 0$ and $T_\zeta = 2$. From then on until $A = 60$, $T_\zeta = 2$ gives the only stable isobar (with the exception of $A = 48$, where $T_\zeta = 4$ is also stable); $A = 64$, for which both $T_\zeta = 2$ and $T_\zeta = 4$ are stable, starts a region with $T_\zeta = 4$ as the stable species, and so on. Again we observe that there are no odd-odd nuclei (odd values of T_ζ for $A = 4n$) in this list.

Finally we turn to the nuclei with *odd mass numbers* ($A = 4n + 1$ and $A = 4n - 1$). They can be treated together for the same reason that atoms near the beginning and end of a period of the periodic table of elements can be compared. The extra electron outside of the closed shell in the lithium atom behaves very similarly to the one "hole" (missing electron) by which the fluorine atom fails to complete a closed shell. Similarly the light $4n + 1$ nuclei have one nucleon outside the n filled levels, whereas the light $4n - 1$ nuclei (see Fig. 1.3) can be considered to consist of n filled levels except for a "hole" (missing nucleon) in the top level. A similar parallelism persists also for the heavier odd nuclei. According to this argument, the symmetry effect ought to be about equally strong in the $4n + 1$ and $4n - 1$ nuclei. The charge effect is also about the same in the two series. The theory thus predicts that the trend toward higher values of T_ζ (due to competition between the charge effect and the symmetry effect) should manifest itself at nearly the same values of the mass number in the two series. This is borne out by the data summarized in Fig. 1.6c.

There is only one stable nuclear species for each odd value of A, whereas there are many even values of A with two or more stable isobars. This fact will be explained by simple symmetry arguments in Section 4.

2. THE SEMI-EMPIRICAL MASS FORMULA OF WEIZSÄCKER

In the previous section we have discussed the effects which influence nuclear stability. We shall extend this treatment in order to obtain a simple interpolation formula for nuclear ground state energies.

"Condensed" nuclear matter seems to be fairly incompressible: the nuclear volume is directly proportional to the mass number.

Furthermore the experimental binding energies show saturation, i.e., the binding energy is roughly proportional to the mass of the nucleus, hence also to its volume. We therefore write the main term in the nuclear energy formula as a "volume energy,"

$$E_{\mathrm{vol}} = -u_v A \qquad (2.1)$$

where u_v is a constant which will be determined by comparison with experiment.

The symmetry effect gives a correction to the volume energy. This effect favors $T_\zeta = 0$ and therefore contributes a positive (repulsive) term with a minimum at $T_\zeta = 0$. We make the rough assumption that this term is proportional to T_ζ^2. The constant of proportionality is expected to depend on A. We shall show in the next section that for a given change in the number of symmetric pairs the change in the potential energy is inversely proportional to the mass number A. We therefore write for the "symmetry energy"

$$E_{\mathrm{sym}} = 4u_\tau \frac{T_\zeta^2}{A} \qquad (2.2)$$

where u_τ is a constant.

The Coulomb energy has already been estimated, and, according to (1.2), it turns out to be

$$E_{\mathrm{Coulomb}} = 4u_c\, Z(Z-1)\, A^{-1/3} \qquad (2.3)$$

The constant u_c is related to the constant r_0 in the nuclear radius formula $R = r_0 A^{1/3}$ through

$$u_c = \frac{3}{20} \frac{e^2}{r_0} \cong 0.15 \text{ Mev} \qquad (2.4)$$

[The choice of the factors 4 in the definition of the constants u_τ and u_c is made here to adhere to the notation of the review paper by Feenberg (47).]

There is, however, another effect which must be included. This is the surface effect (Wick 34). It is a close analogue to the surface tension effect as found in any liquid. The surface tension is explained by the fact that there are fewer "bonds" acting on a surface nucleon than on a nucleon inside nuclear matter; hence the total potential energy is lowered in absolute value compared to what we would get if we just considered a sphere of the size of the nucleus inside a very large volume of condensed nuclear matter.[1] The surface effect acts

---

[1] Other (quantum-mechanical) effects which lead to a surface tension term are discussed by Weizsäcker (35) and Feenberg (41a).

like a repulsive term in the energy. The surface contribution to the energy is proportional to the surface area of the nucleus, i.e., to $A^{2/3}$. We therefore write

$$E_{\text{surf}} = u_s A^{2/3} \tag{2.5}$$

Since the ratio of surface area to the volume of the nucleus decreases as the volume gets bigger, the surface term is most important for the light nuclei. Conversely, the charge effect is most important for the heavier nuclei (large values of Z). Indeed, the very heaviest nuclei are so strongly charged that they are unstable against alpha-particle emission and against fission.

Putting together the various terms, we get the *Weizsäcker semi-empirical formula* for nuclear ground state energies (Weizsäcker 35, Bethe 36a, Feenberg 47):

$$E = -B = -u_v A + 4u_\tau \frac{T_\zeta^2}{A} + 4u_c Z(Z-1) A^{-1/3} + u_s A^{2/3} \tag{2.6}$$

Here B is the binding energy as defined in Section 2 of Chapter I, $E = -B$ is the energy of the ground state of the nucleus. The total energy U, which also includes the rest mass energy, is in these terms

$$U = A \frac{M_n c^2 + M_p c^2}{2} + T_\zeta (M_n c^2 - M_p c^2) + E \tag{2.7}$$

Expression (2.6) is a rough interpolation formula and does not show any of the finer details. It is meant to reproduce only the main features and trends of nuclear energies. For example, let us use (2.7) to calculate the value of T_ζ which leads to the lowest energy U for a given mass number A:

$$(T_\zeta)_{\min} = \frac{1}{2} \frac{u_c (A-1) A^{-1/3} - \frac{1}{4}(M_n c^2 - M_p c^2)}{u_\tau A^{-1} + u_c A^{-1/3}} \tag{2.8}$$

We simplify this expression by retaining only the leading terms and by neglecting the neutron-proton mass difference:

$$(T_\zeta)_{\min} \cong \frac{u_c}{2u_\tau} A^{5/3} \tag{2.9}$$

The ratio of u_c to u_τ enters because the stability against beta-decay is determined by the competition between the charge effect, which favors large neutron excesses, and the symmetry effect, which favors $T_\zeta = 0$. For the same reason the dependence on the mass number is $A^{5/3}$: the charge effect varies like $A^{2/3}$, and this must be divided by the symmetry effect, which varies like A^{-1}.

We now proceed to determine the constants in (2.6). The constant u_c of the Coulomb energy can be determined fairly accurately from

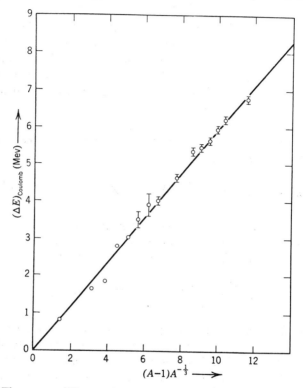

Fig. 2.1. The energy difference between mirror nuclei (corrected for the neutron-proton mass difference) as a function of $(A-1)A^{-1/3}$.

the energy differences between "mirror nuclei" (Stephens 40). The binding energy difference between the pair of nuclei $(A, T_\zeta = +\tfrac{1}{2})$ and $(A, T_\zeta = -\tfrac{1}{2})$ is, according to (2.6),

$$B(A, +\tfrac{1}{2}) - B(A, -\tfrac{1}{2}) = 4u_c \frac{A-1}{A^{1/3}} \qquad (2.10)$$

and contains only the constant u_c. This expression can be compared with the experimental value of this difference, taken from the maximum energies of the positron spectra of the nuclei with $T_\zeta = -\tfrac{1}{2}$. In Fig. 2.1 we have plotted the energy difference (2.10) against $(A-1)A^{-1/3}$. This should yield a straight line passing through the origin, with slope equal to $4u_c$. We see that almost all the points fall on a straight line; the exceptions are among the very lightest nuclei, where special effects may be expected, e.g., the Coulomb exchange energy may be important (Feenberg 42, 46; Phillips 41). We get from this graph $u_c = 0.148$ Mev and the Coulomb radius

$$R_c = 1.465 \times 10^{-13} \times A^{1/3} \text{ cm} \qquad (2.11)$$

Having determined u_c, we can find a suitable value for u_τ by comparing our theoretical expression (2.8) for $(T_\zeta)_\text{min}$ with the values of T_ζ of stable nuclei. In the cases where there are two stable values of T_ζ

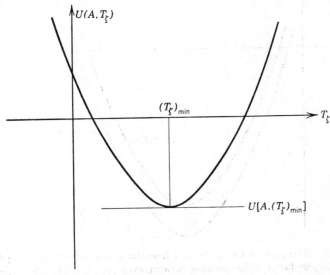

Fig. 2.2.   The total energy U of isobaric nuclei as a function of the neutron excess T_ζ, in the semi-empirical approximation. The curve is a parabola. The value $(T_\zeta)_\text{min}$ at which U has its minimum need not correspond to a real nucleus (i.e., it need not be either integral or half-integral).

for a given A, we use the average value of T_ζ in order to fit (2.8). A reasonable fit is obtained with $u_\tau = 18.1$ Mev. The remaining two constants can be determined by adjusting formula (2.7) to the known nuclear masses. Feenberg (47) finds the following values:

$$\begin{aligned} u_v &\cong 14 \text{ Mev} & u_\tau &\cong 18.1 \text{ Mev} \\ u_c &= 0.146 \text{ Mev} & u_s &\cong 13.1 \text{ Mev} \end{aligned} \qquad (2.12)$$

It should be noted that the constant u_v is not equal to the constant q in the rough relation $B \cong qA$, which is used frequently. q is of the order of 8 Mev for medium-weight nuclei, and it includes the effect

of all terms in (2.6). We emphasize again that the simple formula
(2.6) is not adequate to describe the binding energies of individual
nuclei and should be taken only as a rough representation of the main
features of the dependence of binding energies on mass number and
neutron excess. The constants (2.12) are also only first approximations. Better approximations can be found in the review article of
Feenberg (47).

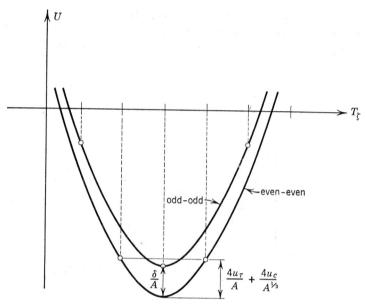

Fig. 2.3a. The nuclear energy U as a function of the neutron excess T_ζ for fixed
even mass number A, differentiating between even-even and odd-odd nuclei. The
figure shows the case most favorable to the stability of an odd-odd nucleus, with a
spacing parameter δ chosen so small as to make an odd-odd nucleus stable. This
case is not observed in nature. This leads to the condition

$$\delta \geq 4u_\tau + 4u_c A^{2/3}$$

on the spacing parameter δ.

The Weizsäcker formula in the form (2.6) indicates that the energies
of isobaric nuclei lie along a parabola with respect to T_ζ, the minimum
of the parabola being at $(T_\zeta)_{\min}$, as shown in Fig. 2.2. We can rewrite
(2.6) in the form

$$U = U[A, (T_\zeta)_{\min}] + \left(\frac{4u_\tau}{A} + \frac{4u_c}{A^{1/3}}\right)[T_\zeta - (T_\zeta)_{\min}]^2 \quad (2.13)$$

where $(T_\zeta)_{\min}$ is given by (2.8). There is only one minimum in this
curve; the nucleus T_ζ lying nearest $(T_\zeta)_{\min}$ is beta-stable and the others

are beta-unstable. The semi-empirical mass formula in this simple
form excludes the possibility of more than one stable isobar. Experimentally, there is only one stable isobar for odd mass numbers; but
there are two and sometimes even three stable isobars for even mass
numbers. These stable nuclei are always of the even-even variety
with the odd-odd ones in between being beta-unstable in both directions. We therefore must add to the Weizsäcker formula a term

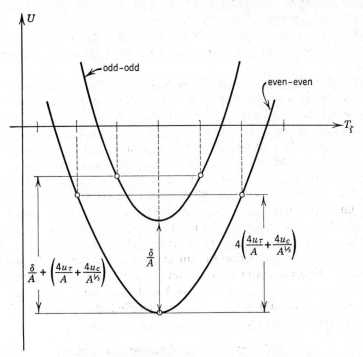

FIG. 2.3b. The nuclear energy U as a function of the neutron excess T_ζ for fixed
even mass number A, differentiating between even-even and odd-odd nuclei. The
figure shows the case most favorable to the occurrence of three stable isobars (all
of them even-even), with the spacing parameter δ chosen so large as to make the
three even-even isobars stable. Since three stable isobars are very rare in nature,
we get the condition

$$\delta \leq 3(4u_\tau + 4u_c A^{2/3})$$

on the spacing parameter δ. This condition is violated only in very few cases.

depending on the type of the nucleus. For our present purposes it
suffices to assume that the even-even isobars lie along one parabola,
and the odd-odd ones along another parabola of the same curvature
and with the same minimum value of T_ζ, but displaced upwards by a
constant amount. We thus add a term

$$\pm \frac{\delta}{2A} \tag{2.14}$$

to (2.13), with the minus sign for even-even nuclei and the plus sign for odd-odd nuclei. δ is taken as a constant. The proportionality to A^{-1} is assumed, since this is a symmetry effect, and we have already assumed this proportionality for the main part of the symmetry effect. It turns out that the energies for the odd nuclei lie about halfway between the energies of nearby even-even and odd-odd nuclei; this was the motivation for adding the same amount (2.14) to the energies of odd-odd nuclei which is subtracted from the energies of even-even nuclei.

The order of magnitude of the symmetry spacing parameter δ can be estimated in a simple way as follows. There is a lower limit on δ because all the odd-odd nuclei are unstable. This is illustrated schematically in Fig. 2.3a, where we have drawn the parabolas for the even-even and the odd-odd isobars in the case most favorable to the stability of the odd-odd species in the middle. The lower limit on δ determined in this way (using the previously determined values of u_r and u_c) ranges from 70 to 100 Mev, the higher values referring to the higher mass numbers. We can also get an upper limit on δ from the condition that triple isobars are very rare occurrences. The case most favorable to the existence of triple isobars is illustrated in Fig. 2.3b. If triple isobars did not occur at all, δ would have to be smaller than three times the above lower limit; since a few triple isobars do exist, we see that the actual value of δ is close to the upper limit, i.e., between 200 and 300 Mev. A more detailed study of beta-decay energies confirms this conclusion and gives the value

$$\delta \sim 270 \text{ Mev} \quad \text{(for medium-weight nuclei)} \tag{2.15}$$

This number must, of course, be divided by the mass number to get the actual spacing between the parabolas for the odd-odd and even-even nuclei.[1]

Bohr and Wheeler (39) used the semi-empirical mass formula (2.13) in their analysis of the fission process. However, they were interested in the finer details of the energy surface, especially the "winding" in the valley of the stable nuclei (Gamow 34). They made this correction by the artifice of replacing the "theoretical" $(T_{\mathfrak{z}})_{\min}$, as

---

[1] The semi-empirical value δ/A overestimates the variation of this spacing with the mass number. The "effective" δ is lower for light-weight nuclei, larger for very heavy nuclei. A better approximation is obtained by using $\delta'/A^{3/4}$ (Fermi, unpublished).

given by (2.7), by a purely empirical parameter giving the bottom of the mass valley for any particular A.   This leads to a considerable improvement in the fit of the formula to the known binding energies and disintegration energies; however, this improvement is at the expense of a complete loss of theoretical foundation, and the formula must then be considered somewhat more empirical.   This and similar formulas will not be discussed here any further (Way 48, Kohmann 48, Feenberg 47, Joliot 45).

Even with all these corrections, certain nuclei show a special stability compared to their neighbors (Mayer 48, Elsasser 33, 34).   The specially stable nuclei seem to be correlated with particular ("magic") numbers of neutrons or protons or both.   These effects will be discussed in Chapter XIV.

3. DETAILED STUDY OF THE SYMMETRY EFFECT

In this section the main argument for the symmetry effect will be put in a more quantitative form.   We shall show that exchange forces lead to a potential energy which has a minimum value for the smallest $|T_\zeta|$.

We assume first that the nuclear potential is of pure Majorana type. We can then estimate the potential energy in the same way as in Chapter III (III,3.2):

$$\bar{V} = -(n_+ p_+ - n_- p_-) \, V_0 \tag{3.1}$$

where n_+ and n_- are the numbers of symmetric and anti-symmetric pairs, p_+ and p_- are the probabilities for interaction between symmetric and anti-symmetric pairs, respectively, and V_0 is the average potential energy (the well depth) within the range b.   In the normal density state p_+ is appreciably larger than p_-.   We therefore get a first estimate for $\bar{V}$ by neglecting the contributions of the anti-symmetric pairs altogether.   According to (III,3.6) p_+ can be split into two factors, g_+ and p.   The value of g_+ can be read off Fig. 3.1 in Chapter III.   It approaches 2 for the limit $p_+ \gg p_-$, in which g_- becomes negligible.   For p we use the asymptotic form of (III,2.8) for $R \gg b$, and get

$$p_+ = g_+ \cdot p \cong 2 \left(\frac{b}{R} \right)^3 \tag{3.2}$$

The nuclear radius R is proportional to $A^{1/3}$, so that we get

$$\left(\frac{b}{R} \right)^3 = \frac{k}{A} \tag{3.3}$$

where k is a constant of proportionality of the order of 2 to 3. Inserting (3.2) and (3.3) into (3.1) gives the result

$$\bar{V} \cong - \frac{2kn_+}{A} V_0 \qquad \text{(pure Majorana force)} \qquad (3.4)$$

which shows that the potential energy has its minimum value for the state which has the maximum number of symmetric pairs.

We now generalize our considerations by introducing a charge-independent nuclear potential whose exchange character is a combination of the Wigner and Majorana types. Wigner (37) first pointed out the great simplifications and the numerous conclusions which are obtained with this assumption of charge- and spin-independent forces. There is still a good possibility that this assumption is not too far from reality. We write the potential energy between two particles as a sum of two terms: one is an ordinary (Wigner) force $V_W(r)$, and the other is a space-exchange (Majorana) force $V_M(r) P^M$:

$$V(r) = V_W(r) + V_M(r) P^M \qquad (3.5)$$

where P^M is the Majorana exchange operator which interchanges the space coordinates of the two nucleons. The total potential energy is the sum of (3.5) over all pairs:

$$V = \sum_{i<j=1}^{A} V_{ij}(r_{ij}) \qquad (3.6)$$

The average value $\bar{V}$ of the potential is given by the following generalization of (3.1):

$$\bar{V} = -(n_+p_+ + n_-p_-)(V_W)_0 - (n_+p_+ - n_-p_-)(V_M)_0 \qquad (3.7)$$

where $(V_W)_0$ and $(V_M)_0$ are the corresponding averages (well depths) within the range b of $V_W(r)$ and $V_M(r)$, respectively. We again neglect p_- compared to p_+ in the normal density state and get the same expression as (3.4) with

$$V_0 = (V_M)_0 + (V_W)_0 \qquad (3.8)$$

This sum determines the attraction between a neutron and a proton in the S state and can therefore be found from the two-body data analyzed in Chapter II.

Let us illustrate the significance of (3.4) by applying it to a calculation of the energy difference between O^{16} and N^{16}. We use the independent-particle picture (Fig. 1.2a for O^{16}, Fig. 1.2b for N^{16}) to describe the nuclei: the only difference between the two nuclei, in our crude estimate, comes from the number of symmetric pairs, n_+. We can find n_+ for these two nuclei by the methods used in Chapter III to get (III,4.27).[1]   This gives for $A = 16$, $T_\zeta = 0$ (Fig. 1.2a):

$$n_+ - n_- = 4 \times 6 - 4 \times \frac{4 \times 3}{2} = 0 \qquad n_+ = 60$$

and for $A = 16$, $T_\zeta = 1$ (Fig. 1.2b):

$$n_+ - n_- = (3 \times 6 + 1 \times 3 + 1 \times 0) - \left(\frac{5 \times 4}{2} + 2 \times \frac{4 \times 3}{2} + \frac{3 \times 2}{2} \right) = -4$$

$$n_+ = 58$$

There are two more symmetric pairs in O^{16} than in N^{16}.   Hence the potential energy $\bar{V}$ in O^{16} is lower than that in N^{16} by an amount

$$\Delta \bar{V} = 2k \frac{2}{A} V_0 \cong 5.3k \text{ Mev} \tag{3.9}$$

where we have used $A = 16$ and $V_0 = 21$ Mev (this estimate comes from the two-body data, discussed in Chapter II).   With an estimated value of k between 2 and 3, we get

$$\Delta \bar{V} \cong 11 \text{ to } 16 \text{ Mev} \qquad \text{(estimated)} \tag{3.10}$$

The actual energy difference between the ground states of N^{16} and O^{16} is within that range.[2]

It would seem unreliable to base any estimate of n_+ on the independent-particle model, which is probably very inaccurate. We shall show, however, that *the values of n_+ are given correctly by the independent-particle model provided that the nuclear potential contains only Wigner and Majorana forces as in* (3.5).   The number n_+ in a nuclear state Ψ is determined by the expression (III,4.26), which gives the difference $n_+ - n_-$ between the number of symmetric and antisymmetric pairs.   Since $n_+ + n_- = \frac{1}{2} A (A - 1)$, we find

$$n_+ = \frac{1}{2} \left[\sum_{i<j=1}^{A} \int \Psi^* P^M_{ij} \Psi \, d\tau + \frac{A(A-1)}{2} \right] \tag{3.11}$$

[1] A pair of particles in the same level contributes $+1$ to $n_+ - n_-$; a pair of identical particles (necessarily in different levels) contributes -1; any other pair (unequal particles in different states) contributes zero.   Note that the result (III,4.27) depended on the assumption $N = Z = $ even.   Hence the value of $n_+ - n_-$ quoted here agrees with (III,4.27) for O^{16}, but not for N^{16}

[2] The difference between the binding energies of O^{16} and N^{16} is about 9.7 Mev. This must be corrected for the charge effect according to (1.6).   After this correction, the energy difference is 13.0 Mev.

This expression is exact. n_+ was found in Chapter III by making assumptions about the wave function Ψ. We first show that the exchange operator $P^M{}_{ij}$ commutes with the Hamiltonian $T+V$ under our assumption about the forces. The potential energy operator (3.6) depends only on the *space* coordinates of the nucleus and is invariant under the exchange of any two space coordinates $(P^M{}_{ij}=P^M{}_{ji})$. Hence $P^M{}_{ij}$ commutes with V. The space coordinates of all nucleons enter into the kinetic energy in exactly the same way. Thus $P^M{}_{ij}$ also commutes with the kinetic energy operator T.

Of course, $P^M{}_{ij}$ does *not* commute with the Coulomb energy term, since the exchange of a neutron and a proton changes the Coulomb energy of the nucleus. However, to the extent that the Coulomb energy can be treated as a small perturbation, we can say that $P^M{}_{ij}$ commutes approximately with the total Hamiltonian, $H=T+V+C$. This approximation restricts us to light- and medium-weight nuclei, since the Coulomb energy term C is by no means very small compared to the potential energy V for heavy nuclei. This is especially true for the dependence of V and C on the neutron excess, in which we are interested here. The expression (3.11) for the number n_+ contains only the operator $P^M{}_{ij}$. In fact, we can consider n_+ the expectation value of the following operator:

$$(n_+)_{\mathrm{Op}} = \frac{1}{2}\left(\sum_{\mathrm{pairs}} P^M{}_{ij} + \frac{A(A-1)}{2}\right) \tag{3.12}$$

This operator commutes with the Hamiltonian $T+V$.

In order to determine the possible values of n_+ for a nucleus with A particles we therefore need not use the actual, complicated wave functions of the system. We can use wave functions appropriate to some fictitious potential, provided that these wave functions go over adiabatically into the correct ones as the fictitious potential is switched off and the true potential is switched on. The fact that the operator $(n_+)_{\mathrm{Op}}$ commutes with the Hamiltonian insures that n_+ stays the same during this switching operation. The fictitious potential we shall choose is simply the potential due to the walls of an impenetrable spherical box in which all the nucleons are enclosed without interacting with each other. The corresponding (independent-particle) wave functions are especially simple, and this fact allows an easy counting of the numbers of symmetric and anti-symmetric pairs.

Of course, the energies and the wave functions of the assembly of nucleons change considerably during this switching operation. However, our estimate (3.4) shows that, to a first approximation, it is sufficient to know the number of symmetric pairs in the actual state of the nucleus in order to estimate the symmetry effect, no matter what are the details of the wave function. This number is given correctly by the independent-particle model. We therefore merely have to pick from the possible values of n_+ the one which leads to the lowest energy according to (3.4).

Before determining n_+ in the general case, we introduce a simple notation to indicate how the particles are distributed between the various energy levels in the box. Let n_1, n_2, n_3, and n_4 denote the number of levels containing 1, 2, 3, and 4 particles, respectively. For example, in Fig. 1.2a, 16 particles are distributed, 4 to each level. This is indicated by the four numbers $n_1 = 0$, $n_2 = 0$, $n_3 = 0$, and $n_4 = 4$. The distribution in Fig. 1.2b is described by $n_1 = 1$, $n_2 = 0$, $n_3 = 1$, $n_4 = 3$. Of course, this description does not tell what levels the particles occupy, but this fact is not important for the symmetry properties of the wave functions. Such distributions of particles among the levels will be called *partitions*. We are using this term rather loosely. The present definition is sufficient for our purposes, however.[1]

One of the four numbers n_1, n_2, n_3, n_4 is redundant because of the following relation between them:

$$n_1 + 2n_2 + 3n_3 + 4n_4 = A \qquad (3.13)$$

where A is the total number of particles. There are therefore three independent numbers necessary and sufficient to describe a partition uniquely, once the total number of particles is given. Their choice is, of course, arbitrary. A convenient choice is the set P, P', P'' defined by[2]

$$P = \tfrac{1}{2}(n_1 + 2n_2 + n_3)$$
$$P' = \tfrac{1}{2}(n_1 + n_3) \qquad (3.14)$$
$$P'' = \tfrac{1}{2}(n_1 - n_3)$$

The partition depicted in Fig. 1.2a is therefore described by $(0,0,0)$, while that of Fig. 1.2b is $(1,1,0)$. We observe that n_4, the number of filled levels, does not enter into (3.14). In other words, P, P', and P'' determine the numbers of particles in the not completely filled levels. An appropriate number n_4 of filled levels has then to be added to make up the total number A of particles according to (3.13).

We have proved in Chapter III, Section 4, that each pair of particles in the same level contributes $+1$ to $n_+ - n_-$, (III,4.26); that each pair

[1] For a more precise definition, see Wigner (37) and Weyl (31).
[2] These numbers are called S, T, and Y, respectively, by Wigner (37).

of identical particles (same spin and type) contributes -1 to $n_+ - n_-$; and that all other pairs contribute nothing.

The proof that the "diagonal" pairs[1] do not contribute anything to $n_+ - n_-$ depended on the fact that the exchange of such a pair leads to a state which violates the Pauli exclusion principle. This is true if all the particles are in filled levels (e.g., Fig. 1.2a). It is not true in general, however. In order to obtain unambiguous answers to the symmetry properties of the wave functions we must specify the way in which the incompletely filled levels are occupied. We shall use a special arrangement of the particles in these levels which we shall call the "*normal*" *arrangement*. It is described as follows: all levels containing one particle contain one neutron with spin up, all levels with two particles contain two neutrons with opposite spin, all levels with three particles contain two neutrons with opposite spin and a proton with spin up. Figures 3.1a through 3.1d are examples of normal arrangements, and Fig. 3.1e illustrates an arrangement which is not normal in our sense. The reason for introducing the normal arrangement lies in its symmetry properties. By virtue of the normal arrangement, every particle in any one level has an identical partner in every other level whose occupation is equal or larger. The exchange of the space coordinates of any "diagonal" pair then leads to a state which violates the Pauli principle.

If we had not specified the normal arrangement, the particle in the top level of Figure 3.1d could have been a proton with spin down (cf. Fig. 3.1e). Its symmetry relation to the particles in the lower level is then not specified completely. Thus the fact that there are three particles in one level and one particle in another level does not yet determine the partition. However, the partition is determined uniquely if the arrangement of the particles within the levels is "normal."

The difference $n_+ - n_-$ is then equal to the number of pairs in equal levels minus the number of pairs of identical particles:

$$n_+ - n_- = [6 \times n_4 + 3 \times n_3 + 1 \times n_2 + 0 \times n_1]$$
$$- [\tfrac{1}{2}(n_1 + n_2 + n_3 + n_4)(n_1 + n_2 + n_3 + n_4 - 1)$$
$$+ \tfrac{1}{2}(n_2 + n_3 + n_4)(n_2 + n_3 + n_4 - 1)$$
$$+ \tfrac{1}{2}(n_3 + n_4)(n_3 + n_4 - 1) + \tfrac{1}{2}n_4(n_4 - 1)] \quad (3.15)$$

This can be rewritten in terms of the mass number A and the partition quantum numbers P, P', and P''. The result is[2]

[1] A "diagonal" pair is a pair of unequal particles in different levels. The connecting line in a scheme of Fig. 3.1 would be neither horizontal nor vertical.

[2] The quantity $n_+ - n_-$ is called Ξ by Wigner (37a), whereas our ξ is his Ξ'.

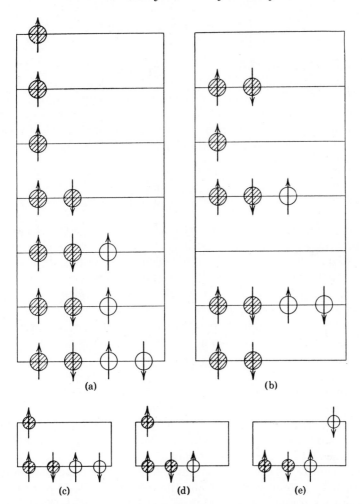

FIG. 3.1.   Examples of arrangements of nucleons in four-particle levels.   Parts (a) through (d) represent "normal" arrangements, whereas part (e) illustrates an arrangement which is not normal in our sense.

$$n_+ - n_- = -\tfrac{1}{8}A^2 + 2A + \tfrac{5}{2} - \xi \qquad (3.16)$$

where

$$\xi = \tfrac{1}{2}\left[(P+2)^2 + (P'+1)^2 + (P'')^2\right] \qquad (3.17)$$

The number of symmetric pairs, n_+, is then given by

$$n_+ = \tfrac{3}{16}A^2 + \tfrac{3}{4}A + \tfrac{5}{4} - \tfrac{1}{2}\xi \qquad (3.18)$$

and substitution into (3.4) gives the following estimate for the nuclear potential energy:

$$\bar{V} \cong -k \left[\frac{3}{8} A + \frac{3}{2} + \frac{5}{2} A^{-1} \right] V_0 + \xi \frac{kV_0}{A} \qquad (3.19)$$

where k is defined by (3.3).

The first term of (3.19) is independent of the neutron excess, and we have decided to ignore the dependence of the kinetic energy $\bar{T}$ on the neutron excess in this chapter. Hence the entire (estimated) dependence of $\bar{T} + \bar{V}$ on the neutron excess arises from the last term of (3.19). Under our rough estimates the "symmetry energy" is given by

$$E_{\text{sym}} \cong \xi \frac{kV_0}{A} \qquad (3.20)$$

where $V_0 = (V_M)_0 + (V_W)_0$ is the well depth in the S state of the neutron-proton system.[1] V_0 is positive; hence the symmetry energy (3.20) favors *low* values of ξ for the nucleus. According to (3.17) this means small values of P, P', P''. Looking back on the definition (3.14) of P, P', P'', we see that we get the *lowest energy if* n_1, n_2, n_3 *are smallest, i.e., if as many particles as possible are in filled levels.*

In any given partition the possible values of the neutron excess are restricted by the Pauli principle. We express this excess by

$$T_\zeta = \tfrac{1}{2}(N - Z)$$

For example, the partition (0,0,0) (see Fig. 1.2a) has only completely filled levels, and therefore the numbers of neutrons and protons must be equal: $(T_\zeta)_{\text{max}} = 0$. The partition (1,1,0) (see Fig. 1.2b) admits three neutrons and one proton outside the filled levels. Hence T_ζ can be as large as $(T_\zeta)_{\text{max}} = 1$, but no larger.

To generalize this, we notice that the normal distribution contains the maximum number of neutrons allowed by the Pauli principle for the partition in question. Comparison of Fig. 3.1a with the definition (3.14) shows that

$$P = T_\zeta = \tfrac{1}{2}(N - Z) \qquad \text{in the normal distribution} \qquad (3.21)$$

We conclude that the neutron excess in any partition (P,P',P'') is limited by

$$\tfrac{1}{2}(N - Z) = T_\zeta \leq P$$

---

[1] This well depth is different in the singlet and triplet spin states. We shall assume that most of the difference can be ascribed to the tensor force, and that the tensor force does not make a large contribution to the symmetry effect in the nuclei under consideration. We shall therefore estimate V_0 in (3.20) from the singlet state of the neutron-proton system.

Since protons and neutrons enter in a perfectly symmetrical way, the proton excess $\frac{1}{2}(Z-N) = -T_\zeta$ is restricted in the same way as the neutron excess. Thus we obtain the *condition upon the possible values of T_ζ in a partition* (P,P',P''):

$$-P \leq T_\zeta \leq P \qquad (3.22)$$

This limitation implies that a nucleus with a large neutron or proton excess (large value of $|T_\zeta|$) must belong to a partition (P,P',P'') with large P, $P \geq |T_\zeta|$. The symmetry energy estimate (3.20) depends on the value of ξ, (3.17), which increases quadratically with P. Thus *the theoretical symmetry energy estimate* (3.20) *has a behavior very similar to the semi-empirical symmetry energy* (2.2). *Expression* (3.20) *increases with increasing* $|T_\zeta|$, *in an approximately quadratic fashion, and it depends inversely on the mass number A.* Furthermore the example of N^{16} and O^{16} has shown that we can get even quantitative agreement in this special instance. The next section will be devoted to a more detailed discussion of the symmetry energy (3.20).

A few words are in place here regarding the limitations of our various estimates. (1) The dependence of the kinetic energy on the neutron excess is not negligible, and it contributes to the actual symmetry effect in nuclei. (2) The contribution of the anti-symmetric pairs to the potential energy is not exactly zero. (3) Our rough estimate (3.4) does not take into account the detailed behavior of the wave function. According to (3.4), all states Ψ_1, Ψ_2, $\cdots$ with the same number of symmetric pairs n_+ (with the same partition P,P',P'') have the same potential energy. This is not correct. However, to the extent that our rough considerations are justified, the states with the same partition are close together in energy compared to the energy separation between states with different partitions.

4. THE SYMMETRY ENERGY AND THE SYSTEMATICS OF STABLE NUCLEI

In any sequence of isobaric nuclei, the one or ones with the lowest energy are stable against beta-decay. The energies of isobaric nuclei are determined primarily by two effects: the symmetry effect and the charge effect. Since we now have a first estimate of the symmetry energy E_{sym}, (3.20), under the assumption of exchange forces, we shall use this estimate to understand the systematics of stable nuclei.

Let us start with nuclei of *odd mass number A*. The neutron excess T_ζ can then assume the values $T_\zeta = \pm\frac{1}{2}, \pm\frac{3}{2}, \pm\frac{5}{2}, \cdots$. We try to determine the partition (P,P',P'') of the ground state of the nucleus which has the neutron excess T_ζ. We must choose that partition

242   VI. Nuclear Spectroscopy I

which gives rise to the lowest value of ξ. Equation (3.17) shows that we must choose the lowest P compatible with T_ζ. According to (3.22), this is $P = |T_\zeta|$. P' and P'' also must be as low as possible, and P' is necessarily positive because of (3.14). Since the nucleus has an odd

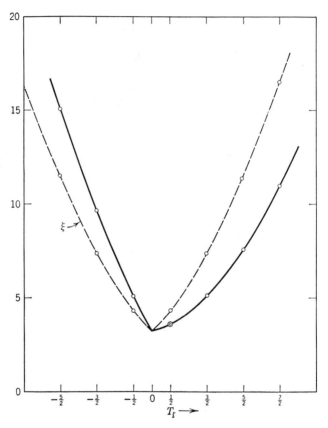

Fig. 4.1. Schematic picture of the dependence of the nuclear energy on the neutron excess T_ζ for nuclei with odd mass number A. The dashed curve shows the symmetry parameter ξ as a function of T_ζ. This parameter is proportional to the symmetry energy E_{sym}. Note the parabolic behavior and the cusp at $T_\zeta = 0$. The solid curve shows $\xi - \frac{3}{2}T_\zeta$, which is an example of the change due to the charge effect. Note that there is only one stable isobar ($T_\zeta = \frac{1}{2}$ in this example). The curves are drawn in, although actually only certain points on them (corresponding to half-integral values of T_ζ) are meaningful.

number of particles, we cannot make n_1 and n_3 both equal to zero. We get the lowest value of P' by making either $n_1 = 1$ and $n_3 = 0$, or else $n_3 = 1$ and $n_1 = 0$. The first choice corresponds to nuclei of type $A = 4n + 1$ (n integral), the second choice to $A = 4n - 1$. The value of

P'' is $+\frac{1}{2}$ in the first case, $-\frac{1}{2}$ in the second case. In either case the value of ξ, (3.17), is equal to

$$\xi = \tfrac{1}{2}T_\zeta^2 + 2|T_\zeta| + \tfrac{13}{4} \qquad \text{(odd nuclei, ground state)} \qquad (4.1)$$

The symmetry energy (3.20) is proportional to ξ. In Fig. 4.1, ξ is plotted against T_ζ. The $|T_\zeta|$ term in (4.1) causes a cusp at $T_\zeta = 0$ in contrast to the assumption of a smooth parabola which was made in the derivation of the semi-empirical Weizsäcker formula (2.2). The increase of the symmetry energy with $|T_\zeta|$ is somewhat stronger than a parabola would indicate. The empirical evidence for the existence of the cusp in the symmetry energy is inconclusive. Figure 4.1 also

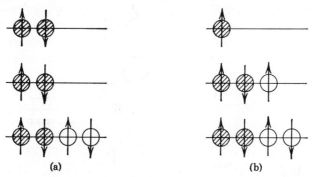

(a)   (b)

Fig. 4.2. Illustration of (a) the partition $(2,0,0)$ and (b) the partition $(1,1,0)$.

shows the inclusion of the charge effect (1.6), which is approximately linear in T_ζ. In the special example of this figure the charge effect is so chosen as to make $T_\zeta = \frac{1}{2}$ the stable isobar.

We now turn to nuclei with *even mass numbers, of type* $A = 4n$ (n *integral*). We again search for the partition of the ground state, i.e., the partition with the lowest ξ which is consistent with (3.14) and (3.22). The optimum value of P is again $P = |T_\zeta|$. Since we now have an even number of nucleons, we try to minimize ξ by making $P' = P'' = 0$. According to the definition (3.14), this choice of P, P', P'' corresponds to $n_1 = n_3 = 0$ and $n_2 = |T_\zeta|$. Since A must be a multiple of 4, this choice is possible only for even values of T_ζ. This is illustrated in Fig. 4.2, where we have assumed there are 4 nucleons outside the filled shells. If T_ζ is even ($T_\zeta = 2$, Fig. 4.2a), all 4 nucleons can be neutrons, giving the partition $(P,P',P'') = (2,0,0)$. On the other hand, if T_ζ is odd ($T_\zeta = 1$, Fig. 4.2b), we must put 3 particles in one level and 1 particle in another level, giving the parition $(P,P',P'') = (1,1,0)$. In general, the ground state partition for $A = 4n$ nuclei with even T_ζ is $(P,P',P'') = (|T_\zeta|,0,0)$ and with odd T_ζ, $(|T_\zeta|,1,0)$.

This characteristic difference between $A = 4n$ nuclei with even and odd T_ζ is an important feature of the theory. The $A = 4n$ nuclei with even T_ζ are even-even nuclei, whereas the $A = 4n$ nuclei with odd T_ζ are odd-odd nuclei. We shall now show that *the theory predicts the instability of all odd-odd nuclei of mass number $A = 4n$.*

To show this we need merely evaluate ξ for the two cases. The result is

$$\xi = \tfrac{1}{2}T_\zeta^2 + 2|T_\zeta| + 4 \qquad \text{(odd-odd nuclei)}$$
$$\xi = \tfrac{1}{2}T_\zeta^2 + 2|T_\zeta| + \tfrac{5}{2} \qquad \text{(even-even nuclei)}$$

(4.2)

This is shown graphically in Fig. 4.3. There are now two different parabolas (each with a cusp at $T_\zeta = 0$ as before), the lower one for the even-even nuclei, the upper one for the odd-odd nuclei. Thus the theoretical symmetry energy estimate (3.20) already includes a term of type (2.14) which had to be introduced artificially into the semi-empirical mass formula. Furthermore the coefficient of this term (which gives the spacing between the two parabolas in the figure) is now no longer an arbitrary parameter but is related to the other constants in the symmetry energy [the spacing between the two parabolas is three times the coefficient of T_ζ^2 according to (4.2)].

The instability of the odd-odd nuclei is a direct consequence of the large spacing between the two parabolas in the figure. If we include the charge effect, the best possibility for making an odd-odd nucleus stable occurs when the minimum of the odd-odd curve coincides with a possible (odd) value of T_ζ. Such a case is shown in Fig. 4.4. We see that even in this most favorable case the odd-odd nucleus has an energy higher than that of the two neighboring, even-even, isobaric nuclei. Thus the two even-even isobars are both stable, and the odd-odd isobar in between undergoes beta-decay in both directions. There are many such cases in the periodic table. All these cases are for even mass numbers A, none for odd A. This is again in agreement with theory: the behavior of ξ for the ground states of odd A nuclei (Fig. 4.1) is smooth, and therefore only one isobar can be beta-stable.[1]

Finally, let us consider the *even mass numbers of type $A = 4n+2$* ($n =$ integral). A simple consideration analogous to the earlier one shows that the partition of the ground state is $(P,P',P'') = (|T_\zeta|,0,0)$ for the (even-even) nuclei with odd T_ζ, and $(P,P',P'') = (|T_\zeta|,1,0)$ for the (odd-odd) nuclei with even T_ζ, with one significant exception,

---

[1] There are a few cases of two stable isobars of odd A nuclei in the periodic table. These are always neighboring isobars, not isobars with an unstable one in between. It is extremely probable that one of the two "stable" isobars is actually unstable, but with a lifetime so long that the radioactivity has so far defied detection.

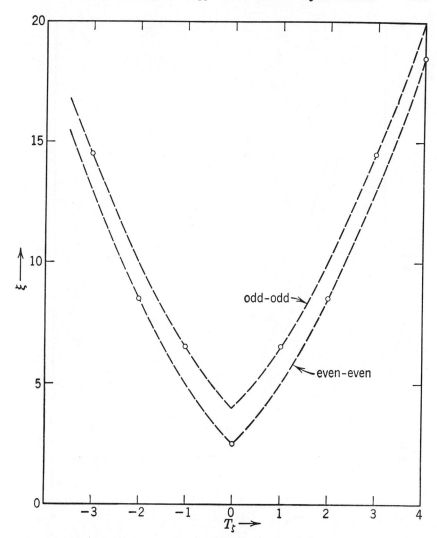

FIG. 4.3. The parameter ξ in the symmetry energy as a function of the neutron excess T_ζ for nuclei with mass numbers $A = 4n$ (n integral). The even-even nuclei (T_ζ even) have lower values of ξ than the odd-odd nuclei (T_ζ odd).

however: the odd-odd nuclei with $Z = N$, $T_\zeta = 0$ form a special case. Figure 1.4b shows that these nuclei have two particles above the filled levels, so that they belong to the same partition, $(P, P', P'') = (1,1,0)$, as their neighboring (even-even) isobars.

The values of ξ for the ground states of the $A = 4n+2$ nuclei are also given by (4.2). (However, the even-even nuclei now have odd

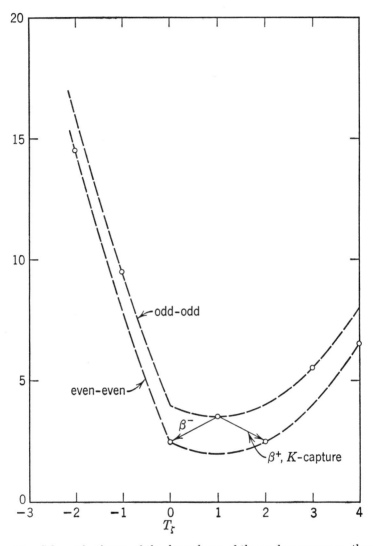

F<small>IG.</small> 4.4. Schematic picture of the dependence of the nuclear energy on the neutron excess T_ζ for nuclei with mass numbers $A = 4n$ (n integral). The example
shown is most favorable to the stability of the odd-odd nucleus with $T_\zeta = 1$; yet
even in this case this nucleus has higher energy than its even-even neighboring
isobars ($T_\zeta = 0,2$) and is therefore unstable. The curves drawn are $\xi - \frac{3}{2}T_\zeta$; the
second term coming from the charge effect.

T_ζ, the odd-odd nuclei have even T_ζ.)   The exceptional $T_\zeta = 0$ nuclei have $\xi = 5$, the same value as their neighboring isobars.   This is shown graphically in Fig. 4.5.   The odd-odd nuclei are again unstable, with the exception of the $T_\zeta = 0$ nuclei which must be treated as special

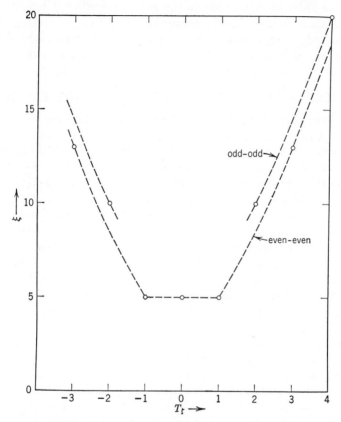

FIG. 4.5.   The parameter ξ in the symmetry energy as a function of the neutron excess T_ζ for nuclei with mass numbers $A = 4n + 2$ (n integral).   Again the odd-odd nuclei ($T_\zeta =$ even) fall on a different (higher) curve than the even-even nuclei ($T_\zeta =$ odd).   The odd-odd nucleus with equal numbers of neutrons and protons ($T_\zeta = 0$) forms an exception, however.   Its symmetry energy (value of ξ) is equal to that of the neighboring even-even isobars.   The stability relations among the nuclei $T_\zeta = 1, 0, -1$ thus depend on the charge effect and the spin effect.

cases.   These special cases have already been discussed in Section 1, where it was shown that the spin dependence of the nuclear forces (which we have neglected in our present rough estimates) is essential for an understanding of the stability of some of these nuclei.

Although the simple estimate (3.20) of the symmetry energy has enabled us to gain a complete understanding of the stability relations of nuclei, this spectacular agreement with experiment is undoubtedly at least partly accidental. After all, in order to understand the stability relations we have to consider cases in which the charge effect is of the same order of magnitude as the symmetry effect. It is doubtful that an effect as strong as the charge effect here can be treated validly by first-order perturbation theory (as we have done). Everything considered, the ease with which this simple theory predicts the stability relations of observed nuclei is perhaps somewhat deceptive.

5. NUCLEAR MAGNETIC MOMENTS IN LIGHT ELEMENTS

The very general arguments of the previous section are not sufficient to predict the magnetic moments of ground states of nuclei, since such a prediction requires a rather detailed description of the states involved. However, Margenau and Wigner (Margenau 40a) have pointed out that considerable partial information concerning the magnetic moments can be obtained from symmetry considerations.

We note that the type of nuclear potential (3.5) which we are using does not contain any spin-orbit coupling. Spin-orbit coupling in nuclei is due to the magnetic fields of the orbital motion and to the tensor forces. The former effect is very small in nuclei; the latter effect has been estimated only very roughly (Phillips 40, Dancoff 39, 40). We shall discuss later some qualitative results of an appreciable spin-orbit coupling, which is, however, still small enough so that it can be treated as a small perturbation.

The expression for the magnetic moment μ of a nucleus under the assumption of no spin-orbit coupling has been given in Chapter I, (I,7.52 and I,7.53). In Chapter I we have applied these expressions to the Schmidt model in which the orbital angular momentum L and the intrinsic spin S are assumed to be due to only one nucleon. Now several nucleons (those outside the filled four-shells) may contribute to the spin angular momentum, and (in principle at least) all nucleons may contribute to the orbital angular momentum.

The considerations of the preceding sections enable us to predict the values of S and g_S for all nuclear ground states. We cannot, however, predict the values of the orbital angular momentum L, nor the way $\mathbf{S}$ and $\mathbf{L}$ combine to form the vector $\mathbf{J}$. The value of g_L is also unknown. In one special case, however, g_L is known: for nuclei composed of an equal number of protons and neutrons ("self-conjugate" nuclei) the assumption of equal neutron-neutron and proton-proton forces implies that the orbital angular momentum is shared equally between the neutrons and the protons. g_L would be unity for a proton and zero for a neutron, so that $g_L = \frac{1}{2}$ in that case.   Sachs (46) has pointed out that this argument can be applied also to the arithmetic mean of the magnetic moments of two mirror nuclei.

We shall now take the following approach: instead of trying to predict magnetic moments and orbital angular momenta from first considerations, let us take the experimentally observed value of J and see how far we can get in predicting the observed magnetic moment.   Since S is known from the general theory, there will be only a few possible values of L, and it will be easy to discriminate between them.   Because of the large values of the spin magnetic moments of the proton and neutron, most of the observed magnetic moments are due to the first term in (I,7.52); therefore an error in g_L is not very decisive.

It is known experimentally that the total angular momenta of all even-even nuclei measured so far are zero, and therefore their magnetic moments are also zero.   Light nuclei of this type, with $T_\zeta = 0$, are composed of an integral number of alpha-particles and hence belong to a partition in which all levels are completely filled [i.e., the partition $(0,0,0)$].   The spins therefore cancel out, and $S = 0$ for those nuclei. For heavier even-even nuclei, the neutron excess is contributed by two neutrons at a time, in successive levels, so that again the spins cancel out.   Since $S = 0$ theoretically and $J = 0$ experimentally, we conclude that the orbital angular momentum L also vanishes for these nuclei. In other words, the individual nucleons move in such a way that the orbital angular momentum of the system as a whole is zero for all even-even nuclei.

We now proceed to find S and g_S for nuclei with *odd* mass numbers. Light nuclei of this kind have all levels except one completely filled. The one remaining level contains either 1 or 3 particles.   For nuclei of type $A = 4n + 1$ the one particle in the top level is the only one contributing to the spin (since all the other spins are saturated); hence the total spin angular momentum is $S = \frac{1}{2}$.   The one "outside" particle is also the only one contributing to the spin part of the magnetic moment; hence $g_S = 5.58$ if the outside particle is a proton, and $g_S = -3.82$ if the outside particle is a neutron.   The situation is exactly the same in the $4n - 1$ nuclei, except that "outside particle" has to be replaced by "outside hole."   In either case, *for all odd nuclei*,

$$S = \tfrac{1}{2}$$

$$g_S = 5.58 \quad \text{if the number of protons is odd} \qquad (5.1)$$

$$g_S = -3.82 \quad \text{if the number of neutrons is odd}$$

Statement (5.1) is expected to be true also for the heavier odd nuclei, since the neutron excess is provided by adding two neutrons at a time to successive levels (see Section 4). However, the approximation of charge- and spin-independent forces gets progressively worse as we go to larger mass numbers (because of the increasing charge effect) and the prediction (5.1) must therefore be taken more cautiously.

We wish to warn the reader at this point against taking the "levels" too literally, say, in terms of an individual-particle model. We are concerned here with the symmetry properties of the wave function under space exchanges. A "filled level" merely means 4 particles completely symmetrical under the exchange of their space coordinates. By the Pauli principle, their spins (and isotopic spins) must then cancel in pairs, and this is all we need in order to prove that the "filled levels" do not contribute to the spin angular momentum or the spin magnetic moment. The strength of these considerations of Margenau and Wigner lies in the fact that so little has to be assumed about the detailed behavior of the wave function.

Before comparing (5.1) with experiment, we give the analogous argument for the four known stable odd-odd nuclei, all of which have equal numbers of protons and neutrons. In order to explain the stability of these elements we have invoked the spin dependence of the nuclear forces in Section 1, which causes the ground state of these elements to be a triplet spin state. In that state, the spins of the "outside" neutron and proton are parallel, and their magnetic moments add up; thus g_S is the sum of the neutron and proton magnetic moments divided by the spin angular momentum S, which is unity. Hence we get, *for odd-odd nuclei with $T_\zeta = 0$,*

$$S = 1 \qquad g_S = 0.88 \qquad (5.2)$$

We now compare these predictions with the experimental material. We start with the self-conjugate odd-odd nuclei, since for them g_L is known to be $\frac{1}{2}$. The relevant data are summarized in Table 5.1. The experimental value of J is given, and the magnetic moment μ_{theor} is calculated for the different values of L compatible with J and the predicted value $S = 1$. The comparison with the experimental values μ_{exp} shows that it is possible to pick one of the admissible values of L as the actual value or as the predominant one.

Only $L = 0$ has been included for the deuteron, in accordance with the considerations of Chapter II. The small deviation between μ_{theor} and μ_{exp} is probably caused by the small admixture of D state ($L = 2$) due to the tensor force. We see that Li^6 has mostly $L = 0$, B^{10} mostly

$L=2$; N^{14} is a mixture with a predominant $L=2$ component, and so is Na^{22}.

The fact that none of the computed values agrees perfectly with the observed ones can be ascribed to three causes: (1) relativistic corrections to the magnetic moments of the individual nucleons; (2) coopera-

TABLE 5.1

Nucleus	J	S	g_S	L	g_L	μ_{theor}	μ_{exp}
H^2	1	1	0.88	0	$\frac{1}{2}$	0.88	0.86
Li^6	1	1	0.88	0	$\frac{1}{2}$	0.88	0.82
				1	$\frac{1}{2}$	0.69	
				2	$\frac{1}{2}$	0.31	
B^{10}	3	1	0.88	2	$\frac{1}{2}$	1.88	1.80
				3	$\frac{1}{2}$	1.60	
				4	$\frac{1}{2}$	1.22	
N^{14}	1	1	0.88	0	$\frac{1}{2}$	0.88	0.40
				1	$\frac{1}{2}$	0.69	
				2	$\frac{1}{2}$	0.31	
Na^{22}†	3	1	0.88	2	$\frac{1}{2}$	1.88	1.75
				3	$\frac{1}{2}$	1.60	
				4	$\frac{1}{2}$	1.22	

† Na^{22} is a radioactive nucleus, but its spin and magnetic moment have been measured (Davis 49). The beta-decay does not influence the dynamical properties of a nucleus.

tive effects, the so-called "exchange magnetic moments," which come into play only when many nucleons are assembled close together;[1] (3) the influence of spin-orbit coupling.

There is no reliable way of treating the *relativistic effects* on the magnetic moments even in the simplest case, the deuteron. However, rough estimates show that the relativistic effects can be large enough to change the observed magnetic moment by an amount of the order of magnitude of 0.1 nuclear magneton. Hence this effect alone might be sufficient to account for most of the deviations in Table 5.1; whether it actually is sufficient is not known at present. As far as *cooperative effects* are concerned, there is some reason to believe that they cancel out in self-conjugate nuclei (Morrison 48, Osborn 50). Finally, the

[1] The cooperative effects can be of two types: (a) the magnetic moments of the various nucleons at close distances may be different from the values at large distances, and (b) there may be contributions to the magnetism of the nucleus from the "exchange currents" set up by the exchange of protons and neutrons. The assumption of exchange forces implies the existence of such exchange currents (Sachs 48, Lamb 38, Siegert 37), but the magnitude of these currents cannot be deduced uniquely from the strength of the exchange forces (Osborn 50).

spin-orbit coupling has the following effect (provided that it is a small perturbation): the wave function no longer has purely one S and L value but becomes a mixture of the various possibilities indicated in the table. The observed magnetic moment is the weighted average of the values in the table, the weights being the probabilities of the various (L, S) combinations in the actual nuclear wave function.[1] In particular, therefore, we should expect the observed magnetic moment to lie between the extremes of the theoretical values. The fact that this is indeed so lends some support to the belief that the spin-orbit coupling is the most important correction of the three discussed here.

We now consider the *odd nuclei*. It is more difficult to make a theoretical prediction of the magnetic moment, since the gyromagnetic ratio for the orbital motion is unknown. We shall give the theoretical values of the magnetic moments for both orbital angular momenta L compatible with the experimentally known values of J and the (theoretically) expected value $S = \frac{1}{2}$ under two assumptions about the orbital gyromagnetic ratio g_L: (1) the Schmidt model (Schmidt 37, Schüler 37, 37a) according to which $g_L = 1$ if Z is odd, $g_L = 0$ if N is odd; and (2) the uniform model (Wigner 37a, Margenau 40a) according to which $g_L = Z/A$. The latter model assumes that the nuclear motion is sufficiently complex to allow us to use statistical considerations; then the orbital angular momentum of the nucleus is distributed evenly among all the particles so that the protons as a whole contribute in proportion to their number. To the extent that the motion in the nucleus is more ordered than that, through shell formation for example, the statistical argument breaks down. The results are summarized in Table 5.2.

The nuclei with mass number 3 have magnetic moments which deviate somewhat from the predicted values. An analysis by Sachs (Sachs 47a, Avery 48, 49) has shown that no reasonable admixture of other possible states gives these results. These deviations are probably due to exchange magnetic moments which contribute about 0.2 nuclear magneton in each case. Hence we should not expect agreement to better than 0.2 nuclear magneton between the simple theory (which neglects these effects) and experiment for the other odd nuclei either. Some calculations (Spruch 50) indicate that the exchange magnetic moment may become even more important as the mass of the nucleus increases.

[1] Note that we are not ascribing the orbital momentum L to the motion of one nucleon only. Hence linear combinations of different L values are possible, in contrast to the one-particle model (see Chapter I, Section 7B) in which the parity rule prevents any such combinations.

For Li^7, a P state is clearly indicated, and the statistical assumption for g_L leads to a very good result.   In Be^9, we are also dealing with a P state; the statistical g_L is not too bad, and the discrepancy is easily

TABLE 5.2

Nucleus	J	S	g_S	L	μ_{theor} Schmidt	Uniform	μ_{exp}
					$g_L = 0$ | $g_L = 1$	$g_L = Z/A$	
H^3	$\frac{1}{2}$	$\frac{1}{2}$	5.58	0	2.79	2.79	2.98
He^3	$\frac{1}{2}$	$\frac{1}{2}$	-3.82	0	-1.91	-1.91	-2.13
Li^7	$\frac{3}{2}$	$\frac{1}{2}$	5.58	1	3.79	3.22	3.25
				2	0.12	-0.90	
Be^9	$\frac{3}{2}$	$\frac{1}{2}$	-3.82	1	-1.91	-1.47	-1.18
				2	1.15	1.95	
B^{11}	$\frac{3}{2}$	$\frac{1}{2}$	5.58	1	3.79	3.25	2.69
				2	0.12	-0.84	
C^{13}	$\frac{1}{2}$	$\frac{1}{2}$	-3.82	0	-1.91	-1.91	0.70
				1	0.64	0.95	
N^{15}	$\frac{1}{2}$	$\frac{1}{2}$	5.58	0	2.79	2.79	$-0.28\dagger$
				1	-0.26	-0.62	
F^{19}	$\frac{1}{2}$	$\frac{1}{2}$	5.58	0	2.79	2.79	2.62
				1	-0.26	-0.61	
Na^{23}	$\frac{3}{2}$	$\frac{1}{2}$	5.58	1	3.79	3.27	2.21
				2	0.12	-0.81	
Al^{27}	$\frac{5}{2}$	$\frac{1}{2}$	5.58	2	4.79	3.75	3.64
				3	0.86	-0.63	
P^{31}	$\frac{1}{2}$	$\frac{1}{2}$	5.58	0	2.79	2.79	1.13
				1	-0.26	-0.61	
Cl^{35}	$\frac{3}{2}$	$\frac{1}{2}$	5.58	1	3.79	3.28	0.82
				2	0.12	-0.81	
Cl^{37}	$\frac{3}{2}$	$\frac{1}{2}$	5.58	1	3.79	3.25	0.68
				2	0.12	-0.85	

† For the sign of the magnetic moment of N^{15} see Proctor (51).

within the error expected as a result of exchange magnetic moments. B^{11} does not fit with any theory.   An admixture of the D state (due to spin-orbit coupling) would perhaps account for the observations. The experimental results in N^{15} and C^{13} indicate clearly that these nuclei are in P states.   It should be emphasized that these are the first two nuclei in the table for which the lowest possible L (i.e., $L=0$ in these cases) does not give a good fit. We shall see later that the independent-particle model predicts P states for these two nuclei. It seems that the Schmidt model gives the best fit for N^{15} and C^{13}. In both cases we find $L=1$.

The theory is no longer so good for the heavier elements. In Na, P, and Cl the magnetic moments fall outside the limits of either L. The deviations are rather large to be explained by exchange magnetic moments. We are entering the region of medium-weight nuclei for which spin-orbit coupling is more important. Indeed, all these magnetic moments fall between the highest and the lowest of the theoretical values and can therefore be explained by assuming appreciable spin-orbit coupling.

The results of this section show that the theory is not adequate to predict the nuclear spins and magnetic moments. However, it gives a rough insight into the implications of the experimental data and allows some interpretation of the observed values.

▶ **6. THE SPECTROSCOPIC CLASSIFICATION
OF NUCLEAR ENERGY LEVELS**

So far we have classified the energy levels only by the partition to which they belong. This suffices to provide an understanding of the systematics of stable nuclei.

We shall now look for other constants of motion which can be used to give a more detailed classification of nuclear levels. The total angular momentum J and the parity are constants of motion in any nucleus. More rules for the classification of energy levels can be obtained if some assumptions about the nuclear forces are made which are only approximately valid. We shall enumerate these assumptions explicitly in this section, although most of them have already been used previously.

We shall make the following two assumptions: (I) *nuclear forces are charge independent;* (II) *the charge effect (Coulomb energy and neutron-proton mass difference) can validly be treated as a small perturbation.*[1]

Assumptions I and II imply the existence of the so-called *isotopic spin multiplets.* We saw one example of an isotopic spin multiplet

---

[1] Although it is usually assumed that the nuclear forces act between pairs of nucleons only, the conclusions below do *not* depend on that assumption. Many-body forces are admitted here, with the one condition that they must be charge independent. It is perhaps useful to point out also that assumptions I and II do *not* exclude strong tensor forces. The isotopic spin multiplets are not destroyed by tensor forces, provided only that the tensor forces as well as the central forces are charge independent.

in Section 1 (Fig. 1.5a).   We shall now discuss isotopic spin multiplets in general.

Suppose that we have a state of the nucleus (A, T_ζ) with the wave function Ψ.   According to assumptions I and II we do not change the dynamical properties of the system if we transform some neutrons into protons, or vice versa.   Hence the same wave function Ψ also describes a possible state of the nuclei $(A, T_\zeta-1)$, $(A, T_\zeta-2)$, $\cdots$ and $(A, T_\zeta+1)$, $(A, T_\zeta+2)$, $\cdots$, the only difference being that some neutron coordinates in the original Ψ are now interpreted as proton coordinates, or vice versa.   There is one important exception to this method of generating wave functions of isobaric nuclei: we must not violate the Pauli principle.   Suppose that our original nucleus had $T_\zeta > 0$, i.e., it was made up of more neutrons than protons.   Let us introduce the symbol m_ζ to denote this initial value of T_ζ.   We can then replace a neutron by a proton, i.e., go to the nucleus with $T_\zeta = m_\zeta - 1$, without fear of violating the Pauli principle, since we have decreased the maximum number of identical particles.   By the same argument, Ψ is an acceptable wave function for the nuclei $T_\zeta = m_\zeta - 2$, $m_\zeta - 3$, etc., all the way to $T_\zeta = -m_\zeta$.   On the other hand, suppose that we replace a proton by a neutron.   The original nucleus $T_\zeta = m_\zeta$ already had a neutron excess; hence this replacement increases the maximum number of identical particles, and the resulting wave function may (but need not) violate the Pauli principle.

We see therefore that for any wave function Ψ there is a maximum value of T_ζ for which Ψ is in agreement with the Pauli principle.   This maximum value of T_ζ is called the *total isotopic spin* and is denoted by T.[1] Ψ is an acceptable wave function for the nuclei

$$T_\zeta = T, T-1, \cdots, -T,$$

and the energy of this state is the same in all these isobaric nuclei (except for the charge effect, of course).   These states of the isobaric nuclei (A, T) to $(A, -T)$ are said to form an *isotopic spin multiplet* with total isotopic spin T.

We now compare ordinary spin multiplets with isotopic spin multiplets.   In an ordinary (mechanical) spin multiplet S, there are $2S+1$ levels with the same energy, corresponding to values of S_z ranging from $+S$ to $-S$.   Analogously, in an isotopic spin multiplet T, there are $2T+1$ levels with the same energy, corresponding to values of T_ζ ranging from $+T$ to $-T$.   In an ordinary spin multiplet the $2S+1$ degenerate levels are levels of the same nuclear species.   On the other

[1] The symbol T for the total isotopic spin quantum number should not lead to confusion with the kinetic energy T in the nucleus.   Both notations are standard.

hand, the degenerate levels in an isotopic spin multiplet belong to $2T+1$ different nuclear species (ranging from $T_{\zeta}=+T$ to $T_{\zeta}=-T$). The $(2S+1)$-fold degeneracy in an ordinary spin multiplet can be lifted by a perturbation (an electric or magnetic field, for example). The $(2T+1)$-fold degeneracy in an isotopic spin multiplet is in practice lifted by the charge effect (compare Figs. 1.5a and 1.5d).

We have seen before that knowledge of a state Ψ in a nucleus $T_{\zeta}=m$ allows us to predict that the same state occurs in the isobaric nuclei $T_{\zeta}=m_{\zeta}-1$, $T_{\zeta}=m_{\zeta}-2$, $\cdots$, $T_{\zeta}=-m_{\zeta}$. To illustrate the applications of this theorem, consider Fig. 6.1, which is a conceivable level system for an isobaric sequence of nuclei with an even mass number A. Suppose that we know (experimentally) the levels of the nucleus $T_{\zeta}=1$. We can then make the following predictions:

(1) There are exactly the same number of levels with the same excitation energies in the mirror nucleus $T_{\zeta}=-1$.[1]

(2) All the levels known in the nucleus $T_{\zeta}=1$ also occur in the nucleus $T_{\zeta}=0$. However, $T_{\zeta}=0$ has additional levels (isotopic spin singlets) without "partners" in $T_{\zeta}=1$.

(3) Some, but not all, of the levels known in $T_{\zeta}=1$ are also found in the nuclei $T_{\zeta}=2$ and $T_{\zeta}=-2$. The levels which occur only in $T_{\zeta}=0$ are isotopic spin singlets, those which occur in $T_{\zeta}=1,0,-1$ (but no higher $|T_{\zeta}|$) are isotopic spin triplets, the others are isotopic spin quintets and higher multiplets.

Predictions (1), (2), and (3) are valid if the charge effect is neglected. To the extent that the charge effect is a small perturbation, the correction caused by it is nearly the same for all levels of a given nucleus T_{ζ}. Thus all the levels of a given species T_{ζ} are shifted upwards in energy by equal amounts. The magnitude of the shift depends on T_{ζ}, of course. An example of this is provided by the levels of the mirror nuclei B^{11} and C^{11} which are shown in Fig. 6.2 (Hornyak 50, Johnson 51, Lauritsen 51). We have drawn the ground states at energy $E=0$, and to the extent that the charge effect is the same from state to state, one should expect corresponding levels at the same excitation energies on the figure. It is apparent that the theoretical prediction is in excellent agreement with the experimental findings; there is only one level which does not seem to have a partner (7.5 Mev in C^{11});[2] future

---

[1] This prediction actually depends only on the assumed equality of neutron-neutron and proton-proton forces and does not require the full charge-independence assumption.

[2] The 6.48-Mev C^{11} state is undoubtedly an unresolved doublet corresponding to the 6.76-Mev and 6.81-Mev B^{11} states; a similar statement holds for the uppermost levels on the figure.

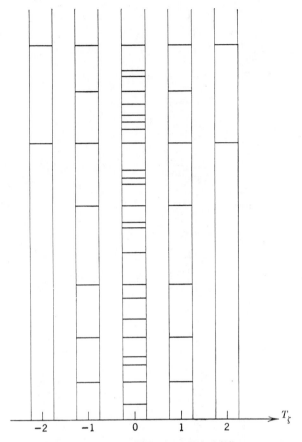

FIG. 6.1. A schematic level system of isobaric nuclei of different neutron excess T_ζ, neglecting the charge effect. The levels occurring in $T_\zeta = 0$ only are isotopic spin singlets; the levels which occur in only the three nuclei $T_\zeta = 1, 0, -1$ are isotopic spin triplets; the levels which occur in the five nuclei $T_\zeta = 2, 1, 0, -1, -2$ are isotopic spin quintets. All levels in $T_\zeta = 1$ have partners in $T_\zeta = -1$, the mirror nucleus, and also in $T_\zeta = 0$. Not all levels in $T_\zeta = 1$ have partners in $T_\zeta = 2$ or $T_\zeta = -2$. The charge effect distorts this figure by raising all levels of a given species T_ζ by a certain amount, the amount depending on T_ζ (larger for larger number of protons, i.e., for smaller T_ζ).

work may well remove this one discrepancy. The small shifts in excitation energies of corresponding levels are to be expected, and they have a reasonable order of magnitude.

The charge effect cannot always be treated as a small perturbation. An example of this is provided by the mirror nuclei C^{13} and N^{13} whose low-lying levels are shown in Fig. 6.3. The first excited level in C^{13} is at 3.10 Mev, whereas in N^{13} it is at 2.4 Mev. This large difference was explained by Wigner. He pointed out

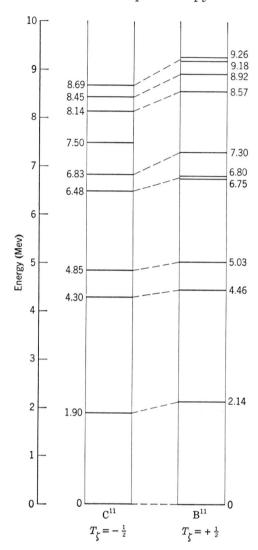

FIG. 6.2. Low-lying energy levels of B^{11} and C^{11}. The ground states are "partners" and so are the various excited states. The B^{11} levels were found from the $B^{10}(d,p)B^{11}$ reaction, the C^{11} levels from the $B^{10}(d,n)C^{11}$ reaction. [Data for this figure were taken from Hornyak (50), Johnson (51), and Lauritsen (51).]

that the separation energy S_n of a neutron from C^{13} is 4.88 Mev, above the 3.10-Mev level, whereas the separation energy S_p of a proton from N^{13} is only 1.92 Mev, below the 2.4-Mev level. Hence the 2.4-Mev level in N^{13} is unstable against proton emission, whereas the "mirror" (3.10-Mev) level in C^{13} is stable against particle (neutron) emission. Under these circumstances the Coulomb energy can no longer be treated as a small perturbation. A more detailed treatment

(Ehrman 51), using the theory of nuclear reactions, gives an estimate for the actual energy shift in this case, which then agrees with experiment as to order of magnitude (the theory does not allow a very detailed comparison).

The existence of corresponding levels in mirror nuclei depends on the assumption of equal neutron-neutron and proton-proton forces but does not require the full charge-independence hypothesis. The evidence for full isotopic spin multiplets in light nuclei is considerably weaker than for corresponding levels in mirror nuclei. The two best

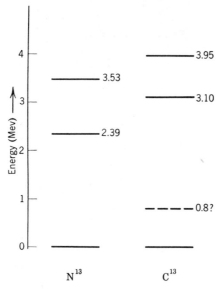

FIG. 6.3.   Low-lying energy levels of N^{13} and C^{13}, with the ground state drawn at zero energy for both species. The large discrepancy in excitation energy between the 2.39-Mev level in N^{13} and the 3.10-Mev level in C^{13} is attributed to the fact that the Coulomb energy cannot be treated as a small perturbation in this case. The 3.10-Mev C^{13} state is stable against neutron emission, whereas the 2.39-Mev N^{13} state is unstable against proton emission. The 0.8-Mev C^{13} level has not been established beyond doubt. [Data taken from Hornyak (50).]

cases are the nuclei with $A = 10$ and $A = 14$ (Sherr 49). The levels of O^{14}, N^{14}, and C^{14} are shown in Fig. 6.4. After correction for the charge effect, we see that the following three states form an isotopic spin triplet: the ground state of O^{14}, the 2.3-Mev excited state of N^{14}, and the ground state of C^{14}. This assignment is strengthened by the properties of the beta-decay of O^{14} and C^{14}. The C^{14} decay is very slow, indicating that the ground state of N^{14} is very different in structure from the ground state of C^{14} (see Chapter XIII). On the other hand, the O^{14} nucleus decays predominantly to the 2.3-Mev level of

N^{14}, and this decay is very fast, indicating that the 2.3-Mev level of N^{14} has very similar properties to the ground state of O^{14}.

Prediction (2) is also borne out by the data of Fig. 6.4. C^{14} has an excited level at 5.6 Mev, and a doubtful excited level at 6.1 Mev.

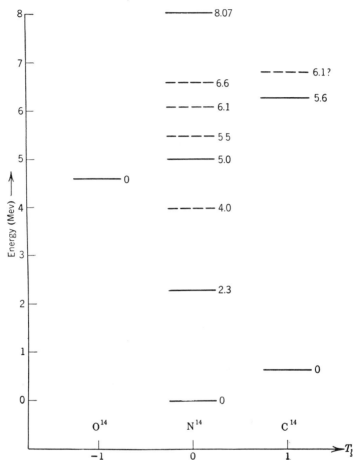

FIG. 6.4. Energy levels of O^{14}, N^{14}, and C^{14}. The ground states of O^{14} and C^{14} together with the 2.3-Mev N^{14} state form an isotopic spin triplet. The 8.07-Mev N^{14} state and the 5.6-Mev C^{14} state may also be corresponding states. No state in N^{14} corresponding to the doubtful 6.1-Mev C^{14} level is known.

If the ground state of C^{14} corresponds to the 2.3-Mev level of N^{14}, these two excited states of C^{14} should correspond to levels in N^{14} at 7.9 Mev and 8.4 Mev, respectively. There is a well-established level in N^{14} at 8.07 Mev, which may correspond to the 5.6-Mev state in C^{14}. The doubtful 6.1-Mev level in C^{14}, on the other hand, does not seem to have a partner in N^{14}.   Only more experimental evidence will tell whether this is a real contradiction to theory.

On the whole, the theoretical interpretation of the data on light nuclei is still in a very early state.   Considerably more work is needed before the implications of these data will be fully explored.   At present the data are not in disagreement with the assumption of charge independence of nuclear forces (i.e., with the existence of isotopic spin multiplets), but the data are not yet conclusive.

It is possible to use the concept of partition to develop a spectroscopic classification of nuclear energy levels much more detailed than the one which we have discussed so far (Wigner 37, Hund 37, Wigner 41).   Unfortunately this more detailed classification is based on the assumption that the tensor forces (spin-orbit coupling) can be neglected in a first approximation.   This assumption is probably adequate for the discussion of the gross features of nuclear stability (see Section 4).   It is, however, too crude to lead to a practically useful spectroscopic classification of energy levels.   If the forces were really charge- and spin-independent, certain levels (those belonging to the same space wave function and hence to the same partition) would coincide in energy to form "supermultiplets."   If the effect of spin-dependent forces (which can be of type $\mathbf{d}_1 \cdot \mathbf{d}_2$ or tensor forces) were small, the actual levels arising from this "supermultiplet" would still be close together in energy compared to the separations between different supermultiplets.   There is no experimental evidence for such a grouping of levels in light nuclei, and theoretical work (Feingold 50) has indicated that the effect of the tensor forces is by no means small. Thus the partition quantum numbers cannot be used as the basis of a detailed classification of energy levels.   On the other hand, partition quantum numbers (P, P', P'') sometimes can be assigned to nuclear levels, and this assignment can be used to draw some conclusions in special cases (Guthrie 42).

We therefore arrive at the following general scheme for classification of energy levels of light nuclei: each level has a definite angular momentum J and parity π.   In addition, the levels of isobaric nuclei can be grouped into isotopic spin multiplets.   Under certain conditions, partition quantum numbers (P, P', P'') can also be assigned to individual levels.

This classification scheme is very much less extensive than the one available for energy levels of atoms (Condon 35).   The reason is our ignorance concerning the nuclear forces as well as our inability to treat nuclear many-body problems by simple approximations.   In atoms the nucleus exerts a predominant force of attraction, so that an independent-particle model is a good first approximation which can be used to classify atomic energy levels. There is no similar first approximation known for nuclei which could claim corresponding accuracy. However, recent successes of the shell model (see Chapter XIV) indicate that the independent-particle model is perhaps not so bad an approximation as it was hitherto assumed to be.

We can summarize the achievements of the general theory of nuclear spectroscopy as follows:

(1) We have obtained a qualitative understanding of the main factors determining the stability of nuclear species (Section 1).

(2) This qualitative understanding could be used to establish a semi-empirical formula for nuclear binding energies which gives a satisfactory summary of the main outlines of the experimental material (Section 2).

(3) A rough estimate of the symmetry effect due to the exchange nature of nuclear forces (Section 3) has enabled us to understand the main outlines of the table of stable nuclei (Section 4).

(4) Some information has been obtained regarding magnetic moments, and this information could be used to interpret the experimental material (Section 5).

(5) A study of the constants of motion of nuclear systems has provided us with a rudimentary framework for the classification of nuclear energy levels (Section 6).

SYMBOLS

A Mass number of the nucleus $[=N+Z]$ (Section 1)

b Range of the nuclear force   (3.2)

B Binding energy of the nucleus   (2.6)

c Speed of light   (Section 1)

C Operator for the Coulomb energy of the nucleus   (Section 3)

$\bar{C}$ Expectation value of C (1.2)

d Distance between nearest neighbors in the nucleus; for the definition of d, see Chapter III, Section 3   (3.2)

E_{Coulomb} Coulomb energy of the nucleus in the Weizsäcker formula $[=\bar{C}]$ (2.3)

E_{rest} Rest mass energy of N neutrons and Z protons separated from each other   (1.5)

E_{surf} Surface energy of the nucleus in the Weizsäcker formula (2.5)

E_{sym} Symmetry energy of the nucleus in the Weizsäcker formula (2.2)

E_{vol}	Volume energy of the nucleus in the Weizsäcker formula (2.1)
g_L	Gyromagnetic ratio for the orbital part of the nuclear magnetic moment; for its definition, see Chapter I, Section 7 (Section 5)
g_S	Gyromagnetic ratio for the spin part of the nuclear magnetic moment; for its definition, see Chapter I, Section 7 (Section 5)
$g_+(d/b)$	Relative probability of interaction for a symmetric pair; for its definition, see Chapter III, Section 3 (3.2)
H	Nuclear Hamiltonian $[=T+V+C]$ (Section 3)
J	Total angular momentum quantum number of the nucleus (Section 5)
k	Constant appearing in $(b/R)^3 = kA^{-1}$; k is estimated to lie between 2 and 3 (3.3)
L	Orbital angular momentum quantum number of the nucleus (Section 5)
$\text{Li}^6{}^*$	The excited state of Li^6 which "corresponds" to the ground states of He^6 and Be^6 (Section 1)
m	Mass of the electron (Section 1)
$m_{\mathfrak{k}}$	Value of $T_{\mathfrak{k}}$ for some definite nucleus (Section 6)
M_n	Mass of the neutron (Section 1)
M_p	Mass of the proton (Section 1)
n	An integer (Section 1)
n_+	Number of symmetric pairs (3.1), (3.11), (3.18)
n_-	Number of anti-symmetric pairs (3.1)
$(n_+)_{\text{Op}}$	Operator for the number of symmetric pairs (3.12)
n_1	Number of "levels" occupied by 1 nucleon (3.13)
n_2	Number of "levels" occupied by 2 nucleons (3.13)
n_3	Number of "levels" occupied by 3 nucleons (3.13)
n_4	Number of "levels" occupied by 4 nucleons (3.13)
N	Number of neutrons in the nucleus $[=A-Z]$ (1.1)
p	Probability of interaction for a pair regardless of its symmetry $[=p(b/R)]$; for its definition see Chapter III, Section 2 (3.2)
p_+	Probability of interaction for a symmetric pair (3.1), (3.2)
p_-	Probability of interaction for an anti-symmetric pair (3.1)
P	Partition symbol $[=\frac{1}{2}(n_1+2n_2+n_3)]$ (3.14)
P'	Partition symbol $[=\frac{1}{2}(n_1+n_3)]$ (3.14)
P''	Partition symbol $[=\frac{1}{2}(n_1-n_3)]$ (3.14)

P^M Majorana exchange operator   (3.5)

$P^M{}_{ij}$ Majorana exchange operator for particles i and j (3.11)

q Constant in the interpolation formula $B \cong qA$ for the nuclear binding energy $[q \cong 8 \text{ Mev}]$ (Section 2)

R Nuclear radius   (1.2)

R_c Coulomb radius of the nucleus   (2.11)

S Spin angular momentum quantum number of the nucleus (Section 5)

S_n Separation energy of a neutron   (Section 6)

S_p Separation energy of a proton   (Section 6)

S_z z component of the spin angular momentum of the nucleus (Section 6)

T Isotopic spin quantum number [= the maximum value of T_ζ for a set of "corresponding" levels in isobaric nuclei] (Section 6)

T Operator for the kinetic energy of the nucleus   (Section 3)

$\bar{T}$ Expectation value of the kinetic energy operator T (Section 3)

T_ζ Neutron excess $[= \tfrac{1}{2}(N - Z)]$ (1.1)

$(T_\zeta)_{\max}$ Maximum neutron excess T_ζ consistent with the partition (P, P', P'') (Section 3)

$(T_\zeta)_{\min}$ Value of the neutron excess T_ζ which leads to the minimum total energy U (maximum binding energy) for a given mass number A (2.8), (2.9)

u_c Constant appearing in the Weizsäcker formula for the Coulomb energy   (2.3), (2.4)

u_s Constant appearing in the Weizsäcker formula for the surface energy   (2.5)

u_v Constant appearing in the Weizsäcker formula for the volume energy   (2.1)

u_τ Constant appearing in the Weizsäcker formula for the symmetry energy   (2.2)

U Total energy of the nucleus   (2.7)

V Operator for the potential energy of the nucleus as a whole (3.6)

$\bar{V}$ Expectation value of the nuclear potential energy V (3.1)

V_0 Well depth of the nuclear potential between two nucleons, in the square well approximation   (3.1)

$V_{ij}(r_{ij})$ Nuclear potential between the pair of nucleons i, j separated by the distance r_{ij} (3.6)

$(V_M)_0$ Well depth of the Majorana potential between two nucleons in the square well approximation   (3.7)

$V_M(r)$ Distance dependence of the Majorana exchange potential between two nucleons   (3.5)

$(V_W)_0$ Well depth of the Wigner potential between two nucleons in the square well approximation   (3.7)

$V_W(r)$ Potential of the Wigner (non-exchange) force between two nucleons at separation r (3.5)

Z Number of protons in the nucleus   (1.1)

δ Constant in the Weizsäcker formula, related to the energy difference between even-even and odd-odd isobars   (2.14)

ΔE_c Energy difference between two isobaric nuclei due to the charge effect   (1.6)

$\Delta \bar{V}$ Difference in $\bar{V}$ between two isobaric nuclei   (3.9)

μ Magnetic moment of the nucleus, in nuclear magnetons (Section 5)

μ_{exp} Experimental value of μ (Section 5)

μ_{theor} Theoretical prediction for the magnetic moment on the assumption of no spin-orbit coupling   (Section 5)

ξ Partition-dependent part of $n_+ - n_-$ (3.16), (3.17)

π Parity of the nucleus   (Section 6)

$\boldsymbol{\sigma}$ Pauli spin vector of a nucleon   (Section 6)

Ψ Wave function of the nucleus   (Section 3)

CHAPTER VII

Nuclear Spectroscopy
II. Special Models

1. INTRODUCTION

The previous chapter is devoted to those aspects of nuclear spectroscopy which can be understood and correlated by means of rather general considerations. The scope of these general methods is considerable, but still rather narrowly circumscribed. We can get qualitative information for the over-all properties of atomic nuclei, but it is much more difficult to obtain any quantitative information, and of course special properties of individual nuclear species (e.g., spin, magnetic moment, excited states, deviation of binding energy from the smooth semi-empirical formula, etc.) cannot be predicted at all.

In view of this situation, considerable effort has been devoted to finding more detailed descriptions of nuclear states which can still be treated with the mathematical methods at our disposal, without being too sweeping simplifications of the actual conditions. This chapter is devoted to a short exposition of these attempts. It will be seen that there are scattered successes in various places, but that most of these attempts can be considered failures. The various models which were invented to describe the behavior of nuclei prove to be insufficient if an attempt is made to put them on some solid theoretical foundation, or to subject them to really detailed comparison with experiment.

We shall start with a discussion of the uniform model, since this model is most closely allied to the general considerations of the previous chapter. We shall then treat the independent-particle model in some detail. The alpha-particle model and the liquid drop model will be treated rather summarily, since they seem to be even farther from the truth than the first two.

▶ ## 2. THE UNIFORM MODEL OF WIGNER (37a, 40)

A. Theory

It was shown in the preceding chapter that very general symmetry arguments can be used to explain the stability of nuclei. These arguments can be extended to give quantitative information concerning nuclear binding energies. This extension is based on the assumption that the motion in nuclei is sufficiently complicated so that statistical considerations can be used. All the details of nuclear motion are ignored, and only the main qualitative features are retained. This model of the nucleus is therefore called the "uniform model." The uniform model fails to the extent that there exist in nuclei shell structure effects (compare the discussion of magnetic moments in the preceding chapter, and the evidence presented in Chapter XIV).

The theory starts with the assumption of charge- and spin-independent forces. For simplicity, let us start by considering Majorana forces only. The potential energy operator is then given by (VI,3.5) and (VI,3.6), with the Wigner term omitted. The expectation value of the potential energy was estimated there by the use of the assumption that the anti-symmetric pairs do not contribute appreciably to the nuclear potential energy $\bar{V}$. We now make a somewhat closer estimate as follows. The Majorana part of the potential energy gives[1]

$$(\psi, V_M \psi) = \sum_{ij} (\psi, V_M(r_{ij}) P^M{}_{ij} \psi) \tag{2.1}$$

where the sum is extended over all pairs of nucleons, counting each pair only once. We introduce the "projection" operators

$$\pi_{ij}{}^{\pm} = \tfrac{1}{2} (1 \pm P^M{}_{ij}) \tag{2.2}$$

which select the part of the wave function which is symmetric (anti-symmetric) under the space interchange of particles i and j. Expression (2.1) becomes

$$(\psi, V_M \psi) = \sum_{ij} (\psi, V_M(r_{ij}) \pi_{ij}{}^{+} \psi) - \sum_{ij} (\psi, V_M(r_{ij}) \pi_{ij}{}^{-} \psi) \tag{2.3}$$

Consider the first sum in (2.3). Because of the projection operator the interaction is computed only for the pairs which are symmetrical under space exchanges. Let us introduce the *average Majorana interaction* $\bar{V}_M{}^s$ *between a symmetric pair of particles*

$$\bar{V}_M{}^s = \frac{\sum_{ij} (\psi, V_M(r_{ij}) \pi_{ij}{}^{+} \psi)}{\sum_{ij} (\psi, \pi_{ij}{}^{+} \psi)} \tag{2.4}$$

In Chapter VI we have estimated $\bar{V}_M{}^s$ to be equal to $-p_+(V_M)_0$, where $(V_M)_0$ is the "well depth" of the Majorana force. Equation

[1] We use the notation $(\psi, V\psi)$ for $\int \psi^* V \psi \, d\tau$.

(2.4) represents a refinement of this estimate. The sum in the denominator of (2.4) is just $\bar{n}_+$, the number of symmetric pairs. In the same way we can introduce $\bar{V}_M{}^a$, the average interaction between anti-symmetric pairs, by replacing $\pi_{ij}{}^+$ with $\pi_{ij}{}^-$. The expectation value (2.3) of the Majorana part of the potential energy becomes

$$(\psi, V_M \psi) = \bar{V}_M{}^s \, \bar{n}_+ - \bar{V}_M{}^a \, \bar{n}_- \qquad (2.5)$$

So far, no approximations have been made. *The uniform model of Wigner now assumes that the average interaction integrals, $\bar{V}_M{}^s$ and $\bar{V}_M{}^a$, between symmetric and anti-symmetric pairs are smooth functions of the mass number A and, to a good approximation, independent of the neutron excess $T_\zeta = \tfrac{1}{2}(N - Z)$ and of other properties of the nucleus.* This approximation disregards all special features of individual nuclear species. The results of the uniform model must therefore be considered a refinement of the semi-empirical treatment of the nuclear energy surface rather than detailed predictions of all relevant nuclear properties. For example, the uniform model makes no attempt to determine the orbital angular momentum L of the nuclear ground state, or its magnetic moment.

It is useful to rewrite formula (2.5) in the alternative form:

$$(\psi, V_M \psi) = \tfrac{1}{2} (\bar{V}_M{}^s - \bar{V}_M{}^a) (\bar{n}_+ + \bar{n}_-) + \tfrac{1}{2} (\bar{V}_M{}^s + \bar{V}_M{}^a) (\bar{n}_+ - \bar{n}_-) \qquad (2.5')$$

Under the assumptions of the uniform model the first term is the same for all isobars, whereas the second term determines the stability relations in an isobaric sequence. The difference between the numbers of symmetric and anti-symmetric pairs has already been evaluated in Section 3 of Chapter VI.

Since a pair of space anti-symmetric particles must stay apart from each other (the wave function must be zero when they are at the same place), the average interaction integral for anti-symmetric pairs is necessarily smaller in absolute value than the interaction integral for symmetric pairs.

Formula (2.5') shows why it might be justifiable to neglect the variation of the interaction integrals in an isobaric sequence. The quantity $\bar{n}_+ - \bar{n}_-$ is a very rapidly varying function of T_ζ, and the variations of the interaction integrals are expected to be considerably smaller and smoother, so that these variations can validly be neglected in a first approximation.

The uniform model makes no attempt to calculate the interaction integrals. However, an estimate of their variation with mass number is possible. The interaction between a pair of particles comes only from distances of the order of magnitude of the range of nuclear forces.

The probability $p(b/R)$ of finding two particles that close together is inversely proportional to the volume of the nucleus, provided that this volume is much larger than the effective volume of interaction. Hence we shall assume that the average interaction integrals $\bar{V}$ are proportional to A^{-1}. Of course, for light nuclei the nuclear volume is not large compared to the volume of interaction; hence we should include in the estimate of the interaction integrals a surface term similar to the surface term in the Weizsäcker semi-empirical mass formula. This has not been done in most of the work on the uniform model, although the possibility has been recognized in the first paper of Wigner on this subject (Wigner 37a).

We now remove our assumption that the nuclear forces are of the Majorana type only, and we include a Wigner force in the theory. The equivalent of (2.5) for the Wigner force has the minus sign replaced by a plus sign, since the Wigner force does not change sign for antisymmetric pairs. We then get for the expectation value of the total potential energy

$$(\psi,\, V\psi) \;=\; -L\,(\bar{n}_+ - \bar{n}_-) - L'\,\tfrac{1}{2}A(A-1) \tag{2.6}$$

where

$$L \equiv -\tfrac{1}{2}(\bar{V}_M{}^s + \bar{V}_M{}^a) - \tfrac{1}{2}(\bar{V}_W{}^s - \bar{V}_W{}^a)$$

$$L' \equiv -\tfrac{1}{2}(\bar{V}_M{}^s - \bar{V}_M{}^a) - \tfrac{1}{2}(\bar{V}_W{}^s + \bar{V}_W{}^a) \tag{2.7}$$

The signs have been chosen so that L and L' are expected to be positive quantities for forces obeying the saturation requirements. We have also used the fact that the sum of the number of symmetric and antisymmetric pairs is equal to the total number of pairs, $\tfrac{1}{2}A(A-1)$.

We now proceed to the determination of the kinetic energy on the basis of the uniform model. We consider all the nuclear particles as moving independently in a sphere of the nuclear volume, except for the requirements of the exclusion principle; this "Fermi gas" is assumed to be completely degenerate, i.e., the particles are crowded into the lowest few levels consistent with the Pauli principle. In terms of the notation of the preceding chapter, using the "normal form" defined there, the number of neutrons with spin up is $n_1 + n_2 + n_3 + n_4$, the number of neutrons with spin down is $n_2 + n_3 + n_4$, etc. There are four kinds of particles here, and the kinetic energy of the Fermi gas is (see Chapter III; $M =$ mass of each nucleon, $R =$ radius of sphere):

$$T = \frac{3}{40}\,(36\pi)^{2/3}\,\frac{\hbar^2}{MR^2}\cdot[(n_1+n_2+n_3+n_4)^{5/3}$$
$$+\,(n_2+n_3+n_4)^{5/3} + (n_3+n_4)^{5/3} + (n_4)^{5/3}] \tag{2.8}$$

This quantity is not the kinetic energy in the actual nucleus but a lower limit for it: the correlations between positions of the particles make the wave function less smooth in configuration space and therefore raise the kinetic energy. However, we shall assume that this effect depends mostly on the mass number and is the same, to a good approximation, for all partitions and all isobars. This assumption may well be wrong; there does not seem to be any simple way of estimating the kinetic energy by taking correlations into account. It is customary to expand (2.8) under the assumption that n_1, n_2, and n_3 (and hence the partition quantum numbers P, P', P'') are small compared to the mass number. This gives, using $R = r_0 A^{1/3}$,

$$T = T_0 A \left[1 + \frac{40}{9A^2} \eta + \cdots \right] \qquad (2.8')$$

where T_0 and η are defined by

$$T_0 = \frac{3}{40} (9\pi)^{2/3} \frac{\hbar^2}{M r_0{}^2}$$

$$\eta = \tfrac{1}{2} [P^2 + (P')^2 + (P'')^2]$$

$\qquad\qquad\qquad\qquad\qquad\qquad (2.9)$

The leading term of (2.8') is proportional to the mass number A and is the same for isobaric nuclei. The term which distinguishes between isobars depends on the partition (symmetry properties) of the wave function through the combination η (2.9). In order to get the lowest energy for the nucleus, we want η to be small. The kinetic energy term favors the stability of nuclei with small values of $|T_\zeta|$.

The estimate of the kinetic energy is very critical for the determination of the binding energy: the kinetic energy neutralizes more than half of the potential energy in actual nuclei, so that the observed binding energy is a small difference of large quantities. A small fractional error in the kinetic energy estimate therefore leads to a large fractional error in the binding energy. It is not altogether clear whether the rough approximations used here give a sufficiently accurate estimate of the kinetic energy.

The charge effect and its influence on the energy in the uniform model is taken over directly from the Weizsäcker formula; see (VI,2.3).

For purposes of later discussion, we shall divide the total energy U of the nucleus in the Wigner uniform model into two parts, the first of which is independent of T_ζ and hence is the same for all isobars:

$$U(A,T_\zeta) = U_0(A) + [U(A,T_\zeta) - U_0(A)] \qquad (2.10)$$

$U_0(A)$ can be suitably defined by

$$U_0(A) = (\tfrac{1}{8}A^2 - 2A - \tfrac{5}{2})L - \tfrac{1}{2}A(A-1)L' + AT_0$$
$$+ (1 - 2A^{-1})A^{5/3}u_c + \tfrac{1}{2}A(M_n c^2 + M_p c^2) \quad (2.11)$$

If we use $r_0 = 1.465 \times 10^{-13}$ cm as in Section 2 of Chapter VI, the constant T_0 is about 13 Mev; the constant $u_c = 0.148$ Mev was introduced in Chapter VI in connection with the Weizsäcker formula. The apparent dependence of $U_0(A)$ on the square of the mass number is not real because the interaction integrals which enter into L and L' are assumed to vary like A^{-1}.

The second part of (2.10) is concerned with the comparison between isobars. Collecting the various formulas and using the quantity ξ of the preceding chapter, we get

$$U(A,T_\zeta) - U_0(A)$$
$$= \frac{L_1}{A}\xi + \frac{T_1}{A}\eta - 4u_c \frac{T_\zeta(A-1-T_\zeta)}{A^{1/3}} + (M_n c^2 - M_p c^2)T_\zeta \quad (2.12)$$

Here the quantity L_1 is defined by $L \equiv L_1 A^{-1}$ and is expected to be constant. It will be determined by comparison with the experimental data concerning isobars. The constant T_1 is given by $T_1 \equiv (\tfrac{40}{9})T_0$ and is estimated to be equal to about 60 Mev. The third and the fourth terms represent the differential effect between isobars of the Coulomb energy and the neutron-proton mass difference (the charge effect).

Since we shall be concerned only with ground state properties of nuclei, we shall restrict ourselves to the lowest partition (lowest values of ξ and η) for each nuclear species. These partitions, and the corresponding values of ξ, have been determined in Section 4 of Chapter VI. An explicit formula was given there for ξ; there exists a similar explicit formula for η. We collect both of them here for easier reference:

$$\xi = \tfrac{1}{2}T_\zeta^2 + 2|T_\zeta| + \tfrac{13}{4} \quad \text{odd } A$$
$$\xi = \tfrac{1}{2}T_\zeta^2 + 2|T_\zeta| + \tfrac{5}{2} \quad \text{even-even nuclei}$$
$$\xi = \tfrac{1}{2}T_\zeta^2 + 2|T_\zeta| + 4 \quad \text{odd-odd nuclei with } N \neq Z \quad (2.13)$$
$$\xi = 5 \quad \text{odd-odd nuclei with } N = Z$$

and

$$\eta = \tfrac{1}{2}T_\zeta^2 + \tfrac{1}{4} \quad \text{odd } A$$
$$\eta = \tfrac{1}{2}T_\zeta^2 \quad \text{even-even nuclei}$$
$$\eta = \tfrac{1}{2}T_\zeta^2 + \tfrac{1}{2} \quad \text{odd-odd nuclei with } N \neq Z \quad (2.14)$$
$$\eta = \tfrac{1}{2} \quad \text{odd-odd nuclei with } N = Z$$

The expression of the Wigner uniform model for the symmetry energy is given by the first two terms of (2.12) (the last two terms represent the charge effect):

$$E_{\text{sym}} = \frac{L_1\xi + T_1\eta}{A} \qquad (2.15)$$

This represents a refinement of expression (VI,3.20). Formula (2.15) becomes very similar to (VI,3.20) if the contribution of the kinetic energy is neglected, i.e., if we put $T_1 = 0$, for then both (2.15) and (VI,3.20) predict that the symmetry energy is proportional to ξ and inversely proportional to the mass number A. Although L_1 could in principle be found from the wave function ψ of the nucleus, in practice it serves merely as an adjustable parameter in the theory which can be chosen to give the best fit to the experiments.

However, even rather rough estimates show that T_1 is by no means negligible compared to L_1. We can estimate L_1 as in Chapter VI by neglecting the contributions of the anti-symmetric pairs and estimating the probability of interaction of the symmetric pairs. Formula (VI,3.20) then gives the estimate

$$L_1 \cong kV_0 \qquad (2.16)$$

where k, defined by (VI,3.3), is expected to be between 2 and 3, and V_0 can be estimated, from the two-body problems, to be of the order of 20 Mev. Hence our estimate for L_1 lies between 40 and 60 Mev, whereas the value of T_1 as estimated from (2.8′) and (2.9) is about 60 Mev.

The symmetry energy under the assumption $T_1 = 0$ has been discussed in detail in Section 4 of Chapter VI. Let us now investigate the consequences of the contribution of the kinetic energy to the symmetry effect. η, (2.14), differs from ξ, (2.13), qualitatively through the absence of the term proportional to $|T_\zeta|$, and quantitatively through the smaller difference between even-even and odd-odd nuclei. The absence of the $|T_\zeta|$ term in η implies that there is no "cusp" for $T_\zeta = 0$. Thus, to the extent that the kinetic energy contribution to E_{sym} is important, the "cusp" at $T_\zeta = 0$ is less pronounced than in Figs. 4.1 to 4.5 of Chapter VI.

The second effect of the kinetic energy is to decrease the energy separation between the curves for the even-even and odd-odd nuclei in Fig. 4.4 of Chapter VI. We can see this by considering the ratio ρ of this spacing to the coefficient of T_ζ^2 in the symmetry energy. According to (2.13), (2.14), and (2.15) this ratio is given by

$$\rho = \frac{3L_1 + T_1}{L_1 + T_1} \qquad (2.17)$$

Since L_1 and T_1 are both inherently positive quantities, (2.17) implies that we get the largest spacing between the two parabolas for the even-even and odd-odd nuclei (compared to the curvature of the parabolas) if $T_1 = 0$. Since T_1 is actually expected to be of the same order of magnitude as L_1, the spacing between the parabolas is decreased considerably.

The uniform model is based on assumptions which are likely to lose their validity both for very low and moderately high mass numbers. In very light nuclei, it is not likely that special properties of individual nuclear species (such as shell effects, for example) can be ignored without appreciable errors. Hence Wigner applied the uniform model to the study of nuclei beyond O^{16}. On the high mass number side, there are several reasons for the model to break down. First, the increasing relative importance of the Coulomb energy makes the basic approximation of charge independence of the forces in the nucleus less applicable. Eventually the Coulomb repulsion mixes up terms belonging to different partitions, and the space symmetry properties of the wave function cease to play an important role. Second, the total number of nucleon pairs increases very rapidly with the mass number; thus a shift of a few pairs from an anti-symmetric to a symmetric character, say, represents a smaller effect on a relative basis. Furthermore the average coefficients L and L' decrease in magnitude, so that one pair with special properties (say, with a particularly strong interaction) can upset the statistical considerations quite easily. For $A = 50$, the number of pairs $\frac{1}{2}A(A-1) = 1225$, and a shift of a few pairs either way represents an effect of only 1 percent or less. It is therefore unlikely that the uniform model should be applicable to nuclei of mass numbers larger than 50. Of course, an appreciable tendency toward shell structure or spin-orbit coupling or both would invalidate the uniform model even in the remaining region of mass numbers, $16 \lesssim A \lesssim 50$.

The main content of the uniform model can be formulated by stating that it gives essentially a theoretical justification of the semi-empirical mass formula of Weizsäcker without attempting any detailed predictions about individual nuclei. The mass formula of Weizsäcker is modified as follows:

(1) A term in $|T_\zeta|$ appears which leads to a cusp in the parabolas at $T_\zeta = 0$. This cusp is less pronounced, however, than in our rough estimate (VI,3.20).

(2) The existence of separate, spaced parabolas for even-even and odd-odd nuclei of the same mass number is a natural consequence of the theory. The spacing is somewhat less than in our rough estimate (VI,3.20).

(3) The odd-odd nuclei with $Z = N$ ($T_\zeta = 0$) constitute a special case (see Section 4 of Chapter VI).

(4) The constants L_1 and T_1 in the symmetry energy can be estimated theoretically to be of the order of 40 to 60 Mev and around 60 Mev, respectively.

(5) The model is expected to be adequate for mass numbers between 16 and 50.

B. Comparison with Experiment

We now compare the uniform model with experiment. It is by its very nature restricted to a rather narrow range of A, and we shall investigate only the nuclei within that range ($16 \lesssim A \lesssim 50$).

Let us start with the energy differences between isobars. The energy difference $[U(A,T_\zeta) - U(A, T_\zeta - 1)]$ can be found from the experimental data on the beta-decay (one of the two nuclei T_ζ, $T_\zeta - 1$ is necessarily beta-unstable). After correction for the charge effect,[1] we obtain an experimental value for the difference in the symmetry energies:

$$\Delta E_r = E_{\text{sym}}(A,T_\zeta) - E_{\text{sym}}(A, T_\zeta - 1) = \frac{L_1\Delta\xi + T_1\Delta\eta}{A} \quad (2.18)$$

where $\Delta\xi$ is the difference between ξ, (2.13), for T_ζ and $T_\zeta - 1$, respectively; $\Delta\eta$ is defined in an analogous way.

According to the prediction (2.18), the difference between the symmetry energies is proportional to A^{-1}. This prediction can be tested by plotting the experimental values of ΔE_r for a given type of transition (e.g., odd A nuclei, $T_\zeta = \frac{3}{2}$ to $T_\zeta = \frac{1}{2}$ or vice versa) against the reciprocal of the mass number A. The experimental points should lie on a straight line passing through the origin, of slope equal to

$$L_1\Delta\xi + T_1\Delta\eta$$

Such a plot is shown in Fig. 2.1 for the symmetry energy differences between odd A nuclei with $T_\zeta = \frac{3}{2}$ and $T_\zeta = \frac{1}{2}$. More information about these energy differences can be obtained from the direction of the beta-decay, without knowledge of the decay energy itself, for the

---

[1] This correction is made by assuming that the Coulomb radius R_c is given by $R_c = r_0 A^{1/3}$ with $r_0 = 1.465 \times 10^{-13}$ cm (its value for the mirror nuclei $T_\zeta = \pm\frac{1}{2}$; see Section 2 of Chapter VI).

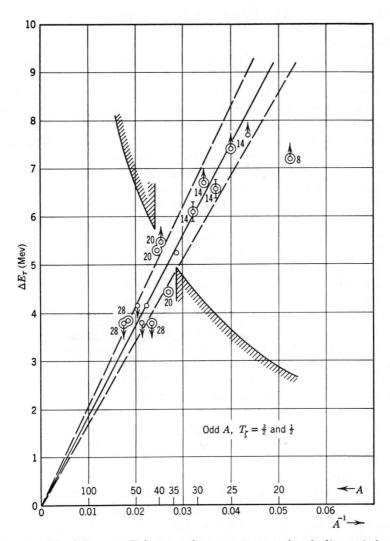

Fɪɢ. 2.1. The difference ΔE_τ between the symmetry energies of adjacent isobars, as a function of the inverse of the mass number A, for nuclei with odd A and $T_\zeta = \frac{1}{2}$ and $\frac{3}{2}$. The circles without arrows represent experimental points. The circles with arrows represent transitions in which only an upper or lower limit for ΔE_τ is known; the arrows point from that limit into the allowed region. The shaded regions are excluded by stability considerations. "Ordinary" transitions are indicated by single circles, whereas "magic" transitions (in which one or both of the nuclei involved contain magic numbers of neutrons or protons) are indicated by double circles. According to the uniform model, all points should be consistent with a straight line passing through the origin. The slope of this straight line is predicted to be $3L_1 + T_1$. The best straight line is drawn in, as well as two dashed straight lines which represent estimates of upper and lower limits for the slope, respectively.

275

direction of the beta-decay implies a limit (upper or lower, as the case may be) on the actual energy difference, and hence a similar limit on the energy difference corrected for the charge effect. These limits are also drawn in on the figure, the shaded areas being excluded regions. It is seen that the experimental points fall on a reasonably good straight line and that the line so drawn avoids the shaded regions. Hence the simple assumption that the symmetry terms are proportional to A^{-1} is seen to be fairly good. (It should be remarked, however, that we have picked a rather favorable case; other classes of transitions show a much wider fluctuation.)

We have also indicated on the figure the points arising from transitions in which one of the two nuclei contains a "magic" number of neutrons or protons (see Chapter XIV). The particular magic number involved is indicated next to each of those points. We see that the points for magic numbers 8, 20, and 28 do deviate from the best straight line more than the others. In each case the deviation is in the right direction (the magic nucleus has higher stability than expected on the uniform model). The magic number 14, on the other hand, does not appear to be very potent; the corresponding points fall right on the best straight line. The presence of these magic numbers makes it much more difficult to test the uniform model. Since the uniform model cannot account for the increased stability of magic nuclei, we should really omit these points from the graph. However, we would then have very few points left; i.e., there are only very few transitions between neighboring isobars for which neither isobar contains a magic number of neutrons or protons.

Since Fig. 2.1 is a plot of $(L_1\Delta\xi + T_1\Delta\eta)/A$ versus $(1/A)$ for a particular class of transitions, the theoretical expression for the slope of the straight line can be deduced from formulas (2.13) and (2.14). For the class of transitions illustrated on the figure, ξ changes by 3, whereas η changes by 1; hence the slope ought to be equal to $3L_1 + T_1$. Such an analysis can be made for various classes of transitions and the results used to determine L_1 and T_1 experimentally (Goldin 50, Frisch 50). Unfortunately, the experimental values of the slopes cannot be fitted closely by an expression of type $(L_1\Delta\xi + T_1\Delta\eta)$. If L_1 and T_1 are adjusted to fit the energy differences between isobars with odd mass numbers, *the energy differences between even-even and odd-odd isobars are underestimated by the theoretical formula.*[1]

To explain this discrepancy, it appears reasonable to suppose that

---

[1] This result is not quite conclusive at this time because the present data are not sufficient to define the slopes closely for all the relevant classes of transitions. By using the present uncertainties in the slopes to their full extent, it is possible to get bare agreement for a particular choice of L_1 and T_1. However, it is very likely

there exists a tendency of individual pairs of nucleons to be closely associated with each other in their orbital motion in the nucleus.   For example, adding two neutrons to a nucleus (thereby producing an isotope of the original one with mass number increased by 2) seems to leave many nuclear properties almost unchanged in a large number of isotopes.   As far as nuclear stability is concerned, this pairing of like nucleons has the effect that the nucleus has a tendency to bind odd particles less strongly than particles which come in pairs.   Thus an even-odd nucleus is on the average less strongly held together than an even-even nucleus, because of the one unpaired particle.   An odd-odd nucleus is even less strongly bound, since there are now two unpaired particles.   The "levels" introduced in Chapter VI merely as a device for counting numbers of symmetric and anti-symmetric pairs seem to have a significance beyond their symmetry properties.   We might say, for example, that two nucleons in different "levels" interact less strongly than two nucleons in the same "level"; hence pairs in different "levels" should be counted less strongly than pairs in the same "level."

If the motion in nuclei were analogous to that in a liquid, say, with frequent collisions between particles and a large degree of randomness, it would be hard to understand how the "levels" could have any significance other than a purely mathematical one (e.g., counting of symmetric and anti-symmetric pairs).   On the other hand, if each nucleon, to a valid first approximation, can be assumed to move in the average field created by the others, the "levels" can well assume physical meaning as the levels of a single particle in this average field. Whether this particular explanation is correct is not known at this time.   However, there is every reason to suppose that the motion of nucleons in heavy nuclei is appreciably more ordered (less liquid-like) in *some* sense than was commonly supposed until recently.   This subject will be discussed in more detail in Chapter XIV.

The second, even more serious, difficulty of the uniform model has been stressed by Wigner (40): it is the inability of this model to account for the observed total binding energy of the nucleus.   Let us start by assuming (as we did in Chapter VI) that the anti-symmetric pairs make no contribution to the potential energy $\bar{V}$.   In that case (2.7) implies that $L=L'$, and (2.6) gives the potential energy estimate

$$\bar{V} \cong -2\bar{n}_{+}L \qquad (2.19)$$

that this agreement will disappear as soon as more complete data become available. Better agreement was found by Wigner (40) and Barkas (39a).   The difference can be attributed to the additional data which have become available since that time.

Formula (2.19) represents an advance over the corresponding estimate (VI,3.4) in that we now have an approximate experimental value for L from the study of energy differences between isobars. The best values of L_1 together with $\bar{n}_+ \cong \frac{3}{16}A^2$ lead to the following estimate for the potential energy per particle:

$$\frac{\bar{V}}{A} \cong 9 \text{ to } 18 \text{ Mev} \qquad (2.20)$$

The value (2.8') of the kinetic energy is a lower limit, since correlations in the wave function increase the kinetic energy. Thus the kinetic energy per particle is at least as large as

$$\frac{\bar{T}}{A} \geq T_0 \cong 13 \text{ Mev} \qquad (2.21)$$

Comparison of (2.20) and (2.21) shows that the binding energy of the nucleus must be less than 5 Mev per particle *before* the correction for the Coulomb effect. This is a very serious discrepancy, since we have underestimated the kinetic energy and overestimated the potential energy.

We have stated without proof that (2.19) is an overestimate of $|\bar{V}|$. According to (2.7) the ratio L'/L is decreased by anti-symmetric Majorana interactions and increased by anti-symmetric Wigner interactions. In order to give saturation, the Majorana forces must predominate over the Wigner forces by a ratio of at least 4:1. Thus the contribution of the anti-symmetric pairs decreases L'/L below the value 1 which we have assumed in (2.19). The potential energy per particle then becomes even less than our estimate (2.20).

Recent work of Wigner (unpublished) has shown that the discrepancy in the total binding energy can be explained by taking into account the tensor forces which have been neglected so far. However, this refinement of the model decreases the theoretical energy difference between even-even and odd-odd nuclei, thereby making that disagreement with experiment even worse. Probably this poor success of the uniform model is due to the fact that the ground state of the nucleus (which determines the nuclear binding energy) should be described not by a uniform model but by a shell (independent particle) model. It is possible that the uniform model will prove more adequate for the description of excited nuclear states (Hurwitz 51).

3. THE INDEPENDENT-PARTICLE MODEL

A. Introduction

The independent-particle model is based on the assumption that each nucleon moves independently of all other nucleons in a common

potential field. This field represents the average effect of all interactions with other nucleons, and it is the same for each particle.
Every nucleon is then considered an independent particle, and the
presence of other particles moving in the same field exerts its influence
only by means of the requirements of the Pauli principle, which
excludes identical particles from occupying the same quantum state.
The independent-particle method is therefore expected to give a good
approximation if the assumption of an average field is justified. This
assumption is justified if the motions of the various nucleons in the
nucleus are not closely correlated with each other (the assumption
fails, for example, if there is a strong tendency toward clustering into
alpha-particles inside the nucleus).

The average field acting on a nucleon, due to the motion of the other
nucleons, could be computed if these motions were known. If we
assumed that the independent-particle model provides a good approximation, we could find the average field from the independent-particle
wave function. This computed average field in general would be
different from the initially assumed average field which was used to
find the wave function. The Hartree-Fock "self-consistent field"
method determines the best (= self-consistent) wave function for the
system by the requirement that the average field computed from the
wave function be identical with the initially assumed average field.
For nuclei only one self-consistent field computation has been done
(for He^4; Matricon 38), with rather good results (which, however, can
be obtained for He^4 with much less labor by using the variational
method with a reasonable trial wave function). For the nuclei to
which the independent-particle model is usually applied, i.e., for
$5 \leq A \leq 16$, no self-consistent field calculation has ever been attempted.
Instead, the wave functions have been chosen from the point of view of
mathematical convenience. There are, therefore, two separate sources
of error in the nuclear calculations with the independent-particle
model: the general inadequacy of the model, and the lack of "self-
consistency" of the wave functions.

Mathematically the assumption of independent (not correlated)
motions for the nucleons means that the wave functions for the system
as a whole can be written in product form, each factor describing the
motion of one nucleon:

$$\psi = \varphi_1(q_1)\ \varphi_2(q_2)\ \cdots\ \varphi_A(q_A) \tag{3.1}$$

Here q_i stands for the coordinates (space, spin, and isotopic spin)
of the ith nucleon. A typical $\varphi(q)$ has the form

$$\varphi(q) = u(x,y,z)\ f(\zeta,\eta) \tag{3.2}$$

where x,y,z are the space coordinates, ζ is the mechanical spin coordinate, and η is the isotopic spin coordinate of the nucleon (see Chapter III, Section 5); the function $f(\zeta,\eta)$ could, for instance, stand for a neutron with spin pointing up: $f(\zeta,\eta) = \alpha(\zeta)\nu(\eta)$.

Expression (3.1) is not an acceptable wave function for particles obeying the exclusion principle, since it is not anti-symmetric under the exchange of any two q's. However, we can get properly anti-symmetric wave functions by linear combinations of functions of the type (3.1). We shall not need the details of this method here.

The assumption that the average field is a central field allows us to classify the one-particle wave functions $u(x,y,z)$, just as in atoms, with a principal quantum number n and an orbital angular momentum quantum number l. The principal quantum number n is related to the number of nodes in the radial part $R(r)$ of $u(x,y,z) = R(r) Y_{lm}(\theta,\phi)$ through

$$\text{Number of radial nodes} = n - l - 1 \qquad (3.3)$$

The sequence of levels arranged in order of increasing energy depends on the nature of the potential.

We give here the sequence of levels for three characteristic central fields. The levels are written in the usual spectroscopic notation, and the equality sign denotes levels with equal energies:

I. *Shielded Inverse Square Force.* $V = -\text{const } r^{-1} \exp(-\alpha r)$.

$$(1s), (2s), (2p), (3s), (3p), (3d), (4s), (4p), (4d), (4f), \cdots \qquad (3.3a)$$

II. *Oscillator Force.* $V = \text{const } r^2$.

$$(1s), (2p), (3d) = (2s), (4f) = (3p), (5g) = (4d) = (3s) \cdots \qquad (3.3b)$$

III. *Spherical Well.*[1] $V = 0$ for $r < b$, $V = V_0$ for $r > b$, $V_0 \to \infty$.

$$(1s), (2p), (3d), (2s), (4f), (3p), (5g), (4d), (3s), \cdots \qquad (3.3c)$$

The shielded inverse square force is important in atoms. Its potential differs from the other two by its large negative value in the center, which depresses the energy of the states in which the particle is found mostly at the center. These are the states with low orbital angular momenta, especially the s states. The average potential energy in nuclei is expected to differ qualitatively from the shielded inverse square potential and be more like the oscillator—or the spherical well—potential. A most characteristic difference is found in the fact that, in the latter two potentials, the second level is a $2p$ state

---

[1] Taken from Margenau (34), who also discusses the case of finite V_0.

and not a $2s$ state as in the atomic potential.   In general, the order of levels in (3.3b) and (3.3c) is quite similar but differs completely from the order in the inverse square field.

If we now try to build up a "periodic system of nuclei," in analogy with the Bohr explanation of the periodic system in atoms, we should expect the $(1s)$ level to be filled up first.   It can accommodate four particles and is filled at He^4.   The next level to fill up is the $(2p)$ level.   Since an orbital angular momentum of one unit has three directions of orientation, the $(2p)$ orbit can hold $3 \times 4 = 12$ particles and is filled at O^{16}.   It is somewhat harder to predict which orbit is filled next.   It would be the $(3d)$ orbit in an infinitely deep spherical well (which is certainly too strong an idealization) and could be either $(2s)$ or $(3d)$ in an oscillator potential.   Until rather recently no one had tried to extend the concept of shells much beyond O^{16}, since the independent-particle model was not expected to yield an adequate approximation for nuclei heavier than that if conventional nuclear forces were assumed to act.   Lately there has been much experimental evidence that this model is much better than anyone had believed (see Chapter XIV).   We shall restrict ourselves here to the nuclei between $A = 5$ and $A = 16$, whose lowest states should belong to the configuration $(1s)^4(2p)^{A-4}$.

B. The P Shell Configurations

We now investigate in greater detail what quantum states can be obtained from the $(1s)^4(2p)^{A-4}$ configuration for the nuclei with A between 5 and 16.

We start with the simplest case: $A = 5$.   The closed $(1s)$ shell can be ignored for our purposes since its spin and angular momentum are zero.   Since the one particle outside the closed shell has an angular momentum $l = 1$, our system is in a P state.   The parity is -1 since the $(2p)$ levels have odd parity and there is an odd number (one) of particles in the $(2p)$ shell.   We can ascribe a partition to this state, and this partition is evidently $(\frac{1}{2},\frac{1}{2},\frac{1}{2})$, corresponding to a situation in which only one particle is outside the closed four-groups.   (See Chapter VI.)

For $A = 6$ there are two particles in the $(2p)$ shell.   By the vector rule of composition of angular momenta, the orbital angular momenta of these two p particles can combine to give $L = 0, 1, 2$.   We now determine the symmetry properties (partition) of these three terms.   A p particle can have its orbital angular momentum directed in any one of three ways: $m = 1, 0, -1$.   The corresponding three wave functions have the form

$$u(x,y,z) = -\frac{x+iy}{\sqrt{2}}\,g(r) \equiv -\frac{p_x+ip_y}{\sqrt{2}} = p_+ \qquad (m=1)$$

$$u(x,y,z) = z\,g(r) \equiv p_z \qquad\qquad\qquad (m=0) \qquad (3.4)$$

$$u(x,y,z) = \frac{x-iy}{\sqrt{2}}\,g(r) \equiv \frac{p_x-ip_y}{\sqrt{2}} = p_- \qquad (m=-1)$$

where $g(r)$ is a function of $r=|\mathbf{r}|$ only, and the functions p_x, p_y, p_z, p_+, and p_- are defined by (3.4). These three one-particle wave functions can be thought of as the three components of a vector $\mathbf{p}$. Let us call $\mathbf{p}(1)$ the vector whose components represent the possible wave functions of the first p particle, and $\mathbf{p}(2)$ the vector representing the second p particle. The two-particle wave function which describes the state formed by the two particles is a bilinear combination of the components of the two vectors $\mathbf{p}(1)$ and $\mathbf{p}(2)$. We get the S state $(L=0)$ wave function[1] by combining the two vectors so as to form a scalar:

$$\psi_S = \mathbf{p}(1)\cdot\mathbf{p}(2) \qquad (S \text{ state}) \qquad (3.5a)$$

The three wave functions of the P state are obtained by forming the three components of the cross product vector:

$$\psi_P = \mathbf{p}(1)\times\mathbf{p}(2) \qquad (P \text{ state}) \qquad (3.5b)$$

The five wave functions of the D state are the five components of a symmetric tensor:

$$\psi_{D,\pm 2} = p_\pm(1)\,p_\pm(2)$$

$$\psi_{D,\pm 1} = p_\pm(1)\,p_z(2) + p_z(1)\,p_\pm(2) \qquad (D \text{ state}) \qquad (3.5c)$$

$$\psi_{D,0} = 3\,p_z(1)\,p_z(2) - \mathbf{p}(1)\cdot\mathbf{p}(2)$$

The S and the D states are symmetric with respect to the space exchange of the two particles; the P state is anti-symmetric. The parity of all three states is "even."

The Majorana part of the nuclear forces acts repulsively in anti-symmetric states and attractively in symmetric ones; hence the S and D states are low and the P state high in energy.

The symmetry properties of the S and D states can be expressed also in terms of the partition quantum numbers. We compare the symmetry here with the symmetry conditions in the normal distribution of Section 3 of Chapter VI. The S and D states are symmetric

---

[1] The wave functions (3.5) are not normalized. The correctly normalized functions are given in Appendix A, Section 5, by using expression (A,5.1) with $j=j'=1$ and $J=0,1,2$, respectively.

with respect to the two particles; hence their symmetry corresponds to that of a normal distribution in which the two particles are in the same "level." We therefore obtain the occupation numbers $n_1 = 0$, $n_2 = 1$, $n_3 = 0$, which give rise to the parition $(P,P',P'') = (1,0,0)$.

The symmetry properties of the P state can also be expressed in terms of the partition quantum numbers. Since the P state wave function (3.5b) is anti-symmetric under the exchange of the space coordinates of the two particles outside the closed shell, the symmetry corresponds to the occupation numbers $n_1 = 2$, $n_2 = 0$, $n_3 = 0$, which give rise to the partition $(P,P',P'') = (1,1,1)$.[1]

The cases of more than two particles in the $(2p)$ shell are somewhat more complicated (Feenberg 37b,c; Hund 37), and we shall not treat them in detail. We restrict ourselves to the listing of the low-lying states only. According to the considerations of Chapter VI, the energy of the states is determined to a first approximation by their partition and, more specifically, by the value ξ (VI,3.17) belonging to this partition. High values of ξ correspond to higher energies, low values to lower energies. We shall list only those states of the configuration $(1s)^4 (2p)^{4-4}$ which belong to the lowest partition (the one with the smallest ξ) consistent with the configuration. These states are listed in Table 3.1. They are expected to correspond to the low-lying levels of nuclei with T_ζ near zero and mass number A between 4 and 16.

It should be emphasized that the states listed here are the low-lying levels only for those nuclei which can belong to the partition indicated in each case. For example, the partition $(0,0,0)$ is listed for $A = 12$. This partition implies an equal number of neutrons and protons (see Chapter VI); hence the states listed apply only to C^{12}. The nucleus N^{12}, with one more proton ($T_\zeta = -1$), does not possess any of these states. Rather, its low-lying levels belong to the partition $(1,1,0)$ and are presumably the states of partition $(1,1,0)$ arising from the configuration $(1s)^4 (2p)^{4-4}$. These states, and similar ones for other mass numbers in this region, are listed by Feenberg and Phillips (37c). We shall not treat them here.

A striking feature of this table is its symmetry about the middle, $A = 10$. Except for the sign of P'' in the partition symbol, the lowest partition and the states belonging to it are the same for the nuclei $A' = x$ and $A' = 12 - x$. The x "holes" in the second case act very similarly to the x particles in the p shell in the first case. This is well

---

[1] One may be confused by the apparent contradiction of having an anti-symmetric state although both particles are in the same $(2p)$ level. Actually the $(2p)$ level consists of three sublevels ($m = -1, 0, +1$). Hence an anti-symmetric combination like (3.5b) is possible, the two particles being in different substates.

known from the theory of atomic spectra. Correspondingly, the nuclei with $A = 10$ have the largest number of low-lying states.

Table 3.1 contains one definite prediction which can be checked directly against experiment. To the extent that *all* the low-lying levels of a nucleus belong to the configuration $(1s)^4(2p)^{A-4}$, they must all have the same parity, $+1$ for even A, -1 for odd A. There are three cases at present which seem to contradict this rule. The beta-decay of C^{14} to N^{14} has a very long half-life; this slow decay is difficult to explain unless it is assumed that a parity change occurs during the

TABLE 3.1

LOW-LYING STATES OF THE CONFIGURATION $(1s)^4(2p)^{A-4}$

A	Number of p Particles (A')	Parity	Lowest Partition	States of this Configuration Belonging to the Lowest Partition
4	0	$+$	(0,0,0)	S
5	1	$-$	$(\frac{1}{2},\frac{1}{2},\frac{1}{2})$	P
6	2	$+$	(1,0,0)	S, D
7	3	$-$	$(\frac{1}{2},\frac{1}{2},-\frac{1}{2})$	P, F
8	4	$+$	(0,0,0)	S, D, G
9	5	$-$	$(\frac{1}{2},\frac{1}{2},\frac{1}{2})$	P, D, F, G
10	6	$+$	(1,0,0)	S, D, D, F, G
11	7	$-$	$(\frac{1}{2},\frac{1}{2},-\frac{1}{2})$	P, D, F, G
12	8	$+$	(0,0,0)	S, D, G
13	9	$-$	$(\frac{1}{2},\frac{1}{2},\frac{1}{2})$	P, F
14	10	$+$	(1,0,0)	S, D
15	11	$-$	$(\frac{1}{2},\frac{1}{2},-\frac{1}{2})$	P
16	12	$+$	(0,0,0)	S

transition. Then either C^{14} or (more probably) N^{14} would have odd parity (Gerjuoy 51). The second case is exemplified by the 2.4-Mev excited state of N^{13} shown in Fig. 6.3 of Chapter VI. This state is unstable with respect to emission of protons. The emission probability (width) of the level is too large for p wave protons but is reasonable for s wave protons. Since the residual nucleus, C^{12}, presumably has even parity, emission of an s wave proton implies that the metastable level of N^{13} also has even parity, in contradiction to Table 3.1.[1] The third case is the 2.42-Mev excited state of Be^9 which decays by neutron emission to Be^8. Be^8 is known to have even parity since it

---

[1] The mirror nucleus, C^{13}, has been studied by Thomas (50), who finds conclusive evidence for opposite parities of the ground state and the 3.1-Mev state of C^{13}.

decays into two alpha-particles (see Chapter IX, Section 5). The very low neutron width of the Be^9 level, $\Gamma_n \leq 5$ kev (Van Patter 51), makes it likely that this state emits D wave neutrons and hence has the same parity as Be^8, i.e., even. This is in contradiction to Table 3.1.

Although these arguments are not conclusive, they lend weight to the assumption that levels belonging to different configurations are not widely separated in energy from each other, but rather interpenetrate to an appreciable extent. The theory of atomic spectroscopy (Condon 35) shows that appreciable "configuration interaction" can be expected in such a case. The model then fails to give simple predictions which can be proved or disproved by experiment.

The prediction of the orbital angular momenta L for the low-lying levels is a specific prediction obtained from the independent-particle model which cannot be obtained from general considerations such as those of the last chapter. Experimentally L is not known except for the ground states (where it can be inferred from the magnetic moments). Table 3.1 shows only one low-lying level for $A = 15$, which should therefore be the ground state. Thus N^{15} should be in a P state. This checks very well against the measured magnetic moment of N^{15} (see Section 5 of Chapter VI). Similarly, the "closed-shell" nuclei He^4 and O^{16} are in S states as predicted; however, this follows from a more general rule applying to *all* even-even nuclei and should therefore not be taken as a confirmation of the independent-particle model.[1] There are no stable nuclei with $A = 5$, but the scattering experiments with neutrons and protons on He^4 can be interpreted as showing low-lying $L = 1$ (P state) resonances, in agreement with Table 3.1 (Critchfield 49, Goldstein 50).

Nuclei with A between 6 and 14 do not allow such a simple comparison with experiment, since there are several low-lying levels in the table for each case. Until we know which of these levels is the ground state according to the independent-particle model, we cannot compare this model with experimental results concerning the ground state (in particular, the magnetic moment). We therefore need an estimate of the energy differences among low-lying levels.

C. The Energy of the Ground State

We have determined the character of the low-lying levels in the independent-particle model. In order to find out which of these

---

[1] Recent considerations (Jahn 50, Racah 50) have shown that the independent-particle model predicts S states for the even-even nuclei also in the region where the ($3d$) shell is being completed.

levels is the ground state, we need a somewhat closer estimate of the energy.

Let us first discuss the case $A = 6$ with two nucleons in the $(2p)$ shell. Here the question narrows down to the problem which of the two space-symmetric states, the S state or the D state, is lower. This is determined by a perturbation calculation: We take the average of the energy operator over the wave functions, (3.5a) and (3.5c), representing these states and find out which gives rise to a lower value.

The two states are equal with respect to their kinetic energy since both consist of two particles in the $(2p)$ shell. They are different with respect to the potential energy of interaction between the two $(2p)$ particles. The potential is attractive since they are in symmetric states. Therefore, the lower state is the one in which the particles are found closer to each other, i.e., in which the wave functions of the two particles overlap to a stronger degree. The calculation shows that this is the S state. This result can be understood as follows: We first find the probability distribution in space of a single particle in a p state relative to the direction of its angular momentum l. We investigate the state $m = 1$ in which l is oriented along the z axis and find that the square of the one-particle wave function [first line of (3.4)] is proportional to $\sin^2 \theta$, where θ is the angle of the radius vector with the z axis.

Actually, in the state $m = 1$, the vector l is not oriented exactly parallel to the z axis but includes an angle ϑ given by

$$\cos \vartheta = \frac{l_z}{|l|} = \frac{1}{\sqrt{2}}$$

[The magnitude of the square of an angular momentum is $l(l+1)$.] Thus the breadth of the probability distribution-in-θ is partly due to the fact that the direction of l is not strictly parallel to the z axis. We now compare the overlap of the wave functions of two particles in p states for the two cases: (1) the angular momenta add up to a D state; (2) the angular momenta cancel out and give an S state. In the first case the two angular momentum vectors l_1 and l_2 are not strictly parallel, since the maximum z component of the total angular momentum is 2 and not $2\sqrt{2}$. In the second case, however, the two vectors l_1 and l_2 are exactly opposed; their vectorial sum $\mathbf{L}$ is exactly zero. Therefore the probability distributions are narrower in the second case and give rise to a better overlap.

It is found in general, also for more than two particles in the $(2p)$ shell, that the lowest of the low-lying levels is the one with the *smallest angular momentum.*[1]   In the actual calculation we compute the average value of the potential energy between the (2p) particles as given by the independent-particle model.   The result can be expressed as follows (Hund 37, Feenberg 37c, Shimose 38, Racah 42): the difference in energy between two low-lying levels of angular momentum L and L' is given by

$$E(L) - E(L') = \tfrac{1}{2} [L(L+1) - L'(L'+1)] K \qquad (3.6)$$

where K may be shown to be the following integral:

$$K = -\int\int x_1 x_2 z_1 z_2\, g(r_1)\, g(r_2)\, V(r_{12})\, d\tau_1\, d\tau_2 \qquad (3.7)$$

The integral is extended over the configuration space of two (2p) particles whose wave functions were defined in (3.4). $V(r_{12})$ is the potential energy between two particles in a *symmetric* state as a function of their distance.   Since $V(r_{12})$ is attractive, the sign of K is positive.

Table 3.1 shows that the independent-particle model predicts the ground state to be an S state for even mass numbers and a P state for odd mass numbers in the range $4 \le A \le 16$.   The only likely exception is for $A = 10$, where the model predicts two different D states of the same energy.   It is very likely that these states interact strongly in the next approximation and are pushed apart in energy.   Since their predicted excitation is not very large, it is not impossible that the lower one of the two is pushed in energy below the S state.   This seems to be the case experimentally: the measured spin (total angular momentum I) of B^{10} is 3, and the magnetic moment indicates a D state (see Section 5 of Chapter VI).

The prediction of the orbital angular momentum of the ground states of nuclei is a very specific prediction which can be checked easily against experiment.   We therefore review the experimental evidence summarized in Chapter VI (Tables 5.1 and 5.2).   The *odd-odd nuclei* do not fit well at all: Li^6 has the predicted S state, but B^{10} and N^{14} are in D states.   We have seen that B^{10} can perhaps be explained, but the argument does not hold for N^{14}.   The situation is better for the *odd nuclei:* $L = 1$ is a good fit to the magnetic moments of Li^7, Be^9, B^{11}, C^{13}, and N^{15}, i.e., for *all* the odd nuclei in this region whose magnetic moments are known.   There is some indication of an admixture of a D state in B^{11}.   This is not too surprising and is in fact a success rather than a failure of the independent-particle model.   According to Table 3.1, there should be low-lying D states in odd nuclei only for

---

[1] A very simple proof is given by Shimose (38).

$A = 9$ and $A = 11$; hence only these nuclei can have admixtures of D states in appreciable amounts; experimentally no admixtures of states other than P states are indicated for $A = 7,13,15$. The *even-even* *nuclei* again give a check for the theory since they are all in S states. However, $I = 0$ seems to be the rule for *all* even-even nuclei, not just for the ones in this region of mass numbers, so that we probably should explain this rule by much more general (so far unknown) arguments; if so, the check with the independent-particle model in this limited region of mass numbers does not prove very much about the model.

Estimates have been made for the order of magnitude of the integral K. With reasonable values for the force strengths and ranges and the spread of the wave function we get $K \sim 1$ Mev. There is at present no way of checking this value against experiment.

The spacing predicted by (3.6) between the ground state and the first excited state depends on the nucleus we are dealing with. The spacing is smallest for mass numbers $A = 9,11$, where the ground state should be a P state and the first excited state a D state, so that formula (3.6) predicts a separation of $2K \sim 2$ Mev (both these levels, of course, split into two under spin-orbit coupling, giving four levels in all). For nuclei with even mass numbers, the ground states ought to be S states and the first excited levels ought to be D states, formula (3.6) predicting a separation of $3K \sim 3$ Mev. (These levels are not split in the $A = 4k$, $T_{\zeta} = 0$ nuclei and in the $A = 4k+2$, $T_{\zeta} = \pm 1$ nuclei; they are split into four levels each for the $A = 4k+2$, $T_{\zeta} = 0$ nuclei.) The largest separation between ground states and first excited levels is predicted for mass numbers $A = 5,7,13,15$, where the ground state is a P state and the first excited state an F state, with a separation $5K \sim 5$ Mev (each level again splitting into two under spin-orbit coupling). Since we expect the spin-orbit coupling to have appreciable effects on the level structure, these predictions can hardly be tested in detail. However, we should expect to be able to predict something about the number of levels with low excitation, say less than 5 Mev. This number ought to be large (eight) for $A = 6,10,14$ and $T_{\zeta} = 0$, moderate (four) for $A = 9,11$, and very small (two) for $A = 5,7,13,15$ as well as for $A = 8,12$ with $T_{\zeta} = 0$ and for $A = 6,10,14$ with $T_{\zeta} = \pm 1$. Finally, there ought to be no low-lying excited levels at all for He^4 and O^{16}. By and large, these predictions are borne out surprisingly well. Of fourteen nuclei whose low-lying levels are fairly well known by now, there is only one non-conforming case (N^{14}, with considerably too few levels). The complete absence of low-lying levels in O^{16} is a particularly striking confirmation of this picture.

So far we have assumed that the forces are charge and spin independent. At the time these investigations were started, the quadrupole moment of the deuteron had not yet been discovered; hence the assumption was made that all forces are central and that a small admixture of Heisenberg or Bartlett forces or both is required to fit the data on the two-body problem. It seems now that the singlet-triplet splitting in the neutron-proton system is predominantly due to the tensor force. It is not easy to include the tensor force in calculations with the independent-particle model, and no such calculations have been published to date.[1] This must be kept in mind when the predictions of this model, as commonly given, are compared with experimental findings.

▶ D. Nuclear Magnetic Moments on Independent-Particle Model

The orbital angular momenta L of the ground states of the odd nuclei check well against experiment. In order to predict the magnetic moment itself we still need to determine two things: (1) the way in which L and S combine to form a total angular momentum I, and (2) the value of the orbital gyromagnetic ratio g_L, i.e., the share of the orbital angular momentum L contributed by the protons.

The first point was treated by Inglis (36), Dancoff (36), and Furry (36) on the basis of central nuclear forces (this was before the discovery of the quadrupole moment of the deuteron); the spin-orbit coupling was then attributed to relativistic effects. Inglis showed that the main effect (related to the "Thomas factor" in atomic spectroscopy) works in such a way as to make L and S line up parallel to each other for mass numbers below 10, and opposite one another for mass numbers above 10 (the behavior of the "holes" is the opposite of the particles as far as spin-orbit coupling is concerned). The sign of the tensor force as deduced from the deuteron is such that it acts in the same direction.

This prediction seems to work out rather well: the only odd-odd nucleus for which it can be tested, N^{14}, has $I = 1 = |L - S|$, as predicted. The odd nuclei have $I = \frac{3}{2} = L + S$ for $A = 7,9$, and $I = \frac{1}{2} = |L - S|$ for $A = 13,15$. The exception is $A = 11$ with $I = \frac{3}{2} = L + S$.

We now turn to the orbital gyromagnetic ratio g_L (Rose 37). For the odd-odd nuclei we get $g_L = \frac{1}{2}$ from general considerations (equality of neutron-neutron and proton-proton forces), and of course the independent-particle model gives the same result. The odd nuclei are more interesting since g_L is not determined a priori. For nuclei of *mass number* 5 the one outside particle carries all the angular momentum;

---

[1] The work of Feingold (50) indicates that the tensor force is very important and changes the theoretical predictions considerably.

hence $g_L = 1$ if that outside particle is a proton (Li^5) and $g_L = 0$ if it is a neutron (He^5). Both nuclei are unstable, so this cannot be checked by experiment. The same reasoning applies to the end of the period, where there is just one "hole" left in the $(2p)$ shell. In N^{15} that hole is a proton; hence g_L should be equal to unity. This checks quite well with experiment, significantly better than the statistical assumption $g_L = Z/A = \frac{7}{15}$.

For nuclei of *mass number* 7 we can form a P state out of a trilinear combination of three vectors [one for each of the three $(2p)$ particles]:

$$\psi_P = [\mathbf{p}(1)\cdot\mathbf{p}(2)]\,\mathbf{p}(3) + [\mathbf{p}(2)\cdot\mathbf{p}(3)]\,\mathbf{p}(1) + [\mathbf{p}(3)\cdot\mathbf{p}(1)]\,\mathbf{p}(2) \quad (3.8)$$

In each term of (3.8) two of the particles combine into an S state, the remaining particle contributing the net orbital angular momentum. Since (3.8) is completely symmetrical in the three particles, the orbital angular momentum is distributed equally among them, whereas the statistical assumption would imply that it is distributed equally among all seven particles. Hence g_L of Li^7 is $\frac{1}{3}$ on the independent-particle model [one of the three $(2p)$ particles is a proton], compared to $g_L = \frac{3}{7}$ on the basis of the statistical assumption. Experimentally, $g_L = \frac{1}{3}$ and $g_L = \frac{3}{7}$ both fit within the error expected from exchange magnetic moments and other perturbations. In C^{13}, where two of the three holes are protons, $g_L = \frac{2}{3}$ is a somewhat poorer fit than the statistical result $g_L = \frac{6}{13}$. These comparisons may be invalidated by the fact that the function (3.8) predicts a negative quadrupole moment for Li^7, in direct contradiction to experiment (Kusch 49, Welles 42, Present 50, Hummel 51, Inglis 51).

For *mass number* 9 the P state is more complicated than (3.8) since the space wave function cannot be symmetric in more than four of the five $(2p)$ particles. The computation of g_L is straightforward though lengthy. The result is $\frac{1}{3}$ if two of the five $(2p)$ particles are protons, $\frac{2}{3}$ if 3 of the 5 are protons. The agreement with experiment is not very good, either for Be^9 or B^{11}, but D state admixtures can be expected in both cases.

Altogether, the independent-particle model seemed to be successful in predicting angular momenta and magnetic moments. However, the reported positive quadrupole moment of Li^7 and the difficulties with the parity of states of N^{14}, N^{13}, and Be^9 make these successes appear somewhat like unexplained coincidences. In view of the theoretical criticisms which we shall now take up, it would have been surprising indeed if the independent-particle model had been quite as successful as it was believed to be until recently.

E. Criticism of the Independent-Particle Model

The limitation of any independent-particle model lies in its inability to encompass the correlations between the positions and spins of the various particles in the system (Frank 37). As an extreme example, consider the eight-particle system Be^8. This nucleus is known to be dynamically unstable against breakup into two alpha-particles. The wave function after this breakup is concentrated into two entirely separate regions of configuration space, one for each alpha-particle, the positions of four particles being closely correlated with each other but uncorrelated with the positions of the other four (the other alpha-particle). There is no way in which the independent-particle model could do justice to this situation.

There is, of course, no need to go to such extremes. Even in a dynamically stable nucleus we expect that there is some tendency for group formation; particles which attract each other are on the average closer together than particles which repel each other. The wave function of the system as a whole is distorted from that of the independent-particle model in a way to take better advantage of the attractive forces available and to be more effective in avoiding the repulsive forces. The wave function strikes a balance between the desire to minimize the potential energy and the resulting unfavorable increase in the kinetic energy so as to yield the lowest total energy for the ground state of the system.

The problem of the correlation energy has been studied extensively in the theory of the solid state, in connection with the theory of free electrons in metals (Wigner 34, 38). It was found that the correlation energy cannot be neglected by any means; it is a significant part (up to 50 percent) of the binding energy in a metal. Nevertheless, certain qualitative conclusions (e.g., the existence of energy bands, "holes" in almost filled bands, etc.) can be drawn from the independent-particle model in a valid way.

In nuclei the situation is presumably less favorable if one believes in the existence of both attractive and repulsive forces between nuclear particles (the usual exchange forces subject to the saturation conditions). The existence of forces of both signs forces the wave function into strongly correlated behavior to avoid the repulsions which raise the total energy. In contrast to this, if all the forces have the same sign, the assumption that any one particle is acted upon by some "average" field is much closer to the truth, and this assumption is all that is needed for the independent-particle model.

In order to get some idea of the errors in the calculations based on the independent-particle model for nuclei, many investigators have carried out perturbation calculations starting from the independent-particle model as a zero-order approximation (Inglis 37, 38; Nakabayasi 37; Grönblom 37, 38; Margenau 38b, 39; Watenabe 39; Carroll 40; Tyrrell 39, 39a; Kroeger 38). They found that the change in the zero-order wave function introduced by this perturbation procedure is by no means small: if we write the wave function as $\Psi_0 + \Psi_{\text{pert}}$, the condition

$$\int |\Psi_{\text{pert}}|^2 \, d\tau \ll \int |\Psi_0|^2 \, d\tau \qquad (3.9)$$

is rather badly violated, the two integrals being of the same order of magnitude. This large perturbation in the zero-order wave function is due to two causes: (1) the zero-order wave function used as a starting point is not self-consistent in the Hartree-Fock sense, so that part of Ψ_{pert} amounts to a "self-consistency correction" to Ψ_0, which correction does not transcend the limitations of the independent-particle model; (2) the remaining correction to Ψ_0 comes from the correlations between the motions of the particles in the nucleus. It is rather difficult to disentangle these two fundamentally different corrections (Watenabe 39).

Since the perturbation is large, the zero-order wave function commonly used with the independent-particle model is a very poor approximation to the true wave function in a conventional nuclear potential. Consequently, any conclusions drawn from this wave function (such as the nature of the low-lying levels, their separations, etc.) are on a rather uncertain footing.

4. THE ALPHA-PARTICLE MODEL OF THE NUCLEUS

A. Outline of the Theory

Very early in the development of nuclear physics, it was observed that alpha-particles emerge in the decay of heavy radioactive nuclei. This led some investigators to suppose that alpha-particles also exist as stable substructures inside these heavy nuclei before they decay. This view is now rather generally discredited; the study of nuclear reactions has shown that protons and neutrons, as well as alpha-particles, can emerge from a heavy nucleus in a highly excited state, and a better understanding of nuclear forces in general has made it difficult to accept the idea that alpha-particles can maintain their identity for a very long time inside condensed nuclear matter.

A new version of the same idea was later put forth by Wefelmeier (37, 37a), Wheeler (37), Weizsäcker (38), and Fano (37). They were aware of the shortcomings of a naive alpha-particle model and suggested that the alpha-particles, rather than being stable structures inside a nucleus, be considered to have only a short-lived identity. After a certain time t the alpha-particle dissolves into its constituents, and the remains of this and other dissolved alpha-particles rearrange themselves into a new alpha-particle structure, etc. Wheeler attempted to show that this time t is long compared to the periods of vibration and rotation of such a temporary alpha-structure. Then the properties of this alpha-structure would be manifest just as if it were permanent at least as far as the low excited states of this "molecule" are concerned.

We shall not go into the criticisms of the alpha-particle model now; we shall instead discuss its predictions and successes and reserve the criticisms for later.

The first and most obvious success of the alpha-particle model is in the prediction of the binding energies of nuclei which can be formed out of an integral number of alpha-particles. Let us, for example, describe the nucleus O^{16} by the simple "model" of four alpha-particles placed far apart from each other. The total energy of this system is four times the energy of a single alpha-particle, i.e.,

$$4 \times 4.00391 = 16.01564 \text{ mass units}$$

The observed total energy of O^{16} is 16.00 mass units (by definition). If we subtract the masses of eight neutrons and eight protons from these two masses, we get the following result: our model of O^{16} gives a binding energy of 113 Mev, whereas the actual binding energy is 127 Mev. Hence, *without any binding whatsoever between the alpha-particles themselves*, we have predicted almost 90 percent of the observed binding energy.

Clearly, a model of four alpha-particles without any binding is not an adequate description of an O^{16} nucleus. Indeed, although this model is stable against separation into eight neutrons and eight protons, it obviously does not show stability against breakup into four alpha-particles. However, the above result looks encouraging in the sense that the inter-alpha binding energy seems to be small compared to the intra-alpha binding energy (of the order of 10 percent).

We shall therefore see how far we can get by assuming that the alpha-particles maintain their identity long enough so that we can consider the O^{16} nucleus a "polyatomic molecule," made up of four alpha-particles in close proximity. We shall not try to compute the force between two alpha-particles a distance r apart. We shall merely assume that it is similar in character to the force between two

neutral atoms, with the Coulomb repulsion superposed.   The potential
between two neutral atoms which can form a chemical bond is shown
schematically in Fig. 4.1a.   At large distances r, the force is attractive
(van der Waals force) with a fairly long "tail" (the potential

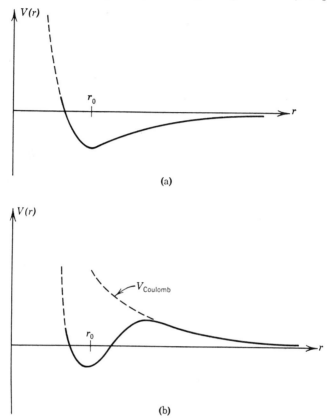

(a)

(b)

Fig. 4.1.   (a) A schematic picture of the potential between two neutral atoms as a
function of their separation r; r_0 is the equilibrium distance.   The curve is dashed
for small separations to indicate that the concept of a potential function $V(r)$
becomes invalid there.   (b) A schematic picture of the potential between two
alpha-particles as a function of their separation r, as assumed in the alpha-particle
model of the nucleus.

decreases like r^{-6}).   For values of r less than the "equilibrium
distance" r_0 the force is repulsive.   Finally, at still smaller values
of r, the two atoms interpenetrate to such an extent that the concept
of a potential depending on their separation becomes meaningless.
This is shown on the figure by a dashed line.   In molecular physics
it is valid to assume that the long-range, attractive van der Waals

forces are additive between the various atoms in the molecule.   This is, of course, not true for the short-range repulsive forces, for which proximity of a third atom disturbs the force between the first two appreciably.

We now add the Coulomb force to our assumed potential between alpha-particles (Fig. 4.1b), and we assume that the part of the potential beyond r_0 is additive between the various alpha-particle pairs.   In that case each alpha-particle "bond" contributes about equally to the total inter-alpha binding energy of a saturated nucleus.   Let $U(\alpha)$ be the total energy of an alpha-particle, and $U(n\alpha)$ be the total energy of the nucleus under consideration.   We then define the "inter-alpha binding energy" B_α by

$$B_\alpha \equiv nU(\alpha) - U(n\alpha) \tag{4.1}$$

and divide it by the total number of bonds.   This number of bonds is found from geometrical considerations; e.g., the O^{16} nucleus is considered a regular tetrahedron with an alpha-particle at each corner and six connecting lines (bonds) between them.   Table 4.1 gives the

TABLE 4.1

Nucleus	Number of Alpha-Particles n	Configuration	Number of Bonds	B_α (Mev)	Inter-alpha Binding Energy per Bond (Mev)
Be^8	2	Dumbbell	1	-0.12	-0.12
C^{12}	3	Triangle	3	7.33	2.45
O^{16}	4	Tetrahedron	6	14.5	2.42
Ne^{20}	5	Trigonal bipyramid	9(8)	19.3	2.14(2.41)
Mg^{24}	6	Octahedron	12(11)	28.8	2.40(2.62)
Si^{28}	7	Pentagonal bipyramid	16	37.8	2.36
S^{32}	8	Hexagonal bipyramid	19	46.8	2.47

results (the numbers in parentheses will be discussed below).   The constancy of the values in the last column of the table is rather encouraging for the alpha-particle model of the nucleus.   A binding energy per bond of the order of 2.5 Mev does not seem unreasonable at first sight.   The most disturbing feature of this table is the lack of alpha-stability of Be^8.   This nucleus should be basic to the theory, since the value of the alpha-binding energy for each bond should be derived from it.

Brown and Inglis (Brown 39b) have pointed out that these values should still be corrected for the Coulomb energy of the saturated nucleus.   However, this

correction does not amount to very much here.   The Coulomb energy consists of
two parts in this model: the internal Coulomb energy of each alpha-particle, which
is taken care of automatically by (4.1), and the Coulomb energy between alphas.
The latter energy, however, is simply proportional to the number of bonds as
long as each bond is associated with the same alpha-alpha distance.   This is
true for the first three nuclei of the table, and approximately true for the others.
It does not seem worth while to make the correction for variable bond distances,
since a similar but unknown correction would have to be made in the computation
of the potential energy per bond (i.e., the more distant bonds would have to be
weighted more lightly, so column four of the table would no longer consist of
integers).   However, the Coulomb correction does change the average nuclear
binding per bond by an amount $4e^2/r_{\alpha\alpha} \cong 1.8$ Mev if we assume an inter-alpha
distance $r_{\alpha\alpha} \cong 3.0 \times 10^{-13}$ cm.   After this correction, the nuclear binding in Be^8 is
about 1.7 Mev and the binding energy per bond is raised to about 4.1 Mev in the
other saturated nuclei.   Thus the discrepancy persists, although it is somewhat
lessened.

Hafstad and Teller (38) point out that the specially strong binding of O^{16} can
be understood in this model by looking at the number of bonds as a function of the
number of alphas, n.   The ratio of the number of bonds to the number of alpha-
particles is 0.5 for Be^8, 1.0 for C^{12}, 1.5 for O^{16}; but from then on the rate of increase
is much less rapid: 1.8 for Ne^{20}, 2.0 for Mg^{24}, 2.3 for Si^{28}, etc.   However, the value
of B_α for Ne^{20} is rather low on this model, even *after* the number of bonds is taken
into account.   (The binding energy per bond in Ne^{20} is only 2.14 Mev compared to
2.35 to 2.47 Mev in the others.)   Wefelmeier (37) suggested that this can be understood on geometrical grounds: Ne^{20} is a double pyramid with a triangular base.
The particles at the top and bottom of this structure are quite far apart and are
"shielded" from each other by the intervening triangle.   Hence we should
count Ne^{20} as having not 9, but 8 "effective" bonds.   If that is done (numbers in parentheses in Table 4.1), the binding energy per bond turns out to be 2.41
Mev, in excellent agreement with that of the other alpha-particle nuclei.   The
corresponding correction for Mg^{24} is not so important, since the top and bottom
particles on the octahedron are separated by a square with a big enough "hole"
in it so that the top-to-bottom bond distance is much smaller than in Ne^{20} and
the bond is much more effective.   This is again in agreement with the bracketed
numbers in Table 4.1.

We shall now give a short outline of the remainder of the theory.
We proceed to find the excited states of the alpha-particle nuclei by
analogy with molecular spectroscopy (Hafstad 38, Dennison 40).
The states are classified into vibrational and rotational levels, and
usually only the rotational levels are considered since they presumably
have lower energies.   The only unknown quantity in the expression for
the excitation energy is then the alpha-alpha distance (this determines
the effective moments of inertia of the "molecule").   Since the
alpha-particles obey Bose statistics, not all rotational states are
actually realized, but only those states in which the wave function
can be made symmetric under the exchange of every two alphas.   This
eliminates a number of low-lying rotational levels which would other-

wise be present. We should perhaps observe that the alpha-particle model, by its very method of construction, can describe only those excited states which belong to the lowest partition (0,0,0) of the $A = 4n$ nuclei. In addition to assuming that the wave function contains groups of four particles, each group showing internal symmetry with respect to space exchanges of the particles, the alpha-particle model assumes that these "groups" are actually separated in space and form individual entities. Conversely, a partition of lower symmetry is necessarily in conflict with the alpha-particle model (some alpha-particles would have to be broken up) and this model cannot encompass excited states with such partitions.

Hafstad and Teller (38) and Kittel (42) have treated the nuclei composed of an integral number of alphas plus or minus one extra particle. This was also done in analogy to molecular physics. This time the analogy refers to the electronic states of molecules: the one "extra" particle or hole is treated as a "light" electron in the "heavy" structure made up of the "stationary" alpha-particles. They get P states for the same odd nuclei for which the independent-particle model gets P states as ground states. A detailed calculation of the magnetic moments on the alpha-model has been made by Bethe (38), Sachs (39), and Inglis (39, 39a, 41), who obtained results which check about as well (or as poorly) against experiment as those of the independent-particle model, although the discrepancies arise with different nuclei. In general, the value of g_L from the alpha-model is more nearly equal to the statistical value Z/A than the values from the independent-particle model. This is to be expected since so much of the orbital motion in the alpha-model is due to motion of the alpha-structure as a whole, in which one neutron is carried along with each moving proton.

The alpha-particle model and the independent-particle model differ strongly regarding the nuclei with mass numbers $A = 4n+2$ (Latimer 37). The alpha-particle model has no adequate method of treating them. They could be described in either of two different ways: as n alphas plus two extra particles, or as $n+1$ alphas plus two "holes." Since the geometric structure differs appreciably in these two models, no definite conclusion can be reached.[1] There is perhaps one predic-

[1] We could try to make a "resonating group" wave function (Wheeler 37a) by a linear combination of the wave functions describing these two models, but this gets us into difficulties rather quickly: without a dynamical theory for the motion of the particles in the alpha-particle model, i.e., without a detailed specification of the alpha-alpha forces and the forces between alpha-particles and extra particles or holes, we cannot know how heavily to weight each component of the mixture.

tion regarding the $4n+2$ nuclei which can be made on the basis of the alpha-model: their binding energies ought to be appreciably lower than the mean of the binding energies of the (saturated) nuclei $4n$ and $4n+4$. Actually, however, the binding energies are about equal to this mean value.

B. Criticism of the Alpha-Particle Model

The main argument for the alpha-particle model comes from the binding energies of the "saturated" nuclei; however, as early as 1934 Elsasser (33, 34) had pointed out that this binding energy argument is not really valid. The fact that the binding energies of alpha-particle nuclei are very nearly integral multiples of the binding energy of the alpha-particle itself merely shows that the average binding energy per nucleon is the same in the alpha-particle as in nuclei made up of them. Indeed, even in non-alpha-particle nuclei the average binding energy per nucleon has roughly the same value as in the alpha-particle. This shows that nuclear matter is in a rather "liquid" state, with no special structure. Of course, there are *short-range* order effects even in liquids (as shown by x-ray diffraction phenomena, for example); similarly in nuclei we should expect to find a considerable amount of local correlation of particles. This is, however, far from Wefelmeier's assumption of a rigid alpha-structure of the nucleus. The short-range, "instantaneous" alpha-groupings which are undoubtedly present continually merge into one another and do not preserve their identity for any appreciable length of time.[1]

A very strong experimental argument against the alpha-particle model comes from the scattering of alpha-particles in helium. The data were analyzed by Wheeler (41, 41a) who found, among other things, two resonance levels[2] with zero total angular momentum, $J = 0$. Their separation in energy is only a few Mev, much too little to be explained as two different levels in an alpha-alpha potential of the type shown in Fig. 4.1. Furthermore a potential of this type would make the upper level very wide, whereas it is actually rather sharp (the width is of the order of 1 Mev). Therefore the *concept of a potential between two "rigid" alpha-particles is not adequate to describe the experiments even at energies of a few Mev*. Rather we

---

[1] Wheeler's early arguments for long-time alpha-groupings were based on rather rough estimates, and later work has shown that the "degree of dissociation" of the alpha-particles inside condensed nuclear matter is very high indeed (Grönblom 39, Wergeland 41).

[2] See Chapter VIII for the significance of resonance levels. Some later evidence throws doubt upon Wheeler's values of J (Hornyak 50).

should interpret at least the second resonance level in the scattering in terms of a dissolution and reordering of the alpha-particles upon close collision.

If the alpha-particles do not even maintain their identity effectively in collisions involving energies of a few Mev, we should expect that they will be very quickly "dissolved" in condensed nuclear matter. Theoretical calculations (Grönblom and Marshak 39, Margenau 41, Wergeland 41) using conventional nuclear forces confirm this expectation.

There is another point worth stressing: even if the potential of Fig. 4.1 could be used to describe the forces between alpha-particles, the analogy to the usual theory of molecular energy levels would still be unsatisfactory. A rough estimate of the likely strength and range of alpha-alpha forces shows that the zero-point vibration amplitude in an alpha-alpha bond is not very much smaller than the alpha-alpha bond distance itself. (Experimental confirmation of this estimate is found in the instability of Be^8 against dissociation into two alpha-particles.) This implies that the vibrational energies are of the same order of magnitude as the rotational energies, so that the separation of the total energy into these two parts becomes useless; a consistent treatment of such an alpha-particle model would have to assume strong vibration-rotation interaction.

The analogy to molecules is questionable for nuclei with one extra particle (or hole) outside of the alpha-structure. The Born-Oppenheimer (27) approximation treats the extra particle as a rapidly moving entity of negligible weight. This approximation corresponds to the zero-order term in an expansion in powers of the fourth root of the mass ratio and is therefore valid for molecules where the mass ratio of the electron to nucleus is at most of the order of 10^{-3}. In the alpha-particle model the mass ratio of "extra" particle to alpha-particle is $\frac{1}{4}$, and the fourth root of this is 0.71, hardly negligible compared to unity.

In addition to the shortcomings enumerated so far, the alpha-particle model is considerably less general in its possible applications than the independent-particle model. We recall the difficulties in treating the nuclei of mass number $4n+2$ with this model, and also the exclusion of states belonging to other than the lowest partition in other nuclei.[1]

---

[1] What is in principle a more general method has been proposed by Wheeler (37a) and called the method of "resonating groups." However, in practice this method leads to difficulties of calculation even for the simplest nuclei (Way 39), and the results of these calculations are not very encouraging.

5. THE LIQUID DROP MODEL

It is very tempting to compare the dynamics of a nucleus with that of a liquid drop (Bohr and Kalckar 37). The molecules of the liquid correspond to the nucleons in the nucleus. We find the following points of analogy: The density of a liquid is almost independent of its size, so that the radius R of a liquid drop is proportional to the cube root of the number A of the molecules. The energy necessary to evaporate the drop completely into well-separated molecules is approximately proportional to the number A (this is analogous to the binding energy of a nucleus). The surface tension of the liquid drop causes a correction to this relation, since the binding energy of the surface molecules is somewhat smaller than that of the interior molecules. This gives rise to a term in the total binding energy proportional to $A^{2/3}$. An analogous term has been introduced into the semi-empirical formula for nuclear binding energies (Chapter VI, Section 2).

It is probable that this analogy is only very superficial. The quoted properties of liquid drops can be traced to the following facts: molecules attract one another at distances larger than the dimensions of the electron shells, and this attraction changes to a strong repulsion when the electron shells begin to interpenetrate.

The potential of this force therefore reaches a minimum at distances d_{min} of the order of the size of the electron orbits. Hence stability is reached when the molecules are so arranged that the distance of nearest neighbors is equal to d_{min}. At the present time there is very little evidence of similar behavior of nuclear forces, although such repulsion at small distances has been proposed by Jastrow (50). Another important difference between the dynamics of liquid matter and nuclear matter is found in the wave-mechanical localization of the particles. The average kinetic energy of the molecules in the liquid is of the order of 0.1 ev. The corresponding de Broglie wavelength is of the order of 5×10^{-9} cm, which is very much *smaller* than the distance between molecules. The average kinetic energy of nucleons in nuclei is of the order of 10 Mev with a corresponding $\lambda \sim 10^{-13}$ cm, which is just of the order of internucleon distances. Hence, in liquids, the motion of the constituents can be described in classical terms and their positions can be well defined, compared to their mutual distance, whereas in nuclei the motion is necessarily of quantum character, since the uncertainty in the localization of the constituents is of the order of magnitude of their distance.

In spite of these differences, attempts were made to describe nuclear dynamics in terms of the motion of a liquid drop. The most impor-

5. The Liquid Drop Model

tant motions are the surface vibrations. A deformation of a spherical drop gives rise to periodic oscillations of the surface. We can analyze these vibrations and determine their frequencies ω_l. If the liquid drop picture is correct, the energy values so obtained give an approximate picture of nuclear level schemes.

Consider a spherical drop of radius R. Any deformation of the surface can be described by introducing a function $R'(\theta,\varphi)$ which is the distance of the deformed surface from the center at an angle θ,φ. We consider especially the difference

$$q(\theta,\varphi) = R'(\theta,\varphi) - R \tag{5.1}$$

which can be expanded in spherical harmonics:

$$q(\theta,\varphi) = \sum_{l=0}^{\infty} \sum_{m=-l}^{l} q_{lm} Y_{lm}(\theta,\varphi) \tag{5.2}$$

For the sake of simplicity we discuss cylindrically symmetric deformations, and hence we ignore all terms with $m \neq 0$. It can be shown that the $q_{l,0}$ are "normal coordinates," i.e., that they oscillate harmonically in time:

$$q_{l,0} = q_l \cos(\omega_l t) \tag{5.3}$$

The characteristic frequency ω_l is determined by the dynamics of the vibration. The restoring force is supplied by the surface tension which opposes a deformation of the surface. The surface energy E_s is given by

$$E_s = \alpha S \tag{5.4}$$

where S is the surface area ($S = 4\pi R^2$ for a spherical drop) and α is the coefficient of surface tension.

The formula for the frequency ω_l was first given by Rayleigh (79):

$$\omega_l = \left[\frac{4\pi\alpha}{3\mathfrak{M}} l(l-1)(l+2) \right]^{1/2} \tag{5.5}$$

where $\mathfrak{M}$ is the mass of the drop.

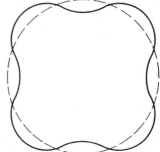

Fig. 5.1. Schematic picture of a typical surface wave of a liquid drop, with $l = 4$.

We shall not give Rayleigh's derivation here, but we shall attempt to explain the qualitative features. Figure 5.1 shows a characteristic deformation. Since the liquid is (by assumption) incompressible, the existence of waves on the surface implies some motion within the liquid. The amplitude of the motion inside the liquid is proportional to the amplitude q_l of the surface vibration, but the factor of proportion-

ality decreases rapidly as we go farther away from the surface. The characteristic distance for this decrease is of the same order of magnitude as the wavelength
λ of the surface wave. In the case of surface vibrations of a liquid drop of radius
R, this wavelength is given by

$$\lambda = \frac{R}{l} \tag{5.6}$$

The mass μ which participates in the vibration inside the liquid is approximately
equal to the mass contained in the outer shell of the drop with a thickness of this
order of magnitude. Hence we get for the mass μ

$$\mu \sim \mathfrak{M} \frac{3\lambda}{R} \tag{5.7}$$

and the kinetic energy T in the vibration is about

$$T \cong \tfrac{1}{2}\mu \dot{q}_l{}^2 \tag{5.8}$$

The restoring force can be estimated from the change in the surface energy. A
plane surface S, which is rippled by a wave of amplitude q_l and wavelength λ, is
larger than a flat surface without ripples by an amount

$$\Delta S \cong \frac{1}{2}\left(\frac{q_l}{\lambda}\right)^2 S \tag{5.9}$$

This relation is approximately true also for a spherical surface. Hence we get
for the change in surface energy of the drop

$$\Delta E_s = \frac{1}{2} k\, q_l{}^2 \qquad k \sim \frac{4\pi R^2 \alpha}{\lambda^2} \tag{5.10}$$

From expressions (5.8) for the kinetic energy and (5.10) for the potential energy,
we get immediately the frequency $\omega_l = (k/\mu)^{1/2}$ which becomes

$$\omega_l \sim \left(\frac{4\pi\alpha l^3}{3\mathfrak{M}}\right)^{1/2} \tag{5.11}$$

when (5.6) is taken into account. Equation (5.11) is equivalent to (5.4) for large
values of l. The specfic properties of the spherical surface change the l^3 appearing
in (5.11) into $l(l-1)(l+2)$. According to (5.5), $\omega_l = 0$ for $l = 1$; this must be so
since a deformation (5.2) with $l = 1$ corresponds to a displacement of the drop as a
whole.

We now apply (5.5) to an actual nucleus. The surface tension
coefficient α can be calculated by using the expression for the surface
energy E_s from the Weizsäcker formula (VI,2.5):

$$E_s = u_s A^{2/3} \qquad u_s \cong 13 \text{ Mev} \tag{5.12}$$

Hence we get from (5.4)

$$\alpha = \frac{u_s A^{2/3}}{4\pi R^2} = \frac{u_s}{4\pi r_0{}^2}$$

where r_0 is the empirical radius: $r_0 \cong 1.4 \times 10^{-13}$ cm. We then get

$$\omega_l \cong \left[l(l-1)(l+2) \frac{u_s}{3r_0{}^2 MA} \right]^{1/2} \tag{5.13}$$

where M is the mass of a single nucleon. The corresponding energy is

$$\hbar \omega_l \cong 14.7 \left[\frac{l(l-1)(l+2)}{A} \right]^{1/2} \text{Mev} \tag{5.14}$$

This value is somewhat too high to account for most low-lying nuclear states. Empirically, the first excited states for nuclei with mass numbers A between 100 and 200 have an excitation energy of the order of 100 kev, whereas (5.14) would predict several Mev.

The frequencies ω_l are reduced somewhat by the Coulomb effect. Whereas the surface tension increases if the drop is deformed, the Coulomb energy decreases upon deformation. This effect reduces the restoring force of the vibration and gives rise to the following expression instead of (5.13) for the frequencies (Frenkel 39, 39a, Rayleigh 82):

$$\omega_l = \left\{ l(l-1) \left[(l+2) - \frac{10\gamma}{2l+1} \right] \frac{u_s}{3r_0{}^2 MA} \right\}^{1/2} \tag{5.15}$$

where γ is the ratio between the Coulomb energy

$$E_c = \frac{3}{5} \frac{(Ze)^2}{R}$$

and the surface tension energy

$$E_s = 4\pi \alpha R^2 = u_s A^{2/3}$$

for the undeformed nucleus; that is, γ is defined by

$$\gamma = \frac{3}{5} \frac{e^2/r_0}{u_s} \frac{Z^2}{A} = 0.0474 \frac{Z^2}{A} \tag{5.16}$$

Expression (5.15) can be understood qualitatively as follows: A surface wave of amplitude q can be obtained from the undeformed sphere by moving half of a surface layer of depth q outward by a distance q. The change in Coulomb energy is

$$\Delta E_c = -\frac{Ze}{R^2} (2\pi R^2 q\rho) q \tag{5.17}$$

where Ze is the charge of the drop, and $\rho = 3Ze/4\pi R^3$ is the charge density. Hence

$$\Delta E_c = \tfrac{1}{2} k_c q^2 \qquad k_c = \frac{3Z^2 e^2}{R^3} \tag{5.18}$$

The total potential energy change is then $\Delta E_s + \Delta E_c$, and we get for the frequency

$$\omega_l = \left(\frac{\mu}{k+k_c}\right)^{1/2}$$

with the help of (5.6), (5.8), (5.10), and (5.16),

$$\omega_l \sim \left[\frac{4\pi\alpha}{3\mathfrak{M}}(l^3 - 5\gamma l)\right]^{1/2} \tag{5.19}$$

This is the asymptotic form of expression (5.15) for $l \gg 1$, provided that α is replaced by $(u_s/4\pi r_0^2)$.

Equation (5.15) leads to somewhat smaller frequencies for heavier nuclei, but it is still insufficient to represent the actual level distances. There are very many more, and more closely spaced, excited states found than (5.15) can predict. If the analogy with a liquid drop is valid at all, the surface vibrations must be considered one very special type of nuclear motion. The actual excited states of nuclei correspond very probably to much more complicated types.

If the liquid is considered compressible (Present 41, Feenberg 41b), longitudinal compressional waves can also be set up in a drop. As long as the compressibility is small, the frequencies of these waves are much higher than the frequencies of the surface waves. We will not consider longitudinal waves here.

The influence of the Coulomb field on the surface deformation becomes important for large Z. We conclude from (5.15) that the frequency becomes imaginary when γ is larger than a certain limiting value γ_c. This value is smallest for $l=2$, where it is $\gamma_c = 2$. If γ is larger than γ_c, the negative Coulomb energy (5.17) overcompensates the surface energy (5.12) and the nucleus is no longer stable with respect to this deformation. We therefore get for the condition of stability against surface deformation from (5.16) (Frenkel 39, 39a, Feenberg 39, Young 39, Bohr 39, Weizsäcker 39, Plesset 41)

$$\frac{3}{5}\frac{e^2/r_0}{u_s}\frac{Z^2}{A} < 2 \qquad \text{or} \qquad \frac{Z^2}{A} < 42.2 \tag{5.20}$$

Any nucleus violating this condition should get deformed and finally should split into two parts. It is interesting to note that the heaviest nuclei are very close to this limit ($Z^2/A = 35.5$ for U^{238}). The condition (5.20) can be considered the main reason for the non-existence of nuclei heavier than those observed.

Nuclei for which Z^2/A is near its limit have a very small deformation frequency ω_2. The amplitude q_0 of an oscillation in the ground state (zero-point oscillation) is $q_0 = (\hbar/2\mu\omega)^{1/2}$ and therefore becomes large for low frequencies. Only a small perturbation from the outside is then necessary to induce an instability, i.e., a breakup of the nucleus. We therefore expect in this model that the nuclei near the limit of Z^2/A are easily induced to perform fission by the additional supply of small amounts of energy. A detailed discussion of the fission mechanism on the basis of this model is given by Bohr and Wheeler (Bohr 39).

We summarize the results of this section: The liquid drop model of the nucleus is not very successful in describing the actual excited states. It gives too large level distances. We conclude that the dynamical motions in the nucleus which are responsible for the excited states are much more complicated than those contained in this model. The liquid drop model is more successful when used to determine the stability of the ground states of nuclei against deformation. The limit for stability against fission is well reproduced, and the underlying idea is well borne out by the fact that nuclei near this limit show the phenomenon of induced fission.

SYMBOLS

A Mass number of the nucleus $[=N+Z]$ (Section 2)

A' Number of nucleons in the P shell for $A \leq 16$ $[=A-4]$ (Section 3)

b Range of the nuclear force   (Section 2)

B_α Inter-alpha binding energy   (4.1)

$d_{\min}$ Distance between two molecules for which the intermolecular potential reaches its minimum value   (Section 4)

E_s Surface energy of a liquid drop   (5.4)

E_{sym} Symmetry energy of the nucleus according to the uniform model   (2.15)

$f(\zeta,\eta)$ A function of the mechanical and isotopic spin coordinates of a nucleon   (3.2)

g_L Orbital gyromagnetic ratio; for its definition see Chapter I, Section 7   (Section 3)

$g(r)$ Radial part of $u(x,y,z)$ for a particle in the P shell   (3.4)

I Total angular momentum quantum number ("spin") of the nucleus in its ground state   (Section 3)

J Total angular momentum quantum number of a nuclear state (not necessarily the ground state)   (Section 4)

k A constant defined in Chapter VI, Section 3; its value is estimated to be between 2 and 3   (2.16)

k Proportionality constant in ΔE_s (5.10)

k_c Coefficient appearing in ΔE_c $[=3Z^2e^2/R^3]$ (5.18)

K Interaction integral for two nucleons in the P shell   (3.6), (3.7)

l Order of a surface vibration of a liquid drop   (Section 5)

l Orbital angular momentum quantum number of a single nucleon   (3.3)

l Orbital angular momentum vector of a single nucleon (Section 3)

L Orbital angular momentum quantum number of the nucleus (Section 2)

L Coefficient of $-(\bar{n}_+ - \bar{n}_-)$ in the potential energy $\bar{V}$, on the uniform model   (2.6), (2.7)

L_1 $\equiv AL$; expected to be independent of the mass number A (2.12)

L' Coefficient of $-(\bar{n}_+ + \bar{n}_-)$ in the potential energy $\bar{V}$, on the uniform model   (2.6), (2.7)

$\mathbf{L}$ Orbital angular momentum vector of the nucleus   (Section 3)

$m = m_l$ Quantum number for the Z component of the angular momentum of a nucleon   (3.4)

M Mass of a nucleon   (Section 2)

M_n Mass of the neutron   (2.11)

M_p Mass of the proton   (2.11)

$\mathfrak{M}$ Mass of a liquid drop   (5.5)

n Principal quantum number of an orbit in the independent-particle model   (3.3)

n Number of alpha-particles in the nucleus   (4.1)

n_1 Number of "levels" occupied by one nucleon; see Chapter VI, Section 3   (Section 2)

n_2 Number of "levels" occupied by two nucleons; see Chapter VI, Section 3   (Section 2)

n_3 Number of "levels" occupied by three nucleons; see Chapter VI, Section 3   (Section 2)

n_4 Number of "levels" occupied by four nucleons; see Chapter VI, Section 3   (Section 2)

$\bar{n}_+$ Number of symmetric pairs in the nucleus   (2.5)

$\bar{n}_-$ Number of anti-symmetric pairs in the nucleus   (2.5)

N Number of neutrons in the nucleus   (Section 2)

p_+ Space wave function of a nucleon in the P shell ($l = 1$) with $m = +1$ $[= -(p_x + ip_y)/\sqrt{2} = -(x + iy)g(r)/\sqrt{2}]$ (3.4)

p_+ Probability of interaction of a symmetric pair   (Section 2)

p_-	Space wave function of a nucleon in the P shell $(l=1)$ with $m=-1$ $[=(p_x-ip_y)/\sqrt{2}=(x-iy)g(r)/\sqrt{2}]$ (3.4)
p_z	Space wave function of a nucleon in the P shell $(l=1)$ with $m=0$ $[=zg(r)]$ (3.4)
$p(b/R)$	Probability of finding two nucleons within the range b of each other (Section 2)
$\mathbf{p}$	Vector with components p_x,p_y,p_z, representing the space wave functions of a single nucleon in the P shell (3.4), (3.5a,b)
P	Partition quantum number; for its definition see Chapter VI, Section 3 (Section 2)
P'	Partition quantum number; for its definition see Chapter VI, Section 3 (Section 2)
P''	Partition quantum number; for its definition see Chapter VI, Section 3 (Section 2)
$P^M{}_{ij}$	Majorana exchange operator for particles i and j (2.1)
q	Coordinates (space, spin, and isotopic spin) of a single nucleon (3.1)
q_0	Amplitude of the surface vibration of a liquid drop in its ground state (zero-point amplitude) (Section 5)
q_l	Amplitude of the surface vibration of order l of a liquid drop (5.3)
q_{lm}	Surface deformation associated with the surface vibration of order l,m of a liquid drop (5.2)
$q(\theta,\varphi)$	Instantaneous deformation of the surface of a liquid drop during a surface vibration (5.1)
r	Distance between alpha-particles in the alpha-particle model of the nucleus (Section 4)
r_0	Constant in the nuclear radius formula $R=r_0\sqrt[3]{A}$ (2.9)
r_0	Equilibrium distance between alpha-particles in the alpha-particle model of the nucleus (Section 4)
r_{ij}	Distance between nucleons i and j (2.1)
$r_{\alpha\alpha}$	Average distance between alpha-particles in the alpha-particle model of the nucleus (Section 4)
R	Nuclear radius (Section 2)
R_c	Coulomb radius of the nucleus (Section 2)
$R(r)$	Radial part of $u(x,y,z)$ (Section 3)
$R'(\theta,\varphi)$	Instantaneous distance of the surface of the liquid drop from its center, during a surface vibration (5.1)
S	Spin angular momentum quantum number of the nucleus (Section 3)

S	Surface area of a liquid drop (5.4)
t	Lifetime of a given alpha-particle structure within the nucleus (Section 4)
T	Kinetic energy of the nucleus (2.8)
T	Kinetic energy of a surface vibration of a liquid drop (5.8)
T_0	Kinetic energy per particle in a nucleus with partition (0,0,0) (2.8'), (2.9)
T_1	$=\frac{40}{9}T_0$; estimated to be about 60 Mev (2.12)
T_ζ	Neutron excess $[=\frac{1}{2}(N-Z)]$ (Section 2)
u_c	Constant appearing in the Weizsäcker formula for the Coulomb energy of the nucleus; for its definition see Chapter VI, Section 2 (2.11)
u_s	Coefficient appearing in the Weizsäcker formula for the surface energy of the nucleus; for its definition see Chapter VI, Section 2 (5.12)
$u(x,y,z)$	Space wave function of a single nucleon (3.2)
U	Total energy (including rest mass energy) of the nucleus $[=U(A,T_\zeta)]$ (2.10)
$U_0(A)$	The part of U which is independent of the neutron excess T_ζ (2.10), (2.11)
$U(n\alpha)$	Total energy (including rest mass energy) of a nucleus composed of n alpha-particles (4.1)
$U(\alpha)$	Total energy (including rest mass energy) of an alpha-particle (4.1)
V	Average potential acting on a nucleon in the independent-particle model of the nucleus (Section 3)
V	Operator for the potential energy of the nucleus as a whole (Section 2)
$\bar{V}$	Expectation value of the potential energy V of the nucleus $[=(\psi,V\psi)]$ (Section 2)
V_M	The part of the total potential energy V of the nucleus contributed by Majorana exchange forces (2.1)
$V(r_{12})$	Potential of the nuclear force between two nucleons at a distance r_{12} (3.7)
$V_M(r_{ij})$	Distance dependence of the Majorana exchange potential between nucleons i and j, at a distance r_{ij} (2.1)
$(V_M)_0$	Well depth of the Majorana exchange potential between two nucleons, in the square well approximation (Section 2)
$\bar{V}_M{}^a$	Average Majorana interaction between an anti-symmetric pair of nucleons (Section 2)

$\bar{V}_M{}^s$	Average Majorana interaction between a symmetric pair of nucleons (2.4)
$\bar{V}_W{}^a$	Average Wigner interaction between an anti-symmetric pair of nucleons (2.7)
$\bar{V}_W{}^s$	Average Wigner interaction between a symmetric pair of nucleons (2.7)
$Y_{lm}(\theta,\varphi)$	Spherical harmonic; for its definition see Appendix A, Section 2 (Section 3)
Z	Number of protons in the nucleus (Section 2)
α	Surface tension of a liquid drop (5.4)
$\alpha(\zeta)$	Spin wave function for a nucleon with spin up (Section 3)
γ	Ratio of Coulomb energy to surface energy of a liquid drop (5.15), (5.16)
γ_c	Critical value of γ for fission instability (Section 5)
Γ_n	Neutron width of a compound state; for its definition see Chapter VIII, Section 3 (Section 3)
ΔE_c	Change in the Coulomb energy of a liquid drop during a surface vibration (5.17), (5.18)
ΔE_s	Change in the surface energy of a liquid drop during a surface vibration (5.10)
ΔE_r	Difference in the symmetry energy of two neighboring isobars (2.18)
ΔS	Change in the surface area of a liquid drop during a surface vibration (5.9)
$\Delta\eta$	Difference in η between two neighboring isobars (2.18)
$\Delta\xi$	Difference in ξ between two neighboring isobars (2.18)
$\eta^{|}$	$\equiv \tfrac{1}{2}\,[P^2+(P')^2+(P'')^2]$ (2.8'), (2.9), and (2.14)
η	The isotopic spin coordinate of a nucleon (3.2)
θ	Angle between the direction of l and the axis of quantization (the z axis) (Section 3)
θ	Colatitude angle for a liquid drop (5.1)
λ	Wavelength of a surface wave of a liquid drop (divided by 2π) (5.6)
μ	That part of the mass $\mathfrak{M}$ of the liquid drop which participates in the surface vibration (5.7)
$\nu(\eta)$	Isotopic spin wave function of a neutron (Section 3)
ξ	The partition-dependent part of $\bar{n}_+ - \bar{n}_-$; for its definition see Chapter VI, Section 3 (2.12), (2.13)
$\pi_{ij}{}^+$	Projection operator for selecting the part of ψ which is symmetric in the interchange of particles i and j (2.2)

π_{ij}^- Projection operator for selecting the part of ψ which is anti-symmetric in the interchange of particles i and j (2.2)

ρ Ratio of the energy spacing between even-even and odd-odd nuclei to the coefficient of T_{ζ}^2 in the energy formula of the uniform model   (2.17)

ρ Charge density of a liquid drop $[=3Ze/4\pi R^3]$ (5.17)

$\varphi(q)$ Wave function of an individual nucleon in the independent-particle model   (3.1)

ψ Nuclear wave function   (Section 2)

ψ_D Wave functions for the D state $(L=2)$ of two nucleons in the P shell   (3.5c)

ψ_P Wave functions for the P state $(L=1)$ of two nucleons in the P shell   (3.5b)

ψ_S Wave function for the S state $(L=0)$ of two nucleons in the P shell   (3.5a)

Ψ Nuclear wave function   (Section 2)

Ψ_0 Zero-order wave function for the nucleus   (3.9)

Ψ_{pert} Difference between the true wave function Ψ and the zero-order wave function Ψ_0 (3.9)

ω_l Circular frequency of the surface vibration of order l of a liquid drop   (Section 5)

CHAPTER VIII

Nuclear Reactions:
General Theory

1. INTRODUCTION

A. Description of a Nuclear Reaction

A nuclear reaction is a process that occurs when a nuclear particle (nucleon or nucleus) gets into close contact with another. Most of the known nuclear reactions are produced by exposing different materials to a beam of accelerated nuclear particles. Usually a strong energy and momentum exchange takes place and the final products of the reaction are one, two, or more nuclear particles leaving the point of close contact in various directions. The products are mostly of a species different from the particles in the original pair. The present chapter contains a wave-mechanical description of nuclear reactions and a general analysis of the phenomena that are expected to occur.

We shall consider nuclear reactions of the type

$$a + X \rightarrow Y + b \qquad (1.1)$$

or, in more compact notation, $X(a,b)Y$. The notation means that particle a strikes nucleus X to produce nucleus Y and an outgoing particle b. "Particles" a and b may be elementary particles (neutrons, protons), but they can also themselves be nuclei (e.g., deuterons or alpha-particles).

Reaction (1.1) is not the most general nuclear reaction. In the general case, an arbitrary number of particles may emerge. This reaction is sufficiently general to include most of the known nuclear reactions at low energy. There is one exception to this, however. We shall be interested in the radiative capture process, where X and a stay together to form a nucleus W while a gamma-ray is emitted:

$$a + X \rightarrow W + \hbar\omega \qquad (1.2)$$

We might have included this as a reaction of type (1.1), provided that we considered the gamma-ray a particle of the same type as a. However, there is good reason for not doing this. The interaction between nuclei and gamma-rays is weak and can be treated as a small perturbation, whereas the interaction of nuclear projectiles (neutrons, protons, deuterons, etc.) with nuclei cannot be treated in that way. Furthermore in (1.2) the number of "particles" does not stay constant throughout the reaction if we admit $\hbar\omega$ as a particle—the gamma-ray is created during the process. For both these reasons (1.2) will be treated separately from reactions of type (1.1) in this section. The inverse reaction to (1.2) is called the photonuclear effect (in analogy to the photoelectric effect). It will be considered in Chapter XII, Section 7.

We are usually interested in the probability of processes of type (1.1) or (1.2) as a function of the energy of the incident particle a, in the energy and the direction of the outgoing particles.

Returning to reactions of type (1.1), we note that formula (1.1) symbolizes only one of the many possible reactions which can occur when a strikes X. We shall be interested in the whole set of reactions

$$a + X \rightarrow \begin{cases} X + a \\ X^* + a \\ Y + b \\ Z_c^* + c \\ \text{etc.} \end{cases} \tag{1.3}$$

The first two reactions (1.3) are distinguished by the fact that the "projectile" a re-emerges after the reaction. The first of these represents *elastic scattering:* the projectile a leaves with the same energy (in the center-of-gravity system), and the target nucleus X is left in its initial state. The second reaction represents *inelastic scattering:* the target nucleus X is forced into an excited state X^*, and the projectile a re-emerges, but with an energy lower than its initial one by the amount of the excitation energy given to the target nucleus. It will prove useful to consider as elastic scattering only those events in which the initial and final states of the target nucleus are completely identical (e.g., there should not be any change of the spin direction of X, even if no excitation energy is involved). We shall therefore include in the inelastic scattering those events in which X changes its internal state in such a way that its energy stays constant, i.e., there is no energy transfer between X and a. (See Section 10.)

B. Channels[1]

All the reactions (1.3), except the elastic scattering, can be sub-divided again according to the quantum state of the residual nucleus and the emerging particle. We denote the states of the nuclei by α', β', γ', $\cdots$, and the states of the incident or emerging particles by α'', β'', γ'', $\cdots$. If particles a, b, etc., are elementary, states α'', β'', etc., refer to their spin orientation. We get the reactions

$$a_{\alpha''} + X_{\alpha'} = \begin{cases} X_{\alpha'} + a_{\alpha''} \\ X_{\beta'} + a_{\beta''} \\ Y_{\gamma'} + b_{\gamma''} \\ \text{etc.} \end{cases} \tag{1.3'}$$

Here α' and α'' are states of the target nucleus and the incident particle, β' and β'', or γ' and γ'', can denote any quantum state of X and a. or Y and b, respectively, which can be created in this reaction. Of course, the conservation laws of energy, angular momentum, and

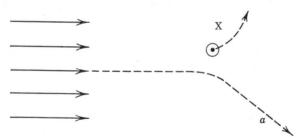

FIG. 1.1.   Elastic scattering, laboratory system.

parity restrict the possible pairs of β' and β'', γ' and γ'', etc. Any such possible pair of residual nucleus and emerging particle, each in a definite quantum state, is called a *reaction channel*. We shall denote channels by single Greek letters, α, β, $\cdots$, which comprise both indices α' and α'', or β' and β''. Channel $X_{\alpha'} + a_{\alpha''}$ is called the *entrance channel* or *initiating channel* of reaction (1.3').

The special position accorded to particle a and nucleus X in (1.3) corresponds to the experimental setup, in which a uniform beam of particles a bombard nucleus X, as in Fig. 1.1. Nucleus X is initially at rest (or moving very slowly in comparison to the projectiles a),

---

[1] The concept of a reaction "channel" was first introduced in the way we use it here by Wigner and Eisenbud (unpublished) and Breit (40).

and all projectiles are moving with the same velocity, indicated by arrows. Figure 1.1 shows one elastic scattering event.

Let us consider the reaction in the system in which the center of mass of the projectile and the target nucleus is at rest. Figure 1.2

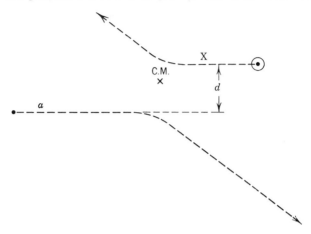

FIG. 1.2.   Elastic scattering in the center-of-mass system (C.M. = center of mass).

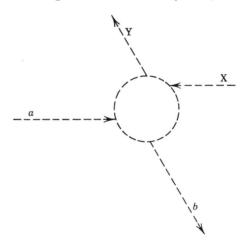

FIG. 1.3.   Nuclear reaction in the center-of-mass system.

shows this for elastic scattering. Since the total linear momentum of the system must be zero both before and after the collision, the particles enter from opposite directions and emerge in opposite directions. Since the mass of target nucleus X usually exceeds that of projectile a, the speed of X is much smaller than the speed of a. The distance d is called the impact parameter.

In Fig. 1.3, we show a general reaction (1.1) in the center-of-mass system. Here we have drawn a sphere around the region where the reaction takes place. To describe a reaction (1.1) in detail, we would have to determine the motion of all the particles in the system (including all the component particles of X and Y) within that region. This is neither possible nor desirable. We are interested only in the probability of getting the final result $Y+b$.

C. Energy Relations

Let us now consider the energy relations occurring in the nuclear reaction. If the incident particle a and the target nucleus X are still very far apart, there is no interaction energy between them, and the total energy E can be expressed as the sum of the kinetic energy ϵ_α of the relative motion of the two partners a and X in channel α, and their internal energies $E_{\alpha'}$ of X and $E_{\alpha''}$ of a:[1]

$$E = \epsilon_\alpha + E_{\alpha'} + E_{\alpha''} \tag{1.4}$$

Since we always consider the center of gravity at rest, the main part of ϵ_α comes from the lighter partner a. Therefore ϵ_α is essentially the kinetic energy of the incoming projectile a. We also refer to ϵ_α as the "channel energy" of the entrance channel α, and we shall sometimes use for it the letter ϵ without index. The kinetic energy $(\epsilon_\alpha)_{\text{lab}}$ of the incident particle in the laboratory system is given by

$$(\epsilon_\alpha)_{\text{lab}} = \frac{M_a + M_X}{M_X} \epsilon_\alpha \tag{1.5}$$

where M_a and M_X are the masses of a and X, respectively. In the same way we define the energies in any other channel into which the reaction may lead. Consider, for example, channel β, which leads to a residual nucleus Y in state β' and an emitted particle b in state β''. The total energy must be equal to the total energy E in the entrance channel. If the partners Y and b are far apart, we can express E in terms of the sum of the kinetic energy ϵ_β and the internal energies $E_{\beta'}$ and $E_{\beta''}$ of the two partners:

$$E = \epsilon_\beta + E_{\beta'} + E_{\beta''}$$

ϵ_β is again called the channel energy and is the sum of the kinetic energies of the outgoing particle b and of the residual nucleus Y in

---

[1] Since the number of neutrons and protons stays constant during the course of nuclear reactions, we do not need to include the rest mass contribution to the energy. $E_{\alpha'}$ in (1.4) is the negative of the binding energy of nucleus X in quantum state α'.

the center-of-gravity system. The channel energy ϵ_β is related to the entrance channel energy ϵ_α by

$$\epsilon_\beta = \epsilon_\alpha + Q_{\alpha\beta} \qquad (1.6)$$

where

$$Q_{\alpha\beta} = E_{\alpha'} + E_{\alpha''} - E_{\beta'} - E_{\beta''} \qquad (1.7)$$

is the "Q value" from channel α to channel β. It is the difference in energy in the outgoing and entrance channels. $Q_{\alpha\beta} = -Q_{\beta\alpha}$ is characteristic of channels α and β and is independent of the channel energies.

We can also express the Q value in terms of the separation energies S_a and S_b of particle a or b from the compound nucleus, and in terms of the excitation energies $E_{\alpha'}{}^*$, $E_{\alpha''}{}^*$ of the partners in channel α and the corresponding excitation energies $E_{\beta'}{}^*$, $E_{\beta''}{}^*$ in channel β:

$$Q_{\alpha\beta} = S_a - S_b + (E_{\alpha'}{}^* + E_{\alpha''}{}^*) - (E_{\beta'}{}^* + E_{\beta''}{}^*) \qquad (1.8)$$

If the value of ϵ_α is such that the channel energy ϵ_β is negative according to (1.6), channel β is "closed." No (α,β) reaction can take place in that case. If $\epsilon_\beta > 0$, we call the channel "open"; the (α,β) reaction is then possible.

In practice the target nucleus, as well as the bombarding particle, is in its ground state. We are often interested in knowing the minimum kinetic energy of a necessary to make the $X(a,b)Y$ reaction occur, without inquiring into the precise channel through which the outgoing particles emerge. The minimum energy corresponds to the channel in which the outgoing particle b and the residual nucleus Y are both in their ground states; we shall call this channel the β_0 channel. The "Q value of the $X(a,b)Y$ reaction" is defined by

$$Q_{ab} = E_{a_0'} + E_{a_0''} - E_{\beta_0'} - E_{\beta_0''} \qquad (1.9)$$

where $E_{a_0'}$, etc., are the energies of the ground states of the particles X, a, Y, and b, respectively. If Q_{ab} is positive, the $X(a,b)Y$ reaction is "exoergic"; it proceeds even with zero kinetic energy in the entrance channel. The kinetic energy in the exit channel β_0 is the maximum kinetic energy which the outgoing particle b and the residual nucleus Y can have. This energy is often used, and we shall call it ϵ_{bY}. It is given by

$$\epsilon_{\beta_0} = \epsilon_{bY} = \epsilon + Q_{ab} \qquad (1.10)$$

where $\epsilon = \epsilon_{\alpha_0}$ is the kinetic energy in the entrance channel (both a and X in their ground states).

If the Q value, Q_{ab}, of the $X(a,b)Y$ reaction is negative, the reaction is "endoergic" and does not proceed unless the channel energy ϵ in the entrance channel exceeds a certain amount. Equation (1.10) implies that ϵ must exceed $-Q_{ab}$ in order that the channel β_0 be "open" (i.e., that ϵ_{bY} be positive). This minimum energy $-Q_{ab}$ for an endoergic reaction is also called the "threshold energy" of the $X(a,b)Y$ reaction.[1]

2. CROSS SECTIONS

A. Geometrical Limitations on Reaction and Scattering Cross Sections

Consider a beam of particles directed at a layer of matter. In most nuclear reactions the effect of this layer is composed additively of the effects of individual units (scattering centers) in the layer; the individual nuclei in the material act as independent scattering centers. The cross section of a reaction is then defined by

$$\sigma = \frac{\text{number of events of given type per unit time per nucleus}}{\text{number of incident particles per unit area per unit time}} \quad (2.1)$$

The concept of a cross section cannot be used if large numbers of nuclei act coherently. This occurs in only one type of nuclear reaction: the scattering (but not the absorption) of a beam of very slow neutrons by crystalline material. In all other cases the cross section (2.1) has a well-defined meaning.

Let us consider a plane wave of particles a incident upon the nucleus X, representing an entrance channel α. Particle a can be re-emitted into the same channel, or it can initiate a nuclear reaction which leads into another channel. We shall separate the elastic scattering events from all the other reactions (1.3) and from (1.2), so that the total cross section $\sigma_t(\alpha)$ for all events which may take place is given by

$$\sigma_t(\alpha) = \sigma_{sc}(\alpha) + \sigma_r(\alpha) \quad (2.2)$$

Here $\sigma_{sc}(\alpha)$ denotes the elastic scattering cross section, and $\sigma_r(\alpha)$ denotes the combined cross section for all events other than elastic scattering. (We include the various inelastic scattering cross sections in σ_r.) We shall refer to σ_r as the "reaction cross section."

We assume for the sake of simplicity that target nucleus X, *as well as projectile* a, *has zero spin.* This assumption is correct only if we use alpha-particles as projectiles, and nuclei with even A as targets. It is certainly incorrect for neutron or proton reactions. Most of the

---

[1] Sometimes a distinction is made between "threshold energy," which then refers to the necessary kinetic energy of a in the *laboratory* system, and the negative Q value, which determines the necessary kinetic energy in the center-of-gravity system. We shall not make this distinction here.

results, however, are not affected by this assumption, which greatly simplifies the treatment. The assumption will be dropped in Section 10, which contains the theory including the effects of the spins.

We can break up each channel α into subchannels (α,l) with given orbital angular momentum l.[1] It is useful to decompose the incident plane wave into spherical harmonics; each spherical harmonic $Y_{l,0}(\theta)$ in this expansion corresponds to a spherical wave in the particular entrance subchannel (α,l). The cross sections can also be subdivided into partial cross sections:

$$\sigma_{sc}(\alpha) = \sum_{l=0}^{\infty} \sigma_{sc,l} \qquad \sigma_r(\alpha) = \sum_{l=0}^{\infty} \sigma_{r,l} \qquad (2.3)$$

where $\sigma_{sc,l}$ and $\sigma_{r,l}$ are the cross sections for the reactions and the elastic scattering events initiated by incident particles with an angular momentum l. σ_l is defined by (2.1) if the numerator contains terms corresponding only to those reactions or scattering events which are initiated by incident particles of given l, the denominator remaining the same. The separation (2.3) of the cross section into additive contributions of given l is possible only for the cross sections integrated over the angles of emergence of the reaction products. The differential cross section for a reaction or scattering in which the emergent particle leaves in a definite direction θ involves interference terms between the contributions from different values of l, since definite phase relations between these contributions exist in the incident plane wave. These interference terms vanish after the integration over the full solid angle.

Geometrical considerations show that there are upper bounds for the partial reaction cross sections $\sigma_{r,l}$. Before deriving the value of these bounds, we give a crude argument for their existence. The significance of the angular momenta in a plane wave can be visualized by dividing up the incident beam into cylindrical zones (see Fig. 2.1). The innermost zone contains particles with impact parameters less than $\lambda = \lambda/2\pi$ ($\lambda =$ de Broglie wavelength of the relative motion). The next zone contains all particles with impact parameters between λ and 2λ. The lth zone contains particles with impact parameters between $l\lambda$ and $(l+1)\lambda$. Then, according to elementary classical mechanics, the incident particles moving in the lth zone have angular momenta (i.e., momentum $\times$ impact parameter) between $Mvl\lambda$ and $Mv(l+1)\lambda$, i.e., between $\hbar l$ and $\hbar(l+1)$.

---

[1] Here and in the following sections we measure angular momenta in units of $\hbar$. The expression "angular momentum l" refers to a state in which the square of the angular momentum has the value $\hbar^2 l(l+1)$.

In quantum mechanics only integral values l of the angular momentum are admitted. It might be thought that this quantization of angular momenta implies also quantization of impact parameters (i.e., motion of the particles only with definite, quantized impact parameters). This interpretation is too rigid, since it is impossible to

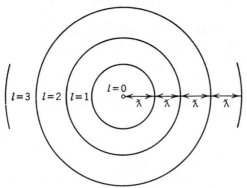

FIG. 2.1. The incident beam is directed perpendicular to the plane of the figure. The particles with a given l hit predominantly the indicated ring-shaped areas.

speak of a well-defined impact parameter in a beam whose particles have a well-defined velocity. However, it is approximately correct to assume that the particles with an angular momentum l move in the lth zone.

The cross-sectional area of the lth zone is $(2l+1)\pi\lambdabar^2$. Since no more particles can be taken out of the beam than are in it originally, we expect that the reaction cross section $\sigma_{r,l}$ cannot be larger than this amount, i.e.,

$$\sigma_{r,l} \leq (2l+1)\pi\lambdabar^2 \tag{2.4}$$

It should be noted that (2.4) does *not* apply to the scattering cross section.

We now proceed to give a more formal derivation of (2.4). The incident beam is represented by a plane wave in the incident channel. We define the channel coordinate $\mathbf{r}_\alpha$ as the vector between the center of the target nucleus X and the projectile a. The plane wave can be written in the form

$$\exp{(i\mathbf{k}_\alpha \cdot \mathbf{r}_\alpha)} = \exp{(ikz)}$$

if we choose the z axis parallel to $\mathbf{k}_\alpha$. The wave vector $\mathbf{k}_\alpha$ is related to the relative velocity $\mathbf{v}_\alpha = \dot{\mathbf{r}}_\alpha$ by

$$\mathbf{k}_\alpha = \frac{M_\alpha \mathbf{v}_\alpha}{\hbar} \qquad M_\alpha = \frac{M_a M_{\mathrm{X}}}{M_a + M_{\mathrm{X}}} \tag{2.5}$$

where the "channel mass" M_α is the reduced mass of a and X. The channel wave number $k_\alpha = |\mathbf{k}_\alpha|$ and the channel wavelength λ_α are related to the channel energy ϵ_α by

$$k_\alpha = \frac{1}{\lambda_\alpha} = \frac{(2M_\alpha\epsilon_\alpha)^{1/2}}{\hbar} \tag{2.6}$$

The plane wave can be expanded into spherical harmonics. For large values of kr this expansion becomes (we drop the index α in the rest of this section)[1]

$$\exp(ikz) \cong \frac{\pi^{1/2}}{kr} \sum_{l=0}^{\infty} \sqrt{2l+1}\ i^{l+1} \left\{ \exp\left[-i(kr - \tfrac{1}{2}l\pi)\right] \right.$$
$$\left. - \exp\left[+i(kr - \tfrac{1}{2}l\pi)\right] \right\} Y_{l,0} \tag{2.7}$$

This expression describes an undisturbed plane wave. The nuclear reaction changes this expression. However, only the outgoing wave which is proportional to $\exp(ikr)$ is changed. Hence the actual wave function in the incident channel has an asymptotic behavior differing from (2.7) in the coefficient of $\exp(ikr)$ only. We write for the wave function in the incident channel, for $kr \gg 1$,

$$\psi(\mathbf{r}) \cong \frac{\pi^{1/2}}{kr} \sum_{l=0}^{\infty} \sqrt{2l+1}\ i^{l+1} \left\{ \exp\left[-i(kr - \tfrac{1}{2}l\pi)\right] \right.$$
$$\left. - \eta_l \exp\left[+i(kr - \tfrac{1}{2}l\pi)\right] \right\} Y_{l,0} \tag{2.8}$$

where the complex number η_l is the coefficient of the outgoing wave with angular momentum l. The scattered wave ψ_{sc} is the difference between the actual wave (2.8) and the incident wave (2.7):

$$\psi_{sc} = \psi(\mathbf{r}) - \exp(ikz)$$
$$= \frac{\pi^{1/2}}{kr} \sum_{l=0}^{\infty} \sqrt{2l+1}\ i^{l+1}\ (1 - \eta_l) \exp\left[+i(kr - \tfrac{1}{2}l\pi)\right] Y_{l,0} \tag{2.9}$$

We obtain the scattering cross section by dividing the number N_{sc} of scattered particles per second by the number N of the incident particles per square centimeter per second. In order to find N_{sc} we enclose the center by a large sphere of radius r_0 and equate N_{sc} to the flux of ψ_{sc} through this sphere:

[1] For the definition of Y_{lm} and more about the expansion of $\exp(ikz)$, see Appendix A.

$$N_{sc} = \frac{\hbar}{2iM} \int \left(\frac{\partial \psi_{sc}}{\partial r} \psi_{sc}{}^{*} - \frac{\partial \psi_{sc}{}^{*}}{\partial r} \psi_{sc} \right) r_0{}^2 \sin \theta \, d\theta \, d\varphi \quad (2.10)$$

where the integral is extended over the surface of the sphere. Because of the orthogonality and normalization of the $Y_{l,0}$ we get

$$N_{sc} = \frac{v\pi}{k^2} \sum_{l=0}^{\infty} (2l+1) \left| 1 - \eta_l \right|^2$$

where v is the velocity of the particles. The value of the flux N in a plane wave exp (ikz) is equal to the velocity v, so that we get for the *scattering cross section*

$$\sigma_{sc,l} = \pi \lambda^2 (2l+1) \left| 1 - \eta_l \right|^2 \quad (2.11)$$

The *reaction* cross section is determined by the number N_a of particles taken out of the beam per second. N_a is the number of particles which enter a sphere of radius r_0 around the center without leaving it again through the entrance channel. It is therefore equal to the net flux into this sphere as computed from the complete wave function ψ (2.8):

$$N_a = - \frac{\hbar}{2iM} \int \left(\frac{\partial \psi}{\partial r} \psi^{*} - \frac{\partial \psi^{*}}{\partial r} \psi \right) r_0{}^2 \sin \theta \, d\theta \, d\varphi \quad (2.12)$$

(The minus sign in front makes the influx N_a positive.) The reaction cross section σ_r is given by N_a/N; thus the contribution of the lth subwave is

$$\sigma_{r,l} = \pi \lambda^2 (2l+1) (1 - |\eta_l|^2) \quad (2.13)$$

Equation (2.13) provides the formal proof of the geometrical limit (2.4) on the reaction cross section, since $|\eta_l|^2$ can never be negative. Furthermore, unless $|\eta_l|^2$ is smaller than or equal to unity, the outgoing wave in (2.8) has a higher intensity than the incoming one. The condition

$$|\eta_l|^2 \leq 1$$

insures that the cross section (2.13) does not become negative.

Inspection of (2.11) and (2.12) leads to an inequality connecting $\sigma_{sc,l}$ and $\sigma_{r,l}$. To get the largest possible scattering cross section we must put $\eta_l = -1$, and this implies that $\sigma_{r,l}$ vanishes. On the other hand, we get the maximum amount removed from the beam when we put $\eta_l = 0$, and this implies $\sigma_{sc,l} = \sigma_{r,l} = (2l+1)\pi\lambda^2$. This is precisely the limiting value (2.4) found qualitatively before. In general, for any given scattering cross section there is a maximum value of the reaction cross section. This is indicated in Fig. 2.2 where the shaded region contains the possible values of $\sigma_{sc,l}$ and $\sigma_{r,l}$.

We see from this figure that there cannot be any reaction without some scattering, although scattering without reaction is possible. This can be understood simply by inspection of the main features of

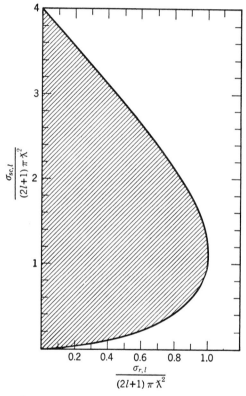

FIG. 2.2. Upper and lower limit of the elastic scattering cross section for a given reaction cross section. Values inside the shaded region are possible; those outside the shaded region are impossible.

the calculation. Any reaction is equivalent to an absorption of the incident wave in the entrance channel. The reaction may lead to an emission of the particle in another channel. It is an absorption as far as the entrance channel is concerned. Any absorption consists of a weakening of the outgoing part of the plane wave. This is equivalent to an addition to the plane wave of an outgoing wave with a phase opposite to the one of the plane wave. This addition appears as a scattered wave. Scattering without absorption occurs if the outgoing part of the plane wave is not weakened in intensity but only shifted in phase.

The maximum value of the scattering cross section is four times the maximum value of the reaction cross section. We see from (2.11) that the phase of η affects the magnitude of σ_{sc}, whereas only $|\eta|^2$ enters into σ_r. *The incoming and outgoing waves are coherent in elastic scattering.* They can interfere, constructively or destructively. The factor 4 noted above comes from the possibility of constructive interference and is therefore absent in the reaction cross section $\sigma_r(\alpha)$.[1]

The *angular distribution* of the scattered beam is also determined by the η_l. Let us ask for the cross section $\sigma_{sc}(\theta)\, d\Omega$ for the scattering into the solid angle element $d\Omega$, which includes the angle θ with the direction of the incident beam (z direction). We determine the number $N_{sc}(\theta)\, d\Omega$ of particles scattered per second into $d\Omega$ by equating it to the flux through a surface element of the sphere of radius r_0:

$$N_{sc}(\theta)\, d\Omega = \frac{\hbar}{2iM}\left(\frac{\partial \psi_{sc}}{\partial r}\psi_{sc}{}^* - \frac{\partial \psi_{sc}{}^*}{\partial r}\psi_{sc}\right)r_0{}^2\, d\Omega \qquad (2.14)$$

This can be calculated from (2.9); we obtain, after division by the ncident flux $N = v$,

$$\sigma_{sc}(\theta)\, d\Omega = \frac{\pi}{k^2}\left|\sum_{l=0}^{\infty}(2l+1)^{1/2}(1-\eta_l)\,Y_{l,0}(\theta)\right|^2 d\Omega \qquad (2.15)$$

Here the contributions of different l's interfere, so that it is no longer possible to write $\sigma_{sc}(\theta)$ as a sum of contributions each of which is due to a specified l.

The η_l do *not* determine the division of the reaction cross section into cross sections for the different reactions leading to the various open channels $\beta \neq \alpha$. We shall need separate assumptions to determine this subdivision.

It is of interest to discuss the limiting case of a "black" nucleus whose radius R is much larger than the wavelength λ. We assume that all particles that strike the nucleus are absorbed by it and therefore lead to a reaction. According to our previous considerations, all particles with $l \leq R/\lambda$ strike the nucleus. Our assumption therefore is expressed by

---

[1] The distinction between outgoing waves which are coherent with the incident wave and those which are incoherent gave the motivation for including in the "reaction" cross section all events in which the target nucleus changes its state; for these outgoing waves are all incoherent with the incident wave and with each other.

$$\eta_l = 0, \quad \text{as long as } l\lambda < R$$
$$\eta_l = 1, \quad \text{for larger values of } l \tag{2.16}$$

Then equations (2.11) and (2.12) give

$$\sigma_r = \sigma_{sc} = \sum_{l=0}^{R/\lambda} (2l + 1)\,\pi\,\lambda^2 \cong \pi R^2$$

We thus obtain the apparently paradoxical result that the total cross section is *twice* the geometrical cross section of the nucleus:

$$\sigma_t = \sigma_{sc} + \sigma_r \cong 2\pi R^2 \tag{2.17}$$

This result has been confirmed experimentally.

The seeming paradox may be explained by a consideration of the meaning of scattering. A picture of the effect of a "black" nucleus is given roughly in Fig. 2.3.

Let us assume that the incident beam contains N neutrons per second per square centimeter. Since the wavelength is small compared with

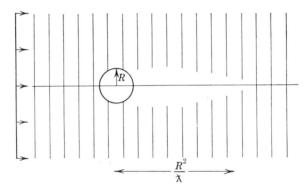

FIG. 2.3.   Shadow scattering.

the radius, we can localize the impact of the incident particles on the nucleus and we find that $N_a = N\pi R^2$ neutrons hit the nucleus per second and are absorbed. There is, however, an additional process: the black nucleus throws a shadow behind it. This shadow cannot be perfectly sharp, because of diffraction effects. Far away, at a distance L from the black object, in the region of Fraunhofer diffraction, the edge of the shadow is blurred over its full extent and the shadow itself has disappeared. The distance L is of the order R^2/λ, or larger. This is a very large distance for most black objects studied in optics, and that is why the approximation of a sharp geometrical shadow is very accurate. In nuclear physics, on the other hand, R^2/λ may be only a few nuclear diameters for fairly energetic projectiles. Thus a number N_{sc} of particles are deviated from their straight path. This number can be determined by the following argument: The shadow behind the nucleus could be produced by replacing the nucleus with a disk of the size πR^2 which emits, toward the right, neutron waves of the same intensity as those in the incident beam, but with opposite phase. The waves emitted from this disk would diverge from the initial direction after a distance R^2/λ. The shadow is equivalent to this wave, and therefore the number N_{sc} is equal to the number $N\pi R^2$ of neutrons emitted by the imaginary disk. Hence the total number of scattered particles per second is $N_{sc} = N\pi R^2$, which leads to a scattering cross section of $\sigma_{sc} = \pi R^2$ in addition to the reaction cross section. The scattering angles of this "shadow scattering" are rather small, of the order λ/R. Nevertheless, the shadow scattering can be distinguished from the incident beam if proper precautions are taken.

B. The Determination of Cross Sections from the Conditions at the Nuclear Surface, for Neutrons with $l = 0$

Nuclear cross sections can be calculated only if the internal structure of the nuclei is known. Expressions (2.11) and (2.13) show that for the elastic scattering cross section and the reaction cross section all necessary information is contained in the magnitudes η_l; they define these two cross sections completely. We therefore investigate the connection between η_l and the internal properties of the nucleus.

No special assumption about the structure of the nuclei has yet been made. At this point we introduce only one general assumption: *the existence of a well-defined nuclear surface.* We assume that the projectile a and the nucleus X have no nuclear interaction if their distance r is larger than the "channel radius" $R = R_X + R_a$. (See Fig. 2.4.) We refer to the region $r > R$ as being "outside the nucleus," whereas $r < R$ is the "interior of the nucleus."[1]

We first restrict ourselves to the case where the incoming particle a is a neutron. This simplifies the calculations and helps to demonstrate the essential points. Then we can describe the relative motion of a and X for $r > R$ by a wave function $\psi(\mathbf{r})$ which corresponds to the relative motion of two particles with no interaction between them:

$$\nabla^2\psi + k^2\psi = 0 \qquad (r > R) \tag{2.18}$$

---

[1] The radius differs from channel to channel. Hence, if different channels are considered, we shall denote the channel radius by R_α, just as we have denoted the channel coordinate by r_α. In this section the subscript is omitted.

Here k is the entrance channel wave number.   Expression (2.18) is incorrect for $r < R$, since the motion of the particle inside the nucleus cannot be described by a wave function which depends on only one coordinate.

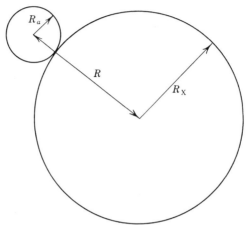

FIG. 2.4.   Definition of channel radius.

For large values of $|\mathbf{r}|$, ψ consists of a superposition of a plane incident wave exp (ikz) and an outgoing spherical wave, as indicated in (2.9).   We are now interested not only in the asymptotic behavior of ψ as given in (2.8) for very large $r = |\mathbf{r}|$, but also in its behavior for smaller values of r, all the way down to the channel radius $r = R$.   The wave function can be written as a sum of subwaves of given orbital angular momentum l:

$$\psi(\mathbf{r}) = \psi(r,\theta) = \sum_{l=0}^{\infty} \frac{u_l(r)}{r} Y_{l,0}(\theta) \qquad (2.19)$$

where $Y_{l,0}$ are the spherical harmonics defined in Appendix A.   We include subwaves with $m = 0$ only, since the incident plane wave exp (ikz) is independent of the azimuthal angle φ.   Furthermore, we shall restrict ourselves for the time being to consideration of the S wave neutrons, i.e., of the $l = 0$ term in (2.19).   As shown by inserting the $l = 0$ term of (2.19) into (2.18), the function $u_0(r)$ satisfies the equation

$$\frac{d^2 u_0}{dr^2} + k^2 u_0 = 0 \qquad (r \geq R) \qquad (2.20)$$

$u_0(r)$ is not determined completely by (2.20) unless boundary conditions are specified.   The general solution of (2.20) is of the form

$$u_0(r) = \mathsf{a} \exp(-ikr) + \mathsf{b} \exp(+ikr) \qquad (r \geq R) \qquad (2.21)$$

where a and b are constants. These constants are determined by the behavior of the wave function far away, i.e., by (2.8). Comparison of (2.21) with (2.8) gives

$$\mathsf{a} = \frac{i\sqrt{\pi}}{k} \qquad \mathsf{b} = -\eta_0 \mathsf{a} \qquad (2.22)$$

The quantity η_0 and hence the coefficient b of the outgoing wave in (2.21) is not determined by the boundary condition at infinity, except that $|\eta_0| \leq 1$. Rather, η_0 is to be found from the theory of nuclear reactions. This theory depends on conditions in the "interior" region, $r < R$. We therefore must connect the quantity η_0, which determines the cross sections, with the conditions at the nuclear surface. We shall describe the behavior of $u_0(r)$ just outside the nuclear surface by the quantity

$$f_0 \equiv R \left[\frac{du_0/dr}{u_0} \right]_{r=R} \qquad (2.23)$$

The quantity f_0 and its analogues for higher values of the angular momentum will be used very often in this chapter. Since the value and derivative of $u_0(r)$ must be continuous at the surface, the magnitude f_0 is completely defined by the conditions in the interior of the nucleus. The entire theory of nuclear reactions as developed here has as its aim to find an approximate expression for the variation of f as a function of the channel energy ϵ. For once f is found, η can be determined from it, and the cross sections from η. At present we are not yet concerned with the essential part of the theory, the determination of f. Rather, we shall indicate only how f can be used to determine η, i.e., how we can find the asymptotic behavior of the wave function for large r if its behavior at $r = R$ is known.

This is very easy for the simplest case of incident neutrons with zero angular momentum $l = 0$. We substitute (2.21) with the coefficients (2.22) into the definition (2.23) and solve for η_0 in terms of f_0. This gives

$$\eta_0 = \frac{f_0 + ikR}{f_0 - ikR} \exp(-2ikR) \qquad (2.24)$$

If the logarithmic derivative f_0 is a real number, (2.24) implies that $|\eta_0|^2 = 1$; hence the reaction cross section $\sigma_{r,0}$ vanishes (see 2.13). A real value of f gives pure scattering without any reaction (without any removal of particles from the entrance channel).

Substitution of (2.24) into (2.11) gives the $l=0$ part of the scattering cross section. This can be written in the form

$$\sigma_{sc,0} = \pi\lambda^2 \left| A_{\text{res}} + A_{\text{pot}} \right|^2 \tag{2.25}$$

where

$$A_{\text{res}} = \frac{-2ikR}{f_0 - ikR} \tag{2.26}$$

$$A_{\text{pot}} = \exp(2ikR) - 1 \tag{2.27}$$

We shall refer to A_{res} as the "internal" or "resonance" scattering amplitude (the latter term is appropriate only under certain conditions; see Section 7), and to A_{pot} as the "potential" or "hard sphere" scattering amplitude. The origin of this name can be seen if we replace the nucleus by a perfectly reflecting sphere with the same radius R. Such a sphere forces the wave function to vanish at $r = R$. According to the definition (2.23) of f_0, this implies $f_0 = \infty$. Equation (2.26) shows that the internal scattering amplitude is zero for a hard sphere; the hard sphere scattering is determined by A_{pot} (2.27).

The separation of the scattering amplitude A into an internal and an external part depends on the assumption of a definite radius R in the channel. To the extent that the channel radius R is indeterminate (e.g., because the nuclear boundary is not perfectly sharp), this separation is only approximate.[1] Furthermore it must be realized that the separation of the scattering amplitude into these two portions has only a theoretical meaning, i.e., it cannot be observed experimentally. The only experimentally measurable quantity is the sum $A_{\text{res}} + A_{\text{pot}}$. In spite of these restrictions, the separation of the scattering amplitude into an internal and an external part is very important for an understanding of the theory of nuclear reactions.

The contribution of the S wave neutrons to the reaction cross section can be found from (2.24) and (2.13). It is

$$\sigma_{r,0} = \pi\lambda^2 \frac{-4kR \operatorname{Im} f_0}{(\operatorname{Re} f_0)^2 + (\operatorname{Im} f_0 - kR)^2} \tag{2.28}$$

where $\operatorname{Re} f_0$ and $\operatorname{Im} f_0$ stand for the real and imaginary parts of f_0, respectively.

---

[1] In principle, we could choose any value $R' > R$ as a radius for the channel, since so far our only condition upon R has been that there shall not be any nuclear interaction for $r \geq R$. In practice, the only choice of R which leads to physically useful results is the smallest R which satisfies this condition, as shown in Fig. 2.4. See, however, Wigner (51).

Since the reaction cross section is an inherently positive quantity, the imaginary part of the logarithmic derivative f_0 must be negative:[1]

$$\text{Im } f_0 \leq 0 \tag{2.29}$$

This can also be seen from (2.24) by imposing the equivalent condition $|\eta_0|^2 \leq 1$.

▶ **C. The Determination of Cross Sections from the Conditions at the Nuclear Surface. General Case**

The relations of Section 2B are restricted to one special case, namely orbital angular momentum $l=0$ and no Coulomb force. We now extend the treatment to the case of arbitrary angular momenta l and (or) charged-particle reactions. The wave function $\psi(\mathbf{r})$, corresponding to the relative motion of the incoming particle a and the target nucleus X, fulfills the equation

$$\nabla^2\psi + \left[k^2 - \frac{2M}{\hbar^2} V(r) \right] \psi = 0 \tag{2.18a}$$

where M is the reduced mass in the channel and $V(r)$ is the potential energy of a and X at separation $r > R$. The radial wave function $u_l(r)$ as defined in (2.19) satisfies a differential equation which can be found by inserting (2.19) into (2.18a):

$$\frac{d^2 u_l}{dr^2} + \left[k^2 - \frac{l(l+1)}{r^2} - \frac{2M}{\hbar^2} V(r) \right] u_l(r) = 0 \tag{2.30}$$

The potential energy $V(r)$ which appears in (2.18a) and (2.30) is the electrostatic potential energy

$$V(r) = \frac{Z_a Z_X e^2}{r} \tag{2.31}$$

where Z_a and Z_X are the charges of a and X, respectively. Equation (2.30) is correct only as long as $r > R$, since the motion inside the nucleus cannot be described by a wave function which depends on only one coordinate.

The two linearly independent solutions of (2.30) which can be found

---

[1] This theorem, as well as the relation between f and the cross sections in general, is well known in many fields; in particular, in electrical engineering, with somewhat different notations. The results will be discussed from a more general point of view in Chapter X. f corresponds to the impedance of a circuit; σ_{sc} and σ_r correspond to the reflection and transmission coefficients, respectively. (The correspondence is not correct as to factors, however.) Relation (2.29) corresponds to the statement that resistances must be positive or zero in a passive linear network

tabulated are the "regular" and "irregular" solutions $F_l(r)$ and $G_l(r)$. They are defined as follows: $F_l(r)$ is a real function which satisfies (2.30) and vanishes for $r=0$. It is then determined completely, except for a numerical coefficient in front. This coefficient is chosen so that the asymptotic behavior of $F_l(r)$ is, for neutrons,

$$F_l(r) \cong \sin (kr - \tfrac{1}{2}l\pi) \qquad \text{neutrons, } kr \gg l \qquad (2.32)$$

For charged-particle reactions the asymptotic behavior is more complicated. To the extent that the shielding by the atomic electrons can be neglected, the asymptotic behavior of the regular solution $F_l(r)$ is

$$F_l(r) \cong \sin [kr - \tfrac{1}{2}l\pi - \gamma \ln (2kr) + \sigma_l]$$
$$\text{charged particles, } kr \gg l \quad (2.33)$$

where γ is a parameter which determines the importance of the Coulomb effects[1] ($v =$ velocity in the channel)

$$\gamma = \frac{Z_a Z_X e^2}{\hbar v} \qquad (2.34)$$

and σ_l is the Coulomb phase shift which determines the purely electrostatic (Rutherford) scattering; it is defined by

$$\exp (2i\sigma_l) = \frac{(l+i\gamma)!}{(l-i\gamma)!} = \frac{(l+i\gamma)(l-1+i\gamma) \cdots (1+i\gamma)}{(l-i\gamma)(l-1-i\gamma) \cdots (1-i\gamma)} \exp (2i\sigma_0) \quad (2.35)$$

The "irregular" solution $G_l(r)$ of (2.30) is defined by its asymptotic behavior for large r:

$$G_l(r) \cong \cos (kr - \tfrac{1}{2}l\pi) \qquad \text{neutrons, } kr \gg l \qquad (2.36)$$

$$G_l(r) \cong \cos [kr - \tfrac{1}{2}l\pi - \gamma \ln (2kr) + \sigma_l]$$
$$\text{charged particles, } kr \gg l \quad (2.37)$$

The differential equation (2.30) implies that the "Wronskian" combination $G(dF/dr) - F(dG/dr)$ is independent of r. It can therefore be determined from the asymptotic forms for large r with the result

$$G_l \left(\frac{dF_l}{dr} \right) - F_l \left(\frac{dG_l}{dr} \right) = k \qquad (2.38)$$

---

[1] This parameter is usually called η in the literature, and was denoted by η in Chapter II, Section 4. We use the notation γ here to avoid confusion with the scattering parameters η_l.

For *neutrons* $[V(r) = 0]$ the solutions $F_l(r)$ and $G_l(r)$ can be written in terms of Bessel functions:

$$F_l(r) = \left(\frac{\pi kr}{2}\right)^{1/2} J_{l+1/2}(kr) \qquad (2.39)$$

$$G_l(r) = -\left(\frac{\pi kr}{2}\right)^{1/2} N_{l+1/2}(kr) \qquad (2.40)$$

where $J_p(z)$ and $N_p(z)$ are the Bessel and Neumann functions of order p, respectively, as defined in Jahnke-Emde (33). Tables of $F_l(r)$ and $G_l(r)$ for neutrons can be found in several places: for example, Morse (45) and Lax (48).

The corresponding functions for charged particles cannot be written in terms of elementary functions. The tabulation of $F_l(r)$ and $G_l(r)$ for charged particles is complicated by the fact that these functions depend not only on kr but also on the charge parameter γ. The extensive tabulations of these functions in connection with proton-proton scattering (Yost 35, 36, Wicher 36) do not cover the region of importance in nuclear reactions, except for very light nuclei. Some values will be given in this chapter. More detailed tables of the quantities of importance for nuclear reactions with charged particles are given by Bloch (51a) and by Christy (48).

For the theory of nuclear reactions, we need the linear combinations of $F_l(r)$ and $G_l(r)$ which correspond to outgoing and ingoing spherical waves. We define $u_l^{(+)}(r)$ and $u_l^{(-)}(r)$ by

$$u_l^{(+)}(r) \equiv G_l(r) + i F_l(r) \qquad \text{neutrons}$$

$$u_l^{(+)}(r) \equiv \exp(-i\sigma_l)[G_l(r) + i F_l(r)] \qquad \text{charged particles} \quad (2.41)$$

$$u_l^{(-)}(r) \equiv \text{complex conjugate of } u_l^{(+)}(r)$$

For neutrons with $l=0$,

$$u_0^{(+)}(r) = \exp(+ikr)$$

and in general the asymptotic behavior of $u_l^{(+)}(r)$ for large r is

$$u_l^{(+)}(r) \cong \exp[i(kr - \tfrac{1}{2}l\pi)] \qquad (kr \gg l) \qquad (2.42)$$

The radial wave function $u_l(r)$ in the outside region can always be written in the form

$$u_l(r) = \mathsf{a}\, u_l^{(-)}(r) + \mathsf{b}\, u_l^{(+)}(r) \qquad (2.43)$$

This reduces to (2.21) for $l=0$ neutrons. The constants a and b are again determined by comparison with the behavior of the wave function at large distances, (2.8).   This gives

$$\mathsf{a} = i^{l+1}\,(2l+1)^{1/2}\,\frac{\sqrt{\pi}}{k} \qquad \mathsf{b} = -\eta_l\,\mathsf{a} \qquad (2.44)$$

The quantity η_l must be connected with the conditions at the nuclear surface.   We therefore introduce the logarithmic derivative of the wave function $u_l(r)$ at the nuclear boundary, f_l, by

$$f_l \equiv R\left[\frac{du_l/dr}{u_l}\right]_{r=R} \qquad (2.45)$$

in complete analogy to (2.23).   In order to get the general expression for η_l in terms of f_l we introduce certain quantities which are completely determined by the conditions *outside* the nucleus: we define the real numbers Δ_l and s_l through

$$R\left[\frac{du_l^{(+)}/dr}{u_l^{(+)}}\right]_{r=R} \equiv \Delta_l + is_l \qquad (2.46)$$

Δ_l and s_l depend on the wave number k, the channel radius R, the angular momentum l, and the charge parameter γ, (2.34).   Comparison of (2.46) and (2.41) shows that Δ_l and s_l are related to the tabulated regular and irregular functions $F_l(r)$ and $G_l(r)$ by

$$\Delta_l = R\left[\frac{G_l\,(dG_l/dr) + F_l\,(dF_l/dr)}{G_l{}^2 + F_l{}^2}\right]_{r=R} \qquad (2.47)$$

$$s_l = R\left[\frac{G_l\,(dF_l/dr) - F_l\,(dG_l/dr)}{G_l{}^2 + F_l{}^2}\right]_{r=R} \qquad (2.48)$$

The numerator of (2.48) is actually independent of R, according to (2.38), and equal to k.   The expression $G_l{}^2 + F_l{}^2$ is unity for neutrons with $l=0$, and larger than unity for $l\neq0$ and (or) charged particles. Since this expression occurs very frequently, it is convenient to introduce a quantity v_l through[1]

$$v_l \equiv \frac{1}{G_l{}^2(R) + F_l{}^2(R)} \qquad (2.49)$$

We shall see in Section 5 that this quantity is very important for the analysis of nuclear reaction data.   A small $v_l \ll 1$ implies that

[1] The Coulomb penetration factor C^2 in Chapter II, Section 4, is equal to (2.49) evaluated for $R=0$ and $l=0$.   Sometimes the quantity $[G_l(R)]^{-2}$ is called a penetration factor.   We shall adhere to the definition (2.49) throughout.   The quantity v_l defined by (2.49) is different from the v_l used in Feshbach (47, 49a).   In these papers the symbol v_l was used for the function $u_l^{(-)}(r)$.

particle a does not penetrate to the nuclear surface appreciably and hence will lead to a weak nuclear reaction. We shall therefore call v_l the "penetration factor"; its significance and behavior will be discussed in more detail in Section 5 of this chapter.

In terms of the penetration factor v_l, the quantity s_l, (2.46) and (2.48), becomes

$$s_l = kRv_l \qquad (2.50)$$

In addition to the quantities Δ_l and s_l, we shall also need the phase of $u_l^{(-)}(r)$ at $r = R$. This phase constant, ξ_l, is defined by

$$\exp(2i\xi_l) = \frac{u_l^{(-)}(R)}{u_l^{(+)}(R)} = \frac{G_l(R) - iF_l(R)}{G_l(R) + iF_l(R)} \exp(2i\sigma_l) \qquad (2.51)$$

where $\sigma_l = 0$ for neutrons, and σ_l is given by (2.35) for charged particles. For neutrons with $l \neq 0$ these phase constants have been tabulated by Morse (45).[1] Tables of ξ_l for charged particles are not available.

For neutrons, ξ_l decreases in absolute value as the penetration factor v_l decreases and ξ_l approaches zero for very low v_l. The limiting values of ξ_l for very high energies (v_l close to 1, $kR \gg l$) and very low energies (v_l close to 0, $kR \ll l$) are [we use the notation $(2l + 1)!! = 1 \times 3 \times 5 \times \cdots \times (2l + 1)$]

$$kR \gg l: \qquad \xi_l \cong -(kR - \tfrac{1}{2}l\pi)$$
$$\text{(for neutrons)} \qquad (2.52)$$
$$kR \ll l: \qquad \xi_l \cong -\frac{(kR)^{2l+1}}{(2l-1)!!\,(2l+1)!!}$$

For charged particles, ξ_l approaches the same limit for high energies (v_l close to 1, $kR \gg l$), but for low energies (v_l close to 0, $kR \ll l$) ξ_l approaches the pure Coulomb phase shift σ_l, (2.35).

We are now in a position to write the relation between η_l and the logarithmic derivative f_l at the nuclear boundary. Substitution of (2.43) with the constants (2.44) into definition (2.45) gives (after some rearrangement)

$$\eta_l = \frac{f_l - \Delta_l + is_l}{f_l - \Delta_l - is_l} \exp(2i\xi_l) \qquad (2.53)$$

Equation (2.53) reduces to (2.24) for neutrons with $l = 0$. Again, a purely real f_l implies $|\eta_l|^2 = 1$, i.e., scattering without any reaction.

[1] The δ_n of Morse (45) in the spherical case (their Table 10) is identical with the negative of our ξ_n. They use the notation $X = kR$ and tabulate $\delta_n = -\xi_n$ in degrees. Feshbach (47, 49a) also use δ_l for $-\xi_l$, but their notation is $x = kR$, $\bar{X} = KR$.

Since $|\eta_l|^2 \leq 1$, the maximum value of the scattering cross section is obtained when $\eta_l = -1$, according to (2.11). A straightforward calculation shows that this gives the following condition upon the logarithmic derivative f_l in (2.53):

$$f_l = \Delta_l + s_l \tan \xi_l \qquad \text{(for } \eta_l = -1) \qquad (2.54)$$

This value of f_l, which gives the maximum scattering cross section, is purely real and therefore corresponds to scattering without any reaction. This is to be expected, since the maximum scattering cross section is obtained when the outgoing wave has the same intensity as the incoming wave but is shifted in phase by exactly 180 degrees.

We can calculate the scattering and reaction cross sections from η_l, (2.53), by the use of (2.11) and (2.13), respectively. We again denote the real and imaginary parts of f_l by Re f_l and Im f_l. The result for the scattering cross section can be written in the form [analogous to (2.25)]

$$\sigma_{sc,l} = (2l + 1)\, \pi\, \lambda^2\, |A^l_{\mathrm{res}} + A^l_{\mathrm{pot}}|^2 \qquad (2.55)$$

where the amplitudes for internal (resonance) scattering and for the "potential" (external) scattering are

$$A^l_{\mathrm{res}} = \frac{-2\,i\,s_l}{(\mathrm{Re}\,f_l - \Delta_l) + i\,(\mathrm{Im}\,f_l - s_l)} \qquad (2.56)$$

$$A^l_{\mathrm{pot}} = \exp{(-2i\xi_l)} - 1 \qquad (2.57)$$

These two equations reduce to (2.26) and (2.27) respectively for $l = 0$ neutrons. Again the potential scattering amplitude is the same as for scattering from an impenetrable sphere of radius R, since A_{res} vanishes in that case ($f_l = \infty$).

The reaction cross section is given by

$$\sigma_{r,l} = (2l + 1)\, \pi\, \lambda^2\, \frac{-4\, s_l\, \mathrm{Im}\, f_l}{(\mathrm{Re}\, f_l - \Delta_l)^2 + (\mathrm{Im}\, f_l - s_l)^2} \qquad (2.58)$$

As before, we conclude from (2.58) that the imaginary part of f_l must be negative or zero. Furthermore the fact that s_l occurs in the numerator provides a proof of our earlier statement that a low penetration factor v_l [and hence low s_l according to (2.50)] leads to a very low reaction cross section.

Although the formulas in the general case are more complex in appearance than the earlier ones for $l = 0$ neutrons, no new physical idea is involved. The properties of the inside of the nucleus enter into these cross sections only through the logarithmic derivative f_l of the wave function $u_l(r)$ at the nuclear boundary $r = R$.

In the following sections certain assumptions will be made regarding the f_l and their dependence on the energy of the incident particles. These assumptions make it possible to calculate the scattering and reaction cross sections by means of the expressions derived in this section.

▶ **D. The Angular Distribution of Elastically Scattered Particles**

The angular dependence of the elastic scattering can be expressed also in terms of the scattering amplitudes A_{res}^l and A_{pot}^l, (2.56) and (2.57). We substitute η_l, (2.53), into (2.15) and rearrange terms to get[1]

$$d\sigma_{sc}(\theta) = \pi\lambda^2 \left| \sum_{l=0}^{\infty} \sqrt{2l+1} \exp(2i\xi_l)(A_{res}^l + A_{pot}^l) Y_{l,0}(\theta) \right|^2 d\Omega$$

$$(2.59)$$

When $A_{res}^l = 0$, (2.59) gives the angular dependence of the scattering from a reflecting sphere surrounded by the same potential field which surrounds the nucleus. The specifically nuclear effects are contained in A_{res}^l, and the effects of the outside potentials are contained in A_{pot}^l. These effects add coherently, i.e., there are interference terms between them.

In the case of charged particles expression (2.59) contains also the scattering by the Coulomb field of the nucleus. The potential scattering alone is in this case identical with the scattering of a hard sphere surrounded by a Coulomb field, and it would give rise to a scattering that differs from Rutherford scattering only with respect to the near encounters which come close to the nuclear surface. Since these near encounters occur only for large scattering angles, the potential scattering alone agrees with ordinary Rutherford scattering at small scattering angles but deviates from Rutherford scattering for large scattering angles.

The series (2.59) converges only slowly for charged particles since every term contributes appreciably to the Coulomb scattering. It is

[1] This formula shows that our designation "scattering amplitude" for A_{res}^l and A_{pot}^l is not entirely accurate. The amplitudes are actually $\exp(2i\xi_l) A_{res}^l$ and $\exp(2i\xi_l) A_{pot}^l$. This constant phase factor makes no difference in the total cross section but shows up in the differential cross section through the cross products in (2.59) between terms with different l. We shall continue, however, to refer to A_{res}^l and A_{pot}^l as the scattering amplitudes of the internal (resonance) scattering and potential scattering, respectively.

therefore necessary to use an equivalent expression in which the main part of the potential scattering amplitude, namely the amplitude of pure Rutherford scattering, is not decomposed into contributions from various values of l. This expression is

$$d\sigma_{sc}(\theta) = \left| \frac{Z_a Z_X e^2}{2Mv^2} \operatorname{cosec}^2 (\tfrac{1}{2}\theta) \exp\left[-2i\gamma \ln \sin (\tfrac{1}{2}\theta)\right] \right.$$

$$\left. -i\lambda\sqrt{\pi} \left\{\sum_{l=0}^{\infty} \sqrt{2l+1} \exp(2i\sigma_l - 2i\sigma_0) \left\{1 - \exp(2i\xi_l - 2i\sigma_l)\right\} \right.\right.$$

$$\times \left.\left[1 + A_{\text{res}}^l\right]\right\} Y_{l,0}(\theta) \right|^2 d\Omega \quad (2.60)$$

with the auxiliary formulas

$$\exp(2i\sigma_l - 2i\sigma_0) = \frac{(l+i\gamma)(l-1+i\gamma)\cdots(1+i\gamma)}{(l-i\gamma)(l-1-i\gamma)\cdots(1-i\gamma)} \quad (2.60a)$$

$$\exp(2i\xi_l - 2i\sigma_l) = \frac{G_l(R) - i\,F_l(R)}{G_l(R) + i\,F_l(R)} \quad (2.60b)$$

where F_l and G_l are the tabulated regular and irregular Coulomb wave functions.

Neither (2.59) nor (2.60) takes into account the influence of the spins of the particles and target nuclei upon the scattering cross section.

The angular dependence of the reaction cross section is not a meaningful concept. This cross section measures the number of particles removed from the primary beam, no matter what happens afterwards. We may be interested in the angular dependence of special nuclear reactions, e.g., the angular distribution of the emitted neutrons in a (p,n) reaction, relative to the direction of the incident beam. The reaction cross section, however, as defined here, includes all the processes which occur. The problem of the angular distribution in individual nuclear reactions (going into a definite channel) is not discussed in detail in this book. Some general theorems about the angular distribution of reaction products will be derived in Chapter X.

E. The Reciprocity Theorem for Nuclear Reactions

So far, we have considered the wave function only in the incident channel α: the reactions leading to different channels were lumped together into the reaction cross section $\sigma_r(\alpha)$. We now give a somewhat more detailed description of the possible reactions.

Let us consider the reaction in which channel α is the entrance channel, and which leads into channel β. The cross section $\sigma(\alpha,\beta)$ for this reaction is defined according to (2.1) by

$$\sigma(\alpha,\beta) = \frac{\text{number of emissions into channel } \beta \text{ per unit time per scattering center}}{\text{number of incident particles in channel } \alpha \text{ per unit area per unit time}} \qquad (2.61)$$

The reaction cross section $\sigma_r(\alpha)$ in channel α is given by

$$\sigma_r(\alpha) = \sum_{\beta \neq \alpha} \sigma(\alpha,\beta) + \sigma_{\text{cap}}(\alpha) \qquad (2.62)$$

It contains the sum of the cross sections into all possible channels β (the sum does not include α, of course), and the "capture cross section" σ_{cap}, which is the cross section for those events in which particle a enters target nucleus X and no other particle is emitted, as described by (1.2).

It is the aim of this chapter to find ways to calculate or to estimate the cross section $\sigma(\alpha,\beta)$. Before we enter into the discussion of these theories, we first establish an important relation between the cross sections of two opposite reactions: $\sigma(\alpha,\beta)$ and $\sigma(\beta,\alpha)$. The two cross sections belong to the inverse reactions

$$a_{\alpha''} + X_{\alpha'} = Y_{\beta'} + b_{\beta''}$$

and

$$b_{\beta''} + Y_{\beta'} = X_{\alpha'} + a_{\alpha''}$$

The relation is quite universal and depends only on the channel wavelengths $\lambdabar_\alpha$ and $\lambdabar_\beta$. It is expressed by

$$\frac{\sigma(\alpha,\beta)}{\lambdabar_\alpha{}^2} = \frac{\sigma(\beta,\alpha)}{\lambdabar_\beta{}^2} \qquad (2.63)$$

where $\lambdabar_\alpha$ and $\lambdabar_\beta$ are the channel wavelengths as defined in (2.6). Before proving this relation, we describe the process in more detail by specifying the relative directions of the incident and the outgoing particles. Let us introduce the differential cross section

$$\sigma(A,B) = \sigma(\alpha; \beta,\theta,\varphi) \, d\Omega \qquad (2.64)$$

which is defined as the cross section for the process in which the incident particle a moves parallel to the z direction, and the outgoing particle b moves within a solid angle element $d\Omega$ whose direction is given by the polar angles θ and φ. There is a corresponding differential cross section for the opposite process,

$$\sigma(-B,-A) = \sigma(\beta,\theta,\varphi; \alpha) \, d\Omega \qquad (2.65)$$

in which the incident particle b enters from the direction θ,φ, and the outgoing particle a leaves within a solid angle element $d\Omega$ which lies parallel to the negative z axis. There is a relation similar to (2.63) between these two differential cross sections,

$$\frac{\sigma(A,B)}{\lambda_\alpha^2} = \frac{\sigma(-B,-A)}{\lambda_\beta^2} \qquad (2.66)$$

The following identities hold:

$$\int \sigma(\alpha; \beta,\theta,\varphi) \, d\Omega = \sigma(\alpha,\beta) \qquad \int \sigma(\beta,\theta,\varphi; \alpha) \, d\Omega = \sigma(\beta,\alpha)$$

if the integrations are extended over all angles, and these identities show that (2.63) follows from (2.66).

We now prove (2.66). Let us consider the reaction which is described by the differential cross section (2.64) as a transition from one state A to another state B of a quantum-mechanical system. State A contains a particle a in a given quantum state α'' and a nucleus X in state α', both moving as free particles. The channel energy lies in the interval between ϵ_α and $\epsilon_\alpha + \Delta\epsilon$, and the direction of the motion of particle a is parallel to the z axis within a small solid angle element $d\Omega$, and directed toward X. State B contains a particle b in the quantum state β'' and the nucleus Y in the quantum state β', moving as free particles with a kinetic energy between ϵ_β and $\epsilon_\beta + \Delta\epsilon$; b is moving away from Y within a solid angle element $d\Omega$ whose direction is given by the angles θ and φ.

We now compare the transition $A \to B$ with the transition $-B \to -A$, where we understand by $-A$ or $-B$ the states A or B with "reversed time," that is, with all motions reversed in direction. The cross section for the transition $-B \to -A$ is obviously $\sigma(-B,-A)$.

The relation between the processes $A \to B$ and $-B \to -A$ is best understood if we enclose our system in a large volume V and consider the probability per unit time $P(A,B)$ of a transition from A to B, and the corresponding probability $P(-B,-A)$ for the opposite transition. These probabilities are related to the cross sections (2.64) and (2.65). $P(A,B)$ is the probability that a particle somewhere within the volume V will hit the target area per unit time, and therefore it is related to $\sigma(A,B)$ by

$$P(A,B) = \frac{v_\alpha \, \sigma(A,B)}{V} \qquad (2.67)$$

where v_α is the relative velocity in channel α. Similarly,

$$P(-B,-A) = \frac{v_\beta \sigma(-B,-A)}{V} \tag{2.68}$$

There is a fundamental relation between the two transition probabilities $P(A,B)$ and $P(-B,-A)$ which is based on the reversibility of transitions between two elementary states of a system. Let us consider a general quantum-mechanical system in state p. We assume that there exists another state q of the same energy. Let T_{pq} be the transition probability per unit time from p to q. If p and q are both single, non-degenerate states (this means: states of statistical weight unity), the transition probability from p to q is equal to the one from $-q$ to $-p$, where the minus signs signify again the time reversal. The state $-q$ differs from q only by the fact that all motions are reversed.

Let us now consider a pair of states P and Q which are defined in such a way that they comprise a number g_P or g_Q, respectively, of single states (g_P and g_Q are their statistical weights); the transition probabilities from P to Q, and vice versa, then fulfill the relation

$$\frac{T_{P,Q}}{g_Q} = \frac{T_{-Q,-P}}{g_P} \tag{2.69}$$

The statistical weights g_A and g_B of the two states A and B are equal to the number of states of a free particle whose energy and direction are found in the interval $\Delta\epsilon$ and $d\Omega$, respectively:

$$g_A = V \frac{(2M_\alpha^3 \epsilon_\alpha)^{1/2}}{(2\pi)^3 \hbar^3} \Delta\epsilon \, d\Omega$$

$$g_B = V \frac{(2M_\beta^3 \epsilon_\beta)^{1/2}}{(2\pi)^3 \hbar^3} \Delta\epsilon \, d\Omega \tag{2.70}$$

so that we get from (2.69)

$$M_\alpha^{3/2} \epsilon_\alpha^{1/2} P(A,B) = M_\beta^{3/2} \epsilon_\beta^{1/2} P(-B,-A) \tag{2.71}$$

Inserting (2.67) and (2.68) into (2.71) leads immediately to the relation (2.66) which we set out to prove.

The relations (2.63) and (2.66) are called the reciprocity theorem for nuclear reactions. The theorem shows that there is a general connection between the cross sections of opposite reactions. A complete proof of this theorem will be found in Chapter X.

3. THE COMPOUND NUCLEUS, CONTINUUM THEORY

A. The Bohr Assumption

The actual nuclear process in a nuclear reaction does not start before the two initial particles a and X have come near enough to one another, within the range of nuclear forces. The nuclear process has ceased when the two products have separated by more than the range. During the time of interaction, a compound system is formed whose properties are decisive for the course of the nuclear reaction.

It was N. Bohr (36, 37) who first pointed out that it is useful to divide the nuclear reaction into two states: (a) the formation of the compound system C, and (b) the disintegration of the compound system into the products of the reaction. The following assumption has been proved valid, or at least approximately valid, in many cases. The two stages (a) and (b) can be treated as independent processes, in the sense that *the mode of disintegration of the compound system depends only on its energy, angular momentum, and parity, but not on the specific way in which it has been produced.* Thus the two steps of the reaction can be considered separate processes following one another. We shall refer to this as the *Bohr assumption.* It is based on the picture of a nucleus as a system of particles with very strong interactions and short-range forces. If the incident particle comes within the range of the forces, its energy is quickly shared among all constituents well before any re-emission can occur. The state of the compound system is then no longer dependent on the way it was formed.

The validity of the Bohr assumption and its limitations can be understood in the following way. Because of the strong interaction between the nucleons, the energy carried by a into X is shared with all other nucleons shortly after contact. This is due to the fact that the "mean free path" Λ of an entering nucleon in nuclear matter is very much smaller than the nuclear radius if the incident energy ϵ is not too high ($\epsilon < 50$ Mev). Λ can be estimated to be roughly $\Lambda \sim 0.4 \times 10^{-13}$ cm if the entering nucleon has a kinetic energy up to about $\epsilon \cong 20$ Mev. For higher energies, Λ increases and is given approximately by Λ (in centimeters) $\sim 1.8 \times 10^{-15} \times E$ (in Mev).

The estimate of Λ is made in the following way: The mean free path is given by $\Lambda = (\sigma\rho)^{-1}$ where σ is the collision cross section with other nucleons, and ρ is the nucleon density inside the nucleus. Recent experiments show that the neutron-proton scattering cross section is approximately given by $\sigma \sim (4 \text{ Mev}/E) \times 10^{-24}$ cm^2 for $E > 10$ Mev, where E is the relative kinetic energy. ρ can be calculated from the approximative formula (I,4.1) for the nuclear radii, $\rho = 3/(4\pi r_0^3)$. The relative energy E is of the order of $E \cong \frac{1}{2}(E_0 + \epsilon)$, where $E_0 \sim 20$ Mev is the average kinetic energy of the nucleons within the nucleus (see p. 355.) We thus get $\Lambda \sim 1.8 \times 10^{-15} \times (\epsilon + E_0)$ cm, where ϵ and E_0 are in Mev.

Once the energy carried in by a is shared with the other nucleons, it takes a great number of energy exchanges, and thus a long time, before enough energy is concentrated on one particle so that it can be re-emitted by the compound system. This can be seen as follows: The total excitation energy E of the compound system is $E = \epsilon + S_a$, where S_a is the separation energy of a from the compound nucleus. Because of the small value of Λ, this energy is quickly shared among the A constituents of C, so that each of them possesses on the average the amount E/A. As long as E/A is small compared to the average separation energy S of a nucleon from C $(E/A \ll S)$, it takes many exchanges before enough energy is concentrated on one particle so that it can be re-emitted. The large number of exchanges is the main reason for the validity of the Bohr assumption. A thorough "mixing" of the energy of the incident particle is expected, so that the state of C before re-emission of another particle shows no traces depending on the special way the excitation energy was delivered.

The conditions for the validity of the Bohr assumption are then (note that $E/A \ll S$ can be written as $(\epsilon/A) + (S_a/A) \ll S$, and that $S_a \sim S$):

$$\Lambda \ll R \qquad \epsilon \ll (A - 1) S$$

Both conditions are fulfilled for nuclei with $A > 10$ as long as $\epsilon < 50$ Mev, since S is of the order of 8 Mev. It should be noted that the above conditions are necessary but not sufficient. There may be other mechanisms within the compound system preventing thorough "mixing" of the energy of the incident nucleon among *all* constituents. One of many possible reasons for the breakdown of the Bohr assumption may be found in the Pauli exclusion principle. Let us describe the nucleus in first approximation as a system of A particles each moving in a given quantum state (independent-particle model; see Chapter XIV). Then the rate of energy exchange of an entering nucleon with the constituents of the target nucleus is smaller than would be expected from the scattering cross section, since the constituents can take up energy only by transitions into unoccupied states. Most of the neighboring states are occupied by other nucleons. Hence the mean free path Λ may be longer than estimated above. It is difficult to analyze, however, to what extent this conclusion still remains valid for the actual nucleus.

More and more evidence has been accumulated recently (see

Chapter XIV) which points toward a different picture of the interior of the nucleus from the one on which the Bohr assumption is based. There are indications of independent orbits of individual nucleons within the nucleus which would lead to the conclusion that the interaction between nucleons within the nucleus is not so strong or so effective as anticipated. If this conclusion is correct, and if it can also be applied to the situation existing during a nuclear reaction, we should be forced to use a different picture for the description of nuclear reactions. The present experimental material is not yet sufficiently complete to decide this question, and we shall assume full validity of the Bohr assumption in this section. For the time being, we shall assume that the state of the compound system and the way in which this system decays do not depend on the way it was formed. The processes following the formation will be assumed to depend only on the total energy, the angular momentum, and the parity of the compound system. These "constants of motion" are the only "memory" the system retains of the way in which it was formed. The particular channel which served as the entrance channel has been "forgotten."

B. Nuclear Reactions, Cross Sections, and Emission Rates

According to the Bohr assumption, we can write the cross section of a nuclear reaction $X(a,b)Y$ in the form

$$\sigma(a,b) = \sigma_C(a)\, G_C(b) \tag{3.1}$$

where $\sigma_C(a)$ is the cross section for the formation of a compound system by particle a incident upon the target nucleus X. $G_C(b)$ is the probability that the compound system C, once formed, decays by emission of a particle b, leaving a residual nucleus Y. $G_C(b)$ is a pure number; the compound system C must decay eventually in some way; $G_C(b)$ is the probability of this special way of decay. It can also be referred to as the "branching ratio" of the reaction into the emission of b. Evidently $\sum_b G_C(b) = 1$ if the sum is extended over all particles b which C can emit.[1]

It is useful to specify the reaction $X(a,b)Y$ in greater detail, by considering the cross section $\sigma(\alpha,\beta)$ corresponding to a specific entrance channel α and specific exit channel β. In other words, we specify the quantum states of all reaction partners before and after the reaction. We therefore write

$$\sigma(\alpha,\beta) = \sigma_C(\alpha)\, G_C(\beta) \tag{3.2}$$

[1] If a light quantum is not considered a particle, the sum is smaller than unity.

where $\sigma_C(\alpha)$ is the cross section for the formation of C through channel α, and $G_C(\beta)$ is the probability that C decays through channel β.

According to the Bohr assumption, the disintegration of the compound system into the different channels β, γ, etc., depends only on the energy E_C, the angular momentum J_C, and the parity of the compound system. There is one important exception to this: the disintegration of C into the channel α by which C was formed. This is a part of what we have defined as elastic scattering in Section 1. The wave which describes the elastic scattering is coherent with the incident wave, and the consequent interference effects [between A_{res} and A_{pot} in (2.25)] show that there is an interrelation between the incident and the scattered wave. We therefore do not apply (3.2) to elastic scattering processes $\sigma(\alpha,\alpha)$. They will be treated separately.

In order to simplify our present considerations, the dependence of the properties of the compound system on the angular momentum J and the parity Π will be ignored in this section. This procedure introduces errors which are not essential in view of the very qualitative nature of our considerations.

We now introduce a few magnitudes which describe the disintegration of the compound system C. We begin with the mean lifetime $\tau(E_C)$ of C before disintegration and define the magnitude

$$\Gamma(E_C) = \frac{\hbar}{\tau(E_C)} \tag{3.3}$$

which is $\hbar$ times the rate of disintegration per unit time.

Γ is an energy and, later on, will play the role of a level width.[1] We therefore call it the "total width" of the state of C with an excitation energy E_C. C can decay into several channels, and its total decay rate Γ can therefore be subdivided into decay rates[2] referring to specific channels:

$$\Gamma(E_C) = \sum_{\beta} \Gamma_\beta(E_C) \tag{3.4}$$

where the sum is extended over all channels into which C can decay, i.e., over all "open" channels. The specific decay rate $\Gamma_\beta(E_C)$ is also a function of E_C and is called the partial width for the decay into channel β.

---

[1] The interpretation of $\Gamma/\hbar$ as a decay rate is more general, however, than the interpretation of Γ as a level width. There are many cases in which the concept of a "level" with a "width" has no meaning; yet Γ, as defined by (3.3), remains a meaningful quantity. To this extent, the word "width" for Γ is misleading.

[2] We shall sometimes call Γ the decay rate, although it is really $\hbar \times$ (decay rate).

The magnitude Γ_β can also be defined as follows: If an assembly of N equal samples of the compound system C is arranged in such a way that, on the average, N stays constant in time (i.e., as many compound systems decay as are produced), then the number of decays into the channel β per unit time is given by $N\Gamma_\beta/\hbar$.

We can now express the branching probability in terms of the decay rates by the relation

$$G_C(\beta) = \frac{\Gamma_\beta}{\Gamma} \tag{3.5}$$

The assumption of the independence of the two processes, the creation and the disintegration of the compound system, makes it possible to derive a connection between the two magnitudes $\sigma_C(\alpha)$ and Γ_α which characterize the rate of two opposite processes (formation and disintegration of the compound nucleus through channel α). The connection is expressed by the following relation (Weisskopf 37, 40):

$$\frac{\sigma_C(\alpha)}{\lambda_\alpha^2 \Gamma_\alpha} = U(E_C) \tag{3.6}$$

where $U(E_C)$ is a function of the excitation energy of the compound nucleus only and *does not depend on channel α*.

Relation (3.6) can be derived from the reciprocity theorem (2.63) if we use the Bohr assumption (3.2) for $\sigma(\alpha,\beta)$ and expression (3.5) for $G_C(\beta)$. Equation (2.63) becomes

$$\frac{\sigma_C(\alpha)}{\Gamma_\alpha \lambda_\alpha^2} = \frac{\sigma_C(\beta)}{\Gamma_\beta \lambda_\beta^2} = U(E_C) \tag{3.7}$$

Since α and β can be any pair of channels which lead to the compound system C, the function $U(E_C)$ must be independent of the channel and we obtain (3.6). The probability $G_C(\beta)$ of the disintegration through a specific channel β can then be written in the form ($k = \lambda^{-1}$)

$$G_C(\beta) = \frac{k_\beta^2\, \sigma_C(\beta)}{\sum_\gamma k_\gamma^2\, \sigma_C(\gamma)} \tag{3.8}$$

where the sum is extended over all channels γ into which C can decay. Hence the cross section (3.2) for the reaction $\alpha \to \beta$ can be computed if the cross sections $\sigma_C(\gamma)$ for the formation of the compound system by all possible channels are known, and if the Bohr assumption is valid. All magnitudes involved in (3.8) are energy dependent. The value of $G_C(\beta)$ for a compound nucleus excited to an energy E_C is given by

(3.8) if the cross sections $\sigma_C(\gamma)$ and the wave numbers k_γ are taken for those channel energies ϵ_γ which produce the compound nucleus with an energy E_C. The same applies to $\sigma_C(\beta)$, k_β, and ϵ_β.

A few qualitative conclusions can be drawn without any detailed determination of the cross sections (Bethe 37, Konopinski 38). It is expected that $\sigma_C(\alpha)$ is, in general, much larger for neutrons than for protons or other charged particles, since the latter must penetrate the Coulomb potential barrier. Thus, according to (3.7), the neutron widths (i.e., the partial widths corresponding to channels with neutron emission) are larger than the proton or alpha-particle widths, except in the case in which the charged particle has much more kinetic energy at its disposal than the neutron. If a reaction with neutron emission is energetically possible, it is generally more likely to occur than any other reaction. Exceptions are found only just at the threshold of a reaction with neutron emission, when the neutron has very small energy. Thus, in reactions which are initiated by a particle a, the cross section $\sigma_C(\alpha)$ can be put approximately equal to the cross section $\sigma(a,n)$ of the (a,n) reaction:

$$\sigma(a,n) \cong \sigma_C(\alpha_0) \tag{3.9}$$

where α_0 is the entrance channel for which the target nucleus X is in its ground state.

4. DETERMINATION OF CROSS SECTIONS, CONTINUUM THEORY

We now proceed to derive an approximate value for the cross section $\sigma_C(\alpha)$ for the formation of the compound system. The method used greatly oversimplifies the actual situation. We do not take into account any individual properties of the nuclei concerned. Accordingly the results must be considered useful only as a first orientation regarding the orders of magnitude to be expected. We base our consideration on *three general assumptions regarding the structure of the nucleus:*

(1) The nucleus has a well-defined surface which is a sphere of radius R. The nuclear forces do not act between a and the nucleus if the distance between a and the center of the nucleus is larger than R.

(2) If the particle a penetrates the nuclear surface, it moves with an average kinetic energy T_{in}, which is much higher than its energy ϵ_α outside. In fact, $T_{in} = \epsilon_\alpha + T_0$, where T_0 is of the order of magnitude of the kinetic energy of intra-nuclear motion. We shall show in this section that $T_0 \sim 20$ Mev if a is a proton or a neutron, and somewhat less if it is an alpha-particle.

(3) Particle a is subject to very strong interactions inside the nucleus, so that it interchanges its energy rapidly with the other nucleons.

In this section we determine the cross section for the formation of the compound nucleus by a crude method (the "continuum theory") which is valid only for energies ϵ_a of at least several Mev. The cross sections obtained are independent of the quantum state or of any other special property of the target nucleus; in fact, they depend only on the type of the incident particle a (whether it is a neutron, proton, or alpha-particle, etc.), on the channel energy ϵ_a, and on the charge and the radius of the target nucleus.

In order to provide a first orientation, we shall derive the value of σ_C on the basis of classical mechanics, neglecting the wave properties of the incident beam. We assume that every particle hitting the nuclear surface will form a compound system. If the incident particle is a neutron $(Z_a = 0)$, the cross section for reaching the nuclear surface is evidently given by the classical "target area":

$$\sigma_C(n) = \pi R^2 \qquad (4.1)$$

In the case of charged particles, the incident beam is deviated by a potential $V(r) = Z_a Z_X e^2 / r$, and the particles reaching the nuclear surface are those whose closest distance of approach to the center would be smaller than R. A simple calculation leads to the following results:

$$\sigma_C(a) = \begin{cases} \pi R^2 \left[1 - \dfrac{V(R)}{\epsilon_\alpha} \right] & \epsilon_\alpha > V(R) \\ 0 & \epsilon_\alpha < V(R) \end{cases} \qquad (4.2)$$

Thus σ_C vanishes below the "barrier energy" $V(R) = Z_a Z_X e^2 / R$ and increases steadily above the barrier up to the asymptotic value πR^2.

We now proceed to a qualitative wave-mechanical discussion of these cross sections. The resulting corrections to the classical expressions (4.1) and (4.2) can be described in terms of two typical wave phenomena:

(A) The position of the particle is undefined within a wavelength λ. This can be approximately accounted for by replacing πR^2 with $\pi(R+\lambda)^2$, and by allowing a small penetration of the particle into the nucleus even if $\epsilon_\alpha < V(R)$.

(B) There is a sudden change of potential when the particle crosses the boundary of the nucleus; this change is caused by the fact that the particle enters into the range of the strongly attractive nuclear forces. The sudden change of potential gives rise to a reflection of the incoming wave at the nuclear surface. This reflection decreases the cross section, especially at low energy.

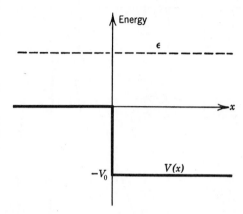

FIG. 4.1.   A sudden change of the potential (from 0 at $x<0$ to $-V_0$ at $x>0$) leads to a reflection from the discontinuity.   The transmission coefficient T is given by (4.3).   It approaches unity for $\epsilon \gg V_0$.

Let us illustrate the effect of this reflection with a simple calculation: A beam of particles of energy ϵ moves in the positive x direction in a potential $V(x)$ given by

$$V(x) = 0 \quad (\text{for } x<0) \qquad V(x) = -V_0 \quad (\text{for } x>0)$$

This potential is illustrated in Fig. 4.1.   The wave number of the particles is

$$k = \frac{(2M\epsilon)^{1/2}}{\hbar} \qquad (\text{for } x<0)$$

$$K = \frac{[2M(\epsilon+V_0)]^{1/2}}{\hbar} \qquad (\text{for } x>0)$$

The particles are partially reflected at $x=0$.   We determine the transmission coefficient T, which is defined as the ratio of the number of particles penetrating into the region $x>0$ to the number of incident particles.   The wave function $\psi(x)$ is given by

$$\psi(x) = \mathsf{A} \exp (ikx) + \mathsf{B} \exp (-ikx) \qquad (\text{for } x<0)$$

$$\psi(x) = \mathsf{C} \exp (+iKx) \qquad (\text{for } x>0)$$

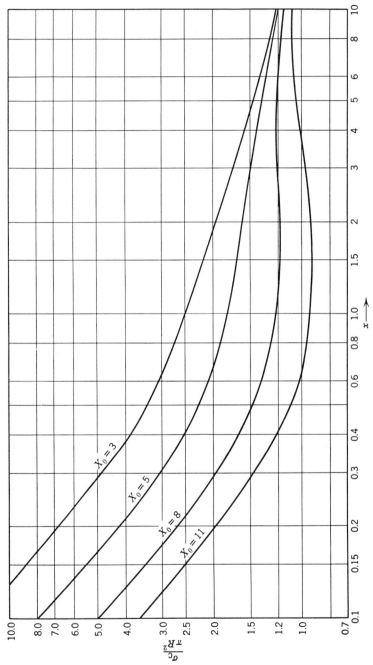

FIG. 4.2. Cross section for the formation of the compound nucleus by neutrons. The abscissa is $x = kR = 0.218\epsilon^{1/2}R$ if ϵ is given in Mev, R in 10^{-13} cm. $X_0 = K_0R$ and is roughly equal to the nuclear radius in units of 10^{-13} cm.

and T is given by

$$\mathsf{T} = \frac{|A|^2 - |B|^2}{|A|^2}$$

By equating the value and the derivative of $\psi(x)$ at $x = 0$, we get

$$\mathsf{T} = \frac{4kK}{(K + k)^2} \tag{4.3}$$

The transmission coefficient T is especially small if $k \ll K$ (at low energies) and approaches unity for high energies ($k \cong K$).

We may consider T an approximate expression for the transmission coefficient of a neutron beam into the nucleus. Combining effects (A) and (B), we get a rough expression for the cross section $\sigma_C(n)$ for formation of the compound nucleus C by neutron bombardment:

$$\sigma_C(n) \cong \pi (R + \lambda)^2 \frac{4kK}{(k + K)^2} \tag{4.4}$$

where K is a wave number which is of the order of magnitude of those occurring within the nucleus ($K \sim 1.0 \times 10^{+13}$ cm^{-1}; see p. 355). While (4.4) is more accurate than the classical approximation (4.1), it is still only a rough interpolation formula. More accurate values of $\sigma_C(n)$ will be derived later on; the results are shown in Figure 4.2.

The cross section (4.4) approaches the classical value πR^2 at high energies, and increases with decreasing energy, but less strongly than $\pi(R + \lambda)^2$, because of the reflection mentioned above in (B). $\sigma_C(n)$ is proportional to $\epsilon^{-1/2}$ at low energies ($\lambda \gg R$). This is the well-known $1/v$ law of neutron absorption, which can be explained as follows: If the wavelength of the neutron becomes large compared with the size of the nucleus, the absorption probability of the neutron wave by the nucleus can depend only on the probability density $I = |\psi|^2$, and no longer on the neutron wavelength, the latter being essentially infinite. Thus the number of absorbed neutrons is proportional to I; the number of incident neutrons per unit area per second, however, is proportional to vI, so that the cross section becomes proportional to $1/v$.

No simple approximate expression like (4.4) can be written for charged particles. Table 4.1 gives the result of the numerical calculation, and Fig. 4.3 illustrates an example. For incident energies ϵ_α above the barrier $V(R)$, we can use the following crude improvement of the classical expression (4.2):

$$\sigma_C \cong \pi \, (R + \lambda)^2 \left[1 - \frac{V(R+\lambda)}{\epsilon_\alpha} \right] \qquad (4.5)$$

It reproduces the calculated values within 15 percent for $\epsilon_\alpha / V(R) > 1.2$. We now proceed to a *wave-mechanical calculation of the cross sections.* We intend to use for this purpose expressions (2.55) to (2.58) by which the scattering and the reaction cross sections are expressed in terms of the logarithmic derivatives f_l at the nuclear surface in the subchannel with angular momentum l.   The functions

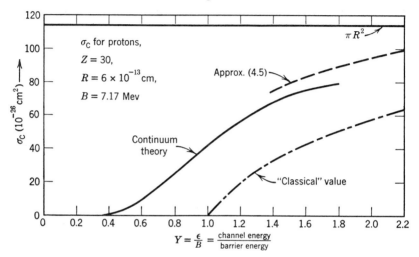

FIG. 4.3.   An example of the cross section for formation of the compound nucleus by protons.   The solid curve represents the best theoretical value, the broken curve represents the approximation (4.5), and the dot-and-dash curve represents the classical value (4.2).   The asymptotic value, πR^2, is also shown.

f_l depend on the conditions inside the nucleus, and we shall derive approximate expressions for f_l from assumptions regarding the interior of the nucleus.

In addition to the three basic assumptions listed at the beginning of this section, we shall now make a fourth assumption (Feshbach 49a):[1]

(4) The number of open channels is very large.

This assumption, unlike the preceding three, is peculiar to the continuum theory of nuclear reactions, and it will be dropped later on in this chapter.   Condition (4) is fulfilled when the incident energy ϵ_α is much higher than the first few excitation energies of the target

[1] A somewhat different assumption, which also leads to a continuum theory of nuclear reactions, was made by Bethe (40).

nucleus. For not too light target nuclei ($A > 50$), this condition is fulfilled for, say, $\epsilon_\alpha > 3$ Mev. It may also be fulfilled for lower energies if the incident particle produces some reaction with a large positive Q value ($Q > 3$ Mev).

Under these conditions we expect that the nuclear particle a which approaches the target nucleus in channel α is very unlikely to reappear in the entrance channel α once it has penetrated into the inside of the nucleus. It may well be reflected back into the entrance channel α at the surface; once inside the surface, however, it exchanges its energy rapidly with the other nucleons, and the chance that it leaves the nucleus by the same channel α is very small if many other channels are available.

We also use the fact that the entering nucleon moves with a high kinetic energy inside, and we assume that the wave function in the entrance channel α would have roughly the form of an *ingoing* wave only (since it does not return):

$$u_l \sim \exp{(-iKr)} \qquad (r < R) \tag{4.6}$$

Here K is a wave number of the order of those that occur when a particle enters the nucleus. Since the logarithmic derivative of u_l must be continuous at $r = R$, comparison with (2.45) gives *the fundamental assumption of the continuum theory of nuclear reactions:*

$$f_l = -iKR \tag{4.7}$$

(independently of l).

It must be emphasized that (4.6) is only a very rough approximation. It is impossible to represent the motion of the incident particle inside the nucleus as a function of r only. Since it is in strong interaction with all other nucleons, (4.6) expresses the fact that nucleons possess on the average a kinetic energy which gives rise to the wave number K, and that they move inward only. It represents the main features of the dependence of the wave function on r, and it will be used only to give an estimate for the logarithmic derivative f.

We shall call this method of determining the cross sections the "continuum theory," because it will not reproduce nuclear resonances. A description of the behavior of $u_l(r)$ for $r < R$ which is different from (4.6) is necessary to extend the considerations to lower energies (see Section 7) where the return of the particle into the entrance channel can no longer be neglected.

Equations (2.55) to (2.58) can now be used to calculate the cross sections. Because of our assumption that particle a is not re-emitted by the compound nucleus into the entrance channel, the reaction

TABLE

THE CROSS SECTION σ_C FOR THE FORMATION OF A COMPOUND NUCLEUS C

The energy ϵ of the incident particle in the center-of-gravity system is measured given by $R = r_0 A^{1/3} + \rho$, where A is the mass number of the target nucleus and given in units of 10^{-26} cm^2. The numbers in parentheses indicate negative powers approximated by the asymptotic formula

$$\sigma_C \cong \pi (R + \lambda)^2 \left[1 - \right.$$

Protons: $r_0 = 1.3 \times 10^{-13}$ cm

Y \ Z	10	20	30	40	50	60	70	80	90
0.2	1.02	56 (3)	40 (4)	39.3(5)	49 (6)	75 (7)	10.3(7)	16.6(8)	30.8(9)
0.3	4.50	78 (2)	15.6(2)	38.8(3)	10.1(4)	30.4(4)	92 (5)	29.5(5)	10.8(5)
0.4	10.3	28.4(1)	11.1(1)	48 (2)	22.6(2)	10.6(2)	48 (3)	23.0(3)	11.7(3)
0.5	16.7	77 (1)	41 (1)	23.1(1)	14.6(1)	91 (2)	56 (2)	36.1(2)	23.6(2)
0.6	20.8	12.7	89 (1)	65 (1)	48 (1)	38 (1)	29 (1)	21.8(1)	16.8(1)
0.7	25.6	18.6	15.4	13.2	11.4	98 (1)	84 (1)	74 (1)	64 (1)
0.8	28.2	24.0	22.2	20.9	19.7	18.3	17.5	16.9	16.2
0.9	31.0	28.5	28.7	28.5	28.6	27.9	27.6	27.4	27.3
1.0	33.4	33.3	35	36	36.9	37	39	39.6	39.9
1.1	35.4	37.1	41	43	45	46	48	50	53
1.2	37.6	40	45	49	52	55	59	61	64
1.3	40	43	49	53	59	62	67	70	74
1.4	42	46	53	58	65	69	75	80	83
1.5	45	49	56	63	70	75	81	87	91
1.6	47	51	59	66	74	79	86	93	98
1.7	50	53	61	69	77	83	91	99	104
1.8	53	54	62	71	80	87	96	104	110
B(Mev)	4.06	6.45	8.28	9.85	11.20	12.6	14.0	15.2	16.3

Protons: $r_0 = 1.5 \times 10^{-13}$ cm

Y \ Z	10	20	30	40	50	60	70	80	90
0.2	74 (2)	32.3(3)	17.9(4)	14.7(5)	14.7(6)	20.3(7)	29.2(8)	38.3(9)	59 (10)
0.3	37 (1)	59 (2)	10.6(2)	23.2(3)	57 (4)	15.0(4)	47 (5)	14.0(5)	45 (6)
0.4	10.2	28.1(1)	96 (2)	38.5(2)	15.4(2)	70 (3)	32 (3)	15.2(3)	75 (4)
0.5	16.3	76 (1)	38.5(1)	21.3(1)	12.3(1)	76 (2)	47 (2)	28.6(2)	17.5(2)
0.6	22.0	12.6	91 (1)	66 (1)	48 (1)	35.4(1)	26 (1)	22 (1)	17.2(1)
0.7	27.1	20.7	17.2	14.3	12.0	10.2	87 (1)	75 (1)	65 (1)
0.8	31.3	27.4	25.4	24.0	22.3	20.9	19.3	18.3	16.9
0.9	35	33.6	33.8	33.4	33.1	32.6	32.2	32.0	32.8
1.0	39	39	42	43	44	45	46	48	46
1.1	42	45	50	52	55	58	61	63	64
1.2	46	50	56	60	65	68	72	76	79
1.3	49	55	62	67	74	78	83	88	93
1.4	52	58	67	74	81	88	94	100	105
1.5	56	62	72	79	87	97	103	110	116
1.6	59	64	75	84	93	103	111	119	127
1.7	61	67	77	88	97	108	117	124	137
1.8	64	68	78	90	101	112	122	128	145
B(Mev)	3.55	5.60	7.17	8.55	9.70	11.0	12.10	13.1	14.15

4.1

BY CHARGED-PARTICLE BOMBARDMENT, AS A FUNCTION OF THE ENERGY ϵ
by $Y = \epsilon/B$, where $B = Z_a Z_X e^2/R$ is the barrier height. The effective radius R is
$\rho = 0$ for protons, $\rho = 1.2 \times 10^{-13}$ cm for alpha-particles. The cross section σ_C is
of 10, e.g., $39(5) = 39 \times 10^{-5}$. For values of $Y \gg 1$ the cross section σ_C can be

$$\left. \frac{R}{(R+\lambda)\,Y} \right] \quad (Y \gg 1)$$

		Alpha-particles: $r_0 = 1.3 \times 10^{-13}$ cm				
Y \ Z	10	20	30	50	70	90
0.2	75 (6)	18.7(10)	52 (14)	93 (20)	54 (25)	29 (29)
0.3	28.5(4)	11.5(6)	10.7(8)	81 (12)	18 (15)	43 (18)
0.4	84 (3)	23.8(4)	11.0(5)	57 (8)	50 (10)	97 (12)
0.5	71 (2)	64 (3)	12.8(3)	28.0(5)	16.5(6)	11.5(7)
0.6	24.9(1)	61 (2)	18.2(2)	22.9(3)	37 (4)	68 (5)
0.7	65 (1)	27.7(1)	14.1(1)	39 (2)	15.1(2)	79 (3)
0.8	11.2	75 (1)	54 (1)	30.3(1)	18.9(1)	11.8(1)
0.9	16.8	13.9	12.4	11.2	97 (1)	85 (1)
1.0	21.8	20.9	20.9	21.3	21.2	21.5
1.1	26.7	27.7	29.3	32.6	36	38
1.2	31.3	34	38	44	49	53
1.3	36	39	45	54	60	67
1.4	39	44	51	62	71	81
1.5	42	49	56	70	81	93
1.6	44	53	61	77	90	105
1.7	46	56	66	84	98	113
1.8	47	59	70	89	105	120
B(Mev)	6.10	10.20	13.50	18.9	23.9	28.2
		Alpha-particles: $r_0 = 1.5 \times 10^{-13}$ cm				
0.2	79 (7)	28.6(11)	76 (15)	64 (21)	34 (26)	44 (31)
0.3	17.9(4)	54 (6)	37 (8)	62 (13)	36 (16)	35 (19)
0.4	61 (3)	15.6(4)	59 (6)	12.3(8)	63 (10)	42 (12)
0.5	59 (2)	51 (3)	63 (4)	14.8(5)	81 (7)	46 (8)
0.6	24.7(1)	56 (2)	15.6(2)	17.3(3)	24.9(4)	42 (5)
0.7	67 (1)	27.9(1)	13.8(1)	39 (2)	13.2(2)	46 (3)
0.8	12.5	81 (1)	58 (1)	32.3(1)	19.4(1)	12.1(1)
0.9	19.2	15.9	14.3	94 (1)	10.3	12.3
1.0	25.6	24.5	24.8	25.1	25.4	25.7
1.1	31.6	33	36	40	42	45
1.2	37	40	46	53	60	66
1.3	42	47	55	65	76	85
1.4	46	53	63	76	89	103
1.5	50	58	70	86	101	117
1.6	53	63	76	95	113	130
1.7	55	68	81	103	123	142
1.8	57	72	86	111	131	153
B(Mev)	5.6	9.1	11.9	16.5	21.2	24.9

cross section σ_r is here identical with the cross section $\sigma_C(\alpha)$ for the formation of the compound nucleus. Hence we can calculate the latter by inserting (4.7) into (2.58):

$$\sigma_C(\alpha) = \pi \,\lambdabar^2 \sum_{l=0}^{\infty} (2l + 1) \frac{4\, s_l \, KR}{\Delta_l^2 + (KR + s_l)^2} \qquad (4.8)$$

The value of K is the only information about the inside of the nucleus which enters into this expression.

The $l=0$ (S wave) part of this expression is particularly simple for neutrons ($\Delta_0 = 0$, $s_0 = kR$):

$$\sigma_{C,0} = \pi \,\lambdabar^2 \frac{4kK}{(k + K)^2} \qquad \text{(neutrons, } l=0\text{)} \qquad (4.9)$$

and can be directly interpreted as the product of the maximum cross section $\pi\lambdabar^2$ and the transmission T as given in (4.3).

The scattering cross section is found by substitution of (4.7) into (2.55), (2.56), and (2.57). It is

$$\sigma_{sc} = \pi \,\lambdabar^2 \sum_{l=0}^{\infty} (2l+1) \left| \frac{2\, i\, s_l}{\Delta_l + i\,(KR+s_l)} + \exp(-2i\xi_l) - 1 \right|^2 \qquad (4.10)$$

The scattering cross section is determined by two effects: the reflection of the incoming wave at the nuclear surface because of the sudden change of wavelength in going from the outside to the inside, and the reflection of the wave at the barrier outside the nuclear surface. These two effects are coherent and therefore cannot be distinguished precisely in the result (4.10). A third possible source of elastic scattering does *not* contribute to (4.10): the compound nucleus, once formed, could in principle decay again into channel α, thereby giving a third contribution to the elastic scattering. However, this contribution has been explicitly excluded by the assumptions of the continuum theory of nuclear reactions. While these three contributions to the elastic scattering process are coherent and can therefore not be distinguished from each other rigorously, it is very important to keep in mind this qualitative breakup into three effects. Indeed, the main difference between the continuum theory and the theory of resonance reactions is directly related to this point (see Section 7).

We must now estimate the wave number K which appears in our expressions. K was defined as the wave number of the wave after it has penetrated the nuclear surface, and its value depends on the type of the particle and on the channel by which it enters the nucleus. Inside the nuclear surface, the wave function of particle a can no longer be expressed as a function of its own coordinates only, and the wave number K of this particle has only qualitative significance. We determine K from the kinetic energy $T_{in} = \hbar^2 K^2 / 2M$ corresponding to this wave number and equate T_{in} to the average kinetic energy of particle a after entering the nucleus.

Let us first assume that particle a is a nucleon (a proton or a neutron). In order to get an approximate idea of the magnitude of K, we estimate the kinetic energies of nucleons inside the nucleus by the same method as in Chapter III, Section 4. The average kinetic energy $\bar{T}$ for a nucleus with radius R containing A particles is given by (III,4.16). However, we must not equate this *average* value to A times the kinetic energy of a particle which is just entering the nucleus from outside. According to the Pauli exclusion principle, the entering nucleon cannot go into any of the filled levels but must assume an energy which corresponds to the top of the Fermi distribution, i.e., its kinetic energy is of the order of ϵ', (III,4.14). Comparison of (III,4.14) with (III,4.14a) gives (with $R = r_0 A^{1/3}$)

$$\frac{2M\epsilon'}{\hbar^2} = \left(\frac{9\pi}{8}\right)^{2/3} \frac{1}{r_0^2} \equiv K_0^2 \tag{4.11}$$

We shall assume that this is the order of magnitude of the wave number of the nucleon a inside the nucleus if it did not carry any kinetic energy with it originally, i.e., if it entered the nucleus with a channel energy $\epsilon \ll \epsilon'$. On the other hand, if its channel energy ϵ is appreciable, we shall assume that the kinetic energy of the entering particle just inside the nuclear surface is the sum of ϵ' (the kinetic energy which it would have if it entered without appreciable channel energy) and its channel energy ϵ outside the nuclear surface. This gives the following expression for the wave number K of the entering nucleon just inside the nuclear surface:

$$K = (K_0^2 + k^2)^{1/2} \tag{4.12}$$

where K_0 is as defined by (4.11) and k is the wave number of the incident particle outside the nucleus. The wave number K_0 does not depend on the number A of nucleons (because of the assumption of constant nuclear density) and is approximately the same for all nuclei. Using $r_0 = 1.5 \times 10^{-13}$ cm, we obtain

$$K_0 \cong 1 \times 10^{13} \text{ cm}^{-1} \quad \text{(for incident nucleons)} \tag{4.13}$$

It is much harder to obtain an estimate for K_0 in case of incident

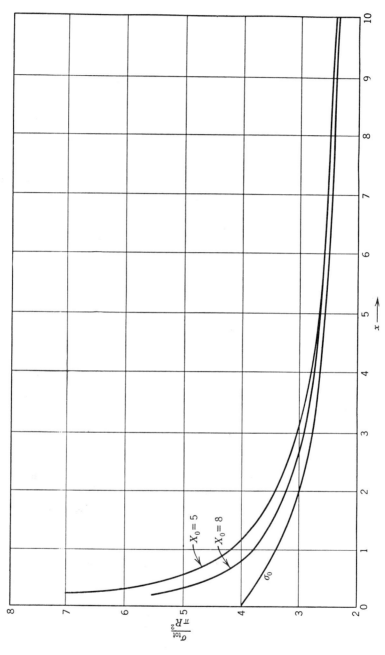

FIG. 4.4.   For descriptive legend see opposite page.

alpha-particles or deuterons. It is perhaps reasonable to assume K_0 to be of the order of the reciprocal of the distances between nucleons within a nucleus. We therefore put tentatively also

$$K_0 \sim 1 \times 10^{13} \text{ cm}^{-1} \qquad \text{(for alpha-particles and deuterons)} \qquad (4.14)$$

The cross sections σ_C evaluated on the basis of (4.8) are found for neutrons in Fig. 4.2; and for protons as well as for alpha-particles in Table 4.1. The value of K_0 enters only in the combination $X_0 = K_0 R$. The neutron curves for $X_0 = 5,7,9$ correspond to elements with a radius of about 5×10^{-13} cm (chlorine), 7×10^{-13} cm (silver), and 9×10^{-13} cm (uranium), respectively. The cross sections for charged particles are given in Table 4.1. In this table two different values of the nuclear radius $R = r_0 A^{1/3}$ have been used: $r_0 = 1.3 \times 10^{-13}$ cm and $r_0 = 1.5 \times 10^{-13}$ cm. The cross sections are quite sensitive to the choice of radius.

In the case of alpha-particles (but *not* of incident nucleons), the channel radius R is the sum of the radius of the target nucleus and the particle radius ρ:

$$R = r_0 A^{1/3} + \rho \qquad (4.15)$$

For the computations of Table 4.1 the particle radius chosen for the alpha-particle was $\rho = 1.2 \times 10^{-13}$ cm. The choice of this value of ρ is rather arbitrary. Our choice is somewhat smaller than the radius of the alpha-particle ($= 2.3 \times 10^{-13}$ cm, according to Bashkin 50). It can be argued that the repulsive Coulomb force is still acting, even when the alpha-particle is partially immersed in the target nucleus, so that ρ should be smaller than the actual radius of the alpha-particle. The above choice of ρ leads to similar values for the radii in determina-

---

FIG. 4.4. Total cross section for neutrons. The abscissa is $x = kR$, where k is the wave number of the neutron (in the center-of-gravity system) and R is the nuclear radius; in terms of the neutron energy ϵ, x is given by $x = 0.218 R \epsilon^{1/2}$, where ϵ is in Mev and R is in 10^{-13} cm. The ordinate is the total cross section, $\sigma_t = \sigma_r + \sigma_{sc} = \sigma_C + \sigma_{sc}$, in units of the cross-sectional area of the nucleus, πR^2. The two upper curves refer to two different values of $X_0 = K_0 R \cong R$ in 10^{-13} cm. The lower curve, labeled σ_0, is drawn in purely for purposes of comparison. σ_0 is the cross section for a perfectly reflecting sphere. We see that at high energies ($kR > 4$) the total cross section is not sensitive to the value of K_0 and is not very different from the cross section for the reflecting sphere (which corresponds to a value of $K_0 = \infty$). Thus the value of the total cross section at high energies can be used to determine the nuclear radius R, but not the "interior" wave number K_0. We also call attention to the fact that the ultimate asymptotic value $\sigma_t = 2\pi R^2$ is approached only very slowly and is *not* a good approximation for neutron energies below 50 Mev. (σ_{tot} in the figure stands for σ_t.)

tions with neutrons and charged particles (see Chapter XI, Section 4) and therefore can be considered a semi-empirical value.

The elastic scattering cross section as given by (4.10) is of interest mainly in the case of neutrons. For charged particles the Coulomb scattering is the dominant part of the elastic scattering and is not of any nuclear interest. Figure 4.4 shows the total cross section $\sigma_t = \sigma_C + \sigma_{sc}$ as a function of energy for neutrons. It is seen that σ_t reaches the asymptotic value $2\pi R^2$ (see p. 324) only at very high energies. For energies below 50 Mev, it is appreciably larger than $2\pi R^2$.

The theory also gives the angular distribution of the elastically scattered neutrons. In the limit of $R \gg \lambda$ the scattering is mostly forward. It is the scattering due to the shadow, as discussed on page 324, and is therefore confined to an angle θ of the order λ/R. Its angular distribution was first derived by Bethe and Placzek (Bethe 37a). They proved that the cross section for the scattering into a solid angle element $d\Omega$ in the direction θ is given by

$$d\sigma_{sc}(\theta) \cong R^2 \left| \frac{J_1(R\theta/\lambda)}{\theta} \right|^2 d\Omega \qquad (4.16)$$

provided $\theta \gg 1$ and $\lambda \ll R$.

5. TRANSMISSION OF POTENTIAL BARRIERS

The cross section for formation of the compound nucleus through the channel α, (4.8), is a sum of terms, each of which corresponds to a definite orbital angular momentum l of the incident particles:

$$\sigma_C(\alpha) = \sum_{l=0}^{\infty} \sigma_{Cl}(\alpha)$$

Each of these partial formation cross sections can be interpreted in the following way. We write

$$\sigma_{Cl}(\alpha) = (2l+1)\pi\lambda^2 T_l(\alpha) \qquad (5.1)$$

and call $T_l(\alpha)$ the transmission coefficient for particle a in channel α. The cross section appears then as the product of the maximum possible cross section [see (2.4)] and the transmission coefficient.

Since the transmission coefficient $T_l(\alpha)$ is of great importance in other connections, we shall derive its value directly from the shape of the potential which acts on particle a in channel α. Let us consider particles with a given angular momentum l in channel α. The effective potential $U_l(r)$ outside the nucleus is given by

$$U_l(r) = V(r) + \frac{\hbar^2 l(l+1)}{2Mr^2} \qquad \text{(for } r > R) \qquad (5.2)$$

Here the first term is the Coulomb potential and the second one is the "centrifugal" potential which appears in the wave equation if it is reduced to the one-dimensional form (2.30). Both effects prevent the particle from entering or leaving the nucleus. We shall call the first the potential barrier, and the second the centrifugal barrier. Although it is impossible to describe by a potential the forces acting on the particle inside the nucleus, we get an *approximate* description by assuming a potential for $r < R$ which would give rise to the wave number K:

$$U_l(r) \cong -U_0 = -\frac{\hbar^2 K_0{}^2}{2M} \qquad \text{(for } r < R) \qquad (5.3)$$

The transmission coefficient $T_l(\alpha)$ gives the fraction of particles incident from $r = +\infty$ which penetrate into the region $r < R$. We therefore calculate the transmission of the potential barrier given by (5.2) and (5.3) and sketched in Fig. 5.1. We assume that this is a one-dimensional problem where the coordinate r runs from $-\infty$ to $+\infty$. A beam is incident from $r = +\infty$ toward $r = 0$ and is partially reflected by the potential; partially it penetrates into the region $r < R$, and proceeds toward $r = -\infty$. Actually, of course, the particles which reach the region $r < R$ amalgamate with the other nucleons and form the compound nucleus. For the sake of a simple one-dimensional calculation, we assume that the beam, once past the potential discontinuity at $r = R$, proceeds undisturbed toward $r = -\infty$.

We therefore write the wave function $u_l(r)$ for $r > R$ as a solution of (2.30) in the form

$$u_l = a u_l{}^{(-)}(r) - b u_l{}^{(+)}(r) \qquad \text{(for } r > R)$$

and for $r < R$ as a traveling wave with a wave number K,

$$u_l = c \exp(-iKr) \qquad \text{(for } r < R)$$

Here $u_l{}^{(+)}$ and $u_l{}^{(-)}$ are the solutions of (2.30) defined by (2.41), and K is given by (4.12). The transmission coefficient is $1 - |b/a|^2$, since $|a^2|$ is the incident and $|b^2|$ the reflected intensity. By equating the value and the first derivative of u_l at $r = R$, we get

$$\frac{b}{a} = \frac{\Delta_l - is_l + iKR}{\Delta_l + is_l + iKR} \exp(2i\xi_l) \qquad (5.4)$$

and thus

$$T_l(\alpha) = \frac{4s_l K R}{\Delta_l{}^2 + (s_l + KR)^2} \tag{5.5}$$

where Δ_l and s_l are defined by (2.46).

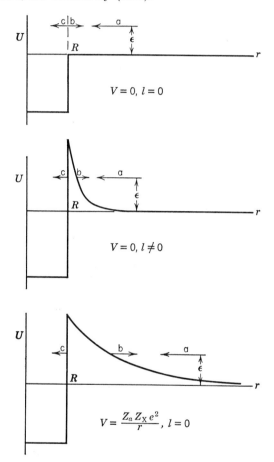

$V = 0,\ l = 0$

$V = 0,\ l \neq 0$

$V = \dfrac{Z_a Z_X e^2}{r},\ l = 0$

FIG. 5.1. Potential barriers: a is the amplitude of the incident beam; b is the amplitude of the reflected beam; c is the amplitude of the transmitted beam.

Even if there is no potential $U(r)$ for $r > R$, as for neutrons with $l = 0$, the transmission coefficient is not unity. For then $\Delta_0 = 0$ and $s_0 = kR$ so that we get the expression (4.3) derived before.

For not too high energies ($k \ll K$), s_l and Δ_l are both small compared to KR. Equation (5.5) then reduces to the following approximate expression [v_l is defined by (2.49) and (2.50)]:

$$T_l(\alpha) \cong \frac{4k}{K} v_l \quad \text{(for } k \ll K) \tag{5.6}$$

It should be noted that the transmission coefficients $T_l(\alpha)$ are independent of the direction of motion. If there were a source of particles in the center of the nucleus, some of the particles would be reflected on reaching the surface from the inside. The ratio between the flux transmitted to the outside and the flux incident on the surface from the inside also would be given by $T_l(\alpha)$.

Expressions for $T_l(\alpha)$ can be calculated exactly for neutrons by using (2.39) and (2.40), together with definitions (2.47) and (2.48) and relation (2.50). We also introduce the definitions

$$x \equiv kR \qquad X \equiv KR$$

$$v_l' \equiv k^{-2} \left[\left(\frac{dG_l}{dr} \right)^2 + \left(\frac{dF_l}{dr} \right)^2 \right]$$

to get the following form for $T_l(\alpha)$, (5.5):

$$T_l(\alpha) = \frac{4\, x\, X\, v_l}{X^2 + (2xX + x^2 v_l')\, v_l} \qquad \text{(neutrons)} \tag{5.7}$$

For small values of l the functions v_l and v_l' are given by

$$v_0 = 1 \qquad\qquad\qquad v_0' = 1$$

$$v_1 = \frac{x^2}{1+x^2} \qquad\qquad v_1' = \frac{1}{x^2} + \left(1 - \frac{1}{x^2}\right)^2$$

$$v_2 = \frac{x^4}{9+3x^2+x^4} \qquad v_2' = \left(1 - \frac{6}{x^2}\right)^2 + \left(\frac{6}{x^3} - \frac{3}{x^2}\right)^2 \tag{5.8}$$

$$v_3 = \frac{x^6}{225+45x^2+6x^4+x^6} \qquad v_3' = \left(1 - \frac{21}{x^2} + \frac{45}{x^4}\right)^2 + \left(\frac{45}{x^3} - \frac{6}{x}\right)^2$$

whereas for very large l the asymptotic forms of v_l and v_l' are

$$v_l \cong \frac{x^{2l}}{[(2l-1)!!]^2} \qquad v_l' \cong \frac{l^2\,[(2l-1)!!]^2}{x^{2l+2}} \tag{5.8'}$$

Expressions (5.8') are valid provided that $x \ll l$. The functions v_l and v_l' are tabulated by Feshbach and Lax (Lax 48).

The calculation of the transmission coefficient $T_l(\alpha)$ is more involved for the case of charged particles. The functions $F_l(x)$ and $G_l(x)$ are difficult to tabulate because they depend on two parameters [x and the charge parameter γ, (2.34)]. One sometimes makes use of the

W.K.B. approximation method, but it should be realized that the W.K.B. approximation is *not very accurate*. This approximation leads to the results

$$
\left.
\begin{array}{l}
s_l(kR) \cong R\,\kappa_l(R) \\
\Delta_l(kR) \cong -\tfrac{1}{2}R[\kappa'(R)/\kappa(R)]
\end{array}
\right\}
\qquad \text{for } U_l(R) < \frac{\hbar^2 k^2}{2M}
$$

$$
\left.
\begin{array}{l}
s_l(kR) \cong R\,\kappa_l(R)\,\exp\left[-2\int_R^{r_0}\kappa_l(r)\,dr\right] \\
\Delta_l(kR) \cong -R[\kappa(R)+\tfrac{1}{2}\kappa'(R)/\kappa(R)]
\end{array}
\right\}
\qquad \text{for } U_l(R) > \frac{\hbar^2 k^2}{2M}
$$

(5.9)

where $\kappa_l(r)$ is the function

$$
\kappa_l(r) \equiv \left(\left|k^2 - \frac{2M}{\hbar^2}\,U_l(r)\right|\right)^{\!\frac{1}{2}}
\tag{5.9'}
$$

$\kappa'(R)$ is its derivative, and r_0 is the classical distance of closest approach for particles of angular momentum $l\hbar$, given by

$$
\kappa_l(r_0) = 0
$$

We emphasize again that the approximation formulas (5.9) sometimes differ from the accurate values even by one or more orders of magni-

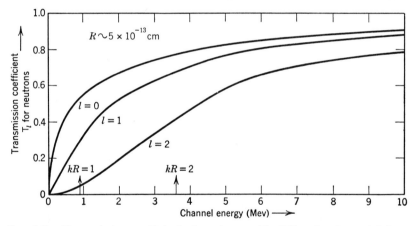

FIG. 5.2. Transmission coefficient of neutrons with different values of l for a nucleus of radius 5×10^{-13} cm. The arrows at the abscissa indicate the energies for which $kR=1$ and $kR=2$. In general, T_l for neutrons approaches unity for $kR \gg l$.

tude, especially if the energy is far below the barrier. Tables of F_l and G_l for charged particles, based on the exact formulas, are given by Bloch (51a).

In order to illustrate the general behavior of these quantities, in Fig. 5.2 we have plotted $\mathsf{T}_l(\alpha)$ against the neutron energy for incident neutrons for various values of l and for a nuclear radius $R = 5 \times 10^{-13}$ cm. Similar curves for protons and a nuclear radius $R = 4.5 \times 10^{-13}$ cm are shown in Fig. 5.3. The particle energy which corresponds to the barrier height is marked with an arrow for each curve. We call attention to the fact that the transmission coefficient $T_l(\alpha)$ is by no means equal to unity at the barrier height. The angular momentum barrier is only subsidiary for charged particles below the barrier height, since the centrifugal potential with its r^{-2} dependence presents a much "thinner" barrier to the protons than the Coulomb repulsion, which is proportional to r^{-1}.

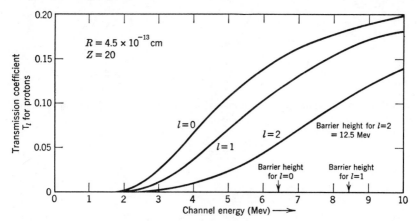

FIG. 5.3. Transmission coefficient of protons with different values of l for a nucleus of radius $R = 4.5 \times 10^{-13}$ and a charge $Z = 20$. The arrows denote the points where the channel energy equals the height of potential barrier. Notice that T_l is appreciably smaller than unity at these points.

For qualitative purposes, a nuclear reaction can be visualized by analogy with a wave guide junction, pictured in Fig. 5.4. The channels are represented by wave guides leading into a common "junction" (the compound nucleus). For neutron channels with $l = 0$ there is no reflection in the wave guides themselves, but there is reflection at the point where the wave in the guide encounters the entrance to the central cavity. In engineering language, this reflection is said to be due to an impedance mismatch (i.e., $f \neq -ikR$, in our terminology). Since the wavelength inside the compound nucleus, K^{-1}, is appreciably shorter than the outside wavelength, k^{-1}, we can represent this impedance mismatch at $r = R$ by letting the incident wave go from a narrow wave guide to a wide opening leading into the cavity itself. This is shown on the figure.

If there is a barrier in one of the channels, the wavelength in the channel is not constant. Rather, the wavelength increases continually as we proceed from infinity farther into the barrier region. If the barrier height exceeds the channel energy ϵ_α, a point is reached where the wave guide "cuts off"; i.e., it becomes so narrow that no traveling wave can propagate at the frequency (energy) in question. Only an exponentially damped wave proceeds farther to reach the cavity itself, in complete analogy with the quantum-mechanical picture of a reaction. This is shown schematically in Fig. 5.5. Channel β has still been assumed to be a neutron channel with $l = 0$, but the other two channels contain barriers and therefore have decreasing diameter (longer channel wavelength) as they get closer to the junction.

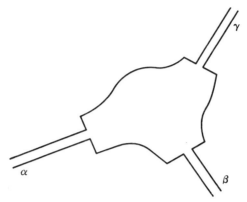

Fig. 5.4. Wave guide junction analogy of a nuclear reaction without potential barriers.

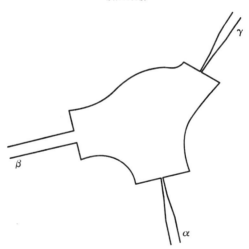

Fig. 5.5. Wave guide junction analogy of a nuclear reaction with potential barriers in channels α and γ.

The reflected wave in that channel through which an incoming wave is sent, α for instance, is due to three causes:

(1) Part of the wave is reflected because of the constriction of the wave guide (the barrier).

(2) There is reflection because of the impedance mismatch at the entrance to the cavity (at $r = R$).

(3) The remainder of the incoming wave then enters the cavity. The cavity

is excited and proceeds to send out waves into all the channels α, β, γ $\cdots$, i.e., in particular also back into channel α itself. This gives a third contribution to the reflected wave in channel α.

In the treatment of nuclear reactions given so far we have neglected this third contribution altogether. The continuum theory of nuclear reactions assumes that there are so many open channels through which the compound nucleus can disintegrate (so many different wave guides leading out of the junction in our figure) that the wave sent back from the cavity into the initial channel has an entirely negligible amplitude (assumption 4). The reflected wave in channel α is then due entirely to the first two contributions, and we can calculate it if we know the properties of the barrier and the amount of impedance mismatch (the ratio of internal to external wave number, K/k) at the entrance to the junction.

Effects (1) and (2) above are not exactly additive. The reflection coefficient in a channel with barrier cannot be written as the product of a barrier reflection coefficient and a reflection coefficient for the impedance mismatch, except as a first approximation. This first approximation is given by formula (5.6): the factor v_l is the reflection coefficient of the barrier, assuming no impedance mismatch at $r = R$; the factor $4k/K$ is the reflection coefficient of the impedance mismatch at $r = R$, assuming no barrier in the guide. Comparison of (5.6) with the exact expression (5.5) shows that this approximate separation of the two kinds of reflection is possible only if both s_l and Δ_l are small compared to KR.

6. THE DECAY OF THE COMPOUND NUCLEUS

A. Competition; Evaporation Model

We discuss in this section the processes occurring *after* the formation of the compound nucleus. On the basis of our assumptions, the probability that the compound nucleus C decays into channel β is given by (3.8) and therefore can be determined from the cross sections σ_C.

We first study the energy distribution of the emitted particles. The kinetic energy in channel β is given by (1.6). Since most of this energy is the kinetic energy of the emitted particle b, and only a small part is the recoil energy of the residual nucleus Y, we consider ϵ_β the kinetic energy of b. We write here

$$\epsilon_\beta = \epsilon_{bY} - E_\beta{}^* \tag{6.1}$$

where ϵ_{bY} is given by (1.10) and represents the maximum value of ϵ_β, which occurs if the residual nucleus Y remains in its ground state. $E_\beta{}^*$ is the excitation energy of Y after the reaction and is the difference between the energy of Y after the reaction and the energy of the ground state of Y. (The possibility that particle b might be in an excited state will be neglected here.) To every level $E_\beta{}^*$ of the residual nucleus there corresponds an energy ϵ_β of the outgoing particle, as long as $E_\beta{}^* < \epsilon_{bY}$. Thus the energy distribution of the emitted particles consists of a series of peaks which are a picture of the spectrum of the residual nucleus, the highest energy corresponding to the lowest level of the residual nucleus. (See Fig. 6.1.)

The relative intensity of the peaks can be estimated by means of expression (3.8). The formation cross section σ_C generally increases

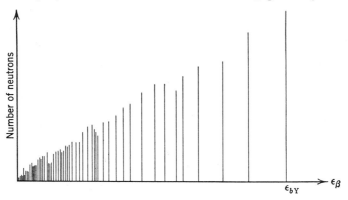

FIG. 6.1.   Energy distribution of emitted neutrons; ideal resolution.

with increasing channel energy (owing to better penetration of the barrier), except for neutrons with $l=0$ where σ_C decreases, but very slowly (proportional to k^{-1} or $\epsilon^{-1/2}$). In all cases the product $k^2 \sigma_C$ which appears in (3.8) is a monotonically increasing function of the

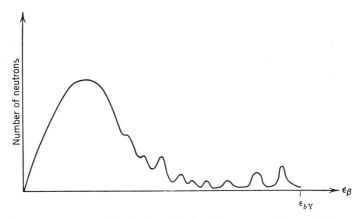

FIG. 6.2.   Energy distribution of emitted neutrons; finite resolution.

channel energy ϵ. Thus we expect the peaks to be stronger, the higher the energy ϵ_β. This tendency should be more pronounced if b is a charged particle, since the potential barrier prevents it from leaving the nucleus with low energy. There are, of course, many individual fluctuations in the intensity from peak to peak which are not taken into account by this treatment. If the energy is high enough, a great many levels of the residual nucleus can be excited. The energy distribution of the particles b becomes continuous when the energies E_β^* are closer together than the definition of the energy in the incident beam, or closer than the energy resolution of the experimental arrangement for detection of the reaction products (see Fig. 6.2). The shape of the distribution function $G_b(\epsilon)\, d\epsilon$ for the number of particles b emitted between ϵ and $\epsilon + d\epsilon$ is then given by

$$G_b(\epsilon)\, d\epsilon = \sum_{\epsilon < \epsilon_\beta < \epsilon + d\epsilon} G_C(\beta) \qquad (6.2)$$

where the sum is extended over the channels β whose energy lies within the energy interval $d\epsilon$. The number of terms in this sum is given by the number of levels of the residual nucleus Y with an excitation energy E_β^* between E and $E - d\epsilon$, where $E = \epsilon_{bY} - \epsilon$. We call this number $w_Y(E)\, d\epsilon$, and $w_Y(E)$ the "level density." We now insert expression (3.8) into (6.2) and remember that the denominator in (3.8) is a sum over all channels and therefore does not depend on ϵ_β. To determine the *relative* intensity distribution of the outgoing particles $I_b(\epsilon)\, d\epsilon$, we need to consider only the numerator of (3.8) and we get

$$I_b(\epsilon)\, d\epsilon = \text{const } \epsilon\, \sigma_C(\beta)\, w_Y(\epsilon_{bY} - \epsilon)\, d\epsilon \qquad (6.3)$$

Here $\sigma_C(\beta) = \sigma_C(\epsilon)$ is a function of the channel energy $\epsilon = \epsilon_\beta$. The factor ϵ replaces the factor k_β^2. The product $\epsilon\sigma_C(\beta)$ is an increasing function of ϵ. $w_Y(\epsilon_{bY} - \epsilon)$ is a strongly decreasing function of ϵ since the level density $w(E)$ increases very rapidly with higher excitation energy E. $I_b(\epsilon)$ exhibits therefore a pronounced maximum. If particle b is a neutron, $\sigma_C(\beta)$ is almost constant; hence the rapid increase of $w(E)$ with E shifts the maximum of $I_b(\epsilon)$ to values of ϵ which are small compared to the maximum energy ϵ_{bY}.

We obtain a rough estimate of the shape of $I_b(\epsilon)$, especially for neutrons, by introducing the following Taylor expansion of the logarithm of the level density

$$\mathfrak{S}(E) = \log w(E)$$

around the maximum energy ϵ_{bY} by which the residual nucleus Y can be excited (Bohr 37; Weisskopf 37, 40; Landau 37):

$$\mathfrak{S}(\epsilon_{bY} - \epsilon) = \mathfrak{S}(\epsilon_{bY}) - \epsilon \left(\frac{d\mathfrak{S}}{dE}\right)_{E = \epsilon_{bY}} + \cdots \qquad (6.4)$$

If this expansion is used to approximate $w(\epsilon_{bY} - \epsilon)$ in (6.3), we can absorb the factor coming from $\mathfrak{S}(\epsilon_{bY})$ into the constant and get

$$I_b(\epsilon) \, d\epsilon = \text{const } \epsilon \, \sigma_C(\epsilon) \exp \left[- \frac{\epsilon}{\Theta(\epsilon_{bY})} \right] d\epsilon \qquad (6.5)$$

where the function Θ is determined by

$$\frac{1}{\Theta(E)} = \frac{d\mathfrak{S}}{dE} \qquad (6.6)$$

Θ has the dimension of an energy and can be interpreted as a nuclear "temperature" in the following way: The logarithm $\mathfrak{S}(E)$ of the level density can be considered (apart from the Boltzmann constant k) the entropy of the residual nucleus in the energy region dE near E. Then (6.6) is the well-known thermodynamical relation between entropy and temperature. (Note that the omission of the Boltzmann constant k in the definition of $\mathfrak{S}$ leads to a temperature which is k times the conventional one and hence has the dimension of an energy.)

For neutrons the function $\sigma_C(\epsilon)$ varies very slowly (except at very low energies), and the distribution $I_b(\epsilon)$ is mainly determined by the factor $\epsilon \exp(-\epsilon/\Theta)$. This is the "Maxwell" energy distribution of molecules evaporated from a surface of temperature Θ. The maximum of $I_b(\epsilon)$ lies at $\epsilon = \Theta$, which should be small compared to ϵ_{bY} in order to make the expansion (6.4) a valid one. If the particles are charged, the distribution is distorted by the factor $\sigma_C(\epsilon)$, which is strongly energy dependent because of the influence of the potential barrier. The maximum of the distribution is then shifted to higher particle energies than $\epsilon = \Theta$, and the approximation (6.4) is correspondingly poorer.

The application of the temperature concept to nuclear reactions can be understood in the following way: The incident particle a enters the target nucleus and forms a highly excited compound nucleus. The excitation energy can be considered heat energy delivered by the impact of a on the target. The heating of the compound system causes an evaporation of neutrons or other particles, and the energy distribution of the emitted neutrons is similar to the Maxwell distribution. The potential barrier distorts the Maxwell distribution for charged particles by depressing the emission of low-energy particles.

The temperature which determines the Maxwell distribution is given by $\Theta(\epsilon_{bY})$:

$$\Theta(\epsilon_{bY}) = \frac{1}{(d\mathfrak{S}/dE)_{E=\epsilon_{bY}}}$$

It is the temperature of the residual nucleus Y at the excitation energy ϵ_{bY}. Here we understand by "temperature of a nucleus with an excitation E" the temperature at which the nucleus would have an average excitation E. It should be noted that the temperature determining the energy distribution of the emitted particles is not the "temperature of the compound nucleus before emission," but the "temperature of the residual nucleus after emission," since ϵ_{bY} is very near the excitation energy in which Y is left in most of the emissions. Evaporation of one particle constitutes a relatively large loss of energy which reduces the temperature considerably. The Maxwell distribution of the emitted particles is determined by the temperature *after* the emission.

In many experimental arrangements it is impossible to distinguish the channel by which a particle b has left the nucleus, or even to determine the energy of b. We are then interested solely in the cross section of an (a,b) reaction, irrespective of the specific channels. This cross section is given by expression (3.1) with

$$G_C(b) = \sum_{\beta} G_C(\beta) \tag{6.7}$$

where the sum is extended over all open channels β which lead to an emission of b.

If the energy of the incident particle is high enough so that the residual nucleus can be left in many different excited states, we can express (6.7) in terms of the level density w. We introduce for this purpose the abbreviation

$$F_b = \sum_{\beta} k_{\beta}^2 \sigma_C(\beta) \tag{6.8}$$

where the sum is extended over all open channels β leading to an emission of b. This sum can be expressed in terms of an integral

$$F_b = F_b(\epsilon_{bY}) = \frac{2M_{\beta}}{\hbar^2} \int_0^{\epsilon_{bY}} \epsilon_{\beta}\, \sigma_C(\epsilon_{\beta})\, w_Y(\epsilon_{bY} - \epsilon_{\beta})\, d\epsilon_{\beta} \tag{6.9}$$

Here $\sigma_C(\epsilon_{\beta})$ is the cross section for the formation of a compound nucleus by a collision with the energy ϵ_{β} between b and the excited nucleus Y*, the latter having an excitation energy $\epsilon_{\beta Y} - \epsilon_{\beta}$. These cross sections depend only on the channel energy ϵ_{β}. They do not depend, in our simplified treatment, on the specific properties of the channels. F_b is a function of the maximum energy ϵ_{bY} which the particle b can acquire (leaving the residual nucleus Y in the ground state). If the level densities $w_Y(\epsilon)$ are known, the functions F_b can be computed for every particle type. According to (3.8) and (6.7), the cross section (3.1) of an (a,b) reaction can then be expressed by

$$\sigma(a,b) = \frac{\sigma_C(a) \, F_b}{\sum_c F_c} \tag{6.10}$$

where the sum is extended over all particle types c emitted in this reaction. It should be emphasized again that this expression can give only a very rough picture of the actual values, since it is based on many approximations. Especially when (6.10) gives rise to cross sections very much smaller than $\sigma_C(a)$ (say less than 10^{-3}), the (a,b) reaction may take place by mechanisms other than the evaporation of b from the compound nucleus.

Some information about the nuclear level density $w(E)$ is necessary in order to evaluate the expressions for the nuclear temperature Θ and for the functions F_b. Our present knowledge of the level spacing in nuclei is very scant, especially at higher excitation energies.[1] We can obtain a rough estimate of the energy dependence of w_Y by a thermodynamical consideration which leads to a plausible energy dependence of the nuclear temperature. The corresponding level density can then be deduced.

The average energy E of a system is a monotonically increasing function of the temperature Θ. If the temperature is very high, so that all degrees of freedom are excited, E is proportional to Θ. This is certainly not the case in a nucleus excited by a normal nuclear reaction. Considering the nucleus very roughly a gas of A particles concentrated in a volume $(4\pi R^3/3)$, we find that this "gas" is degenerate if the excitation energy is of the order of, or less than,

$$\frac{A\hbar^2}{2MR^2} \cong 9A^{1/3} \text{ Mev}$$

Heavy nuclei should therefore be considered, in this approximation, highly degenerate "gases."

---

[1] For calculations of level densities on the basis of rough approximations about nuclear wave functions, see: Bethe (36), Bardeen (37, 38), Van Lier (37), Motz (38), Husimi (38), Sneddon (48).

The function $E(\Theta)$ has a vanishing derivative, $(dE/d\Theta)_{\Theta=0}=0$, for $\Theta=0$. (The specific heat is zero for $\Theta=0$, according to the third law of thermodynamics.) If an expansion of $E(\Theta)$ near $\Theta=0$ in powers of Θ is possible, it must therefore start at least with a quadratic term. We make the assumptions that:

(1) $E=E(\Theta)$ allows a power series expansion around $\Theta=0$.
(2) The leading term of this series is proportional to Θ^2.
(3) The higher powers of Θ can be neglected.

Then we can write ($\mathfrak{a}$ = constant)

$$E = \mathfrak{a}\Theta^2$$

From this we get

$$\mathfrak{S} = \int \frac{dE}{\Theta(E)} = 2(\mathfrak{a}E)^{1/2} + \text{const}$$

and finally for the level density

$$w(E) = \mathfrak{C}\exp[2\sqrt{\mathfrak{a}E}] \tag{6.11}$$

We can try to adjust the constants $\mathfrak{a}$ and $\mathfrak{C}$ so that this equation reproduces our rather scant knowledge of level densities.

The distances between levels around 1 Mev are known in many cases from the investigations of gamma-ray spectra and alpha-ray spectra. The observation of resonances in neutron or proton reactions gives some information about the level density at excitation energies which are equal to or higher than the separation energy of the bombarding particles, which is usually around 6 to 8 Mev. The levels observed around 1-Mev excitation have different angular momenta J and parities II. On the other hand, the slow neutron resonances all have the same parity and only two values of J (see Section 10). This difference was ignored in determining the values of $\mathfrak{C}$ and $\mathfrak{a}$, a procedure consistent with the general approach of this chapter in which selection rules have always been ignored. Furthermore, the values of $\mathfrak{C}$ and $\mathfrak{a}$ listed below apply only to *odd* values of A. Not enough material is available for even A. Since formula (6.11) was fitted to experiment around 1-Mev excitation, it represents the level density in that neighborhood, but it shows a rapid variation below 1 Mev which does not correspond to the facts. Evidently, a statistical formula like (6.11) is not applicable to a region which contains only very few levels.

$$A = 27: \qquad \mathfrak{a} = 0.45 \text{ Mev}^{-1} \qquad \mathfrak{c} = 0.5 \quad \text{Mev}^{-1}$$

$$A = 63: \qquad \mathfrak{a} = 2 \quad \text{Mev}^{-1} \qquad \mathfrak{c} = 0.3 \quad \text{Mev}^{-1}$$

$$A = 115: \qquad \mathfrak{a} = 8 \quad \text{Mev}^{-1} \qquad \mathfrak{c} = 0.02 \text{ Mev}^{-1} \qquad (6.12)$$

$$A = 181: \qquad \mathfrak{a} = 10 \quad \text{Mev}^{-1} \qquad \mathfrak{c} = 0.01 \text{ Mev}^{-1}$$

$$A = 231 \qquad \mathfrak{a} = 12 \quad \text{Mev}^{-1} \qquad \mathfrak{c} = 0.005 \text{ Mev}^{-1}$$

Formula (6.11) with the values shown in (6.12) should *not* be considered quantitatively correct. Formulas (6.11) and (6.12) may serve as a first extremely rough approximate orientation to the general features of the density of nuclear levels.

The nuclear temperature can be expressed as a function of E by the relation

$$\Theta = \left(\frac{E}{\mathfrak{a}}\right)^{1/2} \qquad (6.12\text{a})$$

In order to obtain the temperature determining the Maxwell distribution of outgoing neutrons, E must be put equal to the maximum energy ϵ_{bY}. Table 6.1 shows a few values of Θ for different values of E and A.

TABLE 6.1
Some Typical Nuclear Temperatures (Mev)

E \ A	25	55	115	181	231
5		1.6	0.8	0.7	0.6
10	4.7	2.2	1.1	1.0	0.9
15	5.8	2.7	1.4	1.2	1.1

These temperatures can be obtained by any process leading to the excitation energy E of the compound nucleus which is high enough to give rise to a maximum particle energy ϵ_{bY}. The latter is given by $E = \epsilon_{bY} + S_b$, where S_b is the separation energy of the particle from the compound nucleus.

It must be emphasized that expression (6.11) for the level density of nuclei is nothing more than a first guess. It is very improbable that the actual level densities are represented by such a simple expression. The level densities can be measured experimentally by comparing the energy distribution of the outgoing particles in a nuclear reaction with the theoretical formula (6.3). Reliable techniques for measuring these distributions have only recently been developed (Gugelot 51) and not much knowledge has yet been assembled.

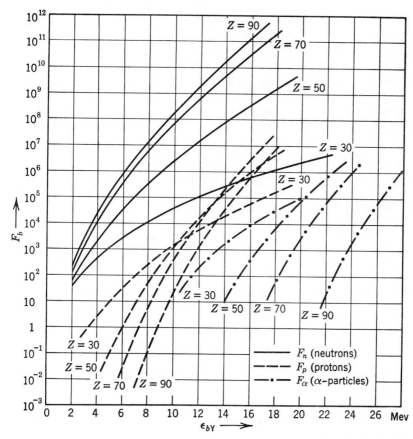

FIG. 6.3.   The functions F_n, F_p, F_α for residual nuclei whose Z is near 30, 50, 70, or 90. These functions are to be used in conjunction with formula (6.10). The curves show the estimated values for residual nuclei with odd A. If A and Z are even, the functions F are smaller by a factor which may be of the order of 10; if A is even and Z is odd, they are larger by a similar factor. The following constants were used: $R = r_0 \cdot A^{1/3}$ with $r_0 = 1.3 \times 10^{-13}$ cm, and formula (6.11) with $c = 0.28$, 0.015, 0.008, or 0.0025 and $a = 2$, 6.5, 10, or 12, respectively, for $Z = 30$, 50, 70, or 90. This graph of the functions F is intended only for illustrative purposes; they are quantitatively unreliable because: (1) formula (6.10) and the constants used for the level density are very hypothetical and certainly inaccurate, and (2) the nuclear radii are probably chosen somewhat too small.

It is expected that the actual level densities deviate from the simple expression (6.11) especially at lower energies, say up to an excitation energy of several Mev. Recent measurements by Kinsey (50) seem to show that the number of levels per Mev does not increase appreciably in the first two or three Mev of excitation. The strong increase sets in at somewhat higher excitation.[1] This would give rise to a more complicated dependence of w on the energy, and to values of the nuclear temperature different from (6.12a).

From the expression (6.11) for the level density, it is possible to calculate the functions F_b defined in (6.8) and (6.9) which serve to compute cross sections according to (6.10). Some typical values of F_b are shown in Fig. 6.3. These values are applicable only if the *residual* nucleus has odd A. In case of a residual nucleus with even mass number A, F_b is higher than shown for odd Z, and lower than shown for even Z. It is difficult to predict these differences quantitatively because of our scant information about level densities.

B. Secondary Nuclear Reactions

In most of the nuclear reactions of type $a+X=Y+b$, the residual nucleus Y is left in an excited state. This surplus energy is emitted by Y, in many cases, in the form of one or several gamma-rays, until the nucleus Y reaches its ground state. In some cases the excitation of Y may be so high that Y is able to emit another particle, say a neutron or a proton. The first reaction is then followed by a "secondary reaction":

$$Y = Z + c$$

in which a particle c is emitted. The actually observed reaction is a bombardment of X by a, followed by an emission of b *and* c, with a residual nucleus Z. In abbreviated form it is represented as an X($a;bc$)Z reaction. The most common reactions of this type are the ($a;2n$) reactions.

An observed X($a;bc$)Z reaction can be due to two different mechanisms:

$$X + a = Y + b \qquad Y = Z + c \qquad \text{(I)}$$

$$X + a = Y' + c \qquad Y' = Z + b \qquad \text{(II)}$$

When the time between the emissions of the first and the second particle becomes very short, e.g., of the order of the transit time of nucleons over nuclear dimensions, we can no longer speak of a defined excited state Y or Y' between the two emissions. The reaction should

---

[1] This behavior may be connected with the fact that the nuclear properties at low excitation can be described by a shell model of independent nuclear particles. (See Chapter XIV.) A simple structure of the nuclear spectra in the region of validity of the shell model would then be expected. The statistical theory of strong interaction, which leads to a high level density, may be applicable at higher excitation energies (Hurwitz 51).

then be described as[1]

$$X + a = Z + b + c \qquad \text{(III)}$$

The last process corresponds to a simultaneous breakup of the compound system into a nucleus Z and two particles, b and c. Process (III) does not correspond to any of the "channels" which we have used so far. It is not probable that process (III) occurs for incident energies less than 100 Mev except among the lightest elements. We shall therefore assume that the reaction $X(a;bc)Z$ is due to process (I) or (II) or both, but not to (III).

We shall denote the cross section for process I by $\sigma(a;b,c)$ and the cross section for process II by $\sigma(a;c,b)$. The observed cross section of the $(a;bc)$ reaction will be called $\bar{\sigma}(a;bc)$. It is the sum of the cross sections for processes I and II:

$$\bar{\sigma}(a;bc) = \sigma(a;b,c) + \sigma(a;c,b)$$

Usually one of these two contributions is much more important than the other, but cases can occur in which $\sigma(a;b,c)$ and $\sigma(a;c,b)$ are of the same order of magnitude. The distinction between processes I and II should not be made, of course, if b and c are the same kind of particle, e.g., in $(a;nn)$ reactions.

According to definition (3.1), the cross section $\sigma(a,b)$ includes also those reactions in which the residual nucleus undergoes a secondary reaction afterwards. We therefore distinguish the cross section $\sigma^*(a,b)$ which comprises only those reactions where the residual nucleus does *not* emit further particles. $\sigma^*(a,b)$ is what we understand conventionally by the cross section of an $X(a,b)Y$ reaction. The following relation holds:

$$\sigma(a,b) = \sigma^*(a,b) + \sum_c \sigma(a;b,c)$$

We can express the cross section for the $(a;b,c)$ reaction (process I) in the following way:

$$\sigma(a;b,c) = \sigma_C(\alpha) \sum_\beta{}' G_C(\beta)\, G_{Y\beta'}(c) \qquad (6.13)$$

Here α is the entrance channel, and the prime on the sum indicates that it is extended only over those channels β in which the residual nucleus Y is excited highly enough to emit a particle c. $G_C(\beta)$ is the relative probability (a pure number) that the compound nucleus C

---

[1] The following reactions may be regarded as examples of (III): $n+d=p+n+n$; $p+B^{11}=3\alpha$.

will decay into channel β, while $G_{Y\beta'}(c)$ is the relative probability that the nucleus Y in state β' (corresponding to channel β) will emit a particle c. All magnitudes in (6.13) can be calculated by the methods developed in this chapter provided that enough is known about the Q values of the various reactions and about the level densities of nuclei Y and Z.

Let us make the simplifying assumption that the residual nucleus Y always emits a particle if its excitation energy is sufficient to do so. Let us call $S_{min}(Y)$ the smallest separation energy of a particle from Y. Our assumption is then expressed by

$$\sum_c G_{Y\beta'}(c) \cong 1 \quad \text{provided that} \quad \epsilon_{bY} - \epsilon_\beta \geq S_{min}(Y)$$

This is equivalent to neglecting the emission of gamma-rays in competition with the emission of particles, an assumption which is in most cases approximately correct except in the immediate neighborhood of the threshold. We can then write

$$\sigma^*(a,b) \cong \sum_\beta{}'' \sigma(\alpha,\beta)$$

where the double prime on the sum indicates that it is extended only over those channels β in which the residual nucleus Y is excited below $S_{min}(Y)$. Let us call ϵ_{sec} the maximum energy available for emission of secondary particles from the first residual nucleus Y, for a given excitation energy in the original compound nucleus. This energy is also the energy of the outgoing particles b in the primary $X(a,b)Y$ reaction at which Y can just start emitting particles (see Fig. 6.4). Thus ϵ_{sec} is given by

$$\epsilon_{sec} = \epsilon_{bY} - S_{min}(Y)$$

We then obtain the following expressions for the "observed" cross section $\sigma^*(a,b)$ of the $X(a,b)Y$ reaction:

$$\sigma^*(a,b) = \sigma(a,b) \qquad \text{(for } \epsilon_{sec} < 0\text{)}$$

$$\sigma^*(a,b) \cong \sigma(a,b) \frac{\int_{\epsilon_{sec}}^{\epsilon_{bY}} I_b(\epsilon)\, d\epsilon}{\int_0^{\epsilon_{bY}} I_b(\epsilon)\, d\epsilon} \qquad \text{(for } \epsilon_{sec} > 0\text{)}$$

where $I_b(\epsilon)\, d\epsilon$ is the relative probability of emission of particles b with energies ϵ_β between ϵ and $\epsilon + d\epsilon$, as given by (6.3).

These expressions can be reduced to a simple form if the first emitted particle b is a neutron. We can then use the approximate

Maxwell distribution (6.5). We ignore the variation of $\sigma_C(\epsilon)$ with the energy ϵ and we assume that $S_{\min}(Y) = \epsilon_{bY} - \epsilon_{sec}$ is very much larger than the temperature Θ of the residual nucleus Y. We then

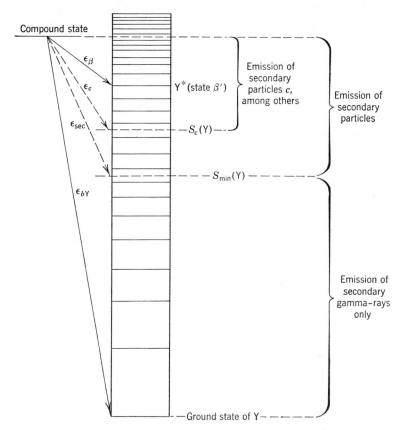

FIG. 6.4. Schematic picture of the energy relationships in the secondary nuclear reaction: $X + a = Y^* + b$, $Y^* = Z + c$. The levels shown are those of the nucleus Y.

get the approximate expression

$$\sigma^*(a,n) \cong \sigma(a,n) \left(1 + \frac{\epsilon_{sec}}{\Theta}\right) \exp\left(-\frac{\epsilon_{sec}}{\Theta}\right) \qquad (6.14)$$

Here Θ is the temperature $\Theta(\epsilon_{bY})$ governing the emission of neutrons. ϵ_{sec} can also be considered the difference $\epsilon_a - \epsilon_{th}$ between the incident energy ϵ_a and the threshold energy ϵ_{th} of the secondary reactions. It is seen that the "observed" $\sigma^*(a,n)$ becomes very much smaller than the "actual" $\sigma(a,n)$ if ϵ_{sec} is larger than the temperature Θ.

Then the secondary reactions take place in almost all cases after the first neutron is emitted.

The cross section of a secondary reaction with emission of particles c following a primary (a,n) reaction can be written in the same approximation as follows [ϵ_c is defined by (6.16) and is indicated in Fig. 6.4]:

$$\sigma(a;n,c) \cong \sigma(a,n) \; \frac{\displaystyle\int_0^{\epsilon_c} \epsilon \exp\left(-\frac{\epsilon}{\Theta}\right) G_{Y\beta'}(c) \, d\epsilon}{\displaystyle\int_0^{\epsilon_{bY}} \epsilon \exp\left(-\frac{\epsilon}{\Theta}\right) d\epsilon} \tag{6.15}$$

The integral in the denominator is approximately equal to Θ^2 provided that $\epsilon_{bY} \gg \Theta$, which is practically always the case. In order to evaluate the integral in the numerator, we express the branching probability $G_{Y\beta'}(c)$ for emission of particles c from the nucleus Y in state β' in terms of the functions F defined by (6.8) and (6.9). The functions F which we shall use here are for emission of particles from Y, not from C, and the level densities which need to be known are the ones in the various secondary residual nuclei Z, Z', etc. ϵ_c is the surplus over the threshold of the $(a;n,c)$ reaction (see Fig. 6.4)

$$\epsilon_c \equiv \epsilon_{bY} - S_c(Y) \tag{6.16}$$

Then the branching probability $G_{Y\beta'}(c)$ is given by

$$G_{Y\beta'}(c) = \frac{F_c(\epsilon_c - \epsilon)}{\displaystyle\sum_{c'} F_{c'}(\epsilon_{c'} - \epsilon)} \tag{6.17}$$

where the functions F are evaluated for the nucleus Y, and the sum in the denominator is extended over all particles c' which Y can emit from state β' with excitation energy $\epsilon_{bY} - \epsilon$. The argument $\epsilon_c - \epsilon$ of F_c is the energy with which particle c is emitted from the nucleus Y in state β'.

Since the functions F for charged particles are highly energy-dependent, the cross section for a secondary charged-particle emission can be found from (6.15) and (6.17) only by direct substitution and numerical evaluation of the integral in the numerator of (6.15). On the other hand, a very simple formula can be given for the $(a;n,n)$ reaction in which both the first and second emitted particles are neutrons. We can assume that neutron emission is predominant as soon as it becomes energetically possible, i.e., $G_{Y\beta'}(n) \cong 1$ if the state β' of Y is excited highly enough so that it can emit neutrons. We then get

$$\sigma(a;n,n) \cong \sigma(a,n) \left[1 - \left(1 + \frac{\epsilon_c}{\Theta} \right) \exp \left(- \frac{\epsilon_c}{\Theta} \right) \right] \qquad (6.18)$$

In this formula ϵ_c is the excess energy over the threshold of the $(a;n,n)$ reaction; it is given by (6.16) with $S_c(Y) = S_n(Y)$, the separation energy of neutrons from Y. Θ is the temperature $\Theta(\epsilon_{bY})$ of the intermediate residual nucleus Y (not of the final residual nucleus Z).

The cross section $\sigma(a,n)$ which appears in (6.14), (6.15), and (6.18) can usually be closely approximated by $\sigma_C(a)$, the cross section for formation of the compound nucleus C by bombardment with particles a.

If the energy of the incident particle becomes sufficiently high, the residual nucleus after emission of the second particle (nucleus Z) may be excited highly enough to emit a third particle.   We then obtain tertiary reactions or reactions of even higher order.

7. RESONANCE THEORY; QUALITATIVE TREATMENT

A. The Occurrence of Resonances

The previous sections were based on assumptions which lead to a cross section $\sigma_C(\alpha)$ for the formation of the compound nucleus which is a monotonic function of the energy. No sharp maxima or minima (resonances) were anticipated. The theory must be extended in order to account for the observed resonance phenomena in nuclear cross sections.[1]

It was assumed in Sections 4 to 6 that the incident particle has no appreciable chance to leave the nucleus through the entrance channel α once it has penetrated into the inside of the nucleus. It is then completely absorbed as far as the wave in channel α is concerned. Such an assumption is justified when the incident energy is high enough to allow the compound nucleus to decay by many channels. It is then very unlikely that the decay takes place by the entrance channel. In the present section, this assumption (4 in Section 4, p. 350) is dropped, and hence the theory is extended to lower incident energies. One of the main consequences is the *appearance of resonances in the cross sections.*

---

[1] The basic papers on resonance reactions are: Bohr (36, 37), Breit (36b), and Peierls (38). The discussion here follows the work of Feshbach et al. (47), Weisskopf (50), and Akhiezer (48). There is considerable literature about the theory of resonance reactions; some of it will be quoted in context in this chapter and in Chapter X.

The wave function u_l just inside the nuclear boundary $(r < R)$ can no longer be represented by (4.6), which symbolizes an ingoing wave only. It now must include also a term representing a wave returning toward the outside. This is indicated by

$$u_l \sim \exp{(-iKr_\alpha)} + \mathsf{b} \exp{(+iKr_\alpha)} \qquad \text{(for } r < R) \qquad (7.1)$$

where b is the (complex) amplitude of the returning wave and depends on the properties of the compound nucleus. At high incident energies we expect b to be close to zero. In absolute value, b is never larger than unity, since no more particles can approach $r_\alpha = R$ from the interior in channel α than have originally penetrated into the inside region.

It must be emphasized again that (7.1) is not an exact representation of the wave function u_l inside the nucleus. For $r < R$, the wave function describing the motion of the incident particle depends on the variables of all other nucleons involved; it is no longer described by a one-particle function $u_l(r_\alpha)$. Relation (7.1) is a very approximate expression which is used to describe only the main features of the dependence of the actual wave function on r_α near the nuclear surface. It expresses the fact that the incident particle possesses an average wave number K, and that it has a finite chance to return into the entrance channel. We are using (7.1) only to determine the logarithmic derivative f_l at the nuclear surface. Expression (7.1) gives rise to a value of f_l different from (4.7), and therefore to different cross sections; (7.1) becomes equivalent to the form (4.6) if $|\mathsf{b}|$ becomes very small. $|\mathsf{b}| \ll 1$ represents the limit of high energies for which the particle has practically no chance to leave the nucleus again by the same channel by which it has entered (assumption 4 of Section 4, p. 350).

Let us now consider the opposite extreme where the energy of the incident particle is so low that *no other channel but the entrance channel is open*, so that the compound system can decay *only* by re-emitting the incident particle with the same energy with which it entered. An example of this is a reaction in which the incident beam consists of neutrons of an energy ϵ, smaller than the lowest excitation energy of the target nucleus, and smaller than the threshold of any nuclear reaction. (In general, an energy $\epsilon < 100$ kev will fulfill this condition if we neglect the possibility of radiative capture and fission.) Then the neutron must leave the compound nucleus again with an energy ϵ.

The wave function inside the surface can then be approximated by

$$u_l \sim \exp{(-iKr_\alpha)} + \exp{[i(Kr_\alpha + 2\varsigma)]} \qquad (7.2)$$

in which the incoming and outgoing waves are equally strong $(|\mathsf{b}| = 1)$, the outgoing wave having a phase shift 2ζ (ζ = real). The boundary condition at $r_a = R$ on the wave function is now

$$f_l = R \left(\frac{du_l/dr}{u_l} \right)_{r=R} = -KR \tan [KR + \zeta(\epsilon)] \qquad (7.3)$$

(7.3) is quite different from (4.7). The phase $\zeta(\epsilon)$ with which the wave returns depends quite sensitively on the complicated interactions which the particle undergoes within the nucleus before it re-emerges near the surface, and is therefore a function of the energy of the entering particle. The cross sections, which follow from (7.3), will be calculated in Section 8. In this section we restrict ourselves to qualitative reasoning, and an attempt will be made to explain or to make plausible the most important qualitative features of the resonance phenomena. The quantitative calculations and the more rigorous derivations are found in the succeeding sections, and in Chapter X.

The re-emergence of the particle gives rise to the *occurrence of resonances* in the compound system. This can be seen qualitatively in the following way:[1] Expression (7.2) shows that the wave function just inside the nuclear surface can be written in the form

$$u \sim C \cos [Kr + \zeta(\epsilon)] \qquad \text{(for } r < R) \qquad (7.4)$$

where C is a constant. This function must be joined smoothly to the wave function u outside the nucleus. We understand by "smooth joining" that the two functions have equal value and equal derivative at $r = R$. Let us, for the sake of simplicity, consider only neutrons of zero angular momentum as incident particles. Then the wave function outside is a periodic function $A \sin (kr + \delta)$ with a wave number k, where A is adjusted so that it corresponds to an incident plane wave e^{ikz} of amplitude unity. The phase δ must be chosen so that $A \sin (kr + \delta)$ joins smoothly to (7.4). k is the wave number of the neutron outside the nucleus, which is much smaller than K, i.e., $k \ll K$. Since we have to join smoothly a periodic function of high wave number K to a periodic function of low wave number k, the amplitude C is, in general, small compared to A in the ratio k/K, as Fig. 7.1a implies. (This is the effect which we called "impedance mismatch" in the preceding section.) There are exceptions, however, if the value of ζ is such that u has a maximum or almost a maximum at $r = R$, $R(u'/u)_{r=R} \cong 0$. Only in this case can the two waves be joined with equal or almost equal amplitudes, as shown in Figs. 7.1b and 7.1c. We conclude from this that the wave function of the

---

[1] The corresponding calculations are given in Section 8A.

incident particle in general penetrates very little into the nucleus. There is, however, a series of energy values ϵ_s, the "resonance" energies, for which $\zeta(\epsilon_s)$ has the right value, so that the tangent of u_l is horizontal at $r = R$. In the neighborhood of these energies the wave penetrates strongly into the nucleus. Hence the particle can enter the nucleus and form a "compound state" only if the energy ϵ is equal or nearly equal to a "resonance" energy ϵ_s.

More conclusions can be drawn from our picture regarding the scattering cross section. The smallness of C/A for energies off resonance implies also that the outside wave assumes a very small

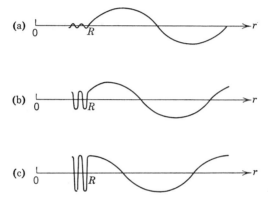

Fig. 7.1. Schematic representation of neutron wave functions at the nuclear surface. The wave functions are indicated as functions of the distance r from the center of the nucleus. $r = R$ is the nuclear radius. Case (a) corresponds to a neutron energy between resonances, case (b) is near resonance, case (c) is in resonance.

value at $r = R$. It almost could be written in the form $A \sin k(r - R)$, which reaches zero at $r = R$. This would be just the solution for the scattering at an impenetrable sphere of radius R, which would force the wave function to vanish at $r = R$. Thus we conclude that the scattering away from resonance ought to be almost identical with that of an impenetrable sphere of radius R.[1]

We expect the following refinements to the conclusions of the previous sections: If the energy of the incident particle is so low that only one channel or only a few channels are open, the cross section σ_C for formation of the compound nucleus is no longer a monotonic function of the energy as given by (4.8). σ_C exhibits resonances for a discrete set of energy values ϵ_s of the incident particle and is very small for all energies ϵ which do not coincide, or nearly coincide, with one of the ϵ_s.

[1] See, however, Wigner (51).

Thus the compound nucleus is formed essentially only in certain discrete energy states. These states are not stationary, since, after some time, they decay by re-emission of the particle which has created them, or by emission of some other particle. We shall call them, therefore, "decaying states." They are in many ways similar to the stationary states of a nucleus.

B. The Compound Nucleus, Level Widths, Qualitative Description

Let us now consider in greater detail the quantum-mechanical system C, consisting of the incident particle a and the target nucleus X, which we have called the "compound system." The system C is created in an excited state in the course of the nuclear reaction, since the entering of the particle a into the target nucleus X not only transmits the kinetic energy of a to the system C but also brings into play the attractive potential energy of the nuclear forces acting between a and X.

Let us first investigate the system C in its lowest possible quantum states. These states lie much lower than those created in collisions between particle a and target nucleus X. C is a nucleus of A constituents, N neutrons, and $A - N$ protons, where A is the total number of nucleons and N the total number of neutrons in the incident particle a and the target nucleus X. This nucleus, *the compound nucleus*, forms a series of stationary states with the excitation energies 0, E_1, E_2, E_3, $\cdots$. These energies are counted from the ground state which, on this scale, has zero energy. These states are stable in the same sense as the stationary states of atoms are. The nucleus would stay indefinitely in one of these states were it not for the electromagnetic radiation, which makes it possible to perform a transition to a lower state with the emission of a light quantum. This stability ceases if the excitation energy is larger than S_{min}, where S_{min} is the smallest of the separation energies S_a of any particle a within the nucleus. If the excitation energy is larger than S_{min}, the spectrum of the nucleus C is, strictly speaking, a continuum, since then particle a can be split off and can assume any amount of kinetic energy. The energy S_{min} plays the same role as the ionization energy in atoms. This is shown schematically in Fig. 7.2.

Why, then, do we observe resonances in the creation of the compound nucleus? Why is the compound nucleus formed only in states with special energies? We shall show in this section that the main reason lies in the long lifetime of the compound nucleus after it is formed. Even if $E > S_{min}$, the peculiar properties of the compound state, especially the strong potential jump at the surface of the nucleus, keep particle a from leaving the compound nucleus for a long time. At

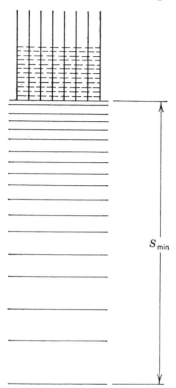

low excess energies, $E - S_{min}$, it is kept within the nucleus almost as rigidly as in the case of $E < S_{min}$, where energy conservation prevents any particle emission whatsoever. Hence the structure of the compound nucleus for $E < S_{min}$ is not qualitatively different from $E > S_{min}$, as will be shown in detail in Sections 8 and 9. The series of discrete energy values continues even above S_{min}, although the states whose energy is higher than S_{min} are not strictly stationary.[1]

The finite lifetime of these states is only partly due to the possibility of the compound nucleus splitting into two parts, the particle a and the residual nucleus. In addition, all the states of a nucleus, with the exception of the ground state, have a finite lifetime because of the possibility of radiative transitions to lower states. The lifetime of the states with $E > S_{min}$ is merely shortened some more by the possibility of ejection of particles. (The emission of beta-rays can be neglected here, since its probability is extremely small compared to all other processes.) The reciprocal value of the lifetime τ_s of the level s is the emission probability per unit time of a gamma-ray or a particle. It is customary to express this value in energy units by multiplying it by $\hbar$:

FIG. 7.2. The spectrum of a nucleus (schematic —the actual number of levels is much greater). Strictly speaking, the spectrum is continuous above S_{min}. We find, however, "decaying" states in the continuum, with properties similar to the stationary states. The true stationary states are indicated by full lines, the decaying states by dashed lines. Several Mev above S_{min} the continuum region is reached, so that there are no decaying states at higher energies.

$$\Gamma^s = \frac{\hbar}{\tau_s} \qquad (7.5)$$

Γ^s is also called the "width" of level s because of the Heisenberg

---

[1] The quantitative calculations underlying these qualitative arguments will be found in Section 9.

uncertainty relation between time and energy: $\Delta t \, \Delta E \cong \hbar$. The fact that state s exists only for a limited time causes an uncertainty in the energy, a width Γ^s.

If the finite lifetime is due to the possibility of different kinds of emissions, the total emission probability Γ^s is the sum of partial probabilities:

$$\Gamma^s = \sum_a \Gamma_a{}^s + \Gamma_{\mathrm{rad}}^s \tag{7.6}$$

where Γ_{rad}^s is the probability per unit time to emit a light quantum,[1] and $\Gamma_a{}^s$ is the same magnitude for a particle a Γ_{rad}^s is also called "radiation width," and $\Gamma_a{}^s$ is a "partial width" corresponding to the emission of a. $\Gamma_a{}^s$ is also referred to as "particle width." The width of levels with $E < S_{\min}$ consists only of the radiation width.

There is one condition on the lifetime which immediately follows from these considerations: In order to obtain a discrete spectrum of levels with an excitation energy larger than $S_{\min}$, the lifetime must be long enough to make the width Γ^s smaller than the distance D_s to the neighboring levels, i.e.,

$$\Gamma^s < D_s \tag{7.7}$$

With sufficient excitation energy E_s, the nucleus C can emit particles a with different energies, corresponding to the different states in which the residual nucleus can be left behind. We can thus subdivide $\Gamma_a{}^s$ into partial widths,

$$\Gamma_a{}^s = \sum_{\alpha'} \Gamma_{a\alpha'}^s \tag{7.8}$$

where $\Gamma_{a\alpha'}^s$ corresponds to the probability of an emission of a with the special condition that the residual nucleus be left in the state α'. We can make (7.8) more specific by introducing the concept of channel. Every decay for which the products are specified completely (including their quantum states) corresponds to a specific channel, which we denote by the letter α. We introduce the channel emission probability or channel width $\Gamma_\alpha{}^s$ and we write for the total width

$$\Gamma^s = \Gamma_{\mathrm{rad}}^s + \sum_\alpha \Gamma_\alpha{}^s \tag{7.9}$$

where the sum is extended over all open channels into which state s

---

[1] The "radiation width" is usually called Γ_γ in the literature. We are using α, β, γ, $\cdots$ to denote particle channels, and therefore employ the notation Γ_{rad} in order to avoid confusion.

can decay. $\Gamma_\alpha{}^s$ can be defined as follows: Let N_s be the population in the excited state s; then $N_s \Gamma_\alpha{}^s / \hbar$ is the number of decays into channel α per unit time.

The total width Γ^s increases with higher excitation energy because of several reasons: first, more particles can be emitted by a higher level; second, more different states α' of the various residual nuclei can be formed, so that the number of terms in (7.9) increases. Because of these two reasons, the number of open channels increases rapidly with increasing excitation energy. Furthermore the probability $\Gamma_\alpha{}^s$ of any single mode of disintegration increases with increasing energy E_s. Thus, at a certain excitation energy E above $S_{\min}$, the average level width Γ^s becomes larger than the average level distance D. Only then does the spectrum of the nucleus become truly continuous.

The existence of quasi-discrete states of the compound nucleus at energies $E > S_{\min}$ can also be understood in another way, by reference to the wave guide analogy mentioned earlier. It is well known that an entirely closed cavity with perfectly reflecting walls has certain definite frequencies with which electromagnetic vibrations can occur inside. Our only experimental knowledge of these resonance states of a cavity comes from a situation in which the cavity is *not* completely closed: In order to make measurements, we must break the wall of the cavity at least once to connect a probe through it. The cavity is then no longer a closed system, and we might think that it no longer has stationary states. The radiation inside the cavity can leak out through the hole which we have made. Nevertheless, it is well known that such measurements are quite possible and reliable, and that the states of the punctured cavity are still almost stationary and very close to the completely stationary states of an ideal, completely closed cavity. The condition that the perturbation introduced by the insertion of the probe be small is that the Q of the cavity shall be very large compared to unity. Q is defined as the ratio of the energy stored inside the cavity to the energy lost through our puncture during one period of vibration. The condition may be expressed in the following form: The lifetime of the state must be long compared to the period of the vibration inside the cavity. We shall see below that this is equivalent to the condition for nuclear resonance reactions that the width be much smaller than the level distance.

C. Interpretation of D and Γ

It is perhaps of some interest to discuss here the physical significance of the level distance D and its connection with some properties of the motion of the nuclear constituents within the nucleus. This motion cannot, in general, be described by a classical picture of moving particles. However, according to the correspondence principle, the highly excited states lend themselves more readily to a classical description. We can build linear combinations of wave functions of a number of neighboring stationary states such that they correspond to a relatively well-defined grouping of particles in space with given velocities, within the limits of accuracy set by the uncertainty principle. The motion of these particles (or, rather, of the maxima in the square of the wave function) corresponds to a good approximation to the motion calculated by classical mechanics. We are here interested in only one feature, the period P of the motion. P is the time after which the initial grouping of particles recurs. We find that the time P is intimately connected with the level distance D of the states used in the linear combination. Let us assume for a moment that the energies E_n of these states (say their number is N) are equally spaced:

$$E_n = E_0 + n\,D$$

We can then write for the linear combination of the N states, whose space dependence is given by φ_n,

$$\psi = \sum_{n=1}^{N} a_n \varphi_n \exp\left(-\frac{iE_nt}{\hbar}\right) = \exp\left(-\frac{iE_0t}{\hbar}\right) \sum_{n=1}^{N} a_n \varphi_n \exp\left(-\frac{inDt}{\hbar}\right)$$

It is evident that $|\psi[t+(2\pi\hbar/D)]|^2 = |\psi[t]|^2$, so that the wave function describes the same configuration at time t as it does at time $t+(2\pi\hbar/D)$. Thus the period of the motion is

$$P = \frac{2\pi\hbar}{D} \tag{7.10}$$

where D is the level distance. This conclusion holds only if the levels are equally spaced, which is approximately the case in simple systems at high excitations.

We cite two elementary examples. First consider a particle of mass M in a one-dimensional potential well of width b and depth V_0, which fulfills the condition $V_0(b^2M/\hbar^2) \gg 1$. The latter condition insures the existence of many stationary states. The energy E_n above the bottom of the well for a high quantum number n is approximately given by $E_n \cong \pi^2n^2\hbar^2/2Mb^2$, and the level distance $D = \pi^2n\hbar^2/Mb^2$. The period P of the corresponding classical motion (oscillation between the two walls of the well) is given by $P = 2b/v$, where v is the velocity inside the well: $v = \sqrt{2E_n/M} = \pi n\hbar/Mb$. Thus the relation $P = 2\pi\hbar/D$ is verified. Another example can be found in the motion of an electron in the Bohr orbits of the hydrogen atom. It can easily be verified that the level distance computed from the Balmer formula corresponds to the period of the motion in the corresponding Bohr orbit.

In complicated systems like atomic nuclei, these considerations lose some of their accuracy, but they still remain valid qualitatively and can be used for a pictorial description. We no longer find approximately equidistant level spacing, but we can consider the average level spacing D an indication of the period of the intranuclear motion. This period turns out to be very large, much larger, for example, than the periods of a one-body motion in a potential well of nuclear size. This is due to the interaction between nucleons, which makes the motion much more involved, so that the time interval between the recurrences of the same configuration becomes very much longer than in any simple motion.

We now extend these considerations to the decaying states. Since these states do not differ essentially from the stationary states, their average level distance D can be used for an estimate of the period P of the motion. Let us in this case apply the concept of period to the recurrence of a very special configuration. We know that a decaying state can be created by a particle a entering into the residual nucleus through the channel α. We single out the configuration which is realized when particle a has just entered into the nucleus, and we ask after what time the particle would reappear at the nuclear surface with the rest of the nucleus arranged in such a way that a is ready to leave through the same channel by which it came in. Such a question can be answered only in a very approximate way: The time P is of the order of the period of the motion, and again we expect the relation $P \sim 2\pi\hbar/D$ to hold.

The recurrence of this configuration does not necessarily mean that particle a will actually leave the compound nucleus. The nuclear surface is equivalent to a strong and sudden change of potential, and the particle is very likely to be reflected at this surface and start the motion inward into the nucleus over again. *This repetition of the motion is essential for the existence of well-defined compound states.* If particle a had left the nucleus after the time $2\pi\hbar/D$, the lifetime τ_s of the state would have been of the order P, and the width $\Gamma^s \cong \hbar/P \cong D/2\pi$ would be of the order D. The states of the compound nucleus are well defined only if $\Gamma^s \ll D$. Thus the lifetime τ_s must be large compared to P; a well-defined state does not yet decay after particle a has once returned to the surface.

We then obtain an interesting interpretation of the significance of the probability $\Gamma_\alpha{}^s$ for the decay through channel α. $\Gamma_\alpha{}^s/\hbar$ is the probability per unit time that the system decays through the channel α if all other channels are closed by some artifice. $\tau_\alpha = \hbar/\Gamma_\alpha{}^s$ should, therefore be the lifetime of the state if only channel α is open. Evidently this lifetime must be at least of the order P. Because of the reflection of a at the inner side of the surface, τ_α may be longer than P. Let us call $\mathsf{T}(\alpha)$ the transmission coefficient toward the outside:

$$\mathsf{T}(\alpha) = \frac{\text{number of successful attempts to escape through channel } \alpha}{\text{number of attempts to escape}}$$

(7.11)

We then get

$$\tau_\alpha \sim \frac{P}{\mathsf{T}(\alpha)}$$

$$\Gamma_\alpha{}^s \sim \mathsf{T}(\alpha) \frac{D}{2\pi} \tag{7.12}$$

which shows that the partial width $\Gamma_\alpha{}^s$ must be smaller than $D/2\pi$. In order to have well-defined levels, $\mathsf{T}(\alpha)$ must be a very small number, making the motion in the state an almost periodic one.

The coefficients $\mathsf{T}(\alpha)$ are precisely the transmission coefficients calculated in Section 5. Since resonance phenomena occur only in the energy region where the wave number k can be assumed small compared to K, we can use here the approximate expression (5.6), which contains two factors: the transmission v_l of the barrier in the channel, and the transmission $4k/K$ of the impedance mismatch at $r=R$. The transmission coefficient depends on the angular momentum of the outgoing (or incoming) particle, on its charge and mass, and on its final wave number k which it assumes at large distances from the nucleus.

We get the following estimate for the channel width from (7.12) and (5.6):

$$\Gamma_\alpha{}^s \sim \frac{4k}{K} v_l \frac{D}{2\pi} \tag{7.13}$$

where k is the wave number of the outgoing particle in channel α resulting from the decay of the compound state s. The factor $4k/K$ comes from the reflection at the surface of the nucleus, and the factor v_l expresses the combined effect of the centrifugal and the Coulomb barriers. For $l=0$ and no Coulomb barrier (in the case of neutrons), we get

$$\Gamma_\alpha{}^s \sim 2 \frac{k}{K} \frac{D}{\pi} \qquad \text{(for } l=0 \text{ neutrons)} \tag{7.14}$$

where k is the wave number of the neutron.

We see from (7.14) that the neutron width of a level is small compared to the level distance only if $k \ll K$. We do not expect resonances, therefore, if the energy of the compound state is so high that the wave number k of the emitted neutron is of the order of K. Actually, the total width Γ^s of a level may become equal to, or larger than, D even at energies where $k < K$, since Γ^s consists of the sum of all partial widths $\Gamma_\alpha{}^s$.

It is useful to split the channel width into two factors,

$$\Gamma_\alpha{}^s = (2kRv_l)\,\gamma_\alpha{}^s \tag{7.15}$$

The first factor $(2kRv_l)$ depends on the channel energy and the conditions *outside* the nucleus. The factor $\gamma_\alpha{}^s$ is called the "reduced width," and it incorporates all the properties of the *interior* of the nucleus. According to (7.13) its order of magnitude can be estimated to be

$$\gamma_\alpha{}^s \sim \frac{D}{\pi KR} \tag{7.16}$$

This relation does not differentiate between different channels. Actually, $\gamma_\alpha{}^s$ may differ strongly in different channels α, but it is expected to be of the order of magnitude shown in (7.16).

The $\gamma_\alpha{}^s$ depend on the excitation energy E_s of the compound nucleus:

$$E_s = \epsilon_{\alpha s} + S_a + E_\alpha$$

where S_a is the separation energy of a, and E_α is the excitation energy of the residual nucleus in channel α. As long as $\epsilon_{\alpha s} \ll E_s$, we can expect that $\gamma_\alpha{}^s$ shows no systematic dependence on $\epsilon_{\alpha s}$, although there may be strong fluctuations between different levels s and different channels α.

The dependence of the particle width $\Gamma_\alpha{}^s$ on the energy $\epsilon_{\alpha s}$ of the particle emitted by the compound state s is mainly determined by the factor $2kRv_l$. The expressions (5.8) for v_l show that, for neutrons, the particle width is proportional to $\epsilon_\alpha{}^{1/2}$ for $l = 0$; it is proportional to $\epsilon_\alpha{}^{l+1/2}$ for $l \neq 0$ as long as ϵ_α is small enough so that the actual expressions (5.8) for v_l can be replaced by the respective first terms. The widths $\Gamma_\alpha{}^s$ for charged particles contain the barrier penetration factor through v_l.

It is necessary to specify the type of levels whose average distance D can be interpreted as the reciprocal of the period of motion. The correspondence principle, as used in the interpretation of D, is applicable only to a series of states which fulfill the following condition: All physical magnitudes which are integrals of motion must have the same value, with the exception of the energy itself. Thus the distance D must be taken between levels of equal J (quantum number of the total angular momentum of the nucleus) and equal parity. It is generally assumed that there are no other integrals for the motion of nucleons within the nucleus because of the strong interactions. If the character of nuclear forces admits more integrals, the meaning of D must be altered. We indicate a few examples.

If there is no coupling between spin and orbital motion in a nucleus, D is the distance between levels of equal L and S. If we were allowed to consider a nucleus a system of independent nucleons moving in a common potential, the energies of the individual nucleons would be integrals, so that D would be the distance between the states of one single nucleon only.

In any of these cases D is just the distance between those states which can be formed by an incoming particle with a definite angular momentum and spin. If there were no interaction between particles, only those states could be formed in which the incoming particle itself is excited. If there is no spin-orbit coupling, only states which have the quantum numbers L and S can be formed, where L and S are those orbital or spin angular momenta, respectively, which occur from the combination of the orbital and spin angular momentum vectors of the particle and the target nucleus.

D. Cross Sections for Nuclear Reactions

The qualitative arguments of the previous sections can be used to construct a formula for the cross sections of nuclear reactions in the resonance region. No mathematical derivation is attempted in this section; it will be given in Section 8B and, more generally, in Section 9 and in Chapter X, Section 4. Here we intend only to make plausible the actual form of the expressions.

We consider the cross section $\sigma(\alpha,\beta)$ of an (α,β) reaction, and we expect that this reaction can take place with appreciable intensity only if the energy of the incident particle is near certain resonance values ϵ_s. Since the resonance energies depend on the angular momentum l of the incident particle, only particles a which have the right value of l can initiate the nuclear reaction near a given resonance.[1] The cross section σ_{Cl} for the formation of the compound nucleus by channel α with angular momentum l was found, in (5.1), to be the product of the maximum possible cross section $(2l+1)\pi\lambda^2$ and the transmission coefficient $T_l(\alpha)$. Equation (5.1) did not take into account any resonance phenomena. We now make the assumption

[1] If the spin of the incident particle is taken into account, more than one l can excite one resonance. We disregard this complication in this section. It will be discussed in Section 10.

that (5.1) is still correct when σ_{Cl} is *averaged over an energy interval which is large enough to contain several resonances.* Hence, in order to obtain the cross section near resonance, we multiply (5.1) by a function $y(\epsilon_\alpha)$, which shows maxima at $\epsilon_\alpha = \epsilon_{\alpha s}$, and whose average is unity. The width of the maxima should correspond to the lifetime of the compound state formed and should therefore be equal to Γ^s, as defined in (7.9).

In analogy with the dispersion theory of light, we choose a special shape for $y(\epsilon_\alpha)$ in the neighborhood of a given resonance energy $\epsilon_{\alpha s}$ by putting

$$y(\epsilon_\alpha) \cong \frac{\alpha}{(\epsilon_\alpha - \epsilon_{\alpha s})^2 + (\frac{1}{2}\Gamma^s)^2} \qquad \text{(for } \epsilon_\alpha \text{ near } \epsilon_{\alpha s}) \qquad (7.17)$$

This distribution has a half-width Γ^s and becomes small when

$$|\epsilon_\alpha - \epsilon_{\alpha s}| \gg \Gamma^s$$

Its average over several resonances can be well approximated by the integral $D^{-1} \int_{-\infty}^{\infty} y(\epsilon)\, d\epsilon$, where D is the level distance. The constant α in the numerator of (7.17) must be chosen so that this average will be unity, i.e., $\alpha = D\Gamma^s/2\pi$. Hence we obtain for the cross section, by using relation (7.12),

$$\sigma_{Cl}(\alpha) = (2l + 1)\, \pi\, \lambda_\alpha^2\, T_l(\alpha)\, y(\epsilon_\alpha)$$

$$\cong (2l + 1)\, \pi\, \lambda_\alpha^2\, \frac{\Gamma_\alpha^s\, \Gamma^s}{(\epsilon_\alpha - \epsilon_{\alpha s})^2 + (\frac{1}{2}\Gamma^s)^2} \qquad (7.18)$$

It is characteristic that this cross section is proportional to Γ_α^s, which is the probability of the opposite process, the decay of the compound nucleus into channel α.

In order to find the cross section for a particular (α,β) reaction, we must multiply $\sigma_C(\alpha)$ by the branching ratio $G_C(\beta) = \Gamma_\beta^s/\Gamma^s$, which is the probability that the compound nucleus, once formed, decays through channel β. [See (3.5).] We then get the following expression for $\sigma(\alpha,\beta)$ in the neighborhood of a resonance $\epsilon_{\alpha s}$, the resonance belonging to the set which is excited by particles of angular momentum l:

$$\sigma(\alpha,\beta) \cong (2l + 1)\, \pi\, \lambda_\alpha^2\, \frac{\Gamma_\alpha^s\, \Gamma_\beta^s}{(\epsilon_\alpha - \epsilon_{\alpha s})^2 + (\frac{1}{2}\Gamma^s)^2} \qquad (7.19)$$

an expression which is called the *Breit-Wigner one-level formula* for nuclear reactions (Breit 36).

It should be noted that the widths Γ_α^s, Γ_β^s depend on the channel energies through the factor $T_l(\alpha)$ or $T_l(\beta)$. They are all functions of ϵ_α, since the exit channel energies ϵ_β are determined by ϵ_α on account of the energy law. Thus the values of Γ_α^s and Γ_β^s at an energy, say, slightly below resonance are somewhat different from their values at an energy slightly above resonance. In contrast to this, the width expressed by (7.13) represents the emission probability into channel α by the compound state s; and, in evaluating the latter quantity, the value of k must be taken at the energy with which the particle would leave the decaying state, i.e., at $\epsilon_\alpha = \epsilon_{\alpha s}$.

The more mathematical theory (Sections 8 and 9 of this chapter, and Chapter X) shows that the parameter $\epsilon_{\alpha s}$ in (7.19) is independent of the channel energy ϵ_α only for S-wave neutron resonances. In all other cases $\epsilon_{\alpha s}$ is itself a function of the channel energy ϵ_α. It is customary to neglect the energy dependence of the widths Γ_α^s and of $\epsilon_{\alpha s}$ in fitting the Breit-Wigner formula to experimental data. However, there are cases where this neglect is not justified (Thomas 51).

Equation (7.19) must not be applied to the (α, α) process, the elastic scattering, because of the interference effects between the re-emission of particle a by the compound nucleus and the scattering at the nuclear surface, as well as at the potentials outside the nucleus. The expression we obtain for the elastic scattering process is derived in Section 8B, and it is

$$\sigma_{sc,l} = \sigma_l(\alpha, \alpha) = (2l + 1)\,\pi\,\lambda_\alpha^2 \left| \frac{i\Gamma_\alpha^s}{(\epsilon_\alpha - \epsilon_{\alpha s}) + \frac{1}{2}i\Gamma^s} + A_{\text{pot}}^l \right|^2 \quad (7.20)$$

where the first term in the absolute square is the "resonance scattering amplitude," and the second is the "potential scattering amplitude" defined by (2.57). Amplitude A_{pot} corresponds to the scattering which would take place if the nucleus were replaced by a perfectly reflecting sphere of radius R; this process determines $\sigma(\alpha, \alpha)$ off resonance. The "resonance scattering amplitude" represents the scattering due to the re-emission by the compound nucleus into channel α. If (7.19) were used to calculate $\sigma(\alpha, \alpha)$, we would obtain the contribution of the first term only. We refer the reader to Section 10 for the changes introduced in (7.19) and (7.20) when the intrinsic spins are taken into account.

A very important special application of (7.19) is the capture reaction as defined in (1.2). Here the compound nucleus C decays by emitting a gamma-ray to a lower excited state which, in general, is so low that, from then on, the nucleus C can be de-excited only by further gamma-ray emissions. We have called Γ_{rad}^s the probability (times $\hbar$) of the emission of a gamma-ray by the compound nucleus per unit time, and we expect therefore the capture cross section in the neighborhood of a resonance ϵ_{as} with an angular momentum l to be

$$\sigma_{\text{cap}}(\alpha) = (2l + 1) \, \pi \, \lambda_\alpha^2 \, \frac{\Gamma_\alpha^s \, \Gamma_{\text{rad}}^s}{(\epsilon_\alpha - \epsilon_{as})^2 + (\tfrac{1}{2}\Gamma^s)^2} \qquad (7.21)$$

where Γ^s is the total width, including the radiation width,

$$\Gamma^s = \sum_\alpha \Gamma_\alpha^s + \Gamma_{\text{rad}}^s$$

The resonance energies ϵ_{as} are those energies near which the incident particle forms the compound nucleus in one of the quasi-stationary excited states. Every state s of the compound nucleus leads to a resonance in every channel through which this state can be formed. The following relation holds between the resonance energies ϵ_{as} and $\epsilon_{\beta s}$ of two channels α, β, leading to the same compound state s:

$$\epsilon_{\beta s} - \epsilon_{as} = Q_{\alpha\beta}$$

where $Q_{\alpha\beta}$ is the Q value as defined in (1.7). This is identical with relation (1.6) of the channel energies ϵ_α and ϵ_β in general. Hence we obtain the same resonance in an (α,β) reaction and in a (β,α) reaction if the entrance channel energy of the latter is equal to the exit channel energy of the former. It is perhaps more appropriate to write the Breit-Wigner formula (7.19) in the form

$$\sigma(\alpha,\beta) = (2l + 1) \, \pi \, \lambda_\alpha^2 \, \frac{\Gamma_\alpha^s \, \Gamma_\beta^s}{(E - E_s)^2 + (\tfrac{1}{2}\Gamma^s)^2} \qquad (7.22)$$

where E is the excitation energy of the compound nucleus when formed by a channel energy ϵ_α, and E_s is the excitation energy of the quasi-stationary state s in the compound nucleus. We find, according to (1.8),

$$E = \epsilon_\alpha + E_{a'} + E_{a''} + S_a$$

where S_a is the separation energy of a from the compound nucleus, and $E_{a'}$, $E_{a''}$ are the excitation energies of the partners in channel α. The form (7.22) makes it more apparent that the resonance denominator is determined by the properties of the compound nucleus and not by the specific entrance channel.

E. Behavior of Nuclear Cross Sections near Threshold

A nuclear (a,b) reaction shows certain characteristic properties when the channel energy of one of the partners, ϵ_α or ϵ_β, is very near zero (Wigner 48). Let us first consider the case where the energy ϵ_α in the entrance channel is very small. We assume $\epsilon_\alpha \leq \Delta$, where Δ is an energy interval in which all magnitudes involved can be considered constant except those which vanish at $\epsilon_\alpha = 0$. Obviously, the reaction cross section $\sigma(\alpha,\beta)$ at $\epsilon_\alpha \to 0$ is zero unless the reaction is exoergic: $Q_{\alpha\beta} > 0$. The cross section $\sigma(\alpha,\beta)$ can then be written, from (7.22),

$$\sigma(\alpha,\beta) \cong \text{const } \lambda_\alpha{}^2 \, \Gamma_\alpha{}^s \qquad (\text{for } \epsilon_\alpha \to 0)$$

where all magnitudes which do not vanish when $\epsilon_\alpha = 0$ make up the "constant." We get, by using (7.13),

$$\sigma(\alpha,\beta) \cong \text{const } \epsilon_\alpha{}^{-1/2} \, v_l(\epsilon_\alpha) \qquad (\text{for } \epsilon_\alpha \to 0) \qquad (7.23)$$

where the penetration factor $v_l(\epsilon_\alpha)$ depends on the nature of the incident particle. If the incident particle is a neutron, we find, by means of (5.8),

$$\sigma_l(\alpha,\beta) = \text{const } \epsilon_\alpha{}^{l-1/2} \qquad (\text{for } \epsilon_\alpha \to 0) \qquad (7.24)$$

where this cross section applies only for reactions initiated by neutrons with an orbital angular momentum l. Unless selection rules are of importance, the largest contribution comes from neutrons with $l=0$, so that we find for neutron-induced reactions:

$$\sigma(\alpha,\beta) = \text{const } \epsilon_\alpha{}^{-1/2} \qquad \begin{array}{l}(\text{for } \epsilon_\alpha \to 0 \text{ in neutron-induced} \\ \text{reactions}) \end{array} \qquad (7.25)$$

which is the well-known $1/v$ law.

If the incident particle has a charge $Z_a e$, the penetration factor $v_l(\epsilon_\alpha)$ decreases rapidly with decreasing energy ϵ_α. The particles with $l=0$ contribute most; the asymptotic expression for v_0 can be calculated with formulas (5.9). We find that

$$v_0 = \text{const } \epsilon^{-1/2} \exp\left(-\frac{Z_a Z_X e^2}{\hbar v_\alpha}\right) \qquad (\text{for } \epsilon_\alpha \to 0)$$

where v_α is the speed of the particle; therefore we get

$$\sigma(\alpha,\beta) = \text{const } \epsilon_\alpha{}^{-1} \exp\left(-\frac{Z_a Z_X e^2}{\hbar v_\alpha}\right) \qquad \begin{array}{l}(\text{for } \epsilon_\alpha \to 0 \text{ in charged-} \\ \text{particle-induced reactions}) \end{array} \qquad (7.26)$$

It should be noted that the asymptotic value (7.26) is reached only at very low energies. For all except very light nuclei, the energies ϵ_α at which (7.26) is valid are so small that no reaction could be observed with present techniques.

The asymptotic properties of $\sigma(\alpha,\beta)$ for $\epsilon_\beta \to 0$ can also be stated in a similar form. This case occurs only if the reaction is endoergic: $Q_{\alpha\beta} < 0$. We then get from (7.22)

$$\sigma(\alpha,\beta) = \text{const } \Gamma_\beta{}^s = \text{const } \epsilon_\beta{}^{1/2} \, v_l(\epsilon_\beta) \qquad \text{(for } \epsilon_\beta \to 0) \qquad (7.27)$$

Especially, if the outgoing particle is a neutron with angular momentum l,

$$\sigma_l(\alpha,\beta) = \text{const } \epsilon_\beta{}^{l+1/2} \qquad \text{(for } \epsilon_\beta \to 0) \qquad (7.28)$$

In general, most of the neutrons emerging at threshold have $l=0$, so that we set

$$\sigma(\alpha,\beta) = \text{const } \epsilon_\beta{}^{1/2} \qquad \text{(for } \epsilon_\beta \to 0, \text{ outgoing neutrons)} \qquad (7.29)$$

If the emerging particle is charged, we set

$$\sigma(\alpha,\beta) = \text{const } \exp\left(- \frac{Z_a Z_{\mathrm{X}} e^2}{\hbar v_\beta} \right) \qquad \text{(for } \epsilon_\beta \to 0, \text{ charged}$$
$$\text{outgoing particles)} \qquad (7.30)$$

Finally, we consider the asymptotic properties of the elastic scattering. $\sigma(\alpha,\alpha)$ consists of two parts: the resonance and the potential scattering. For charged particles, the potential scattering becomes equal to the Rutherford scattering at low energies, since it is equal to the scattering of a charged reflecting sphere. The influence of the reflection at the nuclear surface on the scattering vanishes at low energies, and only the Coulomb scattering remains. This scattering is much larger than any nuclear effect and is of no interest here. The case of neutron scattering is more interesting. The asymptotic behavior of A_{pot} is determined by the fact that ξ_l becomes very small. We get, from (2.52) and (2.57),

$$A_{\text{pot}}^l \cong -2i\xi_l \cong \frac{2i \, (k_\alpha R)^{2l+1}}{(2l-1)!! \, (2l+1)!!}$$

The amplitude for $l=0$ is by far the largest and is

$$A_{\text{pot}}^{(0)} \cong 2ik_\alpha R$$

The resonance amplitude A_{res} is proportional to $\Gamma_\alpha{}^s$, which also contains the factor $k_\alpha R$. The combined amplitude $A_{\text{res}}^{(0)} + A_{\text{pot}}^{(0)}$ is proportional to k_α which, after squaring, cancels the factor $\lambda_\alpha{}^2$ in (7.20), so that we get

$$\sigma(\alpha,\alpha) \to \text{const} \qquad \text{(for } \epsilon_\alpha \to 0, \text{ elastic scattering of neutrons)} \qquad (7.31)$$

The neutron scattering cross section approaches a constant value as the energy approaches zero.

We have derived the asymptotic relations from the Breit-Wigner formulas, (7.19) and (7.20). They can also be derived from the continuum theory, and their validity is not restricted to the energy region in which resonances occur.

We start from (3.2) and find that $\sigma_C(\alpha)$ for $\epsilon_\alpha \to 0$ is proportional to $\lambda_\alpha^2 T_l(\alpha)$, as seen in (5.1). The dependence on the energy of the

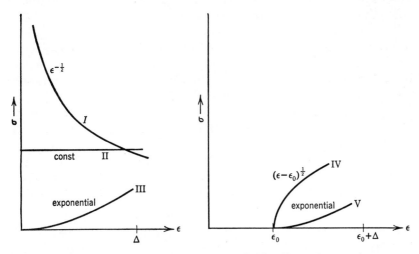

Fig. 7.3.   Behavior of cross sections near threshold.   Curve I: exoergic neutron-induced reaction, (n,a); curve II: elastic scattering of neutrons, (n,n); curve III: exoergic reaction initiated by a charged particle: (p,a) or (α,a); curve IV: endoergic reaction in which a neutron is emitted: (a,n), or inelastic scattering of neutrons (n,n'); curve V: endoergic reaction in which a charged particle is emitted: (a,p) or (a,α). ϵ_0 is the threshold energy of the endoergic reactions. Δ is the energy interval in which all magnitudes except the energy of the particle can be considered constants.

emitted particle is found in $G_C(\beta)$, which, according to (3.8) and (5.1), is proportional to $T_l(\beta)$. Hence we get

$$\sigma_l(\alpha,\beta) = \begin{cases} \text{const } \lambda_\alpha^2 \, T_l(\alpha) & (\text{for } \epsilon_\alpha \to 0) \\ \text{const } T_l(\beta) & (\text{for } \epsilon_\beta \to 0) \end{cases} \qquad (7.32)$$

This is equivalent to our previous relations (7.23) and (7.27), from which all others were derived. The equivalence comes from the fact that, for low energies,

$$T_l(\alpha) \to \frac{4k_\alpha}{K} \, v_l(\alpha)$$

The asymptotic properties are indicated schematically in Fig. 7.3.

▶   **8. RESONANCE THEORY; DETERMINATION
OF CROSS SECTIONS**

A. Pure Resonance Scattering

The conclusions of the previous section were based on qualitative arguments. This section provides a more quantitative formulation of the results as well as a formal derivation.

We consider, first, processes in which the incoming particle must leave by the same channel by which it came in. The only cross section different from zero is the scattering cross section. Let us first discuss the case of neutrons with $l = 0$, which is of the greatest interest. The scattering cross section is given by (2.25), (2.26), and (2.27) and is expressed in these equations as a function of the logarithmic derivative f_0. We now substitute (7.3) for f_0 in order to reproduce the arguments made on page 381.

The general behavior of the logarithmic derivative f_0 as a function of the channel energy ϵ can be estimated as follows: The function $u(r)$ just inside the channel entrance $(r \leq R)$ has the qualitative behavior (7.2)

$$u(r) \sim \exp\,(-iKr) + \exp\,[i(Kr+2\zeta)] = 2 \exp\,(i\zeta)\,\cos\,(Kr+\zeta)$$
$$(\text{for } r \leq R) \qquad (8.1)$$

The cosine depends on the energy ϵ in two ways: through K and through the "inside" phase factor ζ. Nevertheless, the behavior of $\cos\,(Kr+\zeta)$ as a function of energy ϵ is expected to be fairly regular. ζ is a real number under our assumptions (only one channel open), and the cosine can never exceed unity in absolute value. For a constant value of r, say $r = R$, the quantity

$$z(\epsilon) \equiv KR + \zeta(\epsilon) \qquad (8.2)$$

is expected to be a monotonically increasing function of ϵ.[1] Thus $[\cos\,(Kr+\zeta)]_{r=R} = \cos z(\epsilon)$ passes through $+1$, 0, -1, 0, $+1$, etc., as a function of ϵ, as indicated in Fig. 8.1. Of course, the zeros are not equispaced in energy, but the qualitative behavior of $\cos z(\epsilon)$ is the same as an ordinary cosine wave.

The derivative of $u(r)$, evaluated at $r = R$, is given by

$$u'(R) \sim -2\,e^{i\zeta}\,K\,\sin\,(KR+\zeta) = -2\,e^{i\zeta}\,K\,\sin z(\epsilon) \qquad (8.3)$$

which has the same general behavior as a function of energy as $u(R)$.

---

[1] It can be shown in all generality that $df_0/d\epsilon \leq 0$. Hence it follows from (8.4) that $dz/d\epsilon \geq 0$.

However, the zeros of $u(R)$ do not coincide with those of $u'(R)$. Instead, the cosine is zero when the sine is ± 1, and vice versa. This is also indicated in Fig. 8.1.

The logarithmic derivative, $f_0 = Ru'(R)/u(R)$, shows therefore the general behavior of a tangent function. It has a set of zeros, corre-

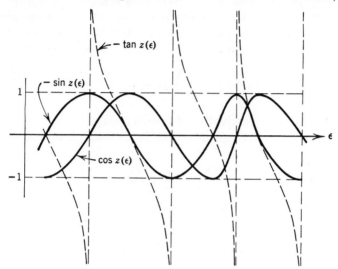

Fɪɢ. 8.1. The wave function $u(R)$ at the channel entrance $r = R$ is proportional to

$$\cos z(\epsilon) \equiv \cos [KR + \zeta(\epsilon)]$$

Its derivative, $u'(R)$, at $r = R$, is proportional to $-\sin z(\epsilon)$. Hence the logarithmic derivative, $f_0 \equiv Ru'(R)/u(R)$, is proportional to $-\tan z(\epsilon)$; this quantity, and hence f_0, has alternating zeros and poles as a function of ϵ.

sponding to the zeros of $u'(R)$, and in between every two zeros a pole, corresponding to a zero of $u(R)$, as shown in Fig. 8.1.

Evaluation of f_0 from (8.1) and (8.3) gives

$$f_0 \sim -KR \tan (KR + \zeta) = -KR \tan z(\epsilon) \qquad (8.4)$$

where $z(\epsilon)$, (8.2), is expected to be a reasonably smooth function of the channel energy. *The main physical results of the theory to be developed now depend on this assumption of a smooth behavior of z as a function of energy.*

We shall be especially interested in the energy regions where f_0 is close to zero, for those are the regions where the resonance scattering amplitude A_{res}, as given by (2.26), becomes very large. The inside wave and the wave outside $r = R$ have roughly equal amplitudes only when the inside wave approaches $r = R$ with almost zero slope, i.e., with f_0 close to zero. We therefore define the "resonance energies" ϵ_s by the condition

$$f_0(\epsilon_s) = -KR \tan z(\epsilon_s) = 0 \qquad (8.5)$$

There is a whole set of such energies. Let us consider any one of them and study the behavior of the resonance scattering amplitude A_{res} for energies ϵ near ϵ_s by a method which we call the "linear approximation method."[1] We expand the function $f_0(\epsilon)$ around its zero at ϵ_s and neglect all but the first (linear) term of this power series:

$$f_0(\epsilon) = \left(\frac{df_0}{d\epsilon}\right)_s (\epsilon - \epsilon_s) + \cdots \qquad (8.6)$$

where $(df_0/d\epsilon)_s$ is the derivative of f_0 with respect to ϵ for $\epsilon = \epsilon_s$. After introducing the positive quantity (see footnote on page 398)

$$\Gamma_0{}^s \equiv -\frac{2kR}{(df_0/d\epsilon)_s} \qquad (8.7)$$

we get the resonance scattering amplitude

$$A_{\text{res}} \cong \frac{i\Gamma_0{}^s}{(\epsilon - \epsilon_s) + i\frac{1}{2}\Gamma_0{}^s} \qquad \text{near resonance} \qquad (8.8)$$

The absolute square of this resonance scattering amplitude

$$|A_{\text{res}}|^2 = \frac{(\Gamma_0{}^s)^2}{(\epsilon - \epsilon_s)^2 + (\frac{1}{2}\Gamma_0{}^s)^2}$$

has the well-known "dispersion" form with a maximum at the resonance energy and a half-width $\Gamma_0{}^s$. We note that $\Gamma_0{}^s$ depends on the energy because of the factor k. We may consider $\Gamma_0{}^s$ approximately a constant, provided that its energy dependence is negligible over the width of the resonance. In the general case we shall define the "width of the resonance" as $\Gamma_0{}^s$ evaluated at $\epsilon = \epsilon_s$:

$$\text{"Width" of resonance} \equiv [\Gamma_0{}^s(\epsilon)]_{\epsilon=\epsilon_s} \qquad (8.9)$$

The resonance scattering amplitude is of the order of unity near resonance within a region of the width $\Gamma_0{}^s$. It is 2 at resonance and therefore much larger than the potential scattering amplitude A_{pot}, (2.27), if $kR \ll 1$. The scattering cross section assumes its maximum value $4\pi\lambda^2$ at resonance. For energies far from resonance, $f_0(\epsilon)$ becomes of the order of KR and higher [see (8.4)], and therefore A_{res}

---

[1] This method is also called the method of perturbation of boundary conditions (Feshbach 44). See also Akhiezer (48).

is much smaller than A_{pot}.[1]   Then the scattering is mainly determined by A_{pot} and is therefore almost equal to the scattering of an impenetrable sphere:

$$\sigma_{sc} \sim \pi \lambdabar^2 \left| A_{\text{pot}} \right|^2 \qquad \text{off resonance} \tag{8.10}$$

This approaches $\sigma_{sc} \cong 4\pi R^2$ if $kR \ll 1$.

We find effects of interference between the two scattering amplitudes when they are of the same order.   It is seen, from (2.27) and (8.8),

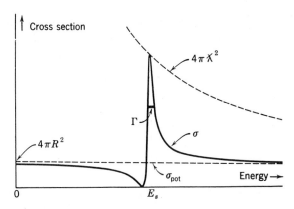

FIG. 8.2.   Elastic scattering cross section for $l=0$ neutrons near a resonance in the compound nucleus.   This curve is drawn on the assumption that the spin I of the target nucleus is zero.   If $I \neq 0$, the theory of Section 10 must be used: The angular momentum S of the compound nucleus is either $I+\frac{1}{2}$ or $I-\frac{1}{2}$.   The curve shown here is then modified as follows: it is multiplied by a constant $g(S)$, (10.6), and to this a non-resonant contribution is added, equal to

$$[1 - g(S)]\pi\lambdabar^{2\prime}|A_{\text{pot}}^2| \cong [1 - g(S)]4\pi R^2$$

Thus, for $I \neq 0$ the peak is less high, and the minimum less deep, than shown here

that the two amplitudes have opposite signs for $\epsilon < \epsilon_s$ and equal signs for $\epsilon > \epsilon_s$, if Γ_0^s is neglected compared to $\epsilon - \epsilon_s$, and if $kR \ll 1$.   Hence we expect destructive interference between resonance and potential scattering, and therefore a minimum in the scattering cross section, if $\epsilon = \epsilon_s - (\Gamma_0^s/2kR)$.   Figure 8.2 illustrates the behavior of the scattering cross section around resonance.

We can get a rough estimate of the width Γ_0^s from (8.7).   We obtain from (8.4)

$$\frac{df}{d\epsilon} = - \frac{d(KR)}{d\epsilon} \tan z - (KR) \sec^2(z) \frac{dz}{d\epsilon} \tag{8.11}$$

[1] Wigner (51) discusses possible exceptions to this rule.

and observe, from (8.5), that z must be a multiple of π at the resonances:

$$z(\epsilon_s) = n\,\pi, \qquad (n \text{ integral})$$

Hence (8.11) gives for $(df/d\epsilon)$ at a resonance

$$\left(\frac{df}{d\epsilon}\right)_s = -KR\left(\frac{dz}{d\epsilon}\right)_s \qquad (8.12)$$

We now use our assumption of a smooth behavior for $z(\epsilon)$ to estimate the crucial magnitude $(dz/d\epsilon)_s$. $z(\epsilon)$ changes by π in going from one value of ϵ_s to the next. Hence *we shall assume that* $dz/d\epsilon \cong \pi/D$, *where D is the energy separation between two resonances.* We write

$$\left(\frac{dz}{d\epsilon}\right)_s \equiv \frac{\pi}{D^*} \qquad (8.13)$$

where D^* is *defined* by (8.13) and is expected to be an energy of the order of the level distance D. If (8.13) is inserted in (8.12), we get from (8.7)

$$\Gamma_0{}^s = \frac{4k}{K}\frac{D^*}{2\pi} \qquad (8.14)$$

The width is small compared to D as long as $k \ll K$. This expression is the same as the one which we derived qualitatively in Section 7C (7.14), for the width of a decaying state of the compound nucleus.

The present discussion of the behavior of the resonance is based on the validity of the linear approximation (8.6). We have made use of this approximation only in a very small energy interval around the resonance ϵ_s. A_{res} is of importance only in that interval in which $f_0(\epsilon) < 1$. If $f_0(\epsilon)$ is larger than unity, we find from (2.26) and (2.27) that $|A_{\text{res}}| < |A_{\text{pot}}|$. We define the energy interval $\Delta\epsilon$ by the condition

$$|\tan z(\epsilon)| < (KR)^{-1} \qquad (\text{for } |\epsilon - \epsilon_s| < \Delta\epsilon) \qquad (8.15)$$

Since KR is much larger than unity, the value of $\tan z(\epsilon)$ remains small in the interval $\Delta\epsilon$, as shown by (8.4). The definition (8.15), together with (8.4), implies that $|A_{\text{res}}| \ll |A_{\text{pot}}|$ for $|\epsilon - \epsilon_s| > \Delta\epsilon$. Since $z(\epsilon)$ changes by π when going from ϵ_s to the next resonance, we conclude that $\Delta\epsilon \ll D$. Hence the expansion (8.6) need only be valid for an energy interval small compared to the distance between resonances. On the other hand, $\Delta\epsilon$ is appreciably larger than the width $\Gamma_0{}^s$ as long as $k R \ll 1$. We can see this by expanding $z(\epsilon)$ in (8.15) in a power series around $\epsilon = \epsilon_s$, which gives

$$\left(\frac{dz}{d\epsilon}\right)_s \Delta\epsilon \cong (KR)^{-1} \tag{8.15a}$$

Comparison of (8.13), (8.14), and (8.15a) leads to the approximate relation

$$\Gamma_0^s \cong 2kR\,\Delta\epsilon$$

which shows that our statement was correct. The width Γ_0^s determines the energy range over which $|A_{\text{res}}| \gtrsim 1$, whereas $\Delta\epsilon$ is the energy range over which $|A_{\text{res}}| \gtrsim |A_{\text{pot}}|$.

Expression (8.13) and the estimate $D^* \sim D$ will be used quite frequently for the estimates of level widths of the type (8.14). A few critical remarks are necessary. Expression (8.1) for the wave function in the interior of the nucleus is highly hypothetical. Actually, the energy dependence $f_0(\epsilon)$ of the logarithmic derivative is determined by the solution of the complete nuclear wave equation. The function $z(\epsilon)$ is then defined by (8.4) as $z(\epsilon) = \tan^{-1}(f_0/KR)$. The only things we know about $z(\epsilon)$ are that it assumes an integer multiple of π at resonances and that its derivative is positive. A function can well go from $n\pi$ to $(n+1)\pi$ as the argument changes from ϵ_s to $\epsilon_s + D$, without having the derivative even close to π/D at either ϵ_s or $\epsilon_s + D$. Two typical unfavorable cases are shown in Figs. 8.3a and 8.3b. The first one is an example which would lead to $D^* > D$ for all resonances, the second one to $D^* < D$. The considerations following (8.1) suggest that $(dz/d\epsilon)_s$ should *not* exhibit such regular bias at the values $z = n\pi$, if the value of K has been chosen correctly. On the basis of our assumptions we expect the variations of $(dz/d\epsilon)_s$ around the mean value π/D to be at random, say as in Fig. 8.3c. However, we cannot exclude the possibility that our assumptions are too simple and that some properties of the internal nuclear structure give rise to a systematic bias of $(dz/d\epsilon)_s$ as in Fig. 8.3a or 8.3b. Our estimate (8.14) of the width would then be invalidated.

We can draw interesting conclusions from a calculation of the amplitude C of the wave inside the nucleus as defined in (7.4). The wave $u_0(r)$ *outside* the nucleus can be written in the form (neutrons, $l=0$)

$$u_0(r) = A \sin (kr + \delta_0) \tag{8.16}$$

where δ_0 is a phase which must be determined by the condition that $f_0 = R(u'/u)_{r=R}$ must be given by (7.3). The value of $u_0(r)$ at $r = R$ can then be expressed in the form $u_0(R) = A[1+(f_0/kR)^2]^{-1/2}$ from (8.16) and $u_0(R) = C[1+(f_0/KR)^2]^{-1/2}$ from (7.4). The equality of these two expressions yields the ratio of the intensities of the waves inside and outside the surface:

$$\left|\frac{C}{A}\right|^2 = \frac{1 + (f_0/KR)^2}{1 + (f_0/kR)^2}$$

In the neighborhood of a resonance energy ϵ_s, we use again the approximate expression (8.6) and obtain with (8.7)

$$\left|\frac{C}{A}\right|^2 = \frac{(\tfrac{1}{2}\Gamma_0{}^s)^2}{(\epsilon - \epsilon_s)^2 + (\tfrac{1}{2}\Gamma_0{}^s)^2}$$

after neglecting $(f_0/KR)^2$ compared to unity. This expression is proportional to $|A_{\text{res}}|^2$ and shows the same resonance peaks and the

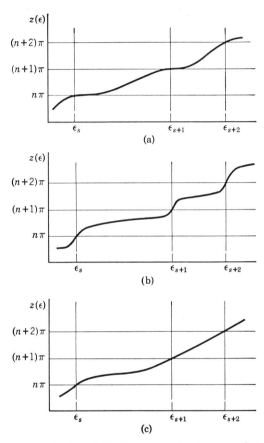

FIG. 8.3.   Schematic behavior of the functions $z(\epsilon)$: (a) would give $D^* > D$; (b) would give $D^* < D$; (c) would give $D^* \sim D$.

same widths.   Outside of the resonance it falls off rapidly to very small values.

Thus it is justified to say that, in the scattering process, the particle enters the nucleus with appreciable probability only near resonance, within an energy interval of about $\Gamma_0{}^s$. Off resonance, the particle is almost entirely reflected at the boundary, and the wave function inside is very weak. That is why the scattering cross section off resonance is well approximated by the effect of an impenetrable sphere of radius R. The resonance scattering is therefore ascribed to the inside of the nucleus; the potential scattering, to its surface.

Let us set aside for a moment our previous assumptions and assume that the particle is able to perform some reactions once it has penetrated to the interior. These reactions may be radiative capture or the ejection of another particle. The cross section σ_r of these reactions is expected to be proportional to the relative intensity $|C/A|^2$ of the "inside" compared to the "outside" wave function. This may help us to understand the fact that the resonance energies are also the maxima for σ_r and that the shapes of the resonances in the reactions are similar to those of $|A_{res}|^2$ in the scattering.

We now generalize our expressions for the scattering cross section to cases of higher angular momentum and to particles other than neutrons. We find the scattering cross section given in terms of the logarithmic derivative f_l by Eqs. (2.55), (2.56), and (2.57). Since we are restricting ourselves to pure scattering processes (no reaction possible; only one open channel), the value of f_l, as defined by (2.45), must be a real number. We introduce the "formal resonance energies" ϵ_s by a requirement analogous to (8.5):

$$f_l(\epsilon_s) = 0 \qquad (8.17)$$

In order to find the energy dependence of the resonance amplitude A_{res}^l, (2.56), in the neighborhood of one of the formal resonance energies ϵ_s, we use the expansion

$$f_l(\epsilon) = (\epsilon - \epsilon_s)\left(\frac{df}{d\epsilon}\right)_s + \cdots$$

and the following abbreviations: the channel width,

$$\Gamma_\alpha{}^s \equiv -\frac{2\,s_l(\epsilon)}{(df_l/d\epsilon)_s} \qquad (8.18)$$

and the "actual resonance energy,"

$$\epsilon_s{}' \equiv \epsilon_s + \frac{\Delta_l(\epsilon)}{(df_l/d\epsilon)_s} \qquad (8.19)$$

$\Gamma_\alpha{}^s$ and $\epsilon_s{}'$ are both functions of the channel energy ϵ, the former through $s_l(\epsilon)$, the latter through $\Delta_l(\epsilon)$. The resonance scattering amplitude (2.56) can then be written in the form

$$A_{res}^l = \frac{i\,\Gamma_\alpha{}^s}{(\epsilon - \epsilon_s{}') + i\frac{1}{2}\Gamma_\alpha{}^s} \qquad (8.20)$$

The differences from the case of neutrons with $l=0$ lie in the expression for the width $\Gamma_\alpha{}^s$, in the shift of the maximum from ϵ_s to $\epsilon_s{}'$, and in the fact that $\epsilon_s{}'$ is no longer a constant but depends on the channel energy ϵ (Thomas 51). The width differs by a penetration factor $s_l/kR = v_l$, according to (2.25):

$$\Gamma_\alpha{}^s \sim v_l \Gamma_0{}^s \tag{8.21}$$

Hence the width is, in general, smaller than the corresponding width for neutrons with $l=0$.

According to (2.11) the scattering cross section for a given l is limited by

$$\left[\frac{\sigma_{sc,l}}{\pi \lambda^2}\right]_{max} = 4\,(2l+1) \tag{8.22}$$

As seen in (2.54), this maximum value is reached when f_l assumes a certain real value. Since the f_l in pure resonance scattering assumes all real values between $+\infty$ and $-\infty$ as the energy changes [see Fig. 8.1], we conclude that *the maximum value* (8.22) *is actually reached for some energy within each scattering resonance peak.* If the resonance is narrow, the energy for which the maximum (8.22) is attained is close to (but not exactly the same as) $\epsilon_s{}'$, (8.19). The energy $\epsilon_s{}'$ determines the maximum of the resonance scattering amplitude $|A^l_{res}|^2$ only, and not the maximum of $|A^l_{res} + A^l_{pot}|^2$, which is involved in (8.22).

B.   Resonance Scattering and Resonance Reactions

We generalize our considerations to include also the possibility that the incoming particle stays in the nucleus and initiates a nuclear reaction. Then the form of the wave function $u(r)$ within the nucleus is symbolized by (7.1), with b an arbitrary number of magnitude $|\mathsf{b}|^2 \leq 1$. The limiting case $|\mathsf{b}|^2 = 1$ leads to pure scattering, and $\mathsf{b} = 0$ leads to the continuum theory. We now consider the intermediate case. Let us write

$$\mathsf{b} = e^{2i\zeta}e^{-2q} \tag{8.23}$$

where ζ and q are real numbers, both being functions of the energy ϵ of the incoming particle. q must be greater than, or equal to, zero, since no more particles can return than entered originally. We then obtain, from (7.1),

$$u_l \approx \mathsf{C} \cos\,(Kr + \zeta + iq) \qquad \text{(for } r < R)$$

where C is a constant independent of r. Hence[1]

---

[1] The logarithmic derivative $R[(du_l/dr)/u_l]_{r=R}$ depends on the channel through which the reaction is initiated. Definition (8.24) refers to the logarithmic derivative in the initiating channel α of the reaction.

$$f_l \equiv R \left[\frac{du_l/dr}{u_l} \right]_{r=R} = -KR \tan\left[z(\epsilon)+iq\right] \qquad (8.24)$$

where z is defined by (8.2).

f_l is now a complex number and gives rise to a non-vanishing reaction cross section. Both the scattering and the reaction cross sections can be expressed in terms of f_l according to equations (2.55) to (2.58).

We shall prove that the cross sections show resonances similar to the ones discussed before, provided that the magnitude q is small compared to unity. A small q indicates that there is only a small probability that the entering particle is diverted into other processes during the time P it needs to return again toward the nuclear surface in channel α. According to the discussion in Section 7C, this is a necessary condition for the existence of well-defined states in the compound nucleus.

We now consider f_l as given in (8.24) as a function of ϵ and q, i.e., $f_l=f_l(\epsilon,q)$. We define a series of "formal resonance energies" in the same way as before:

$$f_l(\epsilon_s, q=0) = -KR \tan z(\epsilon_s) = 0 \qquad (8.25)$$

and we expand f_l in the neighborhood of ϵ_s in a power series in ϵ as well as in q, retaining the leading terms only:

$$f_l(\epsilon) \cong (\epsilon-\epsilon_s)\left(\frac{\partial f_l}{\partial \epsilon}\right)_s + q\left(\frac{\partial f_l}{\partial q}\right)_s$$

$$= (\epsilon-\epsilon_s)\left(\frac{\partial f_l}{\partial \epsilon}\right)_s - iqKR \qquad (8.26)$$

Here we understand by $(\partial f_l/\partial\epsilon)_s$ the derivative of f_l with respect to ϵ at $\epsilon=\epsilon_s$ and $q=0$. It is the derivative appearing in (8.6) and (8.18).

The form (8.26) can be inserted into (2.56) and (2.58). We then obtain simple expressions, valid in the neighborhood of the resonances, by introducing the following magnitudes: the "particle width,"

$$\Gamma_\alpha^s \equiv -\frac{2\,s_l(\epsilon)}{(\partial f_l/\partial\epsilon)_s} \qquad (8.27)$$

the "reaction width,"

$$\Gamma_r^s \equiv -\frac{2qKR}{(\partial f_l/\partial\epsilon)_s} \qquad (8.28)$$

the "total width,"

$$\Gamma^s \equiv \Gamma_r^s + \Gamma_\alpha^s \qquad (8.29)$$

and the "actual resonance energies,"

$$\epsilon_s' \equiv \epsilon_s + \frac{\Delta_l(\epsilon)}{(\partial f_l/\partial \epsilon)_s} \tag{8.30}$$

We then get the elastic scattering cross section from (2.55), where A_{pot}^l is given by (2.57) and the resonance scattering amplitude by

$$A_{\text{res}}^l = \frac{i\Gamma_\alpha{}^s}{(\epsilon - \epsilon_s') + i\frac{1}{2}\Gamma^s} \quad \text{(near resonance)} \tag{8.31}$$

The reaction cross section becomes

$$\sigma_{r,l} = (2l + 1)\,\pi\,\lambda_\alpha{}^2\,\frac{\Gamma_\alpha{}^s\,\Gamma_r{}^s}{(\epsilon - \epsilon_s')^2 + (\frac{1}{2}\Gamma^s)^2} \quad \text{(near resonance)} \tag{8.32}$$

This expression justifies our qualitative development in Section 7D.

We observe that the scattering cross section differs only little from the one calculated for the case of pure scattering in Section 8A. The width $\Gamma_\alpha{}^s$ is given by the same expression, but the denominator of A_{res} contains here the total width Γ^s, whereas in the case of pure scattering it contained only the particle width. The maxima of both the resonance scattering and the reaction cross section occur at $\epsilon = \epsilon_s'$, and the width of the resonances is equal to the total width Γ^s. The existence of an imaginary part of f_l increases the width of the resonances.

Since f_l is no longer purely real, the scattering cross section does *not* reach its maximum value (8.22) in each resonance region. However, the scattering cross section comes close to its maximum value in a channel α for which the channel width $\Gamma_\alpha{}^s$ is much larger than the reaction width $\Gamma_r{}^s$. This condition implies that the various reactions which can occur are unimportant compared to the elastic scattering process, so that the resonance in question shows essentially the "one-channel" behavior of Section 8A.

The formulas developed involve the parameter $q = q(\epsilon)$ which enters into (8.28), about whose behavior we know very little as yet. q is a measure of the probability that the incoming particle stays in the nucleus [see (8.23) and (7.1)]. It depends on the channel energy and on the particular channel α through which the reaction is initiated. In order to use expression (8.32), we must obtain more information about the reaction width $\Gamma_r{}^s$. We employ the reciprocity theorem (2.63) for that purpose.

We shall now be interested in reactions initiated through different channels α and β but leading to the same state s of the compound nucleus. We therefore add subscripts α and β to the reaction widths

$\Gamma_r{}^s$, the channel wavelengths λ, the channel energies ϵ, and the actual resonance energies ϵ_s' in the two channels α and β, respectively. The reaction cross section near resonance in channel α is then, according to (8.32),

$$\sigma_{\alpha r, l} = (2l + 1)\,\pi\,\lambda_\alpha{}^2 \frac{\Gamma_\alpha{}^s\,\Gamma_{r\alpha}{}^s}{(\epsilon_\alpha - \epsilon_{\alpha s}')^2 + \tfrac{1}{4}(\Gamma_\alpha{}^s + \Gamma_{r\alpha}{}^s)^2} \qquad (8.33)$$

where we have written the total width (8.29) explicitly. The same formula gives the reaction cross section near resonance in channel β:

$$\sigma_{\beta r, l} = (2l + 1)\,\pi\,\lambda_\beta{}^2 \frac{\Gamma_\beta{}^s\,\Gamma_{r\beta}{}^s}{(\epsilon_\beta - \epsilon_{\beta s}')^2 + \tfrac{1}{4}(\Gamma_\beta{}^s + \Gamma_{r\beta}{}^s)^2} \qquad (8.34)$$

Let us *assume first that there are only two channels open at the energy under consideration:* channel α and channel β. Radiative capture is neglected. Thus the only possible reactions are the (α,β) and the (β,α) reactions. The reaction cross section $\sigma_{\alpha r}$ in channel α is then the cross section for only one reaction, the (α,β) reaction: $\sigma_{\alpha r} = \sigma_{\alpha\beta}$; and the reaction cross section in channel β is the cross section for only one reaction, the (β,α) reaction: $\sigma_{\beta r} = \sigma_{\beta\alpha}$. The two cross sections (8.33) and (8.34) are cross sections of inverse reactions and must satisfy the reciprocity law (2.63). Substitution of (8.33) and (8.34) into (2.63) gives (using the energy law $\epsilon_\beta = \epsilon_\alpha + Q_{\alpha\beta}$)

$$\frac{\Gamma_\beta{}^s\,\Gamma_{r\beta}{}^s}{(\epsilon_\alpha + Q_{\alpha\beta} - \epsilon_{\beta s}')^2 + \tfrac{1}{4}(\Gamma_\beta{}^s + \Gamma_{r\beta}{}^s)^2} = \frac{\Gamma_\alpha{}^s\,\Gamma_{r\alpha}{}^s}{(\epsilon_\alpha - \epsilon_{\alpha s}')^2 + \tfrac{1}{4}(\Gamma_\alpha{}^s + \Gamma_{r\alpha}{}^s)^2} \qquad (8.35)$$

for *all values of* ϵ_α *near resonance.* All widths Γ are slowly varying functions of the channel energies over the region of resonance. Hence (8.35) can be fulfilled only if: (1) *resonances occur at the same (total) energy in the* (α,β) *and in the* (β,α) *reaction, i.e.,* if

$$\epsilon_{\beta s}' = \epsilon_{\alpha s}' + Q_{\alpha\beta} \qquad (8.36)$$

and (2) the following relations hold:

$$\Gamma_{r\alpha}{}^s = \Gamma_\beta{}^s \qquad \Gamma_{r\beta}{}^s = \Gamma_\alpha{}^s \qquad (8.37)$$

The reaction width for the (α,β) *process is the entrance channel width in the* (β,α) *process, and vice versa.*

If (8.37) is substituted into (8.33), we obtain for $\sigma(\alpha,\beta)$ near resonance the expression (7.19), which was introduced in Section 7D as the Breit-Wigner one-level formula. Hence we have obtained a derivation of this important relation in the special case of two-channel reactions.

These considerations can be extended to the case of several open channels. We then obtain for the reaction width in channel α

$$\Gamma_{r\alpha}{}^{s} = \sum_{\beta \neq \alpha}' \Gamma_{\beta}{}^{s} \qquad (8.38)$$

where the sum is extended over all open channels with the exception of the entrance channel α. The reaction cross section breaks up accordingly into the individual (α,β) cross sections, and the latter can be expressed again by the Breit-Wigner formula (7.19), as in the case of two open channels. If radiative capture is included, the radiation width Γ_{rad}^{s} must be added to (8.38). Hence the assumptions in Section 7D, leading to the Breit-Wigner formula, are justified. A generalization to the case of target nuclei with spin different from zero will be found in Section 10.

Let us consider expression (8.27) for the channel widths in greater detail. We factor out the reduced width according to (7.15) and get

$$\Gamma_{\alpha}{}^{s} = 2k_{\alpha} R \, v_{l\alpha} \, \gamma_{\alpha}{}^{s} \qquad \gamma_{\alpha}{}^{s} = - \left[\left(\frac{\partial f_{l\alpha}}{\partial \epsilon} \right)_{s} \right]^{-1} \qquad (8.39)$$

Here we have used (2.50) for $s_{l\alpha}$ and the notation $v_{l\alpha}$ for the value of the penetration factor v_{l} in channel α. The reduced width $\gamma_{\alpha}{}^{s}$ can be estimated by means of expression (8.13) for f_{l}:[1]

$$\gamma_{\alpha}{}^{s} = \frac{D^{*}}{\pi KR} \sim \frac{D}{\pi KR} \qquad (8.40)$$

This relation is equal to (7.16), and hence we may conclude that the $\Gamma_{\alpha}{}^{s}$ which appears in the Breit-Wigner expressions is also the width which determines the probability of the decay of the compound nucleus through channel α. We prove this relation more accurately (without introducing D^{*}) in Section 9.

The estimate (7.16) for the reduced width is independent of channel α. It serves only to indicate the order of magnitude of $\gamma_{\alpha}{}^{s}$ and must be considered only very approximate. There are differences between the actual values of $\gamma_{\alpha}{}^{s}$ in different channels, as indicated in the more accurate relation (8.39). The actual value of $(df_{l}/d\epsilon)_{s}$ depends on the channel and may differ considerably from one channel to another.

[1] According to the definition (8.39), the reduced width $\gamma_{\alpha}{}^{s}$ is a quantity characteristic of the resonance s and the channel α, and *independent of the channel energy* ϵ_{α}. On the other hand, $\Gamma_{\alpha}{}^{s}$ depends on the channel energy through the factor $2k_{\alpha}Rv_{l\alpha}$. Strictly speaking, the D^{*} appearing in (8.40) and defined by (8.13) is different for different channels α.

We can get a similar estimate for $\Gamma_r{}^s$ by applying (8.13) to (8.28):

$$\Gamma_r{}^s = 4q \frac{D^*}{2\pi} \sim 4q \frac{D}{2\pi} \qquad (8.41)$$

This expression allows a direct interpretation of the physical significance of the reaction width. We go back to Eq. (7.1), which expresses the fact that only the fraction $|b|^2$ of the wave that proceeds into the interior comes back to the nuclear surface through channel α. Thus the fraction $1 - |b|^2 \cong 4q$ of the entering particles is diverted into other processes during the time P, which is the time the particle needs to return to the nuclear surface (compare Section 7C). Therefore $4q/P$ is the probability per unit time for the decay of the compound nucleus by all possible processes except the re-emission of a into the entrance channel α. Because of the relation $P \sim 2\pi\hbar/D$, this decay probability is equal to $\Gamma_r{}^s/\hbar$ as given in (8.41). Hence the reaction width $\Gamma_r{}^s$ can be interpreted as the decay probability of the compound nucleus through all those channels β which lead to a reaction ($\beta \neq \alpha$). This explains the form (8.38) which we quoted above.

It is useful to recapitulate at the end of this section what assumptions and simplifications have been introduced in the derivation of the Breit-Wigner formula. Expressions (2.55) to (2.58) are exact formulas for the cross sections. The Breit-Wigner forms (8.31) and (8.32) are obtained by the expansion (8.26), which is correct only in the neighborhood of the resonance. The function $f_l(\epsilon)$ changes its value appreciably over distances of the order of the level distance D, as the qualitative discussion of its behavior shows. Hence the expansion (8.26) is a good approximation for f_l only over a region which is small compared to D. Therefore the Breit-Wigner formulas are expected to be valid in a region near the resonance which is small compared to D. They are an exact description of the resonance cross sections only if the width of the resonance is very much smaller than the level distance (see Chapter IX, Fig. 2.3). Even then the theory predicts reliably only the *shape* of the resonance. The actual values of the constants are very badly determined. Expressions (8.27) and (8.28) for the widths cannot be directly evaluated since the derivative $(\partial f_l/\partial \epsilon)_s$ is not known. The latter was roughly estimated by setting $D^* \sim D$ in (8.13), from which (8.40) was deduced. Hence, although the prediction of the resonance shape by the Breit-Wigner formulas can be considered very reliable when $\Gamma^s \ll D$, our estimates of the widths must be regarded as a first orientation only.

▶ 9. RESONANCE THEORY; DECAYING STATES
OF THE COMPOUND NUCLEUS

A. The Potential Well Model

We illustrate the existence of decaying quasi-stationary states by an example which is really much too simple to describe an actual nucleus: the potential well. We imagine a single particle moving in the potential V given by

$$V(r) = -V_0 \quad \text{(for } r < b\text{)}$$
$$V(r) = 0 \quad \text{(for } r > b\text{)} \tag{9.1}$$

and we assume that the pure number $2MV_0b^2/\hbar^2 \gg 1$. (In this respect this potential differs from the one assumed between a neutron and a proton in Chapter 2.) Furthermore we restrict ourselves to motions with $l=0$. We put $u(r) = r\varphi(r)$, where $\varphi(r)$ is the wave function, and get for the wave equation of the motion of a particle with energy E:

$$\frac{d^2u}{dr^2} + K^2u = 0 \quad \text{(for } r < b\text{)}$$
$$\frac{d^2u}{dr^2} + k^2u = 0 \quad \text{(for } r > b\text{)} \tag{9.2}$$

where k is the wave number outside the well, and K the wave number inside:

$$k^2 = \frac{2ME}{\hbar^2} \qquad K^2 = \frac{2M(E+V_0)}{\hbar^2} \tag{9.2a}$$

Let us first consider the bound states of the particle in the well. Their energy is negative, $E < 0$, and the particle is restricted to the inside of the well. It is well known that the quantum conditions allow only a discrete set of values $E_1, E_2, \cdots, E_s, \cdots$ for the energy. We can interpret the discrete eigenvalues for negative energies in the following way: The particle within the potential well is not able to leave the well, and it oscillates within the boundaries, since it is reflected at $r=b$. Only those energies E_s are allowed for which the wave is in phase before and after reflection. If this phase relation is violated, the reflection leads to destructive interference, and no stationary state is possible. The situation is changed if $E > 0$, since the particle can then penetrate to the outside of the well. Classically, any particle of positive energy leaves the well at once when it has reached its border. However, the following consideration makes it plausible that in *wave* mechanics "quasi-bound" states must occur if the energy is only slightly higher than zero but much smaller than the depth of the well, i.e., $0 < E \ll V_0$. We make use of the fact derived in Section 5 that a wave of a free particle is reflected strongly when impinging upon a potential step which is almost as high as the kinetic energy of the particle inside. The intensity of the wave which passes over the step is only $4k/K$ times the total "inside" intensity, if K is the wave number of the wave impinging from inside the well, and k is the much smaller wave number outside the potential well. Thus, under the condition $0 < E \ll V_0$, the wave of a particle with an energy E is strongly reflected at $r = b$ and has only a slight chance of getting out of the well. The situation therefore is not wholly different from the case $E < 0$, where the particle cannot get out at all. We must expect the existence of discrete quasi-stationary states with positive energy E_s which exhibit a small leakage to the outside. There are wave functions for all energies $E > 0$. However, if $E \neq E_s$, the reflected wave interferes destructively with the original wave in the interior of the well. Hence the wave function is small inside the well compared to its value outside the well for all energies except the set $E = E_s$.

Let us first consider the truly bound states. Their energy E is negative, and the most general solution of (9.2) is given by [note the condition $u(r) = 0$ for $r = 0$]

$$u(r) = C \sin (Kr) \qquad \text{for } r < b$$
$$u(r) = Ae^{-\alpha r} + Be^{+\alpha r} \qquad \text{for } r > b \qquad (9.3)$$

with $\alpha = (-2ME/\hbar^2)^{1/2}$. Since $e^{+\alpha r}$ increases indefinitely with increasing r (and this is not permissible), we must have

$$B = 0 \qquad (9.4)$$

Both $u(r)$ and du/dr must be continuous at $r = b$; also, not all energies E are compatible with the condition (9.4). There are only certain discrete eigenvalues of the energy (which are the energy values of the bound states) for which (9.2) can be solved.

The situation is different when E becomes positive. Then (9.3) becomes

$$u(r) = Ae^{ikr} + Be^{-ikr} \qquad (\text{for } r > b) \qquad (9.5)$$

Both terms of the solution $r > b$ are bounded for large r, and there is no reason for an additional condition of the type (9.4). Any value of $E > 0$ gives a solution; we are in the continuous spectrum. We now wish to define the quasi-stationary states, and we use for this purpose the property of the leakage of particles from the well into the outside. The solution (9.5) represents for $r > b$ a superposition of an incoming and outgoing wave. We obtain a quasi-stationary state if we postulate that for $r > b$ the solution consists of *outgoing waves only*. This is equivalent to the condition $B = 0$. This restriction again singles out certain definite solutions which describe the "decaying states" and their eigenvalues.

The requirement of only outgoing waves does not correspond precisely to any physically realizable situation. Before the state can decay by emitting outgoing waves, it must first be formed. During the period of formation of the state, incoming waves must be present,

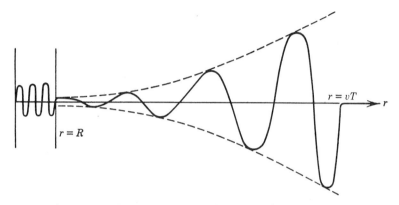

Fig. 9.1.   Schematic picture of the emerging wave of an approximate physical realization of a decaying state. The wave should not approach zero sharply at $r = vT$; rather there is a transition region which is not shown here. For the explanation of the increase in amplitude with increasing r (exaggerated in the figure) see the end of Section 9A.

whereas our requirement $B = 0$ excludes incoming waves altogether at all times. However, we can obtain an *approximate physical realization of a decaying state*, $B = 0$, by considering a system formed a very long time T before we start observation. The wave function $u(r)$ for $r > b$ is then a purely outgoing wave $\exp (+ikr)$ for values of $r \leq vT$ ($v =$ speed of the particle in the outside region), and is zero for $r > vT$. This wave function differs from the wave function of a pure "decaying state" only for very large values of r ($r > vT$) (Breit 35a, 40, Siegert 30, Bloch 40). Such a state is shown schematically in Fig. 9.1.

The restriction of the wave function to outgoing waves can be written in a more convenient form by making use of the logarithmic derivative $f(E)$ defined in (2.23). Since the value of both du/dr and u must be continuous, we get a condition equivalent to (9.4) by postulating that the following condition must hold for the solution

$$u = C \sin Kr$$

inside the well:

$$b \left[\frac{du/dr}{u} \right]_{r=b} \equiv f(E) = ikb \qquad (9.6)$$

the right side of which is just the value of $r(du/dr)/u$ of the outside solution (9.5) if $B = 0$. This leads to the relation

$$f(E) = Kb \cot Kb = ikb \qquad (9.7)$$

We can solve (9.7) numerically, but it will be more instructive to apply the linear approximation method which we have applied before in the resonance scattering problem.

We first impose, not the boundary condition (9.6), but the simpler one:

$$f(E) = Kb \cot Kb = 0 \qquad (9.8)$$

This condition does not contain any imaginary magnitude. We call the positive values of E for which (9.8) is fulfilled E_1, E_2, $\cdots$, E_s, $\cdots$. In order to get the solution for the boundary condition (9.6), we expand the function $f(E)$ around the point E_s as we did in (8.6). Let us call W_s the value of E for which (9.7) is fulfilled; then

$$f(W_s) = ik_s b \qquad (9.8a)$$

where $k_s \equiv (2MW_s/\hbar^2)^{\frac{1}{2}}$ is the corresponding value of k.

We now assume that W_s is near one of the values E_s. $f(W_s)$ can then be expressed by the power series expansion (8.6):

$$f(W_s) = \left(\frac{df}{dE} \right)_s (W_s - E_s) + \cdots \qquad (9.9)$$

By inserting this into (9.6), we get immediately

$$W_s = E_s - i\tfrac{1}{2}\Gamma^s \qquad (9.10)$$

where the "width" Γ^s is defined by

$$\Gamma^s = - \frac{2k_s b}{(df/dE)_s} \qquad (9.11)$$

and k_s is the wave vector corresponding to the resonance energy E_s, i.e., $k_s{}^2 = (2M/\hbar^2)E_s$. Actually, we should set $k_s{}^2 = (2M/\hbar^2)W_s$, but the imaginary part of k enters only in the next approximation.

Expression (9.10) tells us that W_s differs from E_s in first order merely through the addition of an imaginary part to the energy. The center of the levels (real part of the energy W_s) is determined by (9.8) and is therefore identical with the resonance energies of the scattering problem as given by (8.5).[1] Also, the width Γ^s of the virtual levels is equal to the width of the resonance levels, as a comparison of (9.11) with (8.7) reveals. Expression (8.7), however, is dependent on the energy of the incoming particle through the factor k; whereas in (9.11) k must be taken at the resonance energy.

We may well ask what is the physical meaning of a complex energy. The time dependence of the wave function is

$$\psi = \psi(t=0) \exp\left(-\frac{iW_s t}{\hbar}\right)$$

which gives a time dependence for the probability density $|\psi|^2$ of

$$|\psi|^2 = |\psi(0)|^2 \exp\left(-\frac{\Gamma^s t}{\hbar}\right) \tag{9.12}$$

This steady decrease of probability means that the state is continually decaying away with a lifetime $\tau = \hbar/\Gamma^s$. This exponential decrease of probability with time is a direct consequence of our assumption of outgoing waves only. *It also necessitates the condition* $\Gamma^s > 0$; otherwise, the system would gain probability continually, in disagreement with our outgoing wave assumption.

The discrete energy levels which we have just defined must be thought of as being unsharp to the extent Γ^s. We can see this by expanding (9.12) as a Fourier series in time and making the usual quantum-mechanical correspondence $E = \hbar\omega$. We put

$$\psi(t) = (2\pi)^{-1/2} \int_{-\infty}^{+\infty} \zeta(\omega)\, e^{i\omega t}\, d\omega$$

so that

$$\zeta(\omega) = (2\pi)^{-1/2} \int_{-\infty}^{+\infty} \psi(t)\, e^{-i\omega t}\, dt$$

This integral does not converge if we extend it to time $t = -\infty$. However, it is reasonable to start not at $t = -\infty$, but at $t = -T$, where T is some very large time interval. We then find that

$$\zeta(\omega) \sim \frac{1}{i(\omega - E_s/\hbar) - \Gamma^s/2\hbar}$$

---

[1] Since we are considering $l=0$ neutrons, there is no difference between the "formal" resonance energy ϵ_s and the "actual" resonance energy ϵ_s' ($\Delta_l = 0$ for $l=0$ and no charge).

The distribution in energy, i.e., in $\hbar\omega$, is given by $|\zeta(\omega)|^2$ and is therefore proportional to

$$[(\hbar\omega - E_s)^2 + (\tfrac{1}{2}\Gamma^s)^2]^{-1}$$

The half-width of this distribution is Γ^s, which is related to the lifetime τ by (7.5). The energy of such a decaying state cannot be defined more closely than with an uncertainty

$$\Delta E \sim \Gamma^s = \frac{\hbar}{\tau}$$

This situation is by no means peculiar to nuclear physics. Any excited level of an atom is a suitable example. The atom can emit a light quantum, thereby returning to the ground state. The level width Γ^s is related to the emission lifetime in exactly the same way.

A wave function whose absolute square everywhere decreases with time through the factor exp $(-\Gamma^s t/\hbar)$ is in contradiction to the law of conservation of matter, which requires that the integral $\int |\psi|^2 \, dV$ over all space be constant. Actually this integral is infinite for a pure decaying state. We can, however, use the approximate physical realization of such a state, which has been discussed before. The integral $\int |\psi|^2 \, dV$ is then finite because $\psi = 0$ for $r > vT$. Furthermore, the integral is independent of the time t because the exponential decrease of $|\psi(r,t)|^2$ for given r is compensated by the increase in the region of integration.

The wave function which has leaked out of the well is an outgoing spherical wave whose amplitude *increases* with increasing r (see Fig. 9.1). The increase comes from the imaginary part of the wave number $k_s = (2MW_s/\hbar)^{1/2}$. This increase is an expression of the fact that the parts of the wave function farther away from the well correspond to emissions at a time when the intensity inside the well was stronger. The largest amplitude is found in the front of the wave $r = vT$, which corresponds to the particles emitted at the time $t = -T$ when the decay process was started.

B. The Actual Nucleus

So far, our considerations have been based on the example of a particle in a square well. They can be generalized to an actual nucleus. Let us consider a system of A nucleons whose wave function $\Psi(q_1, q_2, \cdots, q_A)$ depends on the coordinates $q_1, q_2, \cdots, q_A$ of all nucleons, which include the position and spin coordinates. Ψ fulfills the wave equation

$$H\Psi = E\Psi \tag{9.13}$$

where H is the Hamiltonian of a system of A nucleons:

$$H = T + V(q_1, \cdots, q_A)$$

T is the operator of the kinetic energy of all A particles, and V is the potential energy depending on the coordinates q_1 to q_A. We shall never make use of the actual expression for H. The energy scale is chosen such that $E = 0$ corresponds to the ground state of the nucleus.

Let us assume that particle a has the smallest separation energy S_{min}. As long as the energy E is smaller than S_{min}, the particle a is bound to the rest of the system, and solutions of (9.13) exist for a series of discrete energy levels only, i.e., $E_0 = 0$, E_1, E_2, $\cdots$, etc. The situation is different for $E > S_{min}$. Particle a is able to emerge from the nucleus (leaving the residual nucleus X behind), and there are no restrictions as to the kinetic energy $\epsilon_a = E - S_{min}$ which a can acquire. The energy spectrum of our system, therefore, is continuous for $E > S_{min}$.

We restrict ourselves first to excitation energies in which only one channel is open. Let us call $\mathbf{r}$ the vector between a and the center of the residual nucleus X after they have been separated. The solutions of the wave equation (9.13) assume a simple form for $r > R$, where R is the channel radius. We can then write

$$\Psi = \chi_0\, \psi(\mathbf{r}) \qquad \text{(for } r > R) \tag{9.14}$$

where χ_0 is the normalized eigenfunction of the residual nucleus in its ground state; χ_0 does not depend on $\mathbf{r}$. We make a further simplifying assumption that the ground state of X has zero angular momentum, so that χ_0 is non-degenerate. $\psi(\mathbf{r})$ is the wave function describing the relative motion of X and a in channel α. It is determined by the wave equation (2.18a).

We now subdivide $\psi(\mathbf{r})$ as in (2.19) into subwaves corresponding to a given angular momentum l and use this for a similar subdivision of the total solution Ψ. Thus

$$\Psi = \sum_l \Psi_l$$

with

$$\Psi_l = \chi_0\, Y_{lm}(\theta,\varphi)\, \frac{u_l(r)}{r} \qquad \text{(for } r > R) \tag{9.15}$$

each Ψ_l being a solution of (9.13) belonging to the eigenvalue E and an angular momentum l. It is practically impossible to solve the wave equation (9.13). However, the only magnitude which enters into our consideration is the logarithmic derivative with respect to r, defined by

$$f_l(E) = R\, \frac{\partial(r\Psi_l)/\partial r}{r\Psi_l} = R\left(\frac{du_l/dr}{u_l}\right)_{r=R} \tag{9.16}$$

The functions $f_l(E)$ are completely determined by the Hamiltonian (9.13), although we shall make no attempt to calculate them. The value of $f_l(E)$ serves as a boundary condition at $r=R$ to the wave equation (2.30) for $u_l(r)$, and determines all cross sections, as demonstrated in the previous sections.

The definition of the "decaying states" introduced in the potential well model can be directly transferred to an actual nucleus. Let us consider the solutions of (9.13) for energies E above the separation energy, $E > S_a$. There is a solution for every value of E whose form for $r > R$ is given in (9.15). The function $u_l(r)$ is, in general, a linear combination of the form

$$u_l(r) = A\, u_l^{(+)}(r) + B\, u_l^{(-)}(r) \tag{9.17}$$

where the ratio A/B is a function of the energy. The functions $u_l^{(+)}(r)$ and $u_l^{(-)}(r)$ are defined in (2.41) and (2.42). *In order to describe a decaying state of our system, the coefficient B in (9.17) must be zero;* $u_l(r)$ then represents an outgoing wave only. This condition is fulfilled for certain values of E, which can be determined by means of the function $f_l(E)$. The condition $B = 0$ is equivalent to

$$f_l(E) = \Delta_l(E) + is_l(E) \tag{9.18}$$

where Δ_l and s_l are as defined in (2.46), (2.47), (2.48). Equation (9.18) says that $f_l(E)$ should be equal to the logarithmic derivative at $r = R$ of a purely outgoing wave $u_l^{(+)}$. Equation (9.18) is a generalization of (9.6) and is fulfilled only for discrete values of E, say $E = W_s$. We determine these values by the method of linear approximation. We first define the energy values E_s by the condition $f_l(E_s) = 0$. We then use again the expansion (9.9) of f_l. Equation (9.18) can then be written in the form

$$\left(\frac{df_l}{dE}\right)_s (W_s - E_s) = \Delta_l + is_l \tag{9.19}$$

We introduce the definitions [$\epsilon_s = E_s - S_a = $ formal resonance energy in channel α]:

$$\gamma_\alpha{}^s = -\left[\left(\frac{df}{dE}\right)_s\right]^{-1} \tag{9.20}$$

$$\delta E_s = -\Delta_l(\epsilon_s)\, \gamma_\alpha{}^s \tag{9.21}$$

$$\Gamma_\alpha{}^s = 2\, s_l(\epsilon_s)\, \gamma_\alpha{}^s = 2k_s R\, v_l(\epsilon_s)\, \gamma_\alpha \tag{9.22}$$

In terms of these constants the approximate value of W_s is found from

(9.19) to be

$$W_s = E_s + \delta E_s - i\tfrac{1}{2}\Gamma_\alpha{}^s \qquad (9.23)$$

W_s is complex. Its real part $E_s + \delta E_s$ agrees with the actual resonance energy (8.19) of the scattering problem.[1] The imaginary part of W_s gives rise to a width $\Gamma_\alpha{}^s$ of the decaying level which is equal to the scattering width $\Gamma_\alpha{}^s$ (8.18), evaluated at the resonance energy. We note that the width (8.18), which occurs in the Breit-Wigner formula, depends on the channel energy ϵ_α through the factor kRv_l. The constant (9.22) is equal to the value of this function at the formal resonance energy.

It is useful to express the partial width for the emission of a in a different way. We determine the width from the flux of the particles a through the channel: the probability per unit time $\Gamma_\alpha{}^s/\hbar$ to emit a particle a is equal to the number of particles per second leaving through the channel. This number can be calculated from the current through a sphere of radius R:

$$\frac{\Gamma_\alpha{}^s}{\hbar} = \frac{\hbar}{2iM_\alpha} \int \left(u_l{}^* \frac{du_l}{dr} - u_l \frac{du_l{}^*}{dr} \right)_{r=R} |Y_{lm}|^2 \, d\Omega$$

Here $d\Omega$ is the solid-angle element in the direction of $\mathbf{r}$. The integration extends over the full solid angle. Using the normalization of Y_{lm}, the definition (9.16), and the boundary condition (9.18), we obtain

$$\Gamma_\alpha{}^s = \frac{\hbar^2 |u_l(R)|^2}{2M_\alpha iR} (f_l - f_l{}^*) = \frac{\hbar^2}{M_\alpha R} s_l \, |u_l(R)|^2$$

We then get, from (2.50),

$$\Gamma_\alpha{}^s = 2k_s R \, v_l \, \gamma_\alpha{}^s$$

where the reduced width (9.20) is now expressed in the form

$$\gamma_\alpha{}^s = \frac{\hbar^2}{2M_\alpha R} |u_l(R)|^2 \qquad (9.24)$$

Equation (9.24) indicates that the reduced width is determined completely by the conditions in the interior of the nucleus, especially by $|u_l(R)|^2$, which is the probability of finding particle a at the surface of the nucleus in channel α.

This result can be interpreted very simply in the case of neutrons with $l = 0$, where $v_l = 1$. The emission probability $\Gamma_\alpha{}^s/\hbar$ must be

---

[1] It should be noted that we are considering here only one open channel, as in Section 8A, in contrast to Section 8B.

equal to the product of the probability $|u_0(R)|^2$ of finding the neutron at $r = R$ and its velocity of escape $v = \hbar k / M_\alpha$. This product gives the same expression that we would get from (9.22) and (9.24).

We now try to evaluate $|u_l(R)|^2$ by using the approximate form (7.2) for $u_l(R)$ inside the nucleus. The phase ζ can be determined for a decaying state s by the condition (9.18) which we have imposed upon f_l. For this evaluation it suffices to replace (9.18) by $f_l = 0$, which was the starting point of the method of linear approximation for f_l. Equation (7.2) can then be written in the form ($C = $ constant)

$$u_s(r) \sim C\,[e^{-iK(r-R)} + e^{+iK(r-R)}] \qquad \text{(for } r < R)$$

and the value in question is $|u_s(R)|^2 \sim 4C^2$. The normalization constant C can be estimated as follows. We have seen, in Section 7, that the particle a spends the time $P_s \sim 2\pi\hbar/D$ in the compound state s before rearriving at the surface. It moves within the nucleus with an average velocity $v \sim \hbar K/M$ and therefore covers an average "path length" $L \sim P_s v \sim 2\pi\hbar^2 K/DM$. This length is much larger than nuclear dimensions, since the particle undergoes many deflections within the nucleus. The average probability of finding it within the length interval dr of this path is dr/L. Since the wave function along this path is approximately $C \exp(iKr)$, we get $dr/L \sim C^2\,dr$, $C^2 \sim L^{-1}$, and $|u_s(R)|^2 \sim 4DM/(2\pi\hbar^2 K)$. Inserting this into (9.24) leads to

$$\gamma_\alpha{}^s \sim \frac{D}{\pi K R} \qquad (9.25)$$

in complete analogy to (8.40).

These considerations can be generalized to the case where several channels are open. We must now impose the boundary condition (9.18) in every open channel simultaneously. We may consider the energy W a function of the logarithmic derivatives $f_{l\alpha}$ in the open channels:

$$W = W(f_{l1}, f_{l2}, \cdots, f_{lN}) \qquad (9.26)$$

where N is the number of open channels: $\alpha = 1, 2, \cdots, N$. We define the formal resonance energy E_s in the compound nucleus by setting all the $f_{l\alpha}$ equal to 0:

$$E_s \equiv W(0, 0, \cdots, 0) \qquad (9.27)$$

We then expand W, (9.26), in a power series around $f_{l\alpha} = 0$ and use (9.18) to determine the values of the various $f_{l\alpha}$ in the decaying state. The result can be written in terms of the following definitions:[1]

---

[1] The definition (9.28) of the partial reduced width in channel α reduces to (9.20) when only one channel is open. The partial derivative in (9.28) is to be evaluated keeping all the other $f_{l\beta} = 0$ ($\beta \neq \alpha$).

$$\gamma_{\alpha l}{}^{s} \equiv -\left(\frac{\partial W}{\partial f_{l\alpha}}\right)_{s} \tag{9.28}$$

$$\delta E_{s} \equiv -\sum_{\alpha=1}^{N} \Delta_{l\alpha}(\epsilon_{\alpha s})\,\gamma_{\alpha l}{}^{s} \tag{9.29}$$

$$\Gamma_{l}{}^{s} \equiv \sum_{\alpha=1}^{N} \Gamma_{\alpha l}{}^{s} \tag{9.30}$$

$$\Gamma_{\alpha l}{}^{s} \equiv 2\,s_{l\alpha}(\epsilon_{\alpha s})\,\gamma_{\alpha l}{}^{s} = 2k_{\alpha s}R_{\alpha}\,v_{l\alpha}(\epsilon_{\alpha s})\,\gamma_{\alpha l}{}^{s} \tag{9.31}$$

In terms of these quantities the energy of the decaying state s, W_{s}, is approximately given by

$$W_{s} = E_{s} + \delta E_{s} - i\tfrac{1}{2}\Gamma_{l}{}^{s} \tag{9.32}$$

The partial widths $\Gamma_{\alpha l}{}^{s}$ are equal to the partial widths which occur in the Breit-Wigner formula, (8.27), evaluated at the formal resonance energy $\epsilon_{\alpha s} = E_{s} - S_{\alpha}$ in each channel. The relation (9.24) between the reduced width $\gamma_{\alpha l}{}^{s}$ and the magnitude of the wave function at the channel entrance remains valid in every open channel.

▶ **10. SPIN AND ORBITAL ANGULAR MOMENTUM**

A. $l = 0$ Neutrons

We have made an important simplification in the previous sections. We have assumed that the incident particle and the target nucleus both have angular momenta ("spins") equal to zero.[1] Only because of this assumption was it possible to describe the incident beam by a simple plane wave exp (ikz). Actually, the incident beam consists of a combination of several waves, each corresponding to a different spin orientation of the incident particle and the target nucleus. We shall show in this section that the inclusion of the spins does not change the results of the continuum theory as developed in Sections 3 and 4. It does introduce some changes in the resonance region.

If the spins of the incident particle and of the target nucleus are zero, the only contribution to the total angular momentum comes from the orbital angular momentum l of the incident particle. That is why we have decomposed the cross sections into parts corresponding to individual values of l. If the spins are different from zero, the total angular momentum J is a combination of three angular momenta: the orbital angular momentum l, the spin $\mathbf{s}$ of the incident particle, and the spin $\mathbf{I}$ of the nucleus (all in units of $\hbar$). It is useful to introduce the

[1] We use the term "spin" for the angular momentum I of the target nucleus, even though this angular momentum may be due mostly to the orbital motions of the nucleons within that nucleus.

vector sum $\mathbf{S}$ of $\mathbf{I}$ and $\mathbf{s}$. $\mathbf{S}$ is called the channel spin.[1] As an example, consider a neutron incident upon a nucleus of spin $\frac{9}{2}$. Here $s = \frac{1}{2}$, $I = \frac{9}{2}$; the channel spin S can assume the value 4 or 5. If we consider the incident neutron in its lth partial wave, the total angular momentum J assumes the values $|l - S|$, $\cdots$, $l + S$. If $l = 1$, we find $J = 4$, 5, 6 for $S = 5$, while $J = 3$, 4, 5 for $S = 4$.

Let us discuss the simplest case, namely, where *only the orbital angular momentum* $l = 0$ *enters*. This is true for very low incident energy, since then the particles with higher angular momenta do not get near enough to the nucleus to initiate a reaction (see p. 319). In this case, the total angular momentum J is made up of s and I alone. It is equal to the channel spin, i.e., $J = S$. We consider only the case $s = \frac{1}{2}$, corresponding to incident neutrons or protons. The treatment can be generalized to any value of s. The channel spin can assume the values $S = I + \frac{1}{2}$ and $S = I - \frac{1}{2}$, except in the case $I = 0$, for which only the first alternative exists. Each value S of the channel spin has $2S + 1$ orientations in space, which are determined by the magnetic quantum number m_S, where $m_S = S, S - 1, \cdots, -S$. We therefore obtain altogether

$$[2(I + \tfrac{1}{2}) + 1] + [2(I - \tfrac{1}{2}) + 1] = 2(2I + 1) = (2s + 1)(2I + 1)$$

states of the channel spin.

An *unpolarized* beam of incident particles impinging upon the nucleus no longer represents one single entrance channel. Such a beam must rather be considered an *incoherent mixture* of incident waves in all the $2(2I + 1)$ entrance channels. Each possible set of spin orientations of the incident particle and the target nucleus corresponds to a different quantum state of the system. In an unpolarized beam, each such state has the same a priori probability, i.e.,

$$[2(2I + 1)]^{-1}$$

The contributions of these individual quantum states add incoherently, since the phase relations between them are random. There are $2S + 1$ elementary states associated with every value of the channel spin S. Thus the relative probability that the incident particles and target nuclei in an unpolarized beam will be found to have the channel spin S is

$$g(S) = \frac{2S + 1}{(2s + 1)(2I + 1)} \tag{10.1}$$

This is the statistical weight of the channel spin S. As an example, consider neutron-proton scattering, where $s = I = \frac{1}{2}$, and S can be

[1] The channel spin S is called j_s by Wigner and Eisenbud (Wigner 47).

either 0 (singlet state) or 1 (triplet state). Formula (10.1) gives $\frac{1}{4}$ for the statistical weight of the singlet state, and $\frac{3}{4}$ for the statistical weight of the triplet state. The scattering cross section for low-energy scattering of an unpolarized beam of neutrons is the weighted average of the singlet and triplet scattering with these statistical weights.

We now consider one specific entrance channel S, m_S. The $l=0$ part of the wave function in this channel, in its dependence on the channel coordinate r, can be written in the form

$$R_0(r) = \frac{u_0(r)}{r}$$

$$u_0(r) = \frac{i\sqrt{\pi}}{k}[\exp(-ikr) - \eta_0(S)\exp(+ikr)]Y_{0,0}(\theta)\chi(S, m_S)$$

(10.2)

where $\chi(S, m_S)$ is the wave function for channel spin S with z-component m_S. Here the constants are chosen such that the incoming wave is equal to the $l=0$ incoming wave in a plane wave $\exp(ikz)$, just as in (2.22). The constant $\eta_0(S)$ depends on the value S of the channel spin; it does not depend on m_S, however, since the states of equal S and different m_S differ only in their spatial orientation and therefore give rise to the same ratio of outgoing to incoming wave.

The value of $\eta_0(S)$ can be quite different for the two possible values of S. Under our assumption $l=0$, the channel spin S is equal to the total angular momentum J of the compound nucleus. The resonance levels of the compound nucleus are at different energies for different values of J. (If two levels of different J should occur at the same energy, we would call it an accidental degeneracy; there is no reason to expect such accidental degeneracies to happen.) Hence, if the channels with channel spin S, say $S=I+\frac{1}{2}$, are in resonance, the other channels ($S=I-\frac{1}{2}$, in our example) are not in resonance. $\eta_0(S)$ is then very different in the two types of channels.

We therefore find two types of resonances for $l=0$ neutrons: one occurring in the channels $S=I+\frac{1}{2}$; the other, in the channels $S=I-\frac{1}{2}$. The cross sections σ_0 for an orbital angular momentum $l=0$ are composed of the (incoherent) contributions of all the $(2s+1)(2I+1)$ entrance channels. All entrance channels belonging to the same value of the channel spin S give rise to the same $\eta_0(S)$, and hence to the same total cross sections. We can therefore write for the cross section due to incoming particles with $l=0$

$$\sigma_0 = \sum_{S=|I-s|}^{I+s} g(S)\,\sigma_0(S)$$

(10.3)

where $g(S)$ is given by (10.1), and $\sigma_0(S)$ is the cross section in one of the entrance channels S. $\sigma_0(S)$ is related to $\eta_0(S)$ by expressions (2.11) and (2.13); $\eta_0(S)$ can be determined from the logarithmic derivative $f_0(S)$ at the surface of the nucleus in each channel, according to (2.24). For $s = \frac{1}{2}$, the sum in (10.3) has only two terms.

In the continuum theory of nuclear reactions (Sections 3 and 4), f_0 is given by (4.7), a value which in this theory is assumed to be independent of the channel spin. Hence $\sigma_0(S)$ for all S is equal to the value computed without consideration of the spins. Since $\sum_S g(S) = 1$, *the inclusion of the spins does not change the final results of the continuum theory.*

The situation is different if resonances occur. In the neighborhood of a resonance ϵ_s occurring, say, in the channels with channel spin S_1, only these channels contribute to the reaction cross section. Channels with a channel spin $S_2 \neq S_1$ do not contribute appreciably, since there is no resonance near ϵ_1 in these other channels. We shall let the channel index α include specification of the channel spin S and its z component m_S. Then the reaction cross section for energies ϵ near ϵ_s is no longer given by (8.32) but rather by

$$\sigma_{r,0} = g(S_1)\,\pi\,\lambda^2\,\frac{\Gamma_\alpha{}^s\,\Gamma_{r\alpha}{}^s}{(\epsilon - \epsilon_s)^2 + (\frac{1}{2}\Gamma^s)^2} \tag{10.4}$$

Here the channel width $\Gamma_\alpha{}^s$ and the reaction width in channel α, $\Gamma_{r\alpha}{}^s$ are defined by (8.27) and (8.38), respectively, with the magnitudes f_l, q, s_l, etc., referring to the channels α with channel spin S_1 (these magnitudes are independent of the z component m_S of S). Equation (10.4) differs from (8.32) through the statistical weight factor $g(S_1)$, which is the relative probability of having the spins of the neutron and target nucleus combine in such a way as to give the correct angular momentum of the resonance level of the compound nucleus $(S = S_1 = J)$.

While it is possible to neglect the contributions of the channels with $S \neq S_1$ to the reaction cross section, this is not possible for the scattering cross section. Even the non-resonant channels, $S \neq S_1$, give rise to scattering of the potential (hard-sphere) type. We therefore get instead (2.25)

$$\sigma_{sc,0} = g(S_1)\,\pi\,\lambda^2\,\big|A_{\mathrm{res}}^{(0)} + A_{\mathrm{pot}}^{(0)}\big|^2 + [1 - g(S_1)]\,\pi\,\lambda^2\,\big|A_{\mathrm{pot}}^{(0)}\big|^2 \tag{10.5}$$

Here the second term represents the non-resonant contribution to the scattering. The amplitude of the potential scattering, $A_{\mathrm{pot}}^{(0)}$, is independent of the channel spin and is given by (2.27). The resonance contribution to the scattering occurs only in the channels with $S = S_1$ [first term of (10.5)]. The resonance scattering amplitude, $A_{\text{res}}^{(0)}$, in these channels is given by (8.31) with $l = 0$.

The scattering cross section for $l = 0$ neutrons has the same qualitative behavior that we derived in Section 8 for spinless particles with $l = 0$ [see Fig. (8.2)]. There is an interference minimum at an energy $\epsilon < \epsilon_s$ and a peak near $\epsilon = \epsilon_s$. The minimum value of the cross section is higher now because of the potential scattering in the non-resonant channels. The maximum value of the scattering cross section is lower than before, approximately by the factor $g(S_1)$.

The statistical weight factor $g(S)$, (10.1), can be written in a simple form for the case where the incident particle has the spin $s = \frac{1}{2}$:

$$g(S) = \frac{1}{2}\left(1 \pm \frac{1}{2I+1}\right) \qquad (\text{for } S = I \pm \tfrac{1}{2}) \qquad (10.6)$$

The fact that channels with different channel spins are associated with different resonance levels of the compound nucleus is a result of our assumption $l = 0$. It implies $\mathbf{J} = \mathbf{S} + l = \mathbf{S}$, so that two channels with different S form compound states of different total angular momentum J, hence with different sets of resonance levels. In the general case, where l is not zero, all those channels contribute to the same resonance which, together with l, can form the compound nucleus in its resonant state J, i.e., all channels for which S lies between $|J - l|$ and $J + l$, and which lead to the correct parity.

B. Particles with Arbitrary l

We now generalize our considerations to include the cases where the incident particle has an orbital angular momentum l different from zero. Again we have to deal with $(2s+1)(2I+1)$ entrance channels, $g(S)$ of them corresponding to each channel spin S; the cross sections, however, are no longer given by (10.4) and (10.5).

In each channel the partial waves of orbital angular momentum l combine with the channel spin S to form a total angular momentum J such that $|l - S| \leq J \leq l + S$. Each partial wave of given orbital angular momentum l can be considered a linear combination of subwaves belonging to each of these values of J.

Consider one such subwave of given l, S, m_s, and J. Since $m_l = 0$ in a plane wave, we restrict ourselves to this value. The spin and angle dependence of this subwave is given by the function $\mathcal{Y}_{Jls}^M$ defined in Appendix A, with $M = m_l + m_s = m_s$. It is, in principle, possible to construct an ingoing wave of this type. It would be of the form

$\exp(-ikr)\,\mathcal{Y}^M_{Jls}$. This is a wave with a well-defined angular momentum l, a "pure" l wave. It is not possible, however, to have both the ingoing and the outgoing waves purely of this type. The outgoing waves generated by this pure ingoing wave are mixtures of all the pure waves l' which are consistent with the same J, M, and S.[1] Thus the orbital angular momentum l' of the outgoing waves may be different from l, provided only that J and M are the same. We shall denote the coefficient of the outgoing wave l', S, J by $-\eta_{ll'}(S,J)$. The wave function in channel α corresponding to the pure ingoing wave l, S, J, M is then

$$u(l,S,J,M;\,\mathbf{r}) = a\,\Big\{\exp\left[-i(kr-\tfrac{1}{2}l\pi)\right]\mathcal{Y}^M_{Jls}$$
$$-\sum_{l'=|J-S|}^{J+S}\eta_{ll'}(S,J)\exp\left[i(kr-\tfrac{1}{2}l'\pi)\right]\mathcal{Y}^M_{Jl's}\Big\} \quad (10.7)$$

Equation (10.7) is the analogue of (2.43) for spinless particles. The possibility of elastic scattering with change of l is a new feature. In the previous sections the scattered wave had the same l as the incoming wave because of the conservation of angular momentum, which was orbital only. The presence of the channel spin S allows changes of l without a change of the total angular momentum J.

Let us consider an example: A neutron beam impinges upon a nucleus with $I=\tfrac{1}{2}$. There are entrance channels with channel spins $S=1$ and $S=0$. Let us consider a neutron entering with $l=0$ in a channel $S=1$. The total angular momentum is $J=1$. The neutron can leave with $l=2$ and $S=1$ without violating the conservation of the total momentum J and without changing the channel spin S.

The coefficients of the outgoing waves $\eta_{ll'}(S,J)$ are independent of the orientation of S, i.e., of m_S. This follows directly from the overall invariance of the problem under rotations of the coordinates and spins simultaneously.

The constant a in (10.7) must be chosen to agree with the incoming l,S,J,M part of a plane wave $\exp(ikz)\,\chi(S,m_S)$ (χ = spin function for the channel spin), since only the outgoing waves can be changed by the presence of the nucleus. The expansion of this plane wave into subwaves with definite l,S,J,M is, for large r:

[1] There are outgoing waves also with different values of the channel spin S. According to our definition, however, these outgoing waves correspond to different channels $\beta \neq \alpha$ and are not qualitatively different from the outgoing waves for other reaction products.

$$\exp{(ikz)}\,\chi(S,m_S)\ =\ \frac{\sqrt{\pi}}{kr}\sum_{l=0}^{\infty}\ \sum_{J=|l-S|}^{+S}\ i^{l+1}(2l+1)^{1/2}$$

$$\times\ C_{ls}(J,M;0,m_S)\left\{\exp{[-i(kr-\tfrac{1}{2}l\pi)]}-\exp{[+i(kr-\tfrac{1}{2}l\pi)]}\right\}\ \mathcal{Y}_{Jls}^{M}\qquad(10.8)$$

where the $C_{ls}(J,M;m_l,m_S)$ are the Clebsch-Gordan coefficients which are given in Appendix A. Note that we always have $M=m_S$. Comparison of the ingoing wave parts of (10.7) and (10.8) then gives (remembering that u is by definition r times the radial wave function)

$$\mathsf{a}\ =\ i^{l+1}\,(2l+1)^{1/2}\,\frac{\sqrt{\pi}}{k}\,C_{ls}(J,M;0,m_S)\qquad(10.9)$$

Equation (10.9) is the generalization of (2.44).

Since the orbital angular momentum l is not conserved during the reaction, it becomes advantageous to combine the waves $u(l,S,J,M;\mathbf{r})$ with the same value of J and S, but with different values of l, into one function, which we shall call $w(S,J,M;\mathbf{r})$. That is, we define w by

$$w(S,J,M;\mathbf{r})\ \equiv\ \sum_{l=|J-S|}^{J+S}\ u(l,S,J,M;\mathbf{r})\qquad(10.10)$$

where each u in the sum is given by (10.7) and (10.9).

The reason for treating all these values of l together is not merely that they transform into each other during the reaction; so do the various possible values of the channel spin S, which we shall still treat separately. The main reason is that there are definite phase relations between the incoming waves of the same S,m_S,J, but different l, contained in the incident plane wave (10.8). Hence the contributions of the various values of l are *coherent* and have to be treated together. On the other hand, the contributions of the various channel spins S and their orientations m_S are incoherent, and we can obtain them finally by a simple averaging process. The scattering without change of energy or S, but with change of l, is therefore to be treated as coherent elastic scattering, while the particles which emerge with the same energy but different channel spin (and perhaps, but not necessarily, different l) can be considered reaction products, and the corresponding cross section can (and will) be included in the reaction cross section.

Let us now determine the elastic scattering cross section for given S,M,J $(m_S=M)$. The scattered wave, w_{sc}, is the difference between w

as given by (10.10) and the terms with the same value of J in the expansion (10.8) of the incident plane wave.   Thus

$w_{sc}(S,J,M\,;\mathbf{r})$

$$= \frac{\sqrt{\pi}}{k} \sum_{l,l'=|J-S|}^{J+S} i^{l+1} \sqrt{2l+1}\; C_{ls}(J,M\,;0,m_s)\,[\delta_{ll'} - \eta_{ll'}(S,J)]$$

$$\times \exp\left[i(kr - \tfrac{1}{2}l'\pi)\right]\, \mathcal{Y}^M_{Jl's} \quad (10.11)$$

For the sake of simplicity we shall derive the formulas only for the cross sections integrated over the solid angle and summed over the directions of the channel spin S of the outgoing particles.[1]   (We have not yet averaged over the orientations of the channel spin S in the incident beam, but we shall do so later.)   The scattered flux into a given solid angle $d\Omega$ is obtained by taking the probability density $|w_{sc}/r|^2$ of the scattered wave at a given r and multiplying by the element of area $r^2 d\Omega$ on the sphere of radius r and by the speed v of the outgoing wave.   The total flux is obtained by integration over $d\Omega$ and summation over spin orientations:

$$\text{Outgoing flux of scattered wave} = v \sum_{\substack{\text{spin} \\ \text{directions}}} \int \left|\frac{w_{sc}}{r}\right|^2 r^2\, d\Omega \quad (10.12)$$

The substitution of (10.11) into (10.12) is greatly simplified by the orthogonality and normalization properties of the spin angle functions $\mathcal{Y}^M_{Jls}$.   (See Appendix A.)   To get the cross section for elastic scattering, we must divide this scattered flux by the flux of the incident plane wave (10.8), i.e., by the speed v.   This gives

$\sigma_{sc}(S,J,M)$

$$= \pi \lambdabar^2 \sum_{l'=|J-S|}^{J+S} \left| \sum_{l=|J-S|}^{J+S} i^{l+1} \sqrt{2l+1}\; C_{ls}(J,M\,;0,m_s)\,[\delta_{ll'} - \eta_{ll'}(S,J)] \right|^2$$

$$(10.13)$$

Equation (10.13) is the generalization of (2.11) and reduces to (2.11) for $S=0$, $J=l=l'$.

---

[1] The restriction to scattering cross sections integrated over the full solid angle gives useful results only for incident neutrons. If charged particles are incident, the total scattering cross section is determined by the Coulomb (Rutherford) scattering.   The generalization of (2.60) for the case of spins is given by Laubenstein (50) and by Blatt and Biedenharn (to be published in 1952).

This rather complicated expression can be simplified by performing the *average* (*not* the sum) over the possible *orientations* $m_s = M$ of the channel spin S in the *incident* wave. These contributions are incoherent as long as the incident beam is unpolarized; hence we can average the cross sections directly:

$$\sigma_{sc}(S,J) = (2S+1)^{-1} \sum_{M = m_s = -S}^{S} \sigma_{sc}(S,J,M) \qquad (10.14)$$

We make use of the following relation between the Clebsch-Gordan coefficients:

$$\sum_{M = -J}^{J} \sum_{m_s = -S}^{S} C_{ls}^{*}(J,M;0,m_s) \; C_{l''s}(J,M;0,m_s) = \frac{2J+1}{2l+1} \delta_{ll''} \qquad (10.15)$$

This is a special case of formula $(A,5.10)$ in Appendix A.

Combination of (10.13), (10.14), and (10.15) gives the elastic scattering cross section for channel spin S and total angular momentum J:

$$\sigma_{sc}(S,J) = \frac{2J+1}{2S+1} \pi \lambda^2 \sum_{l,l' = |J - S|}^{J+S} \left| \delta_{ll'} - \eta_{ll'}(S,J) \right|^2 \qquad (10.16)$$

The diagonal terms of this sum, i.e., with $l = l'$, correspond to elastic scattering without change of orbital angular momentum; the terms with $l \neq l'$ correspond to elastic scattering with change of orbital angular momentum.

We now turn to the reaction cross section. For given values of S, J, $M = m_s$, we obtain the reaction cross section as follows: We find from (10.11) the difference between the incoming spherical wave flux of $w(S,J,M;\mathbf{r})$ and the outgoing spherical wave flux of the same function. This difference must be divided by the flux of the incident plane wave, i.e., by the velocity v. The fluxes are calculated by using formulas similar to (10.12). The result is

$$\sigma_r(S,J,M) = \pi \lambda^2 \sum_{l = |J - S|}^{J+S} (2l+1) \left| C_{ls}(J,M;0,m_s) \right|^2$$

$$- \pi \lambda^2 \sum_{l' = |J - S|}^{J+S} \left| \sum_{l = |J - S|}^{J+S} i^{l+1} \sqrt{2l+1} \; C_{ls}(J,M;0,m_s) \; \eta_{ll'}(S,J) \right|^2 \qquad (10.17)$$

The first term comes from the ingoing part of w; the second (double) sum, from the outgoing wave part. We again average over the orientations m_s of the channel spin in the incident beam and use (10.15).

We then get the *reaction cross section for channel spin S and total angular momentum J of the compound nucleus:*

$$\sigma_r(S,J) = \frac{2J+1}{2S+1}\,\pi\,\lambdabar^2 \sum_{l,l'=|J-S|}^{J+S} (\delta_{ll'} - |\eta_{ll'}|^2) \qquad (10.18)$$

So far we have not mentioned the fact that there exists another quantum number (besides the total angular momentum J) which cannot change during the reaction or scattering: the *parity* Π (Wigner 27). Every quantum state of a mechanical system is either even or odd. Its wave function is multiplied by either $+1$ or -1 if all coordinates x, y, z are replaced by their negative values (the spins are unaffected by the parity operation). Therefore, if the wave function describing the incident particle plus target nucleus was even or odd before the collision, it must remain in the same parity afterwards. The parity of the wave function of the target nucleus, $\Pi(X)$, is the same for all directions of its spin I. The parity of the wave function of the incident particle, $\Pi(a)$, is also independent of the direction of its spin s. $\Pi(a)$ is $+1$ for protons, neutrons, deuterons, and alpha-particles, which are the projectiles mainly used in nuclear reactions. The parity of the wave function describing the relative motion of particle and target nucleus depends on the orbital angular momentum l: it is even for even l, and odd for odd l. Hence, during a *scattering* event, l can only change by an even number: if l was odd originally, it must stay odd; if l was even orginally, it must stay even.

For example, consider a neutron being scattered by a target nucleus of spin $I=\frac{3}{2}$, and assume that the channel spin is $S=1$. Then, as far as conservation of total angular momentum J is concerned, the neutron could come in with $l=0$ ($J=1$) and leave with orbital angular momentum $l=1$. This, however, is forbidden by the conservation of parity. The neutron can come out with $l=2$, provided that l and S add up to $J=1$.

Because of the parity rule, the elastic scattering with change of l is an unimportant phenomenon: At low energies, any process with high l is very improbable. Since $\Delta l \geq 2$, the absorption or the emission of the particle is connected with an l equal to, or larger than, 2. At high energies, on the other hand, inelastic scattering with energy change is highly probable, so that the elastic scattering process in which l changes, but not the quantum state of the target, can be neglected.

We introduce the following notation: Π_C is the parity of the compound nucleus, $\Pi_{\alpha'}$, is the parity of the nucleus X in the quantum state α', $\Pi_{\alpha''}$ is the parity of the projectile a in the quantum state α''. α' and α'' determine the channel α. The *channel parity* Π_{α} is defined by

$$\Pi_{\alpha} \equiv \Pi_{\alpha'}\Pi_{\alpha''} \tag{10.19}$$

The relation between the channel parity and the parity of the compound nucleus is

$$\Pi_C = (-1)^l \, \Pi_{\alpha} \tag{10.20}$$

We also introduce the quantity $\omega_l(\Pi)$, which is unity if $(-1)^l = \Pi$, and zero if $(-1)^l = -\Pi$:

$$\omega_l(\Pi) \equiv \tfrac{1}{2}[1 + (-1)^l\Pi] \tag{10.21}$$

The conservation of parity has the following effect upon formulas (10.16) and (10.18) for the cross sections: we must divide the process into events with parity (of the compound nucleus) $\Pi_C = +1$ and $\Pi_C = -1$. Thus *the elastic scattering cross section for channel spin S, total angular momentum J, and parity Π_C* becomes:

$$\sigma_{sc}(S,J,\Pi_C) = \frac{2J+1}{2S+1} \, \pi \, \lambda^2$$

$$\times \sum_{l,l' = |J-S|}^{J+S} \omega_l(\Pi_{\alpha}\Pi_C) \; \omega_{l'}(\Pi_{\alpha}\Pi_C) \left| \delta_{ll'} - \eta_{ll'}(S,J,\Pi_C) \right|^2 \tag{10.22}$$

In the same way we find the *reaction cross section for channel spin S, total angular momentum J, and parity Π_C of the compound nucleus* from (10.18):

$$\sigma_r(S,J,\Pi_C) = \frac{2J+1}{2S+1} \, \pi \, \lambda^2 \sum_{l,l' = |J-S|}^{J+S} \omega_l(\Pi_{\alpha}\Pi_C) \; \omega_{l'}(\Pi_{\alpha}\Pi_C) \left(\delta_{ll'} - |\eta_{ll'}|^2 \right) \tag{10.23}$$

The cross sections (10.22) and (10.23) still do not represent a full average over the spin directions in the incident beam, since we have restricted ourselves to only one value of the channel spin S. The *cross sections* for unpolarized beams are given by[1]

---

[1] It should be noted that σ_{sc} as given by (10.24) is *not* the cross section for elastic scattering if elastic scattering is defined as scattering without change of energy of the incident particles. Equation (10.24) does not include the cross section for events in which the channel spin S changes during the collision. Such events are included in the reaction cross section according to our definitions. Later on we shall give the expression for the cross section of collisions without energy transfer (the experimental elastic scattering cross section) in the special case where the Breit-Wigner one-level formula is applicable.

$$\sigma_{sc,r} = \sum_{\Pi_C = \pm 1} \sum_{J=0}^{\infty} \sum_{S=|I-s|}^{I+s} g(S)\, \sigma_{sc,r}(S,J,\Pi_C) \qquad (10.24)$$

where $g(S)$ is given by (10.1).

Our previous expression, (10.3), for $l=0$ neutrons was appreciably simpler than (10.24) only because it was assumed that the low energy did not merely prevent particles with $l>0$ from approaching the nucleus, but also prevented particles with $l'>0$ from emerging as scattered particles. Hence the terms with $l'>0$, as well as the terms with $l>0$, are missing from (10.3).

The coefficients $\eta_{ll'}(S,J,\Pi_C)$, which determine the cross sections, are the generalization of the η_l which occur in (2.8) for scattering without spins. We recall that $|\eta_l|^2$ could not exceed 1, otherwise the intensity of the outgoing wave would exceed the intensity of the incoming wave. A similar condition holds for the $\eta_{ll'}(S,J,\Pi_C)$. The combined intensity of all the outgoing waves in (10.7) cannot exceed the intensity of the incoming wave:

$$\sum_{l'=|S-J|}^{S+J} |\eta_{ll'}(S,J,\Pi_C)|^2 \le 1 \qquad (10.25)$$

We do not need to specify which values of l' (even or odd) enter the sum (10.25), since $\eta_{ll'}=0$ when the parity rule is violated.

We now interpret the cross sections (10.22) and (10.23) from the point of view of the continuum theory. Since, in this theory, no wave is reemitted by the compound nucleus, we obtain $\eta_{ll'}(S,J,\Pi_C) = 0$ for $l \neq l'$. The value of $\eta_{ll}(S,J,\Pi_C)$ is determined by the logarithmic derivative $f(S,J)$ of $u(l,S,J,M;r)$ at $r=R$. (f cannot depend on m_s, since the states of different m_s differ only by the orientation in space.) In the continuum theory all logarithmic derivatives are assumed equal and are given by (4.7). Thus all $\eta_{ll}(S,J,\Pi_C)$ belonging to the same l are equal [see (2.53)] and independent of S,J and the parity Π_C. The elastic scattering cross section, as given by (10.22) and (10.24), becomes

$$\sigma_{sc} = \pi \lambda^2 \sum_{S=|I-s|}^{I+s} g(S)\,(2S+1)^{-1} \sum_{J=0}^{\infty} \sum_{l=|J-S|}^{J+S} (2J+1)\,|1-\eta_{ll}|^2$$

Since the parity is unimportant here, the sum is performed over all the values of l indicated. We interchange summations over J and l and use the fact that η_{ll} is independent of J, and that

$$\sum_{J=|l-S|}^{l+S} (2J+1) = (2l+1)(2S+1)$$

This gives

$$\sigma_{sc} = \pi \, \lambdabar^2 \sum_{S=|I-s|}^{I+s} g(S) \sum_{l=0}^{\infty} (2l+1) \, |1 - \eta_{ll}|^2 \qquad (10.26)$$

Since the η_{ll} are independent of S also, we can perform the sum over S explicitly; the statistical weights add up to unity, so that finally

$$\sigma_{sc} = \pi \, \lambdabar^2 \sum_{l=0}^{\infty} (2l+1) \, |1 - \eta_{ll}|^2 \qquad (10.27)$$

This is the same expression as the one we get without any spins whatsoever. A similar statement holds for the reaction cross section in the continuum theory. *The presence of spins does not affect the conclusions of the continuum theory of nuclear reactions.*

We now discuss the cross sections in the resonance region. We restrict ourselves to the case where only one resonance level of the compound nucleus is of importance. The resonance energy will be denoted by ϵ_n, rather than ϵ_s, to avoid confusion with the spin of the incident particle. The resonance level has the angular momentum J and the parity Π_C.

The main difference between these and the expressions in the previous sections comes from the fact that the angular momentum J of the resonance level does *not* determine the orbital angular momentum l of the entering or leaving particle. J is the vector sum of l and the channel spin S: $\mathbf{J} = l + \mathbf{S}$. Hence l can assume the values $|J - S| \cdots J + S$. In the previous sections the channel spin was neglected ($S = 0$) and we had $l = J$. Hence it will be necessary to distinguish partial widths $\Gamma_{\alpha l}{}^n$ of the compound state n corresponding to the decay into channel α with different orbital angular momenta l. The specification of l was unnecessary for the case $S = 0$ since l was uniquely determined by the character of the compound state.

The widths $\Gamma_{\alpha l}{}^n$ are identical with the widths used in preceding sections. They can be split into an external and internal part as in (7.15):

$$\Gamma_{\alpha l}{}^n = 2kR \, v_l \, \gamma_{\alpha l}{}^n$$

where the reduced widths $\gamma_{\alpha l}{}^n$ can be estimated as before in (7.16) in terms of the level distances D. The level distance in question is the distance between levels of the compound nucleus which belong to the same J and the same parity Π_C. D is, therefore, somewhat larger than the distance between nearest levels in the observed spectrum of the compound nucleus.

Let us consider first the cross section of a special nuclear reaction from one channel to another. Let α_S be a given entrance channel of spin S and let $\beta_{S'}$ be an exit channel of spin S'; and let us seek the cross section of the $(\alpha_S, \beta_{S'})$ reaction. It can be shown, but we will not give the proof here in detail, that this cross section near the resonance for an unpolarized beam is given by

$$\sigma(\alpha_S, \beta_{S'}) = \pi \, \lambda_\alpha^2 \, \frac{2J+1}{(2s+1)(2I+1)}$$

$$\times \sum_{l=|J-S|}^{J+S} \sum_{l'=|J-S'|}^{J+S'} \omega_l(\Pi_\alpha \Pi_C) \, \omega_{l'}(\Pi_\beta \Pi_C) \, \frac{\Gamma_{\alpha l}^n \, \Gamma_{\beta l'}^n}{(\epsilon - \epsilon_n)^2 + (\tfrac{1}{2}\Gamma^n)^2} \qquad (10.28)$$

Here I and s are the spins of the target nucleus and the incident particle, respectively. The widths $\Gamma_{\alpha l}^n$ and $\Gamma_{\beta l'}^n$ are the partial widths for the decay with an orbital momentum l or l' into channel α_S or $\beta_{S'}$, respectively. Γ^n is the total width of the level.[1]

The factors ω insure that the parity law is obeyed:

$$(-1)^l \, \Pi_\alpha = \Pi_C = (-1)^{l'} \, \Pi_\beta \qquad (10.29)$$

This parity rule can be expressed in words as follows: If the parities of the entrance channel and exit channel are the same $(\Pi_\alpha = \Pi_\beta)$, the orbital angular momenta l' of the outgoing particles are even (odd) if the orbital angular momenta l of the incoming particles were even (odd); on the other hand, if $\Pi_\alpha = -\Pi_\beta$, the outgoing l' are odd if the incoming l were even, and vice versa. In practice, the channel parity Π_α is equal to the parity of the target nucleus in its ground state, and the channel parity Π_β of the exit channel is equal to the parity of the residual nucleus Y in whichever state it is left.

The general form of (10.28) and especially the statistical factor

$$\frac{(2J+1)}{(2s+1)(2I+1)}$$

can be understood as follows: Let us start from (7.19) for the cross section of an

---

[1] It would have been more consistent to add the subscripts S and S' to the widths also, e.g., $\Gamma_{\alpha l S}^n$ instead of $\Gamma_{\alpha l}^n$. We have omitted these subscripts at the Γ's in formulas (10.28), (10.31), and (10.32) in order to avoid bulky symbols.

(α,β) reaction initiated by a particle with an angular momentum l without channel spin. If the channel spin S is different from zero, not all the incoming particles with orbital angular momentum l form a state with spin J together with the target nucleus. The relative probability $p(J)$ is

$$p(J) = \frac{2J+1}{(2l+1)(2S+1)}$$

Furthermore the relative probability $g(S)$ that s and I give the channel spin S is given by (10.1). Hence we obtain the (α,β) cross section initiated by an orbital momentum l for the case $S=0$ by multiplying (7.19) by $p(J)\cdot g(S)$. The $(\alpha_S,\beta_{S'})$ cross section (10.28) is obtained by summing the result over all possible values of l which can lead to the compound state n and over all possible l' with which it can decay.

It is impossible in most cases to distinguish between channels which differ only in their channel spins. We therefore look for the cross section of a particular nuclear reaction $a+X=Y+b$, where X, as well as Y, is in a definite quantum state. Because of the spins of both partners, the quantum state of the nucleus does not yet determine a definite channel. There are several entrance and several exit channels, according to the value and orientation of the channel spins. Let us call $\bar{\alpha}$ the group of entrance channels, and $\bar{\beta}$ the group of exit channels. The cross section $\sigma(\bar{\alpha},\bar{\beta})$ from $\bar{\alpha}$ to $\bar{\beta}$ in the neighborhood of a resonance is then the sum over the cross sections (10.28) extended over all channel spins S and S' involved. Hence the Breit-Wigner one-level formula for the (α,β) reaction is

$$\sigma(\bar{\alpha},\bar{\beta}) = \sum_{S=|I-s|}^{I+s} \sum_{S'=|I'-s'|}^{I'+s'} \sigma(\alpha_S,\beta_{S'}) \tag{10.30}$$

where I and s are the spins of the residual nucleus and the emitted particle.

Expression (10.30) is a generalization of $\sigma(\alpha,\beta)$ as given in (7.19). In fact, it is a sum of expressions of the form (7.19) corresponding to the transitions from each channel α in $\bar{\alpha}$ to each channel β in $\bar{\beta}$ consistent with conservation of angular momentum and parity. Expression (10.30) does not give any information about the angular distribution of the reaction products, however. Some general theorems about this angular distribution will be proved in Chapter X.

The Breit-Wigner one-level formula for the radiative-capture cross section from a compound state of angular momentum J and parity Π_C is

$$\sigma_{\text{cap}}^{J,\pi_C}(\bar{\alpha}) = \pi \,{\lambda_\alpha}^2 \frac{2J+1}{(2s+1)(2I+1)}$$

$$\times \sum_{S=|I-s|}^{I+s} \sum_{l=|J-S|}^{J+S} \omega_l(\Pi_\alpha \Pi_C) \frac{\Gamma_{\alpha l}{}^n\, \Gamma_{\text{rad}}^n}{(\epsilon_\alpha - \epsilon_n)^2 + (\tfrac{1}{2}\Gamma^n)^2} \qquad (10.31)$$

where Γ_{rad}^n is the radiation width of the level in question.

We now proceed to the elastic scattering in the resonance region. In order to be able to compare with experimentally measured elastic scattering cross sections, we shall give the combined cross section for all processes in which the incident neutron re-emerges without change of energy. This includes events in which the channel spin S changes during the collision—events which are not included in (10.22). We are interested in scattering of the group of $\bar{\alpha}$ entrance channels which differ only by the channel spin S and its z component m_S, but for which the target nucleus is in a definite energy state (the ground state, in practice). We quote the expression for the scattering cross section without giving its derivation. Since the formula is rather complicated, we precede it with an explanation of the meaning of the various terms. The first group of terms gives the resonance scattering without change of either the orbital angular momentum l or the channel spin S. These terms show interference between resonance and potential scattering. The next group of terms refers to the resonance scattering with change of l, but with no change of the channel spin S. This term is part of the elastic scattering as we have defined it so far, and it is contained in (10.22). The contribution of this elastic scattering with change of l, but no change of S, is practically of no importance. The third sum gives the scattering with change of the channel spin S, which is not included in our previous formulas (if was considered part of the reaction cross section). This contribution is of great importance in parity-unfavored[1] slow-neutron-scattering resonances but vanishes for parity-favored resonances if only the lowest possible l contributes appreciably to the cross section. The fourth sum in (10.32) represents the potential scattering which would be present if there were no resonance near the energy ϵ. Finally, the last (fifth) sum subtracts from this potential scattering the contribution of those channels which are affected by the resonance. *The Breit-Wigner one-level formula for the scattering cross section near a resonance of angular momentum J, parity Π_C, produced by channels with parity Π_α, corresponding to particles of spin s ($s = \tfrac{1}{2}$ in practice) and target nuclei of spin I, is*

---

[1] See Table 10.2 for the definition of parity-favored and parity-unfavored resonances.

$$\sigma_{sc} = \pi \lambda^2 \frac{2J+1}{(2s+1)(2I+1)}$$

$$\times \left\{ \sum_{S=|I-s|}^{I+s} \sum_{l=|J-S|}^{J+S} \omega_l(\Pi_\alpha \Pi_C) \left| \frac{i\Gamma_{\alpha l}^{\ n}}{\epsilon - \epsilon_n + i\frac{1}{2}\Gamma^n} + A_{pot}^l \right|^2 \right.$$

$$+ \sum_{S=|I-s|}^{I+s} \sum_{l \neq l' = |J-S|}^{J+S} \omega_l(\Pi_\alpha \Pi_C)\ \omega_{l'}(\Pi_\alpha \Pi_C) \frac{\Gamma_{\alpha l}^{\ n}\ \Gamma_{\alpha l'}^{\ n}}{(\epsilon - \epsilon_n)^2 + (\frac{1}{2}\Gamma^n)^2}$$

$$+ \sum_{S \neq S' = |I-s|}^{I+s} \sum_{l=|J-S|}^{J+S} \sum_{l'=|J-S'|}^{J+S'} \omega_l(\Pi_\alpha \Pi_C)\omega_{l'}(\Pi_\alpha \Pi_C) \frac{\Gamma_{\alpha l}^{\ n}\ \Gamma_{\alpha l'}^{\ n}}{(\epsilon - \epsilon_n)^2 + (\frac{1}{2}\Gamma^n)^2}$$

$$+ \frac{(2s+1)(2I+1)}{2J+1} \sum_{l=0}^{\infty} (2l+1)\ |A_{pot}^l|^2$$

$$\left. - \sum_{S=|I-s|}^{I+s} \sum_{l=|J-S|}^{J+S} \omega_l(\Pi_\alpha \Pi_C)\ |A_{pot}^l|^2 \right\} \tag{10.32}$$

The second summation in the third line of formula (10.32) is a double sum over l as well as l', each running from $|J - S|$ to $J + S$, omitting the terms $l = l'$; equally the first summation in the fourth line is a double sum over S and S', each running from $|I - S|$ to $I + S$, omitting the terms $S = S'$.

Formula (10.32) gives the total (integrated over all angles and summed and averaged over all spin directions) scattering cross section near an isolated resonance. It should be applied to the elastic scattering of neutrons only. For charged particles the total scattering cross section contains also the Rutherford scattering and becomes infinitely large because of the contributions of small-angle scattering. The expression for the differential scattering cross section in a given direction is very much more complicated than (10.32) and will not be discussed here (see footnote on p. 429).

It is of interest to determine the maximum possible value of the scattering cross section in the following special case: Only one channel spin S, total angular momentum J, and parity Π_C contribute to the scattering; and only the lowest orbital angular momentum L consistent with S, J, and Π_C is of importance. The practical value of this special case arises from the analysis of neutron-scattering resonances, which correspond to one definite level of the compound nucleus (with a definite J and Π_C), and for which all but the lowest possible orbital angular momentum l is unimportant because of the centrifugal barrier. The restriction to only one value of the channel spin S will be discussed later on.

Let us first determine the lowest value L of l consistent with S, J, and Π_C. If we ignore the parity rule for the moment, the lowest possible l is equal to $|J - S|$. This is actually the lowest l if the parity rule permits it, i.e., if $(-1)^{J-S} = \Pi_\alpha \Pi_C$. If the parity is unfavorable, the lowest l is $|J - S| + 1$, unless either S or J is zero; then there is no scattering at all from this channel. These statements are summarized in Table 10.1.

TABLE 10.1

MINIMUM VALUE L OF l CONSISTENT WITH GIVEN CHANNEL SPIN S, ANGULAR MOMENTUM OF COMPOUND NUCLEUS J, COMPOUND NUCLEUS PARITY Π_C, AND CHANNEL PARITY Π_α

$(-1)^{J-S} = \Pi_\alpha \Pi_C$	$L \equiv l_{\min} = |J - S|$
$(-1)^{J-S} = -\Pi_\alpha \Pi_C$	$L \equiv l_{\min} = |J - S| + 1$ provided that neither S nor J is zero.
	No l possible if either S or J or both are zero.

Under our restriction that only one value of S, J, and Π_C contributes, we need to consider only one term in the sum (10.24). Furthermore, under the restriction that only the lowest value of l, namely L, contributes, only one term survives in the sum (10.22). This term reaches its maximum value when $\eta_{LL} = -1$ (the other $\eta_{ll'}$ are to be taken equal to $\delta_{ll'}$ under our assumptions). Larger negative values of η_{LL} are inconsistent with (10.25). We then get the following value for the *maximum scattering cross section which can be contributed by one value of J and Π_C if only one channel spin S and only one (the lowest possible) orbital angular momentum $l = L$ is of importance in the scattering:*

$$\sigma_{sc} \leq \frac{2J + 1}{(2s + 1)(2I + 1)} \, 4\pi \lambda^2 \qquad (10.33)$$

For S wave ($l = 0$) neutron resonances of given J, only one value of the channel spin S can contribute, namely $S = J$, and (10.33) is indeed the maximum value of the resonance contribution to (10.5). This maximum is reached in the resonance if no reaction other than elastic scattering is possible (and if radiative capture is negligible). *In S wave neutron resonances a determination of the maximum value of the cross section gives a measure of the angular momentum J of the resonance level of the compound nucleus.* We must correct for the potential scattering due to the non-resonant channels, of course, before evaluating the maximum.

The situation is somewhat more complicated in the case of higher l, since then the spin-flipping (change of channel spin S) process may be possible and is measured experimentally as part of the "elastic" scattering. We shall tabulate the relevant information for the case of neutrons only, i.e., $s = \frac{1}{2}$ (Table 10.2). We observe that the lowest L in the parity-unfavored case·(second line of Table 10.2) is necessarily greater than, or equal to, 1. S wave neutron resonances $(L=0)$ are always parity-favored.

TABLE 10.2

MINIMUM VALUES L OF l AND POSSIBLE CHANNEL SPINS S CONSISTENT WITH A
CHANNEL PARITY Π_α AND WITH A COMPOUND STATE OF GIVEN J AND Π_C

	$I + \frac{1}{2} \leq J$	$I - \frac{1}{2} \geq J$
"Parity-favored" $(-1)^{J-I-\frac{1}{2}} = \Pi_\alpha\Pi_C$	$L = J - (I+\frac{1}{2})$ $S = I+\frac{1}{2}$ (unique S)	$L = (I-\frac{1}{2}) - J$ $S = I-\frac{1}{2}$ (unique S)
"Parity-unfavored" $(-1)^{J-I-\frac{1}{2}} = -\Pi_\alpha\Pi_C$	$L = J - (I-\frac{1}{2})$ $S = I \pm \frac{1}{2}$ Both values of S possible unless $I=0$ ($S=\frac{1}{2}$ only, in that case)	$L = (I+\frac{1}{2}) - J$ $S = I \pm \frac{1}{2}$ Both values of S possible unless $J=0$ ($S=I+\frac{1}{2}$ only, in that case)

In the case of parity-favored resonances (first line of Table 10.2), only one channel spin S contributes to the resonance scattering if higher values of l can be neglected (for slow neutrons). The maximum (10.33) then applies directly, and this maximum is reached if elastic scattering is the predominant reaction. Then a measurement of this maximum determines the angular momentum J of the compound state.

In the case of parity-unfavored resonances (second line of Table 10.2), both channel spins $S = I \pm \frac{1}{2}$ contribute to the resonance scattering; and scattering with change of channel spin S, but without energy change (spin-flipping process), is possible. Hence (10.33) is no longer applicable. It can be shown, however, that (10.33) still gives the right maximum value at resonance to the extent that the interference between resonance and potential scattering is negligible close to the resonance peak. This maximum includes the spin-flipping events and is reached if the scattering without energy change is the predominant reaction. Thus the height of the resonance peak can still be used to determine the J of the compound level, provided that the resonance peak is high compared to the potential scattering background.

A parity-unfavored resonance corresponds to a value of L one higher than we would obtain from consideration of the angular momenta only. For slow neutrons the difference in the penetration factor v_L for parity-favored and parity-unfavored resonances is appreciable. A parity-unfavored resonance is therefore expected to have an abnormally small width.

SYMBOLS

ₔ	Coefficient of exp $(-ikr)$ in $u_0(r)$ (2.21), (2.22)
ₔ	Coefficient of $u_l^{(-)}(r)$ in $u_l(r)$ (2.43), (2.44)
ɑ	Constant appearing in the approximate relation $E = \mathfrak{a}\Theta^2$ between the excitation energy and the temperature of the residual nucleus (6.11)
ₔ	Normalization coefficient in $u(l,S,J,M;\mathbf{r})$ (10.7), (10.9)
a	Incident particle in a nuclear reaction (1.1)
$a_{\alpha''}$	Particle a in quantum state α'' (1.3′)
$a_{\beta''}$	Particle a in quantum state β'' (1.3′)
A	Amplitude of $u(r)$ outside the nuclear surface, for one-channel resonance reactions (Section 7A)
A	Coefficient of exp $(-\alpha r)$ or of exp $(+ikr)$ in the wave function $u(r)$ outside the well (9.3), (9.5)
Ɑ	Constant appearing in $y(\epsilon_\alpha)$ (7.17)
A	Mass number, either of the target nucleus or of the compound nucleus (Section 2A)
A_{pot}	Amplitude for S wave "potential" (hard-sphere) scattering (2.25), (2.27)
A_{pot}^l	Amplitude for potential scattering with orbital angular momentum l (2.55), (2.57)
A_{res}	Amplitude for S wave resonance (internal) scattering (2.25), (2.26)
A_{res}^l	Amplitude for resonance scattering with orbital angular momentum l (2.55), (2.56)
b	Coefficient of exp $(+ikr)$ in $u_0(r)$ (2.21), (2.22)
b	Coefficient of $u_l^{(+)}(r)$ in $u_l(r)$ (2.43), (2.44)
b	Complex amplitude of the wave exp $(+iKr)$ returning from the interior of the compound nucleus (7.1)
b	Outgoing particle in a nuclear reaction (1.1)
b	Width (range) of a square well potential (Section 7C)

$b_{\gamma''}$	Particle b in quantum state γ'' (1.3')
B	Height of the Coulomb barrier $[=Z_aZ_Xe^2/R]$ (Section 4)
B	Coefficient of exp $(+\alpha r)$ or of exp $(-ikr)$ in the wave function $u(r)$ outside the well (9.3), (9.4), (9.5)
c	Outgoing particle in a nuclear reaction (1.3)
C	The compound nucleus (Section 3A)
e	Constant appearing in the approximate level density formula (6.11)
C	Amplitude of $u(r)$ just inside the nuclear surface, for resonance reactions (7.4)
$C_{ls}(J,M;m_l,m_s)$	Clebsch-Gordan (vector addition) coefficient; for its definition, see Appendix A, Section 5 (10.8)
d	Impact parameter of a nuclear collision (Section 1B)
$d\Omega$	Element of solid angle (Section 2A)
$D_s = D$	Level distance in the compound nucleus around the resonance level number s with excitation energy E_s (7.7)
D^*	An energy defined by (8.13), expected to be of the same order of magnitude as the level distance D (8.13), (8.14)
E	Energy of the system; $E=0$ corresponds to all nucleons separated from each other and at rest (1.4)
E	Relative kinetic energy in a nucleon-nucleon collision (Section 3A)
E	Excitation energy of the residual nucleus corresponding to the channel energy ϵ; $E = \epsilon_{bY} - \epsilon$ (Section 6A)
E	Energy of a particle in a one-dimensional model of a nuclear reaction (E corresponds to the channel energy ϵ, not to the excitation energy of the compound nucleus) (9.2a)
E_0	Average kinetic energy of nucleons inside the nucleus, estimated to be about 20 Mev (Section 3A)
$E_{\alpha'}$	Energy of nucleus X in quantum state α' (the negative of its binding energy in that state) (1.4)
$E_{\alpha''}$	Energy of particle a in quantum state α'' (the negative of its binding energy in that state) (1.4)

E_{α_0}' Energy of nucleus X in its ground state α_0' [= the negative of the binding energy of X]   (1.9)

E_{α_0}'' Energy of particle a in its ground state α_0'' [= the negative of the binding energy of a]   (1.9)

$E_{\alpha'}^*$ Excitation energy of nucleus X in quantum state α' (1.8)

$E_{\alpha''}^*$ Excitation energy of particle a in quantum state α'' (1.8)

E_β^* $= E_{\beta'}^* + E_{\beta''}^*$; internal excitation energy in channel β; it is commonly assumed that the outgoing particle is in its ground state so that $E_\beta^* = E_{\beta'}^*$, the excitation energy of the residual nucleus   (6.1)

E_{β_0}' Energy of nucleus Y in its ground state β_0' [= the negative of the binding energy of Y]   (1.9)

E_{β_0}'' Energy of particle b in its ground state β_0'' [= the negative of the binding energy of b]   (1.9)

$E_{\beta'}^*$ Excitation energy of nucleus Y in quantum state β' (1.8)

$E_{\beta''}^*$ Excitation energy of particle b in quantum state β'' (1.8)

$E_C = E$ Excitation energy of the compound nucleus C, measured from its ground state   (Section 3B)

E_n $= E_0 + nD$; nth in a series of equally spaced energy levels   (Section 7C)

E_s Excitation energy of the compound nucleus (measured from its ground state) corresponding to resonance level number s (Sections 7C, 9A)

E_s Energy of stationary state number s in a square well potential   (Section 9A)

f_0 Logarithmic derivative of $u_0(r)$ evaluated at the channel radius $r = R$ (2.23)

$f_0(S)$ Value of the logarithmic derivative f_0 in the channel with channel spin S (Section 10A)

f_l Logarithmic derivative of $u_l(r)$ evaluated at the channel radius $r = R$ (2.45)

$f_{l\alpha}$ Logarithmic derivative f_l in channel α (8.39)

$F_b = F_b(\epsilon_{bY})$ A function related to the branching probability $G_C(b)$ for emission of particles b from the compound nucleus C   (6.8), (6.9)

$F_l(r)$ Regular solution of the extra-nuclear radial equation for collisions with orbital angular momentum l (2.32), (2.33), (2.39)

g_A, g_B, g_P, g_Q	Statistical weight of state A, etc. (Section 2E)
$g(S)$	Statistical weight of channel spin S (10.1), (10.6)
$G_b(\epsilon)\, d\epsilon$	Branching ratio for emission from the compound nucleus of particles b with channel energies between ϵ and $\epsilon + d\epsilon$ (6.2)
$G_C(b)$	Branching ratio (relative decay probability) for the compound nucleus C to decay by emission of particle b (3.1), (6.7)
$G_C(\beta)$	Branching ratio (relative decay probability) for the compound nucleus C to decay through channel β (3.2)
$G_l(r)$	Irregular solution of the extra-nuclear radial equation for collisions with orbital angular momentum l (2.36), (2.37), (2.40)
$G_{Y\beta'}(c)$	Branching ratio (relative decay probability) for the nucleus Y in state β' to decay by emission of particle c (6.13)
$\hbar\omega$	A gamma-ray; the energy of a gamma-ray (1.2)
I	Probability density of the incident wave (Section 4)
I	Angular momentum of the target nucleus X (Section 10A)
$I_b(\epsilon)\, d\epsilon$	Relative number of particles b emitted with channel energies between ϵ and $\epsilon + d\epsilon$ (6.3)
$\operatorname{Im} f_l$	The imaginary part of f_l (2.28), (2.56)
$J = J_C$	Total angular momentum of the system, equal to the angular momentum of the compound nucleus (Sections 3B, 10A)
$J_p(z)$	Bessel function of first kind and order p; for its definition, see Jahnke-Emde (33) (Section 2C)
k_s	$= (2MW_s/\hbar^2)^{1/2}$; wave number of decaying state number s (9.8a)
k_α, k_β	$= |\mathbf{k}_\alpha| = \lambda_\alpha^{-1}$; channel wave number in channel α or β (2.6)
$\mathbf{k}_\alpha$	Wave vector for the relative motion in channel α (2.5)
K	Wave number of a particle just after it enters the compound nucleus (4.3), (4.12)
K_0	$\cong 1 \times 10^{+13}$ cm^{-1}; wave number of a nucleon just after it enters the compound nucleus, if the outside (channel) energy was zero (4.11), (4.13), (4.14)

l	Quantum number for the orbital angular momentum in a channel (Section 2A)
$(2l-1)!!$	$\equiv 1 \times 3 \times 5 \times \cdots \times (2l-1)$; the "double factorial" (2.52)
L	Distance from a "black" nucleus at which the "shadow" becomes blurred completely by diffraction effects $[\cong R^2/\lambda]$ (Section 2A)
L	Orbital angular momentum quantum number of the compound nucleus (Section 7C)
L	"Path length" of a nucleon inside the compound nucleus before rearriving at the nuclear surface (Section 9B)
L	Lowest value of the channel orbital angular momentum l consistent with a channel spin S, a total angular momentum J, and a total (compound nucleus) parity Π_C (Section 10B)
m_S	Magnetic quantum number associated with the channel spin S (Section 10A)
$M = M_\alpha$	Reduced mass for the relative motion in channel α (2.5), (2.30)
M_a	Mass of particle a (1.5)
M_X	Mass of (target) nucleus X (1.5)
M_β	Reduced mass M for the relative motion in channel β (2.70)
N	Incident flux, equal to the number of particles incident per square centimeter per second (Section 2A)
N	Number of open channels at the energy under consideration (Section 9B)
N_a	Number of particles per second taken out of the beam by events other than elastic scattering (2.12)
$N_p(z)$	Neumann function (Bessel function of the second kind) of order p; for its definition, see Jahnke-Emde (33) (2.40)
N_{sc}	Number of scattered particles per second (2.10)
$N_{sc}(\theta)\,d\Omega$	Number of particles per second scattered into the solid-angle element $d\Omega$ around the direction θ with respect to the incident beam (2.14)
p	A non-degenerate quantum state (Section 2E)
$p(J)$	Probability (statistical weight) of a state with total angular momentum J in a system with orbital

	angular momentum l and (channel) spin S, $[=(2J+1)/(2l+1)(2S+1)]$ (Section 10B)
P	A degenerate quantum state (Section 2E)
P	Period of the motion in the compound nucleus (7.10)
$P(A,B)$	Probability per unit time of a transition from state A to state B (2.67)
$P(-B,-A)$	Probability per unit time of a transition from the (time-reversed) state $-B$ to state $-A$ (2.68)
P_s	Period of the motion of the compound nucleus in resonance level number s (Section 9B)
q	A non-degenerate quantum state (Section 2E)
q	A positive real number, related to the amplitude b of the wave $\exp(+iKr)$ returning from the interior of the compound nucleus through $|\mathsf{b}|=\exp(-2q)$; q depends on the channel energy ϵ (8.23)
Q	A degenerate quantum state (Section 2E)
Q_{ab}	Q value (energy release) of the $\mathrm{X}(a,b)\mathrm{Y}$ reaction (1.9)
$Q_{\alpha\beta}$	Q value of the (α,β) reaction (1.6), (1.7)
r	$=|\mathbf{r}_\alpha|$; distance between X and a in channel α (2.7)
r_0	Radius of a large sphere, enclosing the origin, in which the reaction occurs (2.10)
r_0	Constant appearing in the nuclear radius formula $R=r_0A^{1/3}$ (Section 3A)
r_0	Classical distance of closest approach for particles of orbital angular momentum l, defined as the largest root of $\kappa_l(r)=0$ (5.9)
r_α	$=|\mathbf{r}_\alpha|$ (Section 2B)
$\mathbf{r}_\alpha$	Channel coordinate in channel α, equal to the vector separation between X and a (Section 2A)
R	Radius of a "black" nucleus (Section 2A)
R	Channel radius (Section 2B; see also Fig. 2.4)
R_a	Radius of the incident particle a (Section 2B)
R_X	Radius of the target nucleus X (Section 2B)
R_α	Channel radius in channel α (Section 2B)
$\mathrm{Re}\,f_l$	The real part of f_l (2.28), (2.56)
s	Spin of the incident particle a (Section 10A)
$s=s_l(\epsilon)$	A function of the channel energy ϵ which enters into the calculation of the width (2.46), (2.48), (2.50)

$\mathfrak{S}$	$= \log w(E)$; entropy of the residual nucleus at a temperature Θ corresponding to a mean excitation energy E (6.4)
S	Separation energy of a nucleon from the compound nucleus (Section 3A)
S	Spin angular momentum quantum number of the compound nucleus (Section 7C)
S	Channel spin, formed by vector addition of the angular momenta I of the target nucleus and s of the incident particle (Section 10A)
S_1	A particular value of the channel spin S for which there is a resonance near the energy under consideration (Section 10A)
S_2	A value of the channel spin S for which there is no resonance near the energy under consideration (Section 10A)
S_a	Separation energy of particle a from the compound nucleus (1.8)
$S_c(Y)$	Separation energy of particle c from the residual nucleus Y (Section 6B)
$S_{\min}(Y)$	Lowest separation energy of some particle from the residual nucleus Y (Section 6B)
$S_n(Y)$	Separation energy of a neutron from the residual nucleus Y (Section 6B)
$\mathsf{T} = \mathsf{T}(\alpha)$	Transmission coefficient of the nuclear surface (4.3), (7.11)
$\mathsf{T}_l(\alpha)$	Transmission coefficient for collisions through channel α with orbital angular momentum l (5.1), (5.5), (5.6)
T	A very long time interval (Section 9A)
$\bar{T}$	Average kinetic energy of nucleons inside the nucleus (Section 4)
T_0	Kinetic energy of particles of a certain kind inside the nucleus; $T_0 \sim 20$ Mev for nucleons, somewhat less for alpha-particles (Section 4)
T_{in}	Kinetic energy of the incident particle just after it enters the compound nucleus (Section 4)
T_{pq}	Probability per unit time of a transition from quantum state p to quantum state q (Section 2E)
$T_{P,Q}$	Probability per unit time for a transition from state P to state Q (2.69)

$T_{-Q,-P}$	Probability per unit time for a transition from (time-reversed) state $-Q$ to state $-P$ (2.69)
$u'(R)$	The derivative du/dr of the radial wave function $u(r)$ evaluated at the channel radius R (8.3)
$u_0(r)$	S wave radial wave function $[=u_l(r)$ for $l=0]$ (2.19)
$u(l,S,J,M;\mathbf{r})$	r times the wave function for the relative motion in a channel with channel spin S, for collisions with total angular momentum J, z component of total angular momentum M, induced by an ingoing wave with orbital angular momentum l (10.7)
$u_l(r)$	Radial wave function in the incident channel for collisions with orbital angular momentum l (2.19), (2.30)
$u_l^{(+)}(r)$	Outgoing wave solution of the extra-nuclear radial wave equation for orbital angular momentum l (2.41), (2.42)
$u_l^{(-)}(r)$	Ingoing wave solution of the extra-nuclear radial wave equation for orbital angular momentum l (2.41)
U_0	Well depth of a schematic potential inside the nuclear surface, used for the calculation of transmission coefficients (5.3)
$U(E_{\rm C})$	A function of the excitation energy of the compound nucleus (3.6)
$U_l(r)$	Effective potential energy (Coulomb plus centrifugal potential) outside the nuclear surface, for collisions with orbital angular momentum i (5.2)
$v=v_\alpha$	Speed of the relative motion in channel α Section 2A and (2.67)
$v_l=v_{l\alpha}$	Penetration factor in channel α for collisions with orbital angular momentum l; v_l is a function of the channel energy ϵ_α (2.49), (7.23), (8.39)
v_l'	A function appearing in the theoretical expression for the transmission coefficient $T_l(\alpha)$ for neutron channels (5.7), (5.8)
v_β	Speed of the relative motion in channel β (2.68)
$\mathbf{v}_\alpha$	Vector velocity of the relative motion in channel α (2.5)
V	A large volume enclosing the region of interaction (2.67), (2.68)
V	Potential for a one-particle model of a nuclear reaction (Section 4)

V_0	Well depth of the potential V in the interior region for a one-particle model of a nuclear reaction (Section 4)
V_0	Well depth of a square well (9.1)
$V(r)$	Extra-nuclear (electrostatic) potential energy in a channel (2.30), (2.31)
$w(S,J,M;\mathbf{r})$	r times the wave function for the relative motion in a channel with channel spin S, for collisions with total angular momentum J, z component of total angular momentum M, induced by an incident *polarized plane* wave (10.10)
$w_{sc}(S,J,M;\mathbf{r})$	The part of $w(S,J,M;\mathbf{r})$ corresponding to an elastically scattered wave (10.11)
$w_{\mathrm{Y}}(E)$	Level density of the residual nucleus Y at excitation energy E; $w_{\mathrm{Y}}(E)\,dE$ is the number of states of Y with excitation energies between E and $E+dE$ (Section 6A)
W	Nucleus formed by radiative capture of a particle (1.2)
W_s	The (complex) energy of decaying state number s (9.8a)
x	$=kR$; product of the channel wave number and the channel radius (5.7)
X	The target nucleus in a nuclear reaction (1.1)
X*	The target nucleus X in an excited state (1.3)
X	$=KR$; product of the "interior" wave number and the channel radius (5.7)
X_0	$=K_0R$ (Section 4)
$X_{\alpha'}$	The target nucleus X in quantum state α' (1.3')
$y(\epsilon_\alpha)$	A function giving the energy dependence of the reaction cross section near a resonance (Section 7D)
Y	The residual nucleus in a nuclear reaction (1.1)
Y	$=\epsilon/B$; ratio of the channel energy to the height of the Coulomb barrier (Section 4)
$Y_{lm}(\theta,\varphi)$	Spherical harmonic; for its definition see Appendix A, Section 2 (Section 2A)
$\mathcal{Y}^M_{Jls}$	Normalized "spin-angle" harmonic; for its definition see Appendix A, Section 5 (10.7)
$Y_{\gamma'}$	Residual nucleus Y in quantum state γ' (1.3')
z	Channel coordinate along the direction of the incident beam (Section 2A)

$z(\epsilon)$ A quantity related to the radial wave function $u(r)$ at the channel radius $r = R$ (8.2)

Z A residual nucleus   (1.3)

Z_a The charge of particle a, in units of e (2.31)

Z_X The charge of nucleus X, in units of e (2.31)

α Channel index, including both α' and α'' (Section 1B)

α Decay constant for the wave function $u(r)$ of a bound state outside the well   (9.3)

α' Quantum state of a (residual or target) nucleus (Section 1B)

α'' Quantum state of an (incident or outgoing) particle (Section 1B)

α_0 Channel in which both the target nucleus X and the incident particle a are in their respective ground states   (Section 1C)

α_0' Ground state of the target nucleus X   (Section 1C)

α_0'' Ground state of the incident particle a (Section 1C)

$\bar{\alpha}$ Group of channels α belonging to the same quantum state α' of X and α'' of a, but with different channel spins S (Section 10B)

β Channel index, including both β' and β'' (Section 1B)

β' Quantum state of a (target or residual) nucleus (Section 1B)

β'' Quantum state of an (incident or outgoing) particle (Section 1B)

β_0 Channel in which both the residual nucleus Y and the outgoing particle b are in their respective ground states   (Section 1C)

β_0' Ground state of the residual nucleus Y   (Section 1C)

β_0'' Ground state of the outgoing particle b (Section 1C)

$\bar{\beta}$ Group of channels β belonging to the same quantum state β' of Y and β'' of b, but with different channel spins S' (Section 10B)

γ $= Z_a Z_X e^2 / \hbar v$; a parameter measuring the relative importance of Coulomb effects   (2.34)

γ'	Quantum state of a nucleus (target or residual nucleus) (Section 1B)
γ''	Quantum state of a particle (incident or outgoing particle) (Section 1B)
$\gamma_\alpha{}^s$	Reduced partial width of resonance level number s for emission into channel α (7.15), (8.39), (9.20)
$\gamma_{\alpha l}{}^n$	Reduced partial width of resonance level number n for emission into channel α with orbital angular momentum l (Section 10B)
$\gamma_{\alpha l}{}^s$	Reduced partial width of resonance level number s for emission into channel α, with orbital angular momentum l (9.28)
$\Gamma = \Gamma(E_C)$	Total width of a state of the compound nucleus C with excitation energy E_C (3.3)
Γ^n	Total width of resonance level number n (10.28)
Γ^s	Total width of resonance level number s (7.5), (9.10), (9.11)
$\Gamma_a{}^s$	"Particle width" [= partial width of the resonance level number s for emission of particle a] (7.6)
$\Gamma_{a\alpha'}{}^s$	Partial width of resonance level number s for emission of particle a, leaving the residual nucleus in state α' (7.8)
$\Gamma_\alpha{}^s$	Partial width of resonance level number s for emission into channel α (7.9), (9.22)
$\Gamma_{\alpha l}{}^n$	Partial width of resonance level number n for emission into channel α, with orbital angular momentum l (Section 10B)
$\Gamma_\beta = \Gamma_\beta(E_C)$	Partial width of a state of the compound nucleus C with excitation energy E_C for emission into channel β (3.4)
$\Gamma_r{}^s$	Reaction width [= $\hbar$ times the probability per unit time of decay of the compound nucleus in resonance level number s through some channel other than the incident channel α] (8.28)
Γ_{rad}^n	Radiation width of resonance level number n (10.31)
Γ_{rad}^s	Radiation width [= partial width of resonance level number s for emission of a light quantum] (7.6)
$\Gamma_{r\alpha}{}^s$	Reaction width of resonance level number s for reactions initiated through channel α (8.33)

$\Gamma_{r\beta}{}^s$ Reaction width of resonance level number s for reactions initiated through channel β (8.34)

δ Phase shift of $u(r)$ outside the nuclear surface, for one-channel resonance reactions   (Section 7A)

δE_s Level shift of decaying state number s (9.21)

Δ A small energy interval around the threshold of a nuclear reaction   (Section 7E)

$\Delta\epsilon$ A small increment in the channel energy ϵ (Section 2E)

$\Delta\epsilon$ A small energy interval around the resonance energy $\epsilon = \epsilon_s$, defined by condition (8.15)   (8.15a)

$\Delta_l = \Delta_l(\epsilon)$ A parameter entering into the "level shift" for orbital angular momentum l; Δ_l is a function of the channel energy ϵ (2.46), (2.47)

ϵ Channel energy in the entrance channel $[=\epsilon_\alpha]$ (1.10)

ϵ' Maximum kinetic energy of nucleons inside the nucleus (the top of the Fermi distribution)   (4.11)

ϵ_{bY} The highest channel energy ϵ_β in any outgoing channel of an $X(a,b)Y$ reaction, corresponding to leaving the residual nucleus Y in its ground state β_0 (1.10)

ϵ_c Surplus of energy above the threshold of the $(a;b,c)$ reaction   (6.16)

ϵ_n, ϵ_s Channel energy in the incident channel corresponding to resonance level number n or s (Sections 7A, 10B)

ϵ_s "Formal" resonance energy for resonance number s (8.17)

ϵ_s' "Actual" resonance energy for resonance number s; this quantity is a function of the channel energy ϵ (8.19)

ϵ_{sec} $\equiv \epsilon_{bY} - S_{min}(Y)$; maximum energy available for emission of secondary particles from the residual nucleus Y (Section 6B)

ϵ_{th} Threshold energy for secondary reactions   (Section 6B)

ϵ_α Energy of the relative motion in channel α $[=$ the "channel energy" in channel $\alpha]$ (1.4)

$(\epsilon_\alpha)_{lab}$ Laboratory energy of particle a corresponding to the channel energy ϵ_α (1.5)

$\epsilon_{\alpha s}$ Channel energy corresponding to resonance number

s in channel α; this quantity is denoted by ϵ_s if the channel specification is understood   (Section 7C)

$\epsilon_{\alpha s}'$ "Actual" resonance energy for resonance number s in channel α; this quantity is a function of the channel energy ϵ_α; it is denoted by ϵ_s' if the channel specification is understood   (8.33)

$\epsilon_{\beta 0}$ Channel energy in channel β_0 $[=\epsilon_{bY}]$ (1.10)

$\epsilon_{\beta s}$ Channel energy in channel β corresponding to resonance level number s of the compound nucleus (Section 7D)

$\epsilon_{\beta s}'$ "Actual" resonance energy for resonance number s in channel β; this quantity is a function of the channel energy ϵ_β; it is denoted by ϵ_s' if the channel specification is understood   (8.34)

$\zeta = \zeta(\epsilon)$ A real number defining the phase of the amplitude $\mathfrak{b}$ of the wave $\exp(iKr)$ returning from the interior of the compound nucleus   (7.2), (8.23)

$\zeta(\omega)$ Fourier transform of the wave function $\psi(t)$ of a decaying state   (Section 9A)

η_0 $=\eta_l$ for orbital angular momentum $l=0$ (2.22)

$\eta_0(S)$ Coefficient of $\exp(+ikr)$ in $u_0(r)$ for channel spin S (10.2)

η_l Relative amplitude of the outgoing wave with orbital angular momentum l; $\eta_l=1$ corresponds to an undisturbed wave (no reaction or scattering) (2.8)

$\eta_{ll'}(S,J)$ Coefficient of the outgoing wave with orbital angular momentum l' induced by an ingoing wave with orbital angular momentum l, both in a channel with channel spin S and total angular momentum J (10.7)

$\eta_{ll'}(S,J,\Pi_C)$ Coefficient of the outgoing wave with orbital angular momentum l' induced by an ingoing wave with orbital angular momentum l, both in a channel with channel spin S, total angular momentum J, and total (compound nucleus) parity Π_C (10.22)

θ Angle of the outgoing particle with respect to the incident beam, in the center-of-gravity system (Section 2A)

$\Theta = \Theta(E)$ Temperature of the residual nucleus   (6.6)

$\kappa_l(r)$ The local wave number which appears in the

W.K.B. approximation for transmission coefficients (5.9′)

$\lambda = \lambda_\alpha$ de Broglie wavelength of the relative motion in channel α, divided by 2π (Section 2A)

λ_β Channel wavelength λ in channel β (2.63)

Λ Mean free path of a nucleon in nuclear matter (Section 3A)

ξ_l Phase shift for the "potential" scattering with orbital angular momentum l (2.51), (2.52)

Π Parity quantum number   (Sections 3B, 10B)

$\Pi(a)$ Parity of the incident particle a (Section 10B)

Π_C Parity of the compound nucleus, equal to the total parity of the system before and after the reaction (Section 10B)

$\Pi(X)$ Parity of the target nucleus X   (Section 10B)

Π_α Channel parity in channel α (10.19)

$\Pi_{\alpha'}$ Parity of the (target) nucleus X in quantum state α' (Section 10B)

$\Pi_{\alpha''}$ Parity of particle a in quantum state α'' (Section 10B)

ρ Density of nucleons inside the nucleus   (Section 3A)

ρ Difference between the channel radius R_α and the radius R_X of the target nucleus; $\rho = 0$ for nucleons, $\rho \cong 1.2 \times 10^{-13}$ cm for alpha-particles or deuterons (Section 4)

σ Cross section   (2.1)

$\sigma_0(S)$ Cross section for collisions with orbital angular momentum $l = 0$ and channel spin S (10.3)

$\sigma(a,b)$ Cross section of the reaction $X(a,b)Y$ (3.1)

$\sigma^*(a,b)$ The part of $\sigma(a,b)$ attributable to collisions in which the residual nucleus Y is left in a state of low enough excitation so that no further particles (only gamma-rays) are emitted; this is the measured cross section of the $X(a,b)Y$ reaction   (Section 6B)

$\sigma(a;b,c)$ Cross section for the reaction $X+a = Y^*+b$, $Y^* = Z+c$ (Section 6B)

$\sigma(a;c,b)$ Cross section for the reaction $X+a = (Y')^*+c$, $(Y')^* = Z+b$ (Section 6B)

$\bar{\sigma}(a;bc)$ $= \sigma(a;b,c) + \sigma(a;c,b)$; the observed cross section of the $X(a,bc)Z$ reaction   (Section 6B)

$\sigma(a,n)$ Cross section for the reaction initiated by particles a and leading to the emission of neutrons   (3.9)

$\sigma(A,B)$	Differential cross section of the (α,β) reaction (2.64)
$\sigma(-B,-A)$	Differential cross section for the (β,α) (time-reversed) reaction (2.65)
$\sigma_C(a)$	Cross section for formation of the compound nucleus C by bombardment with particles a (3.1)
$\sigma_C(n)$	Cross section for formation of the compound nucleus C by neutron bombardment (4.1), (4.4)
$\sigma_C(\alpha)$	Cross section for formation of the compound nucleus C through channel α (3.2)
$\sigma_{Cl}(\alpha)$	Cross section for formation of the compound nucleus C through channel α by collisions with orbital angular momentum l (5.1)
$\sigma_C(\epsilon_\beta)$	Cross section for formation of the compound nucleus C through collision between a particle b and an excited nucleus Y^*, the states of b and Y^* being such that the collision occurs through channel β with channel energy ϵ_β (6.9)
$\sigma_{\text{cap}}(\alpha)$	Cross section for radiative capture from channel α (2.62), (7.21)
$\sigma_{\text{cap}}^{J,\Pi c}(\bar{\alpha})$	Cross section for radiative capture from the group of channels $\bar{\alpha}$ due to formation of a compound state with total angular momentum J and parity Π_C (10.31)
σ_l	Coulomb phase shift for scattering with orbital angular momentum l (2.35)
$\sigma_{r,l}$	The part of the reaction cross section due to collisions with orbital angular momentum l (2.3), (2.13)
$\sigma_r(S,J)$	Reaction cross section in a channel with channel spin S due to collisions with total angular momentum J, for an unpolarized incident beam (10.18)
$\sigma_r(S,J,M)$	Reaction cross section in a channel with channel spin S due to collisions with total angular momentum J and z component of total angular momentum M (10.17)
$\sigma_r(S,J,\Pi_C)$	Reaction cross section in a channel with channel spin S due to collisions with total angular momentum J and total (compound nucleus) parity Π_C, for an unpolarized incident beam (10.23)
$\sigma_r(\alpha)$	Cross section for all events other than elastic scattering ("reaction cross section") in channel α (2.2)

$\sigma_{sc,0}$ S wave elastic scattering cross section (2.25)

$\sigma_{sc,l}$ That part of the elastic scattering cross section due to collisions with orbital angular momentum l (2.3), (2.11)

$\sigma_{sc}(S,J)$ Cross section for elastic scattering in a channel with channel spin S due to collisions with total angular momentum J, for an unpolarized incident beam (10.14)

$\sigma_{sc}(S,J,M)$ Cross section for elastic scattering in a channel with channel spin S due to collisions with total angular momentum J and z component of total angular momentum M (10.13)

$\sigma_{sc}(S,J,\Pi_C)$ Cross section for elastic scattering in a channel with channel spin S due to collisions with total angular momentum J and total (compound nucleus) parity Π_C, for an unpolarized incident beam (10.22)

$\sigma_{sc}(\alpha)$ Elastic scattering cross section in channel α (2.2)

$\sigma_{sc}(\theta)$ Differential cross section for elastic scattering through an angle θ (Section 2A)

$\sigma_t(\alpha)$ Total cross section in channel α (2.2)

$\sigma(\alpha,\beta)$ Cross section of the (α,β) reaction (2.61)

$\sigma(\alpha;\beta,\theta,\varphi)$ Differential cross section of the (α,β) reaction; θ and φ specify the direction of the outgoing particle (2.64)

$\sigma_{ar,l}$ Reaction cross section for reactions initiated through channel α with orbital angular momentum l (8.33)

$\sigma(\beta,\theta,\varphi;\alpha)$ Differential cross section of the (β,α) reaction; θ and φ specify the direction of the incident particle, while the outgoing particle is emitted along the negative z direction (2.65)

$\tau=\tau_s$ Mean life of state number s of the compound nucleus (7.5)

$\tau(E_C)$ Mean life of the compound nucleus C with excitation energy E_C (3.3)

φ Azimuthal angle of an outgoing particle with respect to the beam direction (Section 2A)

χ_0 Normalized wave function of the residual nucleus in a channel (9.14)

$\chi(S,m_S)$ Spin function for a channel spin S with z component m_S (10.2)

ψ	Wave function of a decaying state in a square well potential (Section 9A)
ψ	$=\psi(\mathbf{r})=\psi(r,\theta)$; wave function for the relative motion in the incident channel (2.8), (9.14)
$\psi(0)$	$=\psi(t=0)$; the decaying state wave function ψ at time $t=0$ (9.12)
ψ_{sc}	Wave function for the elastically scattered wave (2.9)
Ψ	Wave function of a state of an actual nucleus (9.13), (9.14)
Ψ_l	Wave function of a state of an actual nucleus with orbital angular momentum l (9.15)
ω	Circular frequency of a gamma-ray $[=2\pi\nu]$ (1.2)
ω	Circular frequency appearing in the Fourier transform $\zeta(\omega)$ of the wave function $\psi(t)$, corresponding to the energy $E=\hbar\omega$ (Section 9A)
$\omega_l(\Pi)$	Parity-selecting function; it is 1 if $\Pi=(-1)^l$, and it is 0 if $\Pi = -(-1)^l$ (10.21)

CHAPTER IX

Nuclear Reactions; Application
of the Theory to Experiments

1. INTRODUCTION

In this chapter the theory of nuclear reactions will be applied to special reactions, and a comparison will be made between experimental results and theoretical predictions. The broad, general features of different reaction types will be emphasized, and no attempt will be made to include detailed effects which depend on special properties of individual nuclei.

We classify the nuclear reactions into different groups by specifying the nature of the incident particle: we consider nuclear reactions initiated by neutrons, protons, alpha-particles and deuterons. Reactions initiated by gamma-rays will be treated separately in Chapter XII.

We divide the range of energy ϵ of the incident particle roughly into five regions:

I. Low energies: $0 < \epsilon < 1000$ ev.
II. Intermediate energies: 1 kev $< \epsilon < 500$ kev.
III. High energies: 0.5 Mev $< \epsilon < 10$ Mev.
IV. Very high energies: 10 Mev $< \epsilon < 50$ Mev.
V. Ultrahigh energies: 50 Mev $< \epsilon < \infty$.

It is also useful to divide the target nuclei into three categories:

A. Light nuclei: $1 \leq A < 25$.
B. Intermediate nuclei: $25 \leq A < 80$.
C. Heavy nuclei: $80 \leq A < 240$.

We shall classify the nuclear reactions into groups characterized by the nature of the initiating particle, its energy region, and the category to which the target nucleus belongs. This classification determines in general the character of the reactions, the particles which are emitted, their energy distribution, and so on. There is, of course, considerable overlap and a gradual change from one energy region to the next. Many properties of one group can be extended to the neighboring nuclei of another group.

The light nuclei (group A) must be treated individually. It is almost impossible to apply any general rules describing nuclear reactions in that group. The detailed structure of the individual nucleus is decisive for the character and yield of most of the reactions. Separation energies and Q values differ by much larger amounts within group A than within any other group. The assumptions made in the preceding chapter about the interior of the nucleus are not applicable to group A, since there are too few nucleons in these nuclei to form a well-defined interior region. All nucleons are at the "surface" of the nucleus.

We therefore describe only a few characteristic nuclear reactions with light nuclei which show some features different from those observed with intermediate or heavy nuclei. A very detailed description of almost all observed nuclear reactions with light nuclei is found in review articles by Hornyak, Lauritsen, Morrison, and Fowler (Hornyak 48, 50).

The reactions with intermediate or heavy nuclei are of different character in the five energy regions. The outstanding features of these regions can be characterized as follows: Regions I and II are almost exclusively confined to neutron reactions, since charged particles of this energy cannot penetrate to the nucleus. Region I (low energy) is characterized by the preponderance of resonance capture of neutrons in heavy nuclei. The most important reaction in region II is the resonance elastic scattering of neutrons. Energy region III is characterized by the fact that the residual nucleus can be left in several excited states. This leads to inelastic scattering, and to reactions in which the energy of the emitted particles assumes many values. In region IV the energy is high enough to allow secondary nuclear reactions [$(p,2n)$, (p,np), etc.]; in region V the mean free path of a nucleon in nuclear matter becomes comparable to nuclear dimensions, and the compound nucleus description breaks down. We then observe nuclear reactions in which many nucleons are ejected.

One part of the low-energy region I is of special significance: the "thermal" region. A beam of neutrons is called "thermal" if it possesses an energy distribution equal to the Maxwell distribution in a neutron gas at room temperature. Such a beam can be obtained readily from any neutron-producing apparatus in which the neutrons are slowed down in some medium and emerge in equilibrium with the thermal motion. The elastic scattering of "thermal" neutrons and

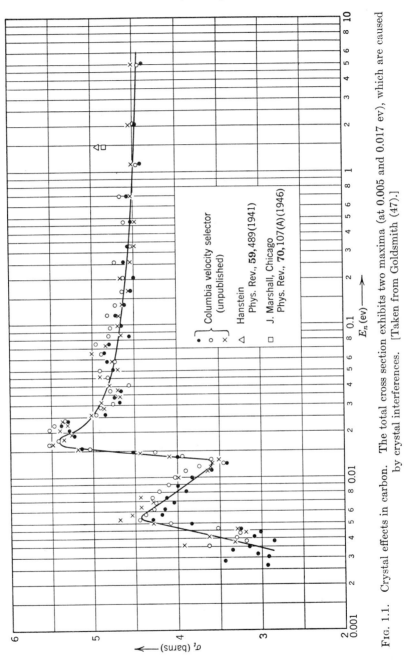

FIG. 1.1. Crystal effects in carbon. The total cross section exhibits two maxima (at 0.005 and 0.017 ev), which are caused by crystal interferences. [Taken from Goldsmith (47).]

TABLE 1.1

REACTIONS WITH INTERMEDIATE AND HEAVY NUCLEI

This table lists the nuclear reactions occurring in each group. The symbols listed refer to the *emerging particle* in a reaction characterized by the type of target, the type of incident particle (columns), and the energy range (rows). The order of symbols in each group corresponds roughly to the order of the yields of the corresponding reactions. Reactions whose yield is usually less than about 10^{-2} of the leading one are omitted.

Abbreviations: el = elastic, inel = inelastic, res = resonances. The abbreviation (res) refers to all reactions listed in the box. The elastic scattering of charged particles is omitted, since it cannot easily be separated from the non-nuclear Coulomb scattering. Fission is also omitted, since it occurs only with a few of the heaviest elements.

Incident Particle → Energy of Incident Particle ↓	Intermediate Nuclei — n	p	α	d	Heavy Nuclei — n	p	α	d
Low 0–1 kev	n(el) γ (res)				γ n(el) (res)			
Intermediate 1–500 kev	n(el) γ (res)	n γ α (res)	n γ p (res)	p n	n(el) γ (res)			
High 0.5–10 Mev	n(el) n(inel) p α (res for lower energies)	n p(inel) α (res for lower energies)	n p α(inel) (res for lower energies)	p n pn $2n$ d(inel)	n(el) n(inel) p γ	n p(inel) γ	n p γ	p n pn $2n$
Very high 10–50 Mev	$2n$ n(inel) n(el) p np $2p$ α three or more particles	$2n$ n p(inel) np $2p$ α three or more particles	$2n$ n p np $2p$ α(inel) three or more particles	p $2n$ pn $3n$ d(inel) tritons three or more particles	$2n$ n(inel) n(el) p pn $2p$ α three or more particles	$2n$ n p(inel) np $2p$ α three or more particles	$2n$ n p np $2p$ α(inel) three or more particles	p $2n$ n np $3n$ d(inel) tritons three or more particles

of neutrons of very low energy ($\epsilon < 1$ ev) frequently displays a very complicated angular and energy dependence with many closely spaced maxima (see Fig. 1.1). These are due to interference effects between the waves scattered from different nuclei within a crystal and are similar to the diffraction of x-rays in crystals. They will not be discussed in this book.

In Table 1.1 the different reaction types are arranged according to the groups in which they appear. The reactions with light nuclei are not listed since they cannot be fitted into any general scheme. The reactions in each group are listed in the order of importance. The reaction which, in general, has the larger cross section precedes the one with lower yield. Reactions are omitted whose cross section is, in general, less than 1 percent of the leading reaction. It should always be kept in mind that there must be many exceptions to any attempt to systematize nuclear reactions. Among the most striking exceptions are some heavy nuclei like Pb, Bi, and others, which exhibit the properties of intermediate nuclei. This behavior is probably connected with the shell structure of nuclei (see Chapter XIV).

In the following sections the different reaction groups will be discussed in more detail. The results from the considerations of Chapter VIII will be compared with the experimental material, and this will help to determine some of the semi-empirical constants which were introduced in the theory, such as the resonance level spacing D and the radiation width Γ_{rad}.

2. NEUTRON-INDUCED REACTIONS

A characteristic feature of neutron-induced reactions is the existence of a well-defined total cross section σ_t which is the sum of the elastic scattering cross section and the reaction cross section. The total cross section can be measured directly by determining the attenuation of a well-collimated neutron beam in passing through a sample of material of known thickness, whereas the measurement of all other cross sections requires the determination of the yield of the reaction and of the strength of the incident beam as well.

The total cross section is ill defined in reactions induced by charged particles, since it contains the Rutherford scattering cross section which becomes extremely large for very small scattering angles. The scattering through very small angles is determined by the Coulomb field far outside the nuclear surface and depends critically on the shielding of the nuclear charge by the atomic electrons. Hence the total cross section in the case of charged particles is mostly an atomic phenomenon.

A. Low and Intermediate Energy, Intermediate Nuclei

Only few neutron reactions can take place with neutrons of low or intermediate energy. For intermediate nuclei the most important reactions are elastic scattering and radiative capture. All other reactions are energetically impossible or negligibly weak. Inelastic neutron scattering is not possible since, in general, the first excited state of the target nucleus is several hundred kilovolts above the ground state. The (n,p) or (n,α) reactions are weak because of the Coulomb barrier which acts as an obstacle to the emission of charged particles with low energy.

The theoretical expressions for the elastic scattering and for the radiative capture are as given in Chapter VIII, Section 7—the Breit-Wigner formulas (VIII,7.20) and (VIII,7.21)—if the spin of the neutron is ignored. The factors which include the spin effect are given for the case $l=0$ in (VIII,10.5) and (VIII,10.4). We expect that most of the observable resonances occur with neutrons of angular momentum $l=0$ or $l=1$; resonances with higher values of l have very small neutron widths $\Gamma_n{}^s$. They are too narrow to be observed.

The most important magnitudes appearing in the Breit-Wigner formula are the widths. The theoretical expression for the neutron width can be taken from (VIII,8.14), (VIII,8.21), and (VIII,5.8); it is

$$\frac{\Gamma_n{}^s}{D^*} = 1.4 \times 10^{-4} \ (\epsilon \text{ in ev})^{1/2} \ v_l \qquad (2.1)$$

where $\Gamma_n{}^s$ is the neutron width evaluated at the energy ϵ near the resonance energy ϵ_s. D^* is *defined* by (2.1), and according to the theory D^* is expected to be of the order of the actual energy separation D between levels of the same angular momentum J and same parity Π_C. The barrier penetration factor v_l was given in (VIII,5.8) for various values of l. The values for $l = 0, 1, 2$ are

$$v_0 = 1 \qquad v_1 = \frac{\epsilon}{\epsilon_0 + \epsilon} \qquad v_2 = \frac{\epsilon^2}{9\epsilon_0{}^2 + 3\epsilon\epsilon_0 + \epsilon^2} \qquad (2.2)$$

where ϵ_0 is defined by

$$kR \equiv \left(\frac{\epsilon}{\epsilon_0}\right)^{1/2} \qquad \epsilon_0 \equiv \frac{\hbar^2}{2MR^2} \cong \frac{21 \text{ Mev}}{(R \text{ in } 10^{-13} \text{ cm})^2} \cong \frac{10 \text{ Mev}}{A^{2/3}} \qquad (2.3)$$

The energy ϵ_0 plays an important role in the estimate of the contributions of different orbital angular momenta l. The relevant quantity here is $kR = (\epsilon/\epsilon_0)^{1/2}$. The neutron widths for angular momenta

$l > (\epsilon/\epsilon_0)^{1/2}$ are much smaller than those for $l = 0$. The neutron widths for orbital angular momenta $l < (\epsilon/\epsilon_0)^{1/2}$ are comparable to the S wave neutron widths. These statements can also be expressed as follows: the neutron widths for an angular momentum l are expected to be small compared to $l = 0$ neutron widths if the neutron energy ϵ is appreciably below the "centrifugal barrier height" for this value of l. The height of the centrifugal barrier is

$$\text{Centrifugal barrier height} = l(l+1)\epsilon_0 \qquad (2.4)$$

Although the *widths* of resonances with high values of l become progressively smaller, this is by no means true of the maximum cross sections in resonance. If the resonance is a pure scattering resonance (as is the case for intermediate-energy neutrons in intermediate nuclei), the maximum cross section is given by (VIII,10.33) and depends only on the resonance energy (i.e., on λ), on the angular momentum J of the resonance level, and on the nuclear spin I of the target nucleus. Hence a completely monoenergetic beam of neutrons incident upon completely stationary target nuclei would yield *all* pure scattering resonances in the compound nucleus, no matter how high the barrier energy. The resonances for neutrons with high values of l would be very narrow, but they would still give a maximum cross section determined from (VIII,10.33).

We must therefore include the effects of finite resolution of the experiments in order to understand under what conditions resonance levels are observed. There are two main effects here: the incident neutrons are not precisely monoenergetic, and the target nuclei are not precisely at rest. The second effect is called the "Doppler broadening" of the resonance. It depends on the temperature of the target, and it can be estimated to be negligible for the data which we are going to discuss here. In order to estimate the first effect, we shall assume that the distribution-in-energy of the incident neutrons is constant within an energy interval $\Delta\epsilon$ about the mean energy $\bar{\epsilon}$, and zero outside this interval. For the narrow resonances under consideration, we can neglect the variation of the neutron width $\Gamma_n{}^s$ across the resonance region and we can neglect the potential scattering. The height of the resonance peak observed experimentally is then, in the two limiting cases,

$$\sigma_{\text{max,exp}} \cong \sigma_{\text{max}} \qquad\qquad \Delta\epsilon \ll \Gamma$$

$$\sigma_{\text{max,exp}} \cong \frac{1}{2}\,\pi\left(\frac{\Gamma}{\Delta\epsilon}\right)\sigma_{\text{max}} \qquad \Delta\epsilon \gg \Gamma \qquad (2.5)$$

Only those resonances will be observed for which $\sigma_{\mathrm{max,exp}}$ exceeds the experimental fluctuations in the measured cross sections.[1]

The second width appearing in the Breit-Wigner formulas is the reaction width $\Gamma_r{}^s$ which, in this case, is equal to the width for the radiative-capture process, since this is the only reaction possible:

$$\Gamma_r{}^s = \Gamma_{\mathrm{rad}}^s \qquad \text{(low- and intermediate-energy neutrons)} \qquad (2.6)$$

The radiation width Γ_{rad}^s has been introduced into the theory as an empirical constant. An attempt at a theoretical determination of this quantity will be made in Chapter XII. Empirically, the radiation width is much smaller than the neutron width for observable levels in intermediate nuclei, in the low- and intermediate-energy region:

$$\Gamma_{\mathrm{rad}}^s \ll \Gamma_n{}^s \qquad \text{(observable resonances of low- and intermediate-}$$
$$\text{energy neutrons in intermediate nuclei)} \qquad (2.7)$$

Thus these resonances are practically pure scattering resonances, and we can use the theory of Chapter VIII, Section 8A, to describe them.

As an example, the total cross section and the radiative-capture cross section of aluminum for intermediate-energy neutrons are given in Fig. 2.1 (Henkel 50). We first observe that the capture cross sections are about three orders of magnitude lower than the total cross sections. Thus the total cross section is practically equal to the elastic scattering cross section.

Neutron scattering resonances are observed at distances D' of roughly 50 kev. This D' is not the "level distance" D which is expected to be of the same order of magnitude as the D^* in (2.1). D is defined to be the distance between levels of equal J and parity. We can use the observed level spacing D' to estimate the spacing D between levels of equal J and parity as follows: We can estimate from (2.1) and (2.5) that only S and P resonances are observable with the energy spread $\Delta\epsilon \sim 5$ kev used in the experiments. Aluminum has only one stable isotope, Al^{27}; hence all the observed resonances are levels in the same compound nucleus, Al^{28}. Al^{27} has a nuclear spin $I = \frac{5}{2}$, and an unknown parity which we call Π_α (it is equal to the channel parity, since an isolated neutron has parity $+1$). If the neutrons responsible for the resonance are S wave neutrons $(l = 0)$, the levels in the compound nucleus have a J of either 2 or 3, and a

---

[1] The estimate (2.5) assumes that the target used for the transmission experiments is thin for all the neutrons, including the resonance neutrons. The expressions are different if the target is thick for resonance neutrons, but thin for neutrons off resonance.

parity $\Pi_C = \Pi_\alpha$. If the neutrons are P wave neutrons $(l=1)$, the compound levels have values of $J = 1, 2, 3,$ or 4, and parity $\Pi_C = -\Pi_\alpha$. Hence there are six types of resonances observed differing in J or parity, and we can conclude therefore that $D \sim 6D' \sim 300$ kev.

Substitution of this value of D into (2.1) gives $\Gamma_n{}^s \cong 13$ kev for S wave resonances near 100 kev, $\Gamma_n{}^s \cong 30$ kev for S wave resonances near

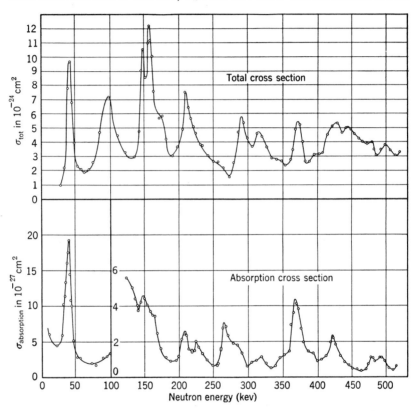

FIG. 2.1.   Neutron cross sections for aluminum, taken from Henkel (50).

500 kev. The corresponding numbers for P wave resonances are 1.2 kev and 10 kev, respectively. Figure 2.1 shows widths of the order of 5 to 10 kev in the lower-energy range, and somewhat larger widths (10 to 20 kev) at higher energies. This is in good agreement with the theoretical predictions.

The capture cross section $\sigma_{\text{cap}}(n)$ shows resonances at the same energies as the total ($\cong$ scattering) cross section. This is to be expected according to the compound nucleus picture, and it serves as a confirmation of that picture. The ratio of resonance capture cross section to resonance scattering cross section varies from level to level.

Fluctuations from the average must occur, since the theory can make predictions only about the average behavior of resonance levels, not about individual levels. According to (VIII,10.4), (VIII,10.5), and (VIII,8.31), the ratio of the capture cross section to the elastic scattering cross section at the resonance peak $(\epsilon = \epsilon_s)$ is approximately [neglecting the potential scattering and using (2.6)]

$$\frac{\sigma_{r,0}}{\sigma_{sc,0}} \cong \frac{\Gamma^s_{\rm rad}}{\Gamma_n{}^s} \qquad (\epsilon = \epsilon_s) \qquad (2.8)$$

The experimental ratio of capture cross section to total cross section is about 10^{-3}. Since, experimentally, the neutron widths are of the order of 5 to 20 kev, we get values of $\Gamma^s_{\rm rad}$ of the order of 3 to 30 ev. Estimates of this sort give the rule

$$\Gamma^s_{\rm rad} \sim 1 \text{ to } 30 \text{ ev} \qquad \text{(for intermediate nuclei)} \qquad (2.9)$$

A cleaner separation between the resonance levels of the compound nucleus is obtained in sulfur, for which the total neutron cross section ($\cong$ elastic scattering cross section) is shown in Fig. 2.2 (data from Adair 49 and Peterson 50). Here the observed level spacing is about 100 kev. Measurements by Blair and Wallace (Blair 50) in $_{23}V^{51}$ indicate a spacing of 25 kev.

The large variations of the level distance from nucleus to nucleus are probably connected with variations in the separation energy S of the neutron from the compound nucleus. The observed resonances correspond to states of the compound nucleus with an excitation energy $E = \epsilon + S$. For the same neutron energy ϵ, E can be quite different in two different compound nuclei. Since the level spacing in a nucleus is a rapidly decreasing function of the excitation energy E, we may expect large fluctuations in the level spacing at the same neutron energy ϵ from nucleus to nucleus. There is, however, a general trend toward smaller level distances for higher mass numbers.

It is characteristic of the intermediate nuclei that the neutron width $\Gamma_n{}^s$ is larger than the radiation width for all observable levels. Since the neutron width decreases with decreasing energy, we get the most unfavorable estimate by choosing a low resonance energy, say 10 ev. We also choose a low level spacing $D \cong 10$ kev. Then (2.1) gives, for an S wave resonance which would be the only observable one at such a low energy, $\Gamma_n{}^s \cong 5$ ev, which is still comparable with the radiation widths (2.9). It is extremely unlikely that a level should be found within 10 ev of the neutron separation energy if the level spacing is 10 kev. Hence all the observed resonances in intermediate nuclei are predominantly scattering resonances. The interaction of neutrons

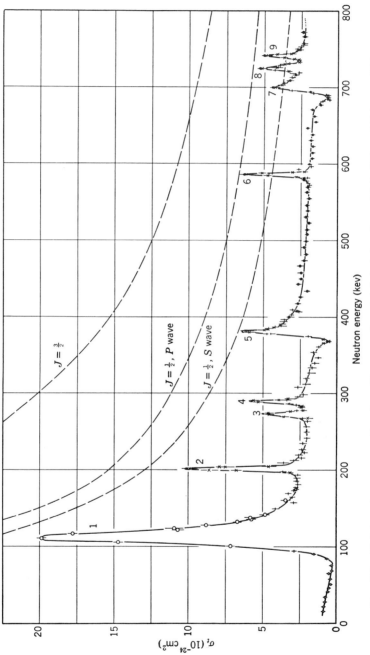

FIG. 2.2.   Total neutron cross section for sulfur; experimental data taken from Adair (49) and Peterson (50).

below 200 kev with intermediate nuclei is a good example of almost pure elastic scattering as described in Section 8A of Chapter VIII.

The theory predicts a characteristic behavior of the elastic scattering cross section near resonance due to the interference of potential and resonance scattering (see Chapter VIII, Section 8). There should be a minimum of the scattering cross section on the low-energy side of a resonance with $l = 0$, and a slower decrease on the high-energy side. The total cross section in sulfur, as shown in Fig. 2.2, consists predominantly of elastic scattering and should exhibit the expected phenomenon. The first, fifth, and seventh resonances show the phenomenon quite clearly. The other resonances belong probably to values of l higher than zero for which the potential scattering is too weak to produce appreciable interference.

The scattering cross section between resonances is given by the potential scattering only and is therefore expected to be the same as that of a repulsive sphere of nuclear size, which approaches $4\pi R^2$ at low energies $\epsilon \ll \epsilon_0$. We must not forget, however, that the interference between potential and resonance scattering is strong even at energies which differ from the resonance energy by much more than the width Γ^s of the resonance. Hence deviations from pure potential scattering are found relatively far from resonance, at distances of the order of $\Delta\epsilon$ as given by (VIII,8.15a).

The maximum value of the cross section gives information about the J of the resonance level. It was shown in Chapter VIII, Section 8, that the scattering cross section reaches its largest possible value in the resonances if the elastic scattering is the dominant reaction. The maximum cross section was found to be $4\pi\lambda^2(2l+1)$ if the spin is disregarded. We must use here the more detailed expression (VIII,10.33), which gives the maximum cross section for energies $\epsilon \ll \epsilon_0$ [ϵ_0 is defined in (2.3)], where only the lowest possible $l = L$ contributes appreciably. Since the spin I of the target nucleus is usually known, J can be deduced from the maximum cross section at resonance with the help of (VIII,10.33). If J and I are known, the two possible values (depending on the parity of the compound nucleus) of the lowest orbital angular momentum L of the resonance neutrons are given in Table 10.2 of Chapter VIII.

The target nucleus in Fig. 2.2, sulfur, is predominantly (95.1 percent) an even-even isotope, S^{32}, which has nuclear spin $I = 0$ and presumably even parity. S wave neutrons then lead to resonances in the compound nucleus, S^{33}, with $J = \frac{1}{2}$ and parity $\Pi_C = +1$. The maximum cross section for those resonances, acording to (VIII,10.33), is $4\pi\lambda^2$; this is drawn in on the figure (labeled $J = \frac{1}{2}$, S wave). Resonances 1, 5, and 7 are probably S wave resonances. P wave neutrons lead to resonances with $J=\frac{1}{2}$ or $J=\frac{3}{2}$ and parity $\Pi_C=-1$. The expected maximum cross sections are also drawn in on the figure (these curves include a rough correction for the potential scattering background which is not present for S wave resonances in this nucleus). Resonances 2, 3, 4, 6, 8, and 9 are probably P wave resonances. Most of them are only partially resolved and therefore do not reach the maximum value.

The three S wave resonances visible on Fig. 2.2 all have the same value of $J(=\frac{1}{2})$ and the same parity. Thus the average level distance between them, $D=300$ kev, is the proper value to substitute into the estimate (2.1). The widths predicted on this basis are within a factor 5 of the theoretical estimate (2.1). Agreement between the rough estimate (2.1) and any single experiment to within a factor of 10 either way is considered satisfactory, but consistent disagreement between (2.1) and a whole set of experiments by the same factor would not be tolerable.

We now turn to the capture cross section and consider especially capture near a resonance with $l=0$. We can use the expression (VIII,10.4) for the reaction cross section and write it in the following form by substituting (VIII,8.39) for the neutron width:

$$\sigma_{\text{cap}}(n) = 2\pi\lambda R \; g(S) \; \frac{\gamma_n{}^s \; \Gamma_{\text{rad}}^s}{(\epsilon-\epsilon_s)^2 + (\frac{1}{2}\Gamma^s)^2} \tag{2.10}$$

where $\gamma_n{}^s$ is the reduced neutron width. We find that $\sigma_{\text{cap}}(n)$ is proportional to λ or $\epsilon^{-1/2}$ at very low energies in contrast to the behavior of the elastic scattering cross section, which approaches a finite value as $\epsilon \to 0$. Although (2.10) is valid only near the resonance, we shall apply it to thermal energies ϵ_{th} by assuming that ϵ_s is the resonance nearest to ϵ_{th}, in which case (2.10) should be qualitatively correct. It is expected that $|\epsilon_{th}-\epsilon_s|$ is of the order of the level distance D and certainly never larger than $D/2$. Hence we may put $|\epsilon_{th}-\epsilon_s|\equiv D/2\zeta$ where $\zeta\geq 1$. We set for a rough estimate $g(S)\cong\frac{1}{2}$ and use the estimate (VIII,8.40) for $\gamma_n{}^s$. Furthermore we assume that $|\epsilon_{th}-\epsilon_s|$ is much larger than Γ^s. This gives for the thermal neutron capture cross section

$$[\sigma_{\text{cap}}(n)]_{th} \cong 4\zeta^2 \frac{\lambda_{th}}{K}\left(\frac{\Gamma_{\text{rad}}^s}{D}\right)$$

$$\cong \zeta^2 \cdot 1100 \left(\frac{\Gamma_{\text{rad}}^s}{D}\right) \times 10^{-24} \text{ cm}^2 \tag{2.11}$$

The experimental values of the capture cross section at thermal energies for intermediate nuclei are of the order of 10^{-25} cm^2 or higher. This indicates that (Γ_{rad}/D) is of the order of 10^{-4} in agreement with the measurement shown in Fig. 2.1 and with similar results. There is a tendency toward larger values of σ_{cap} for larger A, which probably is connected with the decrease of the level distance D with increasing A.

B. Low Energy, Heavy Nuclei

The only reactions possible for low-energy neutrons on heavy nuclei are elastic scattering, radiative capture, and, in a very few cases, neutron-induced fission. The effect of the Coulomb barrier prohibiting the emission of charged particles of low energy is even more pronounced than with intermediate nuclei. Only neutrons with $l = 0$ can produce any reaction in this group, since $\lambda \gg R$.

The low-energy neutron reactions with heavy nuclei are characterized by the fact that the cross sections frequently show resonances very close together in energy. We find distances between resonances of the order of 10 and 100 ev in many heavy elements. However, in certain nuclear species no resonances at all have been found, and it is probable that there exist a large number of heavy nuclei with resonance spacing much larger than 100 ev. In fact, indications have been found (Goldhaber 49, Harris 50) that this is the case in most nuclei with even A. Certainly target nuclei with "magic" numbers (see Chapter XIV) of protons and neutrons show very large resonance spacing in the compound nucleus (many kev's), especially lead and bismuth (Barschall 49).

Small level distances should be connected with very small neutron widths. In fact, (2.1) shows that the neutron widths should on the average be considerably smaller than 1 ev; for a resonance, say, at 10 ev, and a level distance $D \sim 30$ ev, $\Gamma_n{}^s$ becomes of the order of 10^{-2} ev, a value which is in agreement with experimental measurements. However, the total widths of these low-lying resonances were found to be much larger—of the order of 10^{-1} ev. This forces us to conclude that most of the total width is due to the reaction width, which in this case is exclusively radiation width (with the exception of the very few fissionable nuclei). Hence we conclude that $\Gamma_{rad} \sim 0.1$ ev for low-energy neutron resonances in heavy nuclei. In contrast to the situation with intermediate nuclei, *the neutron width is small compared to the radiation width for low-energy neutrons on heavy nuclei.* Resonance capture is stronger than resonance scattering.

The cross section for the radiative capture process [(n,γ) process]

472 IX. Nuclear Reactions; Comparison with Experiments

is given by (2.10), which we write for our present purposes in the form (using $\Gamma_{\text{rad}}^s \cong \Gamma^s$)

$$\sigma_{\text{cap}}(n) = 8\pi\lambda R\, g(S) \left(\frac{\gamma_n{}^s}{\Gamma^s}\right) \left[1 + \frac{4(\epsilon - \epsilon_s)^2}{(\Gamma^s)^2}\right]^{-1} \qquad (2.12)$$

where $\gamma_n{}^s$ is the reduced neutron width. This formula has been checked quantitatively to a very high accuracy. Figure 2.3 shows,

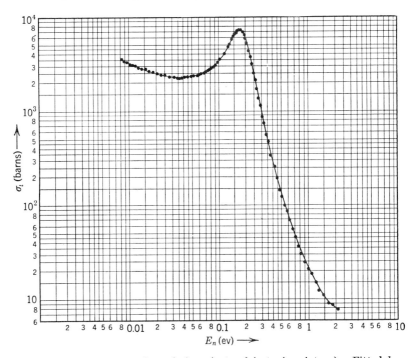

FIG. 2.3. σ_t for neutrons in cadmium (natural isotopic mixture). Fitted by a Breit-Wigner one-level formula with $\epsilon_s = 0.176$ ev, $\sigma_{\max} = 7.2 \times 10^{-21}$ cm^2, $\Gamma^s = 0.115$ ev. [Taken from Goldsmith (47).]

for cadmium, a series of measurements at different energies which are compared with the theoretical Breit-Wigner formula (2.12). The agreement is extremely accurate. The theory of the Breit-Wigner formula is expected to give very reliable results for the shape of resonances if the widths of the resonances are small compared to their separation in energy.

The scattering cross section near resonance is much smaller than the capture cross section, since $\Gamma_{\text{rad}}^s \gg \Gamma_n{}^s$ [see (2.8)]. At larger distances from the resonance, however, σ_{sc} approaches the potential scattering cross section $4\pi R^2$, whereas $\sigma_{cap}(n)$ becomes very much smaller than $4\pi R^2$, except at energies very close to zero. According to (2.12) the capture cross section contains a factor λ which goes to infinity for zero energy. Hence there is always an energy below which σ_{cap} is larger than σ_{sc} since the latter cross section approaches a constant value $4\pi R^2$. This energy is in general very low (lower than thermal energies) except when there is a resonance close to zero energy. The resonance of cadmium shown in Fig. 2.3 is an example of this case.

The total cross section is approximately equal to the capture cross section $\sigma_{cap}(n)$ near resonance. Off resonance the total cross section becomes approximately equal to the S wave potential scattering cross section $4\pi R^2$ except at very low energies where it becomes proportional to $\epsilon^{-1/2}$.

The relevant constants ϵ_s, $\gamma_n{}^s$, $\Gamma_{rad}^s \cong \Gamma^s$ of a resonance are obtained by comparing the experimental results with the theoretical expression (2.12). Most of the experiments measure the total (transmission) cross section. Unlike resonances in intermediate nuclei, the slow neutron resonances in heavy nuclei have to be corrected for the Doppler broadening which is caused by the thermal motion of the nuclei in the target. The relative energy between the neutron and the nucleus is not what it would be for completely stationary nuclei but is spread over an interval $(\Delta\epsilon)_D$ of the order of

$$(\Delta\epsilon)_D \sim \left[\frac{\epsilon kT}{A}\right]^{1/2} \tag{2.13}$$

where kT is the energy of the thermal motion (of the order of 0.025 ev at room temperature) and A is the mass number. The Doppler width is small compared to Γ_{rad}^s for resonance energies $\epsilon_s \sim 1$ ev, but $(\Delta\epsilon)_D$ becomes comparable to Γ_{rad}^s for resonances in the 100-ev range in nuclei of mass number $A \gtrsim 100$.

We have listed in Table 2.1 some of the experimental results of measurements of resonance energies and widths.

A very remarkable feature of the table is the fact that, in heavy nuclei, Γ_{rad}^s is always very near 0.1 ev. In all cases in which it could be measured directly it was found that it fell within the limits

$$0.03 \text{ ev} < \Gamma_{rad}^s < 0.20 \text{ ev} \quad \text{(heavy nuclei)} \tag{2.14}$$

These values are somewhat smaller than the radiation widths in intermediate nuclei.

The measurements of $\Gamma_n{}^s$ can be compared with expression (2.1).

TABLE 2.1

NEUTRON WIDTHS OF RESONANCE LEVELS AND LEVEL DISTANCES†

The first column contains the *target* nucleus. If the mass number is not given, the isotope in question has not been assigned. Then the width can be determined only if the abundances of the isotopes in question are about equal. The second column contains the resonance energy ϵ_s of the neutrons. The third column contains the neutron width $\Gamma_n{}^s$. Since in most cases $g(S)$ is not known, the value in this column is actually $2g(S)\cdot\Gamma_n{}^s$, which is the closest result attainable since $\langle g(S)\rangle_{\mathrm{av}} = \frac{1}{2}$. The fourth column contains the radiation width Γ_{rad}^s wherever it was measured. In all these cases it is almost equal to the total width, $\Gamma^s \cong \Gamma_{\mathrm{rad}}^s$, and the values given are the measured total widths. The fifth column contains the product of the reduced neutron width $\gamma_n{}^s$ as defined in (VIII,7.15) and the nuclear radius. The sixth column contains the magnitude D^* derived from $\Gamma_n{}^s$ according to (2.1). All resonances in this table are assumed to be due to $l = 0$ neutrons because of the low energy ϵ_s. The seventh column contains the level spacing D of levels of equal J and parity. It is very difficult to estimate this spacing from the present observations. If several levels of the same isotope are known, the distance D is put equal to twice the average distance of these levels, assuming that half the resonances belong to the value $J = I + \frac{1}{2}$ and half of them to $J = I - \frac{1}{2}$. (I is the spin of the target nucleus.) If no assignment of resonances to isotopes is possible, the distance D is estimated very roughly from the number of resonances observed. This or other gross uncertainties are indicated by the symbol $\sim D$. According to the theory D^* should be of the same order of magnitude as D.

Target Nucleus	Resonance Energy, ϵ_s	Neutron Width, $\Gamma_n{}^s$	Radiation Width, Γ_{rad}^s	Reduced Neutron Width, $R\gamma_n{}^s$	D^*	D	Reference
	kev	kev		kev $\times$ cm $\times 10^{13}$	kev	kev	
Na^{23}	3	0.17		5.2	16	$\sim$50	Selove 50a
Mg^{24}	2540	150		214	670	1000	McPhail 40
Al^{27}	155	10		63	200	300	Henkel 50
S^{32}	115	25		167	530	300	Peterson 50
Ni	15	3		60	190	200	Barschall 48
	70	5		43	130	200	Barschall 48
	ev	ev		ev $\times$ cm $\times 10^{13}$	ev	ev	
Mn^{55}	345	13		1600	5000	$>$1000	Rainwater 47
Co^{59}	120	2.6		540	1700	$\sim$1000	Wu 47
							Seidl 49
Zn	520	5		500	1600	$>$500	Coster 48

† Most of the material in this table is taken from Teichmann (49).

TABLE 2.1 (*Continued*)

Target Nucleus	Resonance Energy, ϵ_s	Neutron Width, $\Gamma_n{}^s$	Radiation Width, Γ_{rad}^s	Reduced Neutron Width, $R\gamma_n{}^s$	D^*	D	Reference
	ev	10^{-3} ev	ev	ev $\times$ cm $\times 10^{13}$	ev	ev	
Rh[103]	1.3	0.33	0.14	0.65	2.0	>20	Borst 46 Sturm 47
Pd[108]	24	49	0.14	23	73	~50	Coster 48
Ag[107]	45	13		4.5	14	~40	Havens 46
Ag[109]	5.1	11	0.17	12	38	~40	Selove 50
	13	4.8		3	10	~40	Havens 46
Cd[113]	0.18	0.8	0.115	3.2	13	>50	Rainwater 47
In[115]	1.44	2.4	0.09	4.4	14	~100	Havens 47
In[113]	3.8	7		8.2	26	~100	Havens 47
	8.6	40		31	97	~100	Havens 47
Sb	5.8	1		1	3.2	~20	Rainwater 47
	15	8		5	16	~20	Rainwater 47
I[127]	20	2.4		1.2	3.8	~15	Jones 47
Sm	0.096	0.58	0.074	4.4	14	~20	Borst 46 Sturm 47
Eu	0.465	0.9	0.20	2.9	9	~10	Sturm 47
Gd	0.03	0.51	0.05	6.7	21		Sturm 47
Ta[181]	4.1	1.4		1.6	5	~6	Havens 47
	10	2.0		1.4	4.4	~6	Havens 47
	13	0.3		0.2	0.6	~6	Havens 47
	22	3.1		1.5	5	~6	Havens 47
W[182]	4.15	2.3		2.6	8	~8	Havens 47
W[183]	7.8	1.6		1.4	4.5	~8	Havens 47
Au[197]	4.87	21.1	0.17	22	70	>100	Tittman 50

Only the product $g(S)\Gamma_n{}^s$ is measured by the experiments [see (2.12)].[1] In Table 2.1, $g(S)$ has been set equal to $\frac{1}{2}$ which is the average of the two possible values of $g(S)$. *It is seen from Table 2.1 that D^* is in*

[1] $g(S)$ is known when the target nucleus is an even-even nucleus with $I = 0$. Then $g(S) = g(\frac{1}{2}) = 1$. There are methods to determine S from a comparison of scattering and absorption data. For example, S has been determined to be 1 for the Cd[113] resonance by Beeman (47).

general of the order of the level distance D, although there are a number of cases among the heavy elements where D^* is definitely less than D. It is not clear whether this discrepancy falls within the expected fluctuations or whether it signifies a failure of the theory.

Owing to the factor $\epsilon^{-1/2}$, the capture cross section at thermal energies can be appreciable even if there is no resonance in the immediate neighborhood. For an estimate we use again expression (2.11) and get now, with $D\sim30$ ev, $\Gamma^s\sim0.1$ ev: $[\sigma_{\mathrm{cap}}(n)]_{th}\sim 4\zeta^2\times 10^{-24}$ cm^2. This would indicate a minimum thermal capture cross section of the order of 4×10^{-24} cm^2 since $\zeta^2\geq1$. The thermal neutron capture cross section has been measured in almost all elements. Most of the elements show values larger than 5×10^{-24} cm.^{2} There are a few striking exceptions with values below 10^{-24} cm^2. They are Sn, Ba, Pb, and Bi. All four belong to the group of "magic" nuclei (see Chapter XIV), and there is other evidence that these very nuclei have abnormally large level distances.

C. Intermediate Energy, Heavy Nuclei

The low-energy region is distinguished by the fact that for many heavy nuclei the widths of the resonances fulfill the relation $\Gamma_n{}^s \ll \Gamma_{\mathrm{rad}}^s$. $\Gamma_n{}^s$ increases with increasing neutron energy (proportional to $\epsilon^{1/2}$), whereas Γ_{rad}^s is not expected to depend on the neutron energy as long as ϵ varies between 0 and 0.5 Mev. This can be seen as follows: Γ_{rad}^s measures the radiative transition probability from

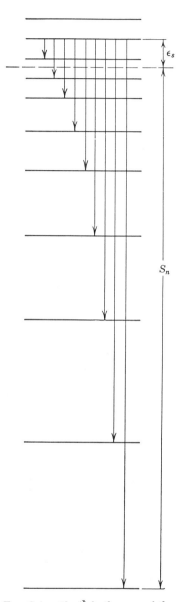

FIG. 2.4. $\Gamma_{\mathrm{rad}}^s/\hbar$ is the sum of the probabilities (per unit time) of all the radiative transitions from the level ϵ_s of the compound nucleus.

the state s of the compound nucleus to lower states as indicated in Fig. 2.4. The excitation energy $E_s = \epsilon_s + S_n$ of state s is very much larger than ϵ_s; an increase of E_s by a small amount should not change Γ_{rad}^s appreciably.

Hence we expect that there exists an energy ϵ_1 at which the S wave ($l=0$) neutron width $\Gamma_n{}^s$ is on the average equal to the radiation width Γ_{rad}^s of the compound state s. According to the relation (VIII,8.14) the corresponding wave number is given by

$$k_1 = (2M\epsilon_1)^{1/2}/\hbar = \tfrac{1}{2}\pi K \frac{\Gamma_{\text{rad}}^s}{D^*} \tag{2.15}$$

Using the same numerical estimates which led to (2.1), we get

$$\epsilon_1 \text{ (in Mev)} \cong 50 \left(\frac{\Gamma_{\text{rad}}^s}{D^*}\right)^2 \tag{2.15a}$$

For $D^* \cong 20$ ev, $\Gamma_{\text{rad}}^s \cong 0.1$ ev, this energy is of the order of a kilovolt. Thus in the intermediate-energy region the neutron width is larger than the radiation width for heavy nuclei also. The character of the neutron reactions in this region is therefore similar to those with intermediate nuclei discussed in Section 2A. However, the level distance is much smaller, so that in most cases it is impossible to resolve the resonances with presently available neutron beams. Furthermore the Doppler width sometimes becomes comparable to the level distance in this region.

It is therefore necessary to average the expressions for the cross sections over an energy interval $\Delta\epsilon$ large compared to the resonance spacing. We consider, for example, the average of the capture cross section $\sigma_{\text{cap}}^l(n)$ of neutrons with an orbital angular momentum l:

$$\langle \sigma_{\text{cap}}^l(n) \rangle_{\text{av}} \equiv (\Delta\epsilon)^{-1} \int_\epsilon^{\epsilon+\Delta\epsilon} \sigma_{\text{cap}}^l(n) \, d\epsilon$$

It was pointed out in Chapter VIII that the average of a cross section over many resonances is of the same order of magnitude as the value we would get for this cross section from the continuum theory. Hence we get from (VIII,3.2) and (VIII,3.5):

$$\langle \sigma_{\text{cap}}^l(n) \rangle_{\text{av}} = \sigma_{\text{C},l}(n) \frac{\Gamma_{\text{rad},l}}{\Gamma_{n,l} + \Gamma_{\text{rad},l}} \tag{2.16}$$

where $\sigma_{\text{C},l}(n)$ is the cross section for formation of the compound nucleus by bombardment with neutrons of orbital angular momentum l. The subscript l on the widths Γ_n and Γ_{rad} denotes the average of these widths over the resonances of given l occurring in the interval $\Delta\epsilon$.

We can evaluate (2.16) by using expression (2.1) for $\Gamma_{n,l}$ and (VIII,5.1) and (VIII,5.6) for $\sigma_{C,l}$:

$$\langle \sigma_{\mathrm{cap}}^l(n) \rangle_{\mathrm{av}} \cong \frac{4\pi(2l+1)}{kK} \frac{v_l}{1 + (\epsilon/\epsilon_1)^{1/2} v_l} \qquad (2.17)$$

The average capture cross section summed over all l

$$\langle \sigma_{\mathrm{cap}}(n) \rangle_{\mathrm{av}} \equiv \sum_{l=0}^{\infty} \langle \sigma_{\mathrm{cap}}^l(n) \rangle_{\mathrm{av}} \qquad (2.18)$$

is plotted in Fig. 2.5 for several values of ϵ_1, together with a few experimental values in the intermediate-energy region. These results point to a value of ϵ_1 of the order of 1 to 10 kev which corresponds to $(\Gamma_{\mathrm{rad}}/D^*) \sim \frac{1}{150}$. This is the expected order of magnitude if Γ_{rad} lies between 0.03 and 0.20 ev.

We can get an approximate expression for $\langle \sigma_{\mathrm{cap}}(n) \rangle_{\mathrm{av}}$ if we assume that $v_l \cong 1$ for $l \leq kR$ and $v_l \cong 0$ for $l > kR$ (see Fig. 5.2 of Chapter VIII, however, for the limitations of such a crude estimate). Then (2.17) and (2.18) can be written in the form

$$\langle \sigma_{\mathrm{cap}}(n) \rangle_{\mathrm{av}} \sim \frac{4\pi k}{K} \frac{(R + \lambda)^2}{1 + (\epsilon/\epsilon_1)^{1/2}}$$

For $\epsilon \gg \epsilon_1$ this becomes approximately equal to

$$\langle \sigma_{\mathrm{cap}}(n) \rangle_{\mathrm{av}} \sim \pi(R + \lambda)^2 \frac{2\pi\Gamma_{\mathrm{rad}}}{D^*} \qquad \text{(for } \epsilon \gg \epsilon_1) \qquad (2.19)$$

We found $\Gamma_{\mathrm{rad}}/D^*$ for heavy nuclei to be of the order of 10^{-2}. The radiative capture cross section for neutrons of 1 Mev is then roughly of the order of 10^{-25} cm^2 for heavy nuclei. Hughes (49, 50a) has measured capture cross sections of heavy nuclei in this energy region, and his results are in good agreement with these estimates (see Fig. 1.2 of Chapter XIV). There are some definite exceptions, such as barium, lead, and bismuth, which show an unusually small $\sigma_{\mathrm{cap}}(n)$ of about 10^{-27} cm^2. They belong to the group of "magic" nuclei and therefore may be assumed to have unusually large level distances D. Intermediate nuclei should have much smaller capture cross sections in this energy region because of their larger level distance D. This larger level distance is only partially compensated by a somewhat higher value of Γ_{rad}. The measurements of Hughes (50a) clearly show this difference between intermediate and heavy nuclei.

So far we have discussed only the reaction cross section and its average over resonances. The average $\langle \sigma_t \rangle_{\mathrm{av}}$ of the total cross section

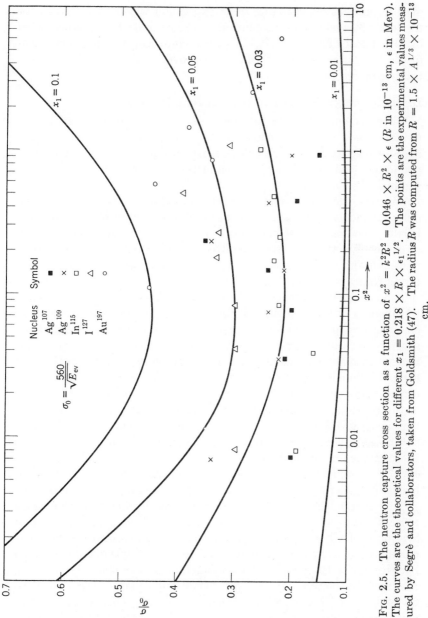

FIG. 2.5. The neutron capture cross section as a function of $x^2 = k^2 R^2 = 0.046 \times R^2 \times \epsilon$ (R in 10^{-13} cm, ϵ in Mev). The curves are the theoretical values for different $x_1 = 0.218 \times R \times \epsilon_1^{1/2}$. The points are the experimental values measured by Segrè and collaborators, taken from Goldsmith (47). The radius R was computed from $R = 1.5 \times A^{1/3} \times 10^{-13}$ cm.

over resonances leads to the same expression which was derived for the total cross section in the continuum theory and which is reproduced in Fig. 4.4 of Chapter VIII.[1]   We therefore can use this curve also in the resonance region for the average over many resonances of the total cross section.

D. High Energy, Heavy and Intermediate Nuclei

When the energy of the incident neutrons is of the order of 1 Mev or higher, new types of processes occur.   We observe inelastic scattering and reactions in which charged particles are emitted.   The compound nucleus can decay by channels different from the entrance channel.

Once the compound nucleus is formed, competition sets in between different modes of decay.   Because of the existence of the Coulomb barrier, the emission of neutrons is more probable than the emission of charged particles.   The re-emitted neutrons can leave the residual nucleus in an excited state, so that we obtain inelastic neutron scattering [(n,n) reaction].

The energy dependence of the cross sections becomes simple when the energy ϵ of the incident neutron is so high that very many neutron channels are open.   This is energetically possible when ϵ is larger than several Mev so that the incident neutron is able to leave the target nucleus in many excited states.   Then it is very improbable that the compound nucleus decays by the entrance channel rather than by one of the many other open channels.   Hence the condition of validity of the continuum theory (Chapter VIII, Section 4) is fulfilled and we may use Fig. 4.2 of Chapter VIII as a good representation of the cross section $\sigma_C(n)$ for the formation of a compound nucleus.

Since the re-emission of neutrons is the most probable process, $\sigma_C(n)$ also represents to a good approximation the cross section for inelastic scattering of neutrons at energies ϵ larger than several Mev.

The energy distribution of the inelastically scattered neutrons reflects the level spectrum of the target nucleus.   As discussed in Section 3 of Chapter VIII, the relative intensities into the different channels of energy ϵ_β are proportional to $\epsilon_\beta \sigma_C(\beta)$, where $\sigma_C(\beta)$ is given by Fig. 4.2 of Chapter VIII as a function of the channel energy ϵ_β. A schematic picture of the expected distribution is shown in Figs. 6.1 and 6.2 of Chapter VIII.   When the incident energy is high, this distribution approximates the "Maxwell" distribution as discussed in Section 6 of Chapter VIII.   Very little is known experimentally

[1] More details can be found in Feshbach (49a).   See footnotes on pages 332 and 333 for differences in notation.

about the energy distribution of the outgoing neutrons.   The experimental results obtained so far seem to be in agreement with the theoretical predictions (Gugelot 51).

The yields of the (n,p) and (n,α) reactions are naturally very small because of the strong competition of the (n,n) process.   By means of (VIII,6.10) we can express the (n,p) cross section in the form

$$\sigma(n,p) = \sigma_C(n) \frac{F_p(\epsilon+Q_{np})}{F_n(\epsilon) + F_p(\epsilon+Q_{np}) + F_\alpha(\epsilon+Q_{n\alpha})} \qquad (2.20)$$

Here Q_{np} and $Q_{n\alpha}$ are the Q values of the (n,p) reaction and (n,α) reaction, respectively, and the values of the functions F can be read from Fig. 6.3 of Chapter VIII.   We have neglected the competition from the radiative capture process and from the (n,d) reaction.   The former is negligible at high neutron energies; the latter is negligible because of the very high threshold energy of the (n,d) reaction in most nuclei.   Usually F_p and F_α in the denominator of (2.20) are small compared to F_n (neutron emission is the most probable mode of decay of the compound nucleus).   An expression similar to (2.20) holds for the cross section of the (n,α) reaction.

If the target nucleus has a high value of Z, the cross sections $\sigma(n,p)$ and $\sigma(n,\alpha)$ obtained from (2.20) become extremely small.   The high Coulomb barrier prevents any appreciable evaporation of charged particles.   Hence it cannot be excluded that some other more complicated mechanisms give rise to small (n,p) or (n,α) yields which, however, may be larger than those predicted by (2.20).   An indication of this effect has been reported by Paul (52).

The radiative capture process competes not only with the re-emission of the neutron through the entrance channel, as in the low-energy region, but also with the emission through other channels.   Hence the capture cross section is expected to be considerably smaller than the one given by (2.19) which was based on the competition with the entrance channel only.

E. Very High Energy, Heavy and Intermediate Nuclei

The neutron cross sections in the very high-energy region have very simple features.   The total, as well as the reaction, cross section should not depend on special properties of the individual nuclei.   The conditions of the continuum theory (Chapter VIII, Section 4) are well fulfilled, and the results as shown in Figs. 4.2 and 4.4 of Chapter VIII are expected to hold.

Let us first discuss the total cross section.   Figure 4.4 of Chapter VIII shows that its value lies near its asymptotic value $2\pi R^2$ but is somewhat larger. In this energy region ($kR > 4$) the total cross section depends but very little on the choice of K_0 which incorporates our assumptions regarding the interior of the nucleus. It is true that a smaller K_0 means a larger reaction cross section, but this difference is compensated by a correspondingly lower scattering cross section. Hence the observed values of σ_t are especially well suited for a determination of the nuclear radius R. Table 2.2 shows a number of nuclear

TABLE 2.2

NUCLEAR RADII

Element	Energy (Mev)	Observed σ_t $(10^{-24}\ \mathrm{cm})^2$	R $(10^{-13}\ \mathrm{cm})$	r_0 $(10^{-13}\ \mathrm{cm})$	Reference
Be	14	0.65	2.4	1.17	Amaldi 46
B	14	1.16	3.4	1.54	Amaldi 46
C	25	1.29	3.8	1.65	Sheer 45
O	25	1.60	4.3	1.71	Sherr 45
Mg	14	1.83	4.5	1.57	Amaldi 46
Al	14	1.92	4.6	1.53	Amaldi 46
	25	1.85	4.6	1.52	Sherr 45
S	14	1.58	4.1	1.30	Amaldi 46
Cl	25	1.88	4.7	1.44	Sherr 45
Fe	14	2.75	5.6	1.46	Amaldi 46
Cu	25	2.50	5.5	1.38	Sherr 45
Zn	14	3.03	5.9	1.48	Amaldi 46
Se	14	3.35	6.3	1.46	Amaldi 46
Ag	14	3.82	6.8	1.44	Amaldi 46
	25	3.70	6.9	1.46	Sherr 45
Cd	14	4.25	7.2	1.48	Amaldi 46
Sn	14	4.52	7.4	1.52	Amaldi 46
Sb	14	4.35	7.3	1.46	Amaldi 46
Au	14	4.68	7.5	1.33	Amaldi 46
Hg	14	5.64	8.3	1.42	Amaldi 46
Hg	25	5.25	8.4	1.44	Sherr 45
Pb	14	5.05	7.8	1.32	Amaldi 46
Bi	14	5.17	7.9	1.34	Amaldi 46

radii determined from such measurements at 14 Mev and 25 Mev by Amaldi (46) and Sherr (45). It should be kept in mind that the radius R may depend on the energy as well as on the nature of the incident particle. R is the distance at which the nuclear forces begin to act. It is defined more exactly as the distance at which the wave number of the incident particle assumes the value K which is characteristic of the wave numbers in the interior of the nucleus. It follows from this definition that R may fluctuate by amounts of the order of $K^{-1} \sim 10^{-13}$ cm. However, no such variation of R with energy is indicated in Table 2.2. In the three elements (Al, Ag, Hg) for which cross sections have been measured both at 14 Mev and at 25 Mev, the implied values of R are very nearly equal to each other.

The reaction cross section σ_r is the sum of the cross sections of all reactions except the elastic scattering and can be measured by determining how many neutrons are removed from a neutron beam, not counting those that are scattered without change of energy.[1] σ_r is almost constant in the energy region considered here. According to Fig. 4.2 of Chapter VIII it lies somewhere between πR^2 and $1.5\pi R^2$, depending on the radius and the value of $K_0 R$. A comparison of experimental results with the theory can be used to determine K_0 since the radius R can be determined independently from total cross section measurements. Table 2.3 contains a number of measurements

TABLE 2.3

NEUTRON REACTION CROSS SECTIONS AT 14 MEV

$(\sigma_r \times 10^{24} \text{ cm}^2)$

Element	Experimental Measurement	Theoretical Estimate	Reference
Al	$\left\{ \begin{matrix} 0.90 \\ 1.06 \end{matrix} \right\}$	1.0	$\left\{ \begin{matrix} \text{Amaldi 46} \\ \text{Phillips (unpublished)} \end{matrix} \right.$
Fe	$\left\{ \begin{matrix} 1.43 \\ 1.45 \end{matrix} \right\}$	1.4	$\left\{ \begin{matrix} \text{Amaldi 46} \\ \text{Phillips (unpublished)} \end{matrix} \right.$
Cd	1.89	2.0	Phillips (unpublished)
Au	2.51	2.2	Phillips (unpublished)
Hg	2.47	2.5	Amaldi 46
Bi	2.56	2.3	Phillips (unpublished)
Pb	$\left\{ \begin{matrix} 2.22 \\ 2.29 \\ 2.56 \end{matrix} \right\}$	2.3	$\left\{ \begin{matrix} \text{Amaldi 46} \\ \text{Gittings 49} \\ \text{Phillips (unpublished)} \end{matrix} \right.$

by Phillips (unpublished) at 14 Mev which show that the theoretical estimate (VIII,4.13), $K_0 \cong 1 \times 10^{-13}$ cm^{-1}, gives a good fit.

The very high-energy region is characterized by the fact that the incident particle possesses enough energy to initiate secondary or tertiary reactions. We expect $(n;2n)$, $(n;np)$, $(n;3n)$ reactions, and so on. Emission of neutrons is usually more probable than emission of charged particles. We shall restrict our discussion to the multiple

[1] The scattering of neutrons without change of energy but with a change in the channel spin (Section 10 of Chapter VIII) is unimportant in this energy range.

emission of neutrons. We simplify expression (VIII,6.18) by the approximation

$$\sigma(n,n) \cong \sigma_C(n) \cong \pi R^2$$

The first approximation corresponds to neglecting the emission of charged particles from the compound nucleus C, and the second is the classical limit of the cross section for formation of the compound nucleus C. We then get

$$\sigma(n;2n) \cong \pi R^2 \left[1 - \left(1 + \frac{\epsilon_c}{\Theta} \right) \exp \left(- \frac{\epsilon_c}{\Theta} \right) \right] \qquad (2.21)$$

Here ϵ_c is the surplus of the incident energy ϵ over the threshold of the $(n;2n)$ reaction: $\epsilon_c = \epsilon - S_n$, where S_n is the separation energy of a neutron from the target nucleus. The temperature Θ is the one which determines the Maxwell distribution of the neutrons emitted in the first step: $\Theta = \Theta(\epsilon)$ [see (VIII,6.12a)]. $\sigma(n;2n)$ becomes almost equal to πR^2 if $\epsilon_c \gg \Theta$. Very little experimental material is available concerning $(n;2n)$ reactions. Some observations seem to indicate that the $(n;2n)$ cross section is sometimes smaller than (2.21). It is necessary to point out that the Bohr assumption may no longer be correct for incident neutrons in the high-energy region. The penetrability of the nuclear surface (VIII,5.7) is almost unity if $\epsilon > 10$ Mev. Hence it is possible that the neutron may leave the compound nucleus before it has shared all its energy with the other nucleons. It may be emitted before "thermal equilibrium" is established. In this case the average energy with which it is emitted is larger than the one expected from the Maxwell distribution. The residua' nucleus is then less excited and may not be able to emit a second neutron. Thus the yield of the $(n;2n)$ reaction would be reduced. Although this argument may be used to explain low $(n;2n)$ cross sections, the experiments are not yet conclusive enough to demand the abandoning of the Bohr assumption.

3. PROTON- AND ALPHA-PARTICLE-INDUCED REACTIONS

A. High Energy, Below Neutron Reaction Threshold

The cross sections of nuclear reactions initiated by protons or alpha-particles are immeasurably small for incident energies below 0.1 Mev, with a few exceptions among the very light nuclei. The Coulomb barrier prevents any appreciable interaction with the nucleus at low energies. We therefore restrict our discussion to high and very high energies.

The character of the reactions initiated by protons or alpha-particles is quite different below and above the threshold energy of the reactions in which neutrons are emitted, the (p,n) or (α,n) reactions, respectively. The threshold energy $-Q_{pn}$ of a (p,n) reaction with a stable target nucleus is always larger than 0.78 Mev: $-Q_{pn} > 0.78$ Mev. If it were less than this amount, the target nucleus, which is an isobar of the residual nucleus, would be unstable and would decay by a negative beta-transition into the residual nucleus. Actually the (p,n) threshold energies are very large for the light nuclei and the lighter of the intermediate nuclei. They are of the order of, but somewhat larger than, the proton Coulomb barrier energies for all nuclei for which $Z = N - 1$, or $Z = N =$ even, or $Z = N - 2 =$ even. This can be seen as follows: In the first case, the (p,n) reaction leads to a mirror nucleus, whose energy differs from that of the target nucleus just by the Coulomb energy, in the positive direction. In the second and third cases, the replacement of a neutron by a proton destroys the symmetry (partition) and adds Coulomb energy. Both factors increase the energy of the nucleus (see Chapter VI). We therefore expect large (p,n) thresholds for nuclei up to $A \cong 40$; e.g., $-Q_{pn} = 4.5$ Mev for Na^{23} as target and $-Q_{pn} = 6.6$ Mev for Cl^{35}.

Protons having an energy below this threshold can give rise only to elastic scattering, inelastic scattering, radiative capture, and perhaps (p,α) reactions. Because of the large Coulomb barrier for alpha-particles, the (p,α) reaction is very much weaker than the others, except in the very few cases in which the (p,α) reaction is highly exoergic. Owing to the absence of neutron emission, the lifetimes of the compound states are relatively long and sharp resonances may be expected. They were observed in many cases by measuring the yield of the radiative capture process as a function of the proton energy. Many sharp resonances have been found with this method by bombarding the following nuclei with protons: Na^{23}, Mg^{25}, Al^{27}, P^{31}, Cl^{37}. Figure 3.1 shows the γ-ray yield as a function of the proton energy in aluminum (Broström 47).

Since these reactions are capture processes, we can use (VIII,10.31) for the cross section. The resonances are too narrow to be resolved in these experiments. It can be shown, however, that the area under the unresolved resonance peak is equal to the area under the (much higher and much narrower) true resonance peak. We shall evaluate this area (the integral of the cross section over an energy region including the resonance peak in question) under the assumption that only the lowest orbital angular momentum $l_{\min} \equiv L$ consistent with the J and parity of the resonance level contributes appreciably to the cap-

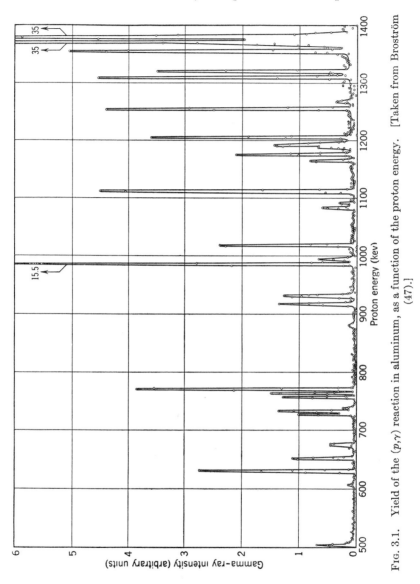

FIG. 3.1.   Yield of the (p,γ) reaction in aluminum, as a function of the proton energy.   [Taken from Broström (47).]

ture.   These minimum angular momenta are tabulated in Table 10.2 of Chapter VIII.   We shall furthermore neglect the energy dependence of the proton width within the resonance region.   We then get from (VIII,10.31)

$$\int \sigma_{\text{cap}}(p) \, d\epsilon = 2\pi^2\lambda^2 \frac{2J+1}{(2I+1)(2s+1)} \frac{\Gamma_p{}^s \, \Gamma_{\text{rad}}^s}{\Gamma^s} \tag{3.1}$$

where Γ_{rad}^s is the radiation width of the resonance level number s, Γ^{s} is its total width, and $\Gamma_p{}^s$ is the width for proton emission.   The latter is the sum of the channel widths for all channels α within the group $\bar{\alpha}$ of effective entrance channels ($l=L$ only, and $S=I\pm\tfrac{1}{2}$):

$$\Gamma_p{}^s = \sum_{S=I\pm\frac{1}{2}} \Gamma_{pSL}^s \tag{3.2}$$

The values of the channel spin S which can contribute are also listed in Table 10.2 of Chapter VIII.   In many cases only one of the two terms in the sum (3.2) is different from zero. $\Gamma_p{}^s$ is given by (VIII,7.13). Because of the barrier penetration factor v_l, $\Gamma_p{}^s$ increases very rapidly with energy.   For example, the proton width in Al^{27} can be estimated from the level distance between levels in Fig. 3.1.   If we assume that most of the levels in the figure are due to S wave protons, we get an experimental value of D of the order of 100 kev.   This implies a proton width $\Gamma_p{}^s$ of the order of 1 ev for $\epsilon = 600$ kev, and of the order of 200 ev for $\epsilon = 1.4$ Mev.   (Both values are calculated for S wave protons.) Since Γ_{rad}^s is not expected to show any marked energy dependence, there will be an energy ϵ_1 at which $\Gamma_{\text{rad}}^s \cong \Gamma_p{}^s$; for energies $\epsilon \gg \epsilon_1$ expression (3.1) depends only on the radiation width.   The maxima of the resonances in Fig. 3.1 do not increase strongly with the energy, and we assume therefore that these resonances lie above ϵ_1 and can be used to determine Γ_{rad}^s.   A comparison of the experimental value of the area under the peaks with the theoretical value (3.1) for $l=0$ or $l=1$ (higher l's are improbable at these energies) gives roughly $\Gamma_{\text{rad}}^s \sim 1$ ev in agreement with (2.9), and also in agreement with the assumption that $\Gamma_p{}^s \gg \Gamma_{\text{rad}}^s$ for the resonances in question.

The inelastic scattering of protons is an important means to determine the level spectrum of the *target* nucleus.   This method is practically restricted to the energy region near or below the (p,n) threshold, since neutron emission is much more probable than re-emission of the proton, if the neutrons can leave the nucleus with energies above 1 Mev.   Therefore the (p,p) reaction for level determinations is applied only to the lighter intermediate nuclei with high (p,n) thresholds.

The heavier nuclei have in general much lower (p,n) thresholds. Furthermore high proton energies must be used in order to penetrate the Coulomb barrier. Hence no appreciable nuclear effects are expected below the (p,n) threshold.

Similar considerations can be applied to alpha-induced reactions below the (α,n) threshold. So far no case is known experimentally

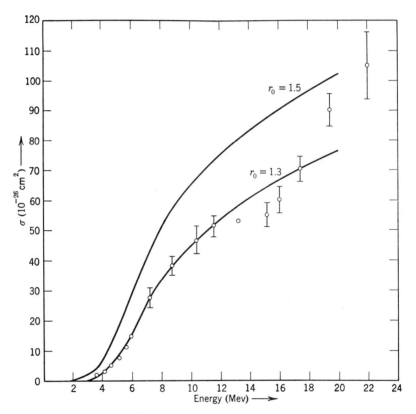

FIG. 3.2a. $\sigma_C(p)$ for Cu^{63}. The solid curves are the theoretical values for $r_0 = 1.3 \times 10^{-13}$ cm and 1.5×10^{-13} cm; the points represent $\sigma = \sigma(p,n) + \sigma(p;2n) + \sigma(p;pn)$ as observed by Ghoshal (50).

in which alpha-resonances below the (α,n) threshold have occurred. The energy of the alpha-particles is too small to penetrate the barrier.

A very promising method of studying resonances with charged particles is the observation of the elastic scattering near resonance. The deviations from pure Rutherford scattering are of two kinds: (1) off resonance the nucleus acts not like a point charge, but like a charged impenetrable sphere of radius R; the correction for this effect is

obtained from formula (VIII,2.60) by putting $A_{res}^l = 0$.   (2) In resonance there is a specifically nuclear contribution to the scattering which
is given by the A_{res}^l in (VIII,2.60).   The scattering amplitude A_{res}^l
near resonance is given by (VIII,8.31).

These formulas are valid under the assumption of spinless projectiles and target nuclei.   They are therefore correct for elastic

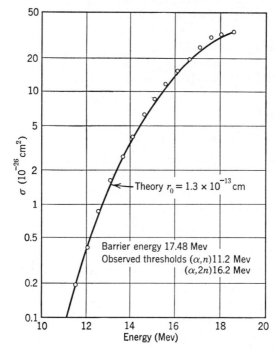

FIG. 3.2b. $\sigma_C(\alpha)$ for Rh^{103}.   The solid curve shows the theoretical values for
$r_0 = 1.3 \times 10^{-13}$ cm; the points are $\sigma = \sigma(\alpha,n) + \sigma(\alpha;2n)$ as observed by Bradt
(47).

scattering of alpha-particles from even-even nuclei, but not for elastic
scattering of protons.   The spin effects do not enter into the scattering
off resonance, but they must be considered within the resonance
region (Laubenstein 50).   The analysis of the energy and angular
dependence of the deviations from Rutherford scattering off resonance
allows in principle a very accurate measurement of the effective nuclear
radius R.   A further analysis of the energy and angular dependence
of the scattering within the resonance regions makes it possible in
principle to assign angular momenta J and parities Π_C to the various
resonance levels of the compound nucleus.   Such analyses have been

carried out so far only for a very few resonances in light nuclei (Rose 40, Wheeler 41, 41a, Critchfield 49). Examples of experimental work are found in Bender (49) and other work of the Wisconsin group.

B. High Energy, Above Neutron Reaction Threshold

If the compound nucleus has enough excitation energy to emit a neutron of 1 Mev or more, the neutron reaction becomes the dominant reaction. The high probability of neutron emission also broadens the levels of the compound nucleus. We can then apply the continuum theory for the cross sections averaged over many resonances and get the values for the cross sections $\sigma_C(p)$ and $\sigma_C(\alpha)$ which are tabulated in Table 4.1 of Chapter VIII. Since the neutron reaction is dominant, its cross section is almost equal to the cross section for formation of the compound nucleus:

$$\sigma(p,n) \cong \sigma_C(p) \qquad \sigma(\alpha,n) \cong \sigma_C(\alpha)$$

The comparison with experimental results is satisfactory in most cases as the examples in Figs. 3.2a, and 3.2b show. However, in order to get agreement with the shape of the excitation functions, nuclear radii had to be chosen which are somewhat smaller than those deduced from neutron experiments. Their value is represented by

$$R = 1.3 \times 10^{-13} \times A^{1/3} \text{ cm}$$

rather than by $1.5 \times 10^{-13} \times A^{1/3}$ cm. It is not certain whether this discrepancy is genuine or due to experimental inaccuracies. Recent measurements by Blaser (51) and co-workers suggest nuclear radii which are more in conformity with those found in neutron experiments.

The cross sections for reactions in which particles other than neutrons emerge are expected to be very small. They are given by expression (VIII,6.10). There is not enough experimental material available to test the theory.

C. Very High Energy

The very high-energy region is characterized by the appearance of secondary reactions. The reaction cross section should be well represented by the continuum theory, as given in Table 4.1 of Chapter VIII. The compound nucleus decays mostly by the emission of a neutron, but the residual nucleus may possess enough energy to emit a second particle. Because of the Coulomb barriers the most common secondary reaction is the $(p;2n)$ or $(\alpha;2n)$ reaction. At still higher energies, tertiary reactions of the type $(\alpha;3n)$ should occur and have been observed.

The higher-order reactions with charged particles have shown good agreement with the theoretical predictions.   We discuss as an example the $(\alpha;n)$ and $(\alpha;2n)$ reactions on silver and the $(\alpha;2n)$ and $(\alpha;3n)$

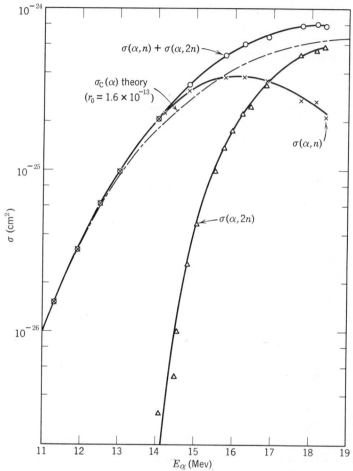

FIG. 3.3.   Cross sections of the Ag^{109} (α,n) and Ag^{109} $(\alpha,2n)$ reactions. [From Bradt (47).   Energy scale and absolute values redetermined by Bleuler, Stebbins, and Tendham (unpublished).]

reactions on bismuth.   Figure 3.3 shows $\sigma(\alpha,n)$ and $\sigma(\alpha;2n)$ on Ag^{109} as a function of energy according to measurements of Bradt and Tendham (Bradt 47).   The graph also contains the theoretical curve for $\sigma_C(\alpha)$, the cross section for the formation of the compound nucleus by alpha-particles. $\sigma(\alpha,n)$ follows the theoretical curve as expected until the threshold for the $(\alpha;2n)$ reaction is reached.   Then $\sigma(\alpha,n)$

drops and the $\sigma(\alpha;2n)$ curve starts rising sharply.   The sum of the two is close to the theoretical curve for $\sigma_C(\alpha)$ with $r_0 = 1.6 \times 10^{-13}$ cm

If we use expressions (VIII,6.14) and (VIII,6.18) to represent $\sigma(\alpha,n)$ and $\sigma(\alpha;2n)$, respectively, we find that the best fit is obtained with a nuclear temperature of $\Theta \cong 1.8$ Mev.   This is the temperature of the evaporation of the first neutron, and it therefore should be given by (VIII,6.12a) with E equal to the maximum energy of the escaping neutrons.   We find $\Theta = 1.3$ Mev for $E = 12$ Mev, in reasonable agreement with the experiments.

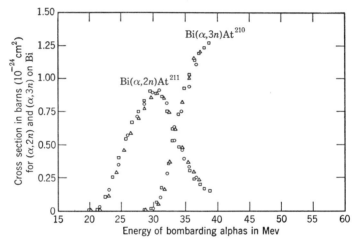

FIG. 3.4. $\sigma(\alpha;2n)$ and $\sigma(\alpha;3n)$ in bismuth as functions of energy. [From Kelly (49).]

The behavior of the cross sections of alpha reactions at higher energies is shown in Fig. 3.4, which contains the measurements of Kelly and Segrè (Kelly 49) for $\sigma(\alpha;2n)$ and $\sigma(\alpha;3n)$ on bismuth.   We observe the characteristic fall of the $(\alpha;2n)$ reaction with the onset of the $(\alpha;3n)$ reaction.   The sum of the two cross sections $[\sigma(\alpha,n)$ is already negligibly small] is a smoothly rising curve and is equal to $\sigma_C(\alpha)$.

A very instructive series of measurements was made by Ghoshal (50) with protons bombarding Cu^{63} and alpha-particles bombarding Ni^{60}.   Both bombardments produce the compound nucleus Zn^{64}. The energy difference between the nuclei Cu^{63} and Ni^{60} is such that a proton energy ϵ_p in the first bombardment and an alpha-particle energy $\epsilon_\alpha = \epsilon_p + 7$ Mev in the second one produce the compound nucleus Zn^{64} in the same state of excitation.   Hence, if the Bohr

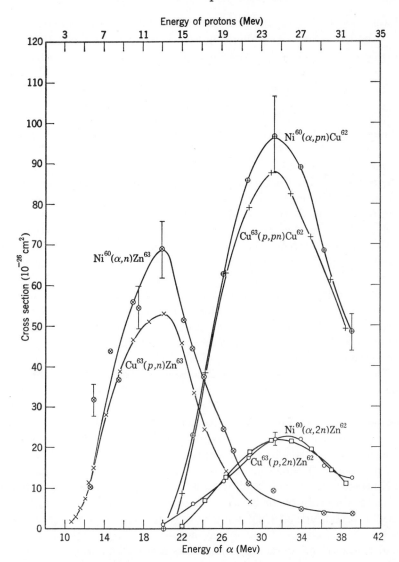

FIG. 3.5.   Cross sections for reactions involving the compound nucleus Zn^{64}, as measured by Ghoshal (50).   At any one energy of the compound nucleus, the Bohr assumption leads us to expect that the ratios of the cross sections for the (a,n), the $(a;2n)$, and the $(a;pn)$ reactions are independent of the nature of the incident particle a (in this case, a is either a proton or an alpha-particle).   The experimental measurements shown here provide confirmation of this theoretical prediction.

assumption is correct, the processes following the two bombardments must be the same. The following reactions were observed:

(1) $Ni^{60}(\alpha,n)Zn^{63}$ (4) $Cu^{63}(p,n)Zn^{63}$

(2) $Ni^{60}(\alpha;2n)Zn^{62}$ (5) $Cu^{63}(p;2n)Zn^{62}$

(3) $Ni^{60}(\alpha;pn)Cu^{62}$ (6) $Cu^{63}(\alpha;pn)Cu^{62}$

The cross sections of these reactions are given by

$$\sigma(a,b) = \sigma_C(a)\ G_C(b)$$

where a stands for the incident proton or alpha-particle and b stands for the reaction products, n, $2n$, pn. According to the Bohr assumption $G_C(b)$ depends only on the excitation of the compound nucleus and therefore is the same for incident protons or alpha-particles if $\epsilon_\alpha = \epsilon_p + 7$ Mev. Hence the ratio of the reaction yields of (1), (2), (3) should be equal to the ratio of the yields of (4), (5), (6). Figure 3.5 shows that this is fulfilled. Actually not only the ratios are equal but also the cross sections themselves are almost the same for incident protons and for incident α's. This is due to the accidental fact that $\sigma_C(\text{proton})$ at an energy ϵ_p is almost equal to $\sigma_C(\text{alpha-particle})$ at the energy $\epsilon_p + 7$ Mev in the energy region observed. These experiments are a good proof for the validity of the Bohr assumption.

The fact that the $(a;2n)$ reactions are about four times weaker than the $(a;pn)$ reactions needs some explanation. We would expect that the reaction emitting a proton is weaker because of the Coulomb barrier effect. However, the product Cu^{62} of the pn process is an odd-odd nucleus, whereas the product of the $2n$ process is an even-even nucleus. As the latter very probably has a much smaller level density, the number of channels leading to a $2n$ decay is reduced compared to the number of channels leading to a pn decay. This effect overcompensates the effect of the barrier. A part of the observed cross section for the production of Cu^{62} may be due to the emission of deuterons rather than of a separated neutron and proton. This effect would also tend to make the apparent $(a;pn)$ cross section higher.

4. NEUTRON-, PROTON-, AND ALPHA-PARTICLE-INDUCED REACTIONS AT ULTRAHIGH ENERGIES

The considerations of Section 3 of Chapter VIII have shown that at ultrahigh energies the mean free path of a nuclear particle within a nucleus becomes of the order of nuclear dimensions. It is then no longer justifiable to consider the Bohr assumption valid since there is not sufficient time to share the energy among all constituents before a particle leaves the compound nucleus. Hence the second phase of the nuclear reaction depends on the initial phase in all details.

At ultrahigh energies it is more suitable to consider separately the interaction of the incoming particle with the individual nucleons of the target nucleus. Because of the small collision cross section the incoming particle hits only one or a few nucleons which, by elastic scattering, obtain a large fraction of the energy of the incoming particle. The secondary nucleon then may be able to leave the nucleus without further collision, or it may divide its energy with a third nucleon; this process may repeat itself until the energy of the nucleons is so low that the previous considerations are applicable. Thereafter the nucleons share their energy with the nucleus as a whole.

We therefore expect the following effects of an ultrahigh energy particle hitting a nucleus: a small number of nucleons (perhaps also an alpha-particle among them) leave the nucleus with energies within or near the "ultrahigh energy" region, say $\epsilon_i > 30$ Mev. The balance ϵ_Θ of the incident energy is transferred to the residual nucleus, which can be considered being "heated" up to a certain nuclear temperature Θ depending on the amount ϵ_Θ. The residual nucleus then "boils off" a number of nucleons with low energies corresponding to the temperature Θ. Hence the outgoing particles are expected to fall into two groups: (1) the fast particles which were emitted immediately by direct collisions with the incident particle or with other particles produced by collisions, and (2) the slow particles which are boiled off after thermal equilibrium has been established in the residual nucleus.[1]

The total cross section for very fast particles is less than the geometrical limit $2\pi R^2$ because nuclear matter is partially transparent. There is a finite probability that a very fast particle passes through the nucleus without any collision. Calculations were performed by Serber and others (Fernbach 49) which are based on the mean free path for collision as estimated in Section 3 of Chapter VIII. They also took into account the change of the wave number from k to K when entering into the interior of the nucleus. The nucleus acts as a refracting and partially absorbing sphere, whereas at lower energies the nucleus was considered a refracting but completely absorbing sphere. The calculations agree fairly well with measurements of total cross sections for "90"-Mev neutrons (Cook 49).

The number and the energy distribution of the emitted particles following an ultrahigh-energy nuclear collision have been studied mostly with photographic plates and cloud chambers. Ultrahigh-

---

[1] The processes described here are treated in greater detail in the following papers: Goldberger (48) and Horning (49).

energy particles falling on a photographic emulsion produce "stars" in which every prong corresponds to a charged particle emitted by the center. The same phenomenon can also be studied in cloud chambers. The energy and charge of a particle are determined from its residual range, from the ionization produced, from the scattering of the particle, and from the number of "delta-rays" (knocked-out electrons from atoms) per unit path length. Indications of a grouping into fast and "boiled-off" particles were found with reactions induced by artificially accelerated particles (Brueckner 49) and by cosmic rays (Hornbostel 49, Brown 49, Camerini 49, Feld 50, and many others).

The reactions induced by cosmic-ray particles are considerably more complicated than any of the events discussed so far, and we shall not give any treatment of nuclear interactions in cosmic rays in this book. The main complicating factors are the uncertainty about the energy, nature, and intensity of the initiating particles in many cases, the difficulty of detecting fast neutrons with a large enough efficiency to make their counting possible, and the occurrence of meson production in nuclear collisions. Although the reaction cross section of a nucleus decreases below the geometrical cross section for energies above about 100 Mev, this decrease does not continue indefinitely. The evidence from the cosmic rays indicates (Rossi 48) that the cross section approaches an approximately constant value at energies above 1 Bev. This value is of the order of 40 percent of the geometrical cross section in light nuclei (air) and of the order of 85 percent of the geometrical cross section in a heavy nucleus like lead.[1] The main process responsible for this roughly constant cross section at cosmic-ray energies is the production of mesons. A discussion of meson production is outside the scope of this book.

5. REACTIONS WITH LIGHT NUCLEI

It is impossible to establish general rules governing the course for nuclear reactions with light nuclei. In this section we discuss a number of characteristic reactions which show features different from those observed with intermediate or heavy nuclei. We refer to the excellent review articles of Hornyak, Lauritsen, et al. (Hornyak 48, 50) for a complete description of most of the nuclear reactions with light nuclei. The importance of special selection rules for reactions involving light nuclei was first stressed by Oppenheimer and Serber (Oppenheimer 37, 38).

---

[1] These numbers are only very rough estimates, since cosmic-ray experiments are subject to many corrections.

A. $B^{10}(n,\alpha)Li^7$

When boron is exposed to slow neutrons, the (n,α) reaction on B^{10} is the leading process. The Q value of this reaction is 2.78 Mev. This reaction is of special interest because (n,α) reactions with slow neutrons do not occur very frequently. In intermediate and heavy nuclei, neutrons in energy regions I and II produce elastic scattering or capture (and in some cases fission). The occurrence of (n,α) reactions is usually excluded because of the preventive effect of the Coulomb barrier. In the case of boron, however, the favorable Q value and the low Coulomb barrier (about 2.5 Mev) between Li^7 and an alpha-particle make it possible that an alpha-particle is emitted by the compound nucleus with considerable probability. Alpha-particle emission competes successfully against neutron capture; the radiative capture cross section is less than 10^{-5} of the (n,α) cross section. The (n,α) reaction on B^{10} can be considered a neutron-induced fission of boron into Li^7 and He^4.

The alpha-particles are emitted into two channels, corresponding to the ground state of Li^7 ($Q=2.78$) and to the first excited state of Li^7 ($Q=2.30$). The emission probabilities for thermal neutron bombardment are in the ratio 93 to 7 in favor of the excited state.

The observed energy dependence of the (n,α) cross section is shown in Fig. 5.1. For neutron energies up to 10 kev it is almost exactly proportional to $\epsilon^{-1/2}$. The qualitative features of this curve can be understood by the Breit-Wigner formula for the reaction cross section, with a reaction width (in this case the width for the emission of the alpha-particles) of the order of 250 kev and a resonance energy of about 100 kev. Such a large width is not unexpected in view of the large level distances in B^{11}, and in view of the weakness of the Coulomb barrier for alpha-emission. The $\epsilon^{-1/2}$ dependence of the cross section at energies below 1 kev follows from the Breit-Wigner formula (VIII, 7.25). It is remarkable and very characteristic of this reaction that the $\epsilon^{-1/2}$ dependence extends to energies up to 10^4 ev. This is due to the large reaction width $\Gamma_\alpha{}^s$. Hence the resonance factor is very slowly varying and the main energy dependence comes from the proportionality to λ.

There exists a mirror reaction to the (n,α) reaction on B^{10}:

$$B^{10}(p,\alpha)Be^7$$

The investigation of this reaction is of interest in the proof of the charge symmetry of the nuclear forces. The mirror of the (n,α) reaction with slow neutrons is a (p,α) reaction with an incident energy ϵ_p

such that the protons arrive slowly at the nuclear surface:

$$\epsilon_p \cong \frac{Ze^2}{R} \cong 2.3 \text{ Mev}$$

We should then expect very similar effects, e.g., two alpha-particle groups also differing in energy by 0.48 Mev with a similar intensity

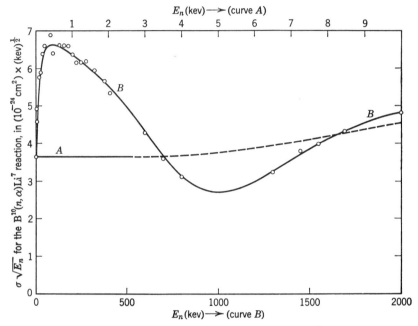

FIG. 5.1. $\sigma(n,\alpha)$ in boron.   This plot shows the product $\sigma \sqrt{\epsilon}$ in order to remove the $\epsilon^{-1/2}$ factor.   There are no reliable measurements between 1 kev and about 10 kev.   The dashed part of curve A is a plausible interpolation.   The horizontal part below 1 kev ($\epsilon^{-1/2}$ dependence) is very well established.   [Values taken from Goldsmith (47).]

ratio.   Be^7 should possess an excited state at roughly the same energy as Li^7.   Recent measurements indicate that this expectation is borne out (Brown 50, Lauritsen 50).   The strong energy dependence of the branching ratio to the two states of Be^7 indicates that a similar behavior may be found in the mirror reaction B$^{10}(n,\alpha)$Li^7.   If this is true, no special importance should be attached to the value of this branching ratio at any one energy (e.g., for thermal neutrons).

B. Proton Reactions with Li^7

When lithium is bombarded with protons, Be^8 is formed as a compound nucleus from Li^7.   Since even the ground state of Be^8 is unstable against decay into two alpha-particles, we expect the following reaction to occur:

$$p + \mathrm{Li}^7 = \mathrm{Be}^8 = \alpha + \alpha$$

The Q value of this reaction is $Q = 17.2$ Mev, so that each alpha-particle gets at least 8.6 Mev, enough to overcome the competition of any other reaction. In spite of this fact we observe also other reac-

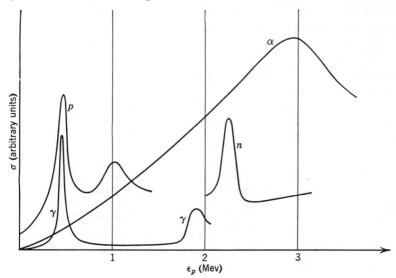

FIG. 5.2. Energy dependence of the cross sections of the (p,γ), (p,n), (p,p), and (p,α) reactions with Li^7. These curves are only schematic. They indicate the general properties but must not be used quantitatively. [From Hornyak (50).]

tions with about equal intensity, i.e., (p,n) and (p,p) reactions, and radiative capture. Figure 5.2 shows the energy dependence of the cross sections.

The radiative capture produces a very hard gamma-ray of energy $\hbar\omega = 17.2 + \epsilon_p$. This is a radiative transition directly to the ground state of Be^8. It also produces a radiation $\hbar\omega = 14.2 + \epsilon_p$ to an excited state of Be^8. The radiative capture process shows a strong resonance at $\epsilon_p = 0.37$ Mev.[1] The (p,n) reaction has a negative Q value: $Q_{pn} = -1.63$ Mev. Neutrons are produced only if $\epsilon_p > 1.63$ Mev. Their channel energy is then $\epsilon_n = \epsilon_p - 1.63$ Mev. Their actual energy depends on the angle of emission. This reaction is one of the best sources of monoenergetic neutrons at low energies. At higher energies

[1] This is the channel energy. The actual proton energy ϵ_p' in the laboratory system is $[1 + (M_p/M_{\mathrm{Li}})]\,\epsilon_p$, where M_{Li} is the mass of Li^7.

a second neutron group occurs as a result of the excited level in Be[7]. The (p,p) reaction is observed as inelastic scattering, leaving the Li[7] nucleus in an excited state of 0.478-Mev excitation.

We find sharp resonances for the emission of protons, neutrons, and gamma-rays, but no sharp resonances at these energes for the emission of alpha-particles. This poses an interesting problem: How is it possible that the compound nucleus created in one of the resonances does not instantly decay into two fast alpha-particles, but lives long enough to emit a gamma-ray or a neutron or a proton, and long enough to account for the narrow width of these levels? The explanation is found in the fact that alpha-particles obey Bose-Einstein statistics (Critchfield 41). Consider the state of the system after the compound nucleus has disintegrated into two alpha-particles. The wave function must be symmetric under the exchange of the two identical particles. This exchange is equivalent to the following two operations: (1) reversing the sign of all position coordinates, i.e., performing the parity operation; (2) interchanging the spins of the two alpha-particles. Since each alpha-particle has spin $I=0$, the second operation gives unity, and the exchange of coordinates which enters into the Bose-Einstein statistics is completely equivalent to the parity operation.[1] The Bose-Einstein statistics of the alpha-particles therefore implies that the parity of the outgoing state must be even. Since the parity is a constant of motion, we conclude that only even-parity states of the compound nucleus can disintegrate into two alpha-particles. Furthermore the parity of the outgoing alpha-particles is determined by the orbital angular momentum l of their relative motion, since the internal parity of each alpha-particle is even. We conclude that the alpha-particles must emerge with even orbital angular momentum l. Since the spin I of each alpha-particle is zero, l is equal to the total angular momentum J, which is a constant of motion. Hence *the compound states which can disintegrate into two alpha-particles have even parity and even angular momentum J.* All other compound states must decay by neutron, proton, or gamma-ray emission exclusively. These other compound states live much longer than the alpha-emitting levels and therefore exhibit sharp resonances. We observe that the second proton resonance does not lead to appreciable gamma-ray emission. This may be accounted for partly by the increased probability for re-emission of the proton as the proton energy

---

[1] This is not true for a reaction involving two deuterons or for proton-proton scattering, since there the spin exchange can give either $+1$ or -1, depending on the spin state (Konopinski 48, Nakano 49).

increases, and may also be due in part to selection rules for the gamma-ray emission.

It should be noted that the nucleus Be^8 formed in the radiative capture of protons by Li^7 decays eventually into two alpha-particles, even though the original compound state, before gamma-ray emission, could not do so. The emission of a gamma-ray may lead to a change of parity Π_C or angular momentum J or both. Thus the state of Be^8 reached after the gamma-ray emission may have the right character (even parity and even J) for disintegration into two alpha-particles. In particular, the lowest two levels of Be^8 (the ground state and the level at 2.9 Mev) are of this type (Wheeler 41, 41a). Hence the ultimate result of the radiative capture process $Li^7(p,\gamma)Be^8$, after one or more gamma-ray emissions, is always a state which disintegrates into two alpha-particles.

A detailed treatment of this and similar reactions involving light nuclei is greatly aided by measurements of the angular distribution of scattered particles and reaction products. The interpretation of these results allows in many cases a fairly definite assignment of J and parity for each compound state. We shall not give any details in this book but shall confine ourselves to a proof of the general theorems which follow from symmetry considerations (Chapter X, Section 3). The angular distribution of the reaction products in the $Li^7(p,n)Be^7$ reaction has been measured by Taschek (48) and analyzed by Breit (48) in terms of possible values of J and the parity of the Be^8 compound states. Considerable work on the interpretation of the $Li^7(p,\alpha)$ reaction in terms of resonance theory has been done by Critchfield (41), Inglis (48), and Heydenburg (48). For a similar analysis of the $F^{19}(p,\alpha)O^{16}$ reaction, see Gerjuoy (40) and Chao (50a).

C. Reactions Leading to the Compound Nucleus N^{15}

The following reactions involve the same compound nucleus N^{15}: $N^{14}(n,p)C^{14}$, $N^{14}(n,\alpha)B^{11}$, $B^{11}(\alpha,n)N^{14}$, $C^{14}(p,n)N^{14}$. The target nucleus in the last reaction is an unstable nucleus, but C^{14} can be provided in sufficient quantities for bombardment because of its very long half-life. The study of these reactions is of special interest because resonances were observed with all of them, and some resonances occurring in different reactions can be ascribed to the same state of the compound nucleus. The situation can best be described by an energy diagram of the type introduced by Hornyak and Lauritsen (48). The middle column of Fig. 5.3 shows the energy states of N^{15}. The numbers indicate the energy in Mev above the ground state of N^{15} which serves as the zero energy point for the whole diagram. The horizontal

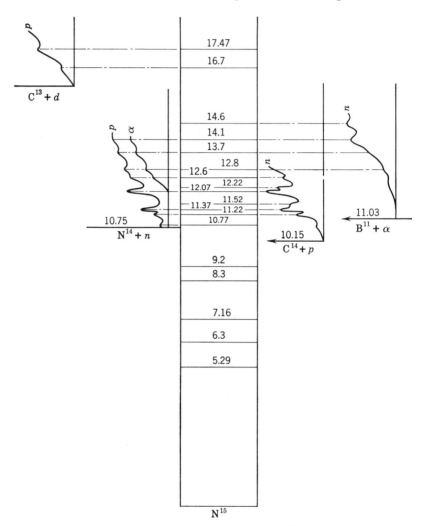

FIG. 5.3.   Energy diagram of the compound nucleus N^{15}. [Simplified version of
the diagram in Hornyak (50).]

lines on the right and on the left indicate the energy of the system
separated into $N^{14}+n$, $C^{14}+p$, $B^{11}+\alpha$, and $C^{13}+d$, each pair in their
ground states and at rest.   The numbers indicate the energies in Mev.
These values serve as zero points for the corresponding channel
energies; e.g., if the compound nucleus N^{15} is created through the chan-
nel $C^{14}+p$ with a channel energy ϵ_p [actual proton energy $\epsilon_p' = \frac{15}{14}\epsilon_p$],
the excitation energy of N^{15} is $10.15 + \epsilon_p$.   The curves plotted above

the channel zero point are the cross section curves of the nuclear reactions initiated by the corresponding channels. The yield is plotted horizontally; the channel energy is plotted vertically starting at the channel zero point in the same scale as the levels. The letter next to the curve denotes the particle emitted in the reaction. For example, the curve above the $(C^{14}+p)$ line denotes the cross section of the (p,n) reaction. It shows several strong resonances which correspond to levels of the compound nucleus N^{15}; e.g., the resonance at $\epsilon_p = 1.92$ Mev indicates a level of N^{15} with an energy of 12.07 Mev.

Table 5.1 shows the resonances observed in the various reactions. The data for the $C^{14}(p,n)$ reaction are taken from Shoupp (49), for the $N^{14}(n,p)$ and $N^{14}(n,\alpha)$ reactions from Stebler (48), and for the $B^{11}(\alpha,n)$ reaction from Walker (49). The energy resolution of Walker's data is not very high, hence only approximate values can be quoted for the resonance energies.

TABLE 5.1

RESONANCE LEVELS IN N^{15} IN VARIOUS REACTIONS, IN Mev†

$C^{14}(p,n)N^{14}$	$N^{14}(n,p)C^{14}$	$N^{14}(n,\alpha)B^{11}$	$B^{11}(\alpha,n)N^{14}$
10.77	.....	.....	....
11.22	11.23	.....	....
11.36	11.38	.....	....
11.52	.....	.....	....
12.07	12.11	12.07	?
12.22	.....	.....	12.3 ± 0.2
12.63	12.43	12.44	?
	12.82	12.84	12.9 ± 0.2
	13.7	13.7	13.6 ± 0.2
			14.1
			14.6

† This material is taken from Hornyak (50).

The $N^{14}(n,p)C^{14}$ and $C^{14}(p,n)N^{14}$ reactions show resonances at the same energies in the compound nucleus, with two exceptions [the (p,n) data do not extend to high enough energies to compare with the last two resonances in the (n,p) reaction]. The appearance of resonances at the same (compound) energies in these two reactions follows directly from the reciprocity theorem (Chapter VIII, Section 2), according to which the cross sections of two inverse reactions must be proportional to each other. There is every reason to believe that the two missing resonances in the (n,p) reaction do exist and were not observed because of experimental difficulties. Similarly, we should expect the $N^{14}(n,\alpha)B^{11}$ and $B^{11}(\alpha,n)N^{14}$ reactions to show resonances at the same energies in the compound nucleus. This is true for the two highest-energy resonances listed in the table. It is very likely that the nominal 12.3 ± 0.2 Mev level in the (α,n) reaction is actually an unresolved superposition of the two resonances at 12.07 and 12.44 Mev in the inverse reaction. It should be emphasized that the occurrence of peaks in the cross sections of *inverse* reactions at the same energies of the compound system provides no confirmation of the compound nucleus theory, since the reciprocity theorem holds even if no long-lived compound state is formed. A check of the compound nucleus theory can be obtained only if peaks are observed at the same (compound) energy for two (or more) reactions which are *not* inverses of each other. Only then can we conclude that compound states are really formed.

There are four compound levels in Table 5.1 which are found decaying through three different channels (by emission of neutrons, protons, and alpha-particles), i.e., at 12.1, 12.44, 12.83, and 13.7 Mev. The existence of these four levels can be considered an indication of the formation of a compound nucleus. No such compound levels are found at lower energies because the Coulomb barrier prevents the emission of the alpha-particles with measurable intensity. At higher energies the various reactions have not yet been studied to a sufficient extent.

Although compound levels which decay through three or more channels are expected to occur whenever three or more channels are open energetically, only very few such coincidences have been observed so far. In most cases the energy relations are not favorable for observation. The channel zero points usually differ by so much energy that we cannot reach the same excitation of the compound nucleus through different channels with presently available Van de Graaff accelerators (which are the main source of precision data on energy levels).

6. DEUTERON-INDUCED REACTIONS

Nuclear reactions initiated by deuterons are of great importance in nuclear physics. In general their yield is much larger than that of corresponding reactions initiated with other charged particles. Deuterons accelerated in cyclotrons are very commonly used for the production of radioactive isotopes.

The theoretical treatment of deuteron-induced reactions is somewhat more difficult than the treatment of other reactions. New types of processes occur with deuterons which are not described by the

schemes introduced in Chapter VIII. The new features can be traced
to the following facts: (a) the deuteron is a very loosely bound structure,
its binding energy of 2.23 Mev being much lower than the average
binding fraction; (b) its charge distribution is very "unsymmetric":
the center of mass and the center of charge (the proton) do not coincide, as they do, e.g., in the alpha-particle. The distance between
the two centers is equal to the "radius" of the deuteron.

According to the regular scheme of nuclear reactions a nucleus
$X(Z,A)$[1] bombarded by deuterons should give rise to a compound
nucleus $C(Z+1, A+2)$ which then decays into several channels:

$$X(Z,A) + d = C(Z+1, A+2) = \begin{cases} Y(Z+1, A+1) + n \\ Y(Z, A+1) + p \\ Y(Z-1, A-2) + \alpha \\ \text{etc.} \end{cases} \quad \text{(I)}$$

The cross sections for this type of nuclear reaction can be calculated
by the methods used in Chapter VIII. Because of the special properties of the deuteron, scheme I is not the only process which takes
place. The following processes occur with appreciable probability:

(II) The "electric" disintegration of the deuteron by the Coulomb
field of the target nucleus (Oppenheimer 35).

(III) The formation of a compound nucleus

$$C'(Z, A+1) \qquad \text{or} \qquad C''(Z+1, A+1)$$

by the absorption of only one constituent of the deuteron. The latter
process is called "stripping" at high energy and "Oppenheimer-
Phillips process" at low energies (Oppenheimer 35a).

We first describe process II: When the deuteron passes by a nucleus
without actually hitting its surface, it is exposed to the Coulomb field
of the nucleus. During its passage the deuteron is under the influence
of an electric field which, from the point of view of the deuteron, varies
with time. Its effect on the deuteron is similar to that of a light wave;
it may cause a disintegration of the deuteron:

$$d + X = X + n + p \quad \text{(II)}$$

Actually the electric field varies quite rapidly at the place of the
deuteron. Let us consider a deuteron with a velocity v passing near
a nucleus; the electric field at the position of the deuteron increases

---

[1] We shall use the notation $X(Z,A)$ for a nucleus X of charge Z and mass number A.

to its maximum and decreases again in a time t of the order of R/v, where R is the radius of the nucleus. For a deuteron of 10 Mev, and $R \sim 0.6 \times 10^{-12}$ cm, we obtain roughly $\hbar\omega \sim 3.3$ Mev for the quantum energy of a light quantum whose frequency is t^{-1}. Hence the Coulomb field, as seen from the deuteron, contains frequencies high enough to cause its disintegration. The cross section for this process is quite large; for nuclei with high Z it is of the same order as the cross sections for other processes (Guth 51, Goldberger 51).

The mechanism of process III is described as follows: Because of the finite size of the deuteron, it may happen that one constituent comes into contact with the nuclear surface before the other one does. Since the nuclear interaction energies are much higher than the binding energy of the deuteron, the nucleon arriving first at the nuclear surface is quickly separated from its partner and forms a compound nucleus C'. If the second nucleon hits the nuclear surface an instant later, the compound nucleus $C(Z+1, A+2)$ is formed just as in process I. If the second nucleon misses the nucleus, however, process III results:

$$d + X(Z,A) = C'(Z, A+1) + p \qquad \text{(IIIa)}$$

$$d + X(Z,A) = C''(Z+1, A+1) + n \qquad \text{(IIIb)}$$

after which the compound nucleus C' or C'' may decay with emission of some other nuclear particle. Process IIIa is the more probable one, especially at low energies, since the electric repulsion keeps the proton away from the target nucleus.

The cross section for these processes is especially simple to compute at very high deuteron energies ϵ_D when the Coulomb repulsion between the nucleus and the deuteron can be neglected: $\epsilon_D \gg Ze^2/R$ (Serber 47). Then the deuterons move in straight lines with constant speed until they collide with the nucleus. The cross section for one nucleon (say the proton) hitting and the other (the neutron) missing is, to a first approximation,

$$\sigma_{\text{III}} = (\pi/2)Rd \qquad (6.1)$$

where d is the average distance between neutron and proton in the deuteron.[1] Equation (6.1) can be explained as follows: Let us consider a deuteron for which the vector $\mathbf{d}$ (from the proton to the neutron) includes an angle θ with the direction of the motion. The cross section for this deuteron to strike the nucleus in such a way that

---

[1] d is of the order of *half* of the decay length (II,2.7) of the wave function for the relative motion of the deuteron, i.e., $d = \frac{1}{2} \times 4.31 \times 10^{-13}$ cm $= 2.2 \times 10^{-13}$ cm. This d is, properly speaking, the "diameter" of the deuteron.

the proton hits but the neutron misses is $2Rd \, |\sin \theta|$ (see Fig. 6.1) if the curvature of the nucleus is neglected, $R \gg d$. As the average value of $|\sin \theta|$ is equal to $\pi/4$, we obtain (6.1).

The nucleon which misses the nucleus proceeds with its original speed, plus whatever was added during the process of breakup. It is reasonable to assume that the breakup leaves the nucleon in a momentum distribution corresponding to the one found in the internal motion of the deuteron. The final momentum of the nucleon after breakup is the vector sum of the momentum $p_0 = (M \epsilon_D)^{1/2}$ coming from the original deuteron motion (M is the mass of *one* nucleon) and the momentum of the internal motion. The contribution of the Coulomb

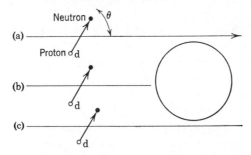

FIG. 6.1. Oppenheimer-Phillips process. Case (a) leads to process IIIb; (b) to I; (c) to IIIa.

field can be neglected at high energies. The average internal momentum p_i in the ground state of the deuteron is of the order $p_i \sim (2MB)^{1/2}$ (B is the binding energy of the deuteron). Hence the final momentum of the escaping particle is roughly within the limits $p_0 - (2MB)^{1/2}$ and $p_0 + (2MB)^{1/2}$. The average angle between the direction of escape and the direction of the incident deuteron beam is approximately given by $(2MB)^{1/2}/p_0$. This distribution has been verified experimentally by Helmholtz and McMillan (47) with 200-Mev deuterons.

At lower energies, $\epsilon_D \sim Ze^2/R$ or smaller, the effect of the Coulomb field plays a decisive role. The orbit of the deuteron is no longer a straight line. The effect of the electrostatic repulsion on the deuteron is complicated by the fact that the electric force does not act on the center of gravity of the deuteron but only on the proton. The neutron therefore is in a more favorable position to reach the nuclear surface than the proton, since the proton needs to reach a distance of only about $R + d$ from the center of the nucleus in order to give the neutron a chance to enter the nucleus. Hence process IIIa is much more probable than IIIb. In fact, if the energy ϵ_D is smaller than Ze^2/R, so that the proton cannot reach the nuclear surface except through a quantum-mechanical penetration of the barrier, process IIIa is the most probable deuteron-induced process. It is called the Oppenheimer-Phillips process.

There does not exist a satisfactory theory which enables us to calculate the cross section σ_{IIIa} of this process even on the basis of the simplified assumptions of Chapter VIII regarding the interior of the nucleus. The main difficulty lies in finding the mathematical form of the wave function of the deuteron near the nucleus. The problem can no longer be split into two parts, one describing the motion of center of gravity of the deuteron and the other the internal motion, since the electric field acts unsymmetrically, on the proton rather than on the center of mass only. Several attempts were made to get an approximate solution (Oppenheimer 35, Volkoff 40, Bethe 38a, Peaslee 48, Butler 50).

We now turn our attention to the compound nucleus C' which is created in process IIIa, and to its excitation energy $E_{C'}$. In contrast to the reactions of type I, the excitation energy of the nucleus C'$(Z, A+1)$ is not determined by the incident energy alone since the stripped nucleon (the proton) can carry off energy.

The conservation of energy gives the following condition:

$$\epsilon_D - B - B(\text{X}) = \epsilon_P + E_{C'} - B(\text{C}') \qquad (6.2)$$

where ϵ_D is the kinetic energy of the deuteron (more precisely, the kinetic energy of the relative motion of deuteron and target nucleus X in the center-of-mass system), $B = 2.23$ Mev is the binding energy of the deuteron, $B(\text{X})$ is the binding energy of the target nucleus X, ϵ_P is the energy of the emerging proton, $E_{C'}$ is the energy of excitation of the compound nucleus C' which is formed by the addition of one neutron to X, and $B(\text{C}')$ is the binding energy of C'. We can solve this equation for the excitation energy of the compound nucleus C'. Using $S_N' = B(\text{C}') - B(\text{X})$ for the separation energy of a neutron from C', we get

$$E_{C'} = \epsilon_D - \epsilon_P - B + S_N' \qquad (6.3)$$

The lowest excitation energy possible is $E_{C'} = 0$, which corresponds to the highest-energy protons which can emerge from this reaction. The highest excitation energy $E_{C'}$ is obtained when no energy at all is carried away by the proton, i.e., when $\epsilon_P = 0$ in (6.3).

The division of the available energy between the entering neutron and the leaving proton is a complicated process. It can be visualized along the following lines: When the neutron touches the nuclear surface, the total energy of the deuteron is partially potential energy (from having run against the Coulomb barrier), partially kinetic (what is left of its original kinetic energy), partially internal (the motion of the neutron relative to the proton within the deuteron). This energy is divided between the leaving proton and the neutron entering the nucleus when the deuteron breaks up. The potential energy remains with the proton since it is caused by the charge. Half of the kinetic energy ϵ_D of the center of mass of the deuteron goes to the neutron, half to the proton. The division of the internal energy into $\epsilon_{in}(N)$ and $\epsilon_{in}(P)$ can take place in many ways, as long as the sum is equal to the binding energy: $\epsilon_{in}(N) + \epsilon_{in}(P) = -B = -2.23$ Mev. The probability of a given division is determined by the internal wave function of the deuteron. Hence the possible excitation energies of C' cover a large energy interval. The neutron may even be left with *negative* kinetic energy in this division. In quantum mechanics negative kinetic energy corresponds to a wave which falls off exponentially and therefore cannot exist in free space over large distances. However, it can cover the small distance between the breakup of the deuteron and the nuclear surface. Hence a neutron breaking loose from a deuteron can enter the nucleus with "negative kinetic energy" and form a compound nucleus with an excitation energy $E_{C'}$, less than the separation energy S_N' of the neutron from C'. It may even produce C' in its ground state. This is in definite contrast to the formation of a compound nucleus by free neutrons, in which case $E_{C'}$ must be larger than S_N'.

The most probable value of the energy ϵ_P of the emerging proton is obtained by assuming that the proton gets half the kinetic energy which the deuteron possesses at the point where it breaks up, all the potential (electrostatic) energy of the deuteron at that place, and half the internal energy $(-B)$ of the deuteron. Let R' be the distance between the deuteron and the center of the target nucleus at the time the deuteron breaks up. Then

$$\langle \epsilon_P \rangle_{av} \cong \frac{1}{2}\left(\epsilon_D - \frac{Ze^2}{R'}\right) + \frac{Ze^2}{R'} - \frac{1}{2}B \qquad (6.4)$$

We estimate R' to be of the order of $R+(d/2)$. Substitution of (6.4) with this value of R' into (6.3) gives for the most probable excitation energy $E_{C'}$ of the compound nucleus $C'=X+N$:

$$\langle E_{C'} \rangle_{av} \cong \frac{1}{2}\left(\epsilon_D - \frac{Ze^2}{R+(d/2)} - B\right) + S_N' \qquad (6.5)$$

The likely values of the excitation energy $E_{C'}$ lie within $\pm B$ of the average value (6.5).

The value of $E_{C'}$ is decisive for the type of process which follows the formation of the compound nucleus. For example, if $E_{C'} < S_N'$, the compound nucleus cannot emit a neutron. It gets rid of the surplus energy either by emission of a gamma-ray, or by emission of another particle b if the separation energy S_b' is less than S_N'. In most cases the gamma-ray emission is the only process occurring.

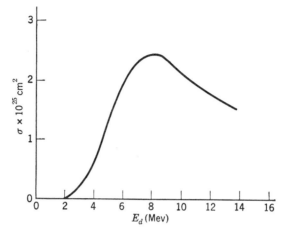

FIG. 6.2.   Cross section of the (d,p) reaction on Cu^{63}, according to Clark and Irvine as quoted by Peaslee (48). The drop at deuteron energies above 8 Mev is attributed to the onset of the $(d;pn)$ reaction.

Hence for $\langle E_{C'} \rangle_{av} < S_N'$, most of the compound nuclei formed are excited below S_N', and we get the (d,p) reaction: $d + X = C' + p$ as the main reaction. If $\langle E_{C'} \rangle_{av} > S_N'$, the compound nucleus C' is mostly left in states in which it is able to emit a neutron, and this is then the most probable reaction. Hence we conclude that for values of $\epsilon_D > \epsilon_D{}^* \equiv Ze^2/[R+(d/2)] + B$, the $(d;pn)$ reaction displaces the (d,p) reaction. Figure 6.2 shows the cross section of a (d,p) reaction on Cu^{63} (measured by Clark and Irvine),[1] which illustrates the characteristic drop of the (d,p) cross section because of the onset of the $(d;pn)$ reaction. The drop occurs above the characteristic energy $\epsilon_D{}^*$ which, for Cu, is of the order of 8 Mev. At energies which are higher than $\epsilon_D{}^*$ the processes of types I and IIIb are no longer negligible compared to the process IIIa leading to the compound nucleus C'.

Because of the Oppenheimer-Phillips process the cross section $\sigma_{C'}$ is higher than other nuclear cross sections with charged particles of

[1] Unpublished but quoted in Peaslee (48).

similar energy.   That is why deuteron reactions are of great practical significance for the production of radioactive isotopes.   In spite of this fact, very little quantitative theoretical work is available on deuteron reactions.   Butler (51) has developed a method to use the deuteron-induced reactions as a tool in nuclear spectroscopy.

In light elements several cases are known where the deuteron produces a compound nucleus C according to the usual process I.   The Coulomb barrier is not high enough to prevent the direct formation of a compound nucleus.   Hence resonances must occur as they do with other elementary particles.   We find listed in Fig. 5.3 two examples of resonances for the $C^{13}(d,p)$ reaction which correspond to compound states of N^{15} at excitation energies of 17.47 Mev and 16.7 Mev, respectively.   The occurrence of resonances shows that a good part of this reaction consists of direct compound nucleus formation. Many and well-defined resonances were also found in the $C^{12}(d,p)$ and $C^{12}(d,n)$ reactions (Bennett 41, Hornyak 50).   The (d,p) resonances and the (d,n) resonances occur at the same energies as we should expect in direct compound nucleus formation according to process I.

SYMBOLS

A	Mass number (Section 1)
A^l_{res}	Amplitude for resonance scattering with orbital angular momentum l; for the definition see Chapter VIII, Section 2 (Section 3A)
B	Binding energy of the deuteron $[= 2.23$ Mev] (Section 6)
$B(C')$	Binding energy of the compound nucleus C' created in the Oppenheimer-Phillips process (6.2)
$B(X)$	Binding energy of the target nucleus X (6.2)
$C(Z,A)$	A (compound) nucleus with Z protons and $A - Z$ neutrons (Section 6)
C'	The compound nucleus created in the Oppenheimer-Phillips process (Section 6)
d	A deuteron (Section 1)
d	The radius of the deuteron $[= 1.1 \times 10^{-13}$ cm] (this is one-fourth of the decay length which appears in the deuteron wave function) (6.1)
$\mathbf{d}$	One-half of the vector separation between the neutron and the proton in the deuteron (Section 6)
D	Average energy spacing between resonance levels of the same total angular momentum J and parity (Section 2A)
D'	The observed energy spacing between resonances; D'

	depends on the energy resolution of the equipment as well as on nuclear properties (Section 2A)
D^*	An energy defined by (2.1), and expected to be of the same order of magnitude as D (2.1)
E	Excitation energy of the compound nucleus (Section 2A)
$E_{C'}$	Excitation energy of the compound nucleus C' created in the Oppenheimer-Phillips process (6.3)
$\langle E_{C'} \rangle_{av}$	Most probable excitation energy of the compound nucleus C' created in the Oppenheimer-Phillips process (6.5)
F_α	A function related to the branching ratio for emission of alpha-particles from the compound nucleus; for its definition see Chapter VIII, Section 6 (2.20)
F_n	A function related to the branching ratio for emission of neutrons from the compound nucleus; for its definition see Chapter VIII, Section 6 (2.20)
F_p	A function related to the branching ratio for emission of protons from the compound nucleus; for its definition see Chapter VIII, Section 6 (2.20)
$g(S)$	Statistical weight of channel spin S (2.10)
$G_C(b)$	Branching ratio for emission of particles b from the compound nucleus (Section 3C)
$\hbar\omega$	Energy of a (capture) gamma-ray (Section 5B)
I	Angular momentum ("spin") of the target nucleus X (Section 2A)
J	Total angular momentum of the compound nucleus C (Section 2A)
k	Wave number of the relative motion before the reaction $[=(2M\epsilon)^{1/2}/\hbar]$ (2.3)
k	Boltzmann constant; $\mathsf{k}\mathsf{T}$ is the average thermal energy at temperature T (2.13)
K	Wave number inside the compound nucleus (2.11)
K_0	Wave number inside the compound nucleus for neutrons with channel energy $\epsilon=0$; $K_0 \cong 1\times10^{13}\,\mathrm{cm}^{-1}$ (Section 2E)
l	Orbital angular momentum of the incident particle (Section 2A)
L	Lowest orbital angular momentum l consistent with the total angular momentum J and the parity Π_C of the compound nucleus (Section 2A)
M	Reduced mass for the relative motion in a channel [$\cong$ the mass of the incident particle] (2.3)

M	Mass of a nucleon (Section 6)
n	A neutron (Section 1)
N	Number of neutrons in the target nucleus (Section 3A)
p	A proton (Section 1)
p_0	Momentum associated with each nucleon in the deuteron in consequence of the motion of the center of gravity of the deuteron $[=(M\epsilon_D)^{1/2}]$ (Section 6)
p_i	Momentum associated with each nucleon in the deuteron in consequence of the internal motion (Section 6)
Q	Q value (energy release) of a nuclear reaction (Section 5A)
$Q_{n\alpha}$	Q value of the (n,α) reaction (2.20)
Q_{np}	Q value of the (n,p) reaction (2.20)
Q_{pn}	Q value of the (p,n) reaction (Section 3A)
r_0	Constant appearing in the nuclear radius formula $R = r_0 A^{1/3}$ (Section 2E)
R	Channel radius (2.3)
R'	Distance between the center of the deuteron and the center of the target nucleus at the time the deuteron breaks up (6.4)
s	Spin of the incident particle in a nuclear reaction (3.1)
S	Channel spin (Section 2A)
S	Separation energy of a particle (neutron) from the compound nucleus (Section 2A)
S_b'	Separation energy of a particle b from the compound nucleus C' formed in the Oppenheimer-Phillips process (Section 6)
S_N'	Separation energy of a neutron from the compound nucleus C' formed in the Oppenheimer-Phillips process (6.3)
T	Temperature of the target substance, in degrees Kelvin (2.13)
v	Speed of the deuteron passing near a nucleus X (Section 6)
v_l	Penetration factor for collisions with orbital angular momentum l (2.1),(2.2)
$X(Z,A)$	Nucleus X with Z protons and $A-Z$ neutrons (Section 6)
Z	Number of protons in the target nucleus (Section 3A)
α	An alpha-particle (Section 1)
α	A channel for a nuclear reaction; the channel index α

	includes specification of the channel spin S (Section 3A)
$\bar{\alpha}$	The group of effective entrance channels for a proton-induced reaction (Section 3A)
γ	A gamma-ray (Section 1)
$\gamma_n{}^s$	Reduced partial width of resonance level number s for emission of neutrons (2.10)
$\Gamma = \Gamma^s$	Total width of resonance level number s (2.5), (3.1)
$\Gamma_{n,l}$	Average value of the neutron width for neutron resonances with orbital angular momentum l (2.16)
$\Gamma_n{}^s$	Neutron width of resonance level number s (2.1)
$\Gamma_p{}^s$	Proton width of resonance level number s (3.1)
Γ_{pSL}^s	Partial width of resonance level number s for emission of protons with channel spin S and orbital angular momentum L (3.2)
$\Gamma_{\mathrm{rad},l}$	Average value of the radiation width for neutron resonances of orbital angular momentum l (2.16)
$\Gamma_r{}^s$	Reaction width of resonance level number s (2.6)
Γ_{rad}^s	$= \Gamma_{\mathrm{rad}}$; radiation width of resonance level number s (2.6), (3.1)
$\Gamma^s = \Gamma$	Total width of resonance level number s (2.5), (3.1)
$\Gamma_\alpha{}^s$	Partial width of resonance level number s for alpha-particle emission (Section 5A)
$\Delta\epsilon$	The range of energies ϵ in the incident beam (Section 2A)
$\Delta\epsilon$	An energy interval large compared to the level distance D in the compound nucleus (Section 2C)
$(\Delta\epsilon)_D$	Energy spread due to the Doppler effect (2.13)
ϵ	Channel energy [= energy of the relative motion in the center-of-mass system] (Section 1)
$\bar{\epsilon}$	Mean energy in the incident beam (Section 2A)
ϵ_0	An energy related to the height of the centrifugal barrier for neutrons (2.3)
ϵ_1	Channel energy ϵ for which the average neutron width for S wave resonances becomes equal to the average radiation width for those resonances (2.15), (2.15a)
ϵ_c	Energy available for the $(n;2n)$ reaction $[=\epsilon-S_n]$ (2.21)
ϵ_D	Channel energy for a deuteron channel (Section 6)
ϵ_i	An energy in the "ultrahigh" region (above 30 Mev) (Section 4)
ϵ_p	Channel energy for a proton channel (Section 3C)

ϵ_P	Energy of the proton in the Oppenheimer-Phillips process (6.2)
$\langle\epsilon_P\rangle_{av}$	Most probable value of the energy of the proton in the Oppenheimer-Phillips process (6.4)
ϵ_s	Channel energy ϵ corresponding to resonance level number s of the compound nucleus (Section 2A)
ϵ_{th}	Thermal energy (a channel energy ϵ of the order of 0.025 ev) (Section 2A)
ϵ_α	Channel energy for an alpha-particle channel (Section 3C)
ϵ_β	Channel energy in channel β (Section 2D)
ϵ_Θ	The part of the energy in a nuclear reaction which goes into "heating" the residual nucleus (Section 4)
ζ	$=\tfrac{1}{2}D/\left|\epsilon_{th}-\epsilon_s\right|$; a real number larger than 1 (2.11)
θ	Angle between $\mathbf{d}$ and the line of motion of the deuteron (Section 6)
Θ	Nuclear temperature of the residual nucleus after emission of the first neutron from the compound nucleus, in Mev (2.21)
λ	de Broglie wavelength of the relative motion, divided by 2π (Section 2A)
Π_C	Parity of the compound nucleus C (Section 2A)
$\sigma(a,b)$	Cross section of the (a,b) reaction (Section 3C)
$\sigma_{C,l}(n)$	Cross section for formation of the compound nucleus by neutrons of orbital angular momentum l (2.16)
$\sigma_C(p)$	Cross section for formation of the compound nucleus by protons (Section 3B)
$\sigma_C(\alpha)$	Cross section for formation of the compound nucleus by alpha-particles (Section 3B)
$\sigma_C(\beta)$	Cross section for formation of the compound nucleus through channel β (Section 2D)
$\sigma_{cap}(n)$	Cross section for the radiative capture of neutrons (Section 2A)
$\langle\sigma_{cap}(n)\rangle_{av}$	Average value of the neutron capture cross section, over many resonances (2.18)
$\langle\sigma_{cap}(n)\rangle_{th}$	Cross section for the radiative capture of thermal neutrons (2.11)
$\sigma^l_{cap}(n)$	Cross section for the radiative capture of neutrons with orbital angular momentum l (Section 2C)
$\langle\sigma^l_{cap}(n)\rangle_{av}$	Average value of the radiative capture cross section for neutrons with orbital angular momentum l, over many resonances (Section 2C)

$\sigma_{\max}$ Maximum (total) cross section in a neutron resonance, for infinite resolution in energy   (2.5)

$\sigma_{\max,\exp}$ Maximum (total) cross section in a neutron resonance, observed experimentally with finite energy resolution $\Delta\epsilon$ (2.5)

$\sigma(n,p)$ Cross section of the (n,p) reaction   (2.20)

$\sigma(p,n)$ Cross section of the (p,n) reaction   (Section 3B)

σ_r The reaction cross section, as distinguished from the cross section for elastic scattering   (Section 2E)

$\sigma_{r,0}$ Reaction cross section for reactions induced by S wave $(l=0)$ particles   (2.8)

$\sigma_{sc,0}$ Elastic scattering cross section of S wave $(l=0)$ particles (2.8)

σ_t Total (elastic scattering + reaction) cross section (Section 2A)

$\sigma(\alpha,n)$ Cross section of the (α,n) reaction   (Section 3B)

$\sigma(\alpha;2n)$ Cross section of the $(\alpha;2n)$ reaction   (Section 3C)

$\sigma(\alpha;3n)$ Cross section of the $(\alpha;3n)$ reaction   (Section 3C)

CHAPTER X

Formal Theory of Nuclear Reactions

In this chapter certain results of the theory of nuclear reactions are derived by methods which are more general than those used in Chapter VIII. The discussions are restricted to some fundamental theorems, some of which were either proved or made plausible by less rigorous means in Chapter VIII.

The scope and the limitations of the theorems will become more obvious in the formal derivations of this chapter. In particular the Breit-Wigner formula for resonance reaction is derived here with much greater generality than in Chapter VIII. It contains, on the other hand, so many adjustable parameters that it must be reduced in most practical cases to the forms used in Chapter VIII.

We have attempted to keep the mathematical complexity within reasonable bounds by restricting the discussion, whenever possible, to the simplest reaction types, namely those in which only uncharged particles with zero spin and zero orbital angular momentum are involved.

1. THE SCATTERING MATRIX

A. The General Form of the Wave Functions

Consider a nuclear system at excitation sufficiently high that the compound nucleus can disintegrate into a number of different channels, which we shall denote by Greek letters α, β, γ, and so on. For simplicity's sake we shall restrict ourselves to the discussion of channels in which there is no "barrier," i.e., to S wave neutron channels, and we shall neglect the influence of intrinsic spins.

The wave functions Ψ of the system at some definite total energy E have a very complicated behavior in that part of the configuration space which corresponds to the compound nucleus, i.e., where all the coordinates r_1, r_2, $\cdots$, r_A of the A nuclear particles are close to each other. On the other hand, in the regions of configuration space corresponding to the various open channels, the behavior is simple: a wave function Ψ describes the relative motion of the particle a and

517

the residual nucleus X in the channel in question, as well as their internal states of excitation appropriate to that channel. Thus, in the region of configuration space corresponding to channel α, say, the wave functions have the form

$$\Psi = \psi(r_\alpha)\, \chi_\alpha \qquad \text{(in channel } \alpha) \qquad (1.1)$$

where χ_α is the eigenfunction of the residual nucleus X in state α. If the emitted particle a is itself a composite system (e.g., an alpha-particle), χ_α is the product of the eigenfunction of X and of a. $\psi(r_\alpha)$ describes the relative motion, and r_α is the "channel coordinate" of Chapter VIII.

The wave function $\psi(r_\alpha)$ contains ingoing as well as outgoing spherical waves. Let v_α be the velocity in channel α, k_α be the channel wave number at the total energy E (of which only part appears as kinetic energy ϵ_α in the channel). We can write $\psi(r_\alpha)$ in the form

$$\psi(r_\alpha) = (A_\alpha\, e^{-ik_\alpha r_\alpha} + A_\alpha{}'\, e^{ik_\alpha r_\alpha})\, (4\pi v_\alpha)^{-1/2}\, r_\alpha{}^{-1} \qquad (1.2)$$

On the right side of the equation the first term in the parentheses, when multiplied by the appropriate time factor, represents an incoming wave; the second one is an outgoing wave. The $(4\pi v_\alpha)^{-1/2}$ could have been absorbed into the (so far arbitrary) constants A and A', but it will be convenient to write it separately.

B. Definition of the Scattering Matrix

If there is only one open channel at energy E, the wave function is uniquely determined by the energy alone.[1] An incoming wave of given strength in this one open channel gives rise to a definite outgoing wave in the same channel. On the other hand, if there are several channels open, the energy alone does not determine the wave function uniquely. This can be seen most easily by observing that there can be an incoming wave in any one of the open channels. The corresponding wave functions are different from each other. If there are N open channels, there are N such wave functions at any one total energy E.

We shall use these N wave functions as our basic set.[2] The wave

---

[1] Except for a constant multiplicative factor which we shall ignore.

[2] This particular basic set is most convenient for the discussion of cross sections. It is not the only possible one, however, and we shall have occasion to use a different set of basic functions in Section 4. In principle, any N linearly independent wave functions can be used as a basic set, and the particular choice used is a matter of convenience only.

function describing a reaction initiated through channel α will be denoted by Ψ_α. The behavior of Ψ_α in the region of configuration space corresponding to some channel β is [see (1.1)]

$$\Psi_\alpha = \psi_{\alpha\beta}(r_\beta)\, \chi_\beta \qquad \text{(in channel } \beta) \qquad (1.3a)$$

If $\beta \neq \alpha$, the wave function for the relative motion corresponds to *outgoing waves only* $(S_{\alpha\beta} = \text{a constant})$:

$$\psi_{\alpha\beta}(r_\beta) = -S_{\alpha\beta} \exp{(ik_\beta r_\beta)}\, (4\pi v_\beta)^{-1/2}\, r_\beta^{-1} \qquad (\beta \neq \alpha) \quad (1.3b)$$

In channel α, on the other hand, there are both an ingoing and an outgoing wave; the ingoing wave has to be normalized to correspond to the rate at which particles a enter through channel α. We shall normalize to unit ingoing flux over the full solid angle, i.e.,

$$4\pi v_\alpha (\psi^*\psi) r_\alpha^2 = 1$$

for the ingoing wave part of $\psi_{\alpha\alpha}(r_\alpha)$. This gives

$$\psi_{\alpha\alpha}(r_\alpha) = [\exp{(-ik_\alpha r_\alpha)} - S_{\alpha\alpha} \exp{(ik_\alpha r_\alpha)}]\, (4\pi v_\alpha)^{-1/2}\, r_\alpha^{-1} \qquad (\beta = \alpha)$$
$$(1.3c)$$

We need N constants $S_{\alpha\beta}$, $\beta = 1,2,\cdots,N$, for a given initiating channel α to describe the asymptotic behavior of the wave function completely. Since α can be any one of the N open channels, there are N^2 constants $S_{\alpha\beta}$ altogether. They can be considered to form an N-by-N matrix, the *scattering matrix* of the system at energy E (Wheeler 37a, Heisenberg 43, Möller 45, Wigner 47, Eisenbud 48).

It is apparent from the definition of the scattering matrix $S_{\alpha\beta}$ that it determines the asymptotic behavior of the wave function in the various channels completely, even in the most general case where the reaction is not initiated merely through one channel, but where there are incoming waves in all the channels [the corresponding wave function is then a linear superposition of the N functions Ψ_α, (1.3)]. Thus the result of any measurement made on the system after the reaction products have separated (e.g., the cross sections for the various possible reactions) is expressible in terms of the scattering matrix. On the other hand, the scattering matrix, describing only the asymptotic behavior of the wave function, does not give us any detailed information about the compound nucleus itself.

The importance of the scattering matrix lies in the following fact: we can prove that it must possess certain properties under very general assumptions about the physical process taking place in the "interior region" (compound nucleus, cavity, or whatever the case may be). These properties of the scattering matrix relate cross sections for different reactions to each other, quite independently of the detailed reaction mechanism.

C. Cross Sections Expressed in Terms of the Scattering Matrix

We first determine the flux of the outgoing spherical wave in channel $\beta \neq \alpha$, from (1.3b). This flux is the product of the probability density $\psi^*\psi$, the channel velocity v_β, and the surface area of the sphere through which the flux is going, $4\pi r_\beta^2$:

$$\text{Outgoing flux in channel } \beta = \psi_{\alpha\beta}^*\psi_{\alpha\beta}\, v_\beta\,(4\pi r_\beta^2) = |S_{\alpha\beta}|^2 \quad (1.4)$$

In order to find the incoming flux we compare the incoming spherical wave part of (1.3c) with the $l=0$ incoming spherical wave part of the spherical harmonic expansion of the plane wave, exp (ikz), formula (VIII,2.7). Since the plane wave exp (ikz) has flux equal to v, the incoming spherical wave part of our $\psi_{\alpha\alpha}$, (1.3_c), corresponds to a plane wave of flux $k_\alpha^2/\pi = (\pi\lambda_\alpha^2)^{-1}$. Dividing the outgoing flux (1.4) by the incident plane wave flux, we get the following result for the *transfer cross section from channel α to channel β* (i.e., the $l=0$ part of this cross section):

$$\sigma_{\alpha\beta} = \pi\lambda_\alpha^2\,|S_{\alpha\beta}|^2 \qquad (\beta \neq \alpha) \tag{1.5}$$

The cross section for elastic scattering, $\sigma_{\alpha\alpha}$ with $l=0$ has already been determined in Chapter VIII, Section 2. Comparison of our present definition of $S_{\alpha\alpha}$, (1.3c), with the $l=0$ term of (VIII,2.8) shows that $S_{\alpha\alpha}$ is identical with the quantity η_0 of Chapter VIII. Hence the $l=0$ scattering cross section is given by (VIII,2.11), which in our present notation becomes

$$\sigma_{sc,0} = \sigma_{\alpha\alpha} = \pi\lambda_\alpha^2\,|1 - S_{\alpha\alpha}|^2 \tag{1.6}$$

We can write (1.5) and (1.6) for transfer and scattering cross sections in the unified form

$$\sigma_{\alpha\beta} = \pi\lambda_\alpha^2\,|\delta_{\alpha\beta} - S_{\alpha\beta}|^2 \tag{1.7}$$

It is apparent that all these cross sections vanish if the scattering matrix is equal to the unit matrix, $S_{\alpha\beta} = \delta_{\alpha\beta}$. This was the motivation for the minus sign in the definition of $S_{\alpha\beta}$, (1.3b) and (1.3c).

The "reaction cross section" of the previous chapters is the sum of all the transfer cross sections to channels $\beta \neq \alpha$, i.e.,

$$\sigma_r = \pi\lambda_\alpha^2 \sum_{\beta \neq \alpha} |S_{\alpha\beta}|^2 \tag{1.8}$$

In Chapter VIII this same cross section was expressed in terms of $\eta = S_{\alpha\alpha}$ as

$$\sigma_r = \pi \lambda_\alpha^2 \left(1 - |S_{\alpha\alpha}|^2\right) \tag{1.9}$$

The equivalence of (1.8) and (1.9) is a result of the first conservation theorem to be proved in the next section.

We shall disregard the possibility of radiative capture throughout the remainder of this discussion. Although this process could be included in the scattering matrix in principle, it would complicate the formulation without any gain in clarity.

As long as the particles taking part in the reaction (including the target nucleus and the various residual nuclei) have no spins, formulas (1.5) to (1.9) can be generalized quite easily for (orbital) angular momenta $l \neq 0$. We merely replace $\exp(\pm ikr)$ in the definition of $S_{\alpha\beta}$, (1.3b) and (1.3c) by $\exp[\pm i(kr - \frac{1}{2}l\pi)]$, and replace $\pi \lambda_\alpha^2$ by $(2l+1)\pi \lambda_\alpha^2$. The presence of a Coulomb barrier does not change anything, since we are concerned only with the asymptotic behavior of the wave functions for large values of r. If the Coulomb field is screened by the atomic electrons (as it always is in practice), the asymptotic behavior of the wave function for orbital angular momentum l is still of the form $\exp[\pm i(kr - \frac{1}{2}l\pi)]$.

If there are spins in the various channels, the formulas become very much more complicated. We shall not discuss them here. The reader is referred to the paper by Wigner and Eisenbud (Wigner 47). (The scattering matrix is called U in that paper.)

2. CONSERVATION AND RECIPROCITY THEOREMS FOR NUCLEAR REACTIONS

A. Ingoing and Outgoing Waves

The wave functions of the preceding section describe a steady-state situation in which the ingoing wave in the entrance channel has constant amplitude everywhere; the particles which go in to react are continually being replenished at the same rate. Let us now consider the case where an ingoing spherical wave in channel α is turned on for some finite time T and then shut off again. Let us represent this wave function by the picture of a wave guide junction, with the various channels $\alpha, \beta, \cdots$ leading into it. Then, at some time before the reaction, the wave function is as depicted schematically in Fig. 2.1a: there are no waves in any channels except channel α, and in that channel there is a wave train of finite length going toward the junction

X. Formal Theory of Nuclear Reactions

(the compound nucleus). The length of this wave train is $L_\alpha = v_\alpha T$, where v_α is the velocity in channel α.[1]

Now consider a later time, after the reaction has already taken place. The wave function is then as shown in Fig. 2.1b: there are outgoing (finite) wave trains in all channels, including channel α (re-emitted wave). The length of the outgoing wave train in channel β is $L_\beta = v_\beta T$, since the time T during which the reaction products pass into a stationary detector in one of the channels is approximately[1]

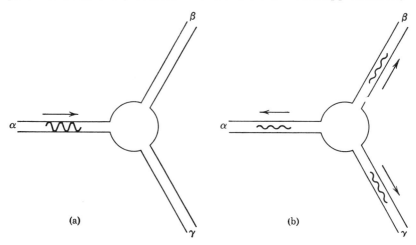

<table>
<tr><td>(a)</td><td></td><td>(b)</td><td></td></tr>
</table>

Fɪɢ. 2.1. Picture of a three-channel junction. (a) (Before) There is a wave train moving toward the junction (compound nucleus) in channel α, none in the other channels. (b) (After) There are outgoing wave trains in all the channels. The amplitudes of these outgoing waves are determined by the scattering matrix $S_{\alpha\beta}$.

equal to the time T during which the incoming spherical wave had been switched on earlier.

Since we now have finite wave trains, the wave function can be normalized to unit total probability:

$$\int \Psi^* \Psi \, d\tau = 1 \qquad (2.1)$$

Consider first the normalization integral for Fig. 2.1a, before the

---

[1] Strictly speaking, it is not possible to have a wave train of finite length L, with sharp boundaries. Even if the edges are sharp at some initial time, as time goes on the edge becomes less sharp; the effective length L of the wave train increases as time goes on. We can estimate the magnitude of this boundary region: it is of the order of a few de Broglie wavelengths, and it increases by that order of magnitude as the wave train passes through the compound nucleus region and re-emerges in another channel. Thus, if we make the length L of the wave train large compared to a de Broglie wavelength $\lambda = \hbar/Mv$, we can neglect these edge effects altogether. We shall do so in the remainder of the discussion.

reaction.   The wave function vanishes everywhere except in channel α, and there it has the form (over the length L_α where it does not vanish)

$$\Psi_{\alpha,in} = C \exp\left(-ik_\alpha r_\alpha\right) (4\pi v_\alpha)^{-1/2} r_\alpha^{-1} \chi_\alpha \qquad (2.2)$$

C being the normalization constant.   The integrals over the internal coordinates of χ_α and a_α in χ_α give unity, so that we get

$$\int \Psi_{\alpha,in}{}^* \, \Psi_{\alpha,in} \, d\tau = |C|^2 \int |\exp\left(-ik_\alpha r_\alpha\right)|^2 (v_\alpha)^{-1} \, dr_\alpha$$

$$= |C|^2 \frac{L_\alpha}{v_\alpha} = |C|^2 \, T = 1$$

Thus the C in (2.2) can be taken as

$$C = T^{-1/2} \qquad (2.2a)$$

where T is the time during which the ingoing wave is switched on.

The scattering matrix, by definition, determines the amplitudes of the outgoing waves in the various channels once the amplitude of the ingoing wave is given.   Equation (1.3b) gives for the form of the outgoing wave in channel β in Fig. 2.1b:

$$\Psi_{\alpha,\text{ out through }\beta} = C \left(-S_{\alpha\beta}\right) \exp\left(ik_\beta r_\beta\right) (4\pi v_\beta)^{-1/2} r_\beta^{-1} \chi_\beta \qquad (2.3)$$

where C is still given by (2.2a).   The probability of finding the reaction products in channel β is then

$$\int |\Psi_{\alpha,\text{ out through }\beta}|^2 \, d\tau = |C|^2 \, |S_{\alpha\beta}|^2 \frac{L_\beta}{v_\beta} = |S_{\alpha\beta}|^2 \qquad (2.4)$$

Incidentally, these formulas apply also to the case where we look at the outgoing particles in the same channel $\beta = \alpha$ through which the ingoing wave had been sent earlier.

B. The Conservation Theorems

It follows from the wave equation

$$H\Psi = i\hbar \, \frac{\partial \Psi}{\partial t} \qquad (2.5)$$

that the time derivative of the scalar product $(\Psi,\Psi) \equiv \int \Psi^* \Psi \, d\tau$ is zero:

$$\frac{\partial}{\partial t} (\Psi,\Psi) = \left(\frac{\partial \Psi}{\partial t}, \Psi\right) + \left(\Psi, \frac{\partial \Psi}{\partial t}\right)$$

$$= \frac{i}{\hbar} (H\Psi,\Psi) - \frac{i}{\hbar} (\Psi,H\Psi) = 0 \qquad (2.6)$$

since H is a Hermitean operator. We now use this constancy of the normalization of the wave function (of the total probability of finding particles anywhere) to derive a conservation theorem for nuclear reactions: we have chosen Ψ_α, (2.2) and (2.2a), so that before the reaction $(\Psi,\Psi) = 1$. This must also be true after the reaction. According to (2.4), each channel β then contributes an amount $|S_{\alpha\beta}|^2$ to the total probability (Ψ,Ψ). Hence we have proved the *first conservation law*

$$\sum_\beta |S_{\alpha\beta}|^2 = 1 \qquad (2.7)$$

This constitutes the formal proof of the equivalence of (1.8) and (1.9) for the over-all reaction cross section.

This conservation law is an expression of the conservation of probability. The left side of (2.7) is the probability that the reaction leads into some one of the available channels, and this probability is, of course, unity. There is one proviso, however: the enumeration of the possible outcomes of the reaction must be complete. If a channel has been left out by mistake, the sum (2.7) is less than unity. In practice, this may occur in connection with the radiative-capture transitions which we have not treated on an equal footing with the particle channels. To do this properly, we should have to include the coordinates of the electromagnetic field into the formulation of the scattering matrix; this would merely complicate matters without adding anything essential.

If two different wave functions Ψ and Φ satisfy the same wave equation, their scalar product (Ψ,Φ) is independent of time:

$$\frac{\partial}{\partial t} (\Psi,\Phi) = \left(\frac{\partial \Psi}{\partial i}, \Phi\right) + \left(\Psi, \frac{\partial \Phi}{\partial t}\right)$$

$$= \frac{i}{\hbar} (H\Psi,\Phi) - \frac{i}{\hbar} (\Psi,H\Phi) = 0$$

[The conservation of the normalization, (2.6), is a special case of this theorem.] In particular, if Ψ and Φ are orthogonal to start out with, they continue to be orthogonal to each other.

We now apply this theorem to nuclear reactions to get a second conservation law. Consider the wave functions Ψ_α and Ψ_β $(\alpha \neq \beta)$ describing reactions with the same compound nucleus, but with ingoing spherical waves sent initially through two different channels. Before the reactions take place, the wave functions Ψ_α and Ψ_β are orthogonal to each other: Ψ_α is zero everywhere except in channel α

[see Fig. 2.1a], and Ψ_β is zero everywhere except in channel β; thus there is no overlap of the wave functions, and their scalar product vanishes.

Consider the same two wave functions *after* the two reactions have taken place. There are outgoing waves in all the channels, waves which are due to both reactions. Nevertheless the total scalar product must still vanish. A typical channel γ contributes the following amount to $(\Psi_\alpha, \Psi_\beta)$

$$\int \Psi^*_{\alpha,\ \text{out through}\ \gamma}\ \Psi_{\beta,\ \text{out through}\ \gamma}\ d\tau = C_\alpha^*\ C_\beta\ S_{\alpha\gamma}^*\ S_{\beta\gamma}\ T' \quad (2.8)$$

where C_α, C_β are the normalization constants (2.2a) for Ψ_α, Ψ_β, respectively, and T' is the time overlap during which the reaction products striking a stationary detector are due to both reactions. This time overlap is the same in all channels γ.

We sum the contributions (2.8) over all channels γ and set the result equal to zero. This gives the *second conservation law:*

$$\sum_\gamma S_{\alpha\gamma}^*\ S_{\beta\gamma} = 0 \qquad (\alpha \neq \beta) \quad (2.9)$$

We observe that the two conservation laws, (2.7) and (2.9), can be written together in the form

$$\sum_\gamma S_{\alpha\gamma}^*\ S_{\beta\gamma} = \delta_{\alpha\beta} \quad (2.10)$$

In matrix notation (2.10) is

$$SS^+ = 1 \quad (2.10')$$

where S^+ is the Hermitean conjugate of S, and 1 is the unit matrix. The two conservation laws imply that *the scattering matrix is a unitary matrix.*

The statement that S is unitary implies a considerable restriction on the number of parameters necessary to describe a reaction. For example, the scattering matrix for a two-channel reaction is a two-by-two matrix with complex coefficients and hence contains $2(2)^2 = 8$ real parameters. However, (2.10) imposes three different restrictive conditions, so that there are only 5 independent parameters left. In general, the scattering matrix for an N channel reaction contains $2N^2$ real parameters, with $\frac{1}{2}N(N+1)$ conditions (2.10) between them.

C. Time Reversal

In many problems of physics the direction of time does not enter explicitly. This is true of most systems in which energy is conserved.

The motion of a planet around the sun, for example, is invariant under time reversal: If a given orbit, $x = f_1(t)$, $y = f_2(t)$, $z = f_3(t)$, satisfies Newton's equations, the "time-reversed orbit"

$$x = f_1(-t) \qquad y = f_2(-t) \qquad z = f_3(-t)$$

is also a possible orbit for the planet, i.e., it also satisfies Newton's equations. A physical system is invariant under reversal of the direction of time if to every possible state of the system there exists a "time-reversed" state which also satisfies the equations of motion.

We shall investigate the operation of time reversal for a quantum-mechanical system (Wigner 32). We can start with a plane wave of free particles, exp (ikz), going in the positive z direction. The "time-reversed" wave is the one going in the opposite direction, exp $(-ikz)$. These two solutions are complex conjugates of each other. We therefore expect that time reversal in general has some relation to taking the complex conjugate of the wave function.

Let us assume for the moment that the Hamiltonian is not only a Hermitean operator $(H^+ = H)$ but also real $(H^* = H)$. We take the complex conjugate on both sides of the wave equation (2.5):

$$H^* \Psi^* = -i\hbar \frac{\partial \Psi^*}{\partial t} = i\hbar \frac{\partial \Psi^*}{\partial(-t)} \tag{2.11}$$

Since $H^* = H$ by assumption, (2.11) shows that the wave function Ψ^* develops in the negative time direction, $-t$, in the same way that Ψ develops in the positive time direction. The reality of the Hamiltonian implies the possibility of time reversal, the wave function of the time-reversed state being just the complex conjugate of the original wave function: $\Psi^{(\mathrm{rev})}(\mathbf{r},t) = \Psi^*(\mathbf{r},-t)$.

While this condition is sufficient for time reversal to be possible, it is not necessary. We need only require that H and H^* are not "essentially" different, i.e., that they differ at most by a unitary transformation U (U independent of time):

$$H^* = U^{-1} H U \tag{2.12}$$

By the same argument as before we see that the time-reversed solution is

$$\Psi^{(\mathrm{rev})}(\mathbf{r},t) = U \Psi^*(\mathbf{r},-t) \tag{2.13}$$

The unitary property of U is necessary to insure that the time-reversed function is properly normalized to unity if the original Ψ was so normalized.

The most important practical case in which time reversal is not simply equivalent to taking the complex conjugate of the wave function is that of intrinsic spins. A particle of spin $\frac{1}{2}$, for example, obeys a wave equation which contains the Pauli spin matrices σ_x, σ_y, σ_z. In the conventional way of writing these matrices, σ_x and σ_z are real, while

$$\sigma_y = \begin{pmatrix} 0 & -i \\ i & 0 \end{pmatrix}$$

is pure imaginary. Thus H^* is not equal to H. The Pauli matrices do not occur by themselves but in combination with other vectors, a typical form being $(\mathbf{\delta \cdot L})$, where $\mathbf{L}$ is the orbital angular momentum vector

$$\mathbf{L} = \mathbf{r} \times \mathbf{p} = -i\hbar \, \mathbf{r} \times \mathbf{\nabla}$$

Then

$$(\mathbf{\delta \cdot L})^* = \sigma_x{}^* L_x{}^* + \sigma_y{}^* L_y{}^* + \sigma_z{}^* L_z{}^* = -\sigma_x L_x + \sigma_y L_y - \sigma_z L_z$$

A simple calculation shows that a unitary transformation with $U = \sigma_y$ brings this back to the original form $(\mathbf{\delta \cdot L})$. Thus time reversal in this case means not only taking the complex conjugate of the wave function but also multiplying it by $U = \sigma_y$, according to (2.13).

This unitary transformation has a simple interpretation. It amounts to reversing the direction in which the spin of the particle is pointing. This can be explained as follows: an intrinsic spin is in many respects similar to a rotating current. If we reverse the sense of time, the current rotates in the opposite direction; hence the spin direction reverses.

This interpretation also points to the one important case where time reversal is not possible, but where energy is nevertheless conserved: the case of a system under the influence of an applied magnetic field. The magnetic field is presumably due to currents in coils outside the limits of the system proper. If the direction of time is reversed, these currents reverse their direction, and so does the magnetic field created by them. In a system subject to magnetic fields, time reversal is possible only if the direction of these fields is reversed simultaneously. Conversely, if the external fields are assumed to maintain their direction, time reversal is not possible for the solutions of the equations of motion. This can be seen formally through the way in which the magnetic field enters into the Hamiltonian, the typical forms being $(\mathbf{L \cdot \mathcal{H}})$ and $(\mathbf{\delta \cdot \mathcal{H}})$. The orbital angular momentum $\mathbf{L} = \mathbf{r} \times \mathbf{p}$ changes its sign upon time reversal; hence $(\mathbf{L \cdot \mathcal{H}})$ also changes its sign unless the magnetic field direction is reversed simultaneously. The spin $\mathbf{\delta}$

behaves very much like the orbital angular momentum $\mathbf{L}$ under time reversal: the directions of both are reversed.

As a final point, we might mention that the possibility of time reversal implies that the wave functions can always be written as real functions. Indeed, if the time-reversed function Ψ^* is also a solution of the wave equation, the real functions

$$\Phi_1 = \Psi + \Psi^* \qquad \Phi_2 = i\,(\Psi - \Psi^*)$$

are acceptable solutions, and we can get a complete set of *real* wave functions for our system. The "reality" relations are somewhat more complicated if spins are present (Wigner 32, 47; Herring 37; Biedenharn 51).

D. The Reciprocity Theorem

We shall assume at first that time reversal is possible and that no spins are present, i.e., that the Hamiltonian is real. Then the time-reversed solution to our Ψ_α (see Figs. 2.1a and 2.1b) is just Ψ_α^*. This time-reversed function has *incoming* waves in all the channels *before* the reaction, the amplitude of the wave in channel β being $-S_{\alpha\beta}^*$; and an *outgoing* wave in the sole channel α *after* the reaction, with amplitude equal to unity.

The functions Ψ_β, $\beta = 1,2,\cdots,N$, form a complete set at energy E. Thus the time-reversed function Ψ_α^* of Ψ_α must be a linear superposition of them:

$$\Psi_\alpha^{(\text{rev})} = \Psi_\alpha^* = \sum_\beta c_\beta\,\Psi_\beta \qquad (2.14)$$

We can determine the constants c_β most easily by looking at both sides of (2.14) some time before the reaction takes place. The amplitude of the ingoing wave in channel γ on the right side is just c_γ (the Ψ_β for $\beta \neq \gamma$ have no ingoing waves in channel γ), whereas on the left side it is $-S_{\alpha\gamma}^*$ according to the last paragraph. Hence $c_\gamma = -S_{\alpha\gamma}^*$ and (2.14) becomes

$$\Psi_\alpha^{(\text{rev})} = \Psi_\alpha^* = -\sum_\beta S_{\alpha\beta}^*\,\Psi_\beta \qquad (2.15)$$

We now exploit this relation between the time-reversed solution and the original solutions to get a reciprocity theorem for nuclear reactions. We compare the amplitudes of the outgoing waves on both sides of (2.15) in a typical channel γ, some time after the reaction has taken place. The left side has an outgoing wave of unit amplitude in channel α and no outgoing waves in any of the other channels; hence the amplitude of the outgoing wave in a typical channel γ is $\delta_{\alpha\gamma}$.

Each Ψ_β on the right side has an amplitude $-S_{\beta\gamma}$ for the outgoing wave in channel γ. Performing the sum in (2.15), we get the relation

$$\sum_\beta S_{\alpha\beta}{}^* S_{\beta\gamma} = \delta_{\alpha\gamma} \qquad (2.16)$$

Equation (2.16) looks very similar to the completeness relation (2.10), but they are not identical, as can be seen by looking at the order of the subscripts in the two equations. In matrix language, (2.16) is

$$S^*S = 1 \qquad (2.16')$$

whereas (2.10) involves the Hermitean conjugate S^+. We combine (2.10') and (2.16'):[1]

$$S^*S = S^+S$$

and cancel out the S on both sides (this is possible since S, being a unitary matrix, is sure to have an inverse). This gives

$$S^* = S^+$$

that is,

$$S_{\alpha\beta}{}^* = S_{\beta\alpha}{}^*$$

Taking the complex conjugate of both sides, we obtain the *reciprocity theorem*

$$S_{\alpha\beta} = S_{\beta\alpha} \qquad (2.17)$$

This theorem states that the probability for a transition proceeding one way in time is equal to the probability for the same transition but with the sense of time reversed.

So far we have neglected intrinsic spins. If they exist, relation (2.17) has to be amended somewhat. We define the "time-reversed channel" $-\alpha$ to channel α as identical to α in all respects except that the spin directions of both the emerging particle and the residual nucleus have been reversed. Then the reciprocity theorem becomes

$$S_{\alpha\beta} = S_{-\beta,-\alpha} \qquad (2.18)$$

Our derivation of the reciprocity theorem makes it apparent that the validity of the theorem depends on the possibility of time reversal. Conversely, in systems which involve external magnetic fields, and in which time reversal is therefore not possible, the reciprocity theorem fails to hold in general. Examples of linear, non-reciprocal networks were given by McMillan (46, 47).

---

[1] We are using the fact that $SS^+ = 1$ implies that $S^+S = 1$ also. This is a general theorem for finite matrices.

The reciprocity theorem (2.17) imposes $\frac{1}{2}N(N-1)$ conditions on the scattering matrix. However, these conditions are not all independent of the previous conditions which assured that S is unitary. The number of independent real parameters in the scattering matrix can be determined most easily by constructing the matrix

$$X = i\,\frac{1-S}{1+S} \tag{2.19}$$

This matrix is called the "reactance matrix" in engineering terminology. A straightforward calculation shows that X is Hermitean if S is unitary; X is obviously symmetric if S is symmetric. Hence, if S is both unitary (conservation law) and symmetric (reciprocity law), X is a real, symmetric matrix. The number of independent real parameters in such a matrix is $\frac{1}{2}N(N+1)$, and this is therefore also the number of real independent parameters in the scattering matrix S.[1]

E. Reciprocity and Detailed Balance

The statement that there is a relation between the probabilities of inverse processes is often based on an application of perturbation theory. If the interaction which produces the transition in question is "weak," the element $S_{\alpha\beta}$ of the scattering matrix for $\alpha \neq \beta$ is proportional to a "matrix element" $H_{\alpha\beta}'$ of the perturbing Hamiltonian between the states α and β. (These considerations have no application at all to nuclear reactions in the energy range considered in this book; but they can be applied, for example, to the emission and absorption of gamma-radiation by nuclei). Since the Hamiltonian is Hermitean, there is a relation between the matrix elements for inverse processes: $H_{\alpha\beta}' = (H_{\beta\alpha}')$.* In the approximation of a "weak" interaction, this implies the *detailed balance theorem*

$$S_{\alpha\beta} = S_{\beta\alpha}{}^* \tag{2.20}$$

It is apparent from this derivation that detailed balance cannot be expected to be as generally valid as reciprocity. In nuclear reactions with spins, for example, the reciprocity relation (2.18) is satisfied, but the law of detailed balance (in which the spin directions are not reversed) in general fails to hold.

[1] The simple way in which the restrictive conditions enter into the reactance matrix, compared to the complicated way in which they enter into the scattering matrix, is a main reason for the use of the reactance matrix in engineering applications. For an alternative way of counting the independent real parameters in S, see Wigner (46).

We can visualize the relation between detailed balance and reciprocity by an example from classical mechanics. Consider the collision between a billiard ball and an object of triangular cross section, pictured in Fig. 2.2a. The initial state, α, and the final state, β, are shown in the figure. The states are specified by the momentum vec-

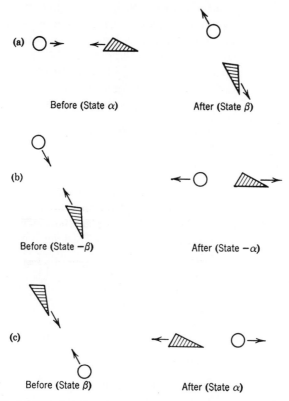

FIG. 2.2.   Illustration of reciprocity and detailed balance.   (a) Picture of a collision between a sphere and an irregularly shaped object.   (b) The time-reversed (reciprocal) collision, which occurs with equal probability.   (c) The opposite collision in the sense of the detailed balance theorem.   This collision occurs with different probability.

tors of the colliding particles without reference to their positions in space. If we reverse the time, we obtain the "reciprocal" process pictured in Fig. 2.2b. This process leads from state $-\beta$ to state $-\alpha$ (notice the reversed directions of the momenta). The transition probability (per unit solid angle) is equal for the two processes, since they can be obtained from each other by reversing the sense of time.

On the other hand, the inverse process in the sense of the detailed balance theorem, $\beta{\rightarrow}\alpha$, pictured in Fig. 2.2c, clearly bears little relation to the original collision; the probabilities are quite different, and detailed balance does not hold for these collisions.

In statistical mechanics the detailed balance theorem, rather than the reciprocity law, is often used. In the discussion of nuclear reactions, however, reciprocity is quite sufficient, and there is every reason for thinking that the reciprocity relations (2.18) hold in nature. There is on the contrary no convincing argument for detailed balance in nuclear reactions. Of course, the difference between reciprocity and detailed balance in nuclear reactions becomes apparent only when the spin directions in the incident and outgoing channels are measured. Averaging over spin directions destroys the distinction in most cases.

▶ 3. THE ANGULAR DISTRIBUTION OF REACTION PRODUCTS

A. The Reaction Amplitude

We shall consider the reaction $a+X=Y+b$ in which all the particles have definite quantum states. This corresponds to a reaction from one definite channel to another definite channel in the sense of Chapter VIII, Section 1. Unlike the work of the preceding sections of the present chapter, however, we shall not restrict ourselves to any one value of the orbital angular momentum of either the incident or the outgoing particles. Since we shall be interested only in one reaction at a time, we shall drop the channel indices α and β on the various quantities of interest, except where confusion might arise.

The behavior of the wave function Ψ in the incident channel is that of a plane wave which we shall normalize to unit flux:

$$\text{Incident plane wave} = \exp{(ikz)} \, (v_\alpha)^{-1/2} \, \chi_\alpha \qquad (3.1)$$

The outgoing wave in channel β has the form

$$\text{Outgoing wave} = q(\theta) \exp{(ikr)} \, r^{-1} \, (v_\beta)^{-1/2} \, \chi_\beta \qquad (3.2)$$

Here θ is the angle between the direction of the incident beam (the z direction) and the direction in which the particles b are observed.[1] The internal wave functions χ_α, χ_β of the various particles taking part in the reaction involve specification of the direction of the spins of the particles, if they do not all have zero spin. The function $q(\theta)$ will be called the "reaction amplitude of the $\alpha \rightarrow \beta$ reaction."

The differential reaction cross section for the (α,β) reaction is given by

$$d\sigma = |q(\theta)|^2 \, d\omega \qquad (3.3)$$

[1] We use the center-of-mass system throughout this discussion.

If spins are involved, this is the cross section for the case in which the incident particle a, the target nucleus X, the emerging particle b, and the residual nucleus Y all have definite spin states.   We shall use the single index ρ to indicate all this information; that is, ρ consists of four different spin indices.   If the incident beam is unpolarized, and if the detector is not sensitive to spin directions, the observed reaction cross section is obtained by averaging over the spin directions of a and X, and summing over the spin directions of b and Y.   As before, we shall call the spin of the incident particle s and of the target nucleus i. The observed reaction cross section of the (α,β) reaction is then

$$d\sigma = (2s+1)^{-1} (2i+1)^{-1} \sum_{\rho} |q_\rho(\theta,\varphi)|^2 \, d\omega \qquad (3.4)$$

We have written the reaction amplitude in (3.3) as a function of θ only, assuming implicitly that it is independent of the azimuthal angle φ.   This is an immediate consequence of the symmetry of the experimental set-up with respect to rotations about the z axis, as long as only one target nucleus at a time is involved in the reaction and no spins are present.   On the other hand, if the spin directions are specified, there is no longer symmetry about the z axis.   Hence the individual reaction amplitudes q_ρ in (3.4) depend on φ as well as on θ. The reaction cross section (3.4) observed with an unpolarized beam, however, is again independent of the azimuthal angle φ, since after averaging over spin directions the symmetry around the z axis is re-established.

B. The Conservation of Parity

If the wave function Ψ describing the reaction has a definite value of the parity, there are certain restrictions on the form the cross sections can take.   Before discussing these restrictions, however, let us first consider under what conditions the wave function Ψ has a definite parity (Wigner 27).   There are three cases of importance in nuclear reactions:

(1) At low energies the angular momentum "barrier" prevents particles with orbital angular momentum $l>0$ from reaching the nuclear surface.   The only particles effective in producing the reaction are the ones with $l=0$.   Thus, in spite of the fact that the plane wave (3.1) contains contributions from all values of l, and hence does not have a definite parity, the state of the compound nucleus formed in the reaction has a definite parity, equal to the product of the parities of the incident particle a and the target nucleus X (since the $l=0$ partial wave has even parity).

(2) If we are dealing with a resonance reaction in the region where the levels of the compound nucleus are widely separated compared to their width, any one resonance level of the compound nucleus has a definite parity. If only this one level is important in producing the reaction (i.e., if the Breit-Wigner one-level dispersion formula is applicable), the wave function for the reaction has the parity of this state of the compound nucleus.

(3) Finally, for reactions involving very light nuclei, it may happen that X and a are actually identical particles, or else that the reaction products Y and b are identical particles. An example of the first kind are the D-D reactions: $d(d,n)\mathrm{He}^3$ and $d(d,p)\mathrm{H}^3$; an example of the second kind is the reaction $\mathrm{Li}^7(p,\alpha)\mathrm{He}^4$. In a channel containing two identical particles *without spins*, an inversion of the space coordinates (parity operator) is equivalent to an exchange of the two identical particles. Two identical particles have definite properties under such an exchange: either the wave function is unchanged (Bose-Einstein statistics) or it changes sign (Fermi-Dirac statistics).[1] In the first case the parity has to be even, in the second case it has to be odd, as long as no spins are involved.

The situation is more complicated when spins are involved. Then an inversion of space alone is not equivalent to an exchange of the two particles, and the parity is correspondingly left undetermined. This is the case in the D-D reactions: two deuterons in either of the two spin states $S=0, 2$ have even parity, while two deuterons in the spin state $S=1$ have odd parity. If the relative spin orientations are unknown, so is the parity.

We now discuss the consequences of the assumption of a definite parity for the wave function on the angular distribution of the reaction products. In the outgoing channel the parity operation corresponds to replacing θ by $\pi-\theta$ and φ by $\varphi+\pi$. If the parity is definite, we have the following relation between the reaction amplitudes:

$$q_\rho(\pi-\theta,\ \varphi+\pi) = \Pi\ q_\rho(\theta,\varphi) \qquad (3.5)$$

(the spin index ρ is the same on both sides of the equation because the parity operator leaves the spins unchanged). Here $\Pi = \pm 1$ is the parity of the relative motion in channel β, not the parity of the wave function as a whole. The latter is given by

$$\text{Parity of } \Psi = \Pi \times (\text{parity of Y}) \times (\text{parity of } b) \qquad (3.6)$$

If we substitute (3.5) into (3.4), we obtain the result for the differential

[1] In practice spinless particles always obey Bose-Einstein statistics.

reaction cross section:

$$d\sigma(\pi - \theta, \varphi + \pi) = d\sigma(\theta, \varphi)$$

Since we have already shown that the cross section (averaged over spins) is independent of the azimuthal angle φ, this implies

$$d\sigma(\pi - \theta) = d\sigma(\theta) \qquad (3.7)$$

In words: *If the wave function for the reaction has definite parity, the differential reaction cross section is symmetric about $\theta = 90°$ (in the center-of-gravity system).* If the cross section is expressed as a polynomial in $\cos \theta$, only even powers of the cosine appear. If it is expressed in terms of Legendre polynomials, only Legendre polynomials with even indices are required. It does not matter for the theorem whether the parity is $+1$ or -1, so long as it has a definite value. Conversely, a study of the differential cross section for a reaction under conditions of definite parity does not lead to a parity assignment. In particular, the parity of any isolated resonance level of the compound nucleus cannot be determined by a study of the angular distribution of the reaction products.

C. Limitations Imposed by the Complexity of the Incident Beam

It often happens that only a restricted range of orbital angular momenta $l \leq L$ are effective in producing the reaction. The following theorem holds under these conditions: If the incident beam of particles is unpolarized, the cross section depends on the angle θ in a way which is no more complicated than would be obtained from the angular dependence of the effective incident beam, i.e., $d\sigma$ involves no powers of $\cos \theta$ higher than $(\cos \theta)^{2L}$.

The theorem is trivial if the spins i, s, i', s' of target nucleus, incident particle, residual nucleus, and outgoing particle are all zero. Consider incident particles with orbital angular momentum $l = L$. The outgoing particles also have $l = L$; hence the reaction amplitude $q(\theta)$ behaves like a spherical harmonic $Y_{L,0}(\theta)$, of order L; the highest power of $\cos \theta$ in this spherical harmonic is $(\cos \theta)^L$. The cross section $d\sigma$, (3.3), then contains no powers of $\cos \theta$ higher than $(\cos \theta)^{2L}$. The waves with values of l lower than L give rise to even lower powers of $\cos \theta$. Hence the theorem is proved.

The proof of the theorem for the case of particles with spin is much more laborious.[1] We start this proof with a new derivation for the

---

[1] We follow the procedure of Yang (48). For alternative derivations, see Myers (38), Critchfield (41), Eisner (47), Wolfenstein (48), and Eisenbud (51). Whereas the theorems discussed here limit the form of the angular distribution considerably,

536   X. Formal Theory of Nuclear Reactions

case of no spins, which can be adapted quite easily to the more complicated (and more significant) case in which spins are present. Therefore we shall consider first spinless particles with orbital angular momentum $l = L$, and we shall be interested in wave functions Ψ_m which have the following behavior in the incident channel:

$$\text{Incoming wave of } \Psi_m = \exp\left[-i(kr - \tfrac{1}{2}L\pi)\right] r^{-1} v_\alpha^{-1/2} Y_{Lm}(\theta,\varphi) \quad (3.8)$$

In practice, only the Ψ_m with $m = 0$ is excited in the reaction, but we shall be concerned with all $2L+1$ of them here. The outgoing wave in channel β has the form (3.2) with a reaction amplitude which depends on the value of m and will be called $q_m(\theta,\varphi)$ (for $m \neq 0$, it depends on φ as well as on θ).

We now perform a rotation R of the system of coordinates which transforms the angles θ,φ on the unit sphere into new angles θ',φ'. We shall denote θ,φ by the single symbol ω in what follows, and similarly θ',φ' by ω'.

We shall consider a second set of wave functions Φ_m with the following property: each Φ_m is the same function of the rotated angles ω' as Ψ_m was of the original angles ω, i.e., the incoming wave of Φ_m looks just like the incoming wave of Ψ_m, (3.8), except that $Y_{Lm}(\omega)$ is replaced by $Y_{Lm}(\omega')$. Then the *outgoing* wave of the new function Φ_m in channel β has the form

$$\text{Outgoing wave of } \Phi_m = q_m(\omega') \exp(ikr)\, r^{-1} v_\beta^{-1/2} \quad (3.9)$$

with the *same* reaction amplitude q_m as before, except that q_m now has the argument ω' rather than ω.

We can express the new functions Φ_m in terms of the old functions Ψ_m. Consider the incoming wave of Φ_m. Its angular dependence is given by $Y_{Lm}(\omega')$. We can write this as a linear superposition of spherical harmonics $Y_{Lm}(\omega)$ as follows:

$$Y_{Lm}(\omega') = \sum_{m'} \mathfrak{D}_{L,mm'}(\mathsf{R})\, Y_{Lm'}(\omega) \quad (3.10)$$

We have given the coefficients of this expansion a subscript L to denote the orbital angular momentum involved, and we have also indicated explicitly that they depend on the particular rotation R under consideration.

---

the proof given here does not lend itself to an explicit determination of the differential cross section in terms of the scattering matrix. For this explicit form, the reader is referred to the paper by Wigner and Eisenbud (Wigner 47) and to a paper by Blatt and Biedenharn (to appear in Rev. Mod. Phys. in 1952).

Equation (3.10) implies the following relation between the new wave functions Φ_m and the old wave functions Ψ_m:

$$\Phi_m = \sum_{m'} \mathfrak{D}_{L,mm'}(\mathsf{R})\, \Psi_{m'} \qquad (3.11)$$

We use (3.11) for the behavior of the wave functions in the outgoing channel to get a relation between the reaction amplitudes $q_m(\omega)$ at two different angles ω and ω':

$$q_m(\omega') = \sum_{m'} \mathfrak{D}_{L,mm'}(\mathsf{R})\, q_{m'}(\omega) \qquad (3.12)$$

The cross section (3.3) depends on the absolute square of q_0. We now use (3.12) to express $q_{m=0}(\omega')$ in terms of $q_{m'}(0)$, where the latter is the reaction amplitude for a fixed direction $\omega = 0$, say the pole of a unit sphere around the center. Let us call R the rotation which turns the pole into the direction ω' on the sphere. Then (we omit the subscript L)

$$q_0(\omega') = \sum_{m'} \mathfrak{D}_{0m'}(\mathsf{R})\, q_{m'}(0) \qquad (3.13)$$

and its absolute square is

$$|q_0(\omega')|^2 = \sum_{m'}\sum_{m''} [\mathfrak{D}_{0m'}(\mathsf{R})]^* \,\mathfrak{D}_{0m''}(\mathsf{R})\, [q_{m'}(0)]^*\, q_{m''}(0) \qquad (3.14)$$

In this equation the entire angular dependence of the right side is contained in the expansion coefficients $\mathfrak{D}(\mathsf{R})$. These expansion coefficients are well known (Wigner 31). In particular, for a rotation which sends the pole $\omega = 0$ of the sphere into ω', the coefficient $\mathfrak{D}_{L,0m'}(\mathsf{R})$ is just the complex conjugate of the spherical harmonic $Y_{Lm'}(\omega')$. Since this spherical harmonic contains no power of $\cos\theta$ higher than $(\cos\theta)^L$, and since each term of the sum (3.14) involves no more than two factors $\mathfrak{D}$, the cross section $d\sigma = |q_0(\omega)|^2\, d\omega$ contains no powers of $\cos\theta$ higher than $(\cos\theta)^{2L}$. We have therefore proved the theorem once more, but so far only for the case of no spins.

We now generalize this proof to the case in which spins are present. We shall consider a set of wave functions $\Psi_{m\rho}$ which have the same angular dependence as (3.8), except that we must now add an index ρ to specify the spin orientations of the four particles involved in the reaction (a, X, b, Y). After a rotation, the modified functions $\Phi_{m\rho}$, analogous to the Φ_m before, will be defined in such a way that they are the same functions in the transformed (rotated) coordinate system as the $\Psi_{m\rho}$ were in the old coordinate system. In particular, for example, if the spin of particle a pointed in the old z direction for $\Psi_{m\rho}$, the spin points in the new z' direction for $\Phi_{m\rho}$.

The transformation from the old functions to the new functions is now more complicated than (3.11). We first rotate the space coordinates without doing anything to the spins. The transformation for that is described by (3.11). We must then, however, make a further transformation to get the spins oriented properly with respect to the new (z') axis. The combined transformation is

$$\Phi_{m\rho} = \sum_{m'} \sum_{\rho'} \mathfrak{D}_{L,mm'}(\mathsf{R}) \; \mathcal{G}_{\rho\rho'}(\mathsf{R}) \; \Psi_{m'\rho'} \tag{3.15}$$

where the coefficients $\mathcal{G}_{\rho\rho'}(\mathsf{R})$ determine the "reshuffling" of the spin indices. These coefficients depend on the rotation R. Unlike the $\mathfrak{D}_{mm'}$, however, the $\mathcal{G}_{\rho\rho'}$ are not associated with any one value of angular momentum (in group theoretical language, the $\mathfrak{D}_{L,mm'}$ form an irreducible representation of the rotation group, whereas the $\mathcal{G}_{\rho\rho'}$ form a reducible representation).

The only property of the $\mathcal{G}_{\rho\rho'}$ which we shall use here is that they are *unitary* matrices:

$$\sum_{i\rho} \mathcal{G}_{\rho\rho'}{}^* \, \mathcal{G}_{\rho\rho''} = \delta_{\rho'\rho''} \tag{3.16}$$

This equation implies that an average over all spin directions referred to the old z axis is the same as an average over all spin directions referred to the new z' axis. We shall not give a formal proof of this property here.

The formal proof involves a more detailed specification of the coefficients $\mathcal{G}$. We can see what they must be by taking the spins of the various particles one at a time and referring each one separately to the new z' axis as the reference direction. The transformation coefficients which determine the reshuffling of an individual spin index i, say, under the rotation R, form the set $\mathfrak{D}_{i,mm'}(\mathsf{R})$, i.e., they are the same coefficients as for a rotation of the orbital part of the wave function, except for an angular momentum i rather than L; the m and m' are now the z components and z' components, respectively, of the spin i. The composite coefficients $\mathcal{G}_{\rho\rho'}$ are products of four $\mathfrak{D}$'s, one for each spin in the picture. Since each $\mathfrak{D}_{mm'}$ is a unitary matrix, the direct product of four such $\mathfrak{D}$ matrices is also unitary. This statement merely expresses the fact that an average over all spin directions, weighted equally, is the same no matter to which z axis the spin directions are referred.

We are interested in the reaction amplitudes $q_{m\rho}(\omega)$ with $m=0$. We shall again use the rotation R which sends the pole $\omega=0$ of the sphere into the position ω' to get [in analogy to (3.13)]

$$q_{0\rho}(\omega') = \sum_{m'} \sum_{\rho'} \mathfrak{D}_{L,0m'}(\mathsf{R}) \; \mathcal{G}_{\rho\rho'}(\mathsf{R}) \; q_{m'\rho'}(0) \tag{3 17}$$

This expression depends on the angle ω', i.e., on the rotation R, not merely through the coefficients $\mathfrak{D}_{0m'}(R)$ but also through the coefficients $\mathcal{G}_{\rho\rho'}(R)$. The crucial point is that the latter dependence drops out in the cross section (3.4) because of averaging over spin directions:

$$\sum_{\rho} |q_{0\rho}(\omega')|^2 = \sum_{\rho} \sum_{m'\rho'm''\rho''} \mathfrak{D}_{0m'}^* \, \mathfrak{D}_{0m''} \, \mathcal{G}_{\rho\rho'}^* \, \mathcal{G}_{\rho\rho''} \, [q_{m'\rho'}(0)_{\,\mathsf{J}}]^* \, q_{m''\rho''}(0)$$

We perform the sum over ρ first and use the unitary property (3.16) of the $\mathcal{G}_{\rho\rho'}$ to simplify the result. This gives

$$\sum_{\rho} |q_{0\rho}(\omega')|^2 = \sum_{m'} \sum_{m''} \mathfrak{D}_{0m'}^* \, \mathfrak{D}_{0m''} \left\{ \sum_{\rho'} [q_{m'\rho'}(0)]^* \, q_{m''\rho'}(0) \right\} \quad (3.18)$$

This equation is the analogue of (3.14); it establishes the theorem. As the sum in braces on the right side does not depend on the angle ω', the full angle dependence is again contained in the coefficients $\mathfrak{D}$. The coefficients $\mathcal{G}_{\rho\rho'}$ have dropped out completely. Therefore the highest power of the cosine which can occur in the cross section (3.4) for an unpolarized beam is $(\cos \theta)^{2L}$. This is true in spite of the fact that an orbital angular momentum L can combine with spins s and i in the incident channel to give total angular momenta J as high as $J = L + s + i$, and in spite of the fact that a given resonance level of the compound nucleus through which the reaction may go may therefore have values of J as high as that. Averaging over spin directions reduces the a priori complexity of the outgoing wave from the equivalent of an angular momentum $J = L + s + i$ down to the equivalent of the maximum *orbital* angular momentum L.

This theorem can also be considered an expression of the uncertainty principle for angles. If no orbital angular momenta in excess of L enter the wave function of the incident beam, and if the spin directions are not specified, the angles in the incident beam are determined only to within the uncertainty $\Delta\theta$ given by

$$L \, \Delta\theta \gtrsim \pi$$

The theorem can then be interpreted to mean that the uncertainty in the angle of the outgoing particles is of the same order of magnitude. We cannot improve the definition of the angle by letting the particles perform a nuclear reaction.

In practice, this theorem is important for the analysis of reactions at low energies, where the angular momentum barrier restricts the values of l which can participate in the reaction.

D. Limitations Imposed by the Complexity of the Compound Nucleus

The theorem of the Section 3C does not assert that terms as high as $(\cos \theta)^{2L}$ actually occur in the differential cross section. A very important exception arises in resonance reactions if the resonance level of the compound nucleus has a total angular momentum J which is less than the maximum orbital angular momentum L. Then the complexity of the distribution in angle of the outgoing particles is no higher than $(\cos \theta)^{2J}$. It is limited by the state of the compound nucleus rather than by the orbital angular momenta in the incident beam. This provides a very powerful tool for analyzing the excited states of nuclei. For example, suppose that the differential reaction cross section at a given resonance energy is independent of angle, while resonances at nearby energies show more complicated angular dependences. We can then infer that the level of the compound nucleus involved in this resonance reaction has total angular momentum $J = 0$, if the compound nucleus contains an even number of particles, and $J = \frac{1}{2}$ if this number is odd. In general, for odd A of the compound nucleus, the highest angular dependence is $(\cos \theta)^{2J-1}$ since only even powers of the cosine can enter owing to the definite parity of the wave function.

The proof of this important theorem follows directly from the fact that the Bohr assumption is fulfilled in resonance reactions. Let us first consider the reaction in which all particles have definite spin directions. We shall now break up the single spin index ρ of the previous section into two spin indices κ and λ, where κ specifies the spin directions in the incoming channel α and λ specifies the spin directions in the outgoing channel β. We define $d\sigma_{\alpha\kappa,\beta\lambda}(\omega)$ as the cross section for the (α,β) reaction when κ and λ are the spin directions in the entrance and exit channel, respectively, and when the emission in channel β takes place in the specific direction $\omega = \theta, \varphi$ within the solid angle element $d\omega$.

According to the Bohr assumption we can split this cross section into two factors:

$$d\sigma_{\alpha\kappa,\beta\lambda}(\theta) = \sigma_C(\alpha\kappa)\, G_{\beta\lambda M_J}(\omega)\, d\omega \qquad (3.19)$$

Here $\sigma_C(\alpha\kappa)$ is the cross section for the formation from the channel $(\alpha\kappa)$ of a definite compound state with a given angular momentum J whose z component is M_J; $G_{\beta\lambda M_J}(\omega)\, d\omega$ is the branching probability that this compound state decays in the manner described before. Obviously $\sigma_C(\alpha\kappa)$ does not depend on the angles θ, φ. At the time the compound nucleus is formed, it does not know yet in which direction it is going to disintegrate.   It is essential for the validity of (3.19) that the compound state be created in only one of the $(2J+1)$ substates with different M_J.   If more than one orientation of J is created, (3.19) ought to contain a sum over them.   However, the z component of l is always zero, because of the symmetry of a plane wave beam with respect to rotations about the direction of the beam.   Hence the z component of the total angular momentum, M_J, is the same for all these states: it is determined entirely by the spin directions κ in the incident beam, since the direction of the orbital angular momentum in the incident channel is always the same.   Thus, once the spin directions in the incident channel are specified, the state of the compound nucleus is also uniquely given; it has a definite value of J in any case (being a definite resonance level), and the M_J is now also defined.

The observed cross section with unpolarized beams is obtained by summing over the spin directions of the outgoing channel and averaging over the spin directions of the incoming channel:

$$d\sigma_{\alpha\beta}(\omega) \;=\; (2s+1)^{-1}(2i+1)^{-1} \sum_{\kappa}\sum_{\lambda} \sigma_C(\alpha\kappa)\, G_{\beta\lambda M_J}(\omega)\, d\omega \qquad (3.20)$$

Because of the Bohr assumption, we can write this expression in the following way:

$$d\sigma_{\alpha\beta}(\omega) \;=\; (2s+1)^{-1}(2i+1)^{-1} \sum_{\kappa} \sigma_C(\alpha\kappa) \left[\sum_{\lambda} G_{\beta\lambda M_J}(\omega)\, d\omega \right] \qquad (3.21)$$

If each one of the different square brackets has an angular distribution no more complicated than $(\cos\theta)^{2J}$, their weighted sum (3.21) also has this kind of angular distribution.

The proof of the theorem is therefore reduced to proving that each square bracket in (3.21) has an angular distribution no more complicated than $(\cos\theta)^{2J}$.   For integral J this statement is just a special case of the theorem proved before: we can consider the compound nucleus analogous to a definite incident channel of the previous theorem, with l and $m=m_l$ replaced by J and M_J, respectively, and with $i=s=0$ in the incident channel.   Then the outgoing angular distribution is no more complicated than $(\cos\theta)^{2l} = (\cos\theta)^{2J}$, which is what we needed to prove.   If J is half-integral, a similar consideration gives the same result.   However, the conservation of parity requires that only even powers of $\cos\theta$ can enter.   Hence the highest power for half-integral J is actually $(\cos\theta)^{2J-1}$.

Of course, each square bracket in (3.20) depends not only on θ, but in general also on the azimuthal angle φ (since M_J is not zero in general). However, it is apparent that this dependence on the azimuthal angle must disappear after averaging over the spin directions κ in the incident channel. The incident beam with unspecified spin directions is not changed by rotations about the z axis (direction of the beam); hence the outgoing distribution must also be independent of the azimuthal angle φ.

It appears from these considerations that the angular distribution in a resonance reaction going through one level of the compound nucleus is limited in its complexity by two factors: the complexity of the incident beam (highest value of l effective in producing the compound nucleus), and the complexity (i.e., the total angular momentum J) of the compound state. The more severe of the two limitations determines the actual complexity of the angular distribution of the outgoing particles.

These statements apply only to resonance reactions in the region where one level at a time is excited. As soon as various compound levels interfere, the angular distribution becomes much more complicated (Blatt 51). It is still limited by the complexity of the incident beam, of course (we recall that in the proof of Section 3C no use was made of any property of the compound nucleus). But it is no longer true that the outgoing beam has a definite parity; hence odd powers of $\cos\theta$ can enter, and the angular distribution can be as complicated as $(\cos\theta)^{2J_{max}}$, where J_{max} is the highest J of the various compound states which contribute appreciably to the reaction. A discussion of angular distributions on the basis of the continuum theory of nuclear reactions can be found in Wolfenstein (51).

▶ **4. THE WIGNER MANY-LEVEL FORMULA**

A. The Compound Nucleus as a "Black Box"

The concept of a compound nucleus in nuclear reactions was treated in detail in Chapter VIII. We shall now discuss an alternative, more formal, method of introducing this concept into the theory of nuclear reactions. The method, developed by Wigner and his collaborators,[1] gives a more rigorous justification of the dispersion formula for resonance reactions than the methods of Sections 7 to 9 of Chapter VIII. On the other hand, the general dispersion formula of Wigner (47) is not very useful for the study of nuclear reactions in the continuum region (see Chapter VIII, Section 4), nor does it lead as naturally to

---

[1] Wigner (46, 46a, 46b, 47, 48, 49, 51,) Teichmann (49, 50), Eisenbud (48), Goertzel (48), Moshinsky (51).

order-of-magnitude estimates in the resonance region as the less formal approach of Chapter VIII.

The definition (1.3) of the scattering matrix $S_{\alpha\beta}$ depends only on the asymptotic properties of the wave functions in the various channels. Only these properties are relevant for the general theorems (completeness and reciprocity) in which no assumption is made regarding the kind of event responsible for the reaction. We now introduce the concept of a compound nucleus into the formal theory. We start by ascribing a channel radius R_α to the compound nucleus in each channel α. For values of the channel coordinate $r_\alpha \geq R_\alpha$ the wave function describes the motion of the separated particle a and residual nucleus X (both in definite quantum states) under the action of known forces of non-nuclear origin (the Coulomb and centrifugal forces). On the other hand, for values of $r_\alpha < R_\alpha$, nucleus X and particle a combine into a compound system about whose dynamical behavior we know very little. Thus we do not know the behavior of the wave function in the region of configuration space which corresponds to the compound nucleus (i.e., the region in which all particles are close together).

We do not really need to know all the details of the motion within the compound nucleus in order to obtain all relevant information about nuclear reactions. A complete description of the internal motion within the compound nucleus is neither necessary nor desirable. In Chapter VIII the only property of the internal wave function which we needed was the value of the logarithmic derivative f, (VIII,2.23), at the channel entrance $r = R$ of the particular channel through which the reaction is initiated. In Chapter VIII we also used the Bohr assumption (see Sections 3 and 4). The formalism to be developed now differs from the previous one in its greater generality: we shall not use the Bohr assumption, but instead we shall derive it from the theory for the special case of resonance reactions. Thus the formalism is also applicable to reactions which violate the Bohr assumption. It should be emphasized, nevertheless, that this added generality is obtained at the expense of concreteness in the formulation.

The value of the wave function and the value of its derivative at each channel entrance $r_\alpha = R_\alpha$ defines the complete behavior of the wave function in each channel. Hence all information of interest about the compound nucleus is contained in the specification of the value and derivative of the wave function at each channel entrance.

In the language of electrical engineering, we treat the compound nucleus as a "black box" with N terminals, one for each channel. The voltage and current at each terminal are the only quantities of interest for the behavior of the "black box" toward the outside.

In particular, two different black boxes which give rise to the same currents and voltages at the terminals are equivalent for our purposes. We can think of the value of the wave function and of its derivative as a close analogy to voltage and current, respectively.

It is not possible to specify the value and the derivative of the wave function at each channel entrance arbitrarily. We have seen in Section 1 that there are only N linearly independent wave functions at each energy E; hence there are only N complex parameters (e.g., the coefficient of each wave function Ψ_α) at our disposal. Thus a specification of the derivative of the wave function at each channel entrance (N complex numbers) uniquely determines the value of the wave function at each channel entrance. The electrical analogy is: given the currents into each terminal of the "black box," the voltages are determined by the internal properties of the box; therefore we cannot specify both the voltage and the current at each terminal arbitrarily.

B. The Derivative Matrix

In order to get a formal connection between the values and derivatives of the wave function at each channel entrance, we must use a set of base functions different from the Ψ_α of Section 1 (see 1.3). We shall choose our new base functions in such a way that they will have simple properties at each channel *entrance* rather than a simple asymptotic form. We shall write all the formulas for the special case of $l=0$ and no spins in any channels, i.e., the spins i,s,i',s' of target nucleus, incident particle, residual nucleus (in whatever state it is left), and outgoing particle are assumed to vanish. This is done for the sake of simplicity. Most of the mportant points already appear in this simplest example. The derivation of the many-level formula for arbitrary values of l,i,s,i',s' has been given by Wigner and Eisenbud (47).

We have seen in Section 2 that the possibility of time reversal implies that all the wave functions can be written as real functions (in the absence of spins). We shall choose our new base functions Φ_α as real functions. That is, we use standing waves in all the channels, instead of the traveling waves which appear in (1.1) and (1.3). The most convenient choices are standing waves of the forms $\cos [k(r-R)]$ and $\sin [k(r-R)]$. The first of these has zero derivative at $r=R$, the second has zero value at $r=R$. Hence the use of these functions allows us to relate the value and the derivative of the wave function at each channel entrance. Since there are N linearly independent functions Ψ_α, there must also be N linearly independent standing wave functions

Φ_α in our new basic set. We shall choose Φ_α so that it behaves like $\cos\,[k_\beta(r_\beta-R_\beta)]$, i.e., has zero derivative at $r_\beta=R_\beta$, in all channels except channel α. In channel α, Φ_α is a linear superposition of $\sin\,[k_\alpha(r_\alpha-R_\alpha)]$ and $\cos\,[k_\alpha(r_\alpha-R_\alpha)]$. The coefficient of the sine is normalized for later convenience, in accordance with the choice used by Wigner and Eisenbud (47). The new basic set Φ_α is defined by

$$\Phi_\alpha \,=\, \phi_{\alpha\beta}(r_\beta)\,\chi_\beta \qquad \text{in channel } \beta \qquad (4.1a)$$

where

$$\phi_{\alpha\beta}(r_\beta) \,=\, \Re_{\alpha\beta}\cos\,[k_\beta(r_\beta-R_\beta)]\left(\frac{M_\beta}{4\pi\hbar}\right)^{1/2} r_\beta^{-1} \qquad \text{for } \beta\neq\alpha \quad (4.1b)$$

and

$$\phi_{\alpha\alpha}(r_\alpha) \,=\, \left\{k_\alpha^{-1}\sin\,[k_\alpha(r_\alpha-R_\alpha)] + \Re_{\alpha\alpha}\cos\,[k_\alpha(r_\alpha-R_\alpha)]\right\}\left(\frac{M_\alpha}{4\pi\hbar}\right)^{1/2} r_\alpha^{-1}$$
$$\text{for } \beta=\alpha \quad (4.1c)$$

Here M_β is the reduced mass in channel β, and χ_β is the internal wave function in that channel. The coefficients $\Re_{\alpha\beta}$ $(\alpha,\beta=1,2,\cdots,N)$ form an N-by-N matrix which is called the "derivative matrix" by Wigner and Eisenbud. Since the wave functions Φ_α are purely real functions,[1] the elements of the derivative matrix $\Re_{\alpha\beta}$ are real numbers.

We can visualize this set of wave functions by analogy with the wave guide junction depicted in Fig. 4.1. The state Φ_α is realized by placing perfectly reflecting mirrors into all the channels. This produces standing waves in all channels. The mirrors in the channels $\beta\neq\alpha$ have been put one-quarter channel wavelength out from the entrance to the cavity (the channel radius R_β). Each mirror gives rise to a node in the wave function. By placing the mirror a quarter-wavelength out, we insure a maximum of the wave function at the channel radius itself, corresponding to the $\cos\,[k_\beta(r_\beta-R_\beta)]$ of (4.1b). If the mirror in channel α were also placed a quarter-wavelength away, the whole system (central cavity plus the short channel segments terminated by mirrors) could be considered a new enlarged cavity. It would then have definite resonant states at definite energies. Since we want to obtain a base set Φ_α of wave functions at an arbitrary energy E, we must leave the position of the mirror in channel α adjust-

---

[1] The definitions (4.1) give the behavior of Φ_α in the external region (the channels) only. The behavior in the internal (compound nucleus) region is defined implicitly by requiring smooth joining at each channel entrance. If the Hamiltonian is purely real, $H^*=H$, the wave function Φ_α is real everywhere, not only in the external region.

able. The mirror in channel α must be placed where, at energy E, the wave function would have a node anyhow. Relation (4.1c) shows that this position is determined by the coefficient $\mathcal{R}_{\alpha\alpha}$ (the diagonal element of the derivative matrix) through

$$(r_{\text{mirror}} - R)_\alpha = -k_\alpha^{-1} \arctan (k_\alpha \mathcal{R}_{\alpha\alpha}) \qquad (4.2)$$

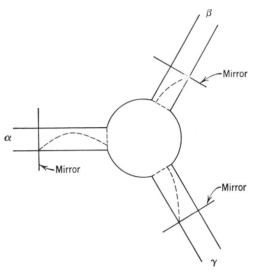

FIG. 4.1. "Black box" with three channels.   Mirrors are set in channels β and γ so that the derivatives of the wave function are zero at the channel entrance.   The position of the mirror in channel α is then a function of the energy, as given in (4.2).

By making one after another of the N channels contain the adjustable mirror, we get N different real wave functions Φ_α which form a complete set of base functions at the energy E.

The definition (4.1) of the set Φ_α gives the behavior of Φ_α in every channel β, for all $r_\beta \geq R_\beta$. It is possible, however, to restate the definition of Φ_α in a form which involves the behavior of the wave function at each channel entrance only:

Φ_α has zero derivative at $r_\beta = R_\beta$ for every channel $\beta \neq \alpha$:

$$\left[\frac{\partial(r_\beta \phi_{\alpha\beta})}{\partial r_\beta}\right]_{r_\beta = R_\beta} = 0 \qquad \text{for } \beta \neq \alpha \qquad (4.3a)$$

and the derivative of Φ_α with respect to r_α at $r_\alpha = R_\alpha$ is given by

$$\left[\frac{\partial(r_\alpha \phi_{\alpha\alpha})}{\partial r_\alpha}\right]_{r_\alpha = R_\alpha} = \left(\frac{M_\alpha}{4\pi\hbar}\right)^{1/2} \qquad \text{for } \beta = \alpha \qquad (4.3b)$$

This alternative definition of Φ_α does not involve any external (channel) quantities, such as the channel velocity or channel energy, with the exception of the channel mass M_α, which was retained for the sake of convenience later on. Thus (4.3) contains only quantities which involve the compound nucleus directly, such as derivatives of the wave function at each channel entrance. The derivative matrix $\mathcal{R}_{\alpha\beta}$ is therefore an "internal" property of the compound nucleus. The compound nucleus appears in the Wigner theory through the derivative matrix only. All other properties of the compound nucleus can be ignored as far as the theory of reactions is concerned. This corresponds to the development in Chapter VIII, where we used only the logarithmic derivatives f_α at the entrance to the incident channels.[1]

The "internal" region which determines the derivative matrix has not been defined unambiguously. The channel radius R_α was defined by the condition that there should not be any nuclear inter-action between the particle a and the residual nucleus X in channel α for any $r_\alpha \geq R_\alpha$. Clearly, if a given value of R_α satisfies this condition, any larger value R_α' will do just as well. We can add arbitrary lengths of each channel to the "internal" region without violating the conditions of the theory. The derivative matrix $\mathcal{R}_{\alpha\beta}'$ appropriate to the extended internal region is different from the derivative matrix $\mathcal{R}_{\alpha\beta}$ for the smaller region. This uncertainty in what we mean by "inter-nal" region is a direct consequence of the fact that we ignore, deliberately, all the properties of the internal region *except* the deriva-tive matrix. We can make the definition of R_α, and hence of the inter-nal region, unique by the requirement that a and X do have a nuclear interaction for $r_\alpha < R_\alpha$ (this is the physical definition of the compound nucleus used in Chapter VIII). Then R_α is the smallest possible value of R_α which satisfies the conditions of the theory (no nuclear interaction outside R_α).

C. The Relation between the Derivative Matrix and the Scattering Matrix

The internal properties of the compound nucleus which are of importance for the outcome of nuclear reactions are all contained in the derivative matrix $\mathcal{R}_{\alpha\beta}$. On the other hand, the cross sections for

---

[1] There are N different f_α at each energy, and $\frac{1}{2}N(N+1)$ different matrix ele-ments $\mathcal{R}_{\alpha\beta}$ (the matrix is symmetric, as we shall show soon). Fewer parameters were necessary in Chapter VIII for the following reasons: In the high-energy region (continuum theory) the Bohr assumption was introduced; in the low-energy region (resonance region) the discussion of the reaction cross sections was restricted to the neighborhood of resonances.

the various reactions and for elastic scattering are expressed simply in terms of the scattering matrix $S_{\alpha\beta}$ (see Section 1C) rather than in terms of the derivative matrix. We must therefore express the scattering matrix in terms of the derivative matrix in order to get from the internal properties of the compound nucleus to the observed cross sections.

The N wave functions Φ_α, (4.1), form a complete set. So do the N wave functions Ψ_α, (1.3). Hence the Φ_α can be expressed as linear superpositions of the Ψ_α:

$$\Phi_\alpha = \sum_\beta C_{\alpha\beta} \Psi_\beta \tag{4.4}$$

We can determine the coefficients $C_{\alpha\beta}$ in this superposition by comparing the behavior of the right and left sides of (4.4) in an arbitrary channel γ, using (1.3) and (4.1), respectively. We equate the coefficients of $\exp(ik_\gamma r_\gamma)$ and of $\exp(-ik_\gamma r_\gamma)$, separately. The first gives, after some simplification,

$$(\delta_{\alpha\gamma} + i\sqrt{k_\alpha}\mathfrak{R}_{\alpha\gamma}\sqrt{k_\gamma})\tfrac{1}{2}\exp(-ik_\gamma R_\gamma) = -i\sqrt{k_\alpha}\sum_\beta C_{\alpha\beta}S_{\beta\gamma} \tag{4.5}$$

The coefficients of $\exp(-ik_\gamma r_\gamma)$ lead to the equation

$$(\delta_{\alpha\gamma} - i\sqrt{k_\alpha}\mathfrak{R}_{\alpha\gamma}\sqrt{k_\gamma})\tfrac{1}{2}\exp(+ik_\gamma R_\gamma) = -i\sqrt{k_\alpha}C_{\alpha\gamma} \tag{4.6}$$

We substitute the value of C from (4.6) into (4.5) to get

$$(\delta_{\alpha\gamma} + i\sqrt{k_\alpha}\mathfrak{R}_{\alpha\gamma}\sqrt{k_\gamma})\exp(-ik_\gamma R_\gamma)$$
$$= \sum_\beta (\delta_{\alpha\beta} - i\sqrt{k_\alpha}\mathfrak{R}_{\alpha\beta}\sqrt{k_\beta})\exp(+ik_\beta R_\beta)S_{\beta\gamma} \tag{4.7}$$

This is a set of N^2 linear equations for the N^2 unknown coefficients of the scattering matrix S. It is easier to write (4.7) in matrix notation by introducing the two following diagonal matrices:

$$B_{\alpha\beta} \equiv \delta_{\alpha\beta}\sqrt{k_\alpha} \tag{4.8}$$

and

$$\omega_{\alpha\beta} \equiv \delta_{\alpha\beta}\exp(-ik_\alpha R_\alpha) \tag{4.9}$$

Relation (4.7) can then be rewritten in the matrix form:

$$(1 + iB\mathfrak{R}B)\omega = (1 - iB\mathfrak{R}B)\omega^{-1}S \tag{4.10}$$

The *solution for the scattering matrix S in terms of the derivative matrix $\mathfrak{R}$ is*

$$S = \omega\frac{1 + iB\mathfrak{R}B}{1 - iB\mathfrak{R}B}\omega \tag{4.11}$$

The physical interpretation of the terms in (4.11) is: the factors ω occur because we are going from the behavior at the nuclear surface, $r = R$, to the behavior at infinity in the channel. These factors amount to a simple change of the "reference plane" in the channel. The fraction in (4.11) can be interpreted as a specifically nuclear scattering matrix which relates the outgoing waves at the surface of the nucleus to the ingoing waves arriving at that surface. The matrix $B\mathfrak{R}B$ is a nuclear reactance matrix which is related to the nuclear scattering matrix in the same way that the reactance matrix X, (2.19), is related to the scattering matrix S. The transformation coefficients B from the derivative matrix to the reactance matrix are necessary because we have insisted on using only "interior" quantities for the definition of the derivative matrix, whereas the natural definition of the reactance matrix involves the channel velocities.

The scattering matrix S is unitary and symmetric, according to the theorems of Section 2. The nuclear scattering matrix $\omega^{-1}S\omega^{-1}$ is therefore also unitary and symmetric. Hence the nuclear reactance matrix $B\mathfrak{R}B$ is Hermitean and symmetric, i.e., real and symmetric. Thus, finally, *the derivative matrix $\mathfrak{R}_{\alpha\beta}$ is real and symmetric*. The reality of $\mathfrak{R}_{\alpha\beta}$ was a direct consequence of our use of real wave functions (standing waves) in its definition. There are $\frac{1}{2}N(N+1)$ independent real matrix elements $\mathfrak{R}_{\alpha\beta}$, and this is just the number of independent real parameters in the scattering matrix. The explicit use of the Bohr assumption would reduce this number of parameters considerably (to $2N$), but we are not using the Bohr assumption here.

The remainder of this chapter will be devoted to finding an expansion for the matrix elements of the derivative matrix as functions of the energy E of the compound nucleus. The expansion gives simple results only in the resonance region, where the levels of the compound nucleus are well separated compared to their widths.

The relation (4.11) between the scattering and derivative matrices was derived for the special case of $l = 0$ and no channel spins. The general relation between the scattering matrix and the derivative matrix is somewhat more complicated, although the essential elements of the derivation are unchanged. The general case is treated by Wigner and Eisenbud (47).

D. The Resonance Levels of the Compound Nucleus

In the definition of the real wave functions Φ_α we had to leave one "mirror" adjustable. Otherwise it would not have been possible to obtain wave functions for every energy E. Conversely, if all the mirrors are fixed, the system possesses a series of discrete states Φ_s ($s = 1,2,3,\cdots$) with definite energies E_s. The discussion in Section 7 of

Chapter VIII has shown that the wave function inside the compound nucleus region is large if the derivatives of the wave function at the various channel entrances are zero. We shall therefore *define the eigenstates of the compound nucleus*, Φ_s, *by the conditions*

$$H\Phi_s = E_s\Phi_s \qquad (4.12a)$$

$$\left[\frac{\partial(r_\alpha\Phi_s)}{\partial r_\alpha}\right]_{r_\alpha=R_\alpha} = 0 \qquad \alpha = 1,2,\cdots,N \qquad (4.12b)$$

$$\int\Phi_s{}^2\, d\tau = 1 \qquad (4.12c)$$

The first of these is the wave equation. As before, we assume that the Hamiltonian H is real, $H^*=H$. The boundary conditions (4.12b) apply to each channel entrance.[1] In terms of Fig. 4.1, these boundary conditions mean that we have put all the mirrors exactly one-quarter channel wavelength out from the channel entrance. There is no longer any adjustable mirror. Since the Hamiltonian is real (by assumption) and the boundary conditions are also real, the wave functions Φ_s are real functions everywhere. Condition (4.12c) is a normalization condition. The integral is to be taken over the "internal" (compound nucleus) region only. It is not necessary to write the normalization in terms of an absolute square of Φ_s, since Φ_s is a real function.

The eigenstates Φ_s, (4.12), form an infinite set. As the energy is increased, more and more channels open up. As soon as a channel opens up, a mirror is placed into it according to (4.12b). Hence the wave functions Φ_s form a discrete set all the way up in energy. These

---

[1] The discussion here is deliberately oversimplified for the sake of compactness and ease of understanding. We assume the "natural" boundary conditions (exponentially decreasing wave functions) in the closed channels. The decay length in a closed channel is an "exterior" quantity, so that our definition of compound states is not entirely independent of the behavior of the system in the exterior region. The strict definition of compound states used by Wigner (47) is phrased in such a way that no "exterior" quantities enter at all. The "interior" (compound nucleus) region of configuration space is enclosed by a surface in configuration space, and a boundary condition analogous to (4.12b) is required everywhere along that surface, the derivative being taken perpendicular to the surface. While this strict definition avoids the use of channel quantities such as the decay length of the wave function in a closed channel, the subsequent development of the theory becomes more difficult since the behavior of the wave function in all the closed channels must be considered explicitly, whereas we shall be able to restrict ourselves to consideration of the behavior of the wave function in the open channels. The more complete theory is needed near the threshold of a new mode of disintegration (Wigner 48).

eigenstates are *not* decaying states; rather they correspond to standing waves. We shall assume that the set Φ_s is a complete set of wave functions for the compound nucleus, so that every wave function (in particular also the function Φ_α at an arbitrary energy E) is a linear superposition of the Φ_s.[1]

The wave equation (4.12a) together with the boundary conditions (4.12b) implies that the Φ_s are orthogonal to each other:

$$\int \Phi_s \Phi_{s'} \, d\tau = 0 \qquad \text{if} \quad E_s \neq E_{s'} \tag{4.13}$$

The integral is again extended over the internal (compound nucleus) region only: all $r_\alpha \leq R_\alpha$.[2] From now on all integrals will be understood to go over the internal region only, unless stated explicitly otherwise.

E. Derivation of the Many-Level Dispersion Formula

In order to derive a compact formula for the elements $\mathcal{R}_{\alpha\beta}$ of the derivative matrix (and hence for the reaction cross sections) we shall expand the N functions Φ_α at an arbitrary energy E in terms of the infinite set Φ_s. This expansion is valid only in the internal (compound nucleus) region. There are therefore two separate steps in the development which is to follow: An expansion must be found valid in the internal region [(4.21)], and afterwards the outside behavior of the Φ_α (and in particular the elements $\mathcal{R}_{\alpha\beta}$ of the derivative matrix) must be determined by joining the wave function in the internal region smoothly onto the wave function in the external region (the channels). This joining leads to the final equation (4.22) for the derivative matrix. As a result the derivative matrix (and through it the cross sections) is expressed completely in terms of parameters connected with the various eigenstates of the compound nucleus, i.e., in terms of energy-independent real parameters.

---

[1] It may appear strange that we must describe a nuclear reaction at any one energy E by N functions Φ_α, where N is the number of open channels, whereas there is only one function, Φ_s, necessary to describe the eigenstate E_s of the compound nucleus. The discrepancy arises from the different regions of interest in the two cases. For the reaction, we are interested in the external region with its N channels. For the eigenstates, we close off the channels by mirrors in fixed positions. The number N of open channels is then irrelevant, and there is only one wave function Φ_s for each eigenstate E_s of the compound nucleus.

[2] Strictly speaking, (4.13) holds if the integral is extended not only over the internal region but also over the entire length of every *closed* channel. If the more stringent boundary conditions of Wigner (47) are used to define the compound states Φ_s (see the footnote on page 550), the orthogonality relation (4.13) holds for the integral extended over the internal region only.

In the region of configuration space corresponding to the compound nucleus, Φ_α, (4.1), at an arbitrary energy E can be written as a linear superposition of the eigenfunctions Φ_s of the compound nucleus:

$$\Phi_\alpha = \sum_{s=1}^{\infty} N_{\alpha s} \Phi_s \qquad (4.14)$$

Since the Φ_s form an orthonormal set [see (4.12c) and (4.13)], we get the usual equation for the coefficients $N_{\alpha s}$ in this expansion:[1]

$$N_{\alpha s} = \int \Phi_\alpha \Phi_s \, d\tau \qquad (4.15)$$

From the wave equations satisfied by Φ_s and by Φ_α, $H\Phi_s = E_s\Phi_s$ and $H\Phi_\alpha = E\Phi_\alpha$, respectively, we can derive an equation for the integral $N_{\alpha s}$, (4.15):

$$(E - E_s)\, N_{\alpha s} = \int (\Phi_s H\Phi_\alpha - \Phi_\alpha H\Phi_s)\, d\tau \qquad (4.16)$$

We now apply Green's theorem to simplify the right side of (4.16), by reducing the volume integral to a surface integral:

$$\int (u\,\nabla^2 v - v\,\nabla^2 u)\, d\tau = \int \left(u\frac{\partial v}{\partial n} - v\frac{\partial u}{\partial n} \right) dS \qquad (4.17)$$

The "surface" here is composite. In each channel β the integral dS extends over the surface of a sphere of radius R_β, so that $dS = R_\beta^2 \, d\Omega_\beta$ in channel β. The normal derivative $\partial u/\partial n$ is the derivative with respect to the channel coordinate r_β, at $r_\beta = R_\beta$.

In a typical channel β, near the channel entrance R_β, the Hamiltonian H can be separated into the internal energies of the residual nucleus X_β and the emerging particle a_β, and the kinetic energy of the relative motion $T_\beta = -(\hbar^2/2M_\beta)\,\nabla_\beta^2$. The internal energies make no contribution to the surface integral in (4.17). Thus we get from (4.17), after integration over the internal coordinates and over the angles in each channel, and after some slight rewriting,

$$\int (\Phi_s H\Phi_\alpha - \Phi_\alpha H\Phi_s)\, d\tau$$

$$= -4\pi \sum_\beta \frac{\hbar^2}{2M_\beta} \left[(r_\beta\phi_{s\beta}) \frac{d(r_\beta\phi_{\alpha\beta})}{dr_\beta} - (r_\beta\phi_{\alpha\beta}) \frac{d(r_\beta\phi_{s\beta})}{dr_\beta} \right]_{r_\beta = R_\beta} \qquad (4.18)$$

---

[1] The possibility of expansion (4.14) is not immediately obvious. The Φ_s have zero derivatives at all channel entrances, whereas the function Φ_α has a finite derivative at the entrance to channel α (see 4.3b). Nevertheless, expansion (4.14) is possible. It is analogous to a Fourier expansion of the function $\sin\theta$ in terms of a cosine series.

Here $\phi_{\alpha\beta}$ is the wave function for the relative motion in channel β appropriate to the total wave function Φ_α; it is defined by (4.1a). $\phi_{s\beta}$ is the corresponding wave function for the relative motion in channel β appropriate to the total wave function Φ_s. Expression (4.18) can be simplified considerably. According to the definition (4.12b) of the eigenfunctions of the compound nucleus, the derivative $d(r_\beta\phi_{s\beta})/dr_\beta$ vanishes at $r_\beta = R_\beta$. According to definition (4.3) the derivative $d(r_\beta\phi_{\alpha\beta})/dr_\beta$ at $r_\beta = R_\beta$ is zero in all channels $\beta \neq \alpha$ and equals $(M_\alpha/4\pi\hbar)^{1/2}$ in channel $\beta = \alpha$. Thus only one term survives in the sum over β, and the right side of (4.16) becomes

$$\int (\Phi_s H\Phi_\alpha - \Phi_\alpha H\Phi_s)\, d\tau = -\left(\frac{\hbar}{2}\right)^{1/2} y_{s\alpha} \qquad (4.19)$$

where the coefficient $y_{s\alpha}$ is defined by[1]

$$y_{s\alpha} \equiv \left(\frac{2\pi\hbar^2}{M_\alpha}\right)^{1/2} R_\alpha\, \phi_{s\alpha}(R_\alpha) \qquad (4.20)$$

The definition (4.20) of $y_{s\alpha}$ is made in such a way that $y_{s\alpha}$ is a parameter characteristic of the resonance state s of the compound nucleus and does not involve any external channel quantities such as the channel velocity, for example. Since (4.20) involves the size of the compound nucleus wave function at the entrance to channel α [the quantity $\phi_{s\alpha}(R_\alpha)$] about which very little is known, the $y_{s\alpha}$ are treated as adjustable parameters of the theory. There are infinitely many of these adjustable parameters, since there are infinitely many resonance levels s.

Comparison of (4.14), (4.16), and (4.19) gives the following expansion of the wave function Φ_α in terms of the eigenfunctions Φ_s of the compound nucleus:

$$\Phi_\alpha = \left(\frac{\hbar}{2}\right)^{1/2} \sum_{s=1}^{\infty} \frac{y_{s\alpha}\,\Phi_s}{E_s - E} \qquad (4.21)$$

Equation (4.21) completes the first step of the proof; we now have an expansion of the wave function Φ_α at arbitrary energy E, valid in the internal (compound nucleus) region.

We now proceed to the second step to find an expression for the derivative matrix in terms of parameters of the compound nucleus. We evaluate both sides of (4.21) at the entrance to a typical channel

---

[1] The constants $y_{s\alpha}$ are identical with the $\gamma_{\lambda s}$ of Wigner and Eisenbud; they use λ to denote resonance levels and s to denote channels.

β. Equations (4.1b) and (4.1c) show that the left side of (4.21) assumes the value $\mathfrak{R}_{\alpha\beta}(M_\beta/4\pi\hbar)^{1/2}R_\beta^{-1}\chi_\beta$ at $r_\beta = R_\beta$. According to the definition (4.20) of $y_{s\beta}$, the wave function Φ_s has the value

$$\Phi_s = y_{s\beta}\left(\frac{M_\beta}{2\pi\hbar^2}\right)^{1/2} R_\beta^{-1}\chi_\beta \qquad \text{at } r_\beta = R_\beta$$

Substitution of these values into (4.21) gives the *Wigner-Eisenbud many-level formula for the derivative matrix* $\mathfrak{R}_{\alpha\beta}(E)$:

$$\mathfrak{R}_{\alpha\beta}(E) = \sum_{s=1}^{\infty} \frac{y_{s\alpha}\, y_{s\beta}}{E_s - E} \qquad (4.22)$$

Formula (4.22) gives the energy dependence of the derivative matrix (and hence also of the cross sections) explicitly in terms of energy-independent parameters of the compound nucleus (i.e., the $y_{s\alpha}$ and E_s). It also shows immediately that the matrix $\mathfrak{R}_{\alpha\beta}$ is real and symmetric (which we have already deduced in Section 4C from the general properties of the scattering matrix).

The derivative matrix has the dimension of a length, according to (4.1c). Hence the parameters $y_{s\alpha}$ have the dimension

$$(\text{energy} \times \text{length})^{1/2}$$

We shall see later on that to a first approximation the partial width $\Gamma_\alpha{}^s$ of the compound state s for disintegration through channel α, as defined in (VIII,7.9), is equal to $2k_\alpha y_{s\alpha}{}^2$. Thus $y_{s\alpha}$ is related to the "reduced" width of Chapter VIII (VIII,7.15) through

$$\gamma_\alpha{}^s \cong \frac{y_{s\alpha}{}^2}{R_\alpha} \qquad (4.23)$$

This formula gives a good approximation only in the resonance region where the compound states are well separated compared to their widths. The parameters $y_{s\alpha}$ do not have any such simple interpretation in the continuum region, nor is expansion (4.22) useful in that region.

F. Discussion of the Many-Level Dispersion Formula

Although there are infinitely many parameters in expansion (4.22), this expansion nevertheless gives specific information about the derivative matrix $\mathcal{R}_{\alpha\beta}$ which cannot be obtained from the general theorems of Section 2.[1]   This information can be summarized as follows:

(1) The poles of $\mathcal{R}_{\alpha\beta}(E)$, i.e., the energies E_s, lie along the real axis. This need not be true for every real function of E: the poles might have come in complex conjugate pairs.

(2) The poles of every matrix element $\mathcal{R}_{\alpha\beta}(E)$ occur at the same energies E_s, i.e., the E_s are independent of α and β.   (From the general theorems we could have inferred only that the poles of $\mathcal{R}_{\alpha\beta}$ and $\mathcal{R}_{\beta\alpha}$ are at the same place.)

(3) The residues of the diagonal elements $\mathcal{R}_{\alpha\alpha}(E)$ at the pole $E = E_s$ are negative (equal to $-y_{s\alpha}{}^2$), and they are related to the residues of the off-diagonal elements $\mathcal{R}_{\alpha\beta}(E)$ at $E = E_s$ (equal to $-y_{s\alpha}y_{s\beta}$).

The third property of the derivative matrix implies that every diagonal element $\mathcal{R}_{\alpha\alpha}(E)$ has a positive derivative everywhere (except at $E = E_s$, where the derivative is not defined), i.e., $\mathcal{R}_{\alpha\alpha}(E)$ looks similar to the tangent function, with one zero between every two poles.[2]

Although these statements represent additional information about the derivative matrix (and hence about the cross sections), this information is hardly sufficient to analyze actual nuclear reactions. Expansion (4.22) is of real use only in the resonance region, where the energy dependence of all but one or two of the terms in the sum can be neglected.

According to (4.22), *the individual resonance states of the compound nucleus make additive contributions to the derivative matrix* $\mathcal{R}$.   The transformation (4.11) from the derivative matrix to the scattering matrix is non-linear.   Hence the individual resonance levels of the compound nucleus do *not* make additive contributions to the scattering matrix itself.   Rather, if two levels of the same J and parity are close together in energy, so that their widths overlap, the resulting cross section is a more complicated function of the energy than we should get from an addition of two Breit-Wigner single-level formulas, or even from the addition of the amplitudes in these formulas.

[1] Wigner (46) also derives certain statements about zeros of scattering and reaction cross sections from this formalism.   It is useful to point out, perhaps, that these statements follow directly from the conservation and reciprocity theorems (which determine the number of independent real parameters in the scattering matrix) without recourse to any more special considerations.

[2] This statement can be generalized to read: the form $\displaystyle\sum_{\alpha}\sum_{\beta} c_\alpha \, \mathcal{R}_{\alpha\beta}(E) \, c_\beta$, with c_α arbitrary real numbers, has a positive derivative with respect to E everywhere where the derivative is defined.   In addition property (3) implies certain inequalities for higher derivatives (see Wigner 47).

Earlier derivations (Bethe 37, 37a; Breit 36b) of the dispersion formula for nuclear reactions were based on an (invalid) application of perturbation theory. In a treatment which considers the possibility of a reaction a small perturbation of the wave function of the incident beam, the nuclear reactance matrix $B\mathfrak{R}B$ is small, in the sense that $(1 - iB\mathfrak{R}B)^{-1}$ can be approximated by $1 + iB\mathfrak{R}B$. Then the scattering matrix S is approximately (from 4.11)

$$S \cong \omega \, (1 + 2iB\mathfrak{R}B) \, \omega \qquad \text{(perturbation theory)} \qquad (4.24)$$

To the extent that this approximation is valid the resonance levels of the compound nucleus make additive contributions not only to the derivative matrix $\mathfrak{R}$, but also to the scattering matrix S. There is good reason to believe, however, that the application of perturbation theory to nuclear reactions in the energy region considered here is not valid, and that the individual resonance levels of the compound nucleus do *not* contribute additively to the scattering matrix.

The sum (4.22) cannot always be estimated by taking a few terms only. A particularly striking example is given by Wigner and Eisenbud: assume that there is no interaction whatsoever in the region where the particles are close together, so that all cross sections vanish. The scattering matrix S is then equal to the unit matrix, $S_{\alpha\beta} = \delta_{\alpha\beta}$. The transformation to the derivative matrix $\mathfrak{R}_{\alpha\beta}$ gives[1]

$$\mathfrak{R}_{\alpha\beta} = \delta_{\alpha\beta} \, k_\alpha \tan (k_\alpha R_\alpha) \qquad \text{(for no interaction)} \qquad (4.25)$$

Expansion (4.22) is then identical with the well-known partial fractions expansion of the tangent function. The cross sections are zero, as they should be. However, this result appears now as a cancellation of the effect of various (purely formal) "resonance levels" with the effect of the transformation (4.11) from the derivative to the scattering matrix.

The basic reason for the usefulness of the dispersion formula for nuclear reactions is to be found in the physics of the problem, not in the mathematical derivation. The physical points have already been discussed at great length in Chapter VIII. We merely recapitulate here that: (1) there is an adequate, although not entirely sharp, physical definition of the channel radius in each channel; (2) there exists a "resonance region" for nuclear reactions at low energies, in which there are well-defined physical resonances in the compound nucleus, these resonances being widely spaced in energy compared to

---

[1] We shall choose finite values of R_α, even though we could pick $R_\alpha = 0$ in this case, in order to bring out the fact that the contributions of the far-away levels can be important in the more physical cases.

their widths; and (3) it is possible to give order-of-magnitude estimates for the partial widths in the various channels at a given resonance (this is equivalent to an estimate of the parameters $y_{s\alpha}$ in the many-level dispersion formula for a given value of s).

We have already mentioned some differences in notation between this presentation of the many-level formula and the original paper by Wigner and Eisenbud (47). Without going into detail, we specify the main differences here:

(1) Channels are denoted here by $\alpha, \beta, \cdots$, whereas Wigner and Eisenbud use sets of two Latin letters l,s for each channel. Channels are called "alternatives" in that paper.

(2) Resonance levels are denoted here by the Latin letter s, whereas Wigner and Eisenbud use the Greek letter λ. The definitions of the resonance energies $E_s(=E_\lambda)$ agree. Our $y_{s\alpha}$ are their $\gamma_{\lambda l s}$.

(3) For the case of no spins, the matrices u and U of Wigner and Eisenbud are identical and are also equal to our scattering matrix $S_{\alpha\beta}$. The possibility of intrinsic spins for the particles in the various channels makes the appearance of the formulas in Wigner and Eisenbud appreciably more complicated than they would be for spinless particles.

G. The Single-Level Breit-Wigner Formula

We shall assume that only one level s contributes appreciably to the sum (4.22). This assumption is always valid over a sufficiently small range of energies E around the resonance energy E_s of this particular compound state. However, in many cases this energy range is too small to be of any practical use. The formulas based on the one-level approximation lead to physically reasonable and useful results only in the low-energy region, where the resonance levels of given angular momentum J and parity are widely spaced compared to their total widths.

Taking only one term of (4.22), we can verify by direct substitution into (4.11) that the corresponding scattering matrix $S_{\alpha\beta}$ is given by

$$S_{\alpha\beta} = \exp\left(-ik_\alpha R_\alpha\right)\left[\delta_{\alpha\beta} - 2i\,\frac{k_\alpha^{1/2}y_{s\alpha}\,k_\beta^{1/2}y_{s\beta}}{(E-E_s) + i\sum_\nu k_\nu y_{s\nu}^{\,2}}\right]\exp\left(-ik_\beta R_\beta\right)$$

$$(4.26)$$

The sum in the denominator is over all channels open at energy E. There is no sum over resonance levels, since we are considering the contribution of only one level.

Direct substitution of this $S_{\alpha\beta}$ into the cross-section formula (1.5) gives the Breit-Wigner single-level formula for the transfer cross section $\sigma_{\alpha\beta}$ ($\alpha \neq \beta$):

$$\sigma_{\alpha\beta} \;=\; \pi\, \lambdabar_\alpha{}^2 \;\frac{\Gamma_\alpha{}^s\,\Gamma_\beta{}^s}{(E-E_s)^2 + (\tfrac12\Gamma^s)^2} \tag{4.27}$$

where the partial widths $\Gamma_\alpha{}^s$ of the resonance level E_s are related to the coefficients $y_{s\alpha}$ through

$$\Gamma_\alpha{}^s \;=\; 2k_\alpha y_{s\alpha}{}^2 \tag{4.28}$$

and where the total width Γ^s of the level is, as before, the sum of all the $\Gamma_\alpha{}^s$. Equation (4.27) is in complete agreement with (VIII,7.19), which was derived in Chapter VIII, Sections 7 and 8, by a less rigorous method. Substitution of (4.26) into (1.6) for the elastic scattering cross section similarly gives the same result (VIII,7.20) which we obtained in Chapter VIII.

The proportionality of the widths $\Gamma_\alpha{}^s$ to the channel wave numbers k_α (for $l=0$ neutron channels) is a direct consequence of the dispersion formula (4.22), since the $y_{s\alpha}$ in (4.28) are compound nucleus quantities by definition, independent of the channel energy. Equation (4.28) represents the justification of the earlier interpretation (4.23) of the parameters $y_{s\alpha}$ in terms of the reduced widths $\gamma_\alpha{}^s$.

If there are barriers in some of the channels, relation (4.28) has to be supplemented by a barrier penetration factor. Relation (4.23) is unchanged. The barrier also produces a shift in energy between the "formal" resonance energy defined by (4.12) and the "actual" resonance energy which appears in the Breit-Wigner formula (see Section 8A of Chapter VIII).

We observe that the transfer cross section (4.27) can be written as a product of two factors, one of which can be interpreted as the cross section for the formation of the compound nucleus from channel α, the other as the branching probability of its disintegration into channel β:

$$\sigma_{\alpha\beta} \;=\; \left[\pi\lambdabar_\alpha{}^2\,\frac{\Gamma_\alpha{}^s\,\Gamma^s}{(E-E_s)^2 + (\tfrac12\Gamma^s)^2}\right]\cdot\left[\frac{\Gamma_\beta{}^s}{\Gamma^s}\right] \tag{4.29}$$

Thus the Bohr assumption is rigorously valid in the resonance region.

While the formal theory of nuclear reactions gives a more rigorous justification of the single-level dispersion formula than the methods of Chapter VIII, and allows us to *prove* the Bohr assumption for reactions involving widely separated resonance levels of the compound nucleus, the formal theory does not allow a simple estimate of the reduced widths $\gamma_\alpha{}^s$. We recall that the estimate (VIII,7.16), which is basic to the interpretation of data on resonance reactions, involves an "internal" quantity, namely the wave number K just *inside* the channel entrance. Hence the formal theory of reactions, which treats the internal region as a "black box," cannot possibly lead to such an estimate.

We have derived the one-level Breit Wigner formula (4.27) on the extreme assumption that the sum (4.22) can be replaced by a single term at energies E close to E_s. This assumption is actually not necessary, even though it is certainly sufficient. Wigner and Eisenbud derive a formula which is very similar in appearance to (4.27) by separating the dominant term from the sum (4.22) and approximating the remainder by an energy-independent matrix. The relation of the quantities $\Gamma_\alpha{}^s$ in (4.27) to the parameters $y_{s\alpha}$ is then different from (4.28), and there is a slight shift in the level energy due to the far-away levels, but formula (4.27) itself still applies.

Wigner (46a) has also given an explicit expression for the cross sections in the case where two resonances of the same J and parity lie close together, so that their widths overlap, but still far apart from all the other resonance levels of the same J and parity. This is a rather unusual case, and it is not clear whether any example of it exists in nature.

The reader is referred to the papers by Wigner (48, 49, 51) and Teichmann (49, 50) for further discussion of the many-level formula (4.22).

SYMBOLS

a	Particle in channel α (Section 1A)
A	Number of nucleons in the system [= mass number of the compound nucleus] (Section 1A)
$A_\alpha = A$	Coefficient of $\exp\,(-ik_\alpha r_\alpha)$ in $\psi(r_\alpha)$ (1.2)
$A_\alpha{}' = A'$	Coefficient of $\exp\,(+ik_\alpha r_\alpha)$ in $\psi(r_\alpha)$ (1.2)
$B = B_{\alpha\beta}$	A diagonal matrix with real matrix elements, defined by (4.8) (4.8)
c_β	Coefficient of Ψ_β in the expansion of $\Psi_\alpha{}^*$ (2.14)
C	Normalization constant of $\Psi_{\alpha,\,\text{in}}$ (2.2), (2.2a)
$C_{\alpha\beta}$	Coefficient in the expansion of Φ_α in terms of the Ψ_β (4.4)
$d\sigma$	Differential cross section for the (α,β) reaction (3.3)
$d\sigma_{\alpha\kappa,\beta\lambda}$	Differential cross section for the (α,β) reaction with spin directions in the incident and outgoing channels specified by κ and λ, respectively (3.19)
$d\tau$	Element of configuration space (2.1)
$d\omega$	Element of solid angle (3.3)
$\mathfrak{D}_{L,mm'}(R)$	Coefficient in the expansion of the spherical harmonic $Y_{Lm}(\omega')$ in terms of $Y_{Lm}(\omega)$, where $\omega' = \theta',\varphi'$ and

	$\omega = \theta, \varphi$ are related to each other through the rotation R (3.10)
E	Energy of the system (compound nucleus) (Section 1A)
E_s	(Formal) resonance energy of the compound (resonance) level number s (4.12a,b)
$f = f_\alpha$	Logarithmic derivative of the wave function at the entrance to the particular channel (α) through which the reaction is initiated; for its definition, see Chapter VIII, Section 2 (Section 4A)
$G_{\beta \lambda M_J}(\omega)$	Branching ratio for decay of the compound state with angular momentum J and z component of angular momentum equal to M_J, by emission through channel β with spin directions specified by λ, in the direction $\omega = \theta, \varphi$ with respect to the incident beam (3.19)
$\mathcal{G}_{\rho \rho'}(\mathsf{R})$	Coefficients determining the "reshuffling" of the spin indices under the rotation R (3.15)
H	Hamiltonian of the system (2.5)
$H_{\alpha \beta}'$	Matrix element of a perturbing Hamiltonian H' between states α and β (Section 2E)
$\mathcal{H}$	Magnetic field vector (Section 2C)
i	Spin of the target nucleus X (Section 3C)
i'	Spin of the residual nucleus Y (Section 3C)
J	Total angular momentum of the system [= angular momentum of the compound nucleus] (Section 3C)
$J_{\max}$	Maximum value of J involved in a reaction (Section 3D)
k_α, k_β	Wave number of the relative motion in channel α or β (Section 1B)
K	Wave number of the relative motion just inside a channel entrance (Section 4G)
l	Orbital angular momentum of the relative motion in a channel (Section 1C)
L	Maximum value of l effective in producing the reaction (Section 3C)
L_α, L_β	Length of the wave packet in channel α [$= v_\alpha T$] or β [$= v_\beta T$] (Section 2A)
$\mathbf{L}$	Orbital angular momentum vector operator [$= \mathbf{r} \times \mathbf{p} = -i\hbar\, \mathbf{r} \times \mathbf{\nabla}$] (Section 2C)
m	Quantum number for the z component of the orbital angular momentum (Section 3C)

M	Reduced mass for the relative motion in a channel (Section 2A)
M_α, M_β	Reduced mass for the relative motion in channel α or β (4.1c)
N	Number of energetically open channels at energy E (Section 1B)
$N_{\alpha s}$	Coefficient in the expansion of Φ_α in a series in the Φ_s (4.14)
$q(\theta)$	Reaction amplitude of the (α,β) reaction (3.2)
$q_\rho(\theta,\varphi)$	Reaction amplitude of the (α,β) reaction with spin directions specified by ρ (3.4)
$q_m(\theta,\varphi)$	Reaction amplitude corresponding to the total wave function Ψ_m (Section 3C)
$q_m(0)$	Value of $q_m(\theta,\varphi)$ at the pole of the sphere (Section 3C)
$q_{m\rho}(0)$	Value of $q_{m\rho}(\omega)$ at the pole of the sphere (3.17)
$q_{m\rho}(\omega)$	Reaction amplitude corresponding to the total wave function $\Psi_{m\rho}$ (3.17)
$\mathbf{r}_i$	Vector position of nucleon number i, $i=1,2,\cdots,A$ (Section 1A)
r_α	Channel coordinate (separation between X and a) in channel α (Section 1A)
r_β	Channel coordinate in channel β (Section 1B)
R	A rotation of the coordinate system (Section 3C)
$R_\alpha = R$	Channel radius in channel α (Section 4A)
R_α'	An alternative (larger) value of the channel radius in channel α (Section 4B)
R_β	Channel radius in channel β (Section 4B)
$\mathcal{R} = \mathcal{R}_{\alpha\beta}$	The derivative matrix (4.1a,b,c)
$\mathcal{R}_{\alpha\beta}'$	The derivative matrix for the alternative choice R_α' of the channel radii (Section 4B)
s	Spin of the incident particle a (Section 3C)
s'	Spin of the outgoing particle b (Section 3C)
S	The scattering matrix, with matrix elements $S_{\alpha\beta}$ (2.10')
S	The channel spin, formed by vector addition of s and i (Section 3B)
$S_{\alpha\beta}$	The scattering matrix (1.3a,b,c)
t	Time coordinate (2.5)
T	The time during which an incoming wave packet passes some stationary point in channel α (Section 2A)

T' The time during which the outgoing wave in channel γ can be due to both the (α,γ) and the (β,γ) reactions (2.8)

T_β Operator for the kinetic energy of the relative motion in channel β (Section 4E)

U A unitary matrix which does not depend on time explicitly   (2.12)

$U_{\alpha\beta}$ $= S_{\alpha\beta}$; this notation is used by Wigner and Eisenbud (Wigner 47)   (Section 1C)

v_α Speed of the relative motion in channel α (1.2)

v_β Speed of the relative motion in channel β (Section 1B)

X The residual nucleus in channel α [= the target nucleus]   (Section 1A)

$\mathcal{X}$ The reactance matrix   (2.19)

$y_{s\alpha}$ A coefficient appearing in the many-level formula; it is related to the reduced width of resonance level number s in channel α (4.20)

Y The residual nucleus in the $X(a,b)Y$ reaction   (Section 3A)

α Channel index   (Section 1A)

$-\alpha$ Channel index for the time-reversed channel of channel α (Section 2D)

β Channel index   (Section 1A)

γ Channel index   (Section 1A)

$\gamma_\alpha{}^s$ Reduced partial width of resonance level number s for decay through channel α; for its definition see Chapter VIII, Section 7   (4.23)

Γ^s Total width of resonance level number s $\left[= \sum_\alpha \Gamma_\alpha{}^s \right]$ (4.27)

$\Gamma_\alpha{}^s, \Gamma_\beta{}^s$ Partial width of resonance level number s for decay through channel α or β (4.27), (4.28)

$\delta_{\alpha\beta}$ Kronecker delta [$= 1$ if $\alpha = \beta$, $= 0$ otherwise]   (1.7)

$\Delta\theta$ Uncertainty in the measurement of angle θ (Section 3C)

ϵ_α Kinetic energy of relative motion in channel α (Section 1A)

η_0 $= S_{\alpha\alpha}$; η_0 is the symbol used for this quantity in Chapter VIII, Section 2   (Section 1C)

θ The angle between the direction of the emergent particle and the incident beam, in the (α,β) reaction (Section 3A)

κ Index specifying the spin directions in the incident channel α (Section 3D)

λ Index specifying the spin directions in the outgoing channel β (Section 3D)

λ_α de Broglie wavelength of the relative motion in channel α, divided by 2π $[=(k_\alpha)^{-1}]$ (Section 1C)

Π Parity of the relative motion in a channel (3.6)

ρ Index specifying the spin directions of a, X, b, and Y in the X(a,b)Y reaction (Section 3C)

$\boldsymbol{\sigma}$ Pauli spin vector, with components σ_x, σ_y, and σ_z (Section 2C)

$\sigma_C(\alpha\kappa)$ Cross section for formation of the compound nucleus through channel α with spin directions specified by κ (3.19)

σ_r Reaction cross section for S wave ($l=0$) collisions (1.8), (1.9)

$\sigma_{sc,0}$ $=\sigma_{\alpha\alpha}$; this symbol was used in Chapter VIII, Section 2 (1.6)

$\sigma_x, \sigma_y, \sigma_z$ The Pauli spin matrices; for their definition see Appendix A, Section 4 (Section 2C)

$\sigma_{\alpha\alpha}$ Elastic scattering cross section in channel α, for S wave ($l=0$) particles (1.6)

$\sigma_{\alpha\beta}$ Cross section for the (α,β) reaction with S wave ($l=0$) particles (1.5)

φ Azimuthal angle (3.4)

$\phi_{\alpha\beta}(r_\beta)$ Wave function for the relative motion in channel β corresponding to the total wave function Φ_α (4.1a)

$\phi_{s\beta}$ Wave function for the relative motion in channel β corresponding to the total wave function Φ_s (Section 4E)

Φ_m Wave function of the same form as Ψ_m, in the new (rotated) coordinate system (Section 3C)

$\Phi_{m\rho}$ Wave function of the same form as $\Psi_{m\rho}$, in the new (rotated) coordinate system (3.15)

Φ_s Wave function for resonant state number s of the compound nucleus (4.12a,b,c)

Φ_α Basic wave function for standing waves; it has non-zero derivative in channel α, vanishing derivatives in all other channels (4.1a,b,c), (4.3a,b)

χ_α Internal wave function in channel α [= the wave

	function of X in state α' times the wave function of a in state α''] (1.1)
χ_β	Internal wave function in channel β [= the wave function of Y in state β' times the wave function of b in state β''] (1.3a)
$\psi = \psi(r_\alpha)$	Wave function for the relative motion in channel α (1.1), (1.2)
$\psi_{\alpha\alpha}(r_\alpha)$	Wave function for the relative motion in channel α corresponding to the total wave function Ψ_α (1.3c)
$\psi_{\alpha\beta}(r_\beta)$	Wave function for the relative motion in channel β corresponding to the total wave function Ψ_α (1.3b)
Ψ_j^1	Wave function of the system (1.1)
Ψ_α	Basic wave function for traveling waves; it has incoming and outgoing waves in channel α, but has only outgoing waves in all other channels (1.3a,b,c)
$\Psi_{\alpha,\,\text{in}}$	Incoming wave in channel α (2.2)
$\Psi_{\alpha,\,\text{out through }\beta}$	Wave function for the part of the wave emerging through channel β (2.3)
Ψ_β	Basic wave function for traveling waves, defined analogously to Ψ_α (Section 2B)
Ψ_m	Total wave function corresponding to an incoming wave with orbital angular momentum L and z component m (Section 3C)
$\Psi_{m\rho}$	Total wave function corresponding to an incoming wave with orbital angular momentum L and z component m, with spin directions specified by ρ (Section 3C)
Ψ^{rev}	Wave function of the time-reversed state (2.13)
ω	Position on the unit sphere, a shorthand notation for the two angles θ and φ (Section 3C)
$\omega = \omega_{\alpha\beta}$	A diagonal matrix with matrix elements of absolute value unity, defined by (4.9) (4.9)

CHAPTER XI

Spontaneous Decay of Nuclei

1. ENERGETIC CONSIDERATIONS

Heavy nuclei, in general, are dynamically unstable. Energy is gained by breaking the nucleus into two parts. However, the parts are held together by very strong forces. It is only because of the quantum-mechanical leakage through potential barriers that some of the heavy nuclei actually do decay into parts. For most of the known heavy nuclei the decay time is so long that no decay has ever been observed.

The dynamic instability of heavy nuclei can be shown by means of the semi-empirical Weizsäcker formula for nuclear energies which was discussed in Chapter VI (VI,2.6). According to this expression any beta-stable nucleus with $A > 85$ is unstable against splitting into two roughly equal parts, since the sum of the energy of the two nuclei $(\frac{1}{2}Z, \frac{1}{2}A)$ is less than the energy of (Z,A).[1] The splitting off of an alpha-particle is energetically favorable for nuclei above $A \cong 191$. The first type of split is called fission, the second alpha-decay.

In order to perform these splits the nucleus must pass through intermediate states whose energy is much higher than the energy of the initial and final stages. This can be seen in the following way: Let us reverse the splitting process by considering two nuclei (Z_1, A_1) and (Z_2, A_2) which are brought together from infinite distance until they merge into the nucleus with $Z = Z_1 + Z_2$, $A = A_1 + A_2$. The potential energy $V(r)$ as a function of the distance of their centers of mass is plotted schematically in Fig. 1.1. As the zero of the energy scale we assume the energy of the two separated nuclei at rest. As long as $r > R \equiv R_1 + R_2$ (R_1 and R_2 are the radii of the two nuclei), the only source of potential energy is the electrostatic repulsion. Hence $V(r) = Z_1 Z_2 e^2 / r$ for $r > R$. For distances r smaller than R the attractive nuclear forces contribute to $V(r)$, and we expect a sharp drop. [It is no longer possible to define $V(r)$ uniquely, since the

---

[1] Throughout this section, we use the abbreviation (Z,A) for a nucleus X with charge Z and mass number A.

potential energy depends on the special conditions under which the merging of the two nuclei take place.] The maximum of the potential energy is therefore near $V(R) = Z_1 Z_2 e^2 / R$. This value is always larger than the difference ΔE between the energy of the nucleus (Z,A) and the sum of the energies of (Z_1, A_1) and (Z_2, A_2). We obtain, for example, in the case of fission into two halves of an Au nucleus $\Delta E = 132$

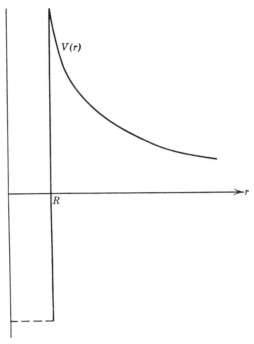

FIG. 1.1. Potential energy of two nuclei as a function of their distance (schematic). $V(r)$ is not well defined for $r < R$.

Mev, whereas $V(R) = 173$ Mev. The alpha-decay of Ra^{126} gives $\Delta E = 4.88$ Mev and $V(R) = 25.7$ Mev. For the very heaviest nuclei, ΔE of the fission split becomes almost equal to $V(R)$. This is why in these nuclei a small excitation, by means of neutron capture or otherwise, can induce fission of the compound nucleus.

The decay of the nucleus (Z,A) can take place only if the potential energy barrier at $r = R$ is overcome. This can be achieved by supplying the necessary energy in the course of a nuclear reaction as in the case of induced fission. An excited compound nucleus is created by bombardment of a target nucleus with nuclear particles of sufficient energy that the excitation energy of the compound nucleus is high enough to overcome the potential barrier. However, this is not the only way. In this chapter we shall consider the spontaneous decay of nuclei in their ground states. The potential barrier is then overcome by means of the quantum-mechanical penetration through potential barriers (Gamow 28, 28a; Gurney 28; Condon 29). The probability of this quantum effect decreases rapidly with increasing mass of the penetrating particle. Hence spontaneous fission is a very rare process, whereas the spontaneous emission of an alpha-particle is a fairly frequent process. We therefore restrict the present considerations to alpha-decay, although the same formalism can be applied to spontaneous fission also.

The energy ϵ_α of the alpha-particle[1] emitted by the "parent" nucleus (Z,A) can be estimated by using the semi-empirical formula (VI,2.6) for the ground-state energies $E(Z,A)$. Assuming that the parent nucleus, and the daughter nucleus $(Z-2, A-4)$, are in their ground states before and after emission, we get

$$\epsilon_\alpha(Z,A) = E(Z,A) - E(Z-2, A-4) + B_\alpha \tag{1.1}$$

where $B_\alpha = 28$ Mev is the binding energy of the alpha-particle. We then get from (VI,2.6), under the assumption $Z \gg 1$ and $A \gg 1$,

$$\epsilon_\alpha(Z,A) = -4u_v - 16u_\tau T_\zeta^2 A^{-2} + 16u_c Z A^{-1/3} - \tfrac{16}{3}u_c Z^2 A^{-4/3}$$
$$+ \tfrac{8}{3}u_s A^{-1/3} + B_\alpha \tag{1.2}$$

The Weizsäcker semi-empirical formula is only an approximation, and we do not expect accurate results from (1.2) after inserting the values (VI,2.12) of the constants. We get for example, for the energy of the alpha-particles emitted by $_{88}\text{Ra}^{224}$, $\epsilon_\alpha = 4.7$ Mev, whereas the actual value is 5.8 Mev.

Formula (1.2) can be used, however, to determine the general trend of the alpha-energies. We determine, for example, the dependence of ϵ_α on the neutron number N of the parent nucleus when Z is kept constant:

$$\left(\frac{\partial \epsilon_\alpha}{\partial N}\right)_z \cong \epsilon_\alpha(Z,A) - \epsilon_\alpha(Z, A-1)$$
$$\cong -16u_\tau T_\zeta A^{-2}\left(1 - \frac{2T_\zeta}{A}\right) - \frac{16}{3}u_c\left(1 - \frac{4}{3}\frac{Z}{A}\right)ZA^{-4/3}$$
$$- \frac{8}{9}u_s A^{-4/3} \tag{1.3}$$

---

[1] ϵ_α is the kinetic energy in the center-of-gravity system and is equal to the Q value of the reaction $(Z,A) = (Z-2, A-4) + \alpha$.

This is a negative number for all values of Z and A. It is of the order
of -0.3 Mev in the region of radioactive nuclei. Hence the alpha-
energy decreases by about that amount when the neutron number of
the parent nucleus is increased by one unit. This tendency is clearly
found in nature. Figure 1.2 shows a graph of the alpha-particle
energies as a function of the mass numbers. The points corresponding

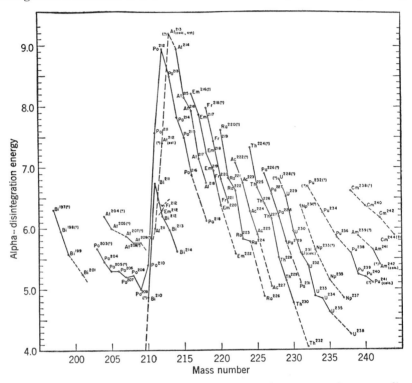

Fig. 1.2. Alpha-decay energies vs. mass number of the parent nucleus, according
to Perlman, Ghiorso, and Seaborg (50).

to equal Z are connected. It is interesting to note that the expected
behavior occurs only for $A > 213$ and for $A < 209$. There is a characteristic break in between which is related to the occurrence of the
"magic" neutron and proton numbers 126 and 82 (Glueckauf 48,
Pryce 50). This will be discussed in Chapter XIV.

2. GENERAL THEORY OF ALPHA-DECAY

The ground state of an alpha-unstable nucleus can be compared
with the state of a compound nucleus in a nuclear reaction; both states
decay by the emission of a particle. We apply the same methods to

the quantum-mechanical description of alpha-decay which we used in Chapter VIII for the description of the decaying compound states.

We first describe the decay in the qualitative terms which were introduced in Chapter VIII, Section 7. The probability $\Gamma_\alpha/\hbar$ per unit time of the emission of an alpha-particle can be written as a product similar to (VIII,7.12):

$$\Gamma_\alpha = \hbar\omega_0\, \mathsf{T}(\alpha) \tag{2.1}$$

where ω_0 is the number of "attempts" per second of the alpha-particle to penetrate through the surface of the nucleus into the outside, and $\mathsf{T}(\alpha)$ is the transmission coefficient of the potential barrier. Because of the periodic character of the motion in a bound state we have identified the time $P = \omega_0^{-1}$ with the classical period of the motion. The use of classical concepts for the description of the ground state or of very low-lying excited states is much less justified than the use of these concepts in the highly excited states of the compound nucleus. Therefore the conclusions drawn are qualitative to a much larger degree than the corresponding conclusions in Chapter VIII. We can use relation (VIII,7.10) between the period and the level distance only as a very rough indication of the orders of magnitude involved (Cohen 50):

$$\omega_0 = P^{-1} \sim \frac{D}{2\pi\hbar} \tag{2.2}$$

where D is the level distance between levels of the same type (angular momentum and parity). $\mathsf{T}(\alpha)$ is the transmission coefficient of a potential barrier of the form shown in Fig. 1.1. The coordinate r used in this figure is the distance between the center of the residual (daughter) nucleus X and the center of the emitted alpha-particle. This coordinate is identical with the "channel coordinate" of Chapter VIII. The channel radius R corresponds to the distance at which the interaction between the alpha-particle and the residual nucleus X becomes small compared to their Coulomb repulsion. The relation between the channel radius R and the individual radii of the nucleus X and the alpha-particle will be discussed later.

In our qualitative picture we assume that the alpha-particle starts out from the interior of the (compound) nucleus with a certain kinetic energy E. It approaches the barrier at $r = R$ from the inside and may or may not pass through the barrier. If it does pass through the barrier, it has the kinetic energy ϵ_α far away (for $r \to \infty$). In this schematic picture we can replace the conditions inside the compound nucleus by a constant potential $V(r) = \epsilon_\alpha - E$ for $r \leq R$. The transmission coefficient under these conditions was determined in Chapter VIII, Section 5. It is given by (VIII,5.5). The wave number K in this formula corresponds to the kinetic energy inside: $K^2 = 2M_\alpha E/\hbar^2$. The magnitudes s_l and Δ_l are defined in terms of the behavior of the wave function in the outside region by (VIII,2.48), (VIII,2.47), and (VIII,2.50). l is the orbital angular momentum of the emerging alpha-particle (in units of $\hbar$).

In the formula for the transmission coefficient $T_l(\alpha)$ (VIII,5.5) we can neglect s_l compared to KR to get

$$T_l(\alpha) \cong \frac{4s_l KR}{(KR)^2 + \Delta_l^2} \qquad (2.3)$$

The decay probability $\Gamma_\alpha/\hbar$ of the compound state into the alpha-channel can then be written

$$\frac{\Gamma_\alpha}{\hbar} = \omega_0 \frac{4s_l KR}{(KR)^2 + \Delta_l^2} \qquad (2.4)$$

In this formula the conditions in the interior of the parent (compound) nucleus enter through ω_0 and KR; the quantities s_l and Δ_l depend on outside conditions and on the value of the channel radius R. Only very crude approximations are available for the "inside" quantities ω_0 and K. We shall adopt the estimate (2.2) for ω_0, and we shall use the value

$$K \sim 1 \times 10^{13} \text{ cm}^{-1} \qquad (2.5)$$

This value corresponds to a kinetic energy of the alpha-particle inside the compound nucleus of the order of 5 Mev. Some of the considerations which enter into that estimate were given in Chapter VIII, Section 5.

The decay probability (2.4) depends very strongly on the energy ϵ_α of the alpha-particle after it emerges from the parent (compound) nucleus. The energy ϵ_α is much less than the height of the barrier (Z = charge of the *residual* nucleus):

$$\text{Barrier height} = \frac{2Ze^2}{R} + \frac{l(l+1)\hbar^2}{2M_\alpha R^2} \equiv V_B \qquad (2.6)$$

Under these conditions s_l is an extremely rapidly varying function of ϵ_α, approaching zero rapidly as ϵ_α approaches zero.

The angular momentum l of the emerging alpha-particle also influences the decay probability. Other things being equal, higher values of l imply somewhat lower decay probabilities. This can be seen from (2.6): higher values of l increase the height of the barrier. The possible values of l for the outgoing alpha-particles are determined by the conservation laws of angular momentum and parity. We shall denote the parent nucleus by C, the daughter nucleus by X (C = X + α); the angular momenta and parities of these two nuclei will be denoted by I_C, I_X and Π_C, Π_X, respectively.

In order to determine the lowest possible value of l we classify the transitions into "parity-favored" and "parity-unfavored" decays. The results are listed in Table 2.1. Parity-unfavored transitions in

TABLE 2.1

MINIMUM VALUE L OF THE ORBITAL ANGULAR MOMENTUM l OF THE ALPHA-PARTICLE IN A TRANSITION $I_C, \Pi_C \rightarrow I_X, \Pi_X$

Parity-favored: $\Pi_C \Pi_X = (-1)^{I_C - I_X}$ $l_{min} \equiv L = |I_C - I_X|$

Parity-unfavored: $\Pi_C \Pi_X = (-1)^{I_C - I_X + 1}$ $l_{min} \equiv L = |I_C - I_X| + 1$
provided that neither I_C nor I_X is zero

which either I_C or I_X or both are zero are absolutely forbidden by the conservation laws.

Alpha-decays involving the ground states of even-even nuclei are presumably parity-favored, with $I_C = I_X = 0$. It is interesting to observe that these decays would be completely forbidden if the parity conditions were unfavorable, i.e., if $\Pi_C = -\Pi_X$. No such case has been found in the natural alpha-emitters. The energetically possible alpha-decays between even-even nuclei with predicted lifetimes [from (2.4)] within the range accessible to experiment are all observed experimentally. *This is a strong argument for the assumption that all even-even nuclei have not merely zero angular momentum I, but also have the same (even) parity Π.*

Expression (2.4) with the estimate (2.2) for ω_0 implies that the alpha-width Γ_α is proportional to the level distance D of the decaying (compound) nucleus near the level that undergoes the decay. This dependence is an expression of the fact that the probability of an alpha-particle appearing at the nuclear surface ready to leave (with the residual particles already arranged into the proper wave function of the residual nucleus X) depends on the dynamics of the nuclear motion in the lowest states of the compound system. If this motion is very simple, both the level distance D and the alpha-width Γ_α are high; if the motion is complicated, both are low. It must be kept in mind that relation (2.2) is extremely crude and does not take into account any special features of the decaying levels. We must expect that there are levels for which the probability of formation of an alpha-particle at the surface is quite different from (2.2).

So far we have used the qualitative arguments of Section 7 of Chapter VIII. We shall now show that the more quantitative methods of Section 9 of that chapter lead to the same results. The parent nucleus in alpha-decay is in a "decaying state" of the type introduced in that section. We can therefore use the analysis of that section directly. The energy W of the decaying state is complex:

$$W = E_s - \tfrac{1}{2}i\Gamma_\alpha \tag{2.7}$$

The real part of W gives the mean energy E_s of the decaying state; the imaginary part contains the alpha-width Γ_α which determines the decay probability, $\Gamma_\alpha/\hbar$. The decaying state is defined by the boundary condition (VIII,9.18) upon the logarithmic derivative $f_l(E)$ at the channel radius R. The alpha-width Γ_α is then given by (VIII,9.20) and (VIII,9.22):

$$\Gamma_\alpha = -2s_l \left[\left(\frac{df_l}{dE} \right)_s \right]^{-1} \tag{2.8}$$

where s_l and the derivative $(df_l/dE)_s$ are evaluated at the real energy E_s which appears in (2.7).[1]

The energy E_s in (2.7) is determined in turn by the condition

$$f_l(E_s) = \Delta_l(E_s) \tag{2.9}$$

This E_s corresponds to the $E_s + \delta E_s$ of (VIII,9.23).

Equations (2.8) and (2.9) cannot be used until some estimate is made of $f_l(E)$. We shall use the same estimate which appeared in the theory of resonance reactions in Chapter VIII, namely

$$f_l(E) \cong -KR \tan z(E) \tag{2.10}$$

and

$$\frac{dz}{dE} \cong \frac{\pi}{D} \tag{2.11}$$

where D is the distance between levels of the same angular momentum and parity.

We need the derivative df_l/dE to evaluate the width Γ_α, (2.8). We neglect the variation of K with energy to get

$$\frac{df_l}{dE} \cong -\frac{\pi KR}{D} \left[1 + \left(\frac{f_l}{KR} \right)^2 \right] \tag{2.12}$$

---

[1] This point is the only difference between the present considerations and those in Section 9 of Chapter VIII. There we made an additional approximation by evaluating s_l and df_l/dE at the "formal" resonance energy for which $f_l(E) = 0$. This is a poor approximation in alpha-decay, since Δ_l, which determines the difference between the "formal" and "actual" resonance energies, is large for energies considerably below the barrier energy.

This value is substituted into (2.8), and (2.9) is used to determine f_l.[1] The result is

$$\Gamma_\alpha \cong \frac{4s_l KR}{(KR)^2 + \Delta_l^2} \frac{D}{2\pi} = T_l(\alpha) \frac{D}{2\pi} \qquad (2.13)$$

Hence the more quantitative treatment of alpha-decay leads to the same result, (2.2) and (2.4), as the earlier qualitative considerations.

The functions s_l and Δ_l in (2.13) must be determined from the solutions of the wave equation in the "outside" (channel) region. It can be shown (Devaney 50) that the W. K. B. approximations to these quantities are satisfactory in the relevant region. The W.K.B. approximation to the penetration coefficient $T_l(\alpha)$, (2.3), is

$$T_l(\alpha) \cong \frac{4K \kappa_l(R)}{K^2 + [\kappa_l(R) + \frac{1}{2}\kappa_l'(R)/\kappa_l(R)]^2} \exp\left[-2 \int_R^{r_0} \kappa_l(r)\, dr\right] \qquad (2.14)$$

where

$$\kappa_l^2(r) \equiv \frac{l(l+1)}{r^2} + \frac{2M_\alpha}{\hbar^2} \frac{2Ze^2}{r} - \frac{2M_\alpha \epsilon_\alpha}{\hbar^2} \qquad (2.15)$$

$\kappa_l'(r)$ is the derivative of $\kappa_l(r)$ in respect to r and r_0 is defined by

$$\kappa_l(r_0) \equiv 0 \qquad (2.16)$$

The exponential in (2.14) is the function introduced by Gamow (28) and Kudar (29). The integral is extended over the region in which the potential barrier is larger than the kinetic energy of the alpha-particle. This is the region into which the alpha-particle could not penetrate if classical mechanics were valid. The Gamow function is a very sensitive function of the energy ϵ_α.

Finally we discuss the significance of the channel radius R which appears in these formulas. This radius cannot be defined very accurately since the "surface of the compound nucleus" is not infinitely sharp. The significance of the channel radius is illustrated in Fig. 2.1. The theory replaces the actual potential energy in its dependence on r by a fictitious one which drops sharply at $r = R$. R is chosen in such a way that the fictitious potential gives the same lifetime as the actual potential. The distance R' at which the actual potential starts deviating from the "outside" behavior should be the sum of the radii of the residual nucleus X and the alpha-particle:

$$R' = R_X + R_\alpha \qquad (2.17)$$

[1] In Section 9 of Chapter VIII we determined f_l at the "formal" resonance energy, i.e., we put $f_l(E_s) = 0$.

The radius of the alpha-particle can be estimated from the scattering of neutrons on alpha-particles and from theoretical considerations (see Chapter V). R_α is probably near 2×10^{-13} cm.

R' is larger than the channel radius R. We therefore write

$$R = R_X + \rho_\alpha \qquad (2.18)$$

where ρ_α is an "effective" radius of the alpha-particle which is less than the actual radius R_α of this particle.

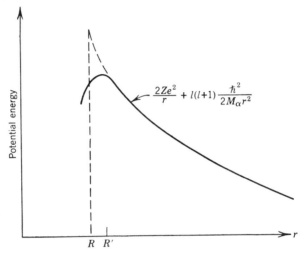

Fig. 2.1. The solid curve shows the actual potential between a nucleus X and an alpha-particle (schematic). The broken curve is the fictitious potential appearing in the alpha-decay theory. The channel radius R is not equal to the distance R' at which the potential energy first deviates from its behavior in the "outside" region. Z is the atomic number of the residual (daughter) nucleus.

The choice of a value of ρ_α for the calculations is somewhat arbitrary, since neither R nor R_X can be defined closer than to within about 0.5×10^{-13} cm. We have made the choice

$$\rho_\alpha = 1.2 \times 10^{-13} \text{ cm} \qquad (2.19)$$

In a few cases (Pb and Bi) R is known from alpha-decay measurements, and R_X is known from neutron measurements (see Chapter IX for the latter). The experimental values are not in disagreement with (2.18) and (2.19).

3. DISCUSSION OF EXPERIMENTAL DATA

According to the theoretical results of the previous section, the probability of the emission of an alpha-particle is an extremely sensi-

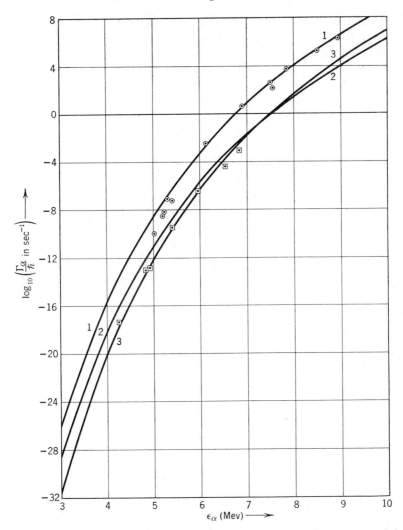

Fig. 3.1. Plot of the emission probability Γ_α as a function of the energy ϵ_α of the alpha-particle. The curves are computed from the theory as follows: curve 1: $Z_{\text{daughter}} = 82$, $R = 9.3 \times 10^{-13}$ cm; curve 2: $Z_{\text{daughter}} = 82$, $R = 7.9 \times 10^{-13}$ cm; curve 3: $Z_{\text{daughter}} = 90$, $R = 9.6 \times 10^{-13}$ cm. In all curves $D = 0.5$ Mev and $K = 10^{13}$ cm^{-1}. The points on the figure correspond to the observed emission probabilities: circles for $Z_{\text{daughter}} = 82$, squares for $Z_{\text{daughter}} = 90$.

tive function of the energy ϵ_α of the alpha-particle. This is illustrated
in Fig. 3.1, where Γ_α is plotted as function of ϵ_α for different nuclei.
A change of energy by one Mev gives rise to a change of Γ_α of about
10^5. This sensitivity makes it possible to apply an expression like
(2.4) for the prediction of experimental values, in spite of the fact
that some of the factors such as ω_0 are known only to within an order of
magnitude. An estimate of only the order of magnitude of Γ_α is
valuable since the range of possible values extends over about 16

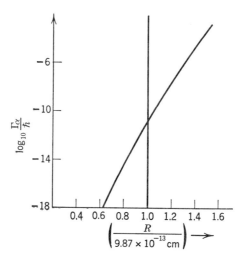

FIG. 3.2. The alpha-emission probability as function of the radius R for
$Z_{\text{daughter}} = 86$, $\epsilon_\alpha = 4.88$ Mev. The ordinate is $\log_{10}(\Gamma_\alpha/\hbar)$, where $\Gamma_\alpha/\hbar$ is
expressed in $\sec^{-1}$.

powers of ten. Although Γ_α depends strongly on the charge Z of
the residual (daughter) nucleus and the channel radius R, the general
trend of the dependence on ϵ_α is the same for all values of Z and R of
importance for naturally radioactive nuclei. The relation between the
logarithm of Γ_α and the energy can be roughly approximated by a
linear law, $\log\Gamma_\alpha \cong a+b\epsilon_\alpha$, or somewhat better by a law of the form
$\log\Gamma_\alpha \cong a-b\epsilon_\alpha^{-1/2}$ (Biswas 49). These relations are usually referred
to as the Geiger-Nuttal law, and they were first found empirically.
It was considered a great success of nuclear theory when Gamow
(28, 28a) was able to explain theoretically the order of magnitude of
the constants involved.

From the observed lifetime $\hbar/\Gamma_\alpha$ of the alpha-decay we can determine some of the constants which appear in the theoretical formula,
(2.4) or (2.13). The most important of these parameters is the channel

radius R. The theoretical value of Γ_α is very sensitive to the value of R. This is shown in Fig. 3.2 for a characteristic example. An increase of the channel radius R by 1×10^{-13} cm (by roughly 10 percent) increases the decay probability by a factor of about 150 for an alpha-energy $\epsilon_\alpha = 5$ Mev. Hence the channel radius R can be determined from the observed Γ_α and ϵ_α with considerable accuracy, in spite of the fact that ω_0 and KR in (2.4) are known only very approximately.

Compared to the sensitive dependence of Γ_α on ϵ_α and R, the dependence on the angular momentum l of the emitted alpha-particle is relatively insignificant. The centrifugal term in (2.6) is small compared to the Coulomb term for low values of l; the ratio of the two is

$$\frac{\text{Centrifugal barrier}}{\text{Coulomb barrier}} = l(l+1)\frac{1.80}{ZR} \tag{3.1}$$

where R is expressed in 10^{-13} cm. For reasonable values, $R \cong 9 \times 10^{-13}$ cm and $Z \cong 85$, this becomes $0.0024\, l(l+1)$, which is completely negligible for $l \leq 4$. The ratio of the two potentials is even smaller for larger values of r, since the centrifugal potential is proportional to r^{-2} whereas the Coulomb potential is proportional to r^{-1}.

Table 3.1 shows the relative values of Γ_α for different values of l,

TABLE 3.1

RATIO OF THE ALPHA-EMISSION PROBABILITY $\Gamma_\alpha(l)$ OF AN ALPHA-PARTICLE WITH AN ANGULAR MOMENTUM l TO THE EMISSION PROBABILITY WITH $l=0$, COMPUTED FOR $Z_{\text{daughter}} = 86$, $R = 9.87 \times 10^{-13}$ cm, $\epsilon_\alpha = 4.88$ MEV

l	$\dfrac{\Gamma_\alpha(l)}{\Gamma_\alpha(0)}$
0	1
1	0.7
2	0.37
3	0.137
4	0.037
5	7.1×10^{-3}
6	1.1×10^{-3}

for $Z = 86$ and $R = 9.87 \times 10^{-13}$ cm. The changes of Γ_α from one value of l to the next are small compared to the inaccuracy of the theoretical estimate (2.2). The theory presented here does not predict any significant difference in alpha-decay lifetimes for values of l differing by as much as 3 units in some cases; for example, Table 3.1 shows that

TABLE 3.2

DETERMINATION OF THE RADII OF ALPHA-UNSTABLE NUCLEI

The first column lists the parent nucleus, the second the daughter nucleus. The symbol $_{83}\mathrm{Bi}^{212}_{129}$ refers to the isotope of Bi $(Z=83)$ of mass number $A=212$ and neutron number $N=A-Z=129$. The next column gives the observed lifetime (s = second, m = minute, h = hour, d = day, y = year). The fourth column gives the alpha-energy in Mev. The fifth column contains a rough estimate of the level distance D near the ground state of the parent nucleus. The channel radius R was computed from these data by using formulas (2.13) to (2.16). The radius R_X in the next-to-last column is the radius of the residual (daughter) nucleus X and was computed from formulas (2.18) and (2.19). The last column shows how closely these radii approximate the simple law $R_X = r_0 A^{1/3}$.

Parent	Daughter	Half-Life	Alpha-energy (eMv)	D (Mev)	R $(10^{-13}$ cm)	R_X $(10^{-13}$ cm)	$r_0 = R_X A^{-1/3}$ $(10^{-13}$ cm)
$_{83}\mathrm{Bi}^{212}_{129}$	$_{81}\mathrm{Tl}^{208}_{127}$	11h	6.20	0.06	8.0	6.8	1.14
$_{83}\mathrm{Bi}^{214}_{131}$	$_{81}\mathrm{Tl}^{210}_{129}$	76d	5.61	0.06	9.2	8.0	1.34
$_{84}\mathrm{Po}^{210}_{126}$	$_{82}\mathrm{Pb}^{206}_{124}$	138.3d	5.40	0.8	8.4	7.2	1.21
$_{84}\mathrm{Po}^{212}_{128}$	$_{82}\mathrm{Pb}^{208}_{126}$	3.0×10^{-7}s	8.95	0.7	9.0	7.8	1.31
$_{84}\mathrm{Po}^{214}_{130}$	$_{82}\mathrm{Pb}^{210}_{128}$	1.5×10^{-4}s	7.83	0.6	9.3	8.1	1.35
$_{84}\mathrm{Po}^{215}_{131}$	$_{82}\mathrm{Pb}^{211}_{129}$	1.8×10^{-3}s	7.50	0.2	9.5	8.3	1.40
$_{84}\mathrm{Po}^{216}_{132}$	$_{82}\mathrm{Pb}^{212}_{130}$	0.158s	6.89	0.5	9.3	8.1	1.35
$_{84}\mathrm{Po}^{218}_{134}$	$_{82}\mathrm{Pb}^{214}_{132}$	$3.05m$	6.12	0.4	9.6	8.4	1.40
$_{85}\mathrm{At}^{215}_{130}$	$_{83}\mathrm{Bi}^{211}_{128}$	10^{-4}s	8.15	0.2	9.3	8.1	1.35
$_{86}\mathrm{Em}^{219}_{133}$	$_{84}\mathrm{Po}^{215}_{131}$	4.7s	6.94	0.03	9.6	8.4	1.39
$_{86}\mathrm{Em}^{220}_{134}$	$_{84}\mathrm{Po}^{216}_{132}$	54.5s	6.39	0.25	9.7	8.5	1.40
$_{86}\mathrm{Em}^{222}_{136}$	$_{84}\mathrm{Po}^{218}_{134}$	3.83d	5.59	0.19	9.7	8.5	1.40
$_{88}\mathrm{Ra}^{223}_{135}$	$_{86}\mathrm{Em}^{219}_{133}$	20.2d	5.82	0.3	9.7	8.5	1.40
$_{88}\mathrm{Ra}^{224}_{136}$	$_{86}\mathrm{Em}^{220}_{134}$	3.8d	5.78	0.08	9.8	8.6	1.42
$_{88}\mathrm{Ra}^{226}_{138}$	$_{86}\mathrm{Em}^{222}_{136}$	1700y	4.88	0.07	9.9	8.7	1.44
$_{89}\mathrm{Ac}^{227}_{138}$	$_{87}\mathrm{Fr}^{223}_{136}$	1810y	5.04	0.06	9.6	8.4	1.39
$_{90}\mathrm{Th}^{227}_{137}$	$_{88}\mathrm{Ra}^{223}_{135}$	93d	6.16	0.04	8.8	7.6	1.26
$_{90}\mathrm{Th}^{228}_{138}$	$_{88}\mathrm{Ra}^{224}_{136}$	2.64y	5.52	0.4	9.5	8.3	1.36
$_{90}\mathrm{Th}^{230}_{140}$	$_{88}\mathrm{Ra}^{226}_{138}$	1×10^5y	4.76	0.5	9.5	8.3	1.36
$_{90}\mathrm{Th}^{232}_{142}$	$_{88}\mathrm{Ra}^{228}_{140}$	1.39×10^{10}y	4.05	0.5	9.8	8.6	1.43
$_{92}\mathrm{U}^{234}_{142}$	$_{90}\mathrm{Th}^{230}_{140}$	2.35×10^5y	4.84	0.8	9.5	8.3	1.35
$_{92}\mathrm{U}^{238}_{146}$	$_{90}\mathrm{Th}^{234}_{144}$	4.51×10^9y	4.25	0.73	9.6	8.4	1.36

the lifetimes for alpha-decay with $l=0,1,2$, and 3 are equal to each other within the likely error of the estimate (2.2).

Table 3.2 collects the relevant data of a number of alpha-emitting nuclei. Only natural alpha-emitters are included. The material in Table 3.2 is taken from a study by Devaney (50).[1] The most important result of this table is the list of channel radii R determined from the natural lifetimes and energies, under the assumption $l=0$ (which, we have just seen, makes very little difference). The radii R_X of the residual (daughter) nuclei, as determined from (2.18) and (2.19), are also listed in Table 3.2. These radii conform surprisingly well to the rule

$$R_X = r_0 A^{1/3} \qquad (3.2)$$

where r_0 is a constant close to 1.4×10^{-13} cm.

There are a few characteristic exceptions to this rule. The radii of Tl^{208} and Pl^{206} appear to be unusually small. These small values are probably spurious and are due to strong deviations of the actual ω_0 in (2.4) from its estimated value (2.2). The parent (compound) nuclei may be especially unsuited for emission of alpha-particles. This would make the characteristic frequency ω_0 very much smaller than the estimate (2.2), leading to a spuriously low value of the channel radius R if (2.2) is used. These deviations from the rule (3.2) are probably connected with the fact that the parent (compound) nuclei in these cases are one nucleon richer, and the daughter nuclei one nucleon poorer, than a "magic" number of nucleons. (See Chapter XIV.)

SYMBOLS

a	Constant appearing in the Geiger-Nuttal law (Section 3)
A	Mass number of a nucleus (parent nucleus in alpha-decay or fission) (Section 1)
A_1	Mass number of a nuclear fragment (Section 1)
A_2	Mass number of a nuclear fragment (Section 1)
b	Constant appearing in the Geiger-Nuttal law (Section 3)
B_α	Binding energy of the alpha-particle $[=28$ Mev] (1.1)
D	Level distance in the compound (parent) nucleus, between levels of the same angular momentum and parity (2.2)

[1] Similar studies were made by Perlman (50) and Kaplan (51).

e	Charge on the proton (Section 1)
E	Kinetic energy of the alpha-particle inside the compound (parent) nucleus (Section 2)
E	Excitation energy in the compound (parent) nucleus (Section 2)
E_s	Real part of W [= mean energy of the decaying state] (2.7)
$E(Z,A)$	Ground-state energy of the nucleus (Z,A) [= the negative of its binding energy] (1.1)
$f_l(E)$	Logarithmic derivative of the radial wave function at the channel entrance; for its definition see Chapter VIII, Section 2 (Section 2)
I	Angular momentum of a nucleus (Section 2)
I_C	Angular momentum of the compound (parent) nucleus (Section 2)
I_X	Angular momentum of the residual (daughter) nucleus (Section 2)
K	Wave number of the alpha-particle inside the compound (parent) nucleus (Section 2)
l	Orbital angular momentum of the emitted alpha-particle (Section 2)
$L = l_{min}$	Minimum value of l consistent with I_C, I_X, Π_C, and Π_X (Section 2)
M_α	Reduced mass for the relative motion of the alpha-particle and the residual (daughter) nucleus [$\cong$ mass of the alpha-particle] (Section 2)
N	Number of neutrons in the compound (parent) nucleus (Section 1)
P	$= \omega_0^{-1}$; the classical period of motion of the compound nucleus (Section 2)
r	Channel coordinate [= the separation between the two nuclear fragments in the breakup of the compound (parent) nucleus] (Section 1)
r_0	Classical distance of closest approach of an alpha-particle to the residual nucleus (2.16)
r_0	Constant appearing in the nuclear radius formula $R = r_0 A^{1/3}$ (3.2)
R	Channel radius for the disintegration $[= R_1 + R_2]$ (Section 1)
R_1	Radius of the nuclear fragment (Z_1, A_1) (Section 1)
R_2	Radius of the nuclear fragment (Z_2, A_2) (Section 1)
R'	Distance at which the nuclear forces between the alpha-

	particle and the residual (daughter) nucleus become active (2.17)
s_l	A function related to the penetration factor; for its definition see Chapter VIII, Section 2 (2.3)
T_ζ	Neutron excess $[=\tfrac{1}{2}(N-Z)=\tfrac{1}{2}A-Z]$ (1.2)
$\mathsf{T}(\alpha)=\mathsf{T}_l(\alpha)$	Transmission coefficient of the barrier for alpha-particles of orbital angular momentum l; for a discussion see Chapter VIII, Section 5 (2.1), (2.3)
u_c	Coefficient of the Coulomb energy term in the Weizsäcker semi-empirical mass formula; see Chapter VI, Section 2 (1.2)
u_s	Coefficient of the surface energy term in the Weizsäcker semi-empirical mass formula; see Chapter VI, Section 2 (1.2)
u_v	Coefficient of the volume energy term in the Weizsäcker semi-empirical mass formula: see Chapter VI, Section 2 (1.2)
u_τ	Coefficient of the symmetry energy term in the Weizsäcker semi-empirical mass formula; see Chapter VI, Section 2 (1.2)
V_B	Height of the potential barrier for emission of alpha-particles of orbital angular momentum l (2.6)
$V(r)$	Potential energy of the two nuclear fragments (Z_1,A_1) and (Z_2,A_2) a distance r apart from each other (Section 1)
W	Complex energy of a decaying state: for discussion see Chapter VIII, Section 9 (2.7)
X	The residual (daughter) nucleus in alpha-decay (Section 2)
$z(E)$	A smoothly increasing function of the excitation energy E of the compound nucleus, assumed to be a linear function of E (2.10), (2.11)
Z	Number of protons in the decaying (parent) nucleus (Section 1)
Z	Number of protons in the residual (daughter) nucleus X (Sections 2, 3)
Z_1	Number of protons in a nuclear fragment (Section 1)
Z_2	Number of protons in a nuclear fragment (Section 1)
(Z,A)	A nucleus with charge Z and mass number A (Section 1)
Γ_α	Width of the compound (parent) state for emission of

-                      alpha-particles; $\Gamma_\alpha/\hbar$ is the probability per unit time of
                       alpha-particle emission   (2.1)

δE_s "Level shift" of a decaying state; see Chapter VIII,
                       Section 9   (Section 2)

ΔE Energy release (Q value) in the breakup $(Z,A) \to (Z_1,A_1)$
                       $+ (Z_2,A_2)$ (Section 1)

Δ_l A function related to the penetration factor; for its
                       definition see Chapter VIII, Section 2   (2.3)

ϵ_α $= \epsilon_\alpha(Z,A)$; energy of the alpha-particle emitted by the
                       parent (compound) nucleus (Z,A) [= the Q value of
                       the reaction $(Z,A) = (Z-2, A-4) + \alpha$]   (1.1)

$\kappa_l(r)$ A function, of the dimension of a wave number, entering
                       into the W. K. B. approximation to the penetration
                       factor   (2.14), (2.15)

Π Parity of a nucleus   (Section 2)

Π_C Parity of the compound (parent) nucleus   (Section 2)

Π_X Parity of the residual (daughter) nucleus   (Section 2)

ρ_α Effective radius of the alpha-particle for alpha-decay,
                       assumed to be 1.2×10^{-13} cm   (2.18), (2.19)

ω_0 Frequency of "attempts" of the alpha-particle to
                       penetrate through the surface of the compound (parent)
                       nucleus   (2.1), (2.2)

CHAPTER XII

Interaction of Nuclei
with Electromagnetic Radiation

1. INTRODUCTION

In the development of atomic physics the interaction of atoms with electromagnetic radiation has been of paramount importance for the understanding of atomic structure. In the case of nuclei, this interaction has not been so important a tool, since, unlike the atomic case, the wavelengths of interest are so short that they cannot be measured by the usual optical devices. The rather indirect methods which must be employed make the energy determination quite inaccurate compared to spectroscopic standards, and the available resolution low. Furthermore in most cases the radiation process is only one of many competing processes (such as particle emission or sometimes even beta-decay) and its probability is correspondingly lower.

For these reasons the study of gamma-rays from nuclei has remained on a rather rudimentary level. The theoretical analysis of the data has usually gone only as far as a general classification of the possible gamma-ray transitions, rough estimates of their lifetimes, and comparison with the available experimental data. There is one distinct exception to this statement: the interaction of electromagnetic radiation with the nuclear two-body systems. There the relevant matrix elements can be calculated more accurately.

Section 2 contains an introduction to the classification of the emitted radiation into multipole types and a discussion of the selection rules for transitions of the various types. Section 3 contains the transition probabilities, the details of the derivations for both Sections 2 and 3 being relegated to Appendix B. These results are applied in Section 4 to the interaction of light with the nuclear two-body systems: the photodisintegration of the deuteron, and its inverse process, the radiative capture of neutrons by protons. The information from these processes checks and supplements our knowledge of the neutron-proton forces from neutron-proton scattering and from the ground state of the deuteron. Section 5 is devoted to the non-radiative de-excitation of nuclei, the so-called internal conversion process. Sections 6 and 7 contain an outline of the theory of isomeric states of nuclei, of radiative capture, and of the nuclear photoeffect. The division there is between transitions involving low-lying nuclear levels (less than a few Mev excitation energy) and transitions involving more highly excited states.

2. MULTIPOLE RADIATION AND SELECTION RULES

A. Multipole Radiation

A complete description of the emission and absorption of light by a quantum-mechanical system such as the nucleus requires the quantum theory of radiation. However, considerable information can be obtained from a study of the classical radiation field emitted by a distribution of charges and currents which vary with time. We consider the case where the source of the radiation is confined to a volume of space small compared to the wavelength of the emitted light. This is true for most electromagnetic radiation which emerges from nuclei: even for a quantum energy $\hbar\omega = 10$ Mev, the wavelength of the light is still of order $\lambdabar = \lambda/2\pi \cong 2 \times 10^{-12}$ cm; most nuclear radiations are of lower energy than that.

It is extremely useful to classify the emitted radiation according to the angular momentum l which is carried by each quantum,[1] and according to its properties under reflection of the coordinates (under the parity operation). It is shown in Appendix B that the angular momentum l of the radiation is determined by the same type of quantum numbers l, m as the angular momentum of a particle; in particular: $l_z = m$, $|l|^2 = l(l+1)$. We shall see that the probability of a radiative transition decreases rapidly as l increases; hence in practice only the one or two lowest values of l consistent with conservation of angular momentum as a whole need to be considered.

For each value of the angular momentum l of the light wave two different waves are possible, the "electric" and the "magnetic" radiation. The need for two types of radiation can be explained as follows: consider a spherical outgoing wave which is emitted by a current distribution near the origin. Since the Maxwell equation for the magnetic field $\mathfrak{IC}$ alone [obtained by eliminating $\mathcal{E}$ from the usual Maxwell equations; see (B,4.2a)] is unchanged by a change of sign of the coordinates, we conclude that we can divide $\mathfrak{IC}(\mathbf{r})$ into an

---

[1] The angular momentum is measured in units of $\hbar$.

even part and an odd part, each of which is separately a solution of the Maxwell equation for $\mathcal{H}$:

Even parity wave: $\mathcal{H}(-\mathbf{r}) = +\mathcal{H}(\mathbf{r})$

Odd parity wave: $\mathcal{H}(-\mathbf{r}) = -\mathcal{H}(\mathbf{r})$

$$(2.1)$$

We shall now show that the parity of $\mathcal{H}$ determines the parity of $\mathcal{E}$. The Maxwell equation (in free space, for a periodically varying field) for $\mathcal{E}$ is

$$-i\omega\mathcal{E} = c \,\text{curl}\, \mathcal{H} \qquad (2.2)$$

It is apparent from (2.2) that an even parity $\mathcal{H}(\mathbf{r})$ leads to an odd parity $\mathcal{E}(\mathbf{r})$, and vice versa. The reason for the choice of $\mathcal{H}$ rather than $\mathcal{E}$ to define the parity of the radiation will become apparent later on.

The opposite parity of $\mathcal{E}$ and $\mathcal{H}$ has the following consequence: consider the Poynting vector $\mathbf{S}$:

$$\mathbf{S} \equiv \frac{c}{4\pi}\, \mathcal{E} \times \mathcal{H} \qquad (2.3)$$

This vector describes the flow of energy in the light wave. Since either $\mathcal{E}$ or $\mathcal{H}$ (but not both) changes sign as $\mathbf{r}$ goes into $-\mathbf{r}$, the direction of $\mathbf{S}$ is reversed. In particular, for an outgoing wave, $\mathbf{S}$ points outward (in the direction of increasing $|\mathbf{r}|$), both at $\mathbf{r}$ and at $-\mathbf{r}$.

The expressions for the electric and magnetic fields in multipole radiation are derived in Appendix B. We quote the results here. We write the field $\mathcal{E}(\mathbf{r},t)$ in the form[1]

$$\mathcal{E}(\mathbf{r},t) = \mathcal{E}(\mathbf{r})\, e^{-i\omega t} + \mathcal{E}^*(\mathbf{r})\, e^{+i\omega t} \qquad (2.4)$$

with a corresponding definition for $\mathcal{H}(\mathbf{r},t)$. The restriction to fields which vary with time according to a definite frequency $\nu = \omega/2\pi$ is convenient and does not lead to any loss of generality. We shall need the differential operator $\mathbf{L}$ and the vector spherical harmonics $\mathbf{X}_{lm}(\theta,\phi)$, defined by

$$\mathbf{L} = -i\,\mathbf{r}\times\nabla \qquad \mathbf{X}_{lm}(\theta,\phi) = \frac{\mathbf{L}\,Y_{lm}(\theta,\phi)}{\sqrt{l(l+1)}} \qquad (2.5)$$

Here Y_{lm} is the usual (scalar) spherical harmonic defined in Appendix A; vector spherical harmonics are discussed in Appendix B. We shall use the symbol κ for the wave number of the emitted light:

[1] This differs from the conventional formulation by a factor of 2. Definition (2.4) makes the transitions to the quantum-mechanical case easier.

$$\kappa = \frac{\omega}{c} = \frac{2\pi\nu}{c} \tag{2.6}$$

We shall also use the functions $u_l^{(+)}(r)$ which were defined in Chapter VIII (VIII,2.32, VIII,2.36, and VIII,2.41 for neutrons) and which represent outgoing waves. In terms of these quantities we now write the *defining expressions* for electric and magnetic multipole radiation of order l,m *outside the source* of the radiation.

The *electric multipole field of order l,m* at the point $\mathbf{r} = r,\theta,\phi$ is given by

$$\boldsymbol{\mathcal{E}}_E(l,m\,;\mathbf{r}) = \frac{i}{\kappa}\,\text{curl}\left[\frac{u_l^{(+)}(r)}{\kappa r}\,\mathbf{X}_{lm}(\theta,\phi)\right]$$

$$\boldsymbol{\mathcal{H}}_E(l,m\,;\mathbf{r}) = \frac{u_l^{(+)}(r)}{\kappa r}\,\mathbf{X}_{lm}(\theta,\phi) \tag{2.7}$$

and the *magnetic multipole field of order l,m* is

$$\boldsymbol{\mathcal{E}}_M(l,m\,;\mathbf{r}) = \frac{u_l^{(+)}(r)}{\kappa r}\,\mathbf{X}_{lm}(\theta,\phi)$$

$$\boldsymbol{\mathcal{H}}_M(l,m\,;\mathbf{r}) = -\frac{i}{\kappa}\,\text{curl}\left[\frac{u_l^{(+)}(r)}{\kappa r}\,\mathbf{X}_{lm}(\theta,\phi)\right] \tag{2.8}$$

The electric multipole fields have non-vanishing radial components of $\boldsymbol{\mathcal{E}}$, and the magnetic multipole fields have non-vanishing radial components of $\boldsymbol{\mathcal{H}}$. The angular momentum carried by one quantum of multipole radiation is $\hbar l$, with z component $\hbar m$. Electric and magnetic multipole radiation of order l,m carry the same angular momentum but differ through their parity. Using the definition (2.1) of the parity, we get

$$\text{Parity of electric multipole } l,m = (-1)^l$$

$$\text{Parity of magnetic multipole } l,m = -(-1)^l \tag{2.9}$$

Thus the parity carried away by electric radiation of order l is the same as the parity carried away in emission of a particle with orbital angular momentum l.

It is apparent from (2.5), (2.7), and (2.8) that the multipole fields of order $l=0$ vanish identically. This is a consequence of the transverse (divergence-free) nature of a light wave in free space.

The radiation fields (2.7) and (2.8) can be multiplied with arbitrary amplitudes. The normalization which we have chosen here is convenient for our purposes, and we consider (2.7) and (2.8) our fundamental fields in the following sense. The electric and magnetic multipole fields form a complete set; any arbitrary field $\mathcal{E}(\mathbf{r})$, $\mathcal{H}(\mathbf{r})$ which obeys the free-space Maxwell equations can be expanded in terms of multipoles:

$$\mathcal{E}(\mathbf{r}) = \sum_{l=1}^{\infty} \sum_{m=-l}^{l} a_E(l,m) \, \mathcal{E}_E(l,m;\mathbf{r}) + a_M(l,m) \, \mathcal{E}_M(l,m;\mathbf{r})$$

$$\mathcal{H}(\mathbf{r}) = \sum_{l=1}^{\infty} \sum_{m=-l}^{l} a_E(l,m) \, \mathcal{H}_E(l,m;\mathbf{r}) + a_M(l,m) \, \mathcal{H}_M(l,m;\mathbf{r})$$

(2.10)

The coefficients $a_E(l,m)$ and $a_M(l,m)$ determine the amplitude of the corresponding multipole radiation and depend on the source of the radiation. The relation between the source of the radiation (the nucleus) and these amplitudes will be investigated in the following section. Meanwhile, however, we can use symmetry considerations to draw some general conclusions about the possible radiative transitions of a nucleus.

B. Selection Rules

We have stated before (and proved in Appendix B) that one quantum of multipole radiation l,m carries with it an angular momentum l with z component m (both measured in units of $\hbar$). If this quantum is emitted by a nucleus in going from the state ψ_a to the state ψ_b, the over-all angular momentum of the system must stay constant during the transition. Thus we must have

$$\mathbf{J}_a = \mathbf{J}_b + \mathbf{l} \tag{2.11}$$

where the vector sum is to be understood in terms of the usual vector addition of angular momenta in quantum mechanics. That is, multipole radiation l,m can be emitted in a transition between two nuclear states ψ_a and ψ_b only if

$$|J_a - J_b| \leq l \leq J_a + J_b \tag{2.12}$$

$$M_a - M_b = m \tag{2.13}$$

where J_a and M_a are the angular momentum and its z component in the nuclear state ψ_a.

Since there does not exist any multipole radiation with $l=0$, relation (2.12) implies that *radiative transitions between two states with angular momentum $J_a = J_b = 0$ are absolutely forbidden*. We shall discuss in Section 5 an alternative mechanism by which the nucleus can transfer its excitation energy to the outside.

In addition to the angular momentum selection rules, (2.12) and (2.13), there are additional selection rules arising from the conservation of parity. The transition probability T_{ab} between the states ψ_a and ψ_b is proportional to the matrix element H'_{ab}:

$$H'_{ab} = \tfrac{1}{2}\int \psi_b{}^* \, (\mathbf{j}\cdot\mathbf{A}) \, \psi_a \, d\tau \qquad (2.14)$$

where $\mathbf{j}$ is the current operator and $\mathbf{A}$ is the vector potential of the emitted radiation. The vector potential $\mathbf{A}$ is proportional to the electric field $\mathbf{\varepsilon}$ in a light wave of definite frequency. Hence $\mathbf{A}$ has the same parity as $\mathbf{\varepsilon}$. The current operator $\mathbf{j}$ has parity -1, since it is an ordinary (polar) vector and hence changes sign under a reflection of the coordinates.[1] The parity of $(\mathbf{j}\cdot\mathbf{A})$ therefore is the opposite of the parity of $\mathbf{\varepsilon}$; since $\mathbf{\varepsilon}$ and $\mathcal{3C}$ always have opposite parity in multipole radiation [see (2.1) to (2.3)], we conclude that $(\mathbf{j}\cdot\mathbf{A})$ has the same parity as the magnetic field in the emitted wave. This was the reason for using $\mathcal{3C}$ in the parity classification (2.1).

The matrix element H'_{ab}, and with it the *transition probability* T_{ab}, *vanishes unless*

$$\begin{aligned} \Pi_a &= \Pi_b \quad &\text{for ``even'' parity radiation} \\ \Pi_a &= -\Pi_b \quad &\text{for ``odd'' parity radiation} \end{aligned} \qquad (2.15)$$

where Π_a and Π_b are the parities of the initial and final states ψ_a and ψ_b, respectively. The parities of the various multipole radiations are given in (2.9). For example, the emission of electric dipole radiation $(l=1)$ is connected with a change of parity of the nucleus, while the emission of magnetic dipole radiation is possible only if the parity does not change.

In atoms the only selection rule of importance is the one for electric dipole emission, i.e., for the emission of the "electric" multipole wave with $l=1$. From (2.12), (2.13), and (2.15) we get the selection rules: $\Delta J = 0, \pm 1$ (but no $0 \to 0$ transitions); $\Delta M = 0, \pm 1$; and opposite parities for the initial and final states. These are indeed the selection rules in atomic radiation.

We shall prove in the next section that the probability of multipole emission decreases rapidly with increasing l. It is of interest, therefore, to find the lowest possible value of l which is consistent with a transition from state ψ_a with angular momentum J_a and parity Π_a to

---

[1] More precisely: because the operator for $\mathbf{j}$ anti-commutes with the parity operator Π: $\mathbf{j}\Pi = -\Pi\mathbf{j}$.

state ψ_b with angular momentum J_b and parity Π_b. Selection rules (2.12) and (2.15) give the results presented in Table 2.1. The need for special consideration of the transitions with $J_a = J_b$ arises from the fact that there are no $l = 0$ multipoles.

TABLE 2.1

The Lowest Order $l_{\min} = L$ of Multipole Radiation in a Transition from J_a,Π_a to J_b,Π_b

(A) $J_a \neq J_b$

	Electric Radiation	Magnetic Radiation
Parity-favored $\Pi_a\Pi_b = (-1)^{J_a - J_b}$	$L = \|J_a - J_b\|$	$L = \|J_a - J_b\| + 1$ except J_a or $J_b = 0$
Parity-unfavored $\Pi_a\Pi_b = (-1)^{J_a - J_b + 1}$	$L = \|J_a - J_b\| + 1$ except J_a or $J_b = 0$	$L = \|J_a - J_b\|$

(B) $J_a = J_b \neq 0$

	Electric Radiation	Magnetic Radiation
$\Pi_a = \Pi_b$	$L = 2$ except $J_a = J_b = \frac{1}{2}$	$L = 1$
$\Pi_a = -\Pi_b$	$L = 1$	$L = 2$ except $J_a = J_b = \frac{1}{2}$

The probabilities of multipole emission will be estimated in Section 6. It turns out that, for the same value of l, emission of electric radiation is much more probable than emission of magnetic radiation. Hence the radiation in the parity-favored case is practically pure electric multipole radiation of order $L = |J_a - J_b|$. The magnetic radiation is weaker, both because it is magnetic and because it needs a higher multipole order. On the other hand, these two effects work against each other in parity-unfavored transitions. Hence we must make closer estimates of the transition probabilities in these transitions, and it may turn out that in some cases the electric and magnetic radiations are of the same order of magnitude. In most cases, however, we expect predominantly magnetic radiation in parity-unfavored transitions.

The $J_a = J_b$ transitions form an exception to this rule. There the $\Pi_a = -\Pi_b$ transitions are practically pure electric (dipole) radiation, whereas the $\Pi_a = \Pi_b$ transitions are in general expected to be practically pure magnetic (dipole) radiation.

3. THE PROBABILITY OF MULTIPOLE EMISSION AND ABSORPTION

A. The Source of the Field

So far we have treated multipole radiation outside the region which produces that radiation, i.e., in free space. We now need the connection between the coefficients $a_E(l,m)$ and $a_M(l,m)$ in (2.10) and the properties of the source which produces this multipole radiation.

Let us first consider as our source a classical system of currents which vary periodically with time:

$$\mathbf{j}(\mathbf{r},t) = \mathbf{j}(\mathbf{r}) \, e^{-i\omega t} + \mathbf{j}^*(\mathbf{r}) \, e^{+i\omega t} \tag{3.1}$$

This distribution of currents is confined to a small region of space of linear dimensions d. The charge density associated with this current distribution is

$$\rho(\mathbf{r},t) = \rho(\mathbf{r}) \, e^{-i\omega t} + \rho^*(\mathbf{r}) \, e^{+i\omega t} \tag{3.2}$$

and the continuity equation requires that

$$i\omega \, \rho(\mathbf{r}) = \text{div } \mathbf{j}(\mathbf{r}) \tag{3.3}$$

The multipole radiation produced by this system of charges and currents is derived in Appendix B. We merely quote the results here. The amplitude of the electric radiation of order l,m is given by[1]

$$a_E(l,m) = -\frac{4\pi}{(2l+1)!!}\left(\frac{l+1}{l}\right)^{1/2}\kappa^{l+2} \, Q_{lm} \tag{3.4}$$

where Q_{lm}, the "electric multipole moment of order l,m," is given by the following approximate expression for long wavelengths ($\kappa d \ll 1$):

$$Q_{lm} = \int r^l \, Y_{lm}^*(\theta,\phi) \, \rho(\mathbf{r}) \, dV \tag{3.5}$$

The integration in (3.5) extends over the entire volume occupied by the charge distribution $\rho(\mathbf{r})$.

It is also shown in Appendix B that the amplitude of the magnetic radiation of order l,m is given by[2]

$$a_M(l,m) = +\frac{4\pi}{(2l+1)!!}\left(\frac{l+1}{l}\right)^{1/2}\kappa^{l+2} \, M_{lm} \tag{3.6}$$

---

[1] The "double factorial" used here is defined by

$$(2l+1)!! \equiv 1 \times 3 \times 5 \times \cdots \times (2l+1)$$

[2] The choice of opposite signs in (3.4) and (3.6) was made so that the multipole moments $Q_{1,0}$ and $M_{1,0}$ have physically reasonable signs [see (3.11) and (3.12)].

where M_{lm}, the "magnetic multipole moment of order l,m," is for long wavelengths given by

$$M_{lm} = - \int r^l \, Y_{lm}{}^*(\theta,\phi) \, \frac{\operatorname{div}(\mathbf{r} \times \mathbf{j})}{c(l+1)} \, dV \qquad (3.7)$$

For later application to radiation emitted from nuclei, it is important to note that a periodic (in time) distribution of charges and currents is not the only possible source of radiation. In view of the intrinsic magnetic moments associated with the spins of the nucleons we must also consider the classical analogue of the radiation from this source, namely radiation emitted by a periodically varying density of magnetization $\mathbf{M}(\mathbf{r},t)$:

$$\mathbf{M}(\mathbf{r},t) \equiv \mathbf{M}(\mathbf{r}) \, e^{-i\omega t} + \mathbf{M}^*(\mathbf{r}) \, e^{+i\omega t} \qquad (3.8)$$

The radiation caused by such a distribution of magnetization is also derived in Appendix B. We quote the result: The electric multipole radiation is given by (3.4) provided that we replace Q_{lm} by Q'_{lm}:

$$Q'_{lm} = - \frac{i\kappa}{l+1} \int r^l \, Y_{lm}{}^*(\theta,\phi) \, \operatorname{div}(\mathbf{r} \times \mathbf{M}) \, dV \qquad (3.9)$$

The magnetic multipole radiation is given by (3.6) provided that we replace M_{lm} by M'_{lm}:

$$M'_{lm} = - \int r^l \, Y_{lm}{}^*(\theta,\phi) \, \operatorname{div} \mathbf{M} \, dV \qquad (3.10)$$

The formulas become relatively simple for the special case of dipole emission. We consider first the expressions for the electric and magnetic dipole moments due to a system of currents $\mathbf{j}(\mathbf{r})$ and charges $\rho(\mathbf{r})$. We shall consider the case where the radiation is emitted with $m = 0$.[1] We then obtain from (3.5) the electric dipole moment

$$Q_{1,0} = \left(\frac{3}{4\pi}\right)^{1/2} \int z \, \rho(\mathbf{r}) \, dV \qquad (3.11)$$

The corresponding magnetic dipole moment is given by (3.7). We can simplify the resulting expression through an integration by parts and obtain:

$$M_{1,0} = \left(\frac{3}{4\pi}\right)^{1/2} \frac{1}{2c} \int (xj_y - yj_x) \, dV \qquad (3.12)$$

---

[1] This is actually the general case, since the other two values of m, $m = \pm 1$, are related by a rotation of coordinates.

By comparing (3.11) and (3.12) we see that the magnetic dipole radiation is weaker than the electric dipole radiation; the current density j is of order $v\rho$, where v is the speed of motion of the charges. Hence a_M is smaller than a_E by a factor of the order of the magnitude v/c. Although we have derived this result only for the dipole radiation, it is true for all multipoles. For the same multipole order l, the intensity of the magnetic radiation is smaller than the intensity of the electric radiation by a considerable factor, which will be estimated in Section 6. It should be emphasized, however, that these rough order-of-magnitude estimates can be modified considerably in special cases by selection rules and other effects.[1]

---

[1] It is sometimes asserted that the ratio $M_{1,0}/Q_{1,0}$ between the magnetic and the electric dipole moment is of the order of κd where d is a length of the order of magnitude of the dimensions of the radiating system. This seems to follow from this argument: The energy radiated per second is proportional to the square of the expression

$$\frac{1}{c} \int (\mathbf{s}\cdot\mathbf{j}) \exp{(i\mathbf{\kappa}\cdot\mathbf{r})} \, dV$$

where $\mathbf{s}$ is the polarization vector and $\mathbf{\kappa}$ is the wave vector of the emitted light and $\exp{(i\mathbf{\kappa}\cdot\mathbf{r})}$ is the retardation factor. When the latter is expanded in a power series

$$\exp{(i\mathbf{\kappa}\cdot\mathbf{r})} = 1 + i(\mathbf{\kappa}\cdot\mathbf{r}) + \cdots$$

the first term of this expansion gives rise to the electric dipole radiation, whereas the second term gives rise to both the magnetic dipole and the electric quadrupole radiation. Hence the intensities of the latter two are smaller than the intensity of the electric dipole radiation by a factor of the order of $(\kappa d)^2$. This argument is wrong. The electric dipole term can be written

$$\frac{1}{c} \int (\mathbf{s}\cdot\mathbf{j}) \, dV = -i\kappa e \int (\mathbf{s}\cdot\mathbf{r}) \, dV$$

since the current $\mathbf{j}$ is the charge e times the time derivative of the displacement $\mathbf{r}$. Thus the electric dipole term is of the order of $e\kappa d$. The term $i(\mathbf{\kappa}\cdot\mathbf{r})$ in the expansion of the exponential gives rise to the following integral (using the notation $\mathbf{n} = \mathbf{\kappa}/\kappa$ for the unit vector in the direction of propagation)

$$\frac{i}{c} \int (\mathbf{s}\cdot\mathbf{j}) \, (\mathbf{\kappa}\cdot\mathbf{r}) \, dV = i\kappa \, (\mathbf{n}\times\mathbf{s}) \cdot \int \frac{\mathbf{r}\times\mathbf{j}}{2c} \, dV + e\kappa^2 \sum_{i,k=1}^{3} s_i n_k \int r_i r_k \, dV$$

The first term on the right side is the magnetic dipole term, which is multiplied by κ just like the electric dipole term (*not* by κ^2). Its order of magnitude is $(\kappa d)(ev/c)$. The second expression is the electric quadrupole term. It is of the order of $e(\kappa d)^2$.

The dipole moments resulting from a distribution of magnetization **M** can be written in the following simple forms, which are obtained by integration by parts from (3.9) and (3.10):

$$M'_{1,0} = \left(\frac{3}{4\pi}\right)^{1/2} \int M_z \, dV \qquad Q'_{1,0} = \left(\frac{3}{4\pi}\right)^{1/2} \frac{i\kappa}{2} \int (\mathbf{r} \times \mathbf{M})_z \, dV$$

B. The Energy Emitted per Second, and Its Angular Distribution

The flow of energy in the multipole radiation is determined by the Poynting vector **S** defined by (2.3). Far away from the source of the radiation, in the "wave zone," $\mathcal{E}$ and $\mathcal{H}$ are perpendicular to each other and to the radial direction **r**, and they are equal in magnitude.[1] Hence in the wave zone we have

$$|\mathbf{S}| \cong \frac{c}{4\pi} \mathcal{E}^2 \cong \frac{c}{4\pi} \mathcal{H}^2 \tag{3.13}$$

Let us draw a large sphere of radius R around the radiating system. At any point of the sphere, $|\mathbf{S}|$ gives the energy escaping per square centimeter per second. We get the energy emitted into the solid angle element $d\Omega$ around the direction θ, ϕ by multiplication of $|\mathbf{S}|$ by the area $R^2 \, d\Omega$ subtended by that solid angle at the surface of our sphere. We call this rate of emission of energy $U(\Omega) \, d\Omega$.

The squares $\mathcal{E}^2$ and $\mathcal{H}^2$ which appear in (3.13) are rapidly varying functions of time. We are interested in their average values. Using (2.4) we get

$$\langle \mathcal{E}^2(\mathbf{r},t) \rangle_{\mathrm{av}} = 2 \, \mathcal{E}^*(\mathbf{r}) \cdot \mathcal{E}(\mathbf{r}) \tag{3.14}$$

and a corresponding equation for the average of $\mathcal{H}^2(\mathbf{r},t)$.

The energy $U_E(l,m;\Omega) \, d\Omega$ in a pure electric multipole radiation l,m with amplitude $a_E(l,m)$, emitted per second into the solid angle element $d\Omega$, can be found from (2.7) (preferably the second of the two equations), (3.13), and (3.14). The result is

$$U_E(l,m;\Omega) = \frac{c}{2\pi\kappa^2} Z_{lm}(\theta,\phi) \, |a_E(l,m)|^2 \tag{3.15}$$

where the angular distribution function $Z_{lm}(\theta,\phi)$ is defined by[2]

---

[1] These statements are only approximately correct, even in the wave zone. The lack of complete transversality of $\mathcal{E}$ and $\mathcal{H}$ in the wave zone is essential for the discussion of the angular momentum carried by the wave.

[2] This angular distribution applies to pure multipole radiation l,m. If the source emits different multipole radiations with comparable intensities, the angular distribution of the emitted light contains interference terms between the different multipoles.

$$Z_{lm}(\theta,\phi) \equiv \mathbf{X}_{lm}^{\ *}\cdot\mathbf{X}_{lm}$$

$$= \frac{1}{2}\left[1 - \frac{m(m+1)}{l(l+1)} \right] |Y_{l,m+1}|^2 + \frac{1}{2}\left[1 - \frac{m(m-1)}{l(l+1)} \right] |Y_{l,m-1}|^2$$

$$+ \frac{m^2}{l(l+1)} |Y_{lm}|^2 \quad (3.16)$$

The energy $U_M(l,m;\Omega)\ d\Omega$ emitted per second into the solid angle element $d\Omega$ by a magnetic multipole radiation is determined by (2.8) (preferably the first equation), (3.13), and (3.14). The result is

$$U_M(l,m;\Omega) = \frac{c}{2\pi\kappa^2}\ Z_{lm}(\theta,\phi)\ |a_M(l,m)|^2 \quad (3.17)$$

We see that *the angular distribution of the emitted energy is the same for electric and magnetic multipole radiation of the same l and m.* Consequently measurements of the angular distribution of the emitted energy determine the multipole order but not the parity of the radiation. On the other hand, the radiations are quite distinct if not merely the energy emitted is measured, but the fields themselves, i.e., if the polarization of the emitted radiation is measured. In the wave zone, the electric and magnetic radiations of the same l and m have polarizations which differ everywhere by 90°. This can be seen by observing that $\boldsymbol{\varepsilon}$ and $\mathfrak{IC}$ are at right angles in the wave zone, and that we get the electric radiation from the magnetic radiation essentially by interchanging $\boldsymbol{\varepsilon}$ and $\mathfrak{IC}$. Hence a measurement of the angular distribution of the polarization allows us to determine the parity of the radiation in addition to the multipole order.

For the special case of dipole radiation with $m=0$ the angular distribution $Z_{1,0}(\theta,\phi)$ is

$$Z_{1,0}(\theta,\phi) = \frac{3}{8\pi} \sin^2 \theta \quad (3.18)$$

This function vanishes at the two poles of the sphere, $\theta=0$ and $\theta=\pi$. This is the well-known result that a dipole does not radiate in the direction of its own axis.

The total energy emitted per second is obtained by integrating (3.15) and (3.17) over the full solid angle. We need the integral (see Appendix B):

$$\int Z_{lm}(\theta,\phi)\ d\Omega = \int \mathbf{X}_{lm}^{\ *}\cdot\mathbf{X}_{lm}\ d\Omega = 1$$

Using this result, we obtain for the energy emitted per second:[1]

Electric radiation: $U_E(l,m) = \dfrac{c}{2\pi\kappa^2}\,|a_E(l,m)|^2$ (3.19)

Magnetic radiation: $U_M(l,m) = \dfrac{c}{2\pi\kappa^2}\,|a_M(l,m)|^2$ (3.20)

The relation between the amplitudes a and the sources of the field has been discussed in Section 3A.

C. Transition to Quantum Mechanics: (1) Emission and Absorption

The transition to quantum mechanics involves two distinct steps. First, light is emitted and absorbed, not continuously, but in quanta of energy $\hbar\omega$. Second, the source (or absorber) of the radiation is a quantum-mechanical system rather than a classical distribution of currents and charges. We shall consider the first step here and reserve the second step for later.

The probability of emission of a light quantum $\hbar\omega$ of given multipole type per unit time is obtained from the rate of emission of energy, (3.19) and (3.20), by dividing by the quantum energy $\hbar\omega$. We call this emission probability $T_E(l,m)$ and $T_M(l,m)$ for electric and magnetic multipole quanta, respectively. Combining the equations of Section 3A with (3.19) and (3.20), we get for the electric radiation

$$T_E(l,m) = \frac{8\pi(l+1)}{l\,[(2l+1)!!]^2}\,\frac{\kappa^{2l+1}}{\hbar}\,\left|Q_{lm} + Q'_{lm}\right|^2 \qquad (3.21)$$

and for the magnetic radiation

$$T_M(l,m) = \frac{8\pi(l+1)}{l\,[(2l+1)!!]^2}\,\frac{\kappa^{2l+1}}{\hbar}\,\left|M_{lm} + M'_{lm}\right|^2 \qquad (3.22)$$

We can make a rough order-of-magnitude estimate of the multipole moments as follows. In the definition (3.5) of Q_{lm} the spherical harmonic is of order unity, while the integral of $\rho(r)$ alone over the charge

---

[1] In contrast to the calculation of the angular distribution of the emitted radiation, the interference terms between different multipole radiations drop out in the expression for the total energy U emitted per second. Hence U is given by

$$U = \sum_{l=1}^{\infty} \sum_{m=-l}^{l} [U_E(l,m) + U_M(l,m)]$$

In practice one, or at most two, of the terms in this sum give most of the contribution to U, as long as the dimensions of the source are small compared to the wavelength of the emitted radiation.

distribution is of the order of the total charge ϵ. Hence we get the following order-of-magnitude estimate for Q_{lm}:

$$Q_{lm} \sim d^l \epsilon \qquad (3.23)$$

where d denotes the linear dimension of the source. If we substitute this into (3.21), we see that the emission probability of a multipole quantum l is proportional to $(\kappa d)^{2l}$. For wavelengths of the light large compared to the dimensions of the source $(\kappa d \ll 1)$ *the emission probability of multipole quanta l is a rapidly decreasing function of l.*

So far we have considered only the emission of light, not its absorption. The absorption can be considered the inverse process to the emission of light, and the two processes are related by the reciprocity law.

Assume that the direction of the incident plane wave of light is the z direction. Then the z component of the orbital angular momentum of the light is zero; the unpolarized plane wave can be split into two circularly polarized components. One of these contains multipole radiation with $m = +1$; the other contains multipole radiation with $m = -1$. The absence of multipole radiation with $m = 0$ in this plane wave is a consequence of the transverse nature of light ($m = 0$ would correspond to a longitudinal wave). Since $m = \pm 1$ are the only multipole radiations contained in the beam, only these multipoles can be absorbed.

We consider an incident beam of light which is not monochromatic but contains a whole range of frequencies. In particular, it covers the region of photon energies which can be absorbed by a nucleus in its ground state a going to some excited level b:

$$\hbar \omega_{ab} = E_b - E_a \qquad (3.24)$$

We denote the number of quanta per square centimeter per second with frequencies between ω and $\omega + d\omega$ by $S(\omega) \, d\omega$. Then it is shown, in Appendix B, that *the probability of excitation of the nucleus to the state b by absorption of electric multipole radiation of order l from this light beam is*

$$A_E(l) = S(\omega_{ab}) \frac{4\pi^3(l+1)(2l+1)}{l\,[(2l+1)!!]^2} \frac{\kappa^{2l-1}}{\hbar} \left[|Q_{l,1} + Q'_{l,1}|^2 + |Q_{l,-1} + Q'_{l,-1}|^2\right] \qquad (3.25)$$

The probability of excitation by absorption of magnetic multipole radiation is obtained from (3.25) by replacing Q and Q' by M and M', respectively.

So long as we do not take into account the radiation damping effects, we cannot obtain the expression for absorption of truly monochromatic radiation.   Actually, the excited state has a width which is due to the fact that it can re-emit the radiation or emit other radiations.   The cross section for absorption of a monochromatic light beam of frequency ω is very large for $\omega = \omega_{ab}$ and approaches zero for frequencies outside the width of the excited level.   The absorption probability (3.25) is related to an integral over this whole frequency width.   While our method does not allow us to find the absorption cross section for monochromatic gamma-rays, this is not a serious difficulty because in practice the frequency spread of the beams used is large compared to the width of the nuclear levels involved.

D. Transition to Quantum Mechanics: (2) The Matrix Elements

So far the electric and magnetic multipole moments Q_{lm} and M_{lm} have been defined in terms of a classical distribution of currents and charges, and of magnetization.   We now take into account the fact that the radiating system (the nucleus) actually must be described by quantum mechanics.

We begin with a single particle of charge e and mass M, without intrinsic spin; this particle is assumed to move in some potential field. Let us consider the radiation emitted by this particle in going from state φ_a to the (lower) state φ_b.   The probability of emission of a given multipole radiation is still given by (3.21) and (3.22), provided only that we replace $\mathbf{j}(\mathbf{r})$ and $\rho(\mathbf{r})$ in the definitions of the multipole moments, (3.5) and (3.7), by the quantum-mechanical analogues:[1]

$$\mathbf{j}(a,b;\mathbf{r}) = \frac{e}{2M} [\varphi_b{}^* (\mathbf{p}\varphi_a) + (\mathbf{p}\varphi_b)^* \varphi_a] \tag{3.26}$$

$$\rho(a,b;\mathbf{r}) = e \, \varphi_b{}^*(\mathbf{r}) \, \varphi_a(\mathbf{r}) \tag{3.27}$$

Here $\mathbf{p} = -i\hbar\boldsymbol{\nabla}$ is the operator for the linear momentum of the particle. We get the electric and magnetic multipole moments for the transition $a \to b$ by replacing $\rho(\mathbf{r})$ in (3.5) by (3.27), and $\mathbf{j}(\mathbf{r})$ in (3.7) by (3.26):

$$Q_{lm}(a,b) = e \int r^l \, Y_{lm}{}^*(\theta,\phi) \, \varphi_b{}^*(\mathbf{r}) \, \varphi_a(\mathbf{r}) \, d\tau \tag{3.28}$$

$$M_{lm}(a,b) = -\frac{1}{l+1} \frac{e}{2Mc} \int r^l \, Y_{lm}{}^*(\theta,\phi) \, \text{div} \, [\mathbf{r} \times \mathbf{j}(a,b;\mathbf{r})] \, d\tau \tag{3.29}$$

We can simplify (3.29) by an integration by parts which shows that the two terms in (3.26) give equal results.   Using the operator $\mathbf{L}$

---

[1] The symmetrization in $\mathbf{j}(a,b;\mathbf{r})$ is necessary so that (3.26) and (3.27) satisfy the continuity equation for a charge density and current density.   For $\varphi_a = \varphi_b$ the charge density $\rho(a,a;\mathbf{r})$ is equal to the charge times the probability density $\varphi_a{}^*\varphi_a$.

defined in (2.5), we obtain

$$M_{lm}(a,b) = -\frac{1}{l+1}\frac{e\hbar}{Mc}\int r^l\, Y_{lm}{}^*(\theta,\phi)\,\text{div}\,(\varphi_b{}^*\mathbf{L}\varphi_a)\,d\tau \quad (3.30)$$

So far no account has been taken of the radiation due to the spin of the particle under consideration. If the particle possesses a spin of $\frac{1}{2}\hbar$, the wave functions φ_a and φ_b are functions of the spin coordinate (which can take only two values, $+1$ and -1) as well as of $\mathbf{r}$. The integration over $d\tau$ in (3.28) to (3.30) then implies also a sum over the two values of the spin coordinate.

In addition to this trivial change, the spin gives rise to a density of magnetization $\mathbf{M}(a,b;\mathbf{r})$ which can also lead to radiative transitions from state φ_a to state φ_b:

$$\mathbf{M}(a,b;\mathbf{r}) = \frac{e\hbar}{2Mc}\,\mu\,\{\varphi_b{}^*\mathbf{\mathfrak{d}}\varphi_a\} \quad (3.31)$$

Here μ is the magnetic moment of the particle expressed in Bohr magnetons (e.g., $\mu = 2.78$ for a proton) and $\mathbf{\mathfrak{d}}$ is the Pauli spin operator with components σ_x, σ_y, and σ_z. The brace in (3.31) denotes a sum over the two values of the spin coordinate only, without an integration over the space coordinate $\mathbf{r}$. This magnetization (3.31) must be inserted into definitions (3.9) and (3.10) for the corresponding multipole moments.

In general the magnetic multipole moments $M'_{lm}(a,b)$ due to the spin are of the same order of magnitude as the magnetic multipole moments $M_{lm}(a,b)$ due to the orbital motion (the current distribution). This can be seen by observing that both orbital momenta and spin momenta are of the order of magnitude of the Planck constant $\hbar$, and that the magnetic moments for the spin and orbital motions are also of the same order of magnitude (namely $e\hbar/2Mc$).

The generalization to systems containing many particles is obtained by a straightforward summation of the expressions for a single particle over all the particles in the system. In nuclei all the nucleons have the same mass M, but only the protons have a charge e. Let $\mathbf{p}_k$ be the momentum operator for the kth proton in the nucleus, and $\mathbf{L}_k$ be the corresponding orbital angular momentum operator (2.5). The wave functions φ_a and φ_b are now functions of the position and spin coordinates of all the particles in the nucleus, and the integration over $d\tau$ implies integration over all the positions as well as sums over all the spin coordinates. The *electric and magnetic multipole moments for nuclear transitions from state φ_a to state φ_b are*

$$Q_{lm}(a,b) = e \sum_{k=1}^{Z} \int r_k^{\ l} \ Y_{lm}{}^*(\theta_k, \phi_k) \ \varphi_b{}^* \ \varphi_a \ d\tau \tag{3.32}$$

$$M_{lm}(a,b) = -\frac{1}{l+1} \frac{e\hbar}{Mc} \sum_{k=1}^{Z} \int r_k^{\ l} \ Y_{lm}{}^*(\theta_k, \phi_k) \ \mathrm{div} \ (\varphi_b{}^* \mathbf{L}_k \varphi_a) \ d\tau \tag{3.33}$$

$$Q'_{lm}(a,b) = -\frac{i\kappa}{l+1} \frac{e\hbar}{2Mc} \sum_{k=1}^{A} \mu_k \int r_k^{\ l} \ Y_{lm}{}^*(\theta_k, \phi_k) \ \mathrm{div} \ (\varphi_b{}^* \mathbf{r}_k \times \mathbf{\delta}_k \varphi_a) \ d\tau \tag{3.34}$$

$$M'_{lm}(a,b) = -\frac{e\hbar}{2Mc} \sum_{k=1}^{A} \mu_k \int r_k^{\ l} \ Y_{lm}{}^*(\theta_k, \phi_k) \ \mathrm{div} \ (\varphi_b{}^* \mathbf{\delta}_k \varphi_a) \ d\tau \tag{3.35}$$

The first two sums go over the protons only, the second two over all the nucleons in the nucleus. The spherical harmonics are evaluated for the position of each particle in turn. μ_k is the intrinsic (spin) magnetic moment of the kth nucleon, measured in Bohr magnetons, and $\mathbf{\delta}_k$ is the corresponding Pauli spin operator. Expressions (3.32) to (3.35) will also be referred to as the *matrix elements* of the various multipole moments between levels a and b.

In the special case of dipole radiation ($l=1$) with $m=0$, the matrix elements are

$$Q_{1,0}(a,b) = e \left(\frac{3}{4\pi} \right)^{1/2} \sum_{k=1}^{Z} \int \varphi_b{}^* \ z_k \ \varphi_a \ d\tau \tag{3.36}$$

$$M_{1,0}(a,b) = \frac{e\hbar}{2Mc} \left(\frac{3}{4\pi} \right)^{1/2} \sum_{k=1}^{Z} \int \varphi_b{}^* \ L_{kz} \ \varphi_a \ d\tau \tag{3.37}$$

$$Q'_{1,0}(a,b) = i \frac{\kappa e\hbar}{4Mc} \left(\frac{3}{4\pi} \right)^{1/2} \sum_{k=1}^{A} \mu_k \int \varphi_b{}^* \ (\mathbf{r}_k \times \mathbf{\delta}_k)_z \ \varphi_a \ d\tau \tag{3.38}$$

$$M'_{1,0}(a,b) = \frac{e\hbar}{2Mc} \left(\frac{3}{4\pi} \right)^{1/2} \sum_{k=1}^{A} \mu_k \int \varphi_b{}^* \ \sigma_{kz} \ \varphi_a \ d\tau \tag{3.39}$$

where L_{kz} and σ_{kz} are the z components of the vectors $\mathbf{L}_k$ and $\mathbf{\delta}_k$, respectively. Relations (3.37) to (3.39) were obtained from (3.33) to (3.35) through integration by parts.

A few words of caution regarding these formulas are warranted. We have used the non-relativistic expression for the current density **j** and have assumed that all electromagnetic effects in a nucleus are created by the motions of the individual nucleons and by their intrinsic magnetic moments. Both assumptions are open to question. If there are exchange forces in nuclei associated with exchange of the nuclear charge between a proton and a neutron, this "exchange current" also gives rise to observable effects. It produces a magnetic moment which is observed as an additional (exchange) magnetic moment in the ground states of nuclei, and which has matrix elements for the emission and absorption of light, thereby adding to the multipole moments.[1] The theory is in a very unsatisfactory state. We should be able to derive all the currents in nuclei from a general theory of nuclear behavior, rather than having to introduce them *ad hoc* as the situation demands. No such general theory is available at present, however.

4. RADIATIVE TRANSITIONS IN THE TWO-BODY PROBLEM

A. Transitions Into and Out of the Continuum; Cross Sections

Formulas (3.21) and (3.22) apply to the emission of light in the transition between two stable states of a nuclear system. In the case of unbound states, such as occur in the collision between a neutron and a proton, the transition probability depends on the flux of the incident wave, and it is more useful to speak about cross sections. The cross section is equal to the transition probability per unit time divided by the flux of the incident wave.

We shall derive first the formula for the neutron-proton capture cross section, i.e., the cross section for the reaction:

$$N + P = D + \hbar\omega \tag{4.1}$$

If the incident neutron and proton did not interact, we could write the initial wave function φ_a in the matrix elements, (3.32) to (3.35), in the form (in the center-of-gravity system)

$$\varphi_a = \exp{(i\mathbf{k}\cdot\mathbf{r})} \tag{4.2}$$

However, this function is not a solution of the wave equation in the initial state. We can obtain a solution by adding the scattered wave to this; for large r this solution assumes the form

---

[1] An investigation by Sachs (51) suggests that these uncertainties are significant for magnetic multipole radiation, but are unimportant for electric multipole radiation.

$$\varphi_a = \exp{(i\mathbf{k}\cdot\mathbf{r})} + f(\theta)\,\frac{\exp{(ikr)}}{r} \qquad \text{(for large } r) \qquad (4.3)$$

This is the wave function of the initial state, which we shall substitute into relations (3.32) to (3.35). The transition probability $T(l,m)$ of a radiative transition with emission of a multipole quantum l,m is then given by (3.21) and (3.22) for electric and magnetic radiations, respectively.

The flux of particles in the wave (4.3) is the density of the plane wave $\exp{(i\mathbf{k}\cdot\mathbf{r})}$, which is unity, multiplied by the relative velocity $v = 2\hbar k/M$ ($\hbar k$ is the momentum and $\frac{1}{2}M$ is the reduced mass in the center-of-mass system). Hence we get the cross section for neutron-proton capture from the transition probability by dividing by the relative velocity v. The result for electric multipole capture is

$$\sigma_{\text{cap}}^{E}(l,m) = \frac{8\pi(l+1)}{l\,[(2l+1)!!]^2}\,\frac{\kappa^{2l+1}}{\hbar v}\,|Q_{lm} + Q'_{lm}|^2 \qquad (4.4)$$

The expression for magnetic multipole capture is obtained by replacing Q and Q' by M and M', respectively.

So far we have ignored the spins of the neutron and proton. Relation (4.4) is applicable if the initial state is a pure state (e.g., the singlet spin state). If the incident beam is unpolarized, the cross section (4.4) must be multiplied by the statistical weight of the initial state, e.g., by $\frac{1}{4}$ for capture from the singlet state.

Expression (4.4) can also be applied to the capture process in other nuclei, i.e., to the reaction

$$a + X = Y + \hbar\omega \qquad (4.5)$$

in which particle a is captured by nucleus X with emission of radiation. However, because of the importance of the formation of an intermediate, compound state in this reaction, it is more useful to employ other methods, which will be discussed in Section 7.

We shall now derive the expression for the cross section of the inverse process, the photodisintegration of the deuteron:

$$\hbar\omega + D = N + P \qquad (4.6)$$

In order to get the cross section for this process, we make use of the detailed balance theorem for inverse processes.[1] We recall that the

---

[1] Since the coupling between matter and radiation is weak ($e^2/\hbar c \ll 1$), the use of the perturbation theory and the detailed balance theorem is justified. It should be realized, however, that the theorem relates capture from the state φ_a, (4.3), to the disintegration into the complex conjugate state $\varphi_a{}^*$. This complex conjugate

transition probability $T_{1 \to 2}$ from state 1 to another state 2 is given by

$$T_{1 \to 2} = \frac{2\pi}{\hbar} |H'_{12}|^2 \rho_2 \qquad (4.7)$$

where H'_{12} is the matrix element of the perturbing Hamiltonian responsible for the transition, and ρ_2 is the number of final states per unit energy interval.

A corresponding formula holds for the inverse transition $2 \to 1$. Furthermore $H'_{12} = (H'_{21})^*$. We therefore obtain the fundamental relation between the transition probabilities of inverse processes:

$$\frac{T_{1 \to 2}}{\rho_2} = \frac{T_{2 \to 1}}{\rho_1} \qquad (4.8)$$

As before, we shall normalize the incident wave to have unit density in space [see (4.3)] so that the cross sections will be obtained from the transition probabilities by division by the velocity v. Substitution into (4.8) yields

$$\frac{d\sigma_{1 \to 2}}{v_2 \rho_2} = \frac{d\sigma_{2 \to 1}}{v_1 \rho_1} \qquad (4.9)$$

In order to treat light quanta and nucleons at the same time we use the relativistic relations between energy, momentum, and speed. Our normalization corresponds to quantization in a "box" of unit volume. The number of final states per unit energy range with the particle moving in a direction within the solid angle element $d\Omega$ is

$$\rho(E) = (2\pi\hbar)^{-3} p^2 \frac{dp}{dE} d\Omega \qquad (4.10)$$

A simple calculation gives

$$v\rho = (2\pi\hbar)^{-3} p^2 d\Omega \qquad (4.11)$$

When this is substituted into (4.9), we get the following relation between the two cross sections:

$$p_1^2 d\sigma_{1 \to 2} = p_2^2 d\sigma_{2 \to 1} \qquad (4.12)$$

(time-reversed) state has the relative momentum $-\hbar\mathbf{k}$ in the opposite direction to the relative momentum for the state φ_a. It also has an incoming spherical wave rather than an outgoing spherical wave. The latter is understandable since the *outgoing* part of the plane wave must be normalized in the photodisintegration process, the *ingoing* part of the plane wave in the capture process. If we want the probability of photodisintegration with a given momentum of the emerging particles, we must relate it to the radiative capture of oppositely directed incoming particles.

In the case of photodisintegration and radiative capture, the momentum of the particles is $p_1 = \hbar k$, and the momentum of the photons is $p_2 = \hbar \omega / c = \hbar \kappa$. Hence we obtain

$$d\sigma_{\mathrm{dis}}(l,m) = \left(\frac{k}{\kappa}\right)^2 d\sigma_{\mathrm{cap}}(l,m) \qquad (4.13)$$

The total disintegration cross section is the integral of $d\sigma_{\mathrm{dis}}$ over the full solid angle. It is related to the total capture cross section (4.4) by

$$\sigma_{\mathrm{dis}}(l,m) = \left(\frac{k}{\kappa}\right)^2 \sigma_{\mathrm{cap}}(l,m) \qquad (4.14)$$

While (4.4) was written only for the total cross section, the angular distribution of the outgoing quanta is given by $Z_{lm}(\theta,\phi)$, (3.16). According to (4.13) this same angular distribution then applies also to the outgoing particles in the disintegration process.

These expressions could be used for photodisintegration of nuclei other than the deuteron, e.g., to find the cross section of a (γ,n) or (γ,p) reaction. Again, however, the existence of an intermediate, compound state makes it more convenient to use other methods, which will be discussed in Section 7.[1]

Expression (4.14) ignores the spins. If the initial state is a mixture of spin states, the proper statistical weights must be used to correct the cross sections. Similarly, a correction must be made if the incident light beam in the photodisintegration process is unpolarized.

B. Radiative Neutron-Proton Capture; Selection Rules

The radiative capture process (4.1) is very improbable compared to elastic neutron-proton scattering at all but the lowest neutron energies.

Of the various multipole radiations which can be emitted in (4.1), the dipoles are the most probable. The selection rules for dipole emission are $\Delta J = 0, \pm 1$ (but no $0 \rightarrow 0$ transitions), and a change of parity for electric dipole emission, but no change of parity for magnetic dipole emission.

The final state of the nuclear system in (4.1) is the ground state of the deuteron, which has $J = 1$ and even parity. Hence we can get dipole emission from initial states (in the continuum) with $J = 0, 1, 2$ and odd parity for electric, even parity for magnetic dipoles. Capture from odd-parity states is very unlikely at low energies, since these

---

[1] In some exceptional cases, e.g., the photodisintegration of Be^9, methods analogous to those used for the deuteron are more appropriate than methods based on the compound nucleus picture (Guth 48, 48a, 49; Mullin 49).

have to be at least $l = 1$ states (P states). At low energies the neutron and proton in a P state do not come close enough together to give rise to an appreciable capture process. Thus electric dipole capture is unimportant.

On the other hand, magnetic dipole capture gives a measurable effect (Fermi 35). The initial state must have even parity and can therefore be either an S state or a D state. The capture from the D state is, of course, unimportant. Thus we are reduced to magnetic dipole capture from either the ^1S or the ^3S state.

The $^3S \rightarrow {}^3S$ capture cross section vanishes for the following reason: the matrix element $M_{1,0}(a,b)$, (3.37), is zero because $\mathbf{L}_p$, the orbital angular momentum of the proton, is half of $\mathbf{L} = \mathbf{L}_n + \mathbf{L}_p$, and the latter gives zero when the system is in an S state. The other matrix element, $M'_{1,0}$, (3.39), vanishes because the spin operators leave the space part of the wave function unchanged, and φ_a is orthogonal to φ_b if both are ^3S states and differ only in energy.

The only capture process of importance is therefore the $^1S \rightarrow {}^3S$ capture. The matrix element $M_{1,0}(a,b)$, (3.37), is again zero, for the same reason as before. On the other hand, the radiation associated with the flipping of the spins of the particles [i.e., the matrix element $M'_{1,0}$, (3.39)] does not vanish. The orthogonality argument fails because the nuclear force in the singlet state is not the same as in the triplet state, hence the space wave functions are not orthogonal to each other.

C. Radiative Neutron-Proton Capture; Computation of the Cross Section and Comparison with Experiment

The operator which appears in the matrix element $M'_{1,0}$, (3.39), can be written in the form

$$\mu_N \mathbf{\delta}_N + \mu_P \mathbf{\delta}_P = \tfrac{1}{2} (\mu_N + \mu_P)(\mathbf{\delta}_N + \mathbf{\delta}_P) + \tfrac{1}{2}(\mu_N - \mu_P)(\mathbf{\delta}_N - \mathbf{\delta}_P) \quad (4.15)$$

The first term on the right side is proportional to the total spin

$$\mathbf{S} = \tfrac{1}{2}(\mathbf{\delta}_N + \mathbf{\delta}_P)$$

of the neutron-proton system. Its value is zero when applied to a singlet state. We therefore need to consider only the second term. It is interesting to observe that the second term would vanish if the neutron and proton had equal magnetic moments.

The final state φ_b in (3.39) is the ground state of the deuteron:

$$\varphi_b = (4\pi)^{-1/2} \frac{u_{0t}(r)}{r} \chi_{1,0} \quad (4.16)$$

where $u_{0t}(r)$ is the radial wave function with asymptotic behavior [$\gamma \equiv$ the inverse of the decay length (II,2.7)]:

$$u_{0t}(r) \cong N e^{-\gamma r} \qquad \text{(for large } r) \qquad (4.17)$$

and with normalization:

$$\int_0^\infty u_{0t}^2(r) \, dr = 1 \qquad (4.18)$$

The initial state φ_a in (3.39) is a ^1S state in the continuum:

$$\varphi_a = \frac{u_{0s}(r)}{kr} \chi_0 \qquad (4.19)$$

where k is the wave number of the relative motion of neutron and proton; $u_{0s}(r)$ is chosen so that it has the asymptotic behavior

$$u_{0s}(r) \cong \sin (kr + \delta_{0s}) \qquad \text{(for large } r) \qquad (4.20)$$

where δ_{0s} is the phase shift in the ^1S state. The choice, (4.19) and (4.20), of the initial function represents (except for an irrelevant phase factor) the S wave part of (4.3); we shall therefore get the correct cross section for the case in which the neutron and proton initially are known to be in the singlet spin state.

The magnetic dipole matrix element (3.39) then is equal to

$$M'_{1,0} = \frac{\sqrt{3}}{2} \frac{e\hbar}{Mck} (\mu_N - \mu_P) \int_0^\infty u_{0s}(r) \, u_{0t}(r) \, dr \qquad (4.21)$$

Substitution into (4.4) (or, rather, its counterpart for magnetic radiation) gives

$$\sigma_{\text{cap}}^M(l=1, m=0) = \frac{2\pi}{3} \frac{e^2}{\hbar c} \left(\frac{\hbar}{Mc} \right)^4 \left(\frac{k^2 + \gamma^2}{k} \right)^3 (\mu_N - \mu_P)^2 I^2 \qquad (4.22)$$

where I is the integral

$$I = \int_0^\infty u_{0s}(r) \, u_{0t}(r) \, dr \qquad (4.23)$$

The capture with emission of an $m=0$ quantum is only one of three possible magnetic dipole capture processes, the other two being emission of quanta with $m=1$ and $m=-1$. The emission of a quantum with $m=+1$ leaves the deuteron in the state with $m=-1$, and vice versa. The cross sections are easily shown to be equal to (4.22). The angular distribution of the emitted radiation is given by the functions Z_{lm} defined in (3.16). If we observe all gamma-rays, irrespective of which final spin state the deuteron is left in, the angular distribution is uniform:

$$\sum_{m=-1}^{+1} Z_{1,m}(\theta,\phi) = \text{constant} \qquad (4.24)$$

This uniform angular distribution of the emitted capture radiation could have been predicted on the basis of the theorems on angular distributions of reaction products, proved in Chapter X. The initial state here is a ^1S state, and we are summing over the spin directions in the final state. The angular distribution can therefore be no more complicated than $(\cos\theta)^{2l} = (\cos\theta)^0 = 1$, i.e., a uniform distribution.

We still need to evaluate the integral (4.23). This requires knowledge of the wave functions of the deuteron in its ground state and of the neutron and proton in the ^1S state in the continuum. To a first approximation, we can neglect the range of the force. That assumption allows us to use the asymptotic forms (4.20) and (4.17) for all values of r. Substitution of (4.17) into (4.18) gives the following value for the normalization constant N in the zero range approximation:

$$N = (2\gamma)^{1/2} \qquad \text{(zero range approximation)} \qquad (4.25)$$

Substitution of (4.17), (4.20), and (4.25) into the definition of I, (4.23), gives

$$I = (2\gamma)^{1/2} \frac{k\cos\delta_{0s} + \gamma\sin\delta_{0s}}{k^2 + \gamma^2} \qquad (4.26)$$

Since we are interested in the capture only near zero energy, we neglect k^2 compared to γ^2, and we use the relation $k\cot\delta_{0s} = -(a_s)^{-1}$, where a_s is the neutron-proton scattering length in the singlet state (see Chapter II, Section 3). We also introduce the binding energy of the deuteron, $B = \hbar^2\gamma^2/M$, and the neutron energy in the *laboratory* system, $E_N = 2\hbar^2k^2/M$. In order to get the observed capture cross section we multiply (4.22) by 3 (since there are 3 possible transitions which are equally likely), and by the probability $(=\frac{1}{4})$ of finding the neutron and proton in the singlet spin state in an unpolarized beam. The result for the capture cross section then is

$$\sigma_{\text{cap}} = \pi \frac{e^2}{\hbar c}\left(\frac{\hbar}{Mc}\right)^2 \frac{B}{Mc^2}(\mu_N - \mu_P)^2 (1 - \gamma a_s)^2 \left(\frac{2B}{E_N}\right)^{1/2}$$

$$\text{(zero range approximation)} \qquad (4.27)$$

The dependence on the energy of the incident neutrons is contained in the last factor, which exhibits the characteristic $1/v$ law of a capture process. If we insert numbers into (4.27), the capture cross section for thermal neutrons ($E_N = 0.025$ ev) turns out to be roughly 0.3×10^{-24} cm^2, in good agreement with the experimental value.

We remark that the factor $(1 - \gamma a_s)^2$ in (4.27) depends on the sign of the scattering length in the singlet state. The assumption of a real, rather than a virtual, singlet state (positive a_s) would have led to a value for the cross section smaller by about a factor of 2, definitely in disagreement with the experimental value. At the time these experiments were performed (1935) the parahydrogen scattering experiment had not even been suggested. The measurement of the neutron capture cross section in hydrogenous materials provided the first proof that there is no bound singlet state of the neutron-proton system (Fermi 35).

The zero range approximation (4.27) is subject to corrections for two reasons: (1) the range of the force is not zero, and (2) the expression (3.31) for the density of magnetization applies only to a single isolated particle, and there is no guarantee that the magnetization in the neutron-proton system is just the sum of (3.31) for the neutron and the proton separately. The range correction cannot be made exactly, but approximate expressions were derived by Bethe and Longmire (Bethe 50) and by Feshbach and Schwinger (Feshbach 51), in terms of the effective ranges r_{0s} and r_{0t} in the singlet and triplet states, respectively. The effective range r_{0t} in the triplet state is known from the scattering data (see Chapter II, Section 3). Hence, if the range correction were the only correction to (4.27), we could derive a value of the singlet effective range r_{0s} from the measured capture cross section. The value so derived is between 2 and 3×10^{-13} cm, in very good agreement with the (somewhat less accurate) value from the scattering data; it is not in disagreement with the assumption of charge independence of the nuclear forces (which would require r_{0s} for the neutron-proton system to be equal to $r_{0s}^{PP} \cong 2.65 \times 10^{-13}$ cm for the proton-proton system.)[1]

Unfortunately, there is little reason to believe that the correction for exchange magnetic moment effects is negligible. The initial and final states are the same, hence the exchange magnetic moment terms are coherent with the terms which we have calculated. A very rough estimate, based on the experimental value of the exchange magnetic moment in H^3 and He^3, leads us to believe that the effect may increase the cross section by up to 4 percent (Austern 50).

[1] There is a small correction caused by the fact that the Coulomb force changes the effective range slightly for the same nuclear force. Unlike the similar correction in the scattering length, (see Chapter II, Section 4), this effect is quite insignificant for the effective range (Chew 49, Bethe 49).

Finally, there is a correction for the effect of the tensor force in the ground state of the deuteron. The presence of the tensor force changes the analysis considerably in principle, but the final effect on the capture cross section is very small (Rarita 41, Hepner 42, Feshbach 51). The capture cross section is decreased by an amount proportional to the percentage of D state in the ground state of the deuteron.

D. Photodisintegration of the Deuteron; Magnetic Dipole Effect

Expression (4.22) gives the capture cross section if the initial state is known to be a singlet spin state and the final state is known to be one particular triplet spin state of the deuteron, namely $m = 0$. We can therefore apply (4.14) directly without corrections for statistical weights of spin states. On the other hand, a correction must be made for the polarization state of the light. In the capture process, the magnetic dipole radiation $l = 1$, $m = 0$ emitted in a particular direction θ with respect to the incident neutron has a definite polarization (in general, elliptic). In the disintegration process the incident light from the θ direction is unpolarized; the probability that the polarization of the incident light is such as to allow magnetic dipole capture is $\frac{1}{2}$. Thus the observed disintegration cross section is only half of (4.14). With this correction we get

$$\sigma_{\text{dis}}^M (l=1, \, m=0) \;=\; \frac{1}{2} \frac{2\pi}{3} \, (\mu_N - \mu_P)^2 \frac{e^2}{\hbar c} \left(\frac{\hbar}{Mc}\right)^2 (k^2 + \gamma^2)\, k^{-1}\, I^2 \quad (4.28)$$

In general, the deuteron is not known to be in the particular spin state $m = 0$ but may just as well be in the spin state $m = 1$ or $m = -1$ with equal probability. However, just as the capture probability turned out to be independent of m, so is the disintegration probability. The weighted average of the disintegration cross section over the three possible values of m of the initial deuteron is therefore also equal to (4.28)

The integral I (4.23) has already been evaluated in the zero range approximation, the result being given in (4.26). Now we can no longer neglect k^2 against γ^2. However, we can still use the relation $k \cot \delta_{0s} = -(a_s)^{-1}$, since the correction terms vanish in the zero range approximation. We then get

$$\sigma_{\text{dis}}^{MD} \;=\; \frac{2\pi}{3} \frac{e^2}{\hbar c} \left(\frac{\hbar}{Mc}\right)^2 (\mu_N - \mu_P)^2 \, \frac{k\gamma \, (1 - \gamma a_s)^2}{(k^2 + \gamma^2)\,(1 + k^2 a_s^2)}$$

$$\text{(zero range approximation)} \quad (4.29)$$

This cross section, corrected for finite range effects, is shown in Fig. 4.1 as a function of the excess energy of the gamma-ray over the binding energy of the deuteron (i.e., the energy which is given to the emerging neutron-proton pair). Near the threshold the cross section is proportional to k, i.e., to the square root of the excess energy. σ reaches a maximum for $k^2 \cong a_s^{-2}$, i.e., at an energy corresponding to the "virtual level" of the neutron-proton system in the singlet state. Thereafter it drops rapidly, first like k^{-1}, later (for $k^2 > \gamma^2$)

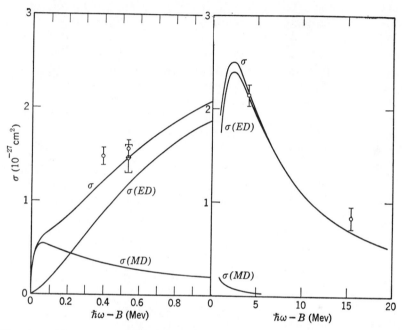

FIG. 4.1. Photodisintegration cross section of the deuteron. ED means electric dipole absorption, MD means magnetic dipole absorption.

like k^{-3}. We observe (see 4.24) that the emerging neutron and proton have spherically symmetric angular distribution. This is to be expected for an S state to S state transition.

E. Photodisintegration of the Deuteron; Electric Dipole Effect

Of the two matrix elements which can contribute to the electric dipole absorption, the absorption caused by the convection current is much stronger than the absorption caused by the intrinsic spins.[1] We

[1] The contributions of Q and Q' to the photodisintegration cross section are coherent in general. However, the cross terms cancel out if we average over spin directions. Thus the contribution of Q' to the measured cross section is smaller than the contribution of Q by a factor of the order of $(\hbar\omega/Mc^2)^2$. Such a small contribution cannot be detected with present experimental techniques.

shall therefore restrict ourselves to the former effect. Since $Q_{1,m}$ contains no spin operators, the transitions are from the ^3S ground state to triplet states in the continuum, and the selection rules for electric dipole transitions require these to be ^3P states.

Since the spins are not involved here, we can ignore the spin functions. Only one term of the sum (3.36) contributes, since there is only one proton. Its coordinate z_1 is one-half of the neutron-proton separation coordinate z which appears in the wave functions.

The function φ_a in (3.36) is given by (4.3), while φ_b is the wave function of the ground state of the deuteron, (4.16). The matrix element (3.36) connects the ground state (an S state) only to the P wave ($l=1$) part of φ_a. At low energies we can neglect the interaction between the neutron and the proton in the P state, i.e., we can set the P wave part of $f(\theta)$ in (4.3) equal to 0. We then get (letting the direction of **k** be the z direction)

$$Q_{1,0} = \frac{\sqrt{3}}{8\pi} e \int z \, e^{-ikz} \frac{u_{0t}(r)}{r} \, dV \qquad (4.30)$$

The integration over the angles can be performed immediately, and it gives

$$Q_{1,0} = -i \frac{\sqrt{3}}{2} \frac{e}{k} \int_0^\infty u_{0t}(r) \, u_{1t}(r) \, r \, dr \qquad (4.31)$$

where $u_{1t}(r)$ is the radial function for the $l=1$ (P wave) component of an undisturbed plane wave $\exp(ikz)$:

$$u_{1t}(r) = \frac{\sin(kr)}{kr} - \cos(kr) \qquad (4.32)$$

It is easily shown that the electric dipole matrix elements $Q_{1,1}$ and $Q_{1,-1}$ vanish with our choice of the z direction.

Since the transition with $m=0$ is the only one which occurs, the angular distribution of the outgoing particles is determined by $Z_{1,0}(\theta,\phi)$, (3.18), i.e., it is proportional to $\sin^2\theta$. Here θ is the angle between the directions of the incident neutron and the outgoing quantum in the capture process, and it is the angle between the directions of the incident quantum and the outgoing neutron in the disintegration process.

The electric dipole photodisintegration cross section can be obtained directly from (4.4), (4.14), and (4.31). The result is (including the correction factor $\frac{1}{2}$ for unpolarized incident light)

$$\sigma_{\text{dis}}^{ED} = \frac{\pi}{3} \frac{e^2}{\hbar c} (k^2+\gamma^2) \, k^{-1} \left(\int_0^\infty u_{0t}(r) \, u_{1t}(r) \, r \, dr \right)^2 \qquad (4.33)$$

In order to evaluate the integral we again use the zero range approximation for the ground-state wave function. The integral can then be evaluated directly, and it gives

$$\int_0^\infty u_{0t}(r)\, u_{1t}(r)\, r\, dr = (2\gamma)^{1/2}\, \frac{2k^2}{(k^2+\gamma^2)^2}$$

(zero range approximation)   (4.34)

Substitution of (4.34) into (4.33) gives the zero range approximation for the electric dipole disintegration cross section. Unlike the magnetic dipole disintegration, the range correction is very easily made here. First of all, we do not need to consider the range of the force in the ^3P state, since we have neglected the effects of this force altogether (i.e., we have set the ^3P phase shift equal to zero). Second, the main contribution to the integral (4.34) comes from values of r outside the range of the nuclear forces.[1] Hence we get an excellent approximation to the integral by continuing to use the asymptotic form (4.17) of $u_{0t}(r)$ for *all* r; the only correction occurs in the normalization constant N, which is no longer equal to $(2\gamma)^{1/2}$.

We now show that the range correction to the normalization constant N involves the same effective range which we have already encountered in the analysis of neutron-proton scattering in Chapter II, Section 3. To prove this, we refer to (II,3.16) and (II,3.17) and use the ground-state wave function for u_0 instead of the wave function appropriate to zero energy. Proceeding in an entirely analogous manner, we get an alternative formula for $k \cot \delta_{0t}$ instead of (II,3.19):

$$k \cot \delta_{0t} = -\gamma + \tfrac{1}{2}\, \rho_{0t}\, (k^2+\gamma^2)$$ (4.35)

where the length ρ_{0t} is given by

$$\rho_{0t} = 2 \int_0^\infty [\exp(-2\gamma r) - N^{-2}\, u_{0t}{}^2(r)]\, dr$$ (4.36)

Comparison of (4.35) with (II,3.19) shows that ρ_{0t} is identical with the effective range for scattering, r_{0t}, (II,3.20), to the accuracy of the shape-independent approximation. The use of the normalization integral (4.18) enables us to solve (4.36) for N to get

$$N = (2\gamma)^{1/2}\, (1-\gamma\rho_{0t})^{-1/2} \cong (2\gamma)^{1/2}\, (1-\gamma r_{0t})^{-1/2}$$ (4.37)

[1] This can be seen by expanding (4.32) for small r. The leading term is proportional to r^2, and there is an extra factor r in the integral, making r^3 in all. Hence the "inside" part of $u_{0t}(r)$ contributes very much less to the integral than the values of r outside the range of the force in the ^3S state.

We now substitute the corrected value of the integral (4.34) into (4.33) to obtain the *cross section for electric dipole photodisintegration of the deuteron:*

$$\sigma_{\text{dis}}^{ED} = \frac{8\pi}{3} \frac{e^2}{\hbar c} \gamma^{-2} \left(\frac{k\gamma}{k^2+\gamma^2}\right)^3 (1 - \gamma r_{0t})^{-1} \qquad (4.38)$$

Near the threshold (k near zero) the cross section goes like k^3, i.e., like $(\hbar\omega - B)^{3/2}$. The cross section reaches a maximum at $k = \gamma$, i.e., $\hbar\omega = 2B = 4.46$ Mev. Thereafter it decreases again. On Fig. 4.1 we have drawn in the electric dipole photodisintegration cross section as a function of the energy.

The order of magnitude of the electric dipole cross section near its maximum can be understood simply. The factor γ^{-2} is proportional to the "geometric size" of the deuteron. The fine structure constant $(e^2/\hbar c) = \frac{1}{137}$ enters because this is a radiation process and this constant is a measure of the strength of the coupling between matter and radiation. The other factors are of order unity near the maximum.

It is interesting to compare the orders of magnitude of the electric dipole and magnetic dipole effects. At energies for which $k^2 \gg \gamma^2$ (i.e., $\hbar\omega \gg B$) the ratio of the two cross sections is constant, and, except for factors of order unity, it is given by

$$\frac{\sigma_{\text{dis}}^{MD}}{\sigma_{\text{dis}}^{ED}} \sim \gamma^2 \left(\frac{\hbar}{Mc}\right)^2 = \frac{B}{Mc^2} \qquad (4.39)$$

This is of the order of magnitude of $(v/c)^2$, where v is the relative velocity in the "outside" region, which makes the predominant contribution to the cross sections. This agrees with the order-of-magnitude estimate which we have made in Section 3 for the ratio of magnetic to electric radiation of the same multipole order. On the other hand, the estimate (4.39) breaks down completely at energies just above threshold, where the magnetic dipole disintegration is the dominant effect. This is a consequence of the selection rules, which allow S state to S state transitions for magnetic dipole absorption but not for electric dipole absorption. This illustrates the limited validity of such order-of-magnitude estimates.

The electric dipole and magnetic dipole effects can be distinguished experimentally by the different angular distribution of the disintegration products. The experimental values of the ratio of the photomagnetic to the photoelectric cross section (Myers 42, Graham 45, Lassen 48, Hamermesh 49, Woodward 49, Meiners 49, Bishop 51) are in satisfactory agreement with theory, considering the errors in both the theory and the experiments.

The total photodisintegration cross section is shown in Fig. 4.1 as a function-of-energy. We have also drawn in on the figure some of the more recent experimental values (Wilson 49, Snell 49, Barnes 50). The agreement is again satisfactory. It should be pointed out that for energies $\hbar\omega > 4$ Mev the total cross section is almost entirely due to the electric dipole effect. Hence the agreement in this region (especially for the 6-Mev gamma-ray from O^{16}) confirms the applicability of the concept of effective range to the analysis of photodisintegration measurements but does not give any new information about the neutron-proton force. A critical discussion of these and other data (Snell 50a, Bishop 50, Hough 50, Phillips 50a, Carver 51) is given by Salpeter (51) and Feshbach (51).

F. Photodisintegration of the Deuteron; Energies above 10 Mev

The approximations which we have made so far fail for photon energies above about 10 Mev. In the calculation of the dipole disintegration probability the detailed behavior of the wave function inside the range of the force becomes important. Furthermore it is no longer possible to neglect the phase shift in the ^3P state for the electric dipole disintegration (the magnetic dipole disintegration probability is negligible compared to the electric dipole effect at these energies). The phase shift in the ^3P state depends critically on the exchange character of the neutron-proton force. For example, it is zero for a Serber force and has opposite sign for pure Wigner and pure Majorana forces. Finally, the transitions due to absorption of quadrupole radiation are no longer completely negligible compared to the dipole-induced transitions.

An even more serious difficulty comes from the neglect of charge exchange currents and relativistic effects in the computation of the radiative transition probabilities. Möller and Rosenfeld (Möller 43) and Sachs (51) have shown that the relevant correction terms are small for electric multipole transitions. However, the argument does not apply to magnetic radiations.

Several calculations have been carried out to find the photodisintegration cross sections above 10 Mev, under various assumptions about the neutron-proton force (Rarita 41a,b; Rose 47; Marshall 49, 50; Levinger 49, 50; Schiff 50, 50a). As expected, the results are sensitive to the force law, and accurate experimental determinations of the disintegration cross section in the 10 to 100 Mev range would give valuable information about the neutron-proton force. The angular distribution of the emitted particles is more sensitive to the details of the force than the total cross section (Rarita 41a,b). Unfortunately, the experimental material available is not sufficient to allow definite conclusions to be drawn. The total cross section has been measured at a gamma-ray energy of $\hbar\omega = 17.6$ Mev (Barnes 50). The value $\sigma = (8.5 \pm 1.2) \times 10^{-28}$ cm^2 is somewhat larger than from an extrapolation of (4.38) to this energy. However, the difference is not large enough to allow any definite conclusions. The angular distribution of the emitted particles has been measured by Fuller (49, 50) in the range $4 < \hbar\omega < 20$ Mev, but again the accuracy is too low to allow any detailed interpretation.

▶   **5. INTERNAL CONVERSION**

A. Conversion Coefficients

A nucleus in an excited state can perform a transition to a lower state not only by emitting a light quantum, but also by transmitting energy directly to the electrons surrounding the nucleus. The transition to a lower state is then connected with the ejection of an atomic electron from a bound orbit. The energy of the ejected electron is equal to the energy lost by the nucleus less the binding energy of the electron in the atom. This process is called "internal conversion." It is sometimes wrongly treated as an internal photoeffect by describing it in the following way: a light quantum emitted by the nucleus is immediately absorbed by the electrons of the atom. Actually, however, the transmission of energy from the nucleus to the electrons is a process which occurs independently of the emission of a light quantum.

As Taylor and Mott (32, 33) have pointed out, the total transition probability $\bar{T}(a,b)$ from a nuclear state a to a nuclear state b is the sum of two terms:

$$\bar{T}(a,b) = T(a,b) + T^{(i)}(a,b) \tag{5.1}$$

where $T(a,b)$ is the radiation transition probability as given by (3.21) and (3.22), and $T^{(i)}(a,b)$ is the probability of internal conversion. The *internal conversion coefficient* α is defined by

$$T^{(i)}(a,b) \equiv \alpha \, T(a,b) \tag{5.2}$$

so that we get

$$\bar{T}(a,b) = (1+\alpha) \, T(a,b) \tag{5.3}$$

The energy is transmitted from the nucleus to the electron by the electromagnetic interaction of the nucleus and the electron. The main contribution comes from the electrostatic Coulomb interaction.

We shall sketch the calculation of $T^{(i)}(a,b)$ by making a number of simplifying assumptions.

(a) We consider only K conversion; that means transmission of energy to electrons in the K shell of the atom.

(b) We restrict ourselves to the electrostatic interaction and use the non-relativistic wave equation for the electron. This is valid only for cases in which all the electron velocities involved are small compared to the velocity of light.

(c) We use a plane wave approximation for the ejected electron. This is correct only if the energy of the ejected electron is large compared to its binding energy in the atom. Let ψ_a and ψ_b be the nuclear wave functions of the nuclear states a and b, which depend on the nucleon coordinates $\mathbf{r}_1 \cdots \mathbf{r}_A$; we assume $E_a > E_b$. Furthermore let v_a, v_b be the electronic wave functions in the K shell and in the continuum after ejection, respectively:

$$v_a = (\pi a^3)^{-1/2} \exp\left(-\frac{R}{a}\right) \qquad \left(a = \frac{a_0}{Z}\right) \tag{5.4}$$

$$v_b = V^{-1/2} \exp(i\mathbf{k}\cdot\mathbf{R}) \tag{5.5}$$

$\mathbf{R}$ is the position vector of the electron with respect to the nucleus, $a_0 = \hbar^2/me^2$ is the Bohr radius of the hydrogen atom, $\mathbf{k}$ is the wave vector of the electron after ejection, and V is the volume of the "box" in which the system is included (this volume drops out in the final result). The transition probability between the initial state $\varphi_a = \psi_a v_a$ and the final state $\varphi_b = \psi_b v_b$ is

$$\text{Transition probability} = \frac{2\pi}{\hbar} |H'_{ab}|^2 z(k) \, d\Omega \tag{5.6}$$

Here H'_{ab} is the matrix element of the interaction energy H' (which we shall assume to be described by the electrostatic interaction between the nucleus and the electron), and $z(k) \, d\Omega$ is the number of states of the ejected electron per unit energy range, for electron directions within the solid angle element $d\Omega$. $z(k)$ is given by

$$z(k) = V \frac{m\hbar k}{(2\pi\hbar)^3} \tag{5.6a}$$

We are interested in the total transition probability $T^{(i)}(a,b)$ between the two nuclear states ψ_a and ψ_b due to internal conversion in the K shell. We must therefore integrate (5.6) over all directions of the ejected electron, and we must multiply by 2 because there are two electrons in the K shell, each of which may be ejected by internal conversion:

$$T^{(i)}(a,b) = 2\frac{2\pi}{\hbar} z(k) \int |H'_{ab}|^2 \, d\Omega \tag{5.7}$$

We assume as interaction energy the electrostatic interaction between the protons in the nucleus and the electron:

$$H' = \sum_{i=1}^{Z} \frac{e^2}{|\mathbf{R}-\mathbf{r}_i|} \tag{5.8}$$

The matrix element H'_{ab} is then equal to

$$H'_{ab} = (\pi a^3 V)^{-1/2} \sum_{i=1}^{Z} \int d^3R \int d\tau \exp(-i\mathbf{k}\cdot\mathbf{R}) \, \psi_b{}^* \frac{e^2}{|\mathbf{R}-\mathbf{r}_i|}$$
$$\times \exp\left(-\frac{R}{a}\right) \psi_a \tag{5.9}$$

where the first integration extends over the coordinates of the electron, the second integration over all the coordinates which occur in the nuclear wave functions. In order to evaluate this integral approximately, we observe that the main contribution to the integration over the electron coordinate $\mathbf{R}$ comes from values of $R \equiv |\mathbf{R}|$ larger than the nuclear coordinates $r_i \equiv |\mathbf{r}_i|$. For $r_i < R$ we can expand $|\mathbf{R}-\mathbf{r}_i|^{-1}$ as follows:

$$\frac{1}{|\mathbf{R}-\mathbf{r}_i|} = \sum_{l=0}^{\infty} \sum_{m=-l}^{l} \frac{4\pi}{2l+1} \frac{r_i{}^l}{R^{l+1}} Y_{lm}(\Theta,\Phi) \, Y_{lm}{}^*(\theta_i,\phi_i) \tag{5.10}$$

Here Θ and Φ are the polar angles of the vector $\mathbf{R}$, and θ_i, ϕ_i are the polar angles of the vector $\mathbf{r}_i$. Substitution of (5.10) into (5.9) gives

$$H'_{ab} = \frac{e}{(\pi a^3 V)^{1/2}} \sum_{l=0}^{\infty} \sum_{m=-l}^{l} \frac{4\pi}{2l+1} Q_{lm}(a,b) \, J_{lm} \tag{5.11}$$

where $Q_{lm}(a,b)$ is the electric multipole matrix element (3.32) and J_{lm} is the integral

$$J_{lm} \equiv \int \exp\left(-\frac{R}{a}\right) \exp(-i\mathbf{k}\cdot\mathbf{R}) \, R^{-(l+1)} Y_{lm}(\Theta,\Phi) \, d^3R \tag{5.12}$$

According to assumption (c) above, we are interested in internal conversion well above the threshold for this process. We can therefore assume that the wavelength $\lambda = k^{-1}$ of the outgoing electron is much smaller than the Bohr radius a of the K shell of the atom, i.e., $ka \gg 1$. In that approximation we can set $\exp(-R/a) \cong 1$ and we can evaluate the integral directly by the use of the addition theorem for the spherical harmonics (see Appendix A, Section 2). Let θ, ϕ be the polar angles of the vector $\mathbf{k}$ with respect to some arbitrary z direction in space. Then[1]

$$J_{lm} = 4\pi\, i^{-l}\, \frac{k^{l-2}}{(2l-1)!!}\, Y_{lm}(\theta,\phi) \qquad (\text{for } ka \gg 1) \qquad (5.13)$$

Substitution of (5.13) into (5.11) gives the following approximate value for the matrix element H'_{ab} of the electrostatic interaction:

$$H'_{ab} = \frac{(4\pi)^2\, e}{(\pi a^3 V)^{1/2}} \sum_{l=0}^{\infty} \sum_{m=-l}^{l} \frac{i^l\, k^{l-2}}{(2l+1)!!}\, Q_{lm}(a,b)\, Y_{lm}(\theta,\phi) \qquad (5.14)$$

We substitute (5.14) into (5.7). The integration is simplified by the orthogonality and normalization of the spherical harmonics. The result for the transition probability per unit time associated with the internal conversion process is

$$T^{(i)}(a,b) = 128\pi\, \frac{me^2}{\hbar^3 a^3} \sum_{l=0}^{\infty} \sum_{m=-l}^{l} \frac{k^{2l-3}}{[(2l+1)!!]^2}\, |Q_{lm}(a,b)|^2 \qquad (5.15)$$

Because of the selection rules, only certain values of l actually occur in the sum (5.15). Furthermore, in practice only the lowest possible value of l gives an appreciable contribution. This lowest value is given in Table 2.1, in the column marked "electric radiation."

In order to get a rough value for the internal conversion coefficient, we shall restrict ourselves to the parity-favored transitions which occur predominantly by emission of electric multipole radiation of the same order $L = l_{\min}$ which contributes to (5.15). In that case we can compare (5.15) directly with the radiative transition probability (3.21), summed over all values of m (we neglect the contribution of Q'_{lm}). The internal conversion coefficient α, (5.2), is then given by ($a_0 = $ Bohr radius of the hydrogen atom)

$$\alpha \cong 16\, \frac{l}{l+1}\, \frac{Z^3}{a_0^4}\, \frac{k^{2l-3}}{\kappa^{2l+1}} \qquad (5.16)$$

Under our approximations it is consistent to neglect the binding energy of the electron in the K shell compared to $\hbar\omega$. Thus we get

[1] See the footnote on page 590 for the definition of the double factorial.

$$\frac{\hbar^2 k^2}{2m} = \hbar\omega - B_K \cong \hbar\omega \tag{5.17}$$

where B_K is the atomic binding energy of an electron in the K shell. Substitution of (5.17) into (5.16) gives the final *approximate value for the internal conversion coefficient $\alpha_K(l)$ for K shell conversion in parity-favored transitions:*

$$\alpha_K(l) \cong Z^3 \left(\frac{e^2}{\hbar c}\right)^4 \frac{l}{l+1} \left(\frac{2mc^2}{\hbar\omega}\right)^{l+5/2} \tag{5.18}$$

This formula is a good approximation only in very special cases, namely for values of $Ze^2/\hbar c \ll 1$ (otherwise the electron wave functions must be treated relativistically) and for transition energies much larger than the binding energy of the K shell electrons:

$$E_a - E_b = \hbar\omega \gg B_K$$

It is seen that the internal conversion increases strongly with Z and with l but decreases with increasing transition energy $\hbar\omega$. Thus internal conversion is an important effect for nuclei of high atomic number in low-energy transitions of high multipole order l.

Our simple derivation would give no internal conversion for nuclear transitions which proceed predominantly by emission of magnetic multipole radiation. This is a result of our restriction to the electrostatic interaction (5.8) between the electrons and the nucleus. If we also consider electromagnetic interactions, we obtain terms in (5.15) which involve the magnetic multipole moments M_{lm} as well as the electric multipole moments Q_{lm}.

Calculations which use less sweeping approximations than the derivation given in this section were performed by many authors (Dancoff 39a; Hebb 38, 40; Drell 49; Lowen 49). Exact calculations, using the relativistic wave functions for the electrons, have been performed by Hulme et al. (32, 36), Taylor (32, 33), Fisk (34, 34a), and recently by Rose et al. (49, 51), Griffith (49), and Reitz (50). Experimental verification of the exact calculations has been obtained by Waggoner (50) and Petch (50). On the other hand, the comparison of exact and approximate calculations for K shell conversion coefficients indicates that the approximate calculations do not yield results of adequate accuracy; experimental evidence (Goldhaber 51) indicates that the approximate calculations for internal conversion in shells other than the K shell also fail to give sufficiently accurate results.

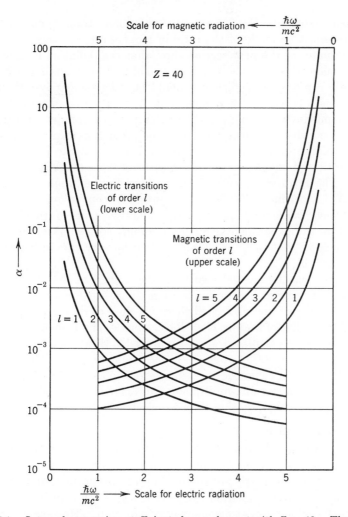

FIG. 5.1. Internal conversion coefficients for an element with $Z = 40$. The lower scale applies to electric radiation, the upper one to magnetic radiation. The number l indicates the multipole order. The values are taken from the tables of Rose et al. (51).

Figure 5.1 shows an example of these internal conversion coefficients for an element with $Z = 40$. In parity-favored transitions the radiation is practically pure electric multipole radiation of the order L listed in Table 2.1, and consequently the electric internal conversion coefficients are appropriate. These coefficients depend on the energy $\hbar\omega$ of the radiation, the lowest permissible multipole order L, and the charge Z of the nucleus. They do not depend on the value of the multipole moments Q_{Lm}. In parity-unfavored transitions a closer estimate must be made of the ratio of magnetic to electric radiation. The estimates of the next section show that the radiation is predominantly magnetic, of order L listed in Table 2.1. Consequently the magnetic conversion coefficients should be used for parity-unfavored transitions. It should be pointed out, however, that the prediction of predominantly magnetic radiation in parity-forbidden transitions is on a somewhat less firm basis than the prediction of predominantly electric radiation in parity-favored transitions. In exceptional cases the electric and magnetic radiation may be of the same order of magnitude. The ratio of electric to magnetic radiation would then enter into the experimentally observed internal conversion coefficient. While such cases may occur, the estimates made in this chapter as well as the experimental evidence summarized in Section 6 lead one to believe that these exceptions should be very rare in low-energy transitions.[1]

Electrons can be ejected also from the L shell of the atom. This process is in general less probable than the K shell conversion, since the probability of finding L shell electrons close to the nucleus is much smaller than that of finding K shell electrons. The L shell conversion coefficients were calculated approximately by Hebb and Nelson (40), Sachs (40), Drell (49), Lowen (49), and Gellman (50). The ratio of K shell to L shell conversion (often referred to as the "K-to-L ratio") decreases with increasing multipole order l; for the same l the ratio is larger for magnetic radiation than for electric radiation.

B. $0 \to 0$ Transitions

A case of special interest arises in the transitions of the nucleus between two states both of which have spin $I = 0$. As we have seen in Section 2, there are no multipoles of order $l = 0$ in the radiation field. Hence no radiative transition can take place. The transition $0 \to 0$ is strictly forbidden for electromagnetic radiation. However, a transition is possible in which the K electrons take over the energy (Fowler 30, Yukawa 35).

It seems at first that the matrix element (5.11) of internal conversion also vanishes, since it is proportional to Q_{lm}. In this case, however,

---

[1] In the literature one very often encounters the erroneous statement that the electric multipole radiation of order l has approximately the same probability as the magnetic multipole radiation of order $l-1$. If this were true, the "mixed" transitions would be the rule rather than the exception. We have pointed out in a footnote on page 592 that the above statement is wrong. The more detailed estimates in Section 6 will give further examples of the difference in transition probability for these two types of transition.

we must also take into account the contribution to the matrix element of the region in which $r_i > R$, which was not included in (5.11) when the expansion (5.10) was used. This is the region of configuration space for which the electron is within the nucleus. Its contribution is negligible in general, but it is most important in the case considered here. Since a transition of the $0 \rightarrow 0$ type does not produce any electromagnetic field outside the nucleus, the energy transfer must take place inside, i.e., for $R < r_i$. In this region we must interchange r_i and R on the right side of (5.10). We need to consider only the term with $l = 0$, which is the only one giving rise to a matrix element between two nuclear states with $I = 0$. We then get

$$H'_{ab} = \frac{e}{(\pi a^3 V)^{1/2}} \sum_{i=1}^{Z} \int d\tau \, \psi_b^* \frac{1}{r_i} \psi_a \int_{R < r_i} d^3R \exp\left(-\frac{R}{a}\right) \exp\left(-i\mathbf{k}\cdot\mathbf{R}\right)$$

(5.19)

Since the intergration over R extends over very small values of R only, we can replace the exponentials by unity:

$$H'_{ab} = \frac{4\pi}{3} \frac{e}{(\pi a^3 V)^{1/2}} \sum_{i=1}^{Z} \int \psi_b^* \, r_i^2 \, \psi_a \, d\tau$$

(5.20)

The sum in (5.20) is of the order of magnitude of the square of the nuclear radius[1] and will be denoted by $\overline{R^2}$. Substitution of (5.20) into (5.7) gives the *transition probability per unit time for* $0 \rightarrow 0$ *transitions:*

$$T^{0 \rightarrow 0}(a,b) = \frac{32}{9} \frac{e^2}{\hbar c} Z^3 \left(\frac{\overline{R^2}}{a_0^2}\right)^2 \left(2 \frac{\Delta E}{mc^2}\right)^{1/2} \frac{mc^2}{\hbar}$$

(5.21)

where $a_0 = \hbar^2/me^2$ is the Bohr radius of the hydrogen atom, and $\Delta E = E_a - E_b - B_K = \hbar^2 k^2/2m$ is the energy of the emerging electron. For $\overline{R^2}$ of the order of $(6 \times 10^{-13} \text{cm})^2$ we get

$$T^{0 \rightarrow 0}(a,b) \sim 0.5 \, Z^3 \left(\frac{\Delta E}{mc^2}\right)^{1/2} 10^4 \text{ sec}^{-1}$$

(5.22)

---

[1] A similar expression is estimated in Section 6 under the assumption of the validity of an independent-particle model. Formulas (6.7) and (6.7a) would give $\overline{R^2} = 3R^2/5$, where R is the radius of the nucleus.

More detailed estimates of the matrix element $\overline{R^2}$ on the basis of the experimental evidence have been made by Drell (50). The matrix element $\overline{R^2}$ is different from zero only if ψ_a and ψ_b have the same parity. Hence a 0→0 transition of this type cannot occur between states of different parity. Still, the lifetime of state ψ_a would not be infinitely long. Other transfer processes can take place whose probabilities are extremely low and negligible in all other cases (emission of two quanta, internal conversion with simultaneous emission of a quantum; see Sachs 40a).

C. Internal Pair Formation

If the energy difference between the nuclear states φ_a and φ_b is larger than $2mc^2$, a new type of internal conversion can occur. The energy can be transmitted to electrons in the "negative-energy states" near the nucleus. These states occur in the relativistic wave equation of the electron. It is well known that Dirac's theory of the positron assumes that the states of negative kinetic energy are occupied by electrons. The lifting of one of these negative-energy electrons into a positive-energy state appears as the creation of an electron-positron pair. This process has been suggested by Oppenheimer and Nedelsky (33) and calculations have been performed by various authors (Jäeger 35; Rose 35, 49a; Thomas 40; Yamaguchi 51).

The probability of internal pair formation is larger than the probability of ejection of a K shell electron if the available energy is appreciably larger than $2mc^2$. An important case of this type is the transition between the first excited state and the ground state of O^{16}. Their energy difference is 6 Mev (Lauritsen 50), and no electromagnetic radiation was observed. Oppenheimer and Schwinger (39) suggested that this absence of radiation can be explained by the assumption that this is a 0→0 transition. For this high energy the internal pair formation process predominates. The electron-positron pairs were found experimentally by several authors (Streib 41, Kojima 43) and have been investigated very carefully by Lauritsen's group (Rasmussen 50, Chao 50). Another case of internal pair formation has been observed in Na^{24} by Rae (49).

Internal pair formation supplements ordinary internal conversion in that the pair formation rate is largest where the internal conversion rate is smallest, namely in the region of low atomic number Z and high transition energies. Horton (48) has suggested that measurement of the angular correlation between the emerging electron and positron would give rather specific information about the multipole order and type of the transition. (See also Rose 49a.)

6. TRANSITIONS BETWEEN LOW-LYING STATES OF NUCLEI

A. Theoretical Estimates

The calculation of the radiative transition probability between two nuclear states a and b is practically impossible except in the case of the deuteron. For all other nuclei the wave functions describing the states are unknown. In spite of this, it is possible to some extent to predict the order of magnitude of the transition probabilities, since they depend very strongly on the multipole order l of the transition.

We restrict ourselves in this section to transitions between nuclear states near the ground state, with energy differences less than several Mev. The wavelength $\lambda = \kappa^{-1}$ of the light is 1.97×10^{-11} cm for 1 Mev and is always large compared to nuclear dimensions. According to (3.32) the electric multipole moments are at most of the order ZeR^l, where R is the radius of the nucleus. As indicated in Section 3, the magnetic multipole moments are smaller than the corresponding electric ones by a factor of the order of v/c. The transition probability corresponding to a multipole moment Q_{lm} or M_{lm} is given by (3.21) and (3.22), respectively. The product $\kappa^l Q_{lm}$ in (3.21) is at most equal to $Ze(\kappa R)^l$, where κR is small compared to unity for the energies $\hbar\omega$ under consideration. We therefore expect the transition probabilities to decrease rapidly with increasing $l_{\min} = L$, where L is as given in Table 2.1.

The ratio between the electric and magnetic multipole moments can be estimated more closely from the structure of expressions (3.32) and (3.33). We use integration by parts to transform (3.33) into the following expression:

$$M_{lm}(a,b) = \frac{1}{l+1} \frac{e}{Mc} \sum_{k=1}^{Z} \int r_k{}^l \, (\mathbf{L}_k Y_{lm})^* \cdot (\varphi_b{}^* \mathbf{p}_k \varphi_a) \, d\tau \qquad (6.1)$$

We estimate the integral as follows: the momentum operator $\mathbf{p}_k$ gives a result of the order of magnitude of Mv, where M is the mass of each nucleon and v is the speed of the nucleons inside the nucleus. Comparison of (6.1) with (3.32) then shows that, except for factors of order unity, the ratio of M_{lm} to Q_{lm} is approximately[1]

$$\frac{M_{lm}}{Q_{lm}} \sim \frac{v}{c} \qquad (6.2)$$

---

[1] It should be realized, of course, that either M_{lm} or Q_{lm} must vanish for given initial and final states, because of the parity selection rule. Relation (6.2) refers to different transitions under otherwise similar conditions.

We have estimated the kinetic energy per nucleon in Chapter VII, Section 2, to be of the order of 10 to 20 Mev. We get an estimate for $(v/c)^2$ by comparing this kinetic energy with the rest energy Mc^2 of the nucleons. Thus $(v/c)^2$ is of the order 0.02 to 0.04.

However, it is not altogether justified to use the full value of v/c for the estimate (6.2). We are interested in transitions between two states a and b. Thus the "effective" speed v for the transition is more nearly the difference between the speeds in the initial and final states. We get an alternative and more useful estimate of the order of magnitude of the ratio of magnetic to electric multipole moments by replacing the operator "div" appearing in (3.33) by R^{-1}, where R is of the order of magnitude of the nuclear radius. The operator $\mathbf{L}$ gives rise to a multiplication by a number of the order l, which roughly cancels the factor $(l+1)^{-1}$ for order-of-magnitude estimates. We then get

$$\frac{M_{lm}}{Q_{lm}} \sim \frac{\hbar}{McR} \tag{6.3}$$

This ratio is, in principle, not different from the ratio v/c which appears in (6.2). The linear dimension R of a quantum-mechanical system is connected with the velocities v by $R \sim \hbar/Mv$, according to the uncertainty principle.

Relation (6.3) lends itself to the following simple interpretation: the electric polarization density P in the nucleus is of the order of the electric moment eR divided by the volume R^3, $P \sim e/R^2$. The corresponding magnetization density M is of the order of the magnetic moments $e\hbar/Mc$ divided by the nuclear volume, $\mathsf{M} \sim (e\hbar/Mc)R^{-3}$. The ratio of these two densities should be of the order of the ratio of the multipole moments, and it is identical with (6.3).

The magnetic multipole moment M'_{lm} contributed by the spins, (3.35), is comparable to the orbital magnetic multipole moment since $\mathbf{L}/(l+1)$ is of the same order of magnitude as $\mu\mathbf{\sigma}$. Actually the intrinsic magnetic moments μ of the nucleons are somewhat larger than unity and therefore $\mu\mathbf{\sigma}$ is probably two to three times larger than $\mathbf{L}/(l+1)$. We shall therefore use the following estimate:

$$\frac{|M_{lm} + M'_{lm}|^2}{|Q_{lm}|^2} \sim 10 \left(\frac{\hbar}{McR}\right)^2 \tag{6.3a}$$

The contribution of the spins to the electric matrix elements, Q'_{lm}, is appreciably smaller than the contribution of the charge density (3.32). If we replace the operator "div" as before by R^{-1}, and neglect factors of order unity, we get, from (3.34) and (3.32),

$$\frac{Q'_{lm}}{Q_{lm}} \sim \frac{\kappa\hbar}{Mc} = \frac{\hbar\omega}{Mc^2} \tag{6.4}$$

For transition energies of a few Mev or less, this ratio is of the order of 10^{-3}. We shall therefore neglect the matrix elements Q'_{lm} in the rest of this chapter.

We emphasize that estimates (6.3a) and (6.4) are only very rough indications of the order of magnitude of the matrix elements. In special cases selection rules and other effects can lead to results which differ considerably from these estimates (e.g., the photodisintegration of the deuteron near threshold; see Section 4).

In order to obtain an estimate of the actual value of the multipole moments we must adopt some kind of nuclear model. The simplest results can be drawn from the independent-particle model, and there are experimental indications (see Chapter XIV) that this model describes low-lying nuclear levels reasonably well. In the independent-particle model a state of the nucleus is described by the quantum numbers of the individual nucleons. The multipole moments, (3.32) to (3.35), between two nuclear states a and b are different from zero only if the two states differ in the quantum numbers of only *one* nucleon. If a and b differed in the quantum numbers of two nucleons, all integrals would vanish for orthogonality reasons, since the operators in the integrals contain the coordinates of only one nucleon at a time.

Let us now consider a transition in which one proton (say nucleon number 1) changes its state. We further assume that the orbital angular momentum of this proton is zero in the final state and is equal to l in the initial state. Then the electric multipole radiation emitted is of order l. We further assume that the transition is parity favored, i.e., the intrinsic spin of the proton in the initial state is parallel to l. Then the two wave functions of the proton have the form

$$\begin{aligned}
w_a &= u_a(r)\, Y_{lm}(\theta,\phi)\, \alpha \\
w_b &= u_b(r)\, (4\pi)^{-1/2}\, \alpha
\end{aligned} \tag{6.5}$$

where α is the spin function for a particle with spin up, and u_a, u_b are functions of $r = |\mathbf{r}|$ only. Substitution into (3.32) gives (remembering that only the first term of the sum over k contributes)

$$Q_{lm} = (4\pi)^{-1/2}\, e\, J_l \qquad \text{(independent-particle model)} \tag{6.6}$$

where

$$J_l = \int_0^\infty r^l\, u_a(r)\, u_b(r)\, r^2\, dr \tag{6.7}$$

We now proceed to estimate the order of magnitude of this radial integral. The simplest estimate is obtained by setting both $u_a(r)$ and $u_b(r)$ equal to the same constant for values of r less than the nuclear radius R, and equal to zero for values of r greater than R. The constant is found from the normalization of the wave functions w_a and w_b and is $(3/R^3)^{1/2}$. With this assumption we get the order-of-magnitude estimate

$$J_l \sim \frac{3R^l}{l+3} \tag{6.7a}$$

Evidently (6.7a) is a very rough estimate. The radial wave functions u_a and u_b are not constant but oscillate in some manner for $r < R$ and drop gradually to zero for $r > R$. We therefore can expect that the actual value of J_l is somewhat smaller than (6.7a). The estimate (6.7a) gives an idea of the order of magnitude which one can anticipate in most transitions between low-lying levels. Values of J_l smaller than (6.7a) by factors, say, up to 30 may well be expected. In some exceptional cases, in which the wave functions u_a and u_b overlap very badly, the integral J_l may even be several orders of magnitude smaller than (6.7a). However, J_l should not be very much larger than (6.7a) as long as the independent-particle model is valid. In view of the very rough nature of these estimates, the special assumption of $l = 0$ in the final state and of a parity-favored transition are not essential for the result.

The estimate of the magnetic multipole moments on the independent-particle model depends more on the details of the model. For example, if there were no spin-orbit coupling, the contribution M'_{lm} of the intrinsic spins to the magnetic multipole moment would vanish completely (an example can be found in Section 4B). However, there is good reason to assume the existence of a spin-orbit coupling in the independent-particle model (see Chapter XIV). Hence we can apply estimate (6.3a) for the ratio of magnetic to electric multipole moments.

If we substitute estimates (6.7a), (6.6), and (6.3a) for the multipole moments into the expressions (3.21) and (3.22) for the transition probabilities, we get the following expression for *electric radiation of multipole order l,*[1]

---

[1] It is possible to generalize expression (6.8) for cases in which the value of l in the final state is not zero. In the general case of an electric transition of multipole order l from an initial state with orbital angular momentum l_1 and total angular momentum J_1 to a final state with orbital angular momentum l_2 and total angular momentum J_2, (6.8) must be multiplied by a statistical factor. Under the assumption that the orbital and total angular momenta are caused by only one particle

$$T_E(l) \cong \frac{2(l+1)}{l\,[(2l+1)!!]^2} \left(\frac{3}{l+3}\right)^2 \frac{e^2}{\hbar c}\,(\kappa R)^{2l}\,\omega$$

$$= \frac{4.4\,(l+1)}{l\,[(2l+1)!!]^2} \left(\frac{3}{l+3}\right)^2 \left(\frac{\hbar\omega}{197\ \mathrm{Mev}}\right)^{2l+1}$$

$$\times\ (R\ \mathrm{in}\ 10^{-13}\ \mathrm{cm})^{2l}\ 10^{21}\ \mathrm{sec}^{-1} \quad (6.8)$$

and, for *magnetic radiation of multipole order l*,

$$T_M(l) \cong \frac{20\,(l+1)}{l\,[(2l+1)!!]^2} \left(\frac{3}{l+3}\right)^2 \frac{e^2}{\hbar c}\left(\frac{\hbar}{McR}\right)^2 (\kappa R)^{2l}\,\omega$$

$$= \frac{1.9\,(l+1)}{l\,[(2l+1)!!]^2} \left(\frac{3}{l+3}\right)^2 \left(\frac{\hbar\omega}{197\ \mathrm{Mev}}\right)^{2l+1}$$

$$\times\ (R\ \mathrm{in}\ 10^{-13}\ \mathrm{cm})^{2l-2}\ 10^{21}\ \mathrm{sec}^{-1} \quad (6.9)$$

Equations (6.8) and (6.9) are only very rough estimates. The actual values are expected to be smaller than these estimates by factors perhaps up to 1000. Exceptional cases of transitions between two states whose wave functions overlap very badly cannot be excluded; in those cases the actual transition probabilities would be very much smaller than the predicted ones (by factors much larger than 10^3). Still these estimates may be of some value for a first orientation since, for gamma-ray energies below 1 Mev, $T_E(l)$ as well as $T_M(l)$ changes by a factor of about 10^6 when l changes by one unit. Expression (6.8) for the electric transition probability can be considered an upper limit as long as the independent-particle model is applicable.

These estimates refer to the transition probability associated with emission of multipole radiation. To get the actual lifetimes we must correct for the transition probability associated with the internal conversion process, i.e., multiply by $(1+\alpha)$, where α is the conversion coefficient. This correction is very important for $\hbar\omega$ in the 100-kev region and medium or heavy elements, especially for high multipole orders l (Axel 49). In many cases the internal conversion coefficient is known experimentally, so that the correction can be made without knowing the multipole order and parity of the transition.

(this assumption is usually made in the nuclear shell model) the statistical factor is:

$$(2l_1+1)(2l_2+1)(2l+1)(2J_2+1)\ [V(l_1l_2l;000)]^2\ [W(l_1J_1l_2J_2;\tfrac{1}{2},l)]^2,$$

where the quantity V is related to the Clebsch-Gordan coefficients and is defined in Appendix A, equation (A,5.8), and W is a coefficient introduced by Racah (42a) [equation (36) page 444 of that paper]. This statistical factor reduces to unity for the case considered in the text $(J_1 = l_1 + \tfrac{1}{2} = l + \tfrac{1}{2};\ J_2 = \tfrac{1}{2},\ l_2 = 0)$.

It can be seen that the magnetic radiation of multipole order l is estimated to be about 100 times less probable than electric radiation of the same order. However, these radiations never compete in a given nuclear transition. A competition between electric and magnetic radiation may occur, in parity-unfavored transitions, between magnetic radiation of order l and electric radiation of the next higher order $l+1$. Estimates (6.8) and (6.9) would predict a difference in the transition probabilities of these two radiations by a factor of about 10^4 for light quanta of energy between 0.1 and 1 Mev. Hence these estimates predict almost pure magnetic radiation in the case of parity-unfavored transitions. This is in contrast to many statements in the literature that magnetic multipole radiation of order l is about as probable as electric multipole radiation of order $l+1$.

Expression (6.6) is calculated for a special model, the independent-particle model, and it is questionable whether it can be used for an estimate of actual transition probabilities. It can be argued in favor of the validity of (6.6) that the multipole moment retains its order of magnitude if the actual states of the nucleus can be expressed as linear combinations of the states of the model, with coefficients which possess random phases.

There are other special models, however, which give rise to quite different expressions for the multipole moments. For example, the transition probability coming from the radiation of the surface vibrations of a liquid drop with a uniform charge distribution gives rise to electric multipoles with $l \geq 2$. It was calculated by Lowen (41), Fierz (43) and Berthelot (44); they obtain

$$
\begin{aligned}
Q_{lm}(a,b) &= 0 &\text{(for } l = 0,1) \\
Q_{lm}(a,b) &= \left(\frac{3}{32\pi}\right)^{1/2} l^{1/2} \left(\frac{\hbar}{AM\omega}\right)^{1/2} Ze\,R^{l-1} &\text{(for } l \geq 2)
\end{aligned} \qquad (6.10)
$$

where AM is the total mass of the nucleus. There are characteristic differences between this expression and the one derived from the independent-particle picture: (1) the matrix element is proportional to Z as a result of the fact that all charges move here in a common motion; (2) Q contains the factor $(\hbar/AM\omega)^{1/2}$ which is the matrix element of the amplitude of an oscillator vibration; hence the transition probability is proportional to ω^{2l} instead of ω^{2l+1}; (3) the nuclear radius R occurs raised to the power $l-1$ instead of l; finally, (4) the electric dipole moment $(l=1)$ vanishes altogether. These differences can be explained by the fact that the liquid drop model and the independent-particle model represent two extreme views of nuclear dynamics. In the former model the motions of the nucleons are highly correlated; in the latter they are completely independent.

Strong correlations between neutron and proton motions, no matter which special model is used, have an effect of great importance for the probability of dipole transitions between low-lying nuclear levels. We shall show that the *assumption of appreciable correlations between neutron and proton motions depresses the values of the electric dipole moments* $Q_{1,m}$ *considerably below the (independent-particle model) estimate* (6.6). In the liquid drop model, an example of extreme correlation, the dipole moments vanish completely. The reduction of the dipole moments can be understood by considering the radiation of a system of equally charged particles, say a nucleus consisting of protons only. In such a system the electric center is the same as the center of mass. For every charge moving to the right there is an equal one moving to the left, since the center of gravity stays at rest (we are neglecting, throughout this chapter, the nuclear recoil upon emission of a gamma-ray). Hence in such a system the dipole moment is always zero; this is true both of the expectation value in any one state and of the matrix element between two different states of such a system.

If it is assumed that adjacent parts of nuclear matter move together, similarly to the flow of a liquid, the radiative effects of the motion are similar to those of a motion of particles of equal charge, the "effective" charge on each particle being $e' = (Z/A)e$. Such a system does not emit any electric dipole radiation. Hence, if models of this type are a valid first approximation to the motion in nuclei, we may expect electric dipole moments much smaller than (6.6) with $l = 1$.

These considerations lead us to expect appreciably lower electric dipole moments than the estimate (6.6) would give. It must be emphasized that the arguments do not apply to higher electric multipole moments. Only in the special case $l = 1$ is there a relation between the operator which enters Q_{lm} and the operator for the position of the center of gravity. Nor do these arguments apply to the magnetic multipole moments; we can use (6.3a) together with (6.6) for all values of l, *including* $l = 1$.

B. Experimental Material; Nuclear Isomers

Many transitions have been observed between nuclear energy states which are accompanied by the emission of a light quantum or by an internally converted electron. Most of these radiative transitions follow a beta-decay in which the product nucleus is left in an excited state as indicated in Fig. 6.1. Excited nuclear states have also been produced by inelastic collisions, by nuclear reactions in which the residual nucleus is left excited, and by electromagnetic excitation (absorption of gamma-rays).

The measurement of the transition probability is difficult if the lifetime of the excited state is very short ($<10^{-9}$ sec). However, because of the strong l dependence of the transition probability, we are led to expect long lifetimes if the difference between the angular momentum of the excited state and the angular momenta of all lower states is large enough. In fact, for radiations of multipole order $l=3$ or higher our estimates, (6.8) and (6.9), give rise to lifetimes longer than 1 sec when the radiated energy is of the order of the energy differences between low-lying nuclear states (0.1 to 0.5 Mev).

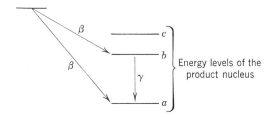

FIG. 6.1.   A beta-decay may lead directly to the ground state (a) of the product nucleus, or it may leave the product nucleus in an excited state (b). In the latter case the excited state emits a gamma-ray or an internal conversion electron.

This is the basis of Weizsäcker's theory of nuclear isomers. Long-lived excited nuclear states were found very early, and Weizsäcker (36) proposed the theory that such a long-lived state could be the first excited state above the ground state, if its angular momentum I happens to be quite different from the angular momentum I_0 of the ground state. Under these conditions the radiation emitted must be of order $l=|I-I_0|$ or $l=|I-I_0|+1$ (see Table 2.1).

We may ask why no long-lived isomeric electronic states are observed in atoms under laboratory conditions. There are many atomic states which can lose their excitation only by emission of radiation of higher multipole order than the usual atomic radiations (electric dipole). However, under laboratory conditions the atoms are not isolated from each other but collide frequently with each other, the mean time between collisions depending on the pressure. An atom in one of these states can lose its excitation by non-radiative collisions with other atoms. Thus the mean lifetime between collisions provides an upper limit for atomic lifetimes. Radiative transitions which by themselves would lead to longer lifetimes have to compete with the collision process and are correspondingly weak and hard to observe. These highly forbidden lines show up more strongly in the spectra of some stars and nebulae. The pressures there are much less than the best vacuum attainable on earth, and the mean time between collisions of atoms is correspondingly much longer. In the nuclear case the collisions between nuclei are completely unimportant, since the nuclei are shielded from each other by their electron clouds and would in any case repel each other electrostatically if brought close together. The non-radiative de-excitation of nuclei is confined to the internal conversion process.

Estimates (6.8) and (6.9) of the transition probabilities must be tested by a comparison with the experimental material. In order to perform this test it is necessary to know the transition probability as well as the multipole type and order of each transition. The order and type of the multipole radiation can be deduced in principle from measurements of the internal conversion coefficients in the different electronic shells; the absolute value of the conversion coefficient as well as the ratio of the K shell to the L shell conversion can be used for this determination. Unfortunately the exact theoretical calculation of the conversion coefficients has not yet been completed. At this time (1951) only the conversion coefficients of the K shell for energies above 150 kev (Rose 49, 51) are calculated with the necessary accuracy. Hence this direct method of multipole determination cannot yet be fully exploited. The multipole type and order can be deduced also from the value of the spin and parity of the initial and final state of the nucleus. The spin value of the ground state is generally known, but the spin of excited states is measured only in very few cases. However, in many instances some conclusions can be drawn about the spin and parity of nuclear states by an analysis of beta-disintegrations or nuclear reactions which lead to the states in question. The study of angular correlations between successive radiations also yields some information. In general, with the methods available at present, the multipole type and order are well established only for relatively few radiative transitions.

We have collected in Table 6.1 a list of some representative cases for which the nature of the radiation seemed to be established.[1] The table contains the theoretical lifetimes of the initial states of the transitions, which are calculated from the radiative transition probabilities, (6.8) and (6.9). The theoretical lifetimes are compared with the experimental values.

The electric transitions by and large show the expected behavior. The experimental lifetimes scatter considerably; they differ from the theoretical estimate (6.8) by factors up to 100. Perhaps it is significant

---

[1] The authors are grateful to M. Deutsch and M. Goldhaber for their extensive help and advice in the discussion of the theoretical estimates and in the collection of data for this table. We also are grateful to W. Frauenfelder and A. de Shalit for valuable help. A much more complete table of isomeric transitions has been compiled by Goldhaber (51).

TABLE 6.1

TEST OF THE LIFETIME ESTIMATES, (6.8) AND (6.9)[1]

The first column lists the nucleus in which the gamma-ray transition occurs, the second column gives the energy of the gamma-ray, in Mev; the next four columns list the data used for the multipole determination: the K shell conversion coefficient α_K, the ratio of K shell to L shell conversion, the spins J_i of the initial state and J_f of the final state of the nucleus. Column 7 lists the multipole type and order; the notation used is E3 for an electric transition of multipole order $l=3$, M4 for a magnetic transition of multipole order $l=4$, etc. Columns 8 and 9 give the theoretical and experimental values of the half-lives; $7(-17)$ means 7×10^{-17} sec; the theoretical values are computed from (6.8) and (6.9), with the correction for internal conversion made as far as possible by use of experimentally determined conversion coefficients; the nuclear radius was assumed to be $R = 1.4 A^{1/3} \times 10^{-13}$ cm; most of the numbers are rounded off to one significant digit. The last column gives the ratio of the theoretical to the experimental lifetime in each case. For sources, see the footnote.

Nucleus	$\hbar\omega$	α_K	K/L	J_i	J_f	Type	Lifetime Theory	Lifetime Experiment	$\left(\dfrac{\text{Theory}}{\text{Exp.}}\right)$
A. Electric Transitions									
N^{13}	2.38	.....	....	$\frac{1}{2},+$	$\frac{1}{2},-$	E1	$7(-17)$	$1(-15)$	0.07
Cd^{111}	0.247	0.054	5.2	..	$\frac{1}{2}$	E2	$1(-8)$	$8(-8)$	0.1
Os^{186}	0.137	0.35	0.6	2	0	E2	$5(-8)$	$8(-10)$	65
Hg^{197}	0.133	~ 0.53	0.3	..	..	E2	$3(-8)$	$7(-9)$	5
Hg^{198}	0.411	0.031	....	..	..	E2	$4(-10)$	$\leq 5(-11)$	≥ 8
In^{114}	0.192	2	1	..	..	E4	$3(4)$	$4(6)$	0.008
Pb^{204}	0.905	0.06	1.5	..	..	E5	$3(3)$	$4(3)$	0.8
B. Magnetic Transitions									
Li^{7}	0.478	.....	....	$\frac{1}{2},-$	$\frac{3}{2},-$	M1	$2(-13)$	$8(-14)$	3
In^{113}	0.39	0.6	5.4	..	$\frac{9}{2}$	M4	$2(4)$	$6(3)$	3
In^{115}	0.338	~ 1	5	..	$\frac{9}{2}$	M4	$6(4)$	$2(4)$	3
Xe^{131}	0.163	~ 20	2.34	..	$\frac{3}{2}$	M4	$2(6)$	$1(7)$	0.2
Ba^{133}	0.276	2.4	3.2	..	..	M4	$1(5)$	$1(5)$	1
Ba^{137}	0.663	0.097	4.8	..	..	M4	$2(2)$	$2(2)$	1

[1] The data for the multipole determination and the lifetime were taken mainly from the compilation of nuclear data by K. Way (50). In addition, the following references were employed: N^{13}: Hornyak 50, Fowler 49, Thomas 50, 51a. The identification of the multipole order is unique since the pair conversion has been measured for the mirror transition in C^{13}. The assignment $\frac{1}{2}$ to the initial state comes from the measured proton width of this (compound) state. A detailed calculation of the theoretical lifetime which uses reasonable wave functions for the

that just among the electric quadrupole radiations one finds some transitions which are considerably faster than the theoretical estimate. This may be connected with the same deviation from the independent-particle model which is responsible for the large values of the static quadrupole moments of some nuclei. There is only one example of an electric dipole transition in Table 6.1, and this occurs in a light nucleus (N^{13}). The theoretical estimate of the lifetime seems to be in fair agreement with experiment; indeed, a more detailed calculation (Thomas 51a) gives agreement within a factor 2. Hence we do not observe here that the dipole moment is appreciably smaller than predicted by the estimate (6.6). This is to be expected, however, since the proton in N^{13} is bound only very weakly to the C^{12} core, the upper one of the two states being energetically unstable against emission of protons. Thus the proton spends a considerable fraction of its time outside the C^{12} core, and hence its motion is well approximated by that of a single particle in a potential well. The theoretical arguments for abnormally small electric dipole moments are presumably applicable only to heavier nuclei, but unfortunately no experimental material on electric dipole radiation is yet available for heavier nuclei.

The magnetic multipole transitions agree fairly well with the estimate (6.9). In particular the magnetic transitions of multipole order $l=4$, which constitute the best-known group of isomers, show surprisingly little deviation from the estimated values. There is a very large group of isomeric transitions to which one can ascribe the multipole order M4 on the basis of the nuclear shell model (see Chapter XIV); this identification is not so certain as the direct verification by the measurement of the conversion coefficients. Therefore these transitions are not listed in Table 6.1. The lifetimes of all these isomers agree very well with the estimate (6.9) (Hill 51, Goldhaber 51, Moszkowski 51).

The transition in Li^7 illustrates the remarks made earlier about parity-unfavored transitions. As far as selection rules are concerned, Li^7 can emit both magnetic dipole and electric quadrupole radiation. However, the theoretical estimates for the transition probabilities

proton in the initial and final states gives much better agreement between the theoretical and experimental values than (6.8). Cd^{111}: Roberts 51, McGinnis 51, and a private communication from M. Goldhaber. Os^{186}: Metzger 51, McGowan 50, 51. Hg^{197}: Frauenfelder 50, Huber 51. Hg^{198}: R. E. Bell, private communication. Li^7: Hornyak 50, Elliot 48, 49, Rose 50, Littauer 50; the assignment of equal parities to the two states is required by the K-capture branching ratio of Be^7. In^{114}: Steffen 51. In^{115}: Bell 49; the beta-decay data give some information about the spin of the initial state. Ba^{137}: Waggoner 50a.

show that the transition proceeds predominantly by emission of magnetic dipole radiation, the electric quadrupole radiation contributing less than 0.01 percent of all decays. This is quite typical of parity-unfavored transitions. There are many examples of the predominance of magnetic radiation (e.g., Hill 51), and so far no exception has been found. It seems therefore reasonable to assume that *most of the radiative transitions between low-lying nuclear levels proceed by emission of pure multipole radiation of the lowest multipole order l permitted by the selection rules, the radiation being electric or magnetic depending on the parity change in the nuclear transition.*

The values in Table 6.1 as well as other experimental material indicate that magnetic transitions are somewhat faster than our estimate (6.9), whereas electric transitions tend to go somewhat slower than (6.8) with the exception of some E2 transitions. Hence, for the same transition energy $\hbar\omega$, the lifetimes of electric and magnetic transitions of the same multipole order l are fairly close together (within a factor of 100) compared to the lifetimes of transitions of different multipole orders $l' \neq l$. Thus there is a rough empirical clustering of isomers into groups, each group corresponding to a definite multipole order (Goldhaber 51). This grouping was first demonstrated empirically by Axel and Dancoff (49); however, these authors suggested a different theoretical interpretation of the groups. Although the grouping is only very approximate, it is nevertheless useful for a quick orientation and in some cases allows prediction of properties of new isomers.

It is worth while to remark that the liquid drop model estimate (6.10) would lead to much poorer agreement with the experimental lifetimes.

Except for a few regions in the periodic table, low-lying long-lived (isomeric) states are the exception and not the rule. In general, the first excited state of a nucleus does not differ from the ground state in spin and parity sufficiently to lead to observable isomerism. Thus any analysis based mostly on isomeric data contains a bias toward long-lived states. There are unfortunately very few reliable data for short-lived transitions. In a few cases, among the very heavy elements, we find excited states which are able to emit alpha-particles as well as gamma-rays. In this case the radiative transition probability can be inferred from the branching ratio between alpha-decay and gamma-ray emission, together with the theoretical estimate of the alpha-decay lifetime given in Chapter XI. Bethe (37) analyzed some gamma-emissions in ThC′ and RaC′ to get radiative transition probabilities of the order of 10^{12} sec^{-1} for energies $\hbar\omega$ in the neighborhood of 1 Mev. According to the estimates given here, these are presumably magnetic dipole or electric quadrupole transitions.

So far there is relatively little evidence for electric dipole transitions between low-lying nuclear levels. Some are known in light nuclei

(N^{13} is probably the best example), and several such lines have been observed in Tc^{96} (Medicus 50). Also, according to M. Goldhaber,[1] application of Bethe's method to more highly excited states in alpha-decaying nuclei gives gamma-decay transition probabilities of the order of 10^{14} sec^{-1}, which may be electric dipole radiation. It should be pointed out, however, that this apparent scarcity of electric dipole transitions is probably spurious. They usually have expected lifetimes which are too short for present measuring techniques; the internal conversion coefficients are also rather low, and accurate measurement of these coefficients has become possible only recently. We may therefore expect to find more examples of electric dipole radiation as experimental work continues. We recall that the theoretical considerations of Section 6A indicate abnormally long lifetimes [compared to the estimate (6.8)] for these transitions. They do *not* indicate that electric dipole transitions should be entirely absent, merely that they should have a lengthened lifetime.

The nuclear shell model (see Chapter XIV) furnishes an argument for the complete absence of dipole transitions between low-lying nuclear states (Mayer 50). According to this model any two low-lying states have the same parity if their J differ by one unit only. If this is so, the parity rule would exclude any electric dipole transition among these states.

C. Directional Correlations between Successively Emitted Gamma-Rays

It is interesting to study the correlation between the directions of two gamma-rays which are emitted in two successive transitions, $a{\to}b$, $b{\to}c$. We illustrate the existence of such correlations with a simple example. Let us assume the following spins of the three states a, b, c, $(E_a > E_b > E_c)$: $I_a = I_c = 0$, $I_b = 1$. Then two successive dipole transitions take place, as indicated in Fig. 6.2. In the transition $a{\to}b$, the three possibilities $\Delta m = +1$, 0, -1 are equally probable. But a transition $a{\to}b$ with $\Delta m = 0$ must be followed by a transition $\Delta m = 0$, in $b{\to}c$; $\Delta m = \pm 1$ is followed by $\Delta m = \mp 1$.

The directional distribution in each

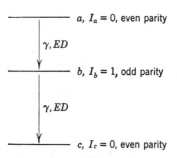

FIG. 6.2. Two successive transitions in the same nucleus lead to an angular correlation between the directions of emission of the two gamma-rays.

[1] Private communication.

of these transitions is given by (3.16). We find that, for electric dipole transitions, the intensity in the direction θ, ϕ is

$$U(\theta,\phi)\,d\Omega = C\,(1 - \cos^2 \theta)\,d\Omega \qquad \text{(for } \Delta m = 0)$$

$$U(\theta,\phi)\,d\Omega = \frac{C}{2}\,(1 + \cos^2 \theta)\,d\Omega \qquad \text{(for } \Delta m = \pm 1) \tag{6.11}$$

Here C is a constant independent of the angles. It follows from (6.11) that the first quantum is equally distributed over all directions since the sum over the three possibilites gives a constant.

The choice of our z direction is quite arbitrary. It determines a polar coordinate system, and it also defines the substates $m = 1, 0, -1$ of state b. Without any loss of generality we may choose the z direction parallel to the direction of the first light quantum. Then the first transition cannot lead to state b with magnetic quantum number $m = 0$ since a dipole emission with $\Delta m = 0$ does not give rise to any radiation in the z direction [see equation (3.18)]. The first transition $a {\rightarrow} b$ is therefore of type $\Delta m = +1$ or $\Delta m = -1$. The second transition $b {\rightarrow} c$ must then be of type $\Delta m = -1$ or $\Delta m = +1$, respectively. Either of these gives rise to the second directional distribution in (6.11). Hence we find that the direction of the second quantum is not arbitrary but is distributed statistically according to the law[1]

$$W(\theta_{12})\,d\Omega = \frac{3}{16\pi}\,(1 + \cos^2 \theta_{12})\,d\Omega \tag{6.12}$$

Here $W(\theta_{12})\,d\Omega$ is the probability that the direction of the second quantum lies within the solid angle element $d\Omega$ at an angle θ_{12} with respect to the first quantum (our z axis). According to (6.12) it is twice as probable that the two light quanta are emitted in the same direction than that they are emitted at right angles to each other; emissions in the same direction and in opposite directions are equally probable.

The case treated here is a special example of two successive gamma-ray transitions. In general, the angular correlation depends on the multipole order of the two emitted quanta and also on the spin values I of the three states. The investigation of such angular correlations as a tool in nuclear spectroscopy was suggested by Dunworth (40) and Hamilton (40). The expected correlations as well as experimental measurements can be found in the papers of Hamilton (40), Goertzel (46), Brady and Deutsch (50), Falkoff (50), and Walter (50).

---

[1] The constant $3/16\pi$ serves to normalize the total emission probability of the second quantum: $\int W(\theta_{12})\,d\Omega = 1$.

In our simple derivation we have assumed that the intermediate state b of the nucleus has a lifetime short enough so that it is not disturbed by outside influences between the time it is formed and the time it emits the second gamma-ray. This may not be true of states which emit multipole radiation of higher-order l. In that case the angular correlation is in general weaker than the one computed from this simple theory (Alder 51) and may also be changed by outside influences (e.g., by the application of an external magnetic field).

We have not made use in the derivation of (6.12) of the type (electric or magnetic) of the assumed dipole radiations. It was pointed out in Section 3B that the angular distribution of the emitted quanta is independent of the parity of the radiation. Hence angular correlation measurements by themselves give information about the angular momenta involved, but not about the parities. Information about the parities may be obtained, however, by observing the polarization of at least one of the two gamma-rays (Falkoff 48, Hamilton 48). Such experiments have been performed by Metzger and Deutsch (Metzger 50), with results which are in good agreement with theoretical expectations and with other measurements (see Brady 50).

An additional complication would occur in the case of parity-unfavored transitions in which electric $(l+1)$ and magnetic (l) radiations are of comparable intensity (Ling 48, Zinnes 50). However, our order-of-magnitude estimates, (6.8) and (6.9), imply that parity-unfavored transitions of energy $\hbar\omega$ less than a few Mev are predominantly of pure magnetic type, with only a very small (less than 1 percent) admixture of electric radiation of order $l+1$. "Mixed" transitions are probably much less frequent than has been supposed in the literature.

The theorems about angular distributions of reaction products in nuclear reactions (see Chapter X) have been extended by Yang (48) to apply to the case discussed here. We shall not go through Yang's proof here, since it is entirely analogous to the proof for nuclear reactions in Chapter X, Section 3. The results are:

(1) The angular correlation between two successive gamma-rays is an even polynomial in $\cos\theta_{12}$.

(2) The highest power in this polynomial is smaller than or equal to $2l_1$ and also smaller than or equal to $2l_2$, where l_1, l_2 are the multipole orders (angular momenta) of the two gamma-rays.

(3) The highest power in this polynomial is also smaller than or equal to $2I_b$, where I_b is the angular momentum of the intermediate nuclear state.

If the gamma-emitting state is produced by emission of a particle from another (compound) nucleus, we may expect an angular correlation between the direction of this particle and the direction of the gamma-ray. We discuss a simple example: let us assume that the initial state of the compound nucleus has spin $I_a = 0$ and that the spin of the residual nucleus in the excited state b is $I_b = 1$, whereas its ground state c has spin $I_c = 0$. We also assume that the particle has no intrinsic spin (e.g., that it is an alpha-particle). The spin relations are the same as in the previous example of the double gamma-ray emission. Again we have three alternative decay schemes, via the substates of b: $m = 1, 0, -1$. If the particle emission leads to substate m, the particle must have been emitted with a wave function

$$R(r) \; Y_{1,-m}(\theta, \phi)$$

in order to fulfill the law of conservation of angular momentum (the angular momentum was zero originally, and therefore the sum of the z components of the angular momentum of the residual nucleus in state b and of the emitted particle must vanish). The angular distribution of the particle is given by $|Y_{1,-m}|^2$:

$$
\begin{aligned}
U_\alpha(\theta, \phi) &= C \cos^2 \theta &&\text{(for } \Delta m = 0) \\
U_\alpha(\theta, \phi) &= \tfrac{1}{2} C \sin^2 \theta &&\text{(for } \Delta m = \pm 1)
\end{aligned}
\tag{6.13}
$$

This is different from the angular distribution of a light quantum emitted in the corresponding transitions. Hence we also get a different angular correlation between the particle and the following quantum. We again choose the z axis parallel to the direction of the particle. Then the only particle emission which can take place is the one with $\Delta m = 0$, since $Y_{1, \pm 1}(\theta = 0) = 0$. Hence according to (6.11) the angular distribution of the gamma-quantum is $C(1 - \cos^2 \theta)$. We get, in contrast to (6.12),

$$W(\theta_{12}) \, d\Omega = \frac{3}{8\pi} \sin^2 \theta_{12} \, d\Omega \tag{6.14}$$

where θ_{12} is the angle between the emitted particle and the gamma-quantum.

The simple discussion here applies to the case where the emitted particle has no intrinsic spin, hence in particular to the angular correlation in the case of alpha-particle emission leading to an excited state of the residual nucleus. Such angular correlations have been observed in nuclear reactions (Arnold 50, Rose 50). Measurements of this sort are very valuable for the study of nuclear spectroscopy.

The general theorems of Yang also apply to this case, provided that we understand by l_1 the orbital angular momentum of the emitted particle. Similar relations can also be derived for angular correlations between beta-rays and subsequent gamma-rays (Falkoff 50a) and between internal conversion electrons and subsequent (or previous) gamma-rays (Ling 48a; Berestetski 48; Gardner 49a, 51; Fierz 49; Lloyd 50, 51, 51a, 51b, 51c; Falkoff 51; Eisenbud 51; Spiers 50).

▶ 7. TRANSITIONS INVOLVING HIGHLY EXCITED STATES

A. General Considerations

Radiative transitions to or from highly excited states play an important role in two phenomena: the radiative capture of neutrons and the nuclear photoeffect. In the first case the neutron enters the target nucleus and forms a compound nucleus in an excited state whose excitation energy E is $E = \epsilon + S_n$, where ϵ is the kinetic energy of the neutron[1] and S_n the separation energy of the neutron from the compound nucleus. Radiative transitions take place from this state to lower ones until the ground state is reached. Experimental evidence in medium and heavy nuclei has shown that about two or three quanta are emitted in succession when slow neutrons are captured (Muehlhause 50, Kinsey 50).

In the nuclear photoeffect, nuclei are exposed to gamma-rays whose energy $\hbar\omega$ is higher than the separation energy of a constituent (neutron or proton) A light quantum is absorbed, and the excited state decays by the emission of a particle. The nuclear photoeffect is a nuclear reaction initiated by a light quantum. Radiative transitions occur between the ground state and an excited state whose excitation energy is higher than the separation energy S_n. (See Figs. 7.1 and 7.2.)

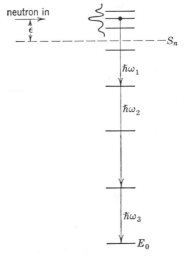

FIG. 7.1. Schematic picture of radiative capture of a neutron. The energy of excitation is released by emission of 2 to 3 gamma-rays in succession.

[1] Strictly speaking, ϵ is the energy of relative motion of the neutron and target nucleus in the center-of-gravity system (the "channel energy" of Chapter VIII). The nuclear recoil upon absorption of the gamma-ray is neglected here.

An exact theoretical description of these processes is impossible, since the radiative transition probabilities can be calculated only if the nuclear wave functions are known. We shall discuss certain methods which can be used to extend the estimates of the transition probabilities of Section 6 to the region of higher excitation.

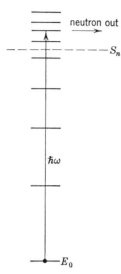

FIG. 7.2. Schematic picture of the nuclear photoeffect with emission of a neutron [the (γ,n) reaction].

In the description of the two processes we make use of the Bohr assumption, i.e., we assume that the process can be divided into two independent steps: (1) the formation of the compound nucleus, and (2) the decay of the compound nucleus by emission of a particle or a light quantum. In both processes only one of the two steps is a radiative transition; in the neutron capture process it is gamma-ray emission from the compound state, in the photoelectric process it is gamma-ray absorption into the compound state.

In both cases the compound state is a state of a nucleus which is excited above the separation energy S_a of some nuclear particle. Hence it is not, strictly speaking, a stationary state but rather a "decaying state" in the sense of Chapter VIII, Section 9. In what follows we shall always treat the states of the compound nucleus as stationary states, although this procedure is rather inaccurate in cases where the excitation energy is so high that the level distance between the compound states is smaller than their width.

B. Sum Rules

The size of matrix elements for radiative transitions is limited by certain relations, called sum rules, which apply to the sum of the squares of the transition matrix elements between one state a of the nucleus and all other stationary states b. The simplest sum rule is the one for the electric dipole matrix elements, which are given in formula (3.36).

Before deriving the sum rule we first introduce the "effective charges for dipole radiation." The operator $\sum_{k=1}^{Z} z_k$ in (3.36) is proportional to the z component of the position of the center of gravity of all the protons. The center of gravity of *all* the nucleons, with z component $G_z = A^{-1} \sum_{k=1}^{A} z_k$, remains at rest (if the nuclear recoil from the gamma-ray is neglected). Hence the transition matrix elements of G_z vanish, and the contribution to the electric dipole radiation comes only from the relative coordinates $\zeta_k = z_k - G_z$. Thus we may replace the sum in (3.36) as follows, without changing the result:

$$e \sum_{k=1}^{Z} z_k \longrightarrow e \sum_{k=1}^{Z} \zeta_k = \sum_{k=1}^{A} e_k' z_k \tag{7.1}$$

where the effective charges e_k' for electric dipole radiation are

$$
\begin{aligned}
e_k' &= e\left(1 - \frac{Z}{A}\right) && \text{(for protons)} \\
e_k' &= -\frac{eZ}{A} && \text{(for neutrons)}
\end{aligned}
\tag{7.2}
$$

These effective charges apply only to electric dipole radiation, since only for this radiation is the matrix element related to the operator for the center of gravity.

In order to derive the dipole sum rule we form the matrix element $p_{kz}(a,b)$ of the z component of the momentum of nucleon number k between nuclear states a and b. The momentum operator is the nucleon mass M times the velocity operator, the latter being the time derivative of the position operator z_k of the nucleon. We therefore get

$$p_{kz}(a,b) = \frac{iM(E_b - E_a)}{\hbar} z_k(a,b) \tag{7.3}$$

We now use the commutation relations

$$\sum_b \left[z_k(a,b)\, p_{k'z}(b,a) - p_{k'z}(a,b)\, z_k(b,a) \right] = i\hbar\delta_{kk'} \tag{7.4}$$

to get the sum rule

$$\frac{2M}{\hbar^2} \sum_b (E_b - E_a)\, |Q_{1,0}(a,b)|^2 = \frac{3}{4\pi} \sum_{k=1}^{A} (e_k')^2 = \frac{3}{4\pi}\frac{NZ}{A} e^2 \tag{7.5}$$

Similar sum rules apply to the other electric dipole matrix elements $Q_{1,m}$ with $m = +1$ and $m = -1$.

The sum must be extended over all energy states of the nucleus. Strictly speaking, this includes also the states in the continuum, where the nucleus can disintegrate by particle emission.[1] In the present considerations we make use of the compound nucleus picture for the states in the continuum (above the lowest particle separation energy S_a). That is, the sum in (7.5) is extended, first over all the stationary bound states of the nucleus, then over the series of quasi-stationary decaying states obtained if the nucleus is excited sufficiently highly to be able to emit particles (see Chapter VIII, Section 9). These states are not strictly stationary, since they have a finite lifetime. Hence the sum rule taken in this way is only approximately correct. The wave function of each decaying state must be normalized by

$$\int_C \left| \varphi_b \right|^2 d\tau = 1 \tag{7.6}$$

where the integration is extended over the region of configuration space corresponding to the compound nucleus, i.e., for which all nucleons are within the radius of the compound nucleus (the "internal" region in the sense of Chapter X).

Another dipole sum rule can be derived by using the following matrix product relation:

$$\sum_b p_{kz}(a,b)\, p_{k'z}(b,a) = (a|p_{kz}p_{k'z}|a) = \langle p_{kz}p_{k'z}\rangle_a \tag{7.7}$$

where the right side represents the expectation value of the operator $p_{kz}p_{k'z}$ in state a. We then get from (7.3)

$$\sum_b (E_b - E_a)^2 \left| Q_{1,0}(a,b) \right|^2 = \frac{3}{4\pi} \left(\frac{\hbar}{M} \right)^2 \left\langle \left(\sum_{k=1}^A e_k{}' \, p_{kz} \right)^2 \right\rangle_a \tag{7.8}$$

Unlike the first dipole sum rule (7.5), relation (7.8) involves not only natural constants but also the expectation value of an operator, $\left(\sum_{k=1}^A e_k{}' \, p_{kz} \right)^2$, in state a of the nucleus. This expectation value can be found only if the wave function of this state is known. However, we can estimate the expectation value by assuming no correlations between the momenta, i.e., $\langle p_{kz}p_{k'z}\rangle_a = 0$ for $k \neq k'$, and by setting all the squares of momenta equal to each other, $\langle p_{kz}{}^2 \rangle_a \cong P^2/3$, where P^2

---

[1] If the sum is taken that way, the states in the continuum must be normalized per unit energy range, and the summation sign for those states replaced by an integration over the continuous energy variable (Bethe 33).

is the average square of the momentum vector of a typical nucleon in the nucleus. This gives the estimate

$$\sum_b (E_b - E_a)^2 \, |Q_{1,0}(a,b)|^2 \sim (4\pi)^{-1} \, e^2 \, \frac{NZ}{A} \left(\frac{\hbar P}{M} \right)^2 \qquad (7.9)$$

These sum rules must be amended if there are exchange forces acting between nucleons (Fock 34, Bloch 36, Feenberg 36b, Siegert 37, Way 37). Then charge is exchanged between the nucleons, so that the position of the charge changes more rapidly than the positions of the nucleons. The velocity of the charges is no longer identical with the velocity of the particles; since the velocity of the charges is larger than the velocity of the particles, sums (7.5) and (7.8) become *larger* also. Bethe and Levinger (Levinger 50) have derived approximate expressions for this increase. They find increases in the sums by factors between 2 and 10, depending on the relative strength of the exchange part of the force and the particular sum rule under consideration. These factors serve only as illustrations, as very radical assumptions were made in the course of their derivation.

We can also derive similar sum rules for the matrix elements of higher multipole transitions (Weisskopf 41). All these sums are of the character of (7.8), i.e., they involve some average value over state a on the right side rather than a combination of natural constants such as (7.5). We find that

$$\sum_b |Q_{lm}(a,b)|^2 = e^2 \left\langle \left| \sum_{k=1}^{Z} r_k^{\,l} \, Y_{lm}(\theta_k, \phi_k) \right|^2 \right\rangle_a \qquad (7.10)$$

In addition to (7.10) other sum rules have been derived by Austern (51) and Sachs (51).

We can estimate the average value in (7.10) as before by neglecting the correlations and assuming a uniform distribution for the nucleons within the nucleus. This gives

$$\sum_b |Q_{lm}(a,b)|^2 \sim \frac{3}{2l+3} \frac{Ze^2}{4\pi} R^{2l} \qquad (7.11)$$

where R is the nuclear radius. It should be emphasized that (7.11) is an *extremely rough estimate* only, since there is little reason to suppose that the correlations between the nucleons in the nucleus [and hence the cross terms in the square which appears in (7.10)] are really completely negligible.

C. Estimates of Matrix Elements Involving Highly Excited Nuclear States

Estimates (6.6) and (6.10) of the multipole moments for transitions between two low-lying nuclear levels were based on simple models. Estimate (6.6) was derived for the motion of one particle (the independent-particle model), (6.10) for the vibration of a liquid drop. These pictures cannot be applied to transitions involving highly excited states (more than a few Mev excitation energy), since the number of levels found at high excitation energies is very much larger than either of these simple models could predict. It is plausible, therefore, that the matrix elements to an individual highly excited level are appreciably smaller than either estimate (6.6) or (6.10), since the transition probabilities must be "divided among many more levels." The need for a reduction in the matrix elements is apparent if the earlier estimates, (6.6) and (6.10), are substituted into the sum rule (7.10); the sum does not even converge.

We shall illustrate this reduction in the matrix elements involving highly excited states by an oversimplified example. Let us assume that the nucleus contains only one charged particle, all other nucleons being neutrons. We shall employ two models, I and II. In model I there is no interaction between the nucleons; they move independently of each other in a common potential V which gives rise to equidistant quantum states with an energy spacing Δ.[1] The levels of the system as a whole are highly degenerate, since a total energy $N\Delta$ can be made up in very many different ways out of energies $n\Delta$ of the individual nucleons (N and n are integers). In model II there are interactions between the nucleons, but they are assumed to be weak enough so that a level of the total system at energy E has a wave function which can be expressed as a linear superposition of model I wave functions for levels $E' = N\Delta$ not very far from E.

Let us consider radiative transitions in model I. Transitions occur between pairs of levels which differ in the state of the proton only but are identical as to the states of all the neutrons. Let us consider two degenerate energy levels, A and B, with energies E_A and E_B, respectively, $E_A > E_B$. For every component level in the lower group B, we can find a combining level in the upper group A simply by lifting the proton up by $(E_A - E_B)/\Delta$ steps. Hence every level in the lower group combines with one level in the upper group, but not vice versa. This is indicated schematically in Fig. 7.3. Let us

---

[1] In this discussion we shall reserve the term "state" for the quantum states of a single nucleon in the potential V and use the term "level" for a quantum state of the system as a whole.

call Q_0 the matrix element of some given multipole type for such a
transition. We assume that its value is roughly the same for all the
transitions possible in model I, no matter how large the energy difference $E_A - E_B$, and we also ignore the
selection rules. These very rough assumptions are made in order to limit
this consideration to its essentials.

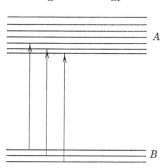

We now change over to model II by
introducing interactions between the
nucleons. Let us first assume that the
interaction is still quite weak, so that the
degenerate levels in group A are split
up by amounts small compared to the
energy spacing Δ. Each level in this
group in model II has a wave function
which is a linear combination of the wave
functions of the corresponding degenerate levels in model I. We shall assume
that these combinations are such that,
on the average, each component level of
group A contributes equally. Similar
statements are assumed to hold for group B. Then there are transitions
between all pairs of levels in the two groups, since each energy level
in the upper group A contains a small part of that specific level of
model I which combines with a specific level in group B. Let g_A be the
number of levels (the degeneracy) in group A. The matrix elements
$Q(a,b)$ between a level a in group A and a level b in group B roughly
fulfill the relation

Fig. 7.3.   A simple example of
a level scheme as described on
this page. $g_A = 7$, $g_B = 3$.   The
levels in group A are degenerate
in model I, and so are the levels
in group B.   In model II the
degeneracy is removed in both
groups of levels.

$$|Q(a,b)|^2 \sim \frac{Q_0{}^2}{g_A} \qquad (7.12)$$

That is, the square of the matrix element is roughly inversely proportional to the number of states in the *upper* group of levels. Note
the peculiar asymmetry with respect to the degeneracy of the two
groups.

If we now let the interaction between nucleons in model II increase,
we may still expect a relation of type (7.12) to hold in a qualitative
way, in the sense that the square of the matrix element is, roughly,
inversely proportional to the number of levels near the upper level
under consideration. We interpret "near" to mean within a given
constant energy interval around the level in question. We can then
rephrase the rule as follows: *The square of the matrix element between*

two levels E_a and E_b is roughly proportional to the average level distance $D(E_>)$ at the energy of the upper level. Here we have introduced the notation

$$E_> = E_a \quad \text{if } E_a > E_b$$
$$E_> = E_b \quad \text{if } E_a < E_b \tag{7.13}$$

This notation is introduced so that, from now on, E_a may denote either the upper or the lower level.

It should be evident from the preceding considerations that this rule has only very qualitative validity. We therefore express the content of the rule in the form

$$\langle |Q_{lm}(a,b)|^2 \rangle_{\text{av}} = q_{lm}(E_a,E_b)\, D_l(E_>) \tag{7.14}$$

where the left side is the average of the square of the multipole matrix elements between the lower level and a large number of upper levels near the upper energy $E_>$. $D_l(E_>)$ is the distance between those levels near $E_>$ which combine with the lower level by the multipole radiation in question. Our rule then leads us to expect that the function q defined by (7.14) is a slowly varying function of the energies E_a and E_b compared to the extremely rapid (exponential) variation of the level distance $D(E_>)$ near the upper energy.

On the other hand, substitution of (7.14) into the sum rule (7.10) shows that q cannot just be set equal to a constant. For simplicity's sake let us assume that E_a is the ground state, $E_a = 0$. Then we can replace the sum in (7.10) by an integral as follows:

$$\sum_b |Q_{lm}(0,b)|^2 \cong \int_0^\infty \langle |Q_{lm}(0,b)|^2 \rangle_{\text{av}} \frac{dE_b}{D_l(E_b)} = \int_0^\infty q_{lm}(0,E_b)\, dE_b \tag{7.15}$$

According to the sum rule (7.10) the last integral must converge, i.e., the function q_l must drop off at high energies E_b. We use estimate (7.11) for the sum, and we assume that q_l is independent of E_b for E_b less than some maximum energy $E_{\text{max},l}$, and zero thereafter. This gives an approximate relation between the (assumed constant) value of q_l and the energy range over which q_l can be assumed to be constant:

$$q_l\, E_{\text{max},l} \sim \frac{3}{2l+3} \frac{Ze^2}{4\pi} R^{2l} \tag{7.16}$$

We now proceed to estimate the value of q by comparing estimate (7.14), which is supposedly appropriate to all energies, with estimate

(6.6), which is valid for transitions between low-lying levels only.[1] Calling the level distance among combining low-lying levels D_0, we obtain the estimate

$$q_l \sim \left(\frac{3}{l+3}\right)^2 \frac{e^2 R^{2l}}{4\pi D_0} \qquad (7.17)$$

Let us now substitute estimate (7.17) into relation (7.16) to find the order of magnitude of the maximum energy for which q_l can be considered to have the constant value (7.17). We replace $(l+3)^2/[3(2l+3)]$ by unity and obtain

$$\frac{E_{\max,l}}{D_0} \sim Z \qquad (7.18)$$

For medium-weight nuclei ($Z \sim 50$) we can estimate $D_0 \sim 0.5$ Mev, which gives $E_{\max,l} \sim 25$ Mev, so that we may be justified in setting q_l equal to the constant value (7.17) up to energies of this order of magnitude. It should be emphasized that the argument which led to this estimate is very uncertain. First of all, estimate (6.6) is only very rough; secondly, the sum rule (7.11) was derived from (7.10) by neglecting correlations. Thus *estimate (7.18) for the maximum energy may well be off by a large factor in either direction.* The estimate is given here merely because of the lack of more precise information.

So far all our estimates have referred to electric multipole transitions. Our estimate $10(\hbar/McR)^2$ of the ratio of magnetic to electric transition probabilities does not depend on the energy of the transition. We shall therefore estimate the *magnetic transition probabilities* by assuming that they are smaller than the electric transition probabilities for the same multipole order l by this constant factor, of the order of 10^{-2}. Hence, in particular, estimate (7.18) of the maximum energy for which a given multipole radiation is effective applies to magnetic radiation as well as to electric radiation.

It should be noted, however, that estimates (7.17) and (7.18) may not apply to electric dipole radiation since there is some indication that estimate (6.6) does not hold in this case.

D. Radiative Capture of Neutrons

After a neutron enters into a nucleus and forms a compound nucleus in some compound state a, there is a certain probability $\Gamma_{\rm rad}/\hbar$ per

---

[1] We do not use estimate (6.10) from the liquid drop model, because it gives poorer agreement with experiment than (6.6), and because there are good reasons (see Chapter XIV) for believing that the independent-particle model gives a better approximation for the wave functions of low-lying nuclear states than the liquid drop model.

unit time that a light quantum is emitted. This probability is the sum of all emission probabilities into states b of the compound system lying below the initial state a. We separate the radiation into the parts coming from different multipole types by writing

$$\Gamma_{\text{rad}} \equiv \sum_{l=1}^{\infty} (\Gamma_{El} + \Gamma_{Ml}) \qquad (7.19)$$

where Γ_{El} is that part of the radiation width of level a which is due to electric multipole emission of order l, and Γ_{Ml} is the corresponding quantity for magnetic multipole emission. Γ_{El} can be expressed as a sum of partial widths for electric multipole transitions of order l into individual lower levels b of the compound nucleus:

$$\Gamma_{El} \equiv \sum_{b} \Gamma_{El}(a,b) \qquad (E_b < E_a) \qquad (7.20)$$

where $\Gamma_{El}(a,b)$ is different from zero only if state b has the right parity and angular momentum so that it can be reached from state a by emission of electric radiation of order l. A similar equation holds for the magnetic radiation width of order l, Γ_{Ml}.

The observed radiation width of a resonance level of the compound nucleus is therefore made up of a very large number of partial widths for individual multipole transitions to individual lower levels. Thus we expect that the radiation widths do not vary much from level to level in the same compound nucleus. This is unlike the expected behavior of particle emission widths (e.g., neutron widths) which can vary widely from one level to the next because of penetration factors and other effects. Large fluctuations in the branching ratios for neutron and gamma-ray emission from level to level should therefore be attributed primarily to the fluctuations in the neutron widths.

We estimate the partial radiation width for electric radiation of order l between the upper state a and the lower state b, $\Gamma_{El}(a,b)$, by combining the general expression (3.21) for the transition probability with estimates (7.14) and (7.17) of the average value of the square of the matrix element. This gives

$$\langle \Gamma_{El}(a,b) \rangle_{\text{av}} \sim \frac{18(l+1)(2l+1)}{l(l+3)^2 \, [(2l+1)!!]^2} \, \frac{e^2}{\hbar c} \, \frac{\hbar\omega}{D_0} \left(\frac{\omega R}{c} \right)^{2l} D_l(E_a) \qquad (7.21)$$

The factor $2l+1$ in the numerator was inserted because the emitted multipole radiation of order l can have $2l+1$ different values of m. Although this is not the correct statistical factor, the error introduced by this approximation is less than the errors due to the various rough estimates which enter into (7.21).

The partial radiation width for magnetic radiation, $\Gamma_{Ml}(a,b)$, is smaller than the corresponding electric width by a factor $10(\hbar/McR)^2$ according to estimate (6.3a).

Before estimating the absolute value of the radiation width, let us start by discussing the spectral distribution of the radiation emitted immediately after capture.[1] In order to get this energy distribution, we must multiply the average partial width (7.21) by the number of lower levels b per unit energy interval, i.e., by $[D_l(E_b)]^{-1}$. Thus the energy distribution $U_l(\hbar\omega)\,d(\hbar\omega)$ of the emitted radiation of order l immediately after capture is

$$U_l(\hbar\omega)\,d(\hbar\omega) = C_l\,(\hbar\omega)^{2l+1}\left[D_l(E_a-\hbar\omega)\right]^{-1} \tag{7.22}$$

where C_l is a constant independent of $\hbar\omega$. The factor $(\hbar\omega)^{2l+1}$ favors the emission of radiation of large quantum energy. The level distance factor favors the emission of radiation of low quantum energy, since D_l is a very rapidly decreasing function of the energy $E_b = E_a - \hbar\omega$. Thus the energy distribution (7.22) has the general shape shown in Fig. 7.4. The maximum of the distribution shifts to higher quantum energies as the multipole order l increases, as is apparent from (7.22). It should be realized that this energy distribution is not really continuous but represents a rough average over a series of discrete peaks, each corresponding to a transition to a given lower state b. Thus, in particular, the smooth curve has no meaning at all for the largest quantum energies which leave the nucleus in the low-lying, widely spaced levels.

We now proceed to estimate the absolute value of the radiation widths for emission of radiation of given multipole type. We replace the sum in (7.20) by an integral and use (7.21) for electric radiation, to get the result

$$\Gamma_{El} \sim \frac{18(l+1)(2l+1)}{l(l+3)^2\,[(2l+1)!!]^2}\,\frac{e^2}{\hbar c}\left(\frac{R}{\hbar c}\right)^{2l}\frac{1}{D_0}\int_0^{E_a}(\hbar\omega)^{2l+1}\frac{D_l(E_a)}{D_l(E_a-\hbar\omega)}\,d(\hbar\omega) \tag{7.23}$$

[1] This is *not* the spectral distribution of the observed neutron capture radiation. When the compound state emits gamma-rays of energy $\hbar\omega$ less than the maximum energy $\hbar\omega_{max} = E_a$ available for capture radiation, the nucleus is left in an excited state. This excited state proceeds to emit more radiation, which is also recorded. For experimental data on the combined distribution of primary and secondary gamma-rays, see, e.g., Kinsey (50) and Hamermesh (51).

This integral can be evaluated if the energy dependence of the level distance is known. The radiation width for *magnetic* radiation differs from (7.23) by a factor $10(\hbar/McR)^2$ according to estimate (6.3a).

In the case of most importance practically, the radiation after capture of a slow neutron, the energy E_a of the compound state which emits the radiation is equal to the neutron separation energy S_n (of

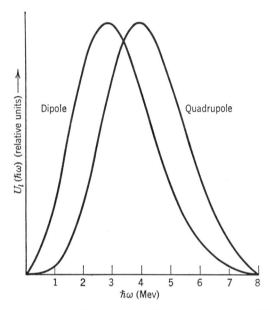

FIG. 7.4. Relative spectral distribution of the first quantum emitted in neutron capture for a nucleus similar to indium. The curves represent a rough schematic estimate of the average over discrete peaks. This distribution can *not* be compared directly with the spectral distribution of gamma-rays observed in neutron capture, since secondary gamma-rays (which contribute to the experimental result) are not included in these theoretical curves.

the order of 8 Mev). In order to get a rough estimate for the radiation width we can use the level density formula as given in Chapter VIII, (VIII,6.11) and (VIII,6.12). The level distance D_0 between low-lying levels is estimated to be of the order of 0.5 Mev for medium-weight and heavy nuclei, and somewhat larger for light nuclei, for which this statistical theory is inapplicable. Table 7.1 contains estimates of the radiation widths of slow neutron capture levels computed with these assumptions from (7.23) for a few representative choices of the neutron separation energy $E_a = S_n$ and of the quantity $\mathfrak{a}$ which appears in the level density formula (VIII,6.11). The choices correspond roughly to nuclei similar to Al, Ag, and W. Only dipole and quadrupole radiation is considered. Higher multipole emissions give rise to much smaller radiation widths and can therefore be ignored.

TABLE 7.1

Nucleus	$E_a = S_n$ (Mev)	a (Mev^{-1})	$\Gamma_{E,1}$ (ev)	$\Gamma_{M,1}$ (ev)	$\Gamma_{E,2}$ (ev)	$\Gamma_{M,2}$ (ev)
Al	8	0.45	680	14	0.36	0.007
Ag	8	6.5	47	0.6	0.04	3×10^{-4}
W	7	10	23	0.18	0.02	2×10^{-4}

The actual value of the radiation width Γ_{rad} of a neutron capture level is the sum (7.19) of the widths of all multipole radiations. The experimental values are quoted in Chapter IX. Γ_{rad} lies between 1 and 30 ev for intermediate nuclei, between 0.03 and 0.20 ev for heavy nuclei. It is seen that the electric dipole widths in Table 7.1 are much larger than the observed values. This may be connected with the earlier surmise that the electric dipole matrix elements are considerably smaller than estimate (6.6), upon which the table is based. The radiation widths obtained from Table 7.1 on the extreme assumption that the electric dipole radiation does not make any significant contribution to Γ_{rad} are of the right order of magnitude. It must be realized, however, that these estimates of radiation widths depend very critically on the expression used for the level distance $D(E)$. In view of the great uncertainty in all these estimates, it is necessary to admit that the theory does not yet make any significant predictions about the absolute magnitude of neutron capture widths. The subject must be re-examined after more becomes known about nuclear level structures.

E. Nuclear Photoeffect

The nuclear photoeffect is the absorption by a nucleus of a light quantum whose energy $\hbar\omega$ is larger than the separation energy S of a constituent, say a proton, a neutron, or an alpha-particle. We then observe (γ,p), (γ,n), or (γ,α) processes, respectively. The simplest example of a nuclear photoeffect is the photodisintegration of the deuteron which was treated in Section 4 on the following basis: the absorption of a light quantum produces a radiative transition from the ground state to a final state in the continuum. Although all nuclear photoeffects can be considered such transitions in principle, it is more natural to apply the Bohr theory of the compound nucleus to these processes if intermediate or heavy nuclei are involved. The process is then divided into two parts: (1) the absorption of the light quantum, creating a compound state with excitation energy $E = \hbar\omega$, and (2) the decay of the compound nucleus through different channels.[1] The cross section can then be written (see VIII,3.1)

$$\sigma(\gamma,b) = \sigma_C(\gamma)\, G_b \qquad \text{(Bohr assumption)} \qquad (7.24)$$

where $\sigma_C(\gamma)$ is the absorption cross section for light of the given frequency, G_b is the branching probability for the decay of the compound state by emission of a particle b. These decay probabilities were discussed in detail in Chapter VIII. For photoeffects well above threshold, we are dealing with the decay of a highly excited compound state, and the expressions of the statistical (evaporation) theory (Chapter VIII, Section 6) should be used to determine G_b. We recall that the most probable process is the emission of a neutron, which leads to a (γ,n) reaction. The residual nucleus may be so highly excited that this reaction is followed by emission of more particles, so that $(\gamma;2n)$, $(\gamma;3n)$ or $(\gamma;np)$ reactions are observed.

It should be noted that some experiments of Wäffler et al. (Hirzel 47) have cast some doubt about the correctness of the Bohr assumption for the nuclear photoeffect. This point will be discussed later on in connection with the experimental material.

In this chapter we are mostly concerned with the first part of the reaction: the absorption of the gamma-ray. We shall assume that the gamma-ray source does not emit monochromatic radiation but emits gamma-rays within a certain energy interval ΔE large compared to the level spacing D of the levels in the compound nucleus at excitation energy $E_a = \hbar\omega$. We shall therefore derive an expression for the cross section of formation of the compound nucleus, $\sigma_C(\gamma)$, which does not show any resonance phenomena but rather represents an average over many resonance peaks.

The expression so derived is valid only in the resonance region of nuclear reactions. We shall nevertheless apply it to find $\sigma_C(\gamma)$ also in the continuum region (well above threshold) where the excitation energy is so high that the widths of the compound levels are larger than the level spacing, so that the levels overlap. It is questionable whether we can then still consider the states of the nucleus well-defined quasi-stationary decaying states. In this section we shall

---

[1] The compound nucleus may also decay by emission of radiation rather than by emission of a particle. In practice the radiation width is small compared to the particle widths for the energies (well above threshold) at which the photoeffect is commonly studied.

assume that this is possible. In our expressions for radiative transitions we consider the upper state a quasi-stationary state with a well-defined wave function.

The excitation probability of the nucleus from the ground state 0 to some definite excited state a through absorption of a given multipole radiation is given by (3.25) with $a \rightarrow 0$ and $b \rightarrow a$. Under our assumptions about the energy spread of the incident gamma-ray beam, many states a will be excited, the total excitation probability being

$$A_E(l) = \sum_{E_a = \hbar\omega}^{\hbar\omega + \Delta E} A_E(l; 0 \rightarrow a) = \left\langle A_E(l; 0 \rightarrow a) \right\rangle_{av} \frac{\Delta E}{D_l} \qquad (7.25)$$

where D_l is the spacing at the energy $E_a = \hbar\omega$ of the levels which combine with the ground state by absorption of electric radiation of order l.

We obtain the cross section for formation of the excited compound nucleus by dividing the total transition probability (7.25) by the flux of incident gamma-rays. We use the quantity $S(\omega)$ introduced in Section 3. The number of quanta in the beam per square centimeter per second is equal to $S(\omega)(\Delta E/\hbar)$. We divide (7.25) by this flux in order to get the *average cross section for creation of the compound nucleus by absorption of electric multiple radiation of order l.* Using (3.25) (neglecting the spin matrix elements Q'), this quantity is

$$\sigma_{Cl}(\gamma) = \frac{4\pi^3(l+1)(2l+1)}{l\,[(2l+1)!!]^2} \kappa^{2l-1} \frac{\langle |Q_{l,1}|^2 + |Q_{l,-1}|^2 \rangle_{av}}{D_l(E_a)} \qquad (7.26)$$

We now use estimate (7.14) for the matrix elements. The level distance cancels out. We shall assume that the quantity q_{lm} is independent of m, so that finally

$$\sigma_{Cl}(\gamma) = \frac{8\pi^3(l+1)(2l+1)}{l\,[(2l+1)!!]^2} \kappa^{2l-1} q_l(0, E_a) \qquad (7.27)$$

Thus the cross section is proportional to the $(2l-1)$th power of the frequency multiplied by a slowly varying function of $E_a = \hbar\omega$. This can also be seen by the following qualitative consideration: The interaction energy between the 2^l pole moment of a charge distribution and the electric field in a light wave is proportional to the lth derivative of the potential or the $(l-1)$th derivative of the field strength. The electric field $\mathcal{E}$ in a light wave containing one quantum is proportional to $\sqrt{\omega}$.[1] Every derivative adds a factor ω/c, so that the $(l-1)$th

---

[1] The energy density $\mathcal{E}^2/4\pi$ is proportional to $\hbar\omega$.

derivative of $\mathcal{E}$ is proportional to the $\omega^{l-1/2}$. The absorption cross section is proportional to the square of the matrix element of the interaction energy, i.e., to ω^{2l-1}. Thus the absorption cross section is proportional to ω^{2l-1}, apart from slowly varying factors which depend on the special properties of the nucleus. This consideration adds independent support to relation (7.14) for the matrix elements.

We now use estimate (7.17) for q_l to get

$$\sigma_{Cl}(\gamma) \sim 18\pi^2 \frac{(l+1)(2l+1)}{l(l+3)^2[(2l+1)!!]^2} \frac{e^2}{\hbar c} \frac{\hbar\omega}{D_0} (\kappa R)^{2l-2} R^2 \quad (7.28)$$

This estimate applies to the absorption of *electric* radiation. The absorption cross section for *magnetic* radiation is smaller than this by the factor $10(\hbar/McR)^2$, according to (6.3a). Equation (7.28) may not apply to electric dipole absorption for the reasons discussed in Section 6, which make it possible that the electric dipole matrix elements are small for transitions with $\hbar\omega \lesssim 15$ Mev.

Hence for $\hbar\omega \lesssim 15$ Mev the main contribution to the gamma-ray absorption cross section probably comes from the magnetic dipole and electric quadrupole absorption only. Expression (7.28) reduces for these two cases to[1]

Magnetic dipole:

$$\sigma_C(\gamma) \sim 4.8 \ (\hbar\omega \text{ in Mev}) \times 10^{-28} \text{ cm}^2$$

Electric quadrupole: (7.29)

$$\sigma_C(\gamma) \sim 1.2 \ (\hbar\omega \text{ in Mev})^3 \left(\frac{R}{6 \times 10^{-13} \text{ cm}}\right)^4 \times 10^{-30} \text{ cm}^2$$

According to these estimates, the magnetic dipole and electric quadrupole absorption are of the same order of magnitude around $\hbar\omega \cong 20$ Mev; at lower energies the magnetic dipole absorption predominates, but not by very much. At energies higher than 20 Mev these estimates break down. The maximum energy for which we can assume that q_l is constant and equal to (7.17) is of the order of 25 Mev according to (7.18). Thus the absorption is very likely much less than estimate (7.29) at energies beyond 20 Mev.

However, at higher energies the absorption is strongly increased by the *onset of electric dipole absorption*. The reasons for the suppression of electric dipole matrix elements discussed in Section 6 are no longer valid at energies beyond about 15 Mev. The contribution of the electric dipole transitions to the photoeffect can be estimated by

---

[1] We assume that $D_0 \cong \frac{1}{2}$ Mev.

the use of the sum rules (7.5) and (7.8) for dipole transitions.[1] For dipole transitions, $l=1$, the sum on the left side of (7.5) is proportional to the integral of the average cross section (7.26) over all quantum energies. Combining (7.5) and (7.26) we get

$$\int \sigma_{C,ED}(\gamma) \, d(\hbar\omega) = 2\pi^2 \frac{e^2}{\hbar c} \frac{NZ}{A} \frac{\hbar^2}{M} \cong 6 \frac{NZ}{A} \times 10^{-26} \text{ Mev-cm}^2 \quad (7.30)$$

Thus for nuclei of $A \cong 100$ the area under the cross-section curve for electric dipole absorption must be of the order of 10^{-24} Mev-cm^2. We also recall that the sum rule (7.5) gives an underestimate of the actual sum if exchange currents are producing part of the radiation. Estimates for the increase of (7.30) due to this effect were given by Levinger and Bethe (50), who showed that the actual sum may be higher than (7.30) by a factor of 2 or more, depending on the relative importance of the exchange forces compared to the ordinary forces.

Following Levinger and Bethe, we use the second sum rule (7.8) to estimate the average energy at which dipole absorption occurs. The sum on the left side of (7.8) is proportional to the integral over all quantum energies of $\hbar\omega \, \sigma_{C,ED}(\gamma)$. Hence the ratio of the two sums (7.5) and (7.8) gives directly the mean energy of the electric dipole absorption (in the sense of a weighted average of the cross section curve). The result is, using (7.9),

$$\text{Mean energy for electric dipole absorption} \cong \frac{4}{3} \frac{P^2}{2M} \quad (7.31)$$

The average kinetic energy $P^2/2M$ of a nucleon inside the nucleus is of the order of 15 Mev (see Chapter VII, Section 2). Hence the average energy of the electric dipole absorption is of the order of 20 Mev. The existence of exchange forces raises both sum (7.5) and sum (7.8). According to the rough estimates of Levinger and Bethe, sum (7.8) is increased more than sum (7.5), so that the exchange forces also increase the average energy of the electric dipole absorption.

Hence the over-all prediction regarding the absorption of light by a nucleus for $\hbar\omega \gtrsim 10$ Mev is as follows: The magnetic dipole and electric quadrupole absorption cross sections follow estimates (7.29) up to about 20 Mev and drop off above this energy; the electric dipole absorption starts coming in significantly around 20 Mev. The latter cross section makes a total contribution (area under the cross section vs. energy curve) given by (7.30), with a correction factor due to exchange forces, and this contribution occurs at energies of the order of

[1] The sum rules are written for the matrix elements $Q_{1,0}$. The corresponding sums for $|Q_{1,1}|^2$ or $|Q_{1,-1}|^2$ give the same result.

magnitude of (7.31), again corrected for exchange forces, i.e., at energies of the order of 20 to 30 Mev. A schematic picture of the expected photoabsorption cross section is shown in Fig. 7.5.

The experiments are not yet sufficiently precise to allow a detailed check against these theoretical predictions. Similarly, the theory as

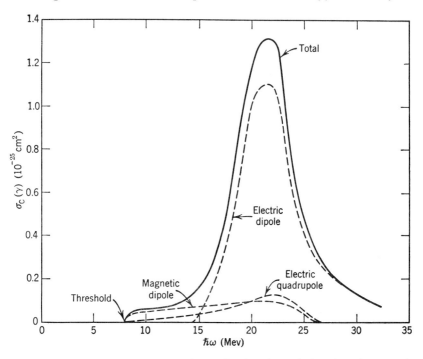

FIG. 7.5. Schematic illustration of the qualitative theoretical expectation regarding the cross section $\sigma_C(\gamma)$ for the formation of an excited nucleus by gamma-ray absorption. The contributions from electric dipole, magnetic dipole, and electric quadrupole radiation are shown separately. The figure is drawn for an intermediate nucleus.

developed here is based on qualitative arguments of a statistical nature, so that we must expect fluctuations from nucleus to nucleus. The theoretical estimates are subject to considerable error and should be interpreted only as giving the general trend of the cross sections.

In order to interpret the experiments we remark that at energies below the threshold of the $(\gamma;2n)$ reaction the (γ,n) reaction cross section is practically equal to the total absorption cross section itself in our picture (the evaporation of charged particles from the excited compound state is much less likely than the evaporation of neutrons). The present experimental material on intermediate and heavy nuclei indicates that the (γ,n) cross section increases rapidly between energies of the order of 10 and 20 Mev (Bothe 39, Baldwin 48, McElhinney 49). The increase between 10 and 17 Mev is not in disagreement with an ω^3 law. The absolute value of the (γ,n) cross section was measured at 17 Mev [$Li^7(p,\gamma)$ source] by several authors (Bothe 39, Wäffler 48, Walker 50, and others). The results disagree somewhat, but for intermediate and heavy nuclei these cross sections are of the order of several 10^{-26} cm^2, increasing with the atomic number A. If most of the photoelectric cross section at 17 Mev is due to absorption of electric quadrupole radiation, (7.29) predicts a proportionality of the cross section to $A^{4/3}$ (the fourth power of the radius R).

At higher energies, and perhaps even at 17 Mev, we expect the electric dipole absorption to become important. Most measurements have shown a strong maximum in the photoelectric cross section which lies somewhere near 20 Mev, depending on the mass number. Lower mass numbers are connected with a higher energy for the maximum cross section (Baldwin 48, Lawson 48, Perlman 48, Strauch 51). The results indicate a value of the order of 10^{-24} Mev-cm^2 for the integral of the cross section over energy. It is therefore probable that the theoretical description is qualitatively correct.[1]

We now turn to the investigation of the products of the nuclear photoeffect. Once the compound nucleus is formed, we expect that it decays into the various channels independently of its mode of formation (Bohr assumption). Specifically, we expect the neutrons to be emitted with a "Maxwell energy distribution" which is governed by the nuclear temperature created by the absorption of the light quantum (Chapter VIII, Section 6). The protons are expected to be emitted much more rarely because of the Coulomb barrier. The latter effect is strongly enhanced by the fact that the emission of a proton with the maximum possible energy is very improbable. The average emission energy of the proton is expected to be much lower because of the strong increase in the number of levels of the residual nucleus with decreasing proton emission energies. The prohibitive effect of the barrier is correspondingly stronger.

---

[1] The discussion of the electric dipole effect here has followed the work of Levinger and Bethe in that we have used sum rules only, without trying to make a detailed model for the final compound state created in the absorption process. More detailed results have been obtained by Goldhaber (48) and by Jensen and his collaborators (Jensen 50a, Steinwedel 50). These authors make use of special models for the mechanism of charge oscillations in the nucleus. The present experiments are perhaps not accurate enough to warrant such detailed comparisons.

Hirzel and Wäffler (47) first pointed out that, in many cases, the relative yield of (γ,n) and (γ,p) reactions does not agree with this theoretical picture. The proton emission was found to be much stronger than expected. The results can be explained by assuming that there exists an alternative mechanism for absorption of photons besides the creation and subsequent decay of a compound state.[1] Let us suppose that this alternative mechanism favors the emission of protons with energies close to the maximum possible one,

$$(\epsilon_p)_{\max} = \hbar\omega - S_p$$

where S_p is the separation energy of a proton. The Coulomb penetration factor at this maximum possible proton energy is very much larger than at the average energy expected on the evaporation model. Hence the ejection of a few protons by this alternative mechanism may be the main part of the (γ,p) process and may thus give rise to a (γ,p) cross section appreciably larger than the one from the compound nucleus effect alone.

Experiments of Diven and Almy (50) support that interpretation. In studying the (γ,p) reaction on silver, they find that the emitted protons can be separated into a low-energy and a high-energy group. The low-energy group shows the general behavior of protons evaporated from a compound nucleus: the protons are emitted with equal probability at all angles, and with an energy distribution similar to the one predicted by the statistical model. The high-energy group is definitely in excess of the amounts expected from evaporation. These protons show a pronounced angular asymmetry, the preferential direction of emission being perpendicular to the incident beam of light quanta. Remarkably similar results have been obtained for rhodium by Curtis et al. (50).

Hirzel and Wäffler (47), Courant (48), and others have suggested that this alternative mechanism is an absorption of the light quantum by a proton at the nuclear surface, which results in ejection of the proton toward the outside before the energy of the proton can be shared with the rest of the nucleus. Such a process is, of course, contrary to the Bohr assumption, since the absorbed energy is not distributed evenly over all constituents of the nucleus. The experimental angular distribution of the high-energy protons is consistent with this direct ejection mechanism. It is to be expected that the direct ejection mechanism accounts for only a minor part of the gamma-ray absorption cross section, the major part of this cross section

---

[1] For an alternative explanation see Schiff (48).

coming from formation of quasi-stationary compound states. Nevertheless, the direct ejection mechanism may be more important for the (γ, p) reaction than the compound nucleus evaporation, since the latter process results predominantly in neutron emissions. The Coulomb barrier is very much easier to penetrate for high-energy, directly ejected protons than for low-energy, evaporated protons.

Presumably the direct ejection mechanism for the protons is most important in heavy nuclei where the Coulomb barrier is high. In light nuclei the lower Coulomb barrier is not so effective in preventing emission of protons from the compound states; hence many, perhaps most, of the protons from photodisintegration of light nuclei can be accounted for by the Bohr assumption, without making use of any alternative mechanism. The experimental measurements of Diven (50) on aluminum and Toms (51) on magnesium can be interpreted completely in terms of compound nucleus formation.

On the basis of this picture most of the *neutrons* ejected in the photoelectric process should result from compound nucleus formation. Price (50) has measured the angular distribution of the total neutron yield in some heavy elements and found an isotropic distribution, in agreement with theoretical expectation. However, we should also expect a small group of high-energy neutrons due to the direct ejection mechanism. This high-energy group would be in excess of the number of neutrons expected from the statistical theory, and would show a non-isotropic angular distribution, with preferential emission at right angles to the gamma-ray beam. There is preliminary evidence for the existence of such a group of neutrons (Poss 50, and private communications from G. A. Price and I. Halpern). In heavy elements this directly ejected group of neutrons accounts for a few percent of the total neutron yield.

Since the direct ejection process does not proceed via the formation of a compound nuclear state, the theory given here does not apply to it.[1]

SYMBOLS

a Incident particle in a nuclear reaction   (4.5)

a A quantum state of the nucleus   (Section 5)

a Radius of the K shell of an atom with atomic number Z, equal to a_0/Z (5.4)

a_0 Bohr radius of the hydrogen atom $[= \hbar^2/m_e e^2 = 5.28 \times 10^{-9}$ cm$]$ (5.4)

$a_E(l,m)$ Amplitude of the electric multipole radiation of order l,m (2.10)

[1] For an attempt at a detailed theory of this process see Courant (51).

$a_M(l,m)$ Amplitude of the magnetic multipole radiation of order l,m (2.10)

a_s Scattering length in the ^1S state of the neutron-proton system; see Chapter II, Section 3   (Section 4)

a A parameter appearing in the level density formula (VIII,6.11)   (Section 7, Table 7.1)

A A degenerate energy level   (Section 7)

$\mathbf{A}$ Vector potential of the radiation field   (2.14)

$A_E(l)$ Probability per unit time of the transition $\psi_a \to \psi_b$ by means of absorption of a light quantum of electric multipole radiation of order l (3.25)

b A quantum state of the nucleus   (Section 5)

B Binding energy of the deuteron $[= \hbar^2\gamma^2/M = 2.226$ Mev$]$ (Section 4)

B A degenerate energy level   (Section 7)

B_K Atomic binding energy of an electron in the K shell (5.17)

c Speed of light   (2.2)

d Linear dimensions of the source of the radiation   (Section 3)

$d\sigma_{1\to 2}$ Differential cross section of the transition $1\to2$ (4.9)

$d\sigma_{2\to 1}$ Differential cross section of the transition $2\to1$ (4.9)

$d\sigma_{\text{cap}}(l,m)$ Differential cross section for radiative neutron proton capture with emission of a quantum of multipole radiation of order l,m (4.13)

$d\sigma_{\text{dis}}(l,m)$ Differential cross section for radiative disintegration of the deuteron by absorption of a quantum of multipole radiation of order l,m (4.13)

$d\tau$ Element of configuration space   (2.14)

$d\Omega$ Element of solid angle   (Section 3)

D A deuteron   (4.1)

D_0 Level distance between *low-lying* states which can combine by emission of multipole radiation of a given type and order   (7.17)

$D(E)$ Level distance at excitation energy E (Section 7)

$D_l(E)$ Distance between those energy levels at excitation energy E which combine with some specified lower level by emission of multipole radiation of order l (7.14)

e Charge on the proton   (3.26)

e_k' Effective charge of nucleon number k for electric dipole radiation   (7.2)

E Excitation energy of the compound nucleus, measured from its ground state   (Section 7)

$E_>$	The larger one of two excitation energies E_a and E_b (7.13)
E_a	Energy of the quantum state ψ_a of the nucleus (3.24)
E_A	Energy of the degenerate level A (Section 7)
E_b	Energy of the quantum state ψ_b of the nucleus (3.24)
E_B	Energy of the degenerate level B (Section 7)
$E_{\max,l}$	Largest excitation energy E for which $q_{lm}(0,E)$ can remain of the same order of magnitude as $q_{lm}(0,0)$ (7.16)
E_N	Energy of the incident neutron in the laboratory system (for neutron-proton capture) $[= 2\hbar^2k^2/M]$ (Section 4)
ε	Electric field vector (Section 2)
$\varepsilon_E(l,m;\mathbf{r})$	Electric field vector in electric multipole radiation of order l,m (2.7)
$\varepsilon_M(l,m;\mathbf{r})$	Electric field vector in magnetic multipole radiation of order l,m (2.8)
$f(\theta)$	Scattering amplitude for neutron-proton scattering (4.3)
g_A	Degeneracy of state A (7.12)
G_b	Branching probability for emission of a particle b from the compound nucleus (7.24)
G_z	z coordinate of the center of gravity of the nucleus (Section 7)
H'	Interaction energy responsible for the internal conversion process (5.8)
H'_{12}	Matrix element for the radiative transition from state 1 to state 2 (4.7)
H'_{ab}	Matrix element for the radiative transition from state a to state b (2.14)
H'_{ab}	Matrix element for the internal conversion transition from (nuclear) state a to state b (5.6), (5.9)
$\mathfrak{H}$	Magnetic field vector (Section 2)
$\mathfrak{H}_E(l,m;\mathbf{r})$	Magnetic field vector in electric multipole radiation of order l,m (2.7)
$\mathfrak{H}_M(l,m;\mathbf{r})$	Magnetic field vector in magnetic multipole radiation of order l,m (2.8)
I	Overlap integral in the expression for the neutron-proton radiative capture cross section (4.23)
I_0	Angular momentum of the nucleus in its ground state (Section 6)
I_a	Angular momentum of the nucleus in state a (Section 6)
I_b	Angular momentum of the nucleus in state b (Section 6)

I_c	Angular momentum of the nucleus in state c (Section 6)
$\mathbf{j}$	Convection current, respectively the operator for this quantity (2.14)
$\mathbf{j}(a,b;\mathbf{r})$	The quantum analogue of the classical convection current for the transition $\varphi_a \rightarrow \varphi_b$ (3.26)
J_a	Angular momentum quantum number of the nucleus in state a (2.12)
J_b	Angular momentum quantum number of the nucleus in state b (2.12)
J_l	$= J_l(a,b)$; radial integral occurring in the matrix element for electric multipole radiation of order l between nuclear states a and b, with the independent-particle model (6.7)
J_{lm}	An integral occurring in internal conversion theory (5.12)
$\mathbf{J}_a$	Angular momentum vector of the nucleus in state a (2.11)
$\mathbf{J}_b$	Angular momentum vector of the nucleus in state b (2.11)
k	$= |\mathbf{k}|$; wave number of the relative motion of neutron and proton (4.3)
k	$= |\mathbf{k}|$; wave number of the electron in the internal conversion process (5.13)
$\mathbf{k}$	Wave vector of the relative motion of neutron and proton (4.2)
$\mathbf{k}$	Wave vector of the electron in the internal conversion process after ejection from the K shell (5.5)
l	Angular momentum quantum number of the radiation [= multipole order] (Section 2 and Appendix B)
$(2l+1)!!$	$\equiv 1 \times 3 \times 5 \times \cdots \times (2l+1)$ (3.4)
$L = l_{\min}$	Lowest value of l consistent with J_a, Π_a, J_b, Π_b (Section 2, Table 2.1)
L_{kz}	z component of $\mathbf{L}_k$ (3.37)
$\mathbf{L}$	Differential operator for the orbital angular momentum vector $[= -i\,\mathbf{r} \times \boldsymbol{\nabla}]$ (2.5)
$\mathbf{L}_k$	Orbital angular momentum operator for the kth nucleon $[= -i\,\mathbf{r}_k \times \boldsymbol{\nabla}_k]$ (3.33)
m	Quantum number associated with the z component of the angular momentum of a quantum of multipole radiation (2.5)
m	Mass of the electron (Section 5)

M	Mass of a nucleon (3.26)
M_a, M_b	Magnetic quantum number of the nucleus in state a or b (2.13)
M_{lm}	Magnetic multipole moment of order l,m associated with the convection current (3.7)
$M_{lm}(a,b)$	Magnetic multipole moment of order l,m associated with the convection current, for the transition $\varphi_a \to \varphi_b$; for one particle (3.29), (3.30); for a many-particle system (3.33)
M'_{lm}	Magnetic multipole moment of order l,m associated with the magnetization (with the spins) (3.10)
$M'_{lm}(a,b)$	Magnetic multipole moment of order l,m associated with the spins, for the transition $\varphi_a \to \varphi_b$ (3.35)
M	Density of magnetization $[= \lvert \mathbf{M} \rvert]$ (Section 6)
M	Density of magnetization (3.8)
$\mathbf{M}(a,b;\mathbf{r})$	Effective magnetization density for the transition $\varphi_a \to \varphi_b$ due to the spin of a particle (3.31)
N	A neutron (4.1)
N	Normalization constant in the wave function of the deuteron (4.17)
p_1	Momentum of the incident particle in the transition $1 \to 2$ (4.12)
p_2	Momentum of the incident particle in the transition $2 \to 1$ (4.12)
$p_{kz}(a,b)$	Matrix element of the z component of the momentum of the kth nucleon for a transition between quantum states a and b of the nucleus (7.3)
p	Momentum operator for a nucleon $[= -i\hbar\mathbf{\nabla}]$ (3.26)
$\mathbf{p}_k$	Momentum operator for the kth nucleon (Section 3)
P	A proton (4.1)
P	Density of electric polarization (Section 6)
P^2	Average square of the momentum of a typical nucleon inside the nucleus (7.9)
$q_{lm}(E_a, E_b)$	$= q_l = q$; a slowly varying function of the energies E_a, E_b; defined by (7.14)
Q_0	Matrix element for a typical single-particle radiative transition (7.12)
Q_{lm}	Electric multipole moment of order l,m associated with the convection current (3.5)
$Q_{lm}(a,b)$	Electric multipole moment of order l,m associated with the convection current, for the transition $\varphi_a \to \varphi_b$; for one particle (3.28); for a many-particle system (3.32)

Q'_{lm} Electric multipole moment of order l,m associated with the magnetization (with the spins)   (3.9)

$Q'_{lm}(a,b)$ Electric multipole moment of order l,m associated with the magnetization (with the spins), for the transition $\varphi_a \rightarrow \varphi_b$ (3.34)

r $= |\mathbf{r}|$; distance from the origin   (2.7)

r $= |\mathbf{r}|$, distance between neutron and proton   (4.3)

r_{0s} Effective range for neutron-proton scattering in the ^1S state; see Chapter II, Section 3   (Section 4)

r_{0t} Effective range for neutron-proton scattering in the ^3S state; see (II,3.20)   (Section 4)

r_i $= |\mathbf{r}_i|$; distance of nucleon number i from the center of gravity of the nucleus   (5.10)

r_k $= |\mathbf{r}_k|$; distance of nucleon number k from the center of gravity of the nucleus   (3.32)

$\mathbf{r}$ Position vector, usually measured from the center of gravity of the nucleus   (Section 2)

$\mathbf{r}$ Vector separation of neutron and proton   (4.2)

$\mathbf{r}_i$ Position vector of nucleon number i, measured from the center of gravity of the nucleus   (5.8), (5.9)

$\mathbf{r}_k$ Position vector of nucleon number k, measured from the center of gravity of the nucleus   (3.34)

R Radius of a large sphere around the radiating system (Section 3)

R $= |\mathbf{R}|$; distance of an atomic electron from the nucleus (5.4)

R Nuclear radius   (6.3)

$\mathbf{R}$ Position vector of an atomic electron, measured from the center of gravity of the nucleus   (5.5)

$\overline{R^2}$ An integral of the order of magnitude of the square of the nuclear radius   (5.20), (5.21)

$S(\omega)$ Flux of the light beam [= number of quanta per square centimeter per second per unit range of the circular frequency ω]   (3.25)

S_a Lowest separation energy of a particle from the nucleus (Section 7)

S_n Separation energy of a neutron   (Section 7)

$\mathbf{S}$ Poynting vector   (2.3)

$\mathbf{S}$ Total spin vector for the neutron-proton system $[= \frac{1}{2}(\mathbf{\delta}_N + \mathbf{\delta}_P)]$ (Section 4)

$T_{1\rightarrow 2}$ Probability per unit time of a transition from state 1 to state 2   (4.7)

T_{ab}	$= T(a,b)$; probability per unit time for a transition between states ψ_a and ψ_b accompanied by emission of electromagnetic radiation (Section 2) and (5.1)
$\bar{T}(a,b)$	Total transition probability (due to radiation and internal conversion) per unit time from state a to state b (5.1)
$T^{0\to 0}(a,b)$	Transition probability per unit time associated with ejection of a conversion electron from the K shell, in a transition between nuclear states a and b with angular momenta $I_a = I_b = 0$ (5.21)
$T^{(i)}(a,b)$	Probability per unit time for a transition between states a and b accompanied by emission of an internal conversion electron (5.1), (5.7)
$T_E(l,m)$	Probability per unit time of emission of a quantum of electric multipole radiation of order l,m (3.21)
$T_M(l,m)$	Probability per unit time of emission of a quantum of magnetic multipole radiation of order l,m (3.22)
$u_{0s}(r)$	Radial wave function for the ^1S state of the neutron-proton system (4.19), (4.20)
$u_{0t}(r)$	Radial wave function for the ^3S (ground) state of the deuteron (4.17), (4.18)
$u_{1t}(r)$	Radial wave function for the ^3P state of the neutron-proton system under the assumption that the neutron-proton force in that state has a negligible effect (4.32)
$u_a(r)$	Radial wave function of a proton in the initial state a of the nucleus (6.5)
$u_b(r)$	Radial wave function of a proton in the final state b of the nucleus (6.5)
$u_l^{(+)}(r)$	Radial wave function for an outgoing wave with orbital angular momentum l; see (VIII, 2.41) (2.7)
$U_\alpha(\theta,\phi)$	Angular distribution of the emission of alpha-particles (6.13)
$U_E(l,m;\Omega)$	$= U(\Omega)$ for electric multipole radiation of order l,m (3.15)
$U_l(\hbar\omega)$	Energy distribution of the multipole radiation of order l emitted immediately after capture (7.22)
$U_M(l,m\,\Omega)$	$= U(\Omega)$ for magnetic multipole radiation of order l,m (3.17)
$U(\Omega)\,d\Omega$	Energy per unit time radiated into the solid angle element $d\Omega$ (Section 3)
v	$= |\mathbf{v}|$; speed of the charges giving rise to the radiation (Section 3)
v	$= 2\hbar k/M$; relative speed of neutron and proton before capture (Section 4)

v_1	Speed of the incident particle in the transition $1 \to 2$ (4.9)
v_2	Speed of the incident particle in the transition $2 \to 1$ (4.9)
v_a	Wave function of an atomic electron in the K shell (5.4)
v_b	Wave function of an atomic electron after ejection from the K shell (5.5)
$\mathbf{v}$	Vector velocity of the charges whose motion gives rise to the radiation (Section 3)
V	Volume of a "box" in which the system is enclosed (5.5)
w_a	Wave function of a proton in the initial state a of the nucleus (6.5)
w_b	Wave function of a proton in the final state b of the nucleus (6.5)
$W(\theta_{12})$	Angular correlation function for successive emission of two nuclear radiations (6.12)
X	Target nucleus in a nuclear reaction (4.5)
$\mathbf{X}_{lm}$	$= \mathbf{X}_{lm}(\theta,\phi)$; vector spherical harmonic; see Appendix B (2.5)
Y	Final nucleus created by radiative capture (4.5)
$Y_{lm}(\theta,\phi)$	Scalar spherical harmonic; see Appendix A (2.5)
z	z component of the position vector $\mathbf{r}$ $[= r \cos \theta]$ (3.11)
$z(k)\, d\Omega$	Number of states of the ejected electron per unit energy range, within the solid angle element $d\Omega$ (5.6a)
$z_k(a,b)$	Matrix element of the z coordinate of the kth nucleon between quantum states a and b of the nucleus (7.3)
Z	Atomic number $[=$ number of protons in the nucleus$]$ (3.32)
$Z_{lm}(\theta,\phi)$	A function determining the angular distribution of multipole radiation of order l,m (3.16)
α	Internal conversion coefficient (5.2)
α	Spin function for a proton with spin up (6.5)
γ	The inverse of the decay length in the ground state of the deuteron $[= 2.32 \times 10^{12}\ \mathrm{cm}^{-1}]$ (4.17)
Γ_{El}	The contribution to Γ_{rad} from emission of electric multipole radiation of order l (7.19)
$\Gamma_{El}(a,b)$	Partial width of compound level a for a transition to level b with emission of electric multipole radiation of order l (7.20)

Γ_{Ml}	The contribution to Γ_{rad} from emission of magnetic multipole radiation of order l (7.19)
$\Gamma_{Ml}(a,b)$	Partial width of compound level a for a transition to level b with emission of magnetic multipole radiation of order l (Section 7)
Γ_{rad}	Radiation width of the compound nucleus in quantum state a (7.19)
δ_{0s}	Phase shift for scattering in the ^1S state of the neutron-proton system (4.20)
δ_{0t}	Phase shift for scattering in the ^3S state of the neutron-proton system (4.35)
Δ	Energy spacing between levels of a single nucleon (Section 7)
ΔE	$= E_a - E_b - B_K$; energy of the conversion electron after ejection from the K shell (5.21)
ΔE	Energy spread in the incident gamma-ray beam (7.25)
ΔJ	$= J_a - J_b$; change in the angular momentum of the nucleus during the transition $a \rightarrow b$ (Section 2)
Δm	Change in the magnetic quantum number m of the nucleus associated with emission of a gamma-ray (Section 6)
ΔM	$= M_a - M_b$ (Section 2)
ϵ	Total charge (3.23)
ϵ	Kinetic energy of a neutron before radiative capture, or after a (γ,n) reaction (Section 7)
ζ_k	$= z_k - G_z$; z coordinate of the kth nucleon measured from the center of gravity of the nucleus (7.1)
θ	Polar angle (colatitude) of the vector $\mathbf{r}$ (2.5)
θ	Polar angle (colatitude) of the wave vector $\mathbf{k}$ of the ejected electron (5.13)
θ_{12}	Angle between the first and second radiation emitted in a cascade nuclear transition $a \rightarrow b \rightarrow c$ (6.12)
θ_i	Polar angle (colatitude) of the position vector $\mathbf{r}_i$ of the ith nucleon (5.10)
θ_k	Polar angle (colatitude) of the position vector $\mathbf{r}_k$ of the kth nucleon (3.32)
Θ	Polar angle (colatitude) of the position vector $\mathbf{R}$ of the electron (5.10)
κ	Wave number of the electromagnetic radiation $[= \omega/c]$ (2.6)
λ	Wavelength of the electromagnetic radiation (Section 2)
$\lambdabar$	$= \lambda/2\pi$; modified wavelength of the electromagnetic radiation (Section 2)

μ Magnetic moment of a nucleon expressed in nuclear magnetons   (3.31)

μ_k Magnetic moment of the kth nucleon expressed in nuclear magnetons   (3.34)

μ_N Magnetic moment of the neutron expressed in nuclear magnetons $[=-1.91]$ (4.15)

μ_P Magnetic moment of the proton expressed in nuclear magnetons $[=+2.79]$ (4.15)

ν Frequency of the electromagnetic radiation $[=\omega/2\pi]$ (Section 2)

Π The parity (space inversion) operator, defined by $\Pi f(\mathbf{r}) = f(-\mathbf{r})$ (Section 2)

Π_a,Π_b Parity quantum number of the nucleus in states a and b (2.15)

ρ Charge density, or the operator for this quantity   (3.2)

ρ_{0t} A length, defined by (4.36), which is very closely equal to the effective range r_{0t} for neutron-proton scattering in the ^3S state   (4.35), (4.36)

$\rho_1=\rho(E)$ Number of states of type 1 per unit energy range (4.8), (4.10)

$\rho_2=\rho(E)$ Number of states of type 2 per unit energy range (4.7), (4.10)

$\rho(a,b;\mathbf{r})$ Quantum analogue of the classical charge density for the transition $a{\rightarrow}b$ (3.27)

$\sigma_{\mathrm{cap}}^E(l,m)$ Cross section for radiative capture with emission of electric multipole radiation of order l,m (4.4)

$\sigma_{\mathrm{cap}}(l,m)$ Cross section for radiative neutron-proton capture with emission of a quantum of multipole radiation of order l,m (4.14)

σ_{cap}^M Total cross section for radiative capture with emission of magnetic multipole radiation   (4.22)

$\sigma_{\mathrm{C}}(\gamma)$ Cross section for excitation of the nucleus to a compound (particle-emitting) state by absorption of a gamma-ray (7.24)

$\sigma_{\mathrm{C},ED}(\gamma)$ The part of $\sigma_{\mathrm{C}}(\gamma)$ due to absorption of electric dipole radiation (7.30)

$\sigma_{\mathrm{C}l}(\gamma)$ The part of $\sigma_{\mathrm{C}}(\gamma)$ due to absorption of multipole radiation of order l (7.26)

$\sigma(\gamma,b)$ Cross section for photodisintegration of a nucleus with emission of a particle b (7.24)

$\sigma_{\mathrm{dis}}^{ED}$ Cross section for radiative disintegration of the deuteron by absorption of electric dipole radiation   (4.33)

$\sigma_{\mathrm{dis}}(l,m)$	Cross section for radiative disintegration by absorption of multipole radiation of order l,m (4.14)
$\sigma_{\mathrm{dis}}^{M}$	Cross section for radiative disintegration of the deuteron by absorption of magnetic multipole radiation (4.28)
σ_{kz}	z component of $\mathbf{\sigma}_k$ (3.39)
$\mathbf{\sigma}$	Pauli spin vector; see Appendix A (3.31)
$\mathbf{\sigma}_k$	Pauli spin vector for the kth nucleon (3.34)
$\mathbf{\sigma}_N$	Pauli spin vector for the neutron (4.15)
$\mathbf{\sigma}_P$	Pauli spin vector for the proton (4.15)
ϕ	Polar angle (longitude) of the wave vector $\mathbf{k}$ of the ejected electron (5.13)
ϕ	Polar angle (longitude) of the position vector $\mathbf{r}$ (2.5)
ϕ_i	Polar angle (longitude) of the position vector $\mathbf{r}_i$ of the ith nucleon (5.10)
ϕ_k	Polar angle (longitude) of the position vector $\mathbf{r}_k$ of the kth nucleon (3.32)
φ_a	Wave function of the nucleus in quantum state a (3.26)
φ_a	Initial state of the system nucleus plus atomic electron $[=\psi_a v_a]$ (Section 5)
φ_b	Wave function of the nucleus in quantum state b (3.26), (7.6)
φ_b	Final state of the system nucleus plus atomic electron, $[=\psi_b v_b]$ (Section 5)
Φ	Polar angle (longitude) of the position vector $\mathbf{R}$ of the electron (5.10)
χ_0	Spin function for the singlet spin state of the neutron-proton system; see Appendix A, Section 4 (4.19)
$\chi_{1,0}$	Spin function for the triplet spin state of the neutron-proton system with $m=0$; see Appendix A, Section 4 (4.16)
ψ_a	Wave function of the nucleus in state a Section 2 and (5.9)
ψ_b	Wave function of the nucleus in state b Section 2 and (5.9)
ω	Circular frequency of the electromagnetic radiation, $[=2\pi\nu]$ (Section 2)
ω_{ab}	Circular frequency associated with the transition between quantum states a and b $[=|E_a-E_b|/\hbar]$ (3.24)
Ω	A direction; this symbol stands for the two polar angles θ and ϕ (Section 3)

CHAPTER XIII

Beta-Decay

1. INTRODUCTION

The evidence that beta-rays are identical with ordinary electrons and positrons is overwhelming. The charge-to-mass ratio, e/m, agrees with the one for electrons within experimental error (Bucherer 09, Neumann 14, Zahn 37, 38) and so does the charge itself. The occurrence of orbital electron capture as an alternative process to β^+-emission shows that the nucleus can accept an ordinary atomic electron in order to effect the transition. This is taken as confirmation of the fact that the β^+-emission itself is emission of an ordinary positron (which is equivalent, in the hole theory, to acceptance by the nucleus of an electron in a negative-energy state). Positrons emitted by nuclei produce annihilation quanta upon encountering ordinary electrons, whereas electrons emitted by nuclei do *not* get captured into occupied orbits, thereby showing that they are identical with the electrons in those orbits (Goldhaber 48a).

The emergence of electrons from nuclei gave rise to the hypothesis that they are an integral part of nuclear matter. At that time (before 1933) the neutron was unknown, and a proton-electron theory of the nucleus seemed reasonable. According to this theory, a nucleus such as $_7N^{14}$ consists of 14 protons (to give the right mass) and 7 electrons (to give the right charge).

A strong argument against this assumption can be based on the measured angular momentum of N^{14}, $J = 1$. On the basis of the proton-electron theory, this nucleus would have an odd number (21) of elementary particles, each of spin $\frac{1}{2}$. Its total angular momentum J would then have to be half-integral, in contradiction to the measurement. This example is typical of all the odd-odd nuclei.

Another argument against the permanent presence of electrons in the nucleus comes from the uncertainty principle. An electron enclosed in a nuclear volume, of dimension R^3 say, must necessarily have a momentum distribution extending out to momenta of order $p_{max} \sim \hbar/R$. The corresponding kinetic energy is (in the extreme

670

relativistic approximation) $E \sim \hbar c / R$. If we use a nuclear radius $R \sim 10^{-12}$ cm, the (kinetic) energy turns out to be of order $E \sim 20$ Mev. In order to keep the electron within the nucleus, the potential energy of attraction between electrons and protons (or neutrons) must be strong enough to more than balance this kinetic energy.[1] There is absolutely no evidence for such a strong attraction between electrons and nuclear matter, and considerable evidence against it (from measurements on the neutron electron interaction). Yet, experiment shows that electrons do come out of nuclei, in the form of beta-rays. We seem to be faced with a contradiction.

This same apparent contradiction had already been encountered in the theory of atomic structure in the problem of the emission and absorption of light by atoms. Electromagnetic radiation does not seem to form an integral part of atomic structure, yet electromagnetic radiation emerges from atoms. In the theory of atomic spectra the contradiction was resolved by assuming that there is a possibility that the atom can change its state under simultaneous emission (or absorption) of a light quantum. While it is commonly said that the light quantum is created during the act of emission, this view is rather superficial. The electromagnetic field and the atom are in interaction all the time. This interaction shows itself not merely through emission and absorption of light but also through small steady disturbances in the atomic structure (Lamb shift and related phenomena, natural level width). Hence we may say that electromagnetic radiation, although not an integral part of actual atomic structure, yet has a kind of latent existence in the atom.

Although the analogy to emission of beta-rays from nuclei seems rather natural, we must overcome another difficulty before we can apply this analogy. This difficulty lies in the apparent lack of conservation of energy, momentum, and angular momentum in beta-decay.

When an atom emits a light quantum, it changes from one well-defined state to another. The emerging light quantum carries away the energy and momentum liberated in the transition. Consequently the energy $\hbar\omega$ of the light quantum is determined, and its momentum is equal and opposite to the momentum of the recoiling atom. By analogy, we should expect that an electron is emitted when a nucleus changes from one well-defined state to another. The emerging electron should then carry away a definite amount of energy, and its

---

[1] Actually, no such strong attractive potential could be maintained for any length of time. It would lead to continuous creation of positron-electron pairs, with a tendency for the resulting space charge to shield the attractive potential (Klein paradox).

momentum should be equal and opposite to the momentum of the recoiling nucleus.

This is not observed. On the contrary, electrons are emitted with all energies smaller than some maximum total energy $E_{\max}$ (this includes the rest energy mc^2). Furthermore the electron does not necessarily leave in the opposite direction from the recoil nucleus. Of course, it would be very surprising if momentum were conserved without energy being conserved; the theory of relativity shows that the two are intimately connected. The angular momentum also fails to be conserved. Consider the beta-decay $C^{14} \rightarrow N^{14}+\beta^-$. The nuclear angular momenta of C^{14} and N^{14} have been measured; they are 0 and 1, respectively. Thus the nuclear angular momentum changes during the transition by an *integral* amount ($\Delta J = 1$). On the other hand, the electron, being a particle of half-integral intrinsic spin, has to carry away a *half-integral* total angular momentum. Thus angular momentum cannot be conserved during this transition.

A clue to the solution of this problem is provided by the fact that the *maximum* energy (including the electron rest energy) of the beta-spectrum is equal to the total energy available from the nuclear transformation. Furthermore the *maximum* momentum which the recoil nucleus receives is in agreement with the one calculated under the assumption that an electron of energy $E_{\max}$ has been emitted in the opposite direction. These facts are explained naturally by the *neutrino hypothesis* due to Pauli.

The neutrino hypothesis postulates the existence of a (so far unobserved) neutral particle of small mass and half-integral spin. This particle, called a neutrino, is assumed to be emitted simultaneously with the observed beta-particle. The electron, neutrino, and product nucleus share among them the energy, momentum, and angular momentum available from the nuclear transition. The beta-particle gets its maximum energy when the neutrino is emitted with zero momentum. This explains the conservation laws found experimentally for the maximum energy and maximum momentum in beta-decay.

Conversely, the difference between the maximum energy $E_{\max}$ of the beta-particle and the total available energy E_0 of the nuclear transformation gives a value for the rest energy $m_\nu c^2$ of the neutrino. Experiments of this type show that the neutrino has a rest energy smaller than 25 kev and equal to zero within the experimental error. The apparent lack of conservation of angular momentum is explained by assigning some half-integral intrinsic spin to the neutrino. We shall assume that the spin of the neutrino is $\frac{1}{2}\hbar$.[1]

---

[1] Calculations with neutrinos of spin $\frac{3}{2}\hbar$ were carried out by Kusaka (41). They appear to exclude this choice on the basis of the shape of the beta-spectrum.

The fact that the neutrino escapes observation is unfortunate but not unexpected. A neutral particle cannot be observed directly with present methods, only indirectly by its effect on charged particles. A neutrino would not be expected to interact very strongly with any known particle. Indeed, we know only one process to which a neutrino can certainly give rise, namely the inverse process to orbital electron capture: a neutrino is absorbed by the nucleus while an electron is emitted (Bethe 34). The cross section for this process can be estimated. It is so small ($\sim 10^{-44}$ cm^2) that the neutrino is able to traverse kilometers of dense matter without a single collision. Direct detection of the neutrino has been considered by Crane (48), Benfield (48), Saxon (49), Barrett (50), and others. Indirect information about the neutrino could be obtained from "double beta-decay"; see Furry (37,39), Racah (37), Majorana (37), Fireman (49).

2. THE NEUTRINO HYPOTHESIS AND THE SHAPE OF THE BETA-SPECTRUM. SELECTION RULES FOR "ALLOWED" TRANSITIONS

We now study the way in which the available energy is divided between the beta-particle and the neutrino, i.e., the shape of the beta-spectrum. We shall first make some simplifying assumptions which can be dropped later. We shall neglect the Coulomb interaction between the electron and the residual nucleus, and the recoil energy of the nucleus.

The Coulomb interaction can be neglected only for the lightest nuclei ($Z \lesssim 10$) and sufficiently high electron energies. The recoil energy is negligible in all cases, since the mass of the nucleus, AM, is much larger than the electron mass m. The maximum recoil energy occurs when all the available energy is given to the electron. If we neglect the rest mass of the neutrino, the electron then has a total energy (including rest energy) of $E_{max} = E_0$, where E_0 is the energy available from the nuclear transition, and a momentum

$$\left(\frac{p_e}{mc}\right)_{max} = \left[\left(\frac{E_{max}}{mc^2}\right)^2 - 1\right]^{1/2}$$

$(p_e)_{max}$ is equal to the maximum recoil momentum P_{max}. We therefore get for the maximum recoil energy E_{rec} (non-relativistic)

$$\left\langle \frac{E_{rec}}{E_{elec}} \right\rangle_{max} = \frac{m}{2AM}\left(\frac{E_{max}}{mc^2} - \frac{mc^2}{E_{max}}\right) \tag{2.1}$$

The second factor is less than 30 for all known beta-transitions, while the first factor is less than 3×10^{-4} for the beta-decay of an isolated neutron and is inversely proportional to the mass number A. Hence we are justified in neglecting the recoil energy. We get an excellent approximation to the momentum P of the recoil nucleus by neglecting the recoil energy and afterwards computing P from the law of conservation of momentum for the recoil nucleus, electron, and neutrino (assuming the initial nucleus was at rest):

$$\mathbf{P} + \mathbf{p}_e + \mathbf{p}_\nu = 0 \qquad (2.2)$$

We start by assuming, as Fermi (34) did, that all possible divisions of energy are equally likely. This statement can be formulated quantitatively as follows: Consider the phase space for the two particles, electron and neutrino. Not all of this phase space is accessible since the sum of the energies is given by the law of conservation of energy:

$$E_e + E_\nu = E_0 \qquad (2.3)$$

We *postulate that the probability of a disintegration leading to a specified* *accessible volume of phase space is directly proportional to that volume.*

Consider the following end state of a disintegration. The electron is contained in the volume element dV_e and has a momentum of magnitude between p_e and $p_e + dp_e$ in a direction within the solid angle element $d\Omega_e$. Corresponding statements hold for the neutrino (neutrino quantities will be denoted by the subscript ν). We express the volume of this state in phase space in its natural units, $h^6 = (2\pi\hbar)^6$. This gives

Volume in phase space $= (2\pi\hbar)^{-6}\, p_e{}^2\, dp_e\, d\Omega_e\, dV_e\, p_\nu{}^2\, dp_\nu\, d\Omega_\nu\, dV_\nu$ (2.4)

We now use the energy law (2.3) to write dp_ν in the form

$$dp_\nu = \left(\frac{\partial p_\nu}{\partial E_0}\right)_{p_e} dE_0 = \frac{E_\nu}{c^2 p_\nu}\, dE_0$$

where the subscript on the partial derivative indicates that the electron momentum is to be kept constant during the differentiation. With this substitution the phase space volume (2.4) assumes the form $\rho(E_0)\, dE_0$, where $\rho(E_0)$ is the "density of final states per unit range of total energy" familiar from perturbation theory; under the assumption of zero rest mass for the neutrino we obtain

$$\rho(E_0) = (2\pi\hbar)^{-6}\, c^{-3}\, p_e{}^2\, (E_0 - E_e)^2\, dp_e\, d\Omega_e\, dV_e\, d\Omega_\nu\, dV_\nu$$

where we have expressed the neutrino energy E_ν in terms of the electron energy E_e and the total energy E_0. According to our assumptions

$\rho(E_0)$ is proportional to the probability that the beta-decay leads to this particular final state.

We observe that this expression predicts that the emission of the electron and the neutrino into all directions is equally likely; in particular, there is no angular correlation between the directions of emission of the two particles. Furthermore, if we imagine that the whole system is enclosed within a large box of volume V, we are equally likely to find the electron and neutrino in any region of the box. Both statements result from the extreme simplifications used in this discussion and will be modified later on.

We are not interested at this time in the position of the emitted particles within our imaginary box. We therefore integrate over dV_e and dV_ν. We shall also not be concerned with the absolute direction of emission of the electron, but only with possible angular correlations between electron and neutrino. We therefore measure the neutrino directions with respect to the direction of the electron, i.e., replace $d\Omega_\nu$ by $d\Omega_{e\nu}$, where $\theta_{e\nu}$ is the angle between electron and neutrino. Integrating over the angles for the electrons gives us the final phase space factor:

$$\rho(E_0) = \frac{V^2}{16\pi^5 \hbar^6 c^3} \, p_e^{\,2} \, (E_0 - E_e)^2 \, dp_e \, d\Omega_{e\nu} \qquad (2.5)$$

If the direction of the neutrino (or, more practically, the direction of the nuclear recoil) is not observed in the experiment, we have to integrate (2.5) over $d\Omega_{e\nu}$ also, which gives an additional factor of 4π. The appearance of the volume V in this expression is of purely formal origin. It will disappear from the final expressions.

The main result contained in (2.5) is the shape of the beta-spectrum. According to (2.5), the distribution-in-momentum of the emitted electrons is given by (omitting the subscript e)

$$P(p) \, dp = C \, p^2 \, (E_0 - E)^2 \, dp \qquad (2.6)$$

where C is a constant. For small momenta this distribution is proportional to p^2, for large momenta (E near E_0) it is proportional to $(E_0 - E)^2$. It vanishes at both limits and has a maximum in the middle. A typical case is shown in Fig. 2.1a.

We now investigate the effect of a possible, small rest mass m_ν of the neutrino on the shape of the beta-spectrum. There is no effect at all for extreme relativistic neutrino energies $E_\nu \gg m_\nu c^2$. Hence we confine ourselves to non-relativistic neutrino energies, $E_\nu - m_\nu c^2 \ll m_\nu c^2$. This is the upper end of the *electron* distribution, where E_e is near

XIII. Beta-Decay

its maximum value, $E_{max} = E_0 - m_\nu c^2$. A simple calculation shows that $\rho(E_0)$ is then proportional to the neutrino momentum, i.e., to $(E_{max} - E_e)^{1/2}$. The electron distribution therefore approaches the upper limit with a vertical tangent instead of a horizontal tangent.[1] This is illustrated schematically in Fig. 2.1b. The best available measurements give a distribution near the maximum electron energy consistent with (2.6) within the experimental error. We can use these measurements to obtain an upper limit for m_ν (Konopinski

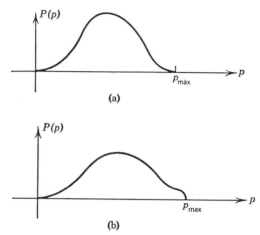

(a)

(b)

FIG. 2.1. $P(p) \, dp$ is the probability of a beta-decay in which the electron is emitted with momentum between p and $p+dp$. The form of $P(p)$ for p near its maximum value depends on the rest mass of the neutrino, $m\nu$. (a) illustrates schematically the case $m_\nu = 0$; (b) the case $m_\nu \neq 0$.

47, Pruett 48, Bowers 49). The result (from the H^3 spectrum measured by Curran 48, 49, and Hanna 49) is: $m_\nu c^2 < 500$ ev, i.e., less than one-hundredth the rest energy of an electron. This determination of the neutrino rest mass depends on the validity of the assumptions made so far, in particular on (1) the assumption of the emission of a single neutrino, and (2) the assumption of a statistical division of the available energy. The neutrino rest mass can also be measured more directly by determining separately the nuclear energy change E_0 and the maximum electron energy E_{max} and using the energy balance $E_0 = E_{max} + m_\nu c^2$. In all cases where direct determinations have been carried out they agree with the indirect determination from the beta-

---

[1] Although the statistical factor gives the general behavior of the beta-spectrum near its end point correctly, the details of the beta-spectrum for finite neutrino rest mass depend on more detailed features of beta-theory than just the statistical factor.

spectrum within the experimental errors. This agreement supports the assumptions listed above.

Before comparing the detailed beta-spectrum with experimental measurements, we must include the effect of the Coulomb force between the beta-particle and the daughter nucleus. In order to do this, we have to retrace the previous argument, filling in some gaps. If we imagine that the whole system is enclosed within a box of volume V, it cannot be true that a decay electron with a given momentum vector $\mathbf{p}_e$ is equally likely to be in any part of the box. Rather, the position and momentum are correlated in the sense that the electron has a direction away from the nucleus which emitted it.

The gap in the argument consisted of the failure to specify the probability of decay more in detail. We shall assume that the decay probability is a product of four factors:

(1) The a priori probability $\rho(E_0)$, (2.5).

(2) The probability of finding the electron within the nuclear volume, i.e., $\int |\psi_e|^2 \, dV_e$ extended over the interior of the nucleus.

(3) The probability of finding the neutrino within the nuclear volume, i.e., $\int |\psi_\nu|^2 \, dV_\nu$ over the interior of the nucleus.

(4) A specifically nuclear factor to be determined from a more detailed theory. We shall assume for the time being that this factor is independent of the distribution of energy between the electron and neutrino.

We can understand the need for factors (2) and (3) by considering the inverse process where an electron and neutrino are put into a box of volume V together with the decay *product* nucleus Y. The rate of the inverse beta-decay, $Y+e+\nu=X$, is proportional to the probability of having Y interact with e and ν at the same time. Hence factors (2) and (3) follow for the inverse beta-decay if we assume that the interactions involved are essentially point interactions. Since the beta-decay and the inverse beta-decay are related by the general reciprocity law for inverse processes (Chapter X, Section 2), we conclude that factors (2) and (3) apply also to the beta-decay itself.

Let us consider the orbital angular momenta l_e and l_ν of the electron and the neutrino after the emission. Since the wavelengths of electron and neutrino are much larger than the nuclear radius, we approximate the integral $\int |\psi_e|^2 \, dV_e$ over the interior of the nucleus by $|\psi_e(0)|^2 \, V_N$, where V_N is the nuclear volume and $\psi_e(0)$ is the electron wave function evaluated at the center of the nucleus. A similar approximation is used for the neutrino factor, (3). The wave function ψ_e for a free electron of wave number $k_e = p_e/\hbar$ emitted with orbital angular momentum

l_e is proportional to $(k_e r_e)^{l_e}$ for small distances r_e from the origin of the coordinate system (the center of the nucleus). Thus in particular $\psi_e(0)$ vanishes except for electrons emitted with zero orbital angular momentum. The same consideration holds for the neutrino. We conclude therefore that the electron and neutrino are emitted only with zero orbital angular momentum as long as the approximations which we have introduced are valid. This rule is in agreement with the intuitive idea that the emitted electron must appear to come from the emitting nucleus. Zero orbital angular momentum means zero impact parameter, i.e., an electron direction straight away from the center of the emitting nucleus.[1]

Actually, the average values of $|\psi_e(r)|^2$ and $|\psi_\nu(r)|^2$ are not exactly equal to their respective values at $r=0$. Hence an emission of the light particles with an orbital angular momentum different from zero is possible, although its probability is relatively much smaller. *We shall call "allowed transitions" the transitions in which both the electron and the neutrino are emitted with zero orbital angular momentum,* and we shall call "forbidden transitions" the relatively weaker ones in which one or both particles are emitted with an orbital angular momentum different from zero.

Let us now consider the intrinsic spin of the emitted particles. Both particles have a spin $\frac{1}{2}$. These two spins can combine to a total intrinsic spin 0 (singlet case) or 1 (triplet case).

The theory, in its present stage, cannot predict which case takes place in the actual beta-decay. The light particles could be emitted either in the singlet state or in the triplet state or in a combination of both. In order to decide this question, we must discuss the consequences of the different possibilities and compare them with the experimental material.

If electron and neutrino are emitted in the singlet spin state, the only angular momentum carried away by the two particles is the orbital angular momentum, and that is zero for allowed transitions. Hence the angular momentum of the daughter nucleus must equal the angular momentum of the parent nucleus. Furthermore, since both the electron and the neutrino are emitted in S states ($l=0$) which have even parity, there cannot be any change in the parity of the nuclear wave functions. We therefore get for the case of singlet emission the *Fermi selection rule for allowed transitions:*

$$\Delta J = 0 \qquad \text{no change of parity} \qquad (2.7)$$

---

[1] This statement is subject, of course, to the usual qualifications due to the Heisenberg uncertainty principle; see Chapter VIII, Section 2.

If the electron and neutrino are emitted in the triplet spin state, i.e., with parallel spins, a different selection rule is obtained. No orbital angular momentum is involved in allowed transitions, and the total angular momentum carried by the two particles is their spin angular momentum, which is now unity. Since the parity operation does not involve the spins, the parity selection rule is as before. We thus get an alternative rule for the case of triplet emission, *the Gamow-Teller selection rule for allowed transitions:*

$$\Delta J = \pm 1 \text{ or } 0 \text{ (except no } 0 \rightarrow 0 \text{ transitions)} \qquad \text{no change of parity}$$
$$(2.8)$$

It must be noted that our distinction between singlet and triplet states of the light particles is justified only in a non-relativistic approach. If a particle possesses a relativistic energy, it is no longer possible to distinguish clearly between orbital and intrinsic angular momentum and to define the parity of the state.[1] On the other hand, the nuclei presumably need not be treated relativistically. Hence we can still use the parity of a nuclear state and certainly the total angular momentum J of the nucleus as good quantum numbers. The more detailed relativistic treatment of the beta-decay shows (see Section 5) that it is justified to maintain selection rules (2.7) and (2.8) in order to distinguish two characteristic ways in which the light particles can be emitted in an allowed transition; the two ways correspond to the singlet and triplet cases in the non-relativistic limit.

Selection rules (2.7) and (2.8) indicate which nuclear transitions could lead to allowed beta-decays in the case of singlet or triplet emission respectively. The transitions which do not fulfill conditions (2.7) for the singlet case or (2.8) for the triplet case involve the emission of a light particle with an orbital angular momentum different from zero. They are therefore forbidden, and it is expected that, other things being equal, allowed beta-decays have larger transition probabilities than forbidden decays.[2] This fact will be used to attempt an experimental decision between the two possibilities.

---

[1] The spin of the so-called "small components" of the four-component Dirac wave function is always opposed to the spin of the "large components." For relativistic energies the two components are of equal order of magnitude. Also the parity of the wave function becomes ambiguous. For a discussion of the parity operation for spin $\frac{1}{2}$ particles see Yang and Tiomno (50).

[2] This statement is made only plausible by our present, non-relativistic treatment of the electron and neutrino, which leads to selection rules (2.7) and (2.8). The non-relativistic argument cannot be regarded as a proof, since the neutrino is always relativistic.

We now turn to the influence of the additional factors, (2) and (3) on page 677, on the shape of the beta-spectrum for allowed transitions. We start out by showing that these factors have no influence on the spectrum shape as long as the Coulomb force between the electron and the daughter nucleus can be neglected. We imagine that the electron is confined to remain inside a box of volume V. Then

$$\int |\psi_e|^2 \, dV_e \cong |\psi_e(0)|^2 \, V_N = \frac{V_N}{V} \qquad (2.9)$$

which is an energy-independent factor. A similar relation holds for the neutrino integral $\int |\psi_\nu|^2 \, dV$. Hence the spectrum shape is completely determined by the statistical factor $\rho(E_0)$, (2.5).

On the other hand, $|\psi_e(0)|^2$ becomes energy-dependent if the Coulomb force on the electron is taken into account. We get an approximate expression for the Coulomb correction to the spectrum shape by treating the electron non-relativistically. This gives

$$F(Z,E) = \frac{|\psi_e(0)|^2}{|\psi_e(0)|^2_{\text{free}}} = \frac{2\pi\eta}{1 - \exp(-2\pi\eta)} \qquad (2.10)$$

where $\eta = Ze^2/\hbar v$ for electrons, $\eta = -Ze^2/\hbar v$ for positrons, v being the speed of the particle far away, Z the atomic number of the *product* (daughter) nucleus. The Coulomb correction enhances the probability of electron emission and decreases the probability of positron emission, especially at low energies. At high energies the Coulomb force loses its effect on the spectrum shape, and the spectrum approaches that computed without the Coulomb correction.

The behavior of the spectrum at very low electron or positron energies can be obtained directly from (2.6) and (2.10). For no Coulomb force, the distribution-in-momentum is proportional to p^2. For electron emission with low momenta p the Coulomb correction factor $F(Z,E)$ becomes inversely proportional to the electron momentum. Hence the electron distribution-in-momentum is proportional to p rather than to p^2 for energies low enough so that $2\pi\eta \gg 1$. For positron emission, the Coulomb correction factor $F(Z,E)$ becomes proportional to $p^{-1} \exp(-c/p)$, where c is a constant. Hence the distribution-in-momentum of low-energy positrons is proportional to $p \exp(-c/p)$, i.e., drops to zero very rapidly. Figure 2.2 illustrates these points in a schematic fashion.

Sometimes the distribution-in-energy rather than the distribution-in-momentum is plotted. Since $c^2 p \, dp = E \, dE$, the former distribution is obtained from the latter by multiplication with E/pc^2. In particular, at energies close to the rest energy mc^2 the energy spectrum for no Coulomb field is proportional to p. If the Coulomb field is taken into account, the energy spectrum at low energies approaches a constant finite value for electrons; it is proportional to $\exp(-c/p)$ for positrons.

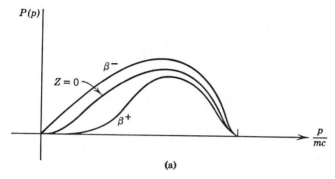

(a)

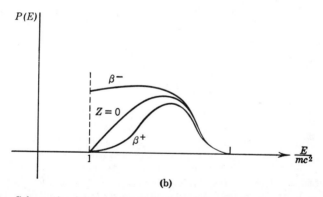

(b)

FIG. 2.2. Schematic picture of the influence of the Coulomb correction upon the spectrum shape of allowed transitions. (a) shows the distribution-in-momentum, i.e., $P(p)\,dp$ is the number of electrons emitted into the momentum interval between p and $p+dp$; (b) shows the distribution-in-energy, i.e., $P(E)\,dE$ is the number of electrons emitted into the energy interval between E and $E+dE$. The curves labeled β^- and β^+ refer to negatron and positron emission, respectively.

The Coulomb effect can be understood qualitatively in the following way: the energy distribution for positive and for negative electrons is the same at the moment of leaving the nucleus. The Coulomb field accelerates the positive electrons and decelerates the negative electrons. Hence the positron spectrum has fewer slow particles, and the negatron spectrum more slow particles, than they would have in the absence of the Coulomb effect. This classical argument would predict no positrons below a certain energy (the barrier energy, $= Ze^2/R$, where R is the nuclear radius). The actual positron spectrum does contain some low-energy positrons, as a result of the quantum-mechanical barrier penetration effect. Indeed, the Coulomb factor (2.10) is the one which occurs in the theory of proton-proton scattering (Chapter II) or in the theory of nuclear reactions induced by charged particles (Chapter VIII). The Coulomb correction becomes important when $2\pi|\eta| = 2\pi Ze^2/\hbar v \gtrsim 1$.

The Coulomb correction factor (2.10) must be amended for two different effects: the relativistic correction, and the correction for screening of the nuclear electric field by the atomic electrons.

If the electron is treated relativistically by means of the Dirac equation, the integral $\int_{nucl} |\psi_e|^2 \, dV$ cannot be replaced by $|\psi_e(0)|^2 \, V_N$ because the radial Dirac function becomes infinite at $r = 0$. The infinity is a very weak one, however, and furthermore the wave function of the electron inside the nucleus itself does not continue to rise indefinitely, since the charge is now distributed over the nuclear volume rather than being a point charge. It is common practice to replace the integral $\int_{nucl} |\psi_e|^2 \, dV$ by $|\psi_e(R)|^2 \, V_N$, where R is the nuclear radius. This approximation does not introduce any serious errors (Good 51).

With this approximation the relativistic Coulomb correction factor (not corrected for screening) becomes (Fermi 34)

$$F(Z,E) = \frac{2(1+s)}{[(2s)!]^2} (2p\rho)^{2s-2} e^{\pi\eta} |(s-1+i\eta)!|^2 \tag{2.11}$$

where $s \equiv [1 - (Ze^2/\hbar c)^2]^{1/2}$; $\rho \equiv R/(\hbar/mc)$, $R \equiv$ nuclear radius; $p \equiv$ electron or positron momentum, in units mc; $\eta \equiv +Ze^2/\hbar v$ for negatron decay; $\eta \equiv -Ze^2/\hbar v$ for positron decay; $v \equiv$ electron or positron speed; $Z \equiv$ charge of final nucleus.

Since the last factor in (2.11) involves a function which has not yet been tabulated, it is useful to get a simple analytic approximation to (2.11) in terms of tabulated functions. The following expression, suggested by Hall (50), is accurate to better than 1 percent in absolute value for all energies and all attainable Z, and even better than that for the shape of the spectrum. This approximation is

$$F(Z,E) \cong \frac{4\pi(1+s)}{[(2s)!]^2} (2p\rho)^{2s-2} (s^2 + \eta^2)^{s-1/2} \exp\left[2\phi\eta - 2s + \frac{s}{6(s^2+\eta^2)}\right] \tag{2.12}$$

where all the symbols are as above and ϕ is defined by $\phi \equiv \arctan(s/\eta)$. For $Z = 0$ this reduces to 1.0046 instead of 1, which gives some indication of the error of this approximation.

The correction for the screening of the field of the residual nucleus by the atomic electrons is more difficult to handle. Fortunately this correction is important only at rather low energies (of the order of 100 kev or less). Rose (36) has shown that the screening correction is quite unimportant for negatron decay, and later calculations (Longmire and Brown 49, Reitz 50) have confirmed this conclusion.

On the other hand, the screening correction is quite important for positron emission. Numerical calculations of Reitz on the ENIAC show that for $Z = 92$ the screening correction amounts to a factor of 2 around 80 kev, and to a factor of 10 at 25 kev.

Collecting the information obtained so far, the *momentum spectrum of the beta-particles in allowed transitions is given by*

$$P(p) \, dp = C \, F(Z,E) \, p^2 \, (E_0 - E)^2 \, dp \qquad (2.13)$$

where C is a constant which in general depends on the specific nuclei involved in the decay, and $F(Z,E)$ is given approximately by (2.10) (for Z less than about 30 and kinetic energies E above a few hundred kev) and more accurately by (2.12) (augmented, for positrons, by the screening correction of Reitz 50).

It is customary in the study of beta-decay to measure all energies in units mc^2, and all momenta in units mc. Thus our *symbol E will be used from now on for E/mc^2, and p for p/mc.*

The distribution-in-momentum $P(p)$ is measured directly by the distribution of curvatures in a magnetic field. Kurie (36) pointed out that the data so obtained can be plotted in a simple manner. It follows from (2.13) that a plot of $[P(p)/Fp^2]^{1/2}$ against energy E is a straight line, intersecting the abscissa at $E = E_0$. The Kurie plot has the advantage that it does not require accurate knowledge of the decay energy E_0, but rather can be used to find E_0 by straight-line extrapolation. It is also a simple and effective way of testing whether a measured beta-spectrum has the allowed shape.[1] A Kurie plot for the beta-decay of S^{35} (taken from Albert and Wu, 48, and Cook et al., 48) is shown in Fig. 2.3. The agreement between theory and experiment is excellent at all but the lowest energies. The deviations from straight-line behavior at extremely low kinetic energies are attributable to experimental errors of various kinds and do not constitute a real disagreement.[2]

In order to see whether this agreement with theory is significant, let us calculate the allowed spectrum under the assumption that *two* neutrinos are emitted in each disintegration. The accessible volume in phase space is determined by the energy law $E_e + E_\nu + E_\mu = E_0$, where we denote the second neutrino by μ. The relevant volume element in phase space is proportional to $p_e^2 \, dp_e \, p_\nu^2 \, dp_\nu \, p_\mu^2 \, dp_\mu$. Elimi-

[1] See Kurie (48), however, for cautions regarding this procedure.

[2] Early measurements of beta-spectra appeared to contradict the Fermi theory. Lawson (39, 40) and Tyler (39) were the first to overcome the experimental difficulties and to get sufficiently accurate measurements to allow a valid comparison with the theory.

nation of the momentum of the second neutrino, similar to the transformation from (2.4) to (2.5), now leads to

$$\rho(E_0) \sim p_e{}^2 \, (E_0 - E_e - E_\nu)^2 \, p_\nu{}^2 \, dp_e \, dp_\nu$$

(we assume zero rest mass for both neutrinos). Since the neutrino ν is just as unobserved as the neutrino μ, we integrate over p_ν between 0 and $(E_0 - E_e)/c$ to get the spectrum shape factor

$$\int \rho(E_0) \, dp_\nu \sim p_e{}^2 \, (E_0 - E_e)^5 \, dp_e \qquad (2.14)$$

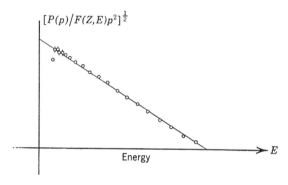

Fig. 2.3. A Kurie plot of the spectrum of S^{35}, taken from Albert and Wu (48). A straight-line plot indicates an allowed spectrum shape; the intercept with the abscissa gives the maximum electron energy. The small deviations at low energies are instrumental.

Distribution (2.14) strongly enhances the low-energy end of the electron spectrum and makes the approach to zero at the upper limit much more rapid than spectrum (2.6), which was based on the emission of only one neutrino. There is no question that (2.14) is in disagreement with the data. The large difference between the shapes (2.6) and (2.14) together with the experimental confirmation of (2.6) (after correction for the Coulomb effect) provides considerable positive support to the single-neutrino hypothesis of Pauli.[1]

3. ORBITAL ELECTRON CAPTURE

Since the nucleus of any atom, radioactive or not, is always surrounded by electrons under laboratory conditions, a nucleus unstable against positron decay can instead capture one of the orbital electrons (Yukawa 35a, Møller 37). This one-sided behavior of positron decay

---

[1] Quite apart from these considerations, it would be awkward to introduce two neutrinos, since they could not be particles of the same kind. In order to obtain conservation of angular momentum in beta-decay, one neutrino would have to have integral spin, the other half-integral spin.

compared to negatron decay does not contradict the basic symmetry between positrons and electrons. If there were positrons around for a nucleus to catch, positron capture would compete with negatron decay just as electron capture competes with positron decay, and with similar energetic relationships. Conversely, there can be unusual conditions in which the nuclei are not surrounded by electrons. In that case orbital electron capture does not occur. In general, the probability of orbital electron capture depends not only on the properties of the nucleus, but also on the properties of the electron cloud around the nucleus (Daudel 47). Thus, the same nuclear transformation occurs with different decay probabilities if the nucleus is surrounded by somewhat different electron clouds (e.g., by being part of different molecules). This effect has been observed (Segrè 49, Leininger 49, Benoist 49, Bouchez 47, 49).

We use statistical considerations for orbital electron capture just as in Section 2. The statistical factor is different now, however, since the electron is in a definite quantum state before its capture. The phase space volume is therefore determined entirely by the energy of the emitted neutrino. This volume is equal to

$$(2\pi\hbar)^{-3} \, p_\nu{}^2 \, dp_\nu \, d\Omega_\nu \, dV_\nu \equiv \rho'(E_\nu) \, dE_\nu$$

As before, we get the statistical factor $\rho(E_\nu)$ from $\rho'(E_\nu)$ by integrating over the possible positions of the particle inside the box, i.e., over dV_ν. Since the neutrino is always emitted in a direction opposite that of the nuclear recoil, there is no question of angular correlation here, and we integrate over the angles $d\Omega_\nu$ also:

$$\rho(E_\nu) = \frac{V}{2\pi^2\hbar^3c^3} \, (E_0 + mc^2 - E_B)^2 \tag{3.1}$$

Here we have assumed zero rest mass for the neutrino and have denoted the available nuclear transformation energy by E_0, the atomic binding energy of the captured electron by E_B.

We shall again assume that the decay probability is given by the four factors enumerated in Section 2. Factor (1) is given by (3.1) for electron capture. We restrict ourselves to *allowed* electron capture transitions. Then the probability of finding the neutrino inside the nuclear volume [factor (3) on our list] is equal to V_N/V, just as before. However, the probability of finding the electron inside the nuclear volume [factor (2)] is changed completely. This factor is no longer proportional to V^{-1}. The electron before capture is bound to the nucleus. Hence the probability of finding it inside the nuclear volume is independent of the size of the box in which the system is enclosed.

The probability depends on the nature of the electron state. It is small for electrons in outlying orbits, and comparatively large for electrons in the inner shells of the atomic structure. By far the largest proportion of the total electron capture probability is due to the capture of electrons from the innermost shell in the atom (this shell is called K shell in x-ray terminology, $1s$ shell in optical spectroscopy). If we neglect relativistic corrections, the probability of finding the K electron inside the nuclear volume is the ratio of this volume, V_N, to the volume enclosed by the first Bohr orbit:

$$\int |\psi_e|^2 \, dV_e = \frac{1}{\pi} \left(\frac{Zme^2}{\hbar^2} \right)^3 V_N$$

This probability must be multiplied by 2 because there are two electrons in the K shell, each of which may be captured by the nucleus.

We shall write the K capture probability in the form:

$$\text{Capture probability} = \frac{\ln 2}{t_K} = C f_K \qquad (3.2)$$

Then t_K is the half-life of the radioactive nucleus if K capture is the only mechanism by which it can disintegrate, i.e., if the energy E_0 liberated by the nuclear transition lies between the limits

$$-(mc^2 - E_B) < E_0 < mc^2$$

For $E_0 > mc^2$, positron emission competes, and the half-life is shorter than t_K. f_K will be defined so that the constant C in (3.2) is the same as in (2.13).[1] The energies E_0 and E_B are again measured in units mc^2. The K electron binding energy E_B is (again in the non-relativistic approximation)

$$E_B \left(= \frac{E_B}{mc^2} \right) = \frac{1}{2} \left(\frac{Ze^2}{\hbar c} \right)^2 \qquad \text{(for a } K \text{ electron)} \qquad (3.3)$$

We then get for the f_K in (3.2)

$$f_K = 2\pi \left(\frac{Ze^2}{\hbar c} \right)^3 \left[E_0 + 1 - \frac{1}{2} \left(\frac{Ze^2}{\hbar c} \right)^2 \right]^2 \qquad (3.4)$$

We emphasize that the Z here is the charge of the *parent* nucleus.

---

[1] Since the spin directions of electron and neutrino are not observed in practice, the phase space factor, (3.2) or (2.5), must be multiplied by the statistical weights of the final states. These statistical weights are 2 for electron capture (emission of one particle of spin $\frac{1}{2}$) and 4 for electron emission (emission of two particles of spin $\frac{1}{2}$ each). This difference accounts for the factor 2 in formula (3.4).

For high values of Z this expression must be corrected for relativistic effects and for the influence of the shielding of the nuclear Coulomb field by the outer electrons. The shielding correction can be made approximately by replacing the actual nuclear charge Z by an "effective charge" which is commonly taken to be $Z - 0.3$ (Bethe 33). The relativistic correction then replaces (3.4) by

$$f_K = 2\pi (2\rho)^{2s-2} \frac{1+s}{(2s)!} \gamma^{1+2s} (E_0 + s)^2 \tag{3.5}$$

The symbols have been defined already in connection with (2.11) and (2.12), except for $\gamma \equiv Ze^2/\hbar c$.

In addition to capturing electrons from the K shell of the atom, the nucleus can also capture electrons from other shells, the most important of these being capture from the L shell. Since the probability of finding an L shell electron within the nuclear volume is much less than that for a K electron, L shell capture is considerably less likely than K capture. It has been observed, however (Pontecorvo 49). With the exception of very low-energy transitions (E_0 negative and not much less in absolute value than $mc^2 - E_B$) the L shell capture can be neglected in the estimate of the electron capture probability. It can happen, however, that the nuclear energy change is low enough so that K shell capture is energetically impossible while L shell capture is still allowed. In that exceptional case the electron capture probability would be almost entirely due to L shell capture.

Orbital electron capture cannot be observed directly, since the whole event takes place within the atom. The only emitted particle is a neutrino which has so far escaped all attempts to detect its presence. The occurrence of orbital electron capture shows itself experimentally through emission of x-rays from the product atom: the product atom is left with a hole in the K shell which is filled by one of the outer electrons, thereby producing x-rays characteristic (in wavelength) of the *product* nucleus. The observation of these x-rays proves that K capture has occurred (Abelson 39). It does not constitute a measurement of the nuclear energy change, however. The nuclear energy change must be found by other means [e.g., the Q value of the (p,n) reaction by which the radioactive nucleus can be formed from the stable one]. In practice, the nuclear energy change E_0 is unknown (or known only within rather wide limits) for most radioactive nuclei which decay exclusively through orbital electron capture.

Since no electron emission takes place in K capture, the entire recoil momentum of the nucleus is due to the emission of the neutrino. The observation of this recoil momentum therefore gives additional support to the neutrino hypothesis (Kan Chang Wang 42, Allen 42, Wright 47, Smith 51).

4. THE HALF-LIVES OF BETA-EMITTERS AND EVIDENCE CONCERNING THE SELECTION RULES IN ALLOWED TRANSITIONS

The probability of decay into a given momentum interval dp of the electron is given by (2.13). We obtain the total probability per unit time that a beta-active nucleus will decay by integrating $P(p)\,dp$ over all electron momenta in the beta-spectrum. This probability also defines the half-life t_- of the beta-decay. We get

$$\beta^- \text{ decay probability} = \frac{\ln 2}{t_-} = C\,f_-(Z,E_0) \qquad (4.1)$$

where $f_-(Z,E_0)$ is the integral

$$f_-(Z,E_0) = \int_0^{p_0} F(Z,E)\,p^2\,(E_0-E)^2\,dp \qquad (4.2)$$

The upper limit of integration, $p_0=(E_0{}^2-1)^{1/2}$, is the maximum momentum in the electron spectrum, expressed in units mc. The integral can be evaluated explicitly for $Z=0$, i.e., if the Coulomb effect on the spectrum is neglected. The result is

$$f_-(0,E_0) = \tfrac{1}{60}\,(E_0{}^2-1)^{1/2}\,(2E_0{}^4-9E_0{}^2-8)$$
$$+ \tfrac{1}{4}\,E_0 \ln\,[E_0 + (E_0{}^2-1)^{1/2}] \quad (4.3)$$

For very large E_0 this function is proportional to $E_0{}^5$. However, in the energy region of interest, $1.1 \le E_0 \le 10$, f_- does not follow an $E_0{}^5$ law but is more nearly proportional to $(E_0-1)^4$. In most cases the Coulomb effect on the spectrum and, through it, on the lifetime cannot be neglected. For values of $Z \ne 0$ the integral (4.2) must be evaluated numerically. Tables and graphs of this function have been given by Feenberg and Trigg (50), Moszkowski (51b), and others.

The probability per unit time of positron emission is found in a similar way. It is

$$\beta^+ \text{ decay probability} = \frac{\ln 2}{t_+} = C\,f_+(Z,E_0) \qquad (4.4)$$

where f_+ is the same integral as (4.2), except that the Coulomb correction factor is the one for positron emission $(\eta = -Ze^2/\hbar v)$. Computed values of f_+ can be found in the references given for f_-.

Unlike negatron emission, however, the observed half-life of a positron emitter is not equal to the t_+ in (4.4). Whenever positron emission is energetically possible, K capture also occurs and shortens the half-life. The probability of electron capture was determined in the previous section [(3.2), (3.4), (3.5)]. If only one nuclear transition can take place, the probability of this transition is the sum of the K capture and positron emission probabilities.   The ratio of K capture to positron emission for allowed transitions is also given in the references quoted above.

In general, a radioactive nucleus starts the decay process from its ground state, since gamma-ray emission from an excited state is usually much more probable than beta-decay.   Isomeric states (see Chapter XII, Section 6) sometimes give exceptions to this rule.   In very many cases, however, the beta-decay proceeds to more than one final nuclear state, i.e., the daughter nucleus may be left in an excited state rather than in its ground state.   The beta-decay is then said to be "complex."   The decay probability of the initial nucleus is the sum of the decay probabilities for the individual transitions in the complex decay.   Since the energy relations for K capture are more favorable than for positron emission, a simple positron decay can be associated with a complex electron capture decay, thereby giving apparently too large a ratio between the K capture and positron emission probabilities.   If the β^- or β^+ decay is complex, the observed spectrum is a superposition of the spectra for the various possible transitions.   Even if the individual spectra have the allowed shape, the composite spectrum shows a more complicated shape (Bethe 39).   Sometimes we can surmise the existence of a complex decay by resolving the observed spectrum into components each of which has the allowed shape (or one of the forbidden shapes; see Section 7).   An unambiguous proof of complexity, however, is obtained best by the detection of time-coincidences between the beta-particles which lead to one of the excited states of the product nucleus and the gamma-rays which are emitted subsequently in the de-excitation of the product nucleus (see Mitchell 48 and the references quoted there).

The factors f_-, f_+, and f_K depend on the conditions outside of the nucleus, since they are determined by phase space considerations and by the effect of the Coulomb field on the electron.   Hence the strictly nuclear properties are contained in the coefficient C, which has the dimensions of an inverse time.   It is customary to define the "comparative half-life" of a simple beta-transition, ft, by

$$ft \begin{cases} \equiv f_-(Z,E_0)\, t & \text{(for } \beta^- \text{ decay)} \\ \equiv [f_+(Z,E_0) + f_K(Z,E_0)]\, t & \text{(for } \beta^+ \text{ decay)} \\ \equiv f_K(Z,E_0)\, t & \text{(for } K \text{ capture without } \beta^+ \text{ decay)} \end{cases} \qquad (4.5)$$

where t is the half-life of the transition, measured in seconds.   If the decay is actually complex, t is the partial half-life for the particular branch in question (i.e., the half-life which would exist if all the other transitions could not occur).

To the extent that the assumption of an allowed spectrum shape is valid, the comparative half-life is related to the constant C which appears in (2.13), (3.2), (4.1), and (4.4) through

$$ft = \frac{\ln 2}{C} \qquad \text{(allowed spectrum shape)} \qquad (4.6)$$

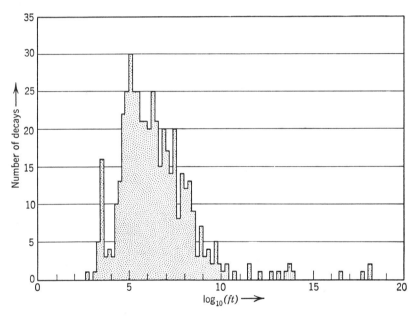

Fig. 4.1.   Frequency distribution of comparative half-lives ft (t is expressed in seconds).   The height of the shaded area indicates the number of decays for which $\log(ft)$ lies within the limits indicated on the abscissa.   Except for the sharp peak around $\log(ft) = 3.5$, there is no special grouping of ft values.   In particular, it is impossible to separate the decays empirically into various "orders of forbiddenness" on the basis of only their lifetimes.

Thus transitions which are equally likely from the point of view of the nucleus have equal comparative half-lives (even though their actual lifetimes may be quite different because of different available energies E_0 or different Z).   Conversely, an unusually large comparative half-life indicates that the nuclear transition is inherently improbable.   This may be due to several causes which will be discussed in later sections of this chapter.

Figure 4.1 shows a plot of the distribution of comparative half-lives of all the well-known transitions (data from the compilation of Feingold 51). There is an almost complete absence of any grouping of these ft values. In the early days of the study of beta-decay, Sargent (33) plotted the lifetimes against the maximum energies, both on logarithmic scales. The points then seemed to fall along several lines, separated from each other, each of slope about 5 (the fifth-power law for the lifetime). If such Sargent curves existed for the data which have accumulated since then, they would appear in Fig. 4.1 as sharp peaks in the distribution of ft values. By and large, no such peaks exist, and it is impossible to group the known beta-decays into "allowed," "first forbidden," "second forbidden," etc., on the basis of the ft values.

The one apparent exception to this rule is the sharp peak around $\log(ft) = 3.5$. It is tempting to assume that these transitions (all of which involve light- or medium-weight nuclei) are the allowed ones, all others being forbidden. However, we shall show in Section 6 that this interpretation is incorrect if "allowed" is defined as in Section 2, i.e., by the change of angular momentum and parity in the nuclear transition. Rather, a good many transitions with $\log(ft)$ around 5 are also allowed in this sense.

There is a general trend in Fig. 4.1 in the direction of decreasing likelihood of high comparative half-lives (ft above 10^{10} sec). This is probably not a true trend. It is difficult to observe a very long half-life if there is a competing transition (to another level of the daughter nucleus) with a much shorter half-life. Most of the observed transitions in the complex decay are then associated with the second branch. In most cases an alternative transition with a branching probability of less than 1 percent escapes detection. The higher the comparative half-life, the higher (on the average) is the actual half-life, and the more likely is the occurrence of a competing, shorter-lived branch in the transition. Indeed, several known decays listed in Feingold's table have been omitted from Fig. 4.1, because the branching probabilities were not known (so that only a lower limit for ft could be deduced, not the actual value).

We shall now list a few special beta-decays in which the initial and final nuclear spins are either known experimentally or can be found on the basis of one of the following semi-empirical rules about nuclear spins:

A. Even-even nuclei have $I = 0$.
B. Mirror nuclei have the same spin.
C. Odd-odd nuclei with $N = Z$ have $I \neq 0$.

Of these, rule A is very well established experimentally and has some theoretical basis in the shell model (Chapter XIV). Rule B is supported by impressive evidence regarding the generally similar behavior of mirror nuclei (see Chapter VI, Sections 2 and 6), but only one experimental measurement has been made (for the H^3–He^3 pair). Rule C is based on the measured spins of H^2, Li^6, B^{10}, N^{14}, and Na^{22} but has no known theoretical foundation.

TABLE 4.1

SOME DECAYS WITH KNOWN SPIN CHANGES

Initial Nucleus	I_i	Final Nucleus	I_f	Log_{10} (ft)
Neutron	$\frac{1}{2}$	H^1	$\frac{1}{2}$	3.2 ± 0.2
H^3	$\frac{1}{2}$	He^3	$\frac{1}{2}$	3.05
He^6	0 (A)	Li^6	1	2.77
Be^7	$\frac{3}{2}$ (B)	Li^7 ground	$\frac{3}{2}$	3.36
		Li^7 exc.	$\frac{1}{2}$?	3.56
F^{18}	$\neq 0$ (C)	O^{18}	0	3.61
Al^{26}	$\neq 0$ (C)	Mg^{26}	0	3.3
Na^{22}	3	Ne^{22} ground	0 (A)	13.8
		Ne^{22} exc.	?	7.4
K^{40}	4	Ca^{40}	0	18.1
Be^{10}	0 (A)	B^{10}	3	13.7
C^{14}	0	N^{14}	1	9.0

The beta-decay of the neutron (Robson 50, Snell 50) is fundamental for the entire theory of the beta-decay, since it establishes the strength of interaction responsible for the decay. The comparison between the beta-decay of the neutron and of H^3 is interesting because the comparative half-life suggests very strongly that the extra neutron in H^3 decays to a proton, to give He^3, just as if the other two nucleons were absent. Both decays would be allowed on either Fermi or Gamow-Teller selection rules.

The next four decays in the table provide *evidence against the Fermi selection rule* (2.7). If the spin assignments of the table are correct, all these decays (with the exception of the ground state to ground state K capture in Be^7) are forbidden by the Fermi selection rule. The comparative half-lives, on the other hand, are close to the fundamental ft value of the neutron, indicating that the transitions are all allowed. Unfortunately there is not a single unquestionable spin assignment on that list. He^6 might have $I = 1$; F^{18} and Al^{26} might have $I = 0$. The spin assignment $I = \frac{1}{2}$ for the excited state of Li^7 is based on the β-γ angular correlation measurement of Rose and Wilson (50) in the $B^{10}(n,\alpha)Li^7$ reaction, which showed no angular correlation. While this measurement strongly suggests $I = \frac{1}{2}$ for Li^{7*}, it does not provide a complete proof.[1] Thus the present evidence against the Fermi selection rule is extremely suggestive but cannot be called conclusive. A measurement of the spin of any one of He^6, F^{18}, or Al^{26} would settle the question completely. We shall assume throughout the rest of this chapter that pure Fermi selection rules are *not* realized in nature; the electron and neutrino are emitted, at least partially, in the triplet (parallel spin) state.

There remains the question whether, in allowed transitions, the electron and neutrino are *always* emitted in the triplet state and never in the singlet state. In this case pure Gamow-Teller selection rules would apply. Consideration of (2.7) and (2.8) shows that this question can be decided by only one kind of transition: $I = 0$ to $I = 0$ without change of parity. Such transitions are allowed by the Fermi selection rule and forbidden by the Gamow-Teller rule. So far no beta-decay of this type is known which can be identified with certainty, but it is too early to exclude its existence completely.[2] Thus we do not know at this time whether the electron and the neutrino are emitted exclusively in the triplet (parallel spin) state.

The next case in Table 4.1, Na^{22}, illustrates the operation of the selection rule for the angular momentum change. The ground state to ground state transition involves a spin change of 3 units and is therefore much less likely intrinsically (the ft value is much higher) than the transition to the excited state of Ne^{22}, for which the spin change is presumably smaller. The same decay also illustrates the remark made before about the difficulty of observing transitions with large ft values. The two competing transitions here have ft values differing by a factor of over 10^6. The ground state to ground state transition involves a larger energy change E_0, hence also a larger value of f. Nevertheless, the partial lifetime for the ground state to ground state transition is about 200 times as long as for the transition to the excited state. Thus the ground state to ground state transitions occur

---

[1] The spin of Be^7 is irrelevant for this argument. If Be^7 had $I = \frac{1}{2}$, the ground state to ground state transition would be forbidden by the Fermi selection rule; if the spin of Be^7 were higher than $\frac{3}{2}$, both transitions would be forbidden. For additional support of the $I = \frac{1}{2}$ assignment of Li^{7*}, see Littauer (50).

[2] There is a possibility that the decay of O^{14} belongs in this category (Sherr 49), but it is not certain that the final (excited) state of N^{14} is really the "analogue" of the C^{14} ground state and hence should have $I = 0$ (see Chapter VI).

only about 0.005 times as often as the others, and they were correspondingly not seen in the earlier work on this decay.[1]

The beta-decays of K^{40} and Be^{10} also illustrate the importance of the selection rules. The corresponding ft values are very high as expected in view of the large spin differences.

It should be remarked that the ft value of a forbidden transition is a rather doubtful concept from the theoretical point of view, since the f was derived on the basis of the spectrum shape for allowed transitions. However, we are using these ft values only very qualitatively as a general indication of forbiddenness. The theory of forbidden transitions (Section 7) justifies this limited use.

Finally, the long comparative half-life of C^{14} shows that long half-lives are not invariably associated with large nuclear spin changes. A possible explanation of the large ft value (almost 10^6 times that of the neutron) can be found in a violation of the parity selection rule, i.e., by assuming that N^{14} has the opposite (presumably odd) parity as C^{14}.[2]

5. DETAILED THEORY OF BETA-DECAY; TRANSITIONS OF ORDER 0

A. The Matrix Element

The theory of beta-decay was first given in a classic paper by Fermi (34). He constructed the theory in complete analogy to the Dirac theory of the emission of light. In the latter theory one considers transitions of a material system (atom or nucleus) from an initial state Φ_i to a final state Φ_f with emission of a light quantum into some definite state (of given direction and polarization) described by the vector potential $\mathbf{A}(\mathbf{r})$. These transitions are caused by the interaction of the system with the radiation field. The probability per unit time of such a transition is given by

$$T = \frac{2\pi}{\hbar} \left| H'_{if} \right|^2 \rho(E) \tag{5.1}$$

where H'_{if} is the matrix element of the interaction responsible for the transition, and $\rho(E)$ is the number of final states of the light quantum per unit range of energy. The matrix element in Dirac's radiation theory is given by

---

[1] For references concerning this and other decays mentioned here, see Feingold (51), Feenberg (50), and Hornyak (50).

[2] See Chapter VII, Section 3, for a discussion of the relevance of this parity assignment for the independent-particle model of these nuclei.

$$H'_{if} = \frac{1}{c} \sum_n \int \mathbf{A}(\mathbf{r}_n) \cdot (\Phi_f{}^* \mathbf{j}_n \Phi_i) \, d\tau \qquad \text{(radiation)} \qquad (5.2)$$

where $\mathbf{A}(\mathbf{r}_n)$ is the vector potential of the emitted light quantum at the position of the nth particle, and $\mathbf{j}_n$ is the current operator for this particle. The sum is taken over all particles in the system. The vector potential $\mathbf{A}(\mathbf{r})$ must be normalized in such a way that it corresponds to exactly one quantum within the box of volume V in which the system as a whole is enclosed.

Fermi describes the probability of beta-decay in a similar way. It is also expressed in the form (5.1); the density of final states $\rho(E)$ is given by (2.5) for electron emission and by (3.1) for electron capture. We restrict the developments of this section to electron emission. They can be readily extended to electron capture.

The matrix element H'_{if} is constructed in analogy to (5.2):

$$H'_{if} = \sum_n \int F(\mathbf{r}_n) \, (\Phi_f{}^* K_n \Phi_i) \, d\tau \qquad \text{(beta-decay)} \qquad (5.3)$$

Here $F(\mathbf{r}_n)$ is a quantity which depends on the emitted "field" (i.e., on the wave functions of the electron and neutrino) at the position of the nth nucleon (the one that undergoes the beta-decay); Φ_i and Φ_f are the wave functions of the initial and final states of the nucleus, respectively; K_n is some operator connected with the beta-decay of the nth nucleon.

The form (5.2) for the matrix element of a radiative transition follows directly from the quantization of the classical equations describing the interaction of moving charges with the electromagnetic field. There is no such classical theory from which we could derive the form of the expressions appearing in (5.3). However, general considerations of invariance together with a requirement of "simplicity" limit the possible choices of $F(\mathbf{r}_n)$ and K_n considerably.[1]

The field expression $F(\mathbf{r}_n)$ must be a linear function of both the electron and the neutrino fields. Let us call the wave function of the emitted electron $\phi_e(\mathbf{r}_e)$ and the wave function of the emitted neutrino $\phi_\nu(\mathbf{r}_\nu)$. Both are Dirac spinor wave functions with four components. $F(\mathbf{r}_n)$ is then a bilinear expression of the form

---

[1] Just as in the discussion of exchange forces in Chapter III, we remark here that, unlike the general invariance requirements, the requirement of "simplicity" is somewhat artificial since it depends on the particular formalism used. The same interaction may appear "simple" in one way of writing it, "complicated" in another formulation.

$$F(\mathbf{r}_n) = \sum_{i=1}^{4} \sum_{j=1}^{4} \xi_{ij} \, \phi_{ei}^*(\mathbf{r}_n) \, \phi_{\nu j}^*(\mathbf{r}_n) \qquad (5.4)$$

where ϕ_{ei} denotes the ith component of the spinor wave function ϕ_e, $\phi_{\nu j}$ denotes the jth component of the spinor wave function ϕ_ν, and each ξ_{ij} is a linear operator upon the electron and neutrino wave functions. The field quantity contains the complex conjugates of ϕ_e and ϕ_ν because the wave function of the final state of the system as a whole appears starred in the matrix element (5.3). For reasons of simplicity we assume that the operators ξ_{ij} do not contain any derivatives. This assumption is equivalent to the exclusion of interactions between the electron-neutrino field and the nucleus which depend on the momenta of the two light particles.[1]   Each ξ_{ij} is then a number, and we can write (5.4) in the short-hand form

$$F(\mathbf{r}_n) = \sum_{i=1}^{4} \sum_{j=1}^{4} \phi_{ei}^*(\mathbf{r}_n) \, \xi_{ij} \, \phi_{\nu j}^*(\mathbf{r}_n) \equiv \{ \phi_e^*(\mathbf{r}_n), \, \xi \, \phi_\nu^*(\mathbf{r}_n) \} \qquad (5.4a)$$

where ξ is the 4-by-4 matrix with the (constant) matrix elements ξ_{ij}. Just as $\mathbf{A}(\mathbf{r})$ in (5.2) had to be normalized to one light quantum in the box of volume V in which the system as a whole is enclosed, so now the wave functions $\phi_e(\mathbf{r}_e)$ and $\phi_\nu(\mathbf{r}_\nu)$ must be normalized to correspond to one electron and one neutrino in the box, respectively. Other than that, ϕ_e and ϕ_ν can be chosen at will from among the possible states of an electron and a neutrino, and (5.1) then gives the probability for emission into that particular state of the electron-neutrino pair.

The operator K_n stands between two nuclear wave functions Φ_i and Φ_f which do not describe the same nucleus. One nucleon has changed from a neutron to a proton or vice versa. In order to give meaning to the integral in (5.3), K_n must contain an operator which, in the function operated on, changes the nth particle from a neutron into a proton or vice versa. Such operators were introduced in Chapter III, Section 5, and are called τ_- (neutron into proton) and τ_+ (proton into neutron), respectively.   We therefore put

$$K_n = \tau_{n,-} \, K'_n \qquad \text{(for negatron decay)}$$
$$K_n = \tau_{n,+} \, K'_n \qquad \text{(for positron decay)}$$

$$(5.5)$$

---

[1] A theory of Uhlenbeck and Konopinski (Konopinski 35) which does involve derivatives of the electron and neutrino wave functions gives appreciably poorer agreement with the present experimental results (although it gave good agreement with the experimental results in 1935) and has been abandoned.

We now make the same assumption of simplicity regarding K'_n as we did for ξ: K'_n does not contain any derivatives; the interaction is supposed to be independent of the momenta of the nucleons as well as of the emitted light particles. Thus K'_n operates exclusively on the spin components of the nucleon wave function. In all generality we must consider the nucleons also relativistic particles; hence K'_n is a 4-by-4 matrix acting on the spinor components of the nth nucleon.[1]

The assumptions of simplicity made so far reduce significantly the possible choices for the operators ξ and K'_n. A further drastic reduction is obtained from the requirement that the quantity

$$F(\mathbf{r}_n)\; \Phi_f{}^* K_n \Phi_i$$

must be a relativistic invariant.

▶ B. Non-relativistic Treatment

Before discussing all possible forms for ξ and K'_n we illustrate the situation by assuming that both the emitted electron and the neutrino are non-relativistic particles with spin $\tfrac{1}{2}$. This assumption is never justified, since the neutrino always moves with the speed of light. Nevertheless, many important aspects of the theory of beta-decay are contained in this simplified treatment, and the extension to the relativistic treatment is straightforward.

Let us consider the bilinear expression (5.4a). In the non-relativistic treatment ϕ_e and ϕ_ν are Pauli (two-component) spin functions, so that the sums over i and j go from 1 to 2, not from 1 to 4. Two Pauli spin functions can combine to form either a scalar (the singlet state) or one of the three components of a vector (one of the three triplet states). These combinations are (see Appendix A, Section 4) the scalar

$$F_s = \phi_{e1}{}^* \phi_{\nu 2}{}^* - \phi_{e2}{}^* \phi_{\nu 1}{}^* = \{\phi_e{}^*, B\,\phi_\nu{}^*\} \tag{5.6}$$

and the vector $\mathbf{F}$ defined by the three functions F_m $(m = 1, 0, -1)$:

$$
\begin{aligned}
F_1 &= \sqrt{2}\,\phi_{e1}{}^* \phi_{\nu 1}{}^* &&= \{\phi_e{}^*, \sigma_1 B\,\phi_\nu{}^*\} \\
F_0 &= \phi_{e1}{}^* \phi_{\nu 2}{}^* + \phi_{e2}{}^* \phi_{\nu 1}{}^* &&= \{\phi_e{}^*, \sigma_0 B\,\phi_\nu{}^*\} \tag{5.7}\\
F_{-1} &= \sqrt{2}\,\phi_{e2}{}^* \phi_{\nu 2}{}^* &&= \{\phi_e{}^*, \sigma_{-1} B\,\phi_\nu{}^*\}
\end{aligned}
$$

---

[1] We assume here that nucleons can be described by the Dirac equation for particles of spin $\tfrac{1}{2}$. The magnetic moments of the neutron and proton show that this cannot be entirely correct. We hope, nevertheless, that the description of the nucleons as Dirac particles gives a good first approximation as far as the theory of beta-decay is concerned.

where the matrix notation is the same as in (5.4a) and the matrices B and σ_m are [1]

$$B = \begin{pmatrix} 0 & 1 \\ -1 & 0 \end{pmatrix} \qquad \sigma_1 = -\frac{1}{\sqrt{2}} (\sigma_x + i\sigma_y)$$

$$\sigma_0 = \sigma_z \qquad\qquad \sigma_{-1} = \frac{1}{\sqrt{2}} (\sigma_x - i\sigma_y) \tag{5.8}$$

Here the quantities σ_x, σ_y, and σ_z are the usual Pauli spin matrices as defined in Appendix A, Section 4. We may consider the three quantities F_m (5.7) components of the vector $\mathbf{F}$:

$$\mathbf{F} = \{\phi_e{}^*, \, \delta B \, \phi_\nu{}^*\} \tag{5.7a}$$

In general, we shall define the "spherical components" A_1, A_0, A_{-1} of a vector $\mathbf{A}$ by relations analogous to (5.8), i.e.,

$$A_1 = -\frac{1}{\sqrt{2}} (A_x + iA_y) \qquad A_0 = A_z \qquad A_{-1} = \frac{1}{\sqrt{2}} (A_x - iA_y)$$

$$\tag{5.8a}$$

With this notation the scalar product of two vectors $\mathbf{A}$ and $\mathbf{B}$ is given by

$$\mathbf{A}\cdot\mathbf{B} = \sum_{\mu=-1}^{1} (-1)^\mu A_\mu B_{-\mu} \tag{5.8b}$$

and the scalar product of $\mathbf{A}^*$ ($* =$ complex conjugate) and $\mathbf{B}$ is given by

$$\mathbf{A}^*\cdot\mathbf{B} = \sum_{\mu=-1}^{1} A_\mu{}^* B_\mu \tag{5.8c}$$

The spherical components of a vector transform under rotations in the same way as the three spherical harmonics of order $l=1$, $Y_{1,m}(\theta,\varphi)$. The spherical components are preferable to the Cartesian components whenever the behavior under rotations of the coordinate system is important.

---

[1] The strict definition of the matrix B is

$$\tilde{\sigma}_x B = -B\sigma_x \qquad \tilde{\sigma}_y B = -B\sigma_y \qquad \tilde{\sigma}_z B = -B\sigma_z$$

where the tilde denotes the transpose of a matrix. The combinations (5.6) and (5.7) differ by a constant factor $\sqrt{2}$ from the (complex conjugates of the) usual singlet and triplet wave functions. This does not matter since any constant multiplier in F can be absorbed into the coupling constant G which we shall introduce anon.

It can be shown that the linear combination (5.6) is invariant under rotations of the coordinate system (transforms like a scalar) whereas the three quantities F_m transform into each other like the three components of a vector. In the non-relativistic treatment we postulate invariance of $F(\mathbf{r}_n)\, \Phi_f{}^* K_n \Phi_i$ under rotations and reflections (but not under Lorentz transformations). Hence, if F_s is chosen for the field quantity F in (5.3), the quantity $\Phi_f{}^* K_n \Phi_i$ must also be a scalar. If the vector $\mathbf{F}$ is chosen for the light particles, the quantity $\Phi_f{}^* K_n \Phi_i$ must also be a vector, and $F(\mathbf{r}_n)\, \Phi_f{}^* K_n \Phi_i$ must be the scalar product of these two vectors. Only one scalar and one vector quantity $\Phi_f{}^* K_n \Phi_i$ can be constructed under our preceding simplifying assumptions (i.e., that K_n is to act solely on the spin coordinates of the nth nucleon). They are obtained by choosing $K_n = 1$ and $K_n = \boldsymbol{\delta}_n$, respectively, where $\boldsymbol{\delta}_n$ is the Pauli spin vector of the nth nucleon. We therefore get two different interactions, the "singlet" and the "triplet" interaction,[1] with the matrix elements

Singlet Interaction

$$H'_{if} = G_s \sum_{n=1}^{A} \int \{ \phi_e{}^*(\mathbf{r}_n),\, B\, \phi_\nu{}^*(\mathbf{r}_n) \}\ (\Phi_f{}^* \tau_{n,-} \Phi_i)\ d\tau \qquad (5.9)$$

Triplet Interaction

$$H'_{if} = G_t \sum_{n=1}^{A} \int \{ \phi_e{}^*(\mathbf{r}_n),\, \boldsymbol{\delta} B\, \phi_\nu{}^*(\mathbf{r}_n) \}\cdot(\Phi_f{}^* \boldsymbol{\delta}_n \tau_{n,-} \Phi_i)\ d\tau$$

$$= G_t \sum_{n=1}^{A} \sum_{m=-1}^{1} \int (-)^m \{ \phi_e{}^*(\mathbf{r}_n),\, \sigma_m B\, \phi_\nu{}^*(\mathbf{r}_n) \}\ (\Phi_f{}^* \sigma_{n,-m} \tau_{n,-} \Phi_i)\ d\tau$$

$$(5.10)$$

where the components $\sigma_{n,m}$ $(m = 1, 0, -1)$ of the nucleon spin vector $\boldsymbol{\delta}_n$ are defined according to (5.8a). The constants G_s and G_t indicate the strength of the interactions.[2]

---

[1] We might have called these interactions the "scalar" and "vector" interaction, respectively, since the first is formed from two scalar quantities, the second is the (scalar) product of two vector quantities. We use a different terminology here in order to avoid confusion with the so-called scalar and vector interactions of the relativistic theory.

[2] It is perhaps desirable to emphasize here that the beta-decay interactions are, to the best of our present knowledge, not related to the interactions between nucleons which are responsible for the nuclear forces. For example, the singlet and triplet interactions used in this chapter refer to the emission of an electron-

We now show that the matrix element (5.9) corresponds to emission of the electron-neutrino pair into the singlet spin state, whereas the matrix element (5.10) corresponds to emission of the electron-neutrino pair into the triplet spin state. Furthermore, we shall show that each term m in the second sum of (5.10) corresponds to emission into the particular triplet state with spin orientation m at the same time that the transforming nucleon flips its spin in the opposite direction, to conserve the angular momentum of the system as a whole. Since the proof is very similar in all cases we shall discuss only one case in detail, namely emission into the triplet state of the electron-neutrino pair with both spins pointing up ($m = 1$). That is, we shall substitute into (5.9) and (5.10) a wave function $\phi_e(\mathbf{r}_e)$ describing an electron with spin up:

$$\phi_{e1}(\mathbf{r}_e) \neq 0 \qquad \phi_{e2}(\mathbf{r}_e) = 0$$

and a similar wave function for the neutrino. According to definition (5.6) the quantity $\{\phi_e{}^*, B \phi_\nu{}^*\}$ then vanishes identically, so that the singlet interaction matrix element (5.9) is zero. The singlet interaction does not lead to any emission into the electron-neutrino state in question, and it is easily shown that a similar result holds for every triplet spin state of the electron-neutrino pair. Therefore the singlet interaction leads to emissions into the singlet spin state exclusively, thus justifying the name. Substitution of the state above into the matrix element for the triplet interaction, (5.10), and comparison with definitions (5.7) shows that the only non-vanishing term corresponds to $m = 1$ in the second sum of (5.10). Thus the term $m = 1$ of the sum in (5.10) corresponds to emission into the triplet spin state of the electron-neutrino pair with both spins pointing up. The nucleon operator K_n corresponding to this emission is

$$\sigma_{n,-m}{}^\tau{}_{n,-} = \sigma_{n,-1}{}^\tau{}_{n,-}$$

This operator changes particle number n from a neutron to a proton (it gives zero if particle n is already a proton), and it flips the spin of this nucleon from the up to the down position (it gives zero if the spin of

neutrino pair into the singlet and triplet spin states, respectively, and have no known connection with the nuclear forces between a pair of nucleons in the singlet and triplet spin states. Similarly, the "tensor" interaction used in beta-decay theory (see Section 5C) is not related to the tensor force between a neutron and a proton. Many investigators have searched for connections between beta-decay and nuclear forces. No such connection has yet been established.

nucleon n already points downwards).   Thus the angular momentum of the system as a whole is conserved, as it must be.[1]

Let us now insert the actual wave functions for ϕ_e and ϕ_ν.   We first neglect the effect of the Coulomb field on the electron and therefore set

$$\phi_e(\mathbf{r}_e) = V^{-1/2} \, u_e \exp\,(i\mathbf{p}\cdot\mathbf{r}_e) \qquad \phi_\nu(\mathbf{r}_\nu) = V^{-1/2} \, u_\nu \exp\,(i\mathbf{q}\cdot\mathbf{r}_\nu) \qquad (5.11)$$

where V is the volume of the imaginary box which encloses the system; u_e and u_ν are two-dimensional Pauli spin functions, normalized to unity and independent of the positions $\mathbf{r}_e$ and $\mathbf{r}_\nu$, respectively (e.g., u_e could be the spin function for a particle with spin up, u_ν the spin function for a particle with spin down); and $\mathbf{p}$ and $\mathbf{q}$ are the momentum vectors of electron and neutrino, respectively, in units mc; $\mathbf{r}$ is expressed in units $\hbar/mc$.   We then get

$$F_s = V^{-1} \{u_e{}^*,\, B\, u_\nu{}^*\} \exp\,[-i(\mathbf{p}+\mathbf{q})\cdot\mathbf{r}]$$

and a corresponding expression for the vector field quantity $\mathbf{F}$.   In all practical cases both momenta $\mathbf{p}$ and $\mathbf{q}$ are small enough so that the argument of the exponential is small compared to unity as long as $\mathbf{r}$ is of nuclear dimensions.   It is therefore justifiable to expand the exponential in powers of the exponent.   This expansion plays a very important role in the classification of the transitions.   Each term leads to a different type.   The power l of the exponent will be called the "order l" of the transition, and this number l also determines the orbital angular momentum carried away by the light particles.

In this section we restrict ourselves to transitions of *zero* order and therefore replace the exponential by unity.   We take into account the value of the wave functions at the center of the nucleus only.   If the wave functions are expanded in terms of spherical harmonics corresponding to different orbital angular momenta l, only the wave with $l=0$ contributes to the value at the origin.   Hence we are restricting ourselves to emissions of light particles with zero orbital angular momentum.

The matrix elements (5.9) and (5.10) can then be written in the form

$$H'_{if} = \frac{G_s}{V} \{u_e{}^*,\, B\, u_\nu{}^*\} \,\langle 1\rangle \qquad \text{(singlet interaction)} \qquad (5.12)$$

---

[1] The requirement that the quantity $F_n(\mathbf{r}_n)\, \Phi_f{}^* K_n \Phi_i$ be invariant under rotations and inversions is equivalent to the requirement that the angular momentum and parity of the system be conserved.

$$H'_{if} = \frac{G_t}{V} \{u_e{}^*, \mathbf{\delta}B\, u_\nu{}^*\} \cdot \langle \mathbf{\delta} \rangle \qquad \text{(triplet interaction)} \qquad (5.13)$$

where the quantities $\langle 1 \rangle$ and $\langle \mathbf{\delta} \rangle$ are defined by

$$\langle 1 \rangle \equiv \sum_{n=1}^{A} \int \Phi_f{}^* \tau_{n,-} \Phi_i \, d\tau \qquad (5.14)$$

$$\langle \mathbf{\delta} \rangle \equiv \sum_{n=1}^{A} \int \Phi_f{}^* \mathbf{\delta}_n \tau_{n,-} \Phi_i \, d\tau \qquad (5.15)$$

These and similar quantities are called "nuclear matrix elements" in the theory of beta-decay. They must be distinguished from the over-all matrix element H'_{if}. Throughout this chapter nuclear matrix elements shall be defined so that they involve only nuclear quantities.

The matrix element H'_{if} as given in (5.12) or (5.13) does not depend on the directions of emission of the light particles in this non-relativistic treatment. Hence there is no electron-neutrino angular correlation in allowed transitions in the non-relativistic limit. The relativistic treatment leads to an angular correlation of order v/c, where v is the speed of the electron.

The selection rules which were derived in Section 2 can be verified directly for the matrix elements (5.14) and (5.15). Expression (5.14) is different from zero only if the Fermi selection rules (2.7) are fulfilled; (5.15) requires the Gamow-Teller selection rules (2.8). This is quite natural, since the replacement of the exponential

$$\exp\left[-i(\mathbf{p} + \mathbf{q}) \cdot \mathbf{r}\right]$$

by unity is equivalent to the assumption made in Section 2 that the light particles do not carry away any orbital angular momentum.

It is now very simple to incorporate the effect of the Coulomb force on the matrix element for allowed transitions. The replacement of the exponential by unity corresponds to the replacement of $\phi_e(\mathbf{r})$ by $\phi_e(\mathbf{r}=0)$. The effect of the Coulomb force on the latter quantity is given by (2.10). Hence the effect of the Coulomb field on allowed transitions is obtained by multiplying (5.12) and (5.13) by $[F(Z,E)]^{1/2}$.

We now determine the factor C which was introduced in (2.13) to include all nuclear properties. The probability $P(p)\, dp$ can be calculated by inserting (5.12) [or (5.13)] and (2.5) into (5.1). In order to get a result which is useful for the evaluation of experiments, we must sum over the spin directions of the electron and the neutrino. Let us call $u_e^{(k)}$ the electron spin function u_e in (5.11) belonging to the spin direction k ($k=1,2$), i.e.,[1]

$$u_e^{(1)} = \begin{pmatrix} 1 \\ 0 \end{pmatrix} \qquad u_e^{(2)} = \begin{pmatrix} 0 \\ 1 \end{pmatrix}$$

Letting $u_\nu^{(k')}$ be the neutrino spin function for neutrino spin direction k', defined in a similar way, we get

$$\{u_e^{(k)*}, B\, u_\nu^{(k')*}\} = \begin{cases} 0 & \text{if } k=k' \\ 1 & \text{if } k=1,\ k'=2 \\ -1 & \text{if } k=2,\ k'=1 \end{cases}$$

Thus we find

$$\sum_{k,k'=1}^{2} \left| \{u_e^{(k)*}, B\, u_\nu^{(k')*}\} \right|^2 = 2 \tag{5.16a}$$

and as the result of an entirely analogous calculation

$$\sum_{k,k'=1}^{2} \{u_e^{(k)*}, \sigma_m B\, u_\nu^{(k')*}\}^* \{u_e^{(k)*}, \sigma_{m'} B\, u_\nu^{(k')*}\} = 2\,\delta_{mm'} \tag{5.16b}$$

By comparing the result for $P(p)\,dp$ with (2.13) we obtain for the constant C one of the two values C_s or C_t, depending on which interaction was used. We introduce a fundamental time constant t_0 for the beta-decay through the definition

$$t_0 = 2\pi^3 \frac{(mc^2)^2 (\hbar/mc)^6}{G^2} \frac{\hbar}{mc^2} \tag{5.17}$$

In terms of this time constant the values of C for the singlet and triplet interactions are

$$C_s = \frac{2}{t_0} |\langle 1 \rangle|^2 \qquad\qquad \text{(singlet interaction)}$$

$$\tag{5.18}$$

$$C_t = \frac{2}{t_0} \sum_{m=-1}^{1} |\langle \sigma_m \rangle|^2 \equiv \frac{2}{t_0} |\langle \boldsymbol{\sigma} \rangle|^2 \qquad \text{(triplet interaction)}$$

We can determine the order of magnitude of the time constant t_0 from the beta-decay of the neutron, which is the simplest beta-decay. In this case the nuclear matrix element (5.14) is equal to unity, and

---

[1] These two spin functions are commonly called α and β, respectively (see Appendix A, Section 4). We use the present notation here because it is more adaptable to the later relativistic theory.

the value of $C = \ln(2)/ft$ is of the order of 6×10^{-4} sec^{-1}. Hence t_0 is of the order of 3000 sec, or about an hour.[1] This fundamental time constant is extremely long compared to the periods of nuclear motion. As Lord Rutherford once put it, "From the point of view of the nucleus, beta-decay practically never happens." As a result of this very long time constant *beta-stability or beta-instability of a nucleus has no influence on its dynamical behavior* (spin, magnetic moment, level spectrum, behavior in nuclear reactions, etc.). Beta-unstable nuclei differ from beta-stable ones only through the accident of having a lower-energy neighboring isobar. The small strength of the beta-decay interaction also implies that it is unlikely that this interaction is responsible for the nuclear forces.

The formulas have been written so far for a transition between two definite nuclear states. This case is seldom observed in practice, since the initial nucleus may have its spin I_i oriented in any direction in space, and the final nucleus can have its spin I_f oriented in those ways which are consistent with the spin direction of the initial nucleus and with the selection rules. It is permissible to assume that the initial spin orientation was along the z axis of the coordinate system, since the decay probability cannot depend on our choice of a z axis in space. Having done this, however, we must perform the sum over all possible orientations of I_f in order to obtain the observed transition probability.

The non-relativistic theory leads to two possible interactions, (5.12) and (5.13), but there is no reason to believe that the true beta-decay interaction is one *or* the other of these two. Rather, it may be a linear combination, with two constants G_s and G_t, one for each interaction. The matrix element H'_{if} in (5.1) is then the sum of the two separate matrix elements. Thus in the general case we might expect that the transition probability is not just the sum of the two separate transition probabilities for the two interactions but also involves an interference term between the two matrix elements. In the present case, however, these interference terms vanish because of the orthogonality of the singlet and triplet spin functions.

---

[1] A closer estimate of t_0 requires the results of the relativistic theory (Section 5C) and a careful estimate of the magnitude of the matrix element (5.15) which is given in Section 6. The relativistic treatment leads to the same result as (5.18) for the neutron, except that the factor 2 is replaced by 1. The combination $|\langle \mathbf{\sigma} \rangle|^2$ which appears in (5.18) turns out to be equal to 3 for the decay of the neutron. If we assume that most of the true beta-decay interaction is of the "triplet" (i.e., Gamow-Teller) type, we get $3/t_0 \cong 6 \times 10^{-4}$ sec^{-1}, or $t_0 \cong 5 \times 10^3$ sec. We shall use this estimate of t_0 throughout this chapter.

▶ **C. Relativistic Treatment**

We now drop the oversimplification of Section 5B and treat the light particles correctly as particles with spin $\frac{1}{2}$ which move with velocities which are close to the light velocity for the electron and equal to it for the neutrino. Hence they must be described by Dirac's relativistic wave equation.

In order to construct the correct interaction types we also must introduce relativistic wave functions for the heavy particles (nucleons). However, at the end we will make use only of the non-relativistic limit of these wave functions since the velocities of the nucleons are small compared to c. Hence the treatment will be relativistic with respect to the light particles only.

The following modifications of the results of Section 5B appear in this treatment:

(a) There are five different types of interaction instead of two under the same conditions.

(b) The transitions can be classified into two distinct groups, the "ordinary" ones and the "relativistic" ones. The ordinary transitions are direct generalizations of those appearing in the non-relativistic case, and they obey the same selection rules. The relativistic transitions obey selection rules different from (2.7) and (2.8) and involve nuclear matrix elements which are of the order of v/c, where v is the velocity of the nucleons. They represent a new type of transition and cannot be considered generalizations of the non-relativistic case.

(c) There is an angular correlation between electron and neutrino in allowed transitions.

In order to avoid confusion with the usual terminology we shall reserve the term "*allowed*" for *ordinary transitions of order* $l=0$. Konopinski (41, 43) includes the relativistic transitions of order 0 among his "first forbidden" transitions. We shall not use his classification here.

We first investigate the form of the field quantity F, (5.4). In the relativistic treatment, ϕ_e and ϕ_ν are *four*-component spinor wave functions, so that ξ in (5.4a) is a 4-by-4 matrix. Furthermore we are now interested in the transformation properties of F not merely under rotations and inversions, but also under Lorentz transformations. Pauli (36) has shown that five, and only five, relativistically covariant quantities of the form (5.4a) can be constructed. The first of these is a relativistic scalar:

$$F_S = \{ \phi_e{}^*, B \, \phi_\nu{}^* \} \tag{5.19}$$

where B is the generalization of the 2-by-2 matrix (5.8):[1]

$$B = \begin{pmatrix} 0 & 1 & 0 & 0 \\ -1 & 0 & 0 & 0 \\ 0 & 0 & 0 & 1 \\ 0 & 0 & -1 & 0 \end{pmatrix} \tag{5.20}$$

In order to obtain more symmetrical formulas we introduce the matrix

$$Q \equiv \beta B = B\beta \tag{5.21}$$

where β is the usual Dirac matrix [see Bethe (33) or Schiff (49) for the explicit forms of the Dirac matrices and of the Dirac wave equation]. The scalar field quantity F_s then becomes

$$F_s = \{ \phi_e{}^*, \beta Q\ \phi_\nu{}^* \} \tag{5.22S}$$

We construct the other covariant structures by introducing the following combinations of the four Dirac matrices α_x, α_y, α_z, and β:

$$\sigma_x = -i\alpha_y\alpha_z \qquad \sigma_y = -i\alpha_z\alpha_x \qquad \sigma_z = -i\alpha_x\alpha_y$$
$$\rho_1 = -i\alpha_x\alpha_y\alpha_z \qquad \rho_2 = \alpha_x\alpha_y\alpha_z\beta \tag{5.23}$$

The following relations hold:

$$\alpha_x = \rho_1\sigma_x \qquad \alpha_y = \rho_1\sigma_y \qquad \alpha_z = \rho_1\sigma_z \qquad \rho_1\rho_2 = i\beta \tag{5.24}$$

It should be noted that the σ's and β combine the large components[2] with large ones and the small components with small ones, whereas the two ρ's combine large with small components.

---

[1] We might perhaps expect to find the familiar Dirac matrix β instead of B, since $\{\phi^*, \beta\phi\}$ is known to be an invariant. However, we must keep in mind that there is a star upon both ϕ_e and ϕ_ν in (5.4a). Hence the transformation properties are different. The combination $\beta B \phi^* \equiv Q\phi^*$ transforms like ϕ. It should be mentioned that the requirement of invariance under inversions must be considered carefully in the relativistic treatment (Yang 50). Form (5.19) with (5.20) for B differs from the forms used by Marshak (42) and Critchfield (43) because Pauli (36) assumes a behavior of ϕ under inversion (the parity operation) different from the behavior assumed by Marshak and Critchfield. We follow Pauli (36) because B connects large components to large components, small components to small components, thereby making the correspondence to the non-relativistic treatment much simpler.

[2] In the notation used here, components number 3 and 4 are "large," the other two are "small." For low particle speeds v the "small" components are of the order of v/c compared to the "large" components. We shall use the terminology "large" and "small" even for fast-moving particles for which all components are of the same order of magnitude.

We can then construct a relativistic four-vector $F_{V\mu}$ whose three spatial components and time component are[1]

$$F_{Vi} = \{\phi_e{}^*,\, \alpha_i Q\, \phi_\nu{}^*\} = \{\phi_e{}^*,\, \rho_1\sigma_i Q\, \phi_\nu{}^*\} \qquad (i=1,2,3)$$

$$F_{V0} = \{\phi_e{}^*,\, Q\, \phi_\nu{}^*\}$$

(5.22V)

The next covariant structure is an anti-symmetric tensor

$$F_{T\mu\nu} = -F_{T\nu\mu} \qquad (\mu,\nu=0,1,2,3)$$

whose six non-vanishing components form two spatial vectors

$$F_{Tij} = -F_{Tji} = \{\phi_e{}^*,\, \beta\sigma_k Q\, \phi_\nu{}^*\} \qquad (i,j,k \text{ cyclic})$$

$$F_{Ti0} = -F_{T0i} = \{\phi_e{}^*,\, \rho_2\sigma_i Q\, \phi_\nu{}^*\}$$

(5.22T)

We furthermore construct the axial (pseudo) four-vector

$$F_{Ai} = \{\phi_e{}^*,\, \sigma_i Q\, \phi_\nu{}^*\} \qquad F_{A0} = \{\phi_e{}^*,\, \rho_1 Q\, \phi_\nu{}^*\} \qquad (5.22\text{A})$$

$F_{A\mu}$ behaves like a four-vector under rotations and proper Lorentz transformations but fails to change sign under inversion of the space coordinates. Similarly we can construct a pseudoscalar F_P which behaves like a scalar under rotations and proper Lorentz transformations but changes sign under inversion of the space coordinates

$$F_P = \{\phi_e{}^*,\, \rho_2 Q\, \phi_\nu{}^*\} \qquad (5.22\text{P})$$

Counting each component separately, there are altogether sixteen quantities, and they exhaust all possible bilinear covariant structures of the form (5.4a).[2] There were only four quantities, (5.6) and (5.7), in the non-relativistic case. We note that all sixteen quantities above are functions $F(\mathbf{r})$ of space through the wave functions ϕ_e and ϕ_ν which must be taken at the position $\mathbf{r}=\mathbf{r}_n$ of the transforming nucleon.

In order to construct the matrix element H'_{if} as given by (5.3) we must also determine the matrix K_n appropriate for each choice of the field quantity F. We write K_n in the form (5.5) and postulate invariance of the quantity

---

[1] We use a real time component $x_0=ct$ rather than the imaginary $x_4=ict$; the square of the four-vector $F_{V\mu}$ is then $\displaystyle\sum_{i=1}^{3}(F_{Vi})^2 - (F_{V0})^2$.

[2] For a proof that these structures have the claimed transformation properties, and that they are the only possible ones, see Pauli (36). We note that we construct bilinear covariants of type $\phi^*\cdots\phi^*$ whereas Pauli's covariants are of type $\phi\cdots\phi$. This accounts for the change in the order of the operators [e.g., $\alpha_i Q$ rather than Pauli's $Q\alpha_i$ in (5.22V)]. Our matrix B would be called B^{-1} in Pauli's notation, and it differs from his B^{-1} by a factor i.

$$F(\mathbf{r}_n) \, (\Phi_f{}^*K_n\Phi_i)$$

with respect to rotations, proper Lorentz transformations, and inversion of the space coordinates. This can be obtained only if the combination

$$\Phi_f{}^*K_n\Phi_i = \Phi_f{}^*K'_n\tau_{n,-}\Phi_i \qquad (5.25)$$

has the same transformation properties under these operations as the field quantity F. Hence we must construct covariant structures of the form (5.25) similar to the structures (5.22) for the light particles. We postulate that K'_n does not involve derivatives of the nucleon wave functions. Evidently relativistic wave functions for nucleons are needed here. The operators K'_n are very similar to those used in (5.22); indeed, they differ only through omission of the operator Q (see the footnote on page 706). We put subscripts n on the Dirac matrices to indicate that they operate on the spinor components of the nth nucleon only. Then the covariant entities are obtained from (5.25) with the following choices of K'_n:

Scalar: $\qquad\qquad\qquad\qquad K'_{nS} = \beta_n \qquad\qquad\qquad\qquad (5.25\text{S})$

Four-vector: $\quad K'_{nV,i} = \alpha_{n,i} = \rho_{n,1}\,\sigma_{n,i} \qquad K'_{nV,0} = 1 \qquad (5.25\text{V})$

Tensor: $\qquad\qquad K'_{nT,ij} = \beta_n\,\sigma_{n,k} \qquad (i,j,k \text{ cyclic})$
$$K'_{nT,i0} = \rho_{n,2}\,\sigma_{n,i} \qquad\qquad\qquad\qquad (5.25\text{T})$$

Axial vector: $\qquad K'_{nA,i} = \sigma_{n,i} \qquad K'_{nA,0} = \rho_{n,1} \qquad (5.25\text{A})$

Pseudoscalar: $\qquad\qquad\qquad K'_{nP} = \rho_{n,2} \qquad\qquad\qquad (5.25\text{P})$

We then get the following five different interaction matrix elements H'_{if}, each one of which has an integrand which is a relativistic scalar:

$$(H'_{if})_S = G_S \sum_{n=1}^{A} \int F_S(\mathbf{r}_n) \, (\Phi_f{}^*K_{nS}\Phi_i) \, d\tau \qquad (5.26\text{S})$$

$$(H'_{if})_V = G_V \sum_{n=1}^{A} \Bigg[\int \sum_{j=1}^{3} F_{Vj}(\mathbf{r}_n) \, (\Phi_f{}^*K_{nV,j}\Phi_i) \, d\tau$$
$$- \int F_{V0}(\mathbf{r}_n) \, (\Phi_f{}^*K_{nV,0}\Phi_i) \, d\tau \Bigg] \quad (5.26\text{V})$$

$$(H'_{if})_T = G_T \sum_{n=1}^{A} \Bigg[\int \sum_{\substack{k=1 \\ (ijk \text{ cyclic})}}^{3} F_{Tij}(\mathbf{r}_n) \, (\Phi_f{}^*K_{nT,ij}\Phi_i) \, d\tau$$
$$- \int \sum_{k=1}^{3} F_{Tk0}(\mathbf{r}_n) \, (\Phi_f{}^*K_{nT,k0}\Phi_i) \, d\tau \Bigg] \quad (5.26\text{T})$$

$$(H'_{if})_A = G_A \sum_{n=1}^{A} \left[\int \sum_{k=1}^{3} F_{Ak}(\mathbf{r}_n) \, (\Phi_f{}^*K_{nA,k}\Phi_i) \, d\tau \right.$$

$$\left. - \int F_{A0}(\mathbf{r}_n) \, (\Phi_f{}^*K_{nA,0}\Phi_i) \, d\tau \right] \quad (5.26A)$$

$$(H'_{if})_P = G_P \sum_{n=1}^{A} \int F_P(\mathbf{r}_n) \, (\Phi_f{}^*K_{nP}\Phi_i) \, d\tau \qquad (5.26P)$$

These five quantities are commonly called matrix elements of the scalar, vector, etc., interaction. It should be realized, however, that the integrand in (5.26V) is not a four-vector but the scalar product of two four-vectors, and hence a scalar.

While any one of these five interactions is a possible choice, there is no reason to believe that the true beta-decay interaction is given by one and only one of them. Any linear combination of the five interactions is also a possible interaction (Fierz 37, Groot 50, Bouchez 50). Wigner and Critchfield (Critchfield 41a, 43) have suggested one special linear combination of the five interactions:

$$(H'_{if})_{WC} = (H'_{if})_S - (H'_{if})_A - (H'_{if})_P \qquad (5.27)$$

with the same value of the constant G for the three matrix elements (i.e., the linear combination with $G_S = -G_A = -G_P = G$ and $G_V = G_T = 0$). The choice of this particular linear combination was motivated as follows: We may consider the beta-decay an event involving four particles (neutron, proton, electron, neutrino), all of which have spin $\frac{1}{2}$ and can (presumably) be described by Dirac spinor wave functions. We can look for a matrix element H'_{if} which treats all four particles on an equal footing, i.e., which is either completely symmetric or completely anti-symmetric under the exchange of any two of the four particles. A completely symmetric scalar cannot be constructed from four Dirac wave functions. The only remaining choice, the completely anti-symmetric interaction, is (5.27). The anti-symmetry is not apparent in this way of writing $(H'_{if})_{WC}$, however. Recently there have been suggestions that an interaction of this type, with the same constant G, operates between any four particles of spin $\frac{1}{2}$ (Tiomno 49, Lee 49, Yang 50).

We proceed to evaluate the transition probability (5.1) in the relativistic theory, and we assume first that the effect of the Coulomb field is negligible. We substitute the explicit wave functions ϕ_e and ϕ_ν, (5.11), into the various field quantities $F(\mathbf{r}_n)$, (5.22). The quantities u_e and u_ν are now four-component Dirac spinors rather than two-component Pauli spinors, but (in the absence of the Coulomb effect) they are still independent of the position variables $\mathbf{r}_e$ and $\mathbf{r}_\nu$, respectively. We shall restrict ourselves in this section to *transitions of order* $l=0$ which are obtained by replacing $\exp\left[-i(\mathbf{p}+\mathbf{q})\cdot\mathbf{r}_n\right]$ by unity. We then obtain expressions for the matrix elements (5.26) analogous to (5.12) and (5.13) in the non-relativistic treatment. For example, the matrix element for the scalar interaction (5.26S) becomes

$$(H'_{if})_S = \frac{G_S}{V}\{u_e{}^*, \beta Q\, u_\nu{}^*\}\,\langle\beta\rangle \tag{5.28}$$

where $\langle\beta\rangle$ is the nuclear matrix element of β given by the following definition. The nuclear matrix element of an operator O is defined by (O_n is the operator O acting upon the nth nucleon):

$$\langle O\rangle \equiv \sum_{n=1}^{A} \int \Phi_f{}^* O_n\tau_{n,-}\Phi_i\, d\tau \tag{5.29}$$

Since the nuclear motion can be considered non-relativistic, we get[1]

$$\langle\beta\rangle \cong \langle 1\rangle \tag{5.30}$$

The scalar interaction (5.26) leads to the same matrix element as the non-relativistic singlet interaction and hence also to the same selection rule (2.7).

We find new types of matrix elements when we analyze the other interactions. They give rise to the effect of relativity mentioned at the beginning of this subsection: the existence of "relativistic transitions" which obey selection rules different from those found in the non-relativistic treatment. We demonstrate this fact first for the axial vector interaction. We restrict ourselves again to the transitions of order $l=0$ by replacing $\exp\left[-i(\mathbf{p}+\mathbf{q})\cdot\mathbf{r}_n\right]$ by unity, and we neglect the Coulomb effect on the electrons. We then obtain, in analogy to (5.28),

$$(H'_{if})_A = \frac{G_A}{V}\left[\{u_e{}^*, \boldsymbol{\sigma} Q\, u_\nu{}^*\}\cdot\langle\boldsymbol{\sigma}\rangle - \{u_e{}^*, \rho_1 Q\, u_\nu{}^*\}\,\langle\rho_1\rangle\right] \tag{5.31}$$

Here $\langle\boldsymbol{\sigma}\rangle$ is the nuclear matrix element (5.15) and $\langle\rho_1\rangle$ is defined analogously:

$$\langle\rho_1\rangle \equiv \sum_{n=1}^{A} \int \Phi_f{}^* \rho_1\tau_{n,-}\Phi_i\, d\tau \tag{5.32}$$

---

[1] The approximation (5.30) is accurate provided that the nucleons move slowly enough so that $(v_n/c)^2\ll 1$, where v_n is the speed of a typical nucleon in the nucleus.

The first term of (5.31) is similar to expression (5.13) for the non-relativistic triplet interaction. It leads to an "ordinary" transition which obeys the selection rule (2.8). The second term, however, is of an essentially different type. It represents a "relativistic transition." The operator ρ_1 connects large Dirac components of the nucleon wave functions to small ones. In a non-relativistic approximation for the nucleons we can express the small components in terms of the large ones (see Bethe 33, sec. 8, or Schiff 49, p. 320). We then get the result

$$\langle \rho_1 \rangle \cong - \left\langle \frac{\mathbf{\delta \cdot v}}{c} \right\rangle \qquad \text{(non-relativistic approximation for the nucleons)}$$

$$(5.33)$$

where $\mathbf{v}$ is the non-relativistic operator for the velocity of the nucleons. Relation (5.33) shows that $\langle \rho_1 \rangle$ is smaller than the ordinary matrix elements $\langle 1 \rangle$ and $\langle \mathbf{\delta} \rangle$ by a factor of the order of (v_n/c), where v_n is the average speed of nucleons inside the nucleus.

Even more important than the different orders of magnitude of relativistic transitions compared to ordinary ones are the different selection rules. The product $(\mathbf{\delta \cdot v})$ is a pseudoscalar, i.e., it is invariant under rotations but changes sign under inversion of the space coordinates (the parity operation). Hence (5.33) vanishes unless the following selection rule is satisfied:

$$\Delta J = 0 \qquad \Pi_i = -\Pi_f \qquad (5.34)$$

This selection rule differs from the Fermi selection rule (2.7) in that it requires opposite parities Π_i and Π_f for the initial and final nuclear states.

The interaction types (5.26V) and (5.26T) lead to expressions for the matrix element which are similar to (5.31). We can distinguish two types of terms; one type contains the nuclear matrix element $\langle 1 \rangle$ or $\langle \mathbf{\delta} \rangle$ and leads to "ordinary" transitions; these are transitions encountered in the non-relativistic theory which obey the selection rule (2.7) or (2.8). The other type contains nuclear matrix elements involving the operator ρ_1 or ρ_2 and leads to "relativistic transitions"; these are transitions which are slower than the ordinary ones and which obey different selection rules. The nuclear matrix elements appearing in these expressions are collected in Table 5.1. We notice that the scalar interaction does not lead to any relativistic transitions, whereas the pseudoscalar interaction does not lead to any ordinary transitions. The matrix elements $\langle \beta \rangle$ and $\langle \beta \mathbf{\delta} \rangle$ for ordinary transitions can be

TABLE 5.1

NUCLEAR MATRIX ELEMENTS AND SELECTION RULES FOR TRANSITIONS OF ORDER
$l = 0$

The equation number next to each matrix element gives the appropriate selection rule.

Interaction	Nuclear Matrix Element, Selection Rules			
	Ordinary		Relativistic	
Scalar (5.26S)	$\langle\beta\rangle$	(2.7)	...	
Vector (5.26V)	$\langle 1\rangle$	(2.7)	$\langle\rho_1\mathbf{\sigma}\rangle$	(5.36)
Tensor (5.26T)	$\langle\beta\mathbf{\sigma}\rangle$	(2.8)	$\langle\rho_2\mathbf{\sigma}\rangle$	(5.36)
Axial vector (5.26A)	$\langle\mathbf{\sigma}\rangle$	(2.8)	$\langle\rho_1\rangle$	(5.34)
Pseudoscalar (5.26P)	...		$\langle\rho_2\rangle$	(5.34)

replaced by $\langle 1\rangle$ and $\langle\mathbf{\sigma}\rangle$, respectively, in a non-relativistic approximation for the nucleons. The matrix element $\langle\rho_1\mathbf{\sigma}\rangle$ for relativistic transitions in the vector interaction can be estimated by the same method which was used to obtain (5.33). The result is

$$\langle\rho_1\mathbf{\sigma}\rangle = \langle\mathbf{\alpha}\rangle \cong -\left\langle\frac{\mathbf{v}}{c}\right\rangle$$

(non-relativistic approximation for the nucleons)   (5.35)

The nucleon velocity operator $\mathbf{v}$ changes sign under inversion. The selection rule for this matrix element therefore differs from the Gamow-Teller selection rule (2.8) by requiring opposite parities for the initial and final states:

$$\Delta J = 0, \pm 1, \quad \text{except no } 0\to 0 \text{ transitions}, \quad \Pi_i = -\Pi_f \quad (5.36)$$

The same approximation which led to (5.33) gives zero for the matrix element $\langle\rho_2\rangle$.[1] We can therefore estimate this matrix element to be of order $(v_n/c)^2$ rather than of order v_n/c. Unlike the matrix element $\langle\rho_1\rangle$, the matrix element $\langle\rho_2\rangle$ cannot be estimated properly without a thoroughgoing relativistic theory of nucleons, which we do not possess. The selection rule is the same as for the matrix element $\langle\rho_1\rangle$, since ρ_1 and ρ_2 are both invariant under rotations and both change sign under inversion.

---

[1] As a result of a trivial mistake, Critchfield (42) gives estimates in which the roles of ρ_1 and ρ_2 are interchanged.

Finally, in the non-relativistic approximation for the nucleons[1] the matrix element $\langle \rho_2 \mathbf{d} \rangle$ becomes

$$\langle \rho_2 \mathbf{d} \rangle \cong - \left\langle \frac{\mathbf{d} \times \mathbf{v}}{c} \right\rangle$$

(non-relativistic approximation for the nucleons)　　(5.36a)

and is therefore of order v_n/c. The selection rule is the same one that applies to $\langle \rho_1 \mathbf{d} \rangle$, i.e., (5.36).

Selection rules (5.34) and (5.36) give the following result: *Relativistic transitions of order $l=0$ lead to final states of opposite parity as the initial state, whereas ordinary transitions of order $l=0$ lead to final states of the same parity as the initial state.* Thus, a transition of order $l=0$ from a definite initial state i to a definite final state f can be either of the ordinary type or of the relativistic type, but not both. We shall see in Section 7 that this is true for any given order l.[2]

The factors v_n/c and $(v_n/c)^2$ which occur in the matrix elements of the relativistic transitions reduce their probability considerably compared to the ordinary ones. The relativistic transitions of order $l=0$ have therefore been counted among the "forbidden" transitions. Konopinski (41, 43) groups relativistic transitions of order 0 into the "first forbidden" class. We prefer to avoid this grouping here, since there are large physical differences between these relativistic transitions and the other "first forbidden" transitions.

We now turn to the third effect of relativity mentioned at the beginning of this subsection, namely *the existence of an angular correlation between the directions of emission of the electron and of the neutrino.* We first demonstrate this effect for the scalar interaction (5.26S) and start with the matrix element (5.28). In order to get the emission probability we must sum $|H'_{if}|^2$ over the spin directions of the electron and the neutrino. Let $u_e^{(k)}$ be the Dirac spin function for a positive-energy electron with spin direction k ($k=1,2$). These spin functions are given explicitly, for example, by Schiff (49, see p. 315). We use a similar notation for the neutrino and get, instead of (5.16a), the relativistic generalization

$$\sum_{k,k'=1}^{2} \left| \{ u_e^{(k)*}, \beta Q\, u_\nu^{(k')*} \} \right|^2 = 1 - \frac{v}{c} \cos \theta_{e\nu} \qquad (5.37)$$

---

[1] The fact that this matrix element is of order v/c rather than of order $(v/c)^2$ was pointed out to us by Dr. R. Nataf and, independently, by Dr. E. Feenberg (private communications).

[2] However, it is possible that an ordinary transition of order l and a relativistic transition of order $l-1$ contribute to the same decay $i \to f$.

where v is the speed of the electron and $\theta_{e\nu}$ is the angle between the directions of emission of electron and neutrino.

The evaluation of the sum (5.37) is straightforward but somewhat tedious. A quicker way to perform the sum is as follows: The function $v_\nu = \beta Q u_\nu{}^* = B u_\nu{}^*$ also satisfies the Dirac equation for a neutrino with positive energy, but with reversed momentum $-\mathbf{q}$, and reversed direction of the spin (v_ν is the time-reversed wave function of u_ν; see Chapter X, Section 2). Since we are summing over spin directions anyway, the reversal of the spin direction makes no difference. We then need the sum of $\left|\{u_e{}^*, v_\nu\}\right|^2$ over the spin directions for the two particles. This sum can be reduced to a trace of Dirac operators by introducing operators Λ^+, which give unity when applied to a positive-energy eigenfunction, zero when applied to a negative-energy eigenfunction. These operators are

$$\Lambda_e{}^+ = \frac{E - \boldsymbol{\alpha}\cdot\mathbf{p} - \beta}{2E} \qquad \text{(for an electron with momentum } +\mathbf{p}\text{)}$$

$$\Lambda_\nu{}^+ = \frac{q + \boldsymbol{\alpha}\cdot\mathbf{q}}{2q} \qquad \text{(for a neutrino with momentum } -\mathbf{q}\text{)}$$

where $q = |\mathbf{q}|$ is the (positive) energy of the neutrino, in units mc^2. We now let $k = 3,4$ stand for the two negative-energy solutions and write

$$\sum_{k,k'=1}^{2} \left|\{u_e^{(k)*}, v_\nu^{(k')}\}\right|^2 = \sum_{k,k'=1}^{2} \{u_e^{(k)*}, v_\nu^{(k')}\}\{v_\nu^{(k')*}, u_e^{(k)}\}$$

$$= \sum_{k,k'=1}^{4} \{u_e^{(k)*}, \Lambda_\nu{}^+ u_\nu^{(k')}\}\{u_\nu^{(k')*}, \Lambda_e{}^+ u_e^{(k)}\}$$

$$= \text{trace } (\Lambda_\nu{}^+\Lambda_e{}^+)$$

$$= 1 - \frac{\mathbf{p}\cdot\mathbf{q}}{Eq}$$

where we have used the known traces of Dirac matrices and their products.

This method of evaluation of spin averages is related to the introduction of an "anti-neutrino" which is commonly encountered in the literature. The wave function v_ν may be considered the wave function of an imaginary particle which exists before the beta-decay and whose *absence* is observed as a neutrino after the decay. We prefer to avoid this formulation of beta-decay theory.

It should be remarked that (5.37) does not reduce to (5.16a) even in the limit $(v/c) \to 0$. The discrepancy of a factor 2 is a result of our erroneous non-relativistic treatment of the neutrino in Section 5B. Since the neutrino is always a relativistic particle, the "large" and "small" components of its wave function are of the same order of magnitude, so that the normalization of the "large" components differs by a factor $\sqrt{2}$ from the non-relativistic normalization. We would get the result (5.16a) from (5.37) if the neutrino had a rest mass $m_\nu \neq 0$ and if both electron and neutrino were moving with speeds small compared to the speed of light.

Equation (5.37) shows that there is an angular correlation between the directions of emission of electron and neutrino. For many beta-decays there is a considerable region of the beta-spectrum for which v/c of the electron is close to 1.   The angular correlation predicted by (5.37) is then appreciable: electrons are emitted preferentially in the direction opposite to the neutrino.   On the other hand, since the angular correlation is proportional to the first power of $\cos \theta_{e\nu}$, it gives no contribution in an average over all directions of emission of the neutrino.   Thus the shape of the beta-spectrum is still determined by the statistical factor (2.5).

We now study the angular correlations between electron and neutrino which result from interactions other than the scalar inter- action.   Some new features occur when the light particles are emitted into the triplet state.   As an example, consider the "ordinary" part of the axial vector interaction [see (5.31)].   In order to get the angular correlation, we must sum $|H'_{if}|^2$ over the spin directions of the electron and the neutrino.   The sum, which corresponds to the non-relativistic (5.16), now becomes

$$\sum_{k,k'=1}^{2} \{u_e^{(k)}{}^*, \sigma_m Q\, u_\nu^{(k')}{}^*\}^* \{u_e^{(k)}{}^*, \sigma_{m'}Q\, u_\nu^{(k')}{}^*\}$$

$$= \delta_{mm'}\left(1 - \frac{v}{c}\cos\theta_{e\nu}\right) + (-1)^m \frac{p_{-m}q_{m'} + q_{-m}p_{m'}}{Eq} \quad (5.38)$$

This sum can also be evaluated by the trace method.   Since the calculation involves a few points not apparent in the computation of (5.37), we go through the derivation here.   We again introduce the time-reversed neutrino spinor $v_\nu = Bu_\nu{}^*$, whereupon the left side of (5.38) becomes

$$\sum_{k,k'=1}^{2} \{u_e^{(k)}{}^*, \sigma_m \beta\, v_\nu^{(k')}\}^* \{u_e^{(k)}{}^*, \sigma_{m'}\beta\, v_\nu^{(k')}\}$$

$$= \sum_{k,k'=1}^{2} \{v_\nu^{(k')}{}^*, (\sigma_m \beta)^\dagger\, u_e^{(k)}\} \{u_e^{(k)}{}^*, \sigma_{m'}\beta\, v_\nu^{(k')}\}$$

where the symbol $(\sigma_m \beta)^\dagger$ means the Hermitean conjugate of the matrix $\sigma_m \beta$. The expression is now in the proper form for the application of the projection operators Λ_e^+ and Λ_ν^+ in a manner completely analogous to the one used before. Using the relation $(\sigma_m)^\dagger = (-)^m \sigma_{-m}$, we get

$$(-)^m \text{ trace } (\beta\sigma_{-m}\Lambda_e^+\sigma_{m'}\beta\Lambda_\nu^+)$$

$$= \frac{(-)^m}{4} \text{ trace } (\sigma_{-m}\sigma_{m'}) + \frac{(-)^m}{4Eq} \sum_{\mu,\mu'=-1}^{1} (-)^{\mu+\mu'}p_\mu q_{-\mu'} \text{ trace } (\sigma_{-m}\sigma_{-\mu}\sigma_{m'}\sigma_{\mu'})$$

where we have used the general relation (5.8b) for a scalar product of two vectors **A** and **B**.   Relation (5.38) now follows by straighforward computation using the known traces of Dirac matrices.

The quantities p_m and q_m in (5.38) are formed from the three components of the light particle momenta $\mathbf{p}$ and $\mathbf{q}$ according to (5.8a). When (5.38) is substituted into the expression for $|(H'_{if})_A|^2$ derived from the first term of (5.31) (only the first term should be used since we are considering "ordinary" transitions), we get the following value for the average of $|H'_{if}|^2$ over the spin directions of the outgoing electron and neutrino:

$$\langle |H'_{if}|^2 \rangle_{\mathrm{av}} = \left(\frac{G_A}{2V} \right)^2 \left[\left(1 - \frac{v}{c} \cos \theta_{ev} \right) |\langle \mathbf{\sigma} \rangle|^2 \right.$$
$$\left. + \frac{(\mathbf{p} \cdot \langle \mathbf{\sigma} \rangle^*)\,(\mathbf{q} \cdot \langle \mathbf{\sigma} \rangle) + (\mathbf{q} \cdot \langle \mathbf{\sigma} \rangle^*)\,(\mathbf{p} \cdot \langle \mathbf{\sigma} \rangle)}{Eq} \right] \quad (5.39)$$

Unlike the non-relativistic case, the result (5.39) depends on the orientation of the vector $\langle \mathbf{\sigma} \rangle$ with respect to the directions of $\mathbf{p}$ and $\mathbf{q}$. In practice, we must perform an average over the possible orientations of the angular momentum of the initial nucleus. This can be done as if $\langle \mathbf{\sigma} \rangle$ were a classical vector, since we restrict ourselves to a non-relativistic treatment of the nucleons. We use the classical identity ($\mathbf{A}$ and $\mathbf{B}$ are any two constant vectors):

$$(\mathbf{S}^* \cdot \mathbf{A})\,(\mathbf{S} \cdot \mathbf{B})_{\substack{\mathrm{average\ over\ directions} \\ \mathrm{of\ the\ vector\ } \mathbf{S}}} = \tfrac{1}{3}\,(\mathbf{S}^* \cdot \mathbf{S})\,(\mathbf{A} \cdot \mathbf{B})$$

to obtain the final angular correlation between electron and neutrino in the ordinary transition of the axial vector interaction; this angular correlation is $[1 - \tfrac{1}{3}(v/c) \cos \theta_{ev}]$.

The angular correlations for other interactions and for other types of transitions can be determined by similar methods. They always have the form

$$1 + \lambda \frac{v}{c} \cos \theta_{ev}$$

where λ is a number between 1 and -1. The resulting values of λ are tabulated in Table 5.2. The angular correlations were worked out by Bloch (35) and by Hamilton (47); for Coulomb corrections see Rose (49b) and Greuling (51); $l = 0$ transitions needs no corrections.

We now turn to the determination of emission probabilities. They are given by (5.1) into which the corresponding values of H'_{if} must be inserted. In order to calculate the probability $P(p)\,dp$ for the emission of an electron with the momentum p, we must not only sum $|H'_{if}|^2$ as before over the spin directions of the electron and the neutrino, but we must also integrate over the directions of motion of both particles. This direction appears explicitly only in the angular correlation term. We obtain finally a result of form (2.13) in which the constant C is given by an expression which is analogous to (5.18). For example, we find for the scalar interaction

$$C_s = t_0^{-1}|\langle\beta\rangle|^2 \cong t_0^{-1}|\langle1\rangle|^2$$

where t_0 is defined by (5.17). Similar expressions hold for ordinary and relativistic transitions of the other interactions. The different values of Ct_0 are also tabulated in Table 5.2. The value of C determines the comparative half-life according to (4.6) which is applicable to all transitions of order $l=0$. The shape of the electron spectrum is of the allowed type as given by (2.13), for all $l=0$ transitions.[1]

The results collected in Tables 5.1 and 5.2 can be compared with

TABLE 5.2

ANGULAR CORRELATION BETWEEN ELECTRON AND NEUTRINO AND THE CONSTANT C IN (2.13) AND (4.6) FOR TRANSITIONS OF ORDER 0

The angular correlation is written as $1 + \lambda \dfrac{v}{c} \cos\theta_{e\nu}$.

Interaction	Ordinary Transitions		Relativistic Transitions	
	λ	t_0C	λ	t_0C
Scalar (5.26S)	-1	$\|\langle\beta\rangle\|^2$	...	...
Vector (5.26V)	$+1$	$\|\langle1\rangle\|^2$	$-\frac{1}{3}$	$\|\langle\rho_1\sigma\rangle\|^2$
Tensor (5.26T)	$+\frac{1}{3}$	$\|\langle\beta\sigma\rangle\|^2$	$+\frac{1}{3}$	$\|\langle\rho_2\sigma\rangle\|^2$
Axial vector (5.26A)	$-\frac{1}{3}$	$\|\langle\sigma\rangle\|^2$	$+1$	$\|\langle\rho_1\rangle\|^2$
Pseudoscalar (5.26P)	...	...	-1	$\|\langle\rho_2\rangle\|^2$

experimental data in order to determine which interaction type is realized in nature. Unfortunately the data are not good enough to allow any clear-cut decision. Only very few conclusions can be reached with the present material.

There are very few experimental data available on the angular correlation of electron and neutrino in allowed transitions. [The work of Allen (49) on He[6] shows a weak angular correlation with a λ less than unity and probably negative. This is inconsistent with a pure vector interaction and probably also inconsistent with a pure scalar one. Since the experimental error is considerable, neither the tensor nor the axial vector interaction contradicts the data. The

[1] This fact is one of the reasons for grouping transitions of order $l=0$ together, rather than classing the relativistic transitions into a "first forbidden" group.

Wigner-Critchfield interaction gives a correlation which also fits the present experiments.

According to the evidence presented in Section 4, many allowed transitions violate the selection rule (2.7).   Hence the true beta-decay interaction must contain either tensor or axial vector interactions or a mixture of both.   The only mixture which is definitely excluded is the one with $G_T = -G_A$, which would give rise to a spectrum shape quite different from the allowed shape (2.13) (Fierz 37, Lewis 46) and hence would contradict the experimental data.

▶ 6. DETERMINATION OF MATRIX ELEMENTS; FAVORED AND UNFAVORED TRANSITIONS

The probability of an allowed beta-decay (ordinary transition of order $l=0$) depends on the magnitude of nuclear matrix elements which involve only spin and isotopic spin operators.   For Fermi selection rules the relevant matrix element is $\langle 1 \rangle$, (5.14).   For Gamow-Teller selection rules the transition probability is proportional to $|\langle \mathbf{\sigma} \rangle|^2$, which is defined by (5.15) and (5.18).

These matrix elements are sums of A terms, so that we may suspect that their magnitude is proportional to the mass number A of the radioactive nucleus.   This is, however, not the case, as can be seen very easily by using the "levels" picture of Chapter VI.   Consider a filled level in a typical level occupation scheme, say Fig. 1.2 of Chapter VI.   Let it be occupied by particles 1 through 4.   Then $\tau_{3,-}$ and $\tau_{4,-}$ give 0 because particles 3 and 4 are protons. $\tau_{1,-}$ and $\tau_{2,-}$ do not give 0, but both lead to wave functions which violate the Pauli exclusion principle: 3 neutrons and 1 proton in the same level.   There are no such states in the final nucleus.   Thus particles in "filled levels" do not contribute to the nuclear matrix element.   The contributions come only from the relatively few particles above the filled levels (Nordheim 37).

The "levels" picture also illustrates another important property of the matrix elements, namely the grouping into favored and unfavored transitions.   Before introducing a more exact definition of this distinction in terms of the symmetry properties of the nuclear wave functions (Wigner 39), let us first describe the states of the initial and final nucleus, respectively, in terms of the "levels" picture.   We call a transition *favored* if the nucleon which changes its charge remains in the same level; the transition is *unfavored* if the nucleon must change its level.   We emphasize that the distinction between favored and unfavored transitions is separate from the previous classification into allowed and forbidden transitions.   Both favored and unfavored transitions are allowed.   The classification into allowed and forbidden transitions refers to the possible changes of angular momentum and parity during the transitions.   The classification into favored and unfavored transitions refers to the possible changes in the level occupation schemes (i.e., the possible changes in the behavior of the wave function under exchanges of the space coordinates only; see Chapter VI, Section 3).   The distinction between favored and unfavored transitions is made only for allowed transitions, not for forbidden transitions.

We now show that most of the allowed beta-transitions are unfavored.   For the negative beta-decay we argue as follows: the change of a neutron into a proton without change of level would *increase* the total energy of the nucleus by an amount corresponding to the additional Coulomb energy and would therefore not lead to a spontaneous decay.   Exceptions to this rule are found in only a few cases of light elements of character $A = 4k + 2$ (k integral), e.g., $He^6 \rightarrow Li^6$, which are favored transitions.   These are just the cases for which the spin dependence of the nuclear forces causes a deviation from the general rule that the most stable nucleus is the one with the largest possible number of neutrons in a given level distribution of nucleons (a given "partition"; see Chapter VI, Sections 1 and 3).[1]

For the positive beta-decay the surplus of neutrons makes the allowed transitions unfavored.   The initial nucleus is almost always in its ground state.   Hence, as long as there are fewer protons than neutrons, the protons are all in levels already containing two neutrons, and thus the protons must change their level when they transform into neutrons, thereby making the transition unfavored.   There are two groups of exceptions: (1) the positive beta-transitions in nuclei with mass number $A = 4k + 2$ (k integral) in which one of the two nuclei has equal numbers of neutrons and protons, e.g., $F^{18} \rightarrow O^{18}$, $Al^{26} \rightarrow Mg^{26}$, $P^{30} \rightarrow Si^{30}$, $Cl^{34} \rightarrow S^{34}$, $K^{38} \rightarrow A^{38}$;[2] (2) the transitions between pairs of

---

[1] The decays $Be^{10} \rightarrow B^{10}$ and $C^{14} \rightarrow N^{14}$ illustrate that other considerations play a role besides the arrangements of the nucleons into levels.   Both decays are analogous to the $He^6 \rightarrow Li^6$ decay (they are obtained by adding 1 and 2 alpha-particles, respectively), yet both have very high comparative half-lives.   The high ft value of Be^{10} is due to the large spin change in the transition (see Table 4.1) which makes the decay highly forbidden, even though it might be favored if it were allowed.   The long comparative half-life of C^{14} is not completely understood at this time but may be connected with a change of parity during the transition, thereby making it a forbidden one (Gerjuoy 51, Warshaw 50).

[2] Again there are examples of forbidden transitions within this class, e.g., the ground state to ground state transitions $C^{10} \rightarrow B^{10}$, $O^{14} \rightarrow N^{14}$, $Na^{22} \rightarrow Ne^{22}$.   In all three cases the beta-decay goes predominantly to an excited state of the final nucleus; in the first two of these three decays the transition to the excited state in question is allowed and favored.

mirror nuclei which differ by one unit of charge; except for $H^3 \rightarrow He^3$ these are all positive beta-decays. These exceptional transitions are *favored*, whereas all other allowed positron decays are *unfavored*.

We expect the matrix elements $\langle 1 \rangle$ and $\langle \sigma \rangle$ to be of the order of 1 for favored transitions: the initial wave function and the final wave function (after changing the charge of the transforming nucleon) do not differ, and hence the integrals in (5.14) and (5.15) are of the order of unity.[1] This is particularly evident in the case of beta-transitions between corresponding states of mirror nuclei. There the "levels" picture is not necessary for the conclusion. The initial and final states are "mirror states," i.e., they differ only through the fact that all the protons have been changed into neutrons, and all the neutrons into protons. The similarity of the two wave functions follows from the equality of neutron-neutron and proton-proton forces, without anything being assumed about neutron-proton forces. The experimental evidence for the similarity of mirror nuclei is excellent (see Chapter VI, Section 6). The "levels" picture is required for the conclusion in the case of the $A = 4k + 2$ nuclei.

The *unfavored* transitions are expected to have appreciably smaller matrix elements. In fact, if the "levels" picture were exact, the matrix elements would vanish because the initial and final wave functions are orthogonal. The observed comparative half-lives show the expected difference clearly. In Fig. 4.1, the peak around $\log(ft) \cong 3.5$ represents the allowed and favored transitions. The decay of the neutron belongs in this group. This value of ft is just what we expect from equation (4.6) and Table 5.2 if we assume the matrix elements to be of order 1 and the fundamental time constant t_0 to be about 5×10^3 sec. The second peak in Fig. 4.1, around $\log(ft) = 5$, is undoubtedly attributable to allowed but unfavored transitions. In all cases for which spectra of these transitions have been measured these spectra have turned out to follow the allowed shape. Comparing the ft values of typical favored and unfavored transitions, we conclude that the lack of overlap of the wave functions in unfavored transitions

---

[1] Strictly speaking, the initial and final wave functions are closely alike only if the two states belong to the same "supermultiplet" (see Chapter VI, Section 6). This condition is more stringent than the one imposed so far (that the two states have the same partition). For example, the wave functions may fail to overlap well, because the nucleon has jumped into a different "orbit" of the independent-particle model, even though the symmetry properties under space exchanges (the partition) of the wave function are unchanged. Such an explanation has been advanced for the high ft value of the $C^{14} \rightarrow N^{14}$ transition. See also Section 7D for a discussion of the "l-selection rule" of Nordheim (50).

reduces the square of the matrix element by a factor between 20 and 50.[1]

We now turn to a more exact definition of favored and unfavored transitions and to a quantitative determination of the matrix elements in the case of favored transitions. Since the operators contained in the matrix elements $\langle 1 \rangle$ and $\langle \mathbf{d} \rangle$ do not involve the space coordinates at all, these operators are symmetric under the interchange of the *space* coordinates of any two nucleons. Therefore, if the initial wave function Φ_i has definite properties under such space exchanges (belongs to a definite partition; see Chapter VI), we can infer immediately that the final wave function Φ_f must belong to the same partition. If Φ_i and Φ_f belong to different partitions, the matrix elements vanish.[2] Thus the precise definition of favored and unfavored transitions is: *An allowed transition is said to be favored if the initial and final nuclear wave functions belong to the same partition; otherwise the transition is said to be unfavored.* If the Wigner approximation of charge- and spin-independent nuclear forces were precisely correct, the matrix elements of allowed and favored beta-decays would be of the order of unity, while the matrix elements of allowed but unfavored beta-decays would vanish.

In practice, the Wigner approximation (in which all wave functions belong to definite partitions) is not rigorously correct. Thus allowed but unfavored beta-transitions do occur, but their matrix elements are small compared to unity. Their comparative half-lives are correspondingly lengthened compared to those of favored transitions.

The distinction between favored and unfavored transitions is expected to be sharpest in the region where the Wigner approximation is best, i.e., for light nuclei. As the number of protons increases, the Coulomb forces become more and more effective until eventually the Wigner approximation breaks down altogether and the partitions can no longer be used to classify the wave functions. For higher mass numbers, therefore, the distinction between favored and unfavored transitions is expected to lose its significance. This prediction is borne out rather strikingly by the positron decays of the $A = 4k + 2$ nuclei which were mentioned before. The comparative half-lives of F^{18} and Al^{26} are typical of allowed and favored transitions. P^{30} has

[1] One sometimes finds in the literature the statement that ft values around 10^5 sec correspond to "first forbidden" transitions. There is no convincing evidence for this assertion.

[2] If the final wave function Φ_f contains a mixture of components belonging to various partitions, the nuclear matrix elements for the beta-decay "connect" with only that part of Φ_f which belongs to the same partition as Φ_i.

$ft = 5 \times 10^4$ sec, which is very high for a favored transition, and Cl^{34} has $ft = 3 \times 10^5$ sec, which is not at all different from typical allowed but unfavored decays.

We shall restrict our discussion of the *matrix elements of favored transitions* to transitions between mirror nuclei. The evaluation of the matrix elements $|\langle 1 \rangle|^2$ and $|\langle \sigma \rangle|^2$ is simplified greatly by the observation that they depend only on the partition (P, P', P'') but not on the number of "filled levels" in the language of Chapter VI. This is understandable since a particle inside one of the filled levels cannot make a beta-transition without leading to a state which violates the Pauli exclusion principle, and which is therefore orthogonal to all actual final states Φ_f. We can therefore evaluate the matrix elements by neglecting the filled levels altogether. In the case of beta-decays between mirror nuclei, there are either one or three particles outside the filled levels. In the first case we can evaluate the matrix elements by considering the beta-decay of a single nucleon. In the second case we can also do so, since we may consider three particles in a level a filled level plus a one-particle "hole."

For the decay of a single nucleon the matrix element $\langle 1 \rangle$, (5.14), is just unity since the initial and final states have the same wave function after the proton is changed into a neutron. The Fermi selection rule (2.7), which always holds with this matrix element, can be augmented by further selection rules if the orbital angular momentum L and the spin angular momentum S of the nucleus are also good quantum numbers. This is the case when the angular momentum is due to only one particle (the other nucleons pairing up to give zero angular momentum),[1] or when spin-orbit coupling can be neglected. In either case the values of L and S must be conserved during the transition since the wave function is unchanged, and we get

$$\Delta L = \Delta S = 0 \qquad \text{(Fermi)} \qquad (6.1)$$

The computation of the matrix element $|\langle \sigma \rangle|^2$, (5.15) and (5.18), is slightly more complicated since the value depends on the way in which S and L combine to form the total angular momentum J of the nucleus (or of the particle). Consider a single particle with orbital angular momentum quantum number L and spin angular momentum quantum number $S = \frac{1}{2}$. There are two possible values of the total angular momentum J, $J = L + \frac{1}{2}$ and $J = L - \frac{1}{2}$. The wave function in each case is of the form

---

[1] In this case L is a good quantum number even in the presence of spin-orbit coupling since the two possible values of L, $L = J + \frac{1}{2}$ and $L = J - \frac{1}{2}$, correspond to states of opposite parity and thus do not mix. The assumption of angular momentum due to only one particle is commonly made in the nuclear shell model (see Chapter XIV).

$$\Phi_{JM} = \sum_{m_L + m_S = M} C_{LS}(J,M;m_L,m_S)\, u_{Lm_L}(x,y,z)\, \chi_{Sm_S} \qquad (6.2)$$

where the C_{LS} are the Clebsch-Gordan coefficients of Appendix A, Section 5; $u(x,y,z)$ has the angle-dependence characteristic of a spherical harmonic $Y_{Lm_L}(\theta,\varphi)$, and χ_{Sm_S} is the spin function for a spin $S = \frac{1}{2}$ and its z component m_S (which can be either $\frac{1}{2}$ or $-\frac{1}{2}$). We have omitted the isotopic spin function which indicates that the nucleon is a neutron (for β^- decay). Consider the matrix element $\langle \sigma_x \rangle$, (5.15). In our case the sum in (5.15) reduces to one term and this term involves the operator $\sigma_x \tau_-$ for the nucleon in question. τ_- changes the neutron into a proton, while σ_x reverses the spin direction:

$$\sigma_x \chi_{Sm_S} = \chi_{S,-m_S}$$

Thus, again apart from the isotopic spin function, we get

$$\sigma_x \tau_- \, \Phi_{JM} = \sum_{m_L - m_S = M} C_{LS}(J,M;m_L,-m_S)\, u_{Lm_L} \chi_{Sm_S} \qquad (6.3)$$

Let the final state have total angular momentum J' [which must be one of $J+1$, J, or $J-1$ according to the selection rules (2.8) for this matrix element] with a z component M'. M' must be either $M+1$ or $M-1$. Expression (6.3) gives

$$\int \Phi_{J'M'}^* \, \sigma_x \tau_- \, \Phi_{JM}\, d\tau = C_{L,1/2}(J',M';M+\tfrac{1}{2},\tfrac{1}{2})\, C_{L,1/2}(J,M;M+\tfrac{1}{2},-\tfrac{1}{2})$$
$$\text{(for } M' = M+1)$$
$$\int \Phi_{J'M'}^* \, \sigma_x \tau_- \, \Phi_{JM}\, d\tau = C_{L,1/2}(J',M';M-\tfrac{1}{2},-\tfrac{1}{2})\, C_{L,1/2}(J,M;M-\tfrac{1}{2},\tfrac{1}{2})$$
$$\text{(for } M' = M-1) \qquad (6.4)$$

The relevant Clebsch-Gordan coefficients are tabulated in Appendix A, Section 5. Since the beta-decay probability cannot depend on which direction in space is chosen as the z direction, we can assume $M = J$ without loss of generality. Expression (6.4) must be squared and summed over the two possible final values M'. The calculation of the other matrix elements $\langle \sigma_y \rangle$ and $\langle \sigma_z \rangle$ is completely analogous to the one outlined here. For details see Grönblom (39a) and Wigner (39).

The quantity $|\langle \mathbf{\sigma} \rangle|^2$ vanishes unless the Gamow-Teller selection rules (2.8) are satisfied for the nuclear transition. If the orbital angular momentum L and the spin angular momentum S of the nucleus are good quantum numbers, $\mathbf{\sigma}$ operates only on S and hence we get the additional selection rules

$$\Delta L = 0 \qquad \Delta S = 0, \pm 1 \quad \text{except no } 0 \to 0 \text{ transitions}$$
$$\text{(Gamow-Teller)} \quad (6.5)$$

Under the same conditions, the matrix element $|\langle \mathbf{\sigma} \rangle|^2$ assumes the values given in Table 6.1. For $L = 0$, the value in the upper left corner of the table is the only relevant one.

TABLE 6.1

VALUES OF $|\langle \mathbf{\sigma} \rangle|^2$ FOR BETA-TRANSITIONS BETWEEN MIRROR NUCLEI

Initial $J \rightarrow$	$L + \frac{1}{2}$	$L - \frac{1}{2}$
Final J		
$L + \frac{1}{2}$	$\dfrac{2L+3}{2L+1}$	$4\,\dfrac{L+1}{2L+1}$
$L - \frac{1}{2}$	$\dfrac{4L}{2L+1}$	$\dfrac{2L-1}{2L+1}$

If spin-orbit coupling is important, we cannot predict the value of the matrix element in such a simple way. Feingold and Wigner (unpublished manuscript, 1948) have called attention to the fact that for appreciable but not too strong spin-orbit coupling the results of the table can be used to give upper and lower limits for the matrix element. The actual value of $|\langle \mathbf{\sigma} \rangle|^2$ in that case must lie between its value for a pure $L = J - \frac{1}{2}$ state and a pure $L = J + \frac{1}{2}$ state.

We now apply these results to the measured comparative lifetimes of the Wigner series of mirror nuclei.[1] If Fermi selection rules are supposed to hold, the ft values of all these mirror nuclei should be the same (since the matrix element $\langle 1 \rangle$ is unity for all of them). Actually, most of these decays have log (ft) between 3.5 and 3.7, with a few, but significant, exceptions. The most important exceptions are the neutron and H^3, both of which have lower ft values. The ft value of the neutron is not well enough known at this time, so we use the value from the triton decay for our comparison, $\log(ft) = 3.06$. The discrepancies between the comparative half-lives of H^3 and some of the other Wigner nuclei (e.g., N^{13}) are as large as a factor of 4. It is hard to see how discrepancies of this order of magnitude can arise if mirror nuclei are really as similar to each other as all the other evidence seems to indicate. Here we find another strong argument against pure Fermi selection rules (singlet emission).

The assumption of triplet emission explains the discrepancies easily. Then the values of the matrix elements must be taken from Table 6.1, and they depend on the spin of the nucleus (for mirror nuclei the spins of the initial and the final nucleus are the same). The small ft values of the neutron and of H^3 are explained by the fact that the orbital angular momentum L is zero for these two nuclei, whereas for all other mirror transitions $L \neq 0$. Table 6.1 shows that $|\langle \mathbf{\sigma} \rangle|^2 = 3$ for $L = 0$, and $|\langle \mathbf{\sigma} \rangle|^2$ is much smaller than 3 for higher values of L (in transi-

---

[1] See Feingold (51) for a table of these ft values.

tions between corresponding states of mirror nuclei, the initial and final states have the same values of J and L, of course). A detailed study by Wigner and Feingold (unpublished, 1948) shows that all the ft values are consistent with the matrix element $|\langle \mathbf{\sigma} \rangle|^2$, i.e., with a pure Gamow-Teller interaction.[1] By comparing the ft values of the two decays of Be^7 (to the ground state and to an excited state of Li^7) Moszkowski (51a) arrives at the same conclusion. A small admixture of a Fermi-type interaction cannot be excluded, however. The value of the fundamental time constant t_0 for beta-decay used in this chapter ($t_0 = 5 \times 10^3$ sec) is based on the comparative half-life of H^3 together with the assumption $Ct_0 = |\langle \mathbf{\sigma} \rangle|^2 = 3$.

Similar comparisons can also be made for the other class of allowed and favored transitions, i.e., light nuclei with $A = 4k+2$. The values of $|\langle 1 \rangle|^2$ and $|\langle \mathbf{\sigma} \rangle|^2$ can again be found by general arguments which do not depend on the details of the nuclear wave functions. The comparison with the experimental lifetime gives excellent agreement for the He^6 decay, somewhat poorer agreement for the decays of F^{18} and Al^{26}, and very poor agreement for the heavier nuclei of this sequence. The disagreement is in the direction of longer experimental lifetimes, i.e., the actual values of the matrix elements are smaller than predicted by the theory. This is expected for the heavier nuclei where the Wigner approximation (on which the calculation is based) becomes poorer.

The excellent agreement for the He^6 decay excludes a large admixture of a Fermi-type interaction (Moszkowski 51a), for such an interaction would contribute to the decay probability of H^3 but would not contribute to the decay probability of He^6, according to the selection rules. Moszkowski concludes that the Fermi-type interaction can at most be half as strong as the main Gamow-Teller interaction, and that the assumption of a pure Gamow-Teller interaction is in agreement with the data on H^3 and He^6.[2]

---

[1] However, in some cases we must assume a predominant value of the orbital angular momentum L which is hardly consistent with the measured magnetic moment, unless there are large exchange magnetic moments. For example, the comparative lifetime for the $C^{11} \to B^{11}$ transition seems to imply a predominant D state ($L = 2$), whereas the magnetic moment of B^{11} is much closer to that of a P state ($L = 1$). See Chapter VI, Section 5, for a discussion of the evidence regarding magnetic moments.

[2] It is interesting to observe the excellent overlap of the wave functions of the ground states of He^6 and Li^6 required by these measurements. Since these states are not "corresponding" states (states belonging to the same isotopic spin multiplet; see Chapter VI, Section 6), the excellent overlap of the two wave functions provides a significant confirmation of the supermultiplet theory of Wigner.

The Wigner theory of allowed and favored transitions is borne out by experiment as well as can be expected.[1] The most important result of these considerations is the recognition that *most allowed beta-decays are unfavored and should therefore have comparative half-lives appreciably longer than that of the neutron.* A second, more tentative conclusion is that a pure Gamow-Teller interaction is in agreement with the lifetimes of allowed and favored decays, whereas a large admixture of a Fermi interaction would lead to disagreement.

7. BETA-TRANSITIONS OF HIGHER ORDER

A. Non-relativistic Theory : Selection Rules, Matrix Elements

The considerations of the previous sections are restricted to zero-order transitions, i.e., to transitions in which the light particles are emitted without any orbital angular momentum with respect to the nucleus. Mathematically this restriction was performed by replacing the exponential $\exp[-i(\mathbf{p}+\mathbf{q})\cdot\mathbf{r}_n]$ by unity when evaluating the matrix elements H'_{if}. The consideration of further terms in the expansion of this exponential gives rise to higher-order transitions which in most cases follow selection rules different from (2.7), (2.8), (5.34), and (5.36). Hence beta-transitions can take place also when the previously derived selection rules are violated. These transitions are, however, of higher order and in general much slower than the zero-order transitions.

The expansion into the different orders takes place in the field quantity $F(\mathbf{r}_n)$ defined by (5.4a). In this section we shall always neglect the Coulomb force in the derivations. The effect of the Coulomb force upon the electron will be described without derivation. Hence we substitute the plane wave functions ϕ_e and ϕ_ν as given by (5.11) into the field quantity (5.4a). We introduce the sum $\mathbf{P}=\mathbf{p}+\mathbf{q}$ of the momenta of the two light particles and expand the exponential $\exp(-i\mathbf{P}\cdot\mathbf{r}_n)$ into a series of angular momentum eigenfunctions. We use formula (A,3.5) of Appendix A, letting the direction of the vector $\mathbf{P}$ be denoted by Θ, Φ, and the direction of the position vector of the transforming nucleon by θ_n, φ_n. For all beta-decays known at present, the wave number $P=|\mathbf{P}|$ of the electron-neutrino pair is small enough so that $Pr_n \ll 1$ for all values of r_n less than the nuclear radius R. We can therefore replace the spherical Bessel function $j_l(Pr_n)$ by its approximate value for small Pr_n, which is given by (A,3.3). Hence we can expand the field quantity (5.4a) in the following way:[2]

[1] However, a case of a much too small ft value is reported by Perez-Mendez (50).

[2] We remind the reader of the double factorial notation

$$(2l+1)!! = 1 \times 3 \times 5 \times \cdots \times (2l+1)$$

$$F(\mathbf{r}_n) = \frac{4\pi}{V}\{u_e{}^*, \xi\, u_\nu{}^*\} \sum_{l=0}^{\infty} \sum_{m=-l}^{l} \frac{i^{-l}r_n{}^l}{(2l+1)!!}\, P^l\, Y_{lm}(\Theta,\Phi)\, Y_{lm}{}^*(\theta_n,\varphi_n)$$

$$(7.1a)$$

The operator ξ depends on the choice of interaction and is given in (5.6) and (5.7) for the non-relativistic theory and in (5.22) for the relativistic theory. The terms in the sum of (7.1a) have a simple interpretation: the term l,m corresponds to emission of the electron-neutrino pair into a state with orbital angular momentum l and z component of orbital angular momentum m. In the development of Section 5 only the first term $l=0$ of (7.1a) was taken into account.

We first apply the expansion (7.1a) to the singlet interaction (5.6) and write the corresponding matrix element (5.9) in the form

$$H'_{if} = \frac{4\pi G}{V}\{u_e{}^*, B\, u_\nu{}^*\} \sum_{l=0}^{\infty} \sum_{m=-l}^{l} \frac{i^{-l}}{(2l+1)!!}\, P^l\, Y_{lm}(\Theta,\Phi)\, \langle r^l Y_{lm}{}^* \rangle$$

$$(7.1b)$$

where the nuclear matrix elements are defined by

$$\langle r^l Y_{lm}{}^* \rangle \equiv \sum_{n=1}^{A} \int \Phi_f{}^*\, r_n{}^l\, Y_{lm}{}^*(\theta_n,\varphi_n)\, \tau_{n,-}\, \Phi_i\, d\tau \qquad (7.2)$$

We shall call the orbital angular momentum l of the electron-neutrino pair the "order" of the beta-decay.[1] The order l is of fundamental importance in the theory of forbidden beta-transitions. Because $Pr_n \ll 1$, the successive orders in the sum (7.1b) make successively smaller contributions. Hence it is sufficient to consider only one value of l, namely the smallest one consistent with the selection rules.[2]

The selection rules can be read off directly from the nuclear matrix element (7.2). Letting J_i, Π_i, J_f, and Π_f stand for the spin and parity of the initial and final states, respectively, the selection rules for non-relativistic transitions of order l with emission into the singlet state are

$$|J_i-J_f| \leq l \leq J_i+J_f \qquad \Pi_i = (-1)^l \Pi_f \qquad (7.3)$$

---

[1] It is perhaps useful to point out that the order l refers to the orbital angular momentum of the electron-neutrino pair, not to the orbital angular momentum of the electron by itself, or of the neutrino by itself.

[2] This statement is modified, however, in the relativistic treatment.

The minimum order l for which (7.3) is satisfied is either $|J_i - J_f|$ or $|J_i - J_f| + 1$, depending on the parities Π_i and Π_f. The Fermi selection rule (2.7) is the special case of (7.3) for $l = 0$.

In order to get the beta-decay probability (5.1), we need the sum of $|H'_{if}|^2$ over the spin directions of electron and neutrino and the average over the directions of the momentum vector $\mathbf{P}$.[1] The sum is given by (5.16); the average can be performed simply by using the orthogonality and normalization of the Y_{lm}. We introduce the notation

$$|\langle r^l Y_l \rangle|^2 \equiv \sum_{m=-l}^{l} |\langle r^l Y_{lm}{}^* \rangle|^2 \tag{7.4}$$

and we restrict ourselves to consideration of one order l. The average value of $|H'_{if}|^2$ then is

$$\langle |H'_{if}(l)|^2 \rangle_{\mathrm{av}} = 8\pi \left(\frac{G}{V}\right)^2 \frac{P^{2l}}{[(2l+1)!!]^2} |\langle r^l Y_l \rangle|^2 \tag{7.5}$$

The transition probability is obtained by combining (7.5) with (5.1) and (2.5).

We now proceed to the triplet interaction (5.10). Since the light particles are emitted into the triplet state, the total angular momentum J removed from the nucleus need no longer be equal to the order l of the transition. Using the same approximations as before, we now get

$$H'_{if} = \frac{4\pi G}{V} \sum_{\mu=-1}^{1} \sum_{l=0}^{\infty} \sum_{m=-l}^{l} \frac{(-)^{\mu} i^{-l}}{(2l+1)!!} P^l \{u_e{}^*, \sigma_\mu B\, u_\nu{}^*\}$$
$$\times\ Y_{lm}(\Theta, \Phi)\, \langle r^l Y_{lm}{}^* \sigma_{-\mu} \rangle \tag{7.6}$$

where the nuclear matrix elements are defined by

$$\langle r^l Y_{lm}{}^* \sigma_{-\mu} \rangle \equiv \sum_{n=1}^{A} \int \Phi_f{}^* r_n{}^l Y_{lm}{}^*(\theta_n, \varphi_n)\, \sigma_{n,-\mu}\, \tau_{n,-}\, \Phi_i\, d\tau \tag{7.7}$$

Each term in (7.6) corresponds to a transition in which the electron-neutrino pair carries away an orbital angular momentum l with z component m and a spin angular momentum of unity (triplet state) with z component μ. In order to obtain simple selection rules we introduce the total angular momentum J carried away by the electron-neutrino pair and its z component M. We define the nuclear matrix element:

---

[1] We average over the directions of $\mathbf{P}$, rather than summing, because the statistical factor $\rho(E_0)$, (2.5), already contains a summation over the possible directions of one of the emitted particles.

$$\langle r^l \mathcal{Y}_{Jl}^{M*} \rangle \equiv \sum_{m+\mu = M} C_{l,1}(J,M;m,\mu) \, (-1)^\mu \, \langle r^l Y_{lm}{}^* \sigma_{-\mu} \rangle \qquad (7.8)$$

where the Clebsch-Gordan coefficients C are as defined in Appendix A, Section 5. We define also an operator $\mathcal{Y}_{Jl}^M(\Theta,\Phi,\sigma)$ for the light particles:

$$\mathcal{Y}_{Jl}^M(\Theta,\Phi,\sigma) \equiv \sum_{m+\mu = M} C_{l,1}(J,M;m,\mu) \, Y_{lm}(\Theta,\Phi) \, \sigma_\mu \qquad (7.9)$$

Just as before, we can restrict ourselves to one value of l in the sum (7.6). We introduce (7.8) and (7.9) and use the orthogonality and normalization relations for the Clebsch-Gordan coefficients to get

$$H'_{if}(l) = \frac{4\pi G}{V} \frac{i^{-l}}{(2l+1)!!} P^l \sum_{J=|l-1|}^{l+1} \sum_{M=-J}^{J} \{u_e{}^*, \mathcal{Y}_{Jl}^M B \, u_\nu{}^*\} \langle r^l \mathcal{Y}_{Jl}^{M*} \rangle$$

$$(7\ 10)$$

Each term in (7.10) corresponds to a transition in which the electron-neutrino pair leaves with an orbital angular momentum l, a spin angular momentum 1, a total angular momentum J, and a z component of the total angular momentum equal to M. We again perform a sum over the spin directions of electron and neutrino, and an average over the directions of the vector $\mathbf{P}$. We introduce the notation

$$|\langle r^l \mathcal{Y}_{Jl} \rangle|^2 \equiv \sum_{M=-J}^{J} |\langle r^l \mathcal{Y}_{Jl}^{M*} \rangle|^2 \qquad (7.11)$$

to get

$$\langle |H'_{if}(l)|^2 \rangle_{\mathrm{av}} = 8\pi \left(\frac{G}{V}\right)^2 \frac{P^{2l}}{[(2l+1)!!]^2} \sum_{J=|l-1|}^{l+1} |\langle r^l \mathcal{Y}_{Jl} \rangle|^2 \qquad (7.12)$$

The transition probability is obtained by combining (7.12) with (5.1) and (2.5). Formulas (7.5) and (7.12) apply to transitions between two definite nuclear states. In practice, we must sum over the spin orientations in the final nuclear state.

The selection rules for non-relativistic transitions of order l with emission into the triplet spin state can be read off directly from the nuclear matrix elements (7.8):

$$|l-1| \leq J \leq l+1 \qquad |J_i - J_f| \leq J \leq J_i + J_f \qquad \Pi_i = (-1)^l \Pi_f$$

$$(7.13)$$

The Gamow-Teller selection rule (2.8) is a special case of (7.13), namely the case $l=0$. In that case the first condition (7.13) can be satisfied by only one value of J, namely $J = 1$, and the second and third conditions (7.13) become identical with (2.8).

We need to know the lowest order $l_{min} \equiv L$ consistent with the spin and parity of the initial and final nuclear states. These values are collected in Table 7.2 (page 738) for selection rules (7.3) and (7.13), as well as for selection rules (7.24) and (7.25) which apply to relativistic transitions.

Ordinary (non-relativistic) transitions of order l are classed among the "lth forbidden" transitions by Konopinski (41, 43).

▶ B. Non-relativistic Theory: Angular Correlation, Spectrum Shape, Lifetime

The most interesting factor in (7.5) and (7.12) is

$$P^{2l} = (\mathbf{p}+\mathbf{q})^{2l} = (p^2 + q^2 + 2pq \cos \theta_e)^l \qquad (7.14)$$

This factor contains an *angular correlation* between the directions of emission of electron and neutrino. For a given distribution of energy between the two particles, (7.14) is largest when the electron and neutrino are emitted parallel to each other. This is understandable physically: the angular momentum carried away from the nucleus is, classically speaking, the momentum P times the lever arm, which is of order R, the nuclear radius. Since $PR \ll \hbar$, the possibility of removal of an angular momentum $l\hbar$ with $l \geq 1$ is a quantum-mechanical barrier penetration effect. This accounts for the slowness of transitions of higher order. The penetration of the centrifugal barrier is easier the larger Pr_n. Hence the angular correlation favors large values of the recoil momentum P, and the nuclear matrix elements (7.2) and (7.8) get their main contributions from values of r_n close to the surface of the nucleus. Both effects become more pronounced with increasing l. The relativistic treatment modifies the angular correlation (7.14) by terms of order v/c of the electron.

The shape of the beta-spectrum in higher-order transitions is different from the shape of the zero-order transitions. The factor (7.14) is responsible for this difference and, as long as the Coulomb effects are neglected, we get the correction to the allowed shape (2.6) by integrating (7.14) over all angles $\theta_{e\nu}$ between electron and neutrino. This integral gives $(l+1)^{-1} S_l(p,q)$, where $S_l(p,q)$ is a shape correction factor by which (2.6) must be multiplied in order to give the shape of the spectrum of a transition of order l:

$$S_l(p,q) \equiv \frac{(p+q)^{2l+2} - (p-q)^{2l+2}}{4pq} \qquad (7.15)$$

Expression (7.15) is symmetric in p and q. This shape correction factor favors emissions in which one or the other of the two particles gets most of the available energy; S_l is smallest for $p=q$, where it assumes the value $(2p)^{2l}$. The first few factors S_l are

$$S_0 = 1 \qquad S_1 = 2(p^2+q^2) \qquad S_2 = 3p^4 + 10p^2q^2 + 3q^4$$

The effect of the Coulomb field will not be derived here, but only made plausible. Consider the $l=1$ transitions with the shape correction factor $S_1=2(p^2+q^2)$. The two terms of S_1 have the following interpretation: $2p^2$ corresponds to emission of the electron with orbital angular momentum $l_e=1$ and of the neutrino with orbital angular momentum $l_\nu=0$, the two angular momenta adding up to $l=1$ for the electron-neutrino pair; the other term, $2q^2$, corresponds to emission of the electron with orbital angular momentum $l_e=0$ and of the neutrino with orbital angular momentum $l_\nu=1$, the two angular momenta again adding up to $l=1$ for the electron-neutrino pair. Thus the term $2p^2$ in S_1 is multiplied by the Coulomb plus centrifugal barrier penetration factor for $l=1$ charged particles, which is

$$(1 + \eta^2) \frac{2\pi\eta}{1 - \exp(-2\pi\eta)}$$

The term $2q^2$ in S_1 is multiplied by the Coulomb penetration factor for $l=0$ charged particles, given by (2.10).

More generally, the term $p^{2k}q^{2l-2k}$ $(k=0,1,2,\cdots,l)$ in $S_l(p,q)$ corresponds to emission of the electron with orbital angular momentum $l_e=k$ and of the neutrino with orbital angular momentum $l_\nu=l-k$. This term is multiplied by the Coulomb plus centrifugal barrier penetration factor for charged particles of orbital angular momentum k, which is[1]

$$V_k = \left[1 + \left(\frac{\eta}{1}\right)^2\right]\left[1 + \left(\frac{\eta}{2}\right)^2\right] \cdots \left[1 + \left(\frac{\eta}{k}\right)^2\right] \frac{2\pi\eta}{1 - \exp(-2\pi\eta)} \tag{7.15a}$$

This procedure gives the following non-relativistic shape correction factor $Sc_l(p,q)$ in the presence of the Coulomb effect:

$$Sc_l(p,q) = \frac{1}{2} \sum_{k=0}^{l} \frac{(2l+2)!}{(2k+1)!\,(2l-2k+1)!} V_k(\eta)\, p^{2k}\, q^{2l-2k} \tag{7.16}$$

[1] V_k is closely related to the barrier penetration factor v_l, (VIII,2.49), evaluated for $l=k$ at $R=0$.

This expression reduces to (7.15) in the absence of the Coulomb effect, i.e., when η is set equal to 0. For $l=0$ transitions (7.16) reduces to the Coulomb correction factor $F(Z,E)$, (2.10). The factor

$$\left[1 + \left(\frac{\eta}{1}\right)^2\right] \cdots \left[1 + \left(\frac{\eta}{k}\right)^2\right]$$

in $V_k(\eta)$ is appreciably different from 1 only for very low-energy electrons. To a first approximation we may replace this factor by 1; this is equivalent to neglecting the effect of the centrifugal barrier upon the electron compared to the effect of the Coulomb barrier. In this approximation $V_k \cong F(Z,E)$ becomes independent of k, so that

$$Sc_l(p,q) \cong F(Z,E)\ S_l(p,q) \tag{7.16a}$$

We shall use this approximation presently. It should be emphasized that the correct relativistic theory leads in many cases to spectrum shapes entirely different from Sc_l (see Section 7D).

We proceed to give a very rough estimate of the comparative half-lives of beta-decays for higher-order transitions. The decay probability is given by the integral over the whole spectrum of the probability (5.1). This integral can be performed by inserting either the matrix element (7.5) or the matrix element (7.12), depending on the type of interaction. The following estimates will be so rough that it makes no difference which interaction is chosen. For the singlet interaction we get the result

$$\text{Decay probability} = \frac{2}{t_0} \frac{4\pi}{(l+1)\,[(2l+1)\,!!]^2}\ |\langle r^l Y_l\rangle|^2\, f_l(Z,E_0) \tag{7.17}$$

where $f_l(Z,E_0)$ is a quantity analogous to $f(Z,E_0)$, (4.2), and reduces to (4.2) when $l=0$.[1] $f_l(Z,E_0)$ is defined by

$$f_l(Z,E_0) \equiv \int_0^{p_0} Sc_l(p,q)\ p^2\ (E_0-E)^2\ dp \tag{7.18}$$

The value of this integral can be roughly estimated as follows: We use the approximation (7.16a) for Sc_l. Furthermore, since the main contribution comes from the middle of the spectrum, we replace $S_l(p,q)$ by its value for $p=q$, which is $(2p)^{2l} \cong (p_0)^{2l} = (E_0{}^2-1)^l$. The integral is then reduced to the one which defines the quantity f_- in (4.2), and we get the estimate

---

[1] All formulas here are written for negatron decay. In the case of positron emission, a correction must be applied for K capture. The ratio of K capture to positron emission in transitions of higher order is not the same as in transitions of order zero (Marshak 42, Good 46).

$$f_l(Z,E_0) \sim (E_0{}^2 - 1)^l f_-(Z,E_0) \qquad (7.18a)$$

We must still give an estimate of the square (7.4) of the nuclear matrix element. It must be of the order ρ^{2l}, where ρ is the nuclear radius R expressed in units of $(\hbar/mc)$. The integration over angles gives a factor of the order $(4\pi)^{-1}$ for each term of the sum in (7.4). Not all terms in (7.4) contribute, since some of them vanish as a result of the selection rule for m. The number of contributing terms varies from 1 to $2l+1$, depending on the initial and final spins and parities (Marshak 42); there are statistical factors similar to those encountered in the theory of multipole radiation (Chapter XII, Section 6). Since we are interested only in a very rough estimate, we shall insert a factor $l+1$ to get some average of this effect. Finally, the comparison of allowed and favored transitions with allowed but unfavored transitions indicates that the lack of overlap between the initial and final nuclear wave functions can be expressed by a factor of about 0.05. Thus our estimate is

$$|\langle r^l Y_l \rangle|^2 \sim 0.05 \, \frac{(l+1) \, \rho^{2l}}{4\pi} \qquad (7.18b)$$

It is hardly necessary to point out that this is only an order-of-magnitude result. Actual nuclear matrix elements may deviate from this estimate by very appreciable factors.

We are now in a position to estimate the comparative half-life (the ft value) of higher-order transitions. It should be noted that the f in ft is not f_l, but rather $f=f_0$, the value appropriate for zero-order transitions. Combining the preceding estimates, we get

$$ft \sim 20 \, \frac{[(2l+1)!!]^2}{\rho^{2l} \, (E_0{}^2 - 1)^l} \, t_0 \sim \frac{[(2l+1)!!]^2}{\rho^{2l} \, (E_0{}^2 - 1)^l} \times 10^5 \text{ sec} \qquad (7.19)$$

where t_0 was estimated from the decay of the neutron to be of the order of 5×10^3 sec.

Table 7.1 lists the experimental results regarding the shape and the lifetime of some beta-decays. The shape allows a determination of the order l of the decay. Of the decays listed in the table, all but I^{124} are β^- emitters, and the I^{124} lifetime has been corrected for K capture. It follows from (7.19) that the product

$$ft \, \frac{\rho^{2l} \, (E_0{}^2 - 1)^l}{[(2l+1)!!]^2}$$

should be of the order of $20t_0 \sim 10^5$ sec. This expectation is borne out surprisingly well by the data in Table 7.1   Also included in the table,

TABLE 7.1
BETA-DECAYS OF HIGHER ORDER

Element	Shape (7.16)	E_0	$\log (ft)$	$\log \dfrac{ft\, \rho^{2l}\, (E_0{}^2 - 1)^l}{[(2l+1)\,!!]^2}$
Cl^{38}	Sc_1	10.43	7.44	4.75
K^{42}	Sc_1	8.02	8.02	5.13
Kr^{85}	Sc_1	2.36	9.09	4.59
Rb^{86}	Sc_1	4.57	8.59	5.41
Rb^{88}	Sc_1	11.05	7.39	4.95
Sr^{89}	Sc_1	3.93	8.59	5.27
Sr^{90}	Sc_1	2.04	9.20	5.24
Y^{90}	Sc_1	5.40	7.98	4.94
Y^{91}	Sc_1	4.02	8.68	5.41
I^{124}	Sc_1	5.31	8.05	5.11
Sn^{125}	Sc_1	5.57	8.57	5.69
Cs^{137}	Sc_1	2.02	9.62	5.76
Tl^{204}	Sc_1	2.51	9.69	6.19
Be^{10}	Sc_2	2.10	13.65	4.03
Cl^{36}	$Sc_2?$	2.40	13.49	4.93
K^{40}	Sc_3	3.64	18.05	6.02
C^{14}	$Sc_0?$	1.30	9.05	9.05
Pm^{147}	$Sc_0?$	1.44	7.58	7.58
Np^{238}	$Sc_0?$	3.72	8.35	8.35

however, are a few examples of beta-decays which seem to follow the allowed shape spectrum but which have comparative lifetimes ft considerably larger than 10^5 sec. The non-relativistic theory cannot account for these decays, but we shall see that they can be understood on the basis of the relativistic theory. For references to the data in the table, see Feingold (51), Feenberg (50), Wu (50), Hayward (50) (Sn^{125}), Freedman (50) (Np^{238}), Zeldes (50) (Kr^{85}), and Bunker (51) (Rb^{88}). A more accurate evaluation of f_l for $l \neq 0$ has been made by Davidson (51).

We also mention that the shape of the beta-spectrum is not always a safe guide for the determination of l. The decay of Cl^{36}, for example, appears to follow the Sc_2 shape to a good approximation, but the relativistic theory combined with the measured initial and final spins shows that this cannot be accurately correct (Fulbright 51; Wu 49, 51; Longmire 49a; Townes 49a; Johnson 51). We shall return to the discussion of this decay later on.

▶ C. Relativistic Theory: Selection Rules, Matrix Elements

The relativistic treatment of the transitions of higher order is a generalization of the considerations of Section 5C. No longer will we replace in the matrix element the wave functions of the light particles by their value at the origin. Just as in the non-relativistic case, we obtain transitions of higher order corresponding to higher orbital angular momenta of the light particles. There are two types of transitions in each order l, the "ordinary" and the "relativistic" ones. They obey different selection rules, and only the ordinary ones are direct generalizations of the non-relativistic transitions. The "relativistic" transitions have nuclear matrix elements which are smaller then the ordinary ones by a factor v/c, v being the velocity of the nucleons.

There are certain features in the relativistic treatment of the higher-order transitions which do not appear in the simpler case of zero-order transitions: the shape of the spectrum contains terms of order v/c of the electron, even when the Coulomb effect is not considered; the modifications due to the Coulomb force are quite different from the relativistic Coulomb correction to the zero-order shape.

We use again expansion (7.1a) of the field quantity $F(\mathbf{r})$ which now represents one of the five relativistic field quantities (5.22). We get the decomposition of the matrix element into terms of different order l by substituting (7.1a) into expressions (5.26). For the simplest case, the scalar interaction, we obtain in this way a formula very much like the singlet interaction matrix element (7.1b) of the non-relativistic theory:

$$(H'_{if})_s = \frac{4\pi G}{V} \{u_e{}^*, \beta Q\, u_\nu{}^*\} \sum_{l=0}^{\infty} \sum_{m=-l}^{l} \frac{i^{-l}}{(2l+1)!!} P^l\, Y_{lm}(\Theta,\Phi)\, \langle \beta r^l Y_{lm}{}^* \rangle$$

(7.20)

where the nuclear matrix element $\langle \beta r^l Y_{lm}{}^* \rangle$ is defined in complete analogy to (7.2) and is indeed equal to (7.2) in the non-relativistic approximation for the nucleons.

Just as before, we can restrict ourselves to the lowest order l which is consistent with selection rules (7.3) for the nuclear transition. This lowest order is given in Table 7.2 on page 738. In order to get the beta-decay probability (5.1) we take the sum of $|H'_{if}|^2$ over the spin

directions of electron and neutrino, and the average over the directions of the momentum vector **P**. The sum is given by (5.37), and the
average can be performed exactly as it was performed in arriving at
(7.5). The average value of $|H'_{if}|^2$ in the scalar theory is therefore
[it may be considered the relativistic generalization of (7.5)]

$$\langle |(H'_{if}(l))_s|^2 \rangle_{av} = 4\pi \left(\frac{G}{V} \right)^2 \left(1 - \frac{v}{c} \cos \theta_{e\nu} \right) \frac{P^{2l}}{[(2l+1)!!]^2} |\langle \beta r^l Y_l \rangle|^2 \quad (7.21)$$

where the nuclear matrix element $|\langle \beta r^l Y_l \rangle|^2$ is defined in analogy to
(7.4) and is equal to (7.4) in the non-relativistic approximation for the
nucleons.

When the same method is applied to the axial vector interaction,
we get two types of terms: ordinary and relativistic transitions [com-
pare (5.31) for the case $l=0$]. Written explicitly, the matrix element
H'_{if} of the axial vector interaction for a beta-transition of order l is

$$(H'_{if}(l))_A = \frac{4\pi G}{V} \frac{i^{-l}}{(2l+1)!!} P^l \sum_{J=|l-1|}^{l+1} \sum_{M=-J}^{J} \{u_e{}^*, \mathcal{Y}_{Jl}^M Q\, u_\nu{}^*\} \langle r^l \mathcal{Y}_{Jl}^{M*} \rangle$$

$$+ \frac{4\pi G}{V} \frac{i^{-l}}{(2l+1)!!} P^l \sum_{m=-l}^{l} \{u_e{}^*, \rho_1 Q\, u_\nu{}^*\}\, Y_{lm}(\Theta,\Phi)\, \langle \rho_1 r^l Y_{lm}{}^* \rangle \quad (7.22)$$

The first term of (7.22) is analogous to the non-relativistic (7.10);
it represents an "ordinary" transition and obeys selection rule
(7.13). The second term is of relativistic origin and has no analogue
in the non-relativistic theory; its nuclear matrix element has the
following non-relativistic approximation:

$$\langle \rho_1 r^l Y_{lm}{}^* \rangle \cong -\frac{1}{2c} \left\langle (\mathbf{\sigma \cdot v})\, r^l Y_{lm}{}^* + r^l Y_{lm}{}^* (\mathbf{\sigma \cdot v}) \right\rangle \quad (7.23)$$

(7.23) is a generalization of (5.33). Thus (7.23) is of the order of v/c
of the nucleons compared to the "ordinary" matrix element (7.2);
furthermore the selection rule associated with this matrix element is
different from (7.3), namely

$$|J_i - J_f| \leq l \leq J_i + J_f \qquad \Pi_i = -(-1)^l \Pi_f \quad (7.24)$$

This selection rule is the generalization of (5.34) to transitions of higher
order.

The square of the matrix element $|(H'_{if}(l))_A|^2$ must not only be
averaged over the directions of **P** and summed over the spin orientations of electron and neutrino, but also summed over the orientations

M_f of the final nuclear spin. We shall not go through this calculation here. Suffice it to say that the ordinary transitions give a result proportional to $|\langle r^l \mathcal{y}_{Jl} \rangle|^2$, (7.11), and the formula differs from the non-relativistic (7.12) in only two respects: the factor 2π is replaced by π (see the footnote on page 704), and each term J in the sum (7.12) has associated with it an angular correlation factor of order v/c of the electron. Explicit expressions for ordinary transitions of order $l=1$ are given by Hamilton (47). The relativistic transitions make a contribution to $|(H'_{if}(l))_A|^2$ which is analogous to (7.21) except that the nuclear matrix element is now $|\langle \rho_1 r^l Y_l \rangle|^2$ and the angular correlation factor is now $[1 + (v/c) \cos \theta_{e\nu}]$. There are no interference terms between ordinary and relativistic transitions of the *same* order l, since the two obey different parity selection rules and therefore lead to different final states. However, there may in some cases be interference terms between relativistic transitions of order l and ordinary transitions of order $l+1$.[1] We shall ignore these terms.

The matrix elements and selection rules for transitions of order l with the five interactions (5.26) are tabulated in Table 7.3. This table is the generalization of Table 5.1 to transitions of higher order; it reduces to Table 5.1 in the special case $l=0$.

We can replace β by unity in the ordinary nuclear matrix elements of Table 7.3 since the nucleons are treated non-relativistically. We then obtain the same matrix elements as in the non-relativistic treatment, and hence also the same selection rules, (7.3) and (7.13), respectively.

The relativistic nuclear matrix element of the axial vector interaction and its selection rule have already been discussed in (7.23) and (7.24).

---

[1] This is completely analogous to the emission of electromagnetic multipole radiation: electric and magnetic radiation of the same order l lead to different final states, but there is competition between magnetic radiation of order l and electric radiation of order $l+1$. In a beta-decay between given initial and final states it often happens that a relativistic transition of order l and an ordinary transition of order $l+1$ give comparable contributions to the decay probability. Furthermore, the matrix elements add coherently, so that there is an interference term in the expression for the transition probability. These interference terms will be ignored here. They are listed by Konopinski (41, 43) and Greuling (42) for all the pure interactions; additional interference terms occur if the beta-decay interaction is a mixture of the five pure interactions (Critchfield 43). The interference terms listed in the literature depend on the relative phase of the two nuclear matrix elements in the complex plane. Considerations based on the invariance of the equations under time reversal (see Chapter X, Section 2) fix the relative phase to be either 0 or π, i.e., the matrix elements can be chosen to be real numbers. The argument (Fuchs 51, Longmire 51, Biedenharn 51a) is completely analogous to that of Lloyd (51) regarding the interference terms in electromagnetic multipole radiation between magnetic radiation of order l and electric radiation of order $l+1$.

TABLE 7.2

Minimum Order $l_{\min} \equiv L$ of Beta-Transitions Consistent with Various Selection Rules and Spins J_i, J_f and Parities Π_i, Π_f of Initial and Final Nuclear States

The upper entry in each case refers to $\Pi_i = +\Pi_f$, the lower to $\Pi_i = -\Pi_f$. The listed values of L are valid provided $L \leq J_i + J_f$ for selection rules (7.3) and (7.24), $|L-1| \leq J_i + J_f$ for selection rules (7.13) and (7.25); otherwise the respective transitions cannot take place at all.

	Selection Rule			
$|J_i - J_f|$	Ordinary		Relativistic	
	(7.3)	(7.13)	(7.24)	(7.25)
0	0	0	1	1
	1	1	0	0
1	2	0	1	1
	1	1	2	0
2	2	2	3	1
	3	1	2	2
3	4	2	3	3
	3	3	4	2
4	4	4	5	3
	5	3	4	4

TABLE 7.3

Nuclear Matrix Elements and Selection Rules for Transitions of Order l

The selection rule appropriate to each matrix element is indicated by its equation number.

Interaction	Nuclear Matrix Element and Selection Rule			
	Ordinary		Relativistic	
Scalar (5.26S)	$\langle \beta r^l Y_{lm}{}^* \rangle$	(7.3)	$\cdots\cdots$	
Vector (5.26V)	$\langle r^l Y_{lm}{}^* \rangle$	(7.3)	$\langle \rho_1 r^l \mathcal{Y}_{Jl}^{M*} \rangle$	(7.25)
Tensor (5.26T)	$\langle \beta r^l \mathcal{Y}_{Jl}^{M*} \rangle$	(7.13)	$\langle \rho_2 r^l \mathcal{Y}_{Jl}^{M*} \rangle$	(7.25)
Axial vector (5.26A)	$\langle r^l \mathcal{Y}_{Jl}^{M*} \rangle$	(7.13)	$\langle \rho_1 r^l Y_{lm}{}^* \rangle$	(7.24)
Pseudoscalar (5.26P)	$\cdots\cdots$		$\langle \rho_2 r^l Y_{lm}{}^* \rangle$	(7.24)

TABLE 7.4†

ESTIMATES OF ft FOR BETA-TRANSITIONS ASSOCIATED WITH SINGLE NUCLEAR
MATRIX ELEMENTS

Note: Estimate (7.34) is valid only under conditions (7.27) and (7.28).

A. *Transitions of Order $l \neq 0$*

Interaction	ft for Nuclear Matrix Element	
	Ordinary	Relativistic
Scalar (5.26S)	(7.34)	. . . .
Vector (5.26V)	(7.34)	$180\ A^{2/3} \times (7.34)$ $J = l, l-1$
		$180\ A^{2/3} \times (7.19)$ $J = l+1$
Tensor (5.26T)	(7.34) $J = l, l-1$	$180\ A^{2/3} \times (7.34)$ $J = l, l-1$
	(7.19) $J = l+1$	$180\ A^{2/3} \times (7.19)$ $J = l+1$
Axial vector (5.26A)	(7.34) $J = l, l-1$	$180\ A^{2/3} \times (7.34)$
	(7.19) $J = l+1$	
Pseudoscalar (5.26P)	. . . . .	$180\ A^{2/3} \times (7.34)$

B. *Transitions of Order $l = 0$, Unfavored*

Interaction	ft for Nuclear Matrix Element (sec)	
	Ordinary	Relativistic
Scalar (5.26S)	10^5	. . . .
Vector (5.26V)	10^5	$1.8 \times 10^7 \times A^{2/3}$
Tensor (5.26T)	10^5	$1.8 \times 10^7 \times A^{2/3}$
Axial vector (5.26A)	10^5	$1.8 \times 10^7 \times A^{2/3}$
Pseudoscalar (5.26P)	. .	$3 \times 10^9 \times A^{4/3}$

† We place Table 7.4 here in order to facilitate the joint use of Tables 7.2, 7.3, and 7.4 for analyzing beta-decays.   Table 7.4 is discussed in Section 7D.

The pseudoscalar nuclear matrix element is of similar structure and obeys the same selection rule.   The vector and tensor interaction lead to relativistic nuclear matrix elements which contain the spin operator $\mathbf{\sigma}$.   Hence their selection rule differs from (7.24) and is

$$|l-1| \leq J \leq l+1 \qquad |J_i - J_f| \leq J \leq J_i + J_f$$
$$\Pi_i = -(-1)^l \Pi_f \qquad\qquad (7.25)$$

The approximate expression for the relativistic nuclear matrix element of the vector interaction is a generalization of (5.35) and (5.36a):

$$\langle \rho_1 r^l \mathcal{Y}_{Jl}^{M*} \rangle \cong$$

$$- \frac{1}{2c} \sum_{m+\mu=M} C_{l,1}(J,M;m,\mu) \, (-1)^\mu \, \langle v_{-\mu} r^l Y_{lm}^* + r^l Y_{lm}^* v_{-\mu} \rangle \quad (7.26)$$

If ρ_1 is replaced by ρ_2 on the left side (i.e., if the interaction is the tensor interaction rather than the vector interaction), the vector $\mathbf{v}$ must be replaced by $\mathbf{d} \times \mathbf{v}$ on the right side. Both matrix elements are smaller than nuclear matrix elements of ordinary transitions of the same order l by a factor of the order of v_n/c, v_n being the average speed of the nucleons.

Unfortunately there is in use a considerable variety of notations for these matrix elements. Greuling (42) denotes by $|Q_n(\mathbf{r},\mathbf{r})|^2$ a quantity proportional to our $|\langle r^n Y_n \rangle|^2$, by $|Q_n(\beta \mathbf{r},\mathbf{r})|^2$ a quantity proportional to our $|\langle \beta r^n Y_n \rangle|^2$, etc. Konopinski (41, 43) uses $|\int 1|^2$, $|\int \mathbf{r}|^2$ for $|\langle 1 \rangle|^2$, $|\langle r Y_1 \rangle|^2$, etc., while Critchfield (42) uses [$\mathbf{r},\mathbf{r}$] for $|\langle r^2 Y_2 \rangle|^2$, [$\mathbf{r},\mathbf{r},\mathbf{r}$] for $|\langle r^3 Y_3 \rangle|^2$, etc. Different authors use different numerical coefficients in front of the matrix elements. The notation is particularly confusing for matrix elements connected with emission of the light particles into the triplet spin state. For example, the nuclear matrix element $|\langle r \mathcal{Y}_{01} \rangle|^2$ is often denoted by $|\int (\mathbf{d} \cdot \mathbf{\hat{r}})|^2$, $|\langle r \mathcal{Y}_{11} \rangle|^2$ is denoted by $|\int \mathbf{d} \times \mathbf{r}|^2$, and $|\langle r \mathcal{Y}_{21} \rangle|^2$ is expressed as a tensor, for which Konopinski (41, 43) uses the notation $|\int B_{ij}|^2$ and Critchfield (42) uses the notation [$\mathbf{d},\mathbf{r}$] (again with different numerical coefficients). The easiest way to establish the correspondence of the various notations is to examine the selection rules associated with each nuclear matrix element. Konopinski and Greuling do not distinguish in their notation between matrix elements involving ρ_1 and ρ_2, respectively.

▶ D. Relativistic Theory: Angular Correlation, Spectrum, Lifetime

In order to perform a complete analysis of a particular beta-decay it is necessary to know the spin and the parity of the initial as well as the final state. Once these quantities are known, Tables 7.2 and 7.3 can be used to find the matrix elements and the lowest value L of l which can be responsible for the transition. The results depend, of course, on the type of interaction. A detailed analysis of the observable properties, like spectrum shape, electron-neutrino angular correlation, and lifetime, should lead to a decision as to which type of interaction is realized in nature. Unfortunately, very little is known about the spin and parity of the initial states since they belong to radioactive nuclei. Very few spins of radioactive nuclei are measured. Recently the shell theory of low-lying nuclear states (see Chapter XIV) has been used with considerable success for the prediction of spins and parities (Shull 49, Nordheim 50). However, these predictions are not as yet reliable enough to serve as a basis for conclusions regarding the beta-decay interaction.

Usually there is, for a given interaction type, only one matrix element that contributes predominantly to the transition. However, in many cases there may be two or more whose contribution is of the same order of magnitude. This happens frequently if the lowest permissible $l = L$ of a relativistic matrix element is one unit less than the L of an ordinary one.[1]

We now discuss the angular correlations, spectrum shapes, and lifetimes expected with higher-order transitions on the basis of the relativistic theory. We restrict ourselves to a short statement of the results without attempting any detailed derivation. We refer for this purpose to the literature (Konopinski 41, 43; Critchfield 42, 43; Marshak 42, 46, 49; Greuling 42).

The *electron-neutrino angular correlation* was given in the non-relativistic theory by expression (7.14). The relativistic treatment introduces further terms of order v/c of the electron For example, the scalar interaction (7.21) contains the factor P^{2l}, which gives the non-relativistic correlation (7.14), but it also contains the factor

$$1 - (v/c) \cos \theta_{e\nu}$$

which represents the relativistic effect. In zero-order transitions the latter factor is the only one which occurs. In transitions of higher order, however, the former factor P^{2l} predominates and gives a correlation which favors emissions in the same direction. This result is obtained for all types of beta-decay interaction (Hamilton 47).

The angular correlation factors for ordinary transitions of order $l = 1$ are given by Hamilton (47) for the case in which Coulomb effects can be neglected. The Coulomb correction to these angular correlations has been worked out by Greuling (51). For experimental results see Sherwin (49, 51).

The *spectrum shape* in transitions of higher order is somewhat more complicated than in the non-relativistic discussion of Section 7A. The "large" and the "small" components of an electron (or neutrino) wave of given total angular momentum j_e (or j_ν) have different orbital angular momenta l_e (or l_ν), and this fact complicates considerably the spectrum of a transition of a given order.

We divide the transitions into two groups, A and B. *Group A contains the transitions in which the dominant nuclear matrix element involves* $\mathfrak{Y}_{Jl}^{M*}$ *with* $J = l+1$, *and group B contains all other transitions.* Physically speaking, group A contains all transitions in which the

---

[1] We mention again that ordinary transitions of order l and relativistic ones of order $l-1$ are classified together in the literature as "lth forbidden" transitions.

electron and the neutrino are emitted into the triplet state with the spin parallel to the orbital angular momentum. A transition for which $|J_i - J_f| = l+1$ always belong to group A, since all other matrix elements are excluded on the basis of the selection rules. In general, a transition belongs to group B if $|J_i - J_f| \neq l+1$.

The spectrum shape for transitions in group A is equal to the allowed spectrum shape (2.6) multiplied by the correction factor Sc_l which is defined by (7.16).[1] It should be noted, however, that the Coulomb effect is correctly accounted for only as long as

$$\frac{Ze^2}{\hbar c} = \frac{Z}{137} \ll 1 \tag{7.27}$$

If condition (7.27) is violated, the exact relativistic expressions must be used. Presumably all transitions listed in Table 7.1, except Cl^{36} and the last three, belong to group A, so that the l values were correctly determined from the spectrum shapes by using the factors Sc_l.

The spectrum of transitions in group B is appreciably more complicated. In particular the Coulomb effect on the spectrum shapes of group B transitions is completely different from the Coulomb effect on spectrum shapes of group A transitions. There is one limiting case in which the spectrum shapes of group B transitions can be expressed in a simple form; in addition to (7.27) the following condition must be satisfied:

$$\frac{Ze^2}{R} \gg 2cp \quad \text{or} \quad \frac{Z}{137\rho} \gg 2\frac{p}{mc} \tag{7.28}$$

where the second part of (7.28) gives the condition in the usual non-dimensional form. Condition (7.28) is usually satisfied for beta-transitions in intermediate nuclei, since the barrier energy Ze^2/R is of the order of 6 to 15 Mev, while $2cp$ is usually below 2 to 3 Mev over most of the spectrum. *For transitions of order $l \geq 1$ of group B the shape factor $Sc_l(p,q)$ is replaced by $C_l(p,q)$ when (7.27) and (7.28) are fulfilled*, where

---

[1] The result usually quoted in the literature for the spectrum shapes of group A transitions is (7.16a) rather than (7.16). However, the so-called "small Z" approximation used in the literature to simplify the exact relativistic expressions amounts to neglecting not only terms of order $Ze^2/\hbar c$ but also terms of order $(Ze^2/\hbar v)^2$, where v is the speed of the electron. If the latter terms are retained, the spectrum shape factors of group A transitions reduce to $Sc_l(p,q)$ as long as (7.27) is valid. For numerical calculations see Laslett (50).

$$C_l(p,q) \equiv \left(\frac{Ze^2}{2\hbar c\rho}\right)^2 \sum_{k=0}^{l-1} \frac{(2l+2)!}{(2l-2k-1)!\,(2k+2)!\,(2k+2)} \, V_k(\eta) \, p^{2k}q^{2l-2k-2}$$

$$(7.29)$$

and $V_k(\eta)$ is defined by (7.15a). In the same approximation which gave (7.16a) we get instead of (7.29) the approximate form

$$C_l(p,q) \cong F(Z,E) \, C_l'(p,q)$$

$$(7.29a)$$

$$C_l'(p,q) \equiv \left(\frac{Ze^2}{2\hbar c\rho}\right)^2 \sum_{k=0}^{l-1} \frac{(2l+2)!}{(2l-2k-1)!\,(2k+2)!\,(2k+2)} \, p^{2k}q^{2l-2k-2}$$

The "small Z" approximation often used in the literature gives (7.29a), whereas (7.29) is obtained from the correct relativistic expressions by neglecting terms of the order of $(Ze^2/\hbar c)^2$ but retaining terms of the order of $(Ze^2/\hbar v)^2$.

In approximation (7.29a) the first one of these shape factors, C_1', is a constant. Hence *first-order transitions of group B which satisfy conditions (7.27) and (7.28) simulate the allowed spectrum shape.* The last three entries in Table 7.1 are presumably of this type. The second shape factor, C_2', is

$$C_2'(p,q) = \left(\frac{Ze^2}{2\hbar c\rho}\right)^2 \left(q^2 + \frac{1}{4}\,p^2\right)$$

The factor $q^2 + \frac{1}{4}p^2$ favors emissions in which q is large, i.e., it favors the low-energy end of the electron spectrum. It should therefore be easy to distinguish this shape from $Sc_1(p,q)$. So far, however, the shape C_2 has never been observed. We shall return to this point later.

We shall need the value of $C_l'(p,q)$ for $p=q$ in connection with the lifetime estimates. We define the numbers D_l by

$$D_l \equiv \sum_{k=0}^{l-1} \frac{(2l+2)!}{(2)^{2l}\,(2l-2k-1)!\,(2k+2)!\,(2k+2)}$$

$$(7.30)$$

The first three are $D_1 = \frac{3}{2}$, $D_2 = \frac{75}{32}$, and $D_3 = \frac{2455}{96}$. Then we have

$$C_l'(p,p) = D_l \left(\frac{Ze^2}{\hbar c\rho}\right)^2 (2p)^{2l-2}$$

$$(7.31)$$

We now proceed to estimate *lifetimes of beta-decays*. We shall give an estimate of the decay probability associated with each nuclear matrix element listed in Table 7.3. The results of these estimates are tabulated in Table 7.4, page 739. Actually, any one beta-transition can go via several nuclear matrix elements, the most important competition being between ordinary transitions of order l and relativistic transitions of order $l-1$. Thus the lifetime estimates must be used as follows: for a given transition from an initial nuclear state with angular momentum J_i and parity Π_i to a given final state with angular momentum J_f and parity Π_f, and for an assumed beta-decay interaction we determine the nuclear matrix elements consistent with the selection rules by consulting Tables 7.2 and 7.3; we then use Table 7.4 to estimate the decay probability associated with each of these matrix elements; the actual decay probability is the sum of all these partial ones.[1] Usually the decay probability associated with some one of the nuclear matrix elements predominates over all the others. If this happens, the expected spectrum shape is the one associated with this dominant nuclear matrix element. On the other hand, if two or more nuclear matrix elements give comparable contributions to the total decay probability, the spectrum shape depends on the precise ratio of the two nuclear matrix elements, and there are additional interference terms which we have ignored in this simplified treatment.

As long as the transition is an ordinary one belonging to group A, the estimate of the lifetime is identical with the one made according to the non-relativistic theory, i.e., (7.19).

The lifetime estimate for ordinary transitions of group B differs from (7.19) because of the different spectrum shape. If conditions (7.27) and (7.28) are fulfilled, the only change consists of the replacement of f_l in (7.17) by g_l:

$$g_l(Z,E_0) \equiv \int_0^{p_0} C_l(p,q)\, p^2\, (E_0-E)^2\, dp \qquad (7.32)$$

As before, we estimate this quantity by using (7.29a) instead of (7.29) and replace $C_l{}'(p,q)$ by its value at the midpoint of the spectrum, at $p=q$. This gives

$$g_l(Z,E_0) \cong C_l(\tfrac{1}{2}p_0,\tfrac{1}{2}p_0)\, f_-(Z,E_0) \qquad (7.33)$$

where $C_l(\tfrac{1}{2}p_0,\tfrac{1}{2}p_0)$ is given by (7.31) and $f_-(Z,E_0)$ is as defined in Section 4. The estimate for the comparative half-life ft of an ordinary transition in group B then becomes

---

[1] Tables 7.2, 7.3, and 7.4 have been placed together on pages 738 and 739 because they must be used jointly.

$$ft \sim \frac{20\,[(2l+1)!!]^2\,t_0}{D_l\,(Z/137)^2\,\rho^{2l-2}\,(E_0{}^2-1)^{l-1}} \qquad \text{(for } l \geq 1) \qquad (7.34)$$

where, as before, we take the fundamental time constant t_0 to be approximately 5×10^3 sec. If condition (7.28) is satisfied, this value is smaller than (7.19) by an appreciable factor. Hence, *if transitions of group A and group B of the same order l are both permitted by the selection rules, the transitions of group B $(J=l, J=l-1)$ are expected to dominate over the transition of group A $(J=l+1)$*; i.e., in such a case the transitions of group B make a larger contribution to the total decay probability than the transition of group A.

The lifetime estimates for relativistic transitions differ from (7.19) and (7.34) only by constant factors. With the sole exception of the matrix element $\langle \rho_2 \rangle$ which occurs with the pseudoscalar interaction in $l=0$ transitions, *all relativistic matrix elements are smaller than the corresponding ordinary matrix elements by a factor v_n/c*, where v_n is the speed of nucleons inside the nucleus. This factor has to be squared in computing the transition probability. The exceptional matrix element $\langle \rho_2 \rangle$ is harder to estimate; we shall assume that it is of the order of $(v_n/c)^2$. The factor v_n/c must be estimated, and we shall use the same value as in the case of electromagnetic multipole radiation (see Chapter XII, Section 6):

$$\frac{v_n}{c} \sim \frac{\hbar}{McR} \qquad (7.35)$$

Thus the ft values of relativistic transitions are larger than those of corresponding ordinary transitions by the factor $(McR/\hbar)^2 = 180\,A^{2/3}$.[1]

All the estimates were made for β^- decay. For positron emitters the ft estimates refer to $f_+(Z,E_0)$ times the partial lifetimes for positron emission. To get estimates of actual lifetimes a correction must be made for the K capture process. In many cases the K/β^+ branching ratio is known experimentally.

Table 7.4 on page 739 lists the lifetime estimates for all nuclear matrix elements occurring in Table 7.3. It must be emphasized that, as these estimates are necessarily quite crude, the actual partial ft values may deviate appreciably from the values given in the table. Agreement between these estimates and experiment to within a factor 100 in either direction should be considered satisfactory. For $l=0$ ordinary transitions (the so-called allowed transitions) the estimates

---

[1] The factor v_n/c has been estimated in many different ways in the literature. No estimate, (7.35) included, can claim very much accuracy.

refer to unfavored transitions. Allowed and favored transitions have shorter lifetimes, with ft of the order of 5×10^3 sec.

In order to illustrate the use of Tables 7.2, 7.3, and 7.4, as well as to get some information about the actual nature of the beta-decay inter-action, we proceed to analyze in some detail the decay of Cl^{36}. The initial and final spins are known: $J_i = 2$ (Townes 49a, Johnson 51), $J_f = 0$ (an even-even nucleus). The spectrum shape is close to the Sc_2 shape. The ft value is 3×10^{13} sec (Wu 49, 51; Fulbright 51).

According to the arguments of Sections 4 and 6 the dominant beta-decay interaction must be of the Gamow-Teller type; hence we shall look primarily for a fit with the tensor or axial vector interaction, but we shall give the results for all interactions. Since the initial and final parities are not known, we have to explore the consequences of both possibilities: a parity change, or no change in parity. We start by assuming that the parity changes during the transition $(\Pi_i = -\Pi_f)$. According to Tables 7.2 and 7.3 the scalar interaction then gives no contribution at all. The vector interaction gives no ordinary con-tribution, but the relativistic transition with $J = l = 2$ is permitted. This transition is associated with the matrix element $|\langle \rho_1 r^2 \mathcal{Y}_{22} \rangle|^2$, fol-lows the C_2 shape, and according to Table 7.4 leads to an estimated ft value of 10^{15} sec. The spectrum shape disagrees with the observed one. The tensor interaction contributes an ordinary transition with $l = 1$, $J = 2$ and a relativistic transition with $l = J = 2$. The former dominates with an estimated (Table 7.4) ft value of 10^9 sec, giving the Sc_1 shape for the spectrum. Both the spectrum shape and the com-parative half-life are in gross disagreement with experiment. The axial vector interaction leads to the same disagreement. Finally the pseudoscalar interaction contributes through a transition of order $l = 2$, matrix element $|\langle \rho_2 r^2 Y_2 \rangle|^2$, with spectrum shape C_2 and estimated ft value 10^{15} sec. The spectrum shape disagrees with the observations. Thus we get no fit at all under the assumption of a parity change during the transition, the disagreement being particularly bad for the two most promising interactions (tensor and axial vector).

We therefore make the opposite assumption of no change in parity, $\Pi_i = +\Pi_f$. The scalar interaction gives a transition of order $l = 2$, matrix element $|\langle \beta r^2 Y_2 \rangle|^2$, with spectrum shape C_2 and estimated ft value 7×10^{11} sec. The vector interaction gives both an ordinary and a relativistic transition which have similar estimated partial half-lives: the ordinary transition is of order $l = 2$, matrix element $|\langle r^2 Y_2 \rangle|^2$; its associated spectrum shape is C_2, and ft estimate is 7×10^{11} sec; the relativistic transition is of order $l = 1$ with $J = 2$ (making it a group A transition), with matrix element $|\langle \rho_1 r \mathcal{Y}_{21} \rangle|^2$, associated spectrum shape Sc_1, and estimated $ft \cong 2 \times 10^{12}$ sec. Since two transitions contribute effectively, the spectrum shape is not determined uniquely but depends on the relative size of the two matrix elements, as well as on their relative sign (the latter enters through the interference term in the spectrum shape which we have ignored throughout this discussion) The tensor interaction is completely analogous to the vector interaction in this case, giving the same estimated ft values and the same uncertainty for the spectrum shape. The axial vector interaction, on the other hand, proceeds only via an ordinary transition with $l = J = 2$, matrix element $|\langle r^2 \mathcal{Y}_{22} \rangle|^2$; the spectrum shape associated with this matrix element is C_2, which disagrees with the measured shape; the associated ft value would be 7×10^{11} sec. Finally, the pseudoscalar interaction gives no contribution at all.

We can use this information to narrow down the choice of an acceptable beta-decay interaction. First of all, *if we make the simplest assumption that the data can be described by one and only one of the five interactions (5.26), the tensor interaction is the only choice consistent with all the data.* This is so because the Gamow-Teller selection rules observed for allowed transitions restrict us to either the tensor or the axial vector interaction, while the Cl^{36} decay rules out the axial vector interaction. A more detailed study of the spectrum shape of Cl^{36} indicates that the spectrum can be understood on the basis of the tensor interaction, reasonable values for the matrix elements being used [Wu 51, Fulbright 51; the contrary finding of Longmire et al. (49) was incorrect].

We now consider mixtures of interactions. The most promising combination from an a priori point of view is the Wigner-Critchfield interaction (5.27). This interaction seems to be excluded by the Cl^{36} data: if we assume $\Pi_i = -\Pi_f$, the axial vector part of this interaction would make the dominant contribution through the matrix element $|\langle r \mathcal{Y}_{21} \rangle|^2$, with the Sc_1 shape and an estimated ft value of 10^9 sec, both of which are in bad disagreement with experiment; on the other hand, if we assume $\Pi_i = +\Pi_f$, the axial vector and scalar interactions both contribute, with matrix elements $|\langle r^2 \mathcal{Y}_{22} \rangle|^2$ and $|\langle \beta r^2 Y_2 \rangle|^2$, respectively; both these matrix elements lead to the C_2 shape, in contradiction to experiment.

The discussion of other mixture interactions is simplified greatly if we accept the results of de Groot and Tolhoek (Groot 50). These authors show that a very reasonable symmetry postulate leads to the conclusion that the tensor interaction can be mixed only with the (polar) vector interaction. If we accept this argument, we need to consider mixtures of tensor and polar vector interactions only. The

Cl^{36} decay does not give any information here because the polar vector interaotion leads to the same results as the tensor interaction.[1]

Whereas the Cl^{36} decay is the only one allowing such a clean-cut analysis, there are several other decays which seem to favor the tensor interaction. The spectrum of RaE was analyzed by Konopinski and Uhlenbeck (Konopinski 41). They could obtain agreement between theory and experiment by using the tensor interaction but not by using the axial vector interaction. Two other decays of the same type are the decays of Tc^{99} (Wu 51a) and Cs^{137} (Langer 51). All three have comparative half-lives of the order of 10^{12} sec with a spectrum shape apparently of type Sc_1. They can be understood on the basis of the tensor (or tensor plus axial vector) interaction by assuming that the transitions occur with no change of parity and a spin change of two units. The situation is then very similar to the Cl^{36} decay which we have discussed in detail.[2] The axial vector interaction is excluded; it cannot give rise to transitions with the Sc_1 shape and such a high ft value since the only transitions in group A are ordinary transitions. An ordinary transition of group A with $l = 1$ and $J = 2$ leads to an estimated ft value of the order of 10^9 sec. Further evidence for the tensor interaction can be derived from the decay of Rb^{86} (Muether 50, Macklin 51, Stevenson 50) by a very detailed analysis of all the relevant data.

Nordheim (50, 51) and Mayer (51) have based their analysis on the spin and parity values taken from the shell model for the low-lying nuclear states. They find the expected differences between the ft values for ordinary $l = 1$ transitions in group A ($J = l+1 = 2$, shape Sc_1, ft of the order of 10^8 to 10^9 sec) and the ft values for similar transitions in group B ($J = l = 1$ and $J = l-1 = 0$, shape C_1, ft of the order of 10^6 to 5×10^7 sec) in agreement with the theoretical predictions. Furthermore there also appears to be evidence for an *approximate orbital angular momentum selection rule*. In the shell model the beta-decay of an odd-A nucleus[3] is attributed to the one "odd" particle, and this

---

[1] An argument of Moszkowski (51a) which is based on the lifetimes of some allowed and favored transitions (see Section 6) seems to exclude a large admixture of polar vector interaction. On the other hand, if the spin of the excited state of N^{14} in the O^{14} decay should turn out to be 0, such an admixture would become necessary to explain the data (see Section 4).

[2] The analysis is much less clear cut, however, because either the initial nuclear spin is unknown, or (in the case of Cs^{137}) the final spin J_f is not equal to zero, so that many matrix elements which are excluded for Cl^{36} on the basis of rigorous selection rules must be taken into account in these other transitions.

[3] The application of the shell model to nuclei with even mass numbers is more difficult, and the results are less certain (Nordheim 51).

particle is assigned to a "shell" with some orbital angular momentum l_i in the initial nucleus, l_f in the final nucleus. Nordheim presents evidence that transitions of order l for which

$$|l_i - l_f| \leq l \leq l_i + l_f \qquad (7.36)$$

have nuclear matrix elements of the order of magnitude of our estimates, whereas transitions which violate (7.36) are "l-forbidden" and have appreciably smaller nuclear matrix elements. A consideration of (7.2) or (7.7) supports this rule: if only one nucleon is involved in the beta-decay, and if its orbital angular momentum is a good quantum number, then indeed the matrix elements (7.2) or (7.7) vanish unless condition (7.36) is satisfied. Nordheim has established this approximate selection rule for the special case of transitions of order $l=0$; he shows that transitions of order $l=0$ with $|l_i-l_f|=2$ and $|J_i-J_f|=1$ are appreciably less rapid than $l=0$ transitions which obey (7.36), i.e., for which $l_i=l_f$.

SYMBOLS

A	Mass number of the nucleus (2.1)
A_1, A_0, A_{-1}	Spherical components of the vector $\mathbf{A}$ (5.8a)
A_x, A_y, A_z	Cartesian components of a vector $\mathbf{A}$ (5.8a)
$\mathbf{A}(\mathbf{r}_n)$	Vector potential of the emitted light quantum at the position of the nth particle, in electromagnetic radiation (5.2)
B	A matrix occurring in beta-decay theory; non-relativistic theory (5.8); relativistic theory (5.20)
B_μ	Spherical components of the vector $\mathbf{B}$ [$\mu=1,0,-1$] (5.8b)
$\mathbf{B}$	A vector (5.8b)
c	Speed of light (Section 1)
C	A constant appearing in the expression for the beta-spectrum and for the beta-decay probability (2.6), (2.13), (3.2), (4.1), (4.6)
$C_l(p,q)$	Shape correction factor for group B transitions with Coulomb effect (7.29)
$C_l'(p,q)$	A polynomial in p and q appearing in an approximate expression for the shape correction factor C_l (7.29a)
$C_{LS}(J,M;m_L,m_S)$	Clebsch-Gordan coefficient; see Appendix A, Section 5 (6.2)

C_s	Value of the constant C in (2.13) for the singlet interaction (non-relativistic theory) (5.18)
C_S	Value of the constant C in (2.13) for the scalar interaction (relativistic theory) (Section 5C)
C_t	Value of the constant C in (2.13) for the triplet interaction (non-relativistic theory) (5.18)
dV_e	Volume element for the electron (2.4)
dV_v	Volume element for the neutrino (2.4)
$d\tau$	Element of configuration space (5.2), (5.3)
$d\Omega_e$	Element of solid angle for the direction of the electron (2.4)
$d\Omega_\nu$	Element of solid angle for the direction of the neutrino (2.4)
D_l	A number (7.30)
e	An electron (positive or negative) (Section 2)
E	Average energy of an electron confined within a volume of nuclear dimensions (Section 1)
$E = E_e$	Energy of the electron, usually expressed in units mc^2 (2.6)
E_0	Total energy available for the beta-decay (Section 1)
E_B	Atomic binding energy of the orbital electron before capture (3.1)
E_e	Total energy (including rest energy) of the emitted electron, usually expressed in units mc^2 (2.3)
$E_{\max}$	Maximum electron energy in the beta-spectrum (this is equal to E_0 if the neutrino has no rest mass) (Section 1)
E_μ	Energy of a hypothetical second neutrino (Section 2)
E_ν	Energy of the emitted neutrino (2.3)
$\left\langle \dfrac{E_{\mathrm{rec}}}{E_{\mathrm{elec}}} \right\rangle_{\max}$	Maximum value of the ratio of the energy of the recoil nucleus to the energy of the emitted electron (2.1)
$f_+(Z,E_0)$	A function related to the half-ife of a positron emitter with maximum energy E_0 (4.4)
$f_-(Z,E_0)$	A function related to the half-life of a negatron emitter with maximum energy E_0 (4.1), (4.2)
f_K	A function related to the partial half-life associated with the K capture process (3.2), (3.4), (3.5)
$f_l(Z,E_0)$	A function defined by (7.18) (7.18)

ft	Comparative half-life of a beta-decay (4.5), (4.6)
$\mathbf{F}$	Vector field quantity for the triplet interaction (non-relativistic theory) (5.7a)
$F_{A\mu}$	μth component ($\mu=0,1,2,3$) of the axial vector field quantity for the axial vector interaction (relativistic theory) (5.22A)
F_m	Spherical component ($m=1,0,-1$) of the vector field quantity $\mathbf{F}$ (5.7)
F_P	Pseudoscalar field quantity for the pseudoscalar interaction (relativistic theory) (5.22P)
$F(\mathbf{r}_n)$	"Field" quantity for the beta-decay, evaluated at the position $\mathbf{r}_n$ of the nth nucleon (5.3)
F_s	Field quantity F for the singlet interaction (non-relativistic theory) (5.6)
F_S	Scalar field quantity for the scalar interaction (relativistic theory) (5.19), (5.22S)
$F_{T\mu\nu}$	$\mu\nu$th component ($\mu,\nu=0,1,2,3$) of the anti-symmetric tensor field quantity for the tensor interaction (relativistic theory) (5.22T)
$F_{V\mu}$	μth component ($\mu=0,1,2,3$) of the four-vector field quantity for the vector interaction (relativistic theory) (5.22V)
$F(Z,E)$	Coulomb correction factor for transitions of order zero (2.10), (2.11), (2.12)
$g_l(Z,E_0)$	A function defined by (7.32) (7.32)
G	Interaction constant for the beta-decay interaction (Section 5B)
G_A	Interaction constant for the axial vector interaction (5.26A)
G_P	Interaction constant for the pseudoscalar interaction (5.26P)
G_s	Interaction constant for the singlet interaction (5.9)
G_S	Interaction constant for the scalar interaction (5.26S)
G_t	Interaction constant for the triplet interaction (5.10)
G_T	Interaction constant for the tensor interaction (5.26T)
G_V	Interaction constant for the vector interaction (5.26V)

H'_{if}	Matrix element of the interaction responsible for the transition (5.2), (5.3)
$(H'_{if})_A$	Matrix element of the axial vector interaction (5.26A)
$H'_{if}(l)$	The part of the matrix element H'_{if} corresponding to transitions of order l (7.5)
$(H'_{if}(l))_A$	The part of the matrix element of the axial vector interaction corresponding to transitions of order l (7.22)
$(H'_{if}(l))_S$	The part of the matrix element of the scalar interaction corresponding to transitions of order l (7.21)
$(H'_{if})_P$	Matrix element of the pseudoscalar interaction (5.26P)
$(H'_{if})_S$	Matrix element of the scalar interaction (5.26S)
$(H'_{if})_T$	Matrix element of the tensor interaction (5.26T)
$(H'_{if})_V$	Matrix element of the vector interaction (5.26V)
$(H'_{if})_{WC}$	Matrix element of the Wigner-Critchfield interaction (5.27)
I	Total angular momentum of the nucleus (nuclear spin) in its ground state (Section 4)
I_f	Total angular momentum (nuclear spin) of the final (daughter) nucleus (Section 4)
I_i	Total angular momentum (nuclear spin) of the initial (parent) nucleus (Section 4)
j_e	Total angular momentum of the emitted electron (Section 7D)
j_ν	Total angular momentum of the emitted neutrino (Section 7D)
$\mathbf{j}_n$	Current operator for the nth particle (5.2)
J	Total angular momentum of the outside nucleon in its initial state (6.2)
J	Total angular momentum carried away by the electron-neutrino pair (Section 7A)
J'	Total angular momentum of the outside nucleon in its final state (6.4)
J_f	Total angular momentum (nuclear spin) of the final (daughter) nucleus (Section 7A)
J_i	Total angular momentum (nuclear spin) of the initial (parent) nucleus (Section 7A)
k	An integer (Section 6)

k	An integer equal to the orbital angular momentum of the emitted electron (7.15a)
k_e	Wave number of the emitted electron (Section 2)
K_n	Operator acting on the coordinates of the nth nucleon in the nuclear wave function (5.3)
K'_n	Isotopic-spin-independent part of K_n (5.5)
$K'_{nA,i}, K'_{nA,0}$	Nucleon operators K'_n for the axial vector interaction (5.25A)
K'_{nP}	Nucleon operator K'_n for the pseudoscalar interaction (5.25P)
K'_{nS}	Nucleon operator K'_n for the scalar interaction (5.25S)
$K'_{nT,ij}, K'_{nT,i0}$	Nucleon operators K'_n for the tensor interaction (5.25T)
$K'_{nV,i}, K'_{nV,0}$	Nucleon operators K'_n for the vector interaction (5.25V)
l	Orbital angular momentum carried away by the electron-neutrino pair, equal to the *order* of the beta-transition (Sections 5B and 7A)
l_e	Orbital angular momentum of the emitted electron (Section 2)
l_f	Orbital angular momentum of the outside nucleon in the final (daughter) nucleus (7.36)
l_i	Orbital angular momentum of the outside nucleon in the initial (parent) nucleus (7.36)
$l_{\min}$	Lowest value of the order l consistent with the selection rules for the transition (Section 7B)
l_ν	Orbital angular momentum of the emitted neutrino (Section 2)
L	Orbital angular momentum quantum number of the nucleus as a whole, or of the outside nucleon (Section 6)
L	$\equiv l_{\min}$ (Section 7B)
$\mathbf{L}$	Orbital angular momentum vector operator for the nucleus as a whole, or for the outside nucleon (Section 6)
m	Mass of the electron (2.1)
m	Quantum number for the z component of the orbital angular momentum carried away by the electron-neutrino pair (7.1a)
m_ν	Mass of the neutrino (Section 1)

M	Mass of a nucleon (2.1)
M	z component of the total angular momentum of the outside nucleon in the initial state (6.2)
M	z component of the total angular momentum carried away by the electron-neutrino pair (7.10)
M'	z component of the total angular momentum of the outside nucleon in the final state (6.4)
n	Running index for the nucleons in the nucleus, $n = 1, 2, \cdots, A$ (5.2), (5.3)
N	Number of neutrons in the nucleus (Section 4)
p	Momentum of the emitted electron $[= p_e]$ (2.6)
p_0	Maximum value of the electron momentum in the beta-spectrum (4.2)
p_e	$\equiv |\mathbf{p}_e|$; momentum of the emitted electron (2.4)
p_m	Spherical component of the vector $\mathbf{p}$ $(m = 1, 0, -1)$, formed according to rule (5.8a) (5.38)
$p_{\max}$	Maximum momentum of an electron confined within a volume of nuclear dimensions (Section 1)
p_μ	Momentum of a hypothetical second neutrino (Section 2)
p_ν	$\equiv |\mathbf{p}_\nu|$; momentum of the emitted neutrino (2.4)
$\mathbf{p}$	Vector momentum of the emitted electron $[= \mathbf{p}_e]$ (5.11)
$\mathbf{p}_e$	Vector momentum of the emitted electron (2.2)
$\mathbf{p}_\nu$	Vector momentum of the emitted neutrino (2.2)
P	$\equiv |\mathbf{P}|$; momentum of the recoil nucleus (Section 2)
P	$\equiv |\mathbf{P}|$; momentum carried by the electron-neutrino pair (7.1a)
P, P', P''	Partition quantum numbers; see Chapter VI, Section 3 (Section 6)
$P_{\max}$	Maximum value of the momentum of the recoil nucleus (Section 2)
$P(p)\, dp$	Number of electrons emitted with momenta between p and $p + dp$ (the beta-spectrum) (2.6), (2.13)
$\mathbf{P}$	Vector momentum of the recoil nucleus (2.2)
$\mathbf{P}$	Combined momentum of the electron-neutrino pair $[= \mathbf{p} + \mathbf{q}]$ (Section 7)
q	Energy of the neutrino in units mc^2 $[= |\mathbf{q}|]$ (Section 5C)

q_m	Spherical component of the vector $\mathbf{q}$ $(m=1,0,-1)$, formed according to rule (5.8a) (5.38)
$\mathbf{q}$	Vector momentum of the emitted neutrino, in units mc $[=\mathbf{p}_\nu]$ (5.11)
Q	A 4-by-4 matrix (5.21)
r_e	Distance of the electron from the center of the nucleus (Section 2)
$|\langle r^l Y_l\rangle|^2$	A quantity defined by (7.4) (7.4)
$\langle r^l Y_{lm}{}^*\rangle$	A nuclear matrix element (7.2)
$\langle r^l Y_{lm}{}^*\sigma_{-\mu}\rangle$	A nuclear matrix element (7.7)
$\langle r^l \mathcal{Y}_{Jl}^{M*}\rangle$	A nuclear matrix element (7.8)
$|\langle r^l \mathcal{Y}_{Jl}\rangle|^2$	A quantity defined by (7.11) (7.11)
r_n	Distance of the nth nucleon from the center of the nucleus (7.1a)
$\mathbf{r}_n$	Vector position of the nth nucleon (5.2), (5.3)
R	Nuclear radius (Section 1)
s	An expression appearing in the formula for the relativistic Coulomb correction to transitions of order 0 (2.11)
S	Spin angular momentum quantum number of the nucleus as a whole, or of the outside nucleon (Section 6)
$\mathbf{S}$	Spin angular momentum vector operator for the nucleus as a whole, or for the outside nucleon (Section 6)
$S_l(p,q)$	Spectrum shape correction factor of the non-relativistic theory in the absence of a Coulomb effect (7.15)
$Sc_l(p,q)$	Spectrum shape correction factor of the non-relativistic theory in the presence of the Coulomb effect; this shape correction factor also applies to group A transitions in the relativistic theory (7.16), (7.16a)
t	Half-life of a beta-transition, measured in seconds (4.5)
t_0	Fundamental time constant for the beta-decay, estimated to be of the order of 5×10^3 sec (5.17)
t_+	Partial half-life associated with positron emission (4.4)
t_-	Half-life for negatron decay (4.1)
T	Transition probability per unit time (5.1)

t_K Partial half-life associated with K capture   (3.2)

u_e Spin function for the electron (independent of $\mathbf{r}$) (5.11)

$u_e{}^{(k)}$ Spin function u_e for an electron with spin direction k; non-relativistic theory   (Section 5B); relativistic theory [see Schiff (49), p. 315]   (5.37)

$u_{Lm_L}(x,y,z)$ Wave function of the outside nucleon with an angle-dependence characteristic of a spherical harmonic $Y_{Lm_L}(\theta,\varphi)$ (6.2)

u_ν Spin function for the neutrino (independent of $\mathbf{r}$) (5.11)

$u_\nu{}^{(k')}$ Spin function for a neutrino with spin direction k'; non-relativistic theory   (Section 5B); relativistic theory [see Schiff (49), p. 315]   (5.37)

v Speed of the emitted electron   (Section 2) average speed of nucleons   (Section 7)

v_n Average speed of nucleons inside the nucleus (Section 5C)

$v_{n,\mu}$ μ-compoment of velocity operator of nth nuclear particle   (7.26)

v_ν Time-reversed spin function of the neutrino $[=Bu_\nu{}^*]$ (Section 5C)

$\mathbf{v}$ Non-relativistic operator for the velocity of the nucleons $[=-(i\hbar/M)\nabla]$ (5.33)

$\left\langle\dfrac{\mathbf{v}}{c}\right\rangle$ A nuclear matrix element   (5.35)

V Volume of an imaginary box enclosing the system (2.5)

V_k Coulomb penetration factor for charged particles with orbital angular momentum k (7.15a)

V_N Volume of the nucleus   (2.9)

X Initial (parent) nucleus in beta-decay   (Section 2)

Y Final (daughter) nucleus in beta-decay   (Section 2)

$Y_{lm}(\theta,\varphi)$ Spherical harmonic; see Appendix A, Section 2 (7.1a)

$\mathcal{Y}_{jl}^M(\Theta,\Phi,\sigma)$ Operator for the light particles   (7.9)

Z Atomic number (charge) of the nucleus; for positron and negatron decay Z is the charge of the final (daughter) nucleus; for orbital electron capture Z

	is the charge of the initial (parent) nucleus (Sections 2 and 3)
$\langle 1 \rangle$	A nuclear matrix element (5.14)
$\alpha_{n,i}$	ith Cartesian component of the Dirac matrix $\boldsymbol{\alpha}$ for the nth nucleon (5.25V)
$\alpha_x, \alpha_y, \alpha_z$	Dirac matrices; see Bethe (33) or Schiff (49) for the explicit forms of the Dirac matrices (5.23)
$\langle \alpha \rangle$	A nuclear matrix element (5.35)
β	Dirac matrix; see Bethe (33) or Schiff (49) for the explicit forms of the Dirac matrices (5.21)
β^+	A positron (Section 1)
β^-	A negatron (Section 1)
β_n	Dirac matrix β for the nth nucleon (5.25S)
$\langle \beta \rangle$	A nuclear matrix element (5.29)
$\langle \beta \boldsymbol{\sigma} \rangle$	A nuclear matrix element, defined analogously to $\langle \boldsymbol{\sigma} \rangle$ and equal to $\langle \boldsymbol{\sigma} \rangle$ in the non-relativistic approximation for the nucleons (Section 5C)
$\delta_{mm'}$	Kronecker delta (5.16b)
ΔJ	Change in the total angular momentum (nuclear spin) of the nucleus during the beta-transition (Section 1)
η	$\equiv Ze^2/\hbar v$ for negatron emission (2.10)
η	$\equiv -Ze^2/\hbar v$ for positron emission (2.10)
$\theta_{e\nu}$	Angle subtended by the directions of emission of electron and neutrino (5.37)
θ_n	Polar angle (colatitude) of the position vector $\mathbf{r}_n$ (7.1a)
Θ	Polar angle (colatitude) of the vector $\mathbf{P}$ (7.1a)
λ	A number between $+1$ and -1 appearing in the expressions for the electron-neutrino angular correlation function (Section 5C)
Λ_e^+	Operator selecting positive-energy electron wave functions (Section 5C)
Λ_ν^+	Operator selecting positive-energy neutrino wave functions (Section 5C)
μ	A hypothetical second neutrino (Section 2)
ν	A neutrino (Section 2)
ξ	Matrix with (constant) matrix elements ξ_{ij} (5.4a)
ξ_{ij}	A linear operator on ϕ_{ei} and $\phi_{\nu j}$ (5.4)

Π_f	Parity of the final (daughter) nucleus (5.34)
Π_i	Parity of the initial (parent) nucleus (5.34)
ρ	Nuclear radius measured in units $\hbar/mc$ (2.11)
ρ_1	Dirac matrix connecting large and small components (5.23)
ρ_2	Dirac matrix connecting large and small components (5.23)
$\rho(E_0)$	Density of final states per unit range of the total energy (2.5)
$\rho(E_\nu)$	Statistical factor (density of final states) for orbital electron capture (3.1)
$\rho_{n,1}$	Dirac matrix ρ_1 for the nth nucleon (5.25V)
$\rho_{n,2}$	Dirac matrix ρ_2 for the nth nucleon (5.25T)
$\langle \rho_1 \rangle$	A nuclear matrix element (5.32)
$\langle \rho_1 r^l Y_{lm}{}^* \rangle$	A nuclear matrix element (7.23)
$\langle \rho_1 r^l \mathcal{Y}_{Jl}^{M*} \rangle$	A nuclear matrix element (7.26)
$\langle \rho_1 \mathfrak{d} \rangle$	A nuclear matrix element (5.35)
$\langle \rho_2 \rangle$	A nuclear matrix element, defined analogously to (5.32) (Section 5C)
$\langle \rho_2 \mathfrak{d} \rangle$	A nuclear matrix element (5.36a)
σ_m	Spherical component ($m = 1, 0, -1$) of the vector $\mathfrak{d}$ (5.7), (5.8)
$\sigma_{n,i}$	Cartesian component ($i = 1, 2, 3$) of the Dirac spin matrix $\mathfrak{d}_n$ of the nth nucleon (5.25V)
$\sigma_{n,m}$	Spherical component ($m = 1, 0, -1$) of the Dirac spin matrix $\mathfrak{d}_n$ of the nth nucleon, formed from the Cartesian components of $\mathfrak{d}_n$ according to rule (5.8a) (5.10)
$\sigma_x, \sigma_y, \sigma_z$	Cartesian components of the Pauli spin vector $\mathfrak{d}$; see Appendix A, Section 4 (5.8)
$\sigma_x, \sigma_y, \sigma_z$	Dirac spin matrices (5.23)
$\tilde{\sigma}_x$	Transpose of the matrix σ_x (Section 5B)
$\mathfrak{d}$	Pauli spin vector for the light particles (5.7a)
$\mathfrak{d}_n$	Pauli spin vector of the nth nucleon (5.10)
$\langle \mathfrak{d} \rangle$	A nuclear matrix element (5.15)
$|\langle \mathfrak{d} \rangle|^2$	Absolute square of the vector nuclear matrix element $\langle \mathfrak{d} \rangle$ (5.18)
$\left\langle \dfrac{\mathfrak{d} \cdot \mathbf{v}}{c} \right\rangle$	A nuclear matrix element (5.33)

$\left\langle \dfrac{\boldsymbol{\delta} \times \mathbf{v}}{c} \right\rangle$	A nuclear matrix element (5.36a)
τ_+	Isotopic spin operator changing a proton into a neutron; see Chapter III, Section 5 (5.5)
τ_-	Isotopic spin operator changing a neutron into a proton; see Chapter III, Section 5 (5.5)
$\tau_{n,+}$	Isotopic spin operator τ_+ for the nth nucleon $\cdot$(5.5)
$\tau_{n,-}$	Isotopic spin operator τ_- for the nth nucleon (5.5)
φ_n	Polar angle (longitude) of the position vector $\mathbf{r}_n$ (7.1a)
ϕ	= arc tan (s/η) (2.12)
ϕ_{e1}	First spinor component of the wave function of the emitted electron (5.6)
ϕ_{e2}	Second spinor component of the wave function of the emitted electron (5.6)
$\phi_e(\mathbf{r}_e)$	Wave function of the emitted electron (Section 5A)
$\phi_{ei}(\mathbf{r}_n)$	ith spinor component of the wave function $\phi_e(\mathbf{r}_e)$ of the emitted electron, evaluated at the position of the transforming nucleon, $\mathbf{r}_e = \mathbf{r}_n$ (5.4)
$\phi_{\nu 1}$	First spinor component of the wave function of the emitted neutrino (5.6)
$\phi_{\nu 2}$	Second spinor component of the wave function of the emitted neutrino (5.6)
$\phi_\nu(\mathbf{r}_\nu)$	Wave function of the emitted neutrino (Section 5A)
$\phi_{\nu j}(\mathbf{r}_n)$	jth spinor component of the wave function $\phi_\nu(\mathbf{r}_\nu)$ of the emitted neutrino, evaluated at the position of the transforming nucleon, $\mathbf{r}_\nu = \mathbf{r}_n$ (5.4)
Φ	Polar angle (longitude) of the vector $\mathbf{P}$ (7.1a)
Φ_f	Wave function of the final (daughter) nucleus (5.2), (5.3)
Φ_i	Wave function of the initial (parent) nucleus (5.2), (5.3)
Φ_{JM}	Wave function of the outside nucleon in its initial state (6.2)
$\Phi_{J'M'}$	Wave function of the outside nucleon in its final state (6.4)

χ_{sm_S}	Spin function for the outside nucleon with spin $S = \frac{1}{2}$ and z component of the spin equal to m_S (6.2)
ψ_e	Wave function of the emitted electron (Section 2)
ψ_ν	Wave function of the emitted neutrino (Section 2)
ω	Circular frequency $(=2\pi\nu)$ of·a light quantum (Section 1)

CHAPTER XIV

Nuclear Shell Structure

1. EVIDENCE FOR THE EXISTENCE OF "MAGIC NUMBERS"

As early as 1917 Harkins (17) pointed out that nuclei with even numbers of protons or neutrons are more stable than those with odd numbers. Elsasser (33, 34) found that special numbers of protons or neutrons form particularly stable configurations. We shall list here a series of facts which indicate that we obtain especially stable nuclei when either the number of protons Z or the number of neutrons $N = A - Z$ is equal to one of the following numbers (Mayer 48):

$$2, \quad 8, \quad 14, \quad 20, \quad 28, \quad 50, \quad 82, \quad 126 \qquad (1.1)$$

These values are commonly referred to as magic numbers.

The nuclei for which Z and N are 2, 8, or 14 are well known to be more stable than their neighbors: they are He^4, O^{16}, and Si^{28}. Evidence for the numbers 20, 28, 50, and 82 can be found by counting the numbers S_Z or S_N of stable nuclei with a given value of Z (isotopes) or N (isotones). Table 1.1 lists these numbers S_Z and S_N, and it is seen that they are somewhat larger than the average when Z or N reaches a magic value (1.1). The numbers S_N and S_Z give a rough measure of the stability connected with the value Z or N. A large S_Z, for example, can be interpreted as an indication that the configuration of Z protons increases the binding energy so that we find stable nuclei even if the number N of neutrons deviates appreciably from the optimum value.

It may be noted that Table 1.1 also bears out Harkins' rule that even values of Z or N lead to greater stability than odd values.

The evidence for the neutron magic numbers is much better than for the proton numbers. In fact, there is no evidence in Table 1.1 of any increased stability of nuclei with $Z = 82$.

Impressive evidence for the greater stability of nuclei with magic proton or neutron numbers arises from the abundance in nature of the various nuclear species. High abundance usually goes with high binding energy. In all cases where the binding energies are known,

761

a definite correlation was found between the binding energies and the abundances. It turns out that nuclei with a magic number of nucleons are especially abundant (Mayer 48).

TABLE 1.1

NUMBERS S_N AND S_Z OF STABLE NUCLEI FOR DIFFERENT VALUES OF N AND Z.
(ALPHA-UNSTABLE NUCLEI ARE COUNTED AS STABLE)

C	16	17	18	19	20	21	22	23	24
S_N for $N=C$	3	1	3	0	5	1	3	1	3
S_Z for $Z=C$	4	2	3	3	6	1	5	1	4

C	25	26	27	28	29	30	31	32
S_N for $N=C$	1	3	1	5	1	4	1	3
S_Z for $Z=C$	1	4	1	5	2	5	2	5

C	47	48	49	50	51	52	53	54
S_N for $N=C$	1	4	1	6	1	4	1	3
S_Z for $Z=C$	2	7	2	10	2	8	1	9

C	78	79	80	81	82	83	84	85
S_N for $N=C$	5	1	3	2	7	1	2	2
S_Z for $Z=C$	6	1	7	6	4	1	7	

Strong evidence for the magic neutron number $N=126$ and the magic proton number $Z=82$ is found in the energies of the alpha-particles emitted by some radioactive nuclei (Berthelot 42, Perlman 50, Pryce 50). Figure 1.2 of Chapter XI shows the energy of the alpha-particles as a function of the mass number A of the parent nucleus according to Perlman, Ghiorso, and Seaborg (Perlman 50). The points corresponding to a fixed Z are connected. It was shown in Chapter XI, Section 1 (XI,1.3), that the alpha-energy is expected to increase with decreasing neutron number if the proton number Z is constant. Figure 1.2 of Chapter XI shows that this increase of ϵ_α with decreasing neutron number is found regularly for $A>213$. The increase becomes especially pronounced for $Z=85$ (At) and $Z=84$ (Po) just when the neutron number reaches $N=128$. These are the cases of At^{213} and Po^{212}. In both of these alpha-decays the daughter nucleus has $N=126$ (magic) and hence has an especially low energy. The alpha-particles leading to these products are especially energetic. If the *parent* nucleus is magic ($N=126$), the alpha-energies should be particularly low, since the decay starts from a nucleus of low energy. This is borne out by the facts as seen in Po^{210}, At^{211}, and especially in Bi^{209} which is alpha-stable, whereas the neutron-richer isotopes Bi^{210} and Bi^{211} are alpha-radioactive.

There are also indications of some reduction in energy in nuclei where N is close to a magic number. For example, At^{214} and Po^{213} have an unusually high alpha-energy, although both lead to a daughter nucleus with $N = 127$. The two parent nuclei Po^{211} and At^{212} with $N = 127$ have relatively low alpha-energies, though not quite so low as Po^{210} and At^{211} with $N = 126$. Similar effects are found when the proton numbers of the alpha-active nuclei become magic or one more than magic (Glueckauf 48).

By comparing the alpha-energies (listed in Fig. 1.2 of Chapter XI) of the At isotopes ($Z = 85$), the Po isotopes ($Z = 84$), and the Bi isotopes ($Z = 83$), we find an indication of a drop when Z reaches 83. The drop is even stronger when Z becomes equal to 82, since no Pb isotope ($Z = 82$) is radioactive. Hence $Z = 82$ must represent an especially stable configuration.

Very similar relations exist among the energies of beta-ray emissions. These energies also are abnormally large when the neutron or proton number of the final nucleus assumes a magic value (Suess 52).

A quantitative study (Way 49, Harvey 51) of the irregularities found with magic numbers leads to the conclusion that the energy of a nucleus with a magic number of neutrons or protons is depressed by an amount which is of the order of 1 to 2 Mev compared to the average energy of similar nuclei whose Z or N is not magic. A depression by this amount can explain the larger number of isotopes or isotones as well as the fluctuations of alpha-decay energies.[1]

Very striking evidence of the effect of magic neutron numbers is found in the radiative-capture cross sections for neutrons. Figure 1.1 shows the results of measurements of Hughes and Sherman (Hughes 50a) of the capture cross sections for neutrons which have an average energy of about 1 Mev. It is plainly visible that the nuclei with $N = 50, 82, 126$ have very much lower cross sections than the average in the same region. A low cross section is an indication of large level spacing D in the compound nucleus which is formed by the neutron capture, as can be seen from (IX,2.19).

Similar evidence can be drawn from the thermal neutron capture cross sections. Equation (IX,2.11) shows that they also should be small for large level distances. The latter evidence may be obscured, however, by the accidental proximity of a resonance to the thermal energy region, whereas the capture of fast neutrons depends on the average over many resonances. Hence the evidence from the "high"-energy neutrons is more reliable.

[1] However, a similar study by Low (50) throws some doubt upon the "potency" of the magic number 20.

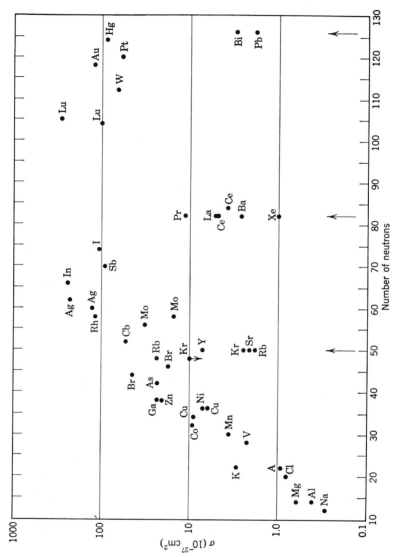

FIG. 1.1. Radiative capture cross section for 1-Mev neutrons as function of the number of neutrons in the target nucleus (reproduced from Hughes 50a). Target nuclei with magic numbers of neutrons give rise to unusually low capture cross sections.

The observed thermal neutron capture cross sections are unusually small for nuclei with magic neutron numbers. Also nuclei with the magic proton numbers 50 (Sn) and 82 (Pb) have much smaller capture cross sections than their neighbors. In the case of lead, the abnormally large spacing between neutron-capturing levels was found directly (Barschall 49).

The low neutron capture cross sections, both at "high" and at thermal energies, provide evidence that magic neutron or proton numbers of the target nucleus are connected with abnormally large level spacing between the levels which are created in the neutron capture. We shall show that the large level spacing between the levels in the compound nucleus can be interpreted as an indication of an abnormally high stability (high binding energy) of the *target* nucleus (Hurwitz 51).

Figure 1.2 is a schematic picture of the level energies of the compound nucleus C together with the energy of the target nucleus X in its ground state plus a neutron at rest. The representation is similar to the one used in the diagrams of Hornyak and Lauritsen (see Fig. 5.3 of Chapter IX); the curve starting at the level $X+n$ depicts schematically the neutron capture cross section. Figure 1.2a represents a normal situation, when neither C nor X is magic. Figure 1.2b corresponds to a case where the target nucleus X has a magic neutron number. Its energy is therefore assumed to be somewhat lower, whereas the energy of the compound nucleus (which has one more neutron) is not depressed. Hence the compound levels into which a neutron of a given energy is captured have a smaller excitation energy in the compound nucleus and therefore a larger level distance. This leads to a small capture cross section.

Figure 1.2c illustrates a case in which both the target nucleus and the compound nucleus are magic. This would happen when the number of *protons* is magic. Then the energy of the ground state of the compound nucleus is also depressed. This, however, does *not* change the conditions at the energy corresponding to the neutron capture. Hence we expect in this case also large level distances and small cross sections.

In this argument we have assumed that only the lowest, or the lowest few, levels of a given nucleus are affected by the "spell" of the magic numbers. The higher levels are assumed to be unchanged, i.e., their absolute energies are *not* lowered appreciably. The evidence from the neutron capture cross sections, and from several other sources, supports this qualitative picture. In particular, we would get completely erroneous conclusions from the assumption that the *entire*

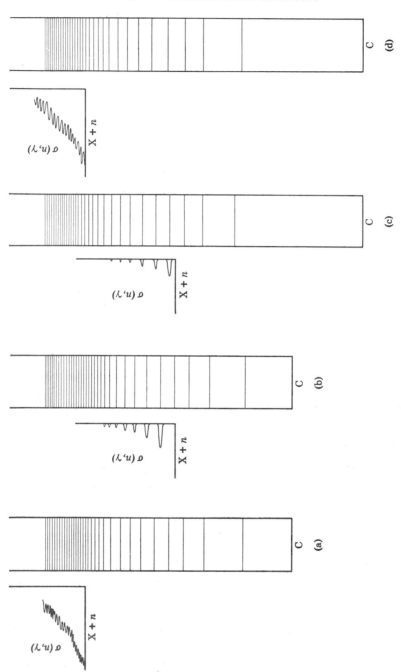

FIG. 1.2. Schematic level diagram of the compound nucleus in the neutron capture process. (a) Target and compound nucleus normal. (b) Target nucleus "magic," compound nucleus normal. (c) Both target and compound nucleus are "magic." (d) Target nucleus normal, compound nucleus "magic."

level system of a magic nucleus is shifted downward in energy by a constant amount.

More evidence in support of the special stability of nuclei with magic neutron or proton numbers can be found from the investigation of fission products. We refer to the excellent summary given by M. Mayer (48).

2. THE NUCLEAR SHELL MODEL

The striking phenomena connected with definite numbers of protons and neutrons have been interpreted as an indication that neutrons and protons within the nucleus are arranged into shells within the nucleus, like electrons in atoms. Each shell is limited to a certain maximum number of nucleons of a given sort. When a shell is filled, the resulting configuration is particularly stable and therefore of low energy.

The theories devised to describe the nature of these shells are all based on the independent-particle model (Haxel 49, Mayer 49, Feenberg 49, Nordheim 49). It is assumed that the nucleons move under the influence of a common potential $V(r)$ and that the interaction between the nucleons can be treated as a small perturbation. This model was discussed in Chapter VII, and it was pointed out that its validity is very questionable. It is therefore very surprising (and so far unexplained) that this model can be used successfully to explain not only the main features of the magic number phenomena, but also more detailed properties such as the spins, magnetic moments, and level spectra of many nuclei.

Three different methods were used to describe the observed shell structure by means of an independent-particle model. We present here only the scheme proposed independently by Haxel, Suess and Jensen, and by M. G. Mayer (Haxel 49, Mayer 49). The other two schemes, by Feenberg (49) and Nordheim (49), are similar in principle.

We start by assuming that the common potential $V(r)$ is an oscillator potential of the form $V = -V_0 + ar^2$. The levels in this potential were listed in Chapter VII (page 280). We consider each group of degenerate (same energy) levels a "shell." These shells are listed in Table 2.1; the angular momenta contained in each shell are given in the second column. Let n be the number of degenerate states within any one shell. Then this shell can accommodate no more than $2n$ neutrons and no more than $2n$ protons, according to the Pauli principle.

It should be mentioned that the assumption of a particular shape for the potential (the oscillator potential) is not essential to the argument. A potential which deviates from the oscillator potential by being flatter near the center and steeper at the edges (like a square well) also gives rise to these shells. The only difference is that states within one shell, but belonging to different values of the orbital angular momentum l, are then no longer precisely degenerate but only approximately so. Larger values of l within a shell have lower energies in this case. The order in which the l values are listed for each shell in Table 2.1

TABLE 2.1

Oscillator Shells	l	Terms (l_j)	Number of Particles	
			In shell	Up to and including shell
I	0	$s_{1/2}$	2	2
II	1	$p_{3/2}, p_{1/2}$	6	8
III	2,0	$d_{5/2}, d_{3/2}, s_{1/2}$	12	20
IV	3,1	$f_{7/2}, f_{5/2}, p_{3/2}, p_{1/2}$	20	40
V	4,2,0	$g_{9/2}, g_{7/2}, d_{5/2},$ $d_{3/2}, s_{1/2}$	30	70
VI	5,3,1	$h_{11/2}, h_{9/2}, f_{7/2},$ $f_{5/2}, p_{3/2}, p_{1/2}$	42	112
VII	6,4,2,0	$i_{13/2}, i_{11/2}, g_{9/2},$ etc.	56	168

corresponds to the order of their energies in such a modified oscillator potential.

The third column of Table 2.1 contains a closer description of the states, which takes into account the fact that the nucleons have an intrinsic spin $\frac{1}{2}$. Each value of l, except $l=0$, gives rise to two states (terms): $j=l+\frac{1}{2}$, $j=l-\frac{1}{2}$. Spectroscopic notation is used here to denote the terms. The letters determine l, and the subscript is equal to j. The next to the last column gives the number of states in each shell, and the last column gives the total number of states in all shells up to and including this shell. It is seen that these total numbers are equal to some of the early magic numbers, but the higher values fail to agree.

In order to get an explanation for the higher magic numbers, a new assumption must be made: We shall suppose that *there exists a spin-orbit coupling which splits the terms $j=l+\frac{1}{2}$ and $j=l-\frac{1}{2}$ by reducing the energy of those terms ($j=l+\frac{1}{2}$) in which the intrinsic spin is parallel to the orbital angular momentum. This effect is assumed to increase with increasing values of l.*[1] Hence the first term listed in the shells of

---

[1] For theoretical discussion regarding this assumption see Keilson (51) and Mayer (50).

Table 2.1 is depressed more than all others. The decrease is supposed to become of the order of the energy difference between two shells for $l=2$ and larger than this difference for $l \geq 3$. We then get a new shell assignment as indicated in Table 2.2. The first two shells are unchanged, since the spin-orbit coupling is weak for $l=1$. The

TABLE 2.2

Nuclear Shells	Terms (l_j)	Number of Particles	
		In shell	Up to and including shell
I	$s_{1/2}$	2	2
II	$p_{3/2}, p_{1/2}$	6	8
IIa	$d_{5/2}$	6	14
III	$s_{1/2}, d_{3/2}$	6	20
IIIa	$f_{7/2}$	8	28
IV	$p_{3/2}, f_{5/2}, p_{1/2}, g_{9/2}$	22	50
V	$g_{7/2}, d_{5/2}, d_{3/2}, s_{1/2}, h_{11/2}$	32	82
VI	$h_{9/2}, f_{7/2}, f_{5/2}, p_{3/2}, p_{1/2}, i_{13/2}$	44	126

depression of the $d_{5/2}$ term in the third shell is assumed to produce an intermediate shell between II and III, called IIa. The same effect is assumed to occur between shells III and IV. From then on the depression of the term of highest j is so strong that it does not form an intermediate shell but must be incorporated into the previous shell. This is shown in Table 2.2 for shells IV, V, and VI. The third and fourth columns give the number of particles per shell and the accumulated numbers, respectively. The latter ones reproduce the magic numbers (1.1) in their entirety, a striking success of this shell model.

Table 2.2 allows prediction of certain regularities in the spins of nuclei if one more assumption is made (Mayer 50): *An even number of nucleons of the same type in a state of given j will always arrange themselves to give a spin 0.*[1] Hence the angular momentum of any

---

[1] For theoretical discussion regarding this rule see Mayer (50), Racah (50a), Kurath (50), and Talmi (51). This rule can be regarded as the opposite to Hund's rule in atomic spectra. Hund's rule states that the multiplicity of the lowest state is the highest possible within the given configuration. The reason is found in the repulsion among electrons which favors a state anti-symmetric in the coordinates and hence symmetric in the spins. The nuclear forces are mainly attractive and favor the state most symmetric in the coordinates. Hence the lowest state must be anti-symmetric in the spins; in most cases this gives rise to a zero spin for even numbers of particles.

shell with even population is zero, and the angular momentum of any shell with odd population must equal the angular momentum of the odd (unpaired) particle. We therefore get the following result for nuclear spins: $I = 0$ for N even, Z even. For N even, Z odd, or for N odd, Z even, the spin I depends on the number C of the odd nucleons ($C \equiv Z$ in the first, $C \equiv N$ in the second case). The number C determines which of the shells is partially filled. It is shell I for $C < 2$, shell II for $2 < C < 8$, etc. The spin of the nucleus can assume only the values j of the terms belonging to this shell. Hence we expect $I = \frac{1}{2}$ for $C < 2$, $I = \frac{3}{2}$ or $\frac{1}{2}$ for $2 < C < 8$; $I = \frac{5}{2}$ for $8 < C < 14$, etc.

This rule is fairly well fulfilled in general. There are only three exceptions, two in shell IIa, and one in IIIa. The two nuclei, F^{19} and Na^{23}, have a spin of $\frac{1}{2}$ and $\frac{3}{2}$, respectively, instead of $\frac{5}{2}$, and Mn^{55} has a spin $\frac{5}{2}$ instead of $\frac{7}{2}$. It may be that the depression of the $d_{5/2}$ term and the $f_{7/2}$ term is not pronounced enough to consider shell IIa different from III, or IIIa different from IV, in all cases.[1] All three exceptions are proton-odd. There is no exception for neutron-odd nuclei. It is quite remarkable that no spin $\frac{1}{2}$ is found in the entire range $28 < C < 50$, and no spin $\frac{3}{2}$ for $50 < C < 82$.

The order in which the terms are listed for each shell in Table 2.2 indicates the order of their energies. It is the order which is in best conformity with the experimental material. For example, the nucleus P^{31} with 15 protons has just 1 proton in shell III; all other nucleons are paired off. Hence the spin of P^{31} should be equal to the spin of the lowest state of shell III: $j = \frac{1}{2}$. By the same reasoning we obtain the spin $\frac{1}{2}$ for Si^{29} with 15 neutrons. Both nuclei actually do have spin $\frac{1}{2}$. Spin $\frac{3}{2}$ is expected for nuclei in which shell IV contains 1 odd nucleon, as in Cu^{63} for example. The situation is somewhat more complicated in shell V, where the two lowest states $g_{7/2}$ and $d_{5/2}$ seem to lie very close together. Sb^{121} with 51 protons (1 in shell V) has spin $\frac{5}{2}$, whereas Sb^{123} with the same number of protons has spin $\frac{7}{2}$.

When a shell contains more than one nucleon, the particles do not necessarily fill up the lowest levels of the shell, because of the so-called *pairing energy*. This is a negative potential energy connected with double occupancy of a level, an energy which is larger the higher the l value of the level. For example, the nucleus As^{75} with 33 protons, 5 of them in shell IV, should have spin $\frac{5}{2}$ if they would fill the

---

[1] The magnetic moment of Mn^{55}, however, is not in agreement with this explanation. An alternative explanation has been suggested, in terms of a relaxation of the rule that a shell with odd population has the angular momentum of the unpaired particle (Goldhaber 51.)

lowest levels in that shell (4 in $p_{3/2}$, 1 in $f_{5/2}$). However, the pairing energy favors the occupancy of the $f_{5/2}$ level ($l=3$) by the proton pairs, leaving the $p_{3/2}$ level for the unpaired proton. Hence the spin of As^{75} is $\frac{3}{2}$. The same argument explains the spin $\frac{3}{2}$ for the nuclei Br^{79} and Br^{81} (7 protons in shell IV).

The pairing energy also explains the fact that the high spins $\frac{11}{2}$ in shell V and $\frac{13}{2}$ in shell VI are never realized in the ground states of nuclei. It always is energetically more favorable to put into these levels a pair of high l ($l = 6$ or 7 respectively) and to put the unpaired nucleon into a level of lower l. Hence nuclei for which C is a few units below 82 (shell V almost completed) have a spin of $\frac{1}{2}$ or $\frac{3}{2}$ rather than $\frac{11}{2}$. The difference between the pairing energy for a pair with low l and a pair with high l is not very large. The states in which the unpaired nucleon is in the level of high spin are therefore observed among the first few excited states, sometimes with excitation energies of a few hundred kev only.

The pairing energy in the $g_{9/2}$ level ($l=5$) of shell IV is not so effective as that in the $h_{11/2}$ and $i_{13/2}$ levels of shells V and VI, on account of the lower l value. Hence we do find a spin $\frac{9}{2}$ among nuclei with an unpaired nucleon in shell IV.

The spins of odd-odd nuclei cannot be predicted without additional assumptions, since it must be known how the spin of the two odd nucleons of different types combine to form the total spin of the nucleus. Some promising attempts in this direction were made by Nordheim (51.)

The shell model also predicts the value of the magnetic moments for the odd-even and even-odd nuclei. The assumption was made that the angular momentum is due to the last odd nucleon only, all other nucleon spins cancelling in pairs. Hence the entire magnetic moment of the nucleus must be produced by this one unpaired nucleon, too. The gyromagnetic ratio g for magnetic moments which are caused by the orbital motion and by the spin of a single particle in a central field (Schmidt model) were given in Chapter I, (I,7.54) and (I,7.55). For a given total angular momentum I we find two possible values of g corresponding to the two possible alignments of the intrinsic spin s and the orbital moment l: $l+s=I$ or $l-s=I$. We shall now show that the nuclear shell model determines which of the two possibilities should be selected for given I. In this model the total spin I is equal to the value of j of the odd nucleon. It is seen in Table 2.2 that, in each shell, there is only one value of l (one letter s, p, d, f, etc.) for each value of j. Thus, for example, a nucleus whose C (odd number of nucleons) belongs in shell IV ($28 < C < 50$) and whose spin is $I = \frac{3}{2}$ must have an orbital momentum $l=1$ (p term, spin parallel) and not

$l=2$ (d term, spin anti-parallel) since no $d_{3/2}$ term is contained in shell IV. Hence the observed value of I determines the orbital momentum l, and (I,7.54) or (I,7.55) with $g_L = 1$ for proton-odd nuclei and $g_L = 0$ for neutron-odd nuclei can be used to calculate the gyromagnetic ratio g.

These calculations do not agree very well with the observations. It was mentioned in Chapter I that the observed magnetic moments do not agree with either of the two possible values predicted by the Schmidt model. They always lie somewhere between the two theoretical values. This result is hard to understand from the point of view of the shell model. The disagreement is especially troublesome for nuclei in which the number of protons is one more than magic as, for example, in Cu^{63} ($Z=29$), Sb^{121}, Sb^{123} ($Z=51$). In these cases we should expect that the core of magic protons is spherically symmetric and that the magnetic moment is due exclusively to the one additional proton. Hence the Schmidt model value ought to agree more closely with the observed one than in other nuclei. This, however, is not the case.[1]

If we relax the exact requirements of the theory somewhat, we can test the prediction of the shell theory in the following way. In general, the observed values lie nearer to one of the two theoretical values than to the other. We can interpret this proximity as an indication of the type of alignment of spin and orbit: if the observed value is near the theoretical value which corresponds to $I = l + s$, we assume that $l = I - s$, and vice versa. This "approximative" determination of l is questionable, since the Schmidt model does not allow any intermediate magnetic moments between the two predicted values. A mixture of the quantum states which correspond to the two alignments is excluded because of the opposite parity of these two states (Margenau 40a).

According to Mayer (50) the value of l can be determined by this method for about 50 nuclei with odd neutrons or odd protons. It is remarkable that this "approximate" determination of l is in almost complete agreement with the prediction of the shell model. Mayer (50) has shown that the resulting l's are the ones that are predicted from the spins I for all nuclei with odd neutron numbers and for all but two nuclei with odd proton numbers. The exceptions are Yb^{173}, which should have $l=3$ but whose magnetic moment is nearer the value for $l=2$, and Eu^{151}, which should have $l=2$ but shows $l=3$.

[1] For attempts at explanations, see Foldy (50a), Bohr (51, 51a), Bloch (51), and de Shalit (51).

The study of the magnetic moments of nuclei reveals another remarkable phenomenon. Although the magnetic moments agree only very approximately with the predictions of the shell model, we sometimes find almost exactly identical magnetic moments in pairs or triplets of isotopes of equal spin but differing by two neutrons. Such groups are Ag^{107} and Ag^{109}; Cs^{133}, Cs^{135}, and Cs^{137}; Tl^{203} and Tl^{205}; In^{113} and In^{115}. Quite independently of the explanation of the actual magnetic moment, this phenomenon indicates that the addition of two neutrons to the nucleus does not change the arrangement of the protons, which are responsible for the magnetic moment in these nuclei. This fact is hard to understand except on the basis of the independent-particle model as a valid first approximation.

There are other examples in which the addition of two neutrons leaves some properties of the nucleus unchanged: each of the two silver isotopes Ag^{107} and Ag^{109} has an isomeric state with almost the same excitation energy and lifetime, although they differ by two neutrons. The two indium isotopes In^{113} and In^{115} have not only similar magnetic moments but also similar quadrupole moments and similar isomeric levels. All three of the nuclei Fe^{56}, Fe^{58}, and Cr^{54} have an excited state with an excitation energy of 830 ± 15 kev (Deutsch 44). They differ by pairs of neutrons or protons. These and many similar examples provide strong support for the existence of relatively independent particle motions within the nucleus.

The assignment of definite l values to proton- or neutron-odd nuclei in the shell model can be used in the theory of beta-decay. The probability of beta-decay depends on the spin difference between the decaying nucleus and the decay product. The prediction of the value of the matrix element entering into the decay probability is greatly improved if not only the spin difference but also the difference in orbital angular momentum l between the two nuclei is known. (See Chapter XIII, Section 7.) Hence the determination of l from the total spin I by means of the shell model can be tested by comparing the resulting conclusions with respect to the beta-decay probabilities with the experimental material. The test was performed by Mayer (50, 51) and Nordheim (50, 51), and the results of the shell theory are in reasonable agreement with experiment. It is a particularly remarkable success of the shell theories that they were able to *predict* that certain beta-transitions should show "forbidden"-type spectra. This prediction depends on the assignment of orbital angular momenta l to the two nuclei involved in the decay. The assignment of l for the stable nucleus (the daughter nucleus) comes from the measured magnetic moment, but the assignment of l for the other, unstable, nucleus represents a severe test for the shell models.[1]

The shell model also furnishes an explanation of the fact that almost all of the isomeric states with long life (see Chapter XII) are found for nuclei where either N or Z is near the end of a shell. We find almost all of them for N or Z between 39 and 49, or between 69 and 81 (Nordheim 49, Feenberg 49).

These "islands of isomerism" can be explained as follows. The terms in one shell do not differ much in energy. The transition from the ground state to the lowest excited state corresponds probably to a transition of the "odd" nucleon from one term in the unfilled shell to another term in the same shell. We expect that these transitions are connected with a large change of spin if subsequent terms in a shell have very different values of j. On the basis of the term order as given in Table 2.2 this happens toward the end of shell IV ($p_{1/2}$ and $g_{9/2}$), of shell V ($s_{1/2}$ and $h_{11/2}$), and of shell VI ($p_{1/2}$ and $i_{13/2}$). Islands of isomerism should occur when the occupation numbers of the shells reach these terms. This happens in shell IV between 39 and 49, in shell V between 69 and 81. The group of isomers corresponding to shell VI (N or Z between 111 and 125) is not very large and not so pronounced as the other two groups. This scheme also provides a method to predict the I differences and the parity differences between isomeric states (Mayer 50, Axel 50, Goldhaber 51, Moszkowski 51).

Let us consider, for example, the nucleus In^{115}. It has 49 protons,

---

[1] It is rather surprising at first sight that this success of the shell models is independent of the particular model employed. The models of Feenberg (49), Nordheim (49), and Mayer (49) (the last being the same as the one of Haxel 49) are quite different in their details. Nevertheless, all three lead to identical predictions as far as analysis of beta-decay data is concerned, in all but a few cases.

The reason is perhaps to be found in the fact that we can get almost as good agreement with beta-decay data for *odd* mass number nuclei by the following simple rules which do not depend on any specific model for the nuclear shell structure:

(1) Every nuclear ground state has, in addition to total angular momentum I and parity II, an orbital angular momentum quantum number L and a spin angular momentum quantum number $S = \frac{1}{2}$.

(2) These values depend only on the number C of odd nucleons. Thus $I(C)$ can be found by examining any one stable nucleus with this number of odd nucleons for which the spin has been measured experimentally.

(3) The values of L and the parity for each C are to be found by comparing the magnetic moment of a representative nucleus (with this odd-nucleon number C) with the Schmidt model, thereby getting $l = L$ and the parity $II(C) = (-1)^L$.

Since all three shell models are devised so as to give agreement with these rules, they necessarily give the same predictions for beta-decay data.

one less than the complete shell IV. Its ground state has spin $\frac{9}{2}$, which indicates that the free space in shell IV is found in the highest level $g_{9/2}$ of the shell. The parity of this state is even ($l=4$). It is expected that the first excited state is the one in which the free space is in the next lower level, $p_{1/2}$. This state would have spin $\frac{1}{2}$ and odd parity. Hence we expect an isomeric transition from this state to the ground state of character M4 (see Chapter XII, Section 6), in agreement with the experiments quoted in Table 6.1 of Chapter XII.

As another example we discuss nuclei with odd neutron numbers N in the range $67 \leq N \leq 81$. The first two levels of shell V are filled, and we have at least 3 neutrons to be placed into the levels $s_{1/2}$, $d_{3/2}$, $h_{11/2}$. In the ground state the $h_{11/2}$ level is occupied by pairs on account of the high pairing energy. Hence the ground states of these nuclei have a spin $\frac{1}{2}$ or $\frac{3}{2}$ and even parity. We expect the following two excited states: one with even parity and spin $\frac{3}{2}$ or $\frac{1}{2}$, respectively, and a higher one with odd parity and spin $\frac{11}{2}$ coming from the configuration where the odd neutron is in the $h_{11/2}$ level. Thus, if the spin of the ground state is $\frac{1}{2}$, we expect an M4 transition from $h_{11/2}$ to $d_{3/2}$ followed by a magnetic dipole transition from $d_{3/2}$ to the ground state $s_{1/2}$. Just this type of spectrum has been observed with nuclei of this category. Each one of the nuclei Sn^{117}, Sn^{119}, Te^{121}, Te^{123}, Te^{125}, and Xe^{129} has a ground state with $I=\frac{1}{2}$, a first excited state with $I=\frac{3}{2}$, and a second excited state with $I=\frac{11}{2}$. The emitted radiation is an M4 radiation followed by an M1 radiation (Goldhaber 51). These examples demonstrate the success of the shell model in the interpretation of nuclear spectra. They also illustrate the striking similarity of nuclear spectra in nuclei differing by pairs of neutrons or protons.

There are strong indications, however, that the coupling rules of the shell model must be modified in a few cases in order to account for some isomeric transitions. In particular, an odd number of particles in a shell does not always give rise to a total angular momentum equal to the j value of the unpaired nucleon. For example, the first excited state in Ag^{107} has a spin $\frac{7}{2}$ (Goldhaber 51), although this value does not occur in the shell of the unpaired nucleon (shell IV). Hence it is assumed that three nucleons in the $g_{9/2}$ level give rise to a total angular momentum $J=\frac{7}{2}$ rather than $J=j=\frac{9}{2}$. This result is not unexpected, since three particles, with $j=\frac{9}{2}$ each, can combine in many ways, resulting in a total J which covers a wide range of values. However, it is a violation of the rule that the spins of all pairs of nucleons cancel in low-lying states, leading to $J=j$. It is rather surprising how rarely this rule is violated in view of the many ways in which the angular momenta j within one level can be combined to a total J different from j.

As a last piece of evidence for shell structure, we mention the nuclear quadrupole moments (Gordy 49, Hill 49a, Townes 49). It was first

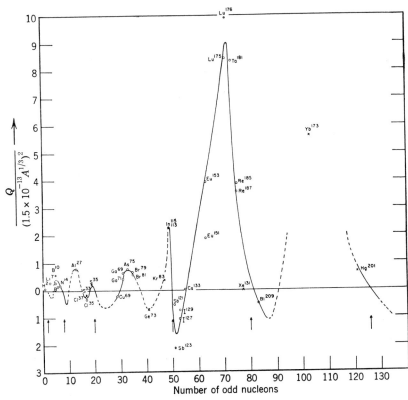

FIG. 2.1. The points are quadrupole moments divided by the square of the nuclear radius, $R^2 = (1.5 \times 10^{-13} \times A^{1/3})^2$. Quadrupole moments of odd-proton, even-neutron and of odd-proton, odd-neutron nuclei (except Li^6 and Cl^{36}) are plotted as circles against number of protons. Quadrupole moments of odd-neutron, even-proton nuclei are plotted as crosses against number of neutrons. Arrows indicate closing of major nucleon shells. The solid curve represents regions where the behavior seems established, the dashed curve represents more doubtful regions. [Reproduced from Townes (49).]

observed by Schmidt (40) that the quadrupole moments Q show certain regularities as indicated in Fig. 2.1. They are large when Z is far from a magic number and are relatively small for Z near magic. A similar dependence on N is indicated but not established. When Z

is higher than, but near to, a magic number, Q is negative; Q is positive for Z lower than, but near, magic.

The independent-particle model suggests that we might be able to ascribe the asymmetry of charge to the last odd proton, whereas all paired nucleons which make up the core of the nucleus are arranged in a spherically symmetric way. In this case the quadrupole moments should vanish or should be very small for nuclei with odd neutrons; the moments for nuclei with odd numbers of protons should be of the order of the quadrupole moment resulting from one particle in a state with orbital angular momentum l and total angular momentum j. The latter value is (Bethe 33, Welles 42)

$$Q = - \frac{2j-1}{2j+2} e^2 \bar{R}^2 \qquad (2.1)$$

where $\bar{R}$ is the average radial extension of the wave function. Expression (2.1) does not check against the observed values. The quadrupole moments observed are usually much larger than (2.1) and are by no means always negative. In order to account for big quadrupole moments like that of Lu^{175} or Ta^{181}, we must assume that at least 30 protons are in non-symmetric quantum states.

It is therefore very probable that the whole nucleus deviates from the spherical shape. In this case the odd particle in an odd nucleus does not move in a spherically symmetric field, and the basis of some of the term assignments is removed (Bohr 51, 51a). A more detailed calculation (Rainwater 50; Maria Mayer, unpublished) shows that such a model can indeed account for the signs and orders of magnitude of the observed quadrupole moments.

3. GENERAL CONSIDERATIONS

The great success of the shell model of nuclei is most surprising and is not yet understood on the basis of our present knowledge about nuclear forces and nuclear dynamics. Reasons were given in Chapter VII, Section 3, for the inadequacy of an independent-particle model on the basis of conventional nuclear forces. The shell evidence not only indicates the validity of such a model but also bases some of its predictions on the actual shape of the potential $V(r)$ common to all nucleons. In order to get shells of the type of Table 2.2, this potential must have a shape between an oscillator potential and a square well.

The one requirement for the validity of the independent-particle model which seems to violate most strongly our ideas of the nucleus is the lack of any effective interaction between nucleons. The existence of orbits in the nucleus with well-defined quantum numbers is possible only if the nucleon is able to complete several "revolutions" in this orbit before being perturbed by its neighbors.   Only then is the width of the level smaller than the distance to other levels, as was demonstrated in Chapter VIII, Section 7.   Hence the effective mean free path of a nucleon in nuclear matter must be somewhat larger than the nuclear dimensions in order to allow the use of the independent-particle model.   This requirement seems to be in contradiction to the assumptions made in the theory of the compound nucleus, Chapter VIII, Section 3.   The study of nuclear reactions indicates that a nucleon, after entering into a nucleus, quickly shares its energy with all the other constituents.

The unexpected indications of a shell structure in the nucleus pose the following fundamental question regarding the nature of nuclear forces.   Can the results be explained on the basis of essentially the same interaction between nucleons which has been hitherto assumed? This interaction is characterized by strong, short-ranged forces of partial exchange character, and it has been supported by the evidence from the scattering experiments between single nucleons in spite of appreciable difficulties of interpretation of the results at high energies (see Chapter IV).   Or do the shell results require us to assume a qualitatively different kind of interaction between nucleons which are densely packed in nuclear matter than between two isolated nucleons? The individual interactions may be weakened (for example, when the density of nucleons reaches nuclear densities) to such an extent that only an over-all average potential remains, without a strong interaction between individual pairs.   Perhaps some such change in our ideas of nuclear interaction is indicated in view of the failure to explain saturation of nuclear forces and nuclear densities with the potentials derived from scattering (see Chapter IV).   On the other hand, the experience gathered from the nuclear reactions contradicts any evidence of weak interaction between nucleons in the nucleus.   We are facing here one of the fundamental problems of nuclear structure which has not yet been solved.

It may be significant that the shell structure evidence is drawn exclusively from the properties of the *ground states* of nuclei or of very low-lying levels.   The stability considerations deal with the energy of the ground state; the neutron capture provided evidence about the energy of the ground state of the target nucleus; the spin and the magnetic moment, as well as the quadrupole moment, are properties of the ground state.   In contrast to this, the evidence for strong interaction found in nuclear reactions is derived from the properties of the compound nucleus which is always formed in a state of high excitation energy. The excitation energy of the compound nucleus is at least equal to the separation energy of the incident particle ($\gtrsim 8$ Mev).

This circumstance suggests the possibility that the shell structure evidence is not necessarily in disagreement with the conventional strong interactions. It is conceivable that the individual motion of the particles is relatively unperturbed in the ground state despite strong interaction. The Pauli principle prevents the transfer of momentum and energy between two nucleons if they are all in their lowest possible energy states, since all states are occupied which can be reached in this transfer. Hence the strong interaction may not become effective at very low excitation and the independent-particle model may assume some validity. When the nucleus is highly excited, the nucleons can transfer energy and momentum and the nucleus can exhibit the characteristic properties of strong energy exchange between the nucleons. It still remains to be proved whether this effect is sufficient to establish independent orbits in low-lying states of nuclei in spite of the existence of strong interactions.[1]

SYMBOLS

a — Coefficient in the oscillator potential $V(r) = -V_0 + ar^2$ (Section 2)

A — Mass number (Section 1)

C — Compound nucleus (Section 1)

C — Number of nucleons of a given type (neutrons or protons) (Section 1)

C — Number of odd nucleons in an even-odd or odd-even nucleus (Section 2)

e — Charge on the proton (2.1)

g — Gyromagnetic ratio of the nucleus; see also Chapter I, Section 7 (Section 2)

g_L — Gyromagnetic ratio associated with the orbital motion; see also Chapter I, Section 7 (Section 2)

I — Total angular momentum quantum number of the nucleus in its ground state (nuclear spin) (Section 2)

j — Total angular momentum quantum number of a nucleon within the nucleus (Section 2)

l — Orbital angular momentum quantum number of a nucleon within the nucleus (Section 2)

---

[1] The electron motion in solid crystal lattices provides an instructive analogy to this situation. It is discussed by Weisskopf (50, 51).

n Number of single-nucleon states of the same energy (within one "shell")   (Section 2)

N Number of neutrons in the nucleus   (Section 1)

Q Electric quadrupole moment of the nucleus; see also Chapter I, Section 7   (2.1)

r Distance of a nucleon from the center of the nucleus (Section 2)

$\bar{R}$ Average radial extension of the wave function of a proton (2.1)

S_N Number of different stable nuclei (isotones) with N neutrons   (Section 1)

S_Z Number of different stable nuclei (isotopes) with Z protons   (Section 1)

$V = V(r)$ Potential acting on a nucleon within the nucleus   (Section 2)

V_0 Value of $V(r)$ at $r = 0$ (the center of the nucleus)   (Section 2)

X The target nucleus in a nuclear reaction   (Section 1)

Z Number of protons in the nucleu   (Section 1)

Angular Momentum Operators
and Eigenfunctions

1. ROTATIONS AND ANGULAR MOMENTA

In classical mechanics as well as in quantum mechanics, the angular momentum of a system is conserved if the equations of motion are invariant under rotations of the coordinate system which is used to describe the motion. This is true of any isolated system, such as a nucleus. It is not true of a system subject to external forces, such as an applied electric or magnetic field (which distinguishes one direction in space from all others).

Let $\varphi(x,y,z)$ be a solution of the wave equation for a single particle. If the wave equation is invariant under rotations about the z direction, say, then the "rotated" function defined by

$$\varphi'(x,y,z) = \varphi(x \cos \vartheta + y \sin \vartheta, \quad y \cos \vartheta - x \sin \vartheta, \quad z) \quad (1.1)$$

is also a solution of the wave equation, since it differs from φ only through a rotation about the z axis through an angle ϑ. We now use the fact that the difference of two solutions is also a solution, and we let ϑ become infinitesimally small to get

$$\varphi' - \varphi = \vartheta \left(y \frac{\partial \varphi}{\partial x} - x \frac{\partial \varphi}{\partial y} \right) \equiv -i\vartheta \, L_z \varphi \quad (1.2)$$

The operator L_z defined by this equation is the angular momentum operator of quantum mechanics in units of $\hbar$. We have therefore proved that $L_z \varphi$ is a solution of the wave equation if φ is a solution and if the wave equation is invariant under rotations of the coordinate system. Hence L_z commutes with the Hamiltonian H. The extension to systems containing more than one particle is straightforward. The angular momentum operator L_z is then the sum of the individual angular momenta of the various particles.

Rotation about the x axis and y axis gives the angular momentum operators L_x and L_y, respectively. The three components of the vector $\mathbf{L}$ satisfy the commutation rules

$$L_x L_y - L_y L_x = iL_z, \cdots \tag{1.3}$$

where the dots indicate the two additional equations obtained by cyclic permutation of the indices. These commutation rules are the basic property of angular momentum operators, i.e., any vector $\mathbf{J}$ whose components J_x, J_y, J_z satisfy the commutation rules (1.3) can be interpreted as an angular momentum. $\mathbf{J}$ can be an operator acting on any arbitrary set of position or spin coordinates of one or several particles.

We can derive a number of important relations by purely algebraic methods using only the commutation rules (1.3) (see Rojansky 42, chap. XIII, or Condon 35, chap. III): J^2 commutes with J_z, and we can show that the eigenvalues of J^2 are of the form $j(j+1)$, where j is either an integer or a half-integer, and the eigenvalues of J_z are $m = j, j-1, j-2, \cdots, -j$. Furthermore, if we denote by Y_{jm} any simultaneous eigenfunction of J^2 and J_z with eigenvalues $j(j+1)$ and m, respectively, the following equations hold:[1]

$$\begin{aligned}
(J_x + iJ_y)\, \mathsf{Y}_{jm} &= \sqrt{(j-m)(j+m+1)}\; \mathsf{Y}_{j,m+1} \\
(J_x - iJ_y)\, \mathsf{Y}_{jm} &= \sqrt{(j+m)(j-m+1)}\; \mathsf{Y}_{j,m-1}
\end{aligned} \tag{1.4}$$

Here Y_{jm} are functions of the variables upon which J operates.

2. SPHERICAL HARMONICS

We now specialize the operator $\mathbf{J}$ to be equal to the differential operator $\mathbf{L}$. The latter can be written in the form

$$L_z = -i\,\frac{\partial}{\partial \phi} \qquad L_x \pm i L_y = \exp\left(\pm i\phi\right)\left[\pm\frac{\partial}{\partial \theta} + i\cot\theta\,\frac{\partial}{\partial\phi}\right] \tag{2.1}$$

Then the functions Y_{jm} are identical with the spherical harmonics. Indeed the spherical harmonics $Y_{lm}(\theta,\phi)$ are defined as normalized simultaneous eigenfunctions of L^2 and L_z with eigenvalues $l(l+1)$ and m, respectively. The spherical harmonic with $m = -l$ satisfies the differential equations $L_z Y = -lY$ and $(L_x - iL_y)Y = 0$. The normalized solution of these two equations is

[1] The algebraic derivation leaves a phase factor undetermined in (1.4). We choose the plus signs in agreement with Condon (35) and Wigner (31), since the Clebsch-Gordan coefficients are given explicitly by them. Bethe (33) uses minus signs instead. Thus our spherical harmonics agree with Bethe's for even m but are the negatives of Bethe's for odd m.

$$Y_{l,-l}(\theta,\phi) = \left[\frac{(2l+1)!!}{4\pi(2l)!!}\right]^{1/2} (\sin\theta)^l \exp(-il\phi) \qquad (2.2)$$

where the "double factorial" $n!!$ is defined by

$$n!! \equiv 2\times4\times6\times\cdots\times n \qquad (n \text{ even})$$
$$n!! \equiv 1\times3\times5\times\cdots\times n \qquad (n \text{ odd})$$

$$(2.3)$$

The half-integral values of l do not give acceptable solutions, since they give rise to probability currents from one pole of the sphere to the other, the two poles acting as a source and sink of probability, respectively.[1]

Restricting ourselves to the integral values of l, therefore, we can find the remaining spherical harmonics Y_{lm} from (2.2) by successive multiplication with the operator L_x+iL_y, according to (1.4). The result can be expressed in the form

$$Y_{lm}(\theta,\phi) = \frac{(-1)^{l+m}}{(2l)!!}\left[\frac{(2l+1)\,(l-m)!}{4\pi\,(l+m)!}\right]^{1/2}(\sin\theta)^m$$
$$\times\frac{d^{l+m}}{(d\cos\theta)^{l+m}}[(\sin\theta)^{2l}]\exp(im\phi) \qquad (2.4)$$

These functions satisfy the relation

$$Y_{lm}{}^* = (-)^m\,Y_{l,-m}$$

They are connected with the Legendre polynomials $P_l(\cos\theta)$ as follows:

$$P_l(\cos\theta) = \left[\frac{4\pi}{2l+1}\right]^{1/2}Y_{l,0}(\theta) \qquad (2.5)$$

The spherical harmonics $Y_{lm}(\theta,\phi)$ form a complete set of functions over the unit sphere. That is, any function $g(\theta,\phi)$ which is square integrable over the full solid angle can be written as a linear combination of the spherical harmonics. Furthermore the spherical harmonics form an orthonormal set:

[1] This argument is due to Nordsieck (unpublished). The usual arguments are: (1) the Y_{lm} with half-integral l are not single-valued, and (2) some of them have singularities at the poles of the sphere. The first argument is fallacious since multiple-valued wave functions cannot be excluded a priori. Only physically measurable quantities, such as probability densities and expectation values of operators, must be single-valued. Double-valued wave functions are used in the theory of particles with intrinsic spin. The second argument is incomplete, since (2.2), for example, has no singularities for $l=\frac{1}{2}$.

$$\int Y_{lm}^{*}\, Y_{l'm'}\, d\Omega \;=\; \delta_{mm'}\, \delta_{ll'} \qquad (2.6)$$

where the integration extends over the full solid angle.

Finally we mention the *addition theorem* of spherical harmonics. [For a proof, see Condon (35) or Bethe (33).] Let θ,ϕ and θ',ϕ' be two points on the unit sphere, and let α be the angle subtended by these two points at the center of the sphere. Then the addition theorem states that

$$Y_{l,0}(\alpha)\, Y_{l,0}(0) \;=\; \left(\frac{2l+1}{4\pi}\right)^{1/2} Y_{l,0}(\alpha) \;=\; \sum_{m=-l} Y_{lm}^{*}(\theta,\phi)\, Y_{lm}(\theta',\phi')$$

$$(2.7)$$

3. EXPANSION OF A PLANE WAVE INTO SPHERICAL WAVES

The wave function of a plane wave of wave number k proceeding along the positive z direction is

$$\exp\,(ikz) \;=\; \exp\,(ikr\cos\theta)$$

This function can be expanded into a series of spherical harmonics. Since it is independent of the azimuthal angle ϕ, the only spherical harmonics entering the expansion are the $Y_{l,0}(\theta)$ with $m=0$. Using (2.6), we obtain

$$\exp\,(ikz) \;=\; \sum_{l=0}^{\infty} A_l(r)\, Y_{l,0}(\theta)$$

$$A_l(r) \;=\; \int Y_{l,0}^{*}(\theta)\, \exp\,(ikr\cos\theta)\, d\Omega$$

$$(3.1)$$

where the integration extends over the full solid angle, but not over the radial coordinate r. The coefficient $A_l(r)$ can be expressed in terms of Bessel functions as follows:

$$A_l(r) \;=\; i^{l}\,\sqrt{4\pi(2l+1)}\; j_l(kr) \;=\; i^{l}\,\sqrt{4\pi(2l+1)}\,\sqrt{\frac{\pi}{2kr}}\; J_{l+1/2}(kr) \quad (3.2)$$

where $J_{\lambda}(z)$ is the Bessel function of first kind and order λ, as defined in Jahnke-Emde (33) or Whittaker (50), and $j_l(z) \equiv \sqrt{\pi/2z}\; J_{l+1/2}(z)$ is the so-called "spherical Bessel function" of the first kind of order l. We are often interested in the asymptotic behavior of $j_l(kr)$ for large and small kr. The dividing line here is not $kr=1$ but rather $kr=l$, i.e., "large" kr means $kr \gg l$, "small" kr means $kr \ll l$. The asymptotic expressions are

$$j_l(kr) \;\cong\; \frac{(kr)^{l}}{(2l+1)!!} \qquad (kr \ll l) \qquad (3.3)$$

$$j_l(kr) \cong \frac{\sin (kr - \frac{1}{2}l\pi)}{kr} \qquad (kr \gg l) \qquad (3.4)$$

The "regular solution" $F_l(r)$ used in Chapter VIII, Section 2, for neutrons, and in other places is related to $j_l(kr)$ through

$$F_l(r) = kr\, j_l(kr)$$

Finally, we can use the addition theorem (2.7) to get an expression for the plane wave in an arbitrary direction Θ,Φ:

$$\exp (i\mathbf{k}\cdot\mathbf{r}) = 4\pi \sum_{l=0}^{\infty} \sum_{m=-l}^{l} i^l\, j_l(kr)\, Y_{lm}{}^*(\Theta,\Phi)\, Y_{lm}(\theta,\phi) \qquad (3.5)$$

Sometimes we are interested only in the S wave part (the $l=0$ part) of the plane wave $\exp (ikz)$. Since $j_0(z) = \sin z/z$ for all values of z, we get

$$l=0 \text{ part of } \exp (ikz) = \sqrt{4\pi} \left[\frac{\sin(kr)}{kr}\right] Y_{0,0} = \frac{\sin(kr)}{kr} \qquad (3.6)$$

4. INTRINSIC SPIN

The algebraic treatment of the commutation rules (1.3) predicts eigenvalues $j(j+1)$ of J^2 with j half-integral, in addition to the integral values which alone could be employed for the spherical harmonics. The simplest example of a half-integral spin is the intrinsic spin of a nucleon which corresponds to the value $j=\frac{1}{2}$ in (1.4). There are only two eigenfunctions for the states of the spin of a single nucleon, namely $Y_{1/2,1/2}$, which describes a particle of spin $\frac{1}{2}$ with the spin direction along the positive z axis of the coordinate system, and $Y_{1/2,-1/2}$, which describes a particle of spin $\frac{1}{2}$ with the spin direction along the negative z axis. We shall refer to these two possibilities as "up" and "down" spin, respectively. To shorten subsequent formulas, we introduce the abbreviations

$$Y_{1/2,1/2} \equiv \alpha \qquad Y_{1/2,-1/2} \equiv \beta \qquad (4.1)$$

We shall also denote the angular momentum vector $\mathbf{J}$ by $\mathbf{s}$. Thus the first equation (1.4) becomes, for $m=\frac{1}{2}$,

$$(s_x+is_y)\, \alpha = 0$$

and for $m=-\frac{1}{2}$,

$$(s_x+is_y)\, \beta = \alpha$$

We can consider α and β the base vectors of a two-dimensional vector space, and the s's as linear operators on this space, expressible in the usual matrix form. According to the two equations just listed, the matrix form of the operator $s_x + is_y$ in this space is

$$s_x + is_y = \begin{pmatrix} 0 & 1 \\ 0 & 0 \end{pmatrix}$$

The so-called Pauli spin matrices σ_x, σ_y, and σ_z are defined by putting $s_x = \frac{1}{2}\sigma_x$, $s_y = \frac{1}{2}\sigma_y$, and $s_z = \frac{1}{2}\sigma_z$. With these definitions, relations (1.4) together with the defining equations $s^2\alpha = \frac{1}{2}(\frac{1}{2}+1)\alpha$, $s^2\beta = \frac{1}{2}(\frac{1}{2}+1)\beta$, $s_z\alpha = \frac{1}{2}\alpha$, and $s_z\beta = -\frac{1}{2}\beta$ give

$$
\begin{array}{llll}
\sigma_z\alpha = \alpha & (\sigma_x + i\sigma_y)\alpha = 0 & (\sigma_x - i\sigma_y)\alpha = 2\beta & \sigma^2\alpha = 3\alpha \\
\sigma_z\beta = -\beta & (\sigma_x + i\sigma_y)\beta = 2\alpha & (\sigma_x - i\sigma_y)\beta = 0 & \sigma^2\beta = 3\beta
\end{array}
\tag{4.2}
$$

These relations give the following explicit forms for the Pauli spin matrices:

$$
\sigma_x = \begin{pmatrix} 0 & 1 \\ 1 & 0 \end{pmatrix} \qquad
\sigma_y = \begin{pmatrix} 0 & -i \\ i & 0 \end{pmatrix} \qquad
\sigma_z = \begin{pmatrix} 1 & 0 \\ 0 & -1 \end{pmatrix} \tag{4.3}
$$

We see that these matrices satisfy the multiplication rules:

$$
\sigma_x{}^2 = \sigma_y{}^2 = \sigma_z{}^2 = 1
$$
$$
\sigma_x\sigma_y = i\sigma_z \qquad \sigma_y\sigma_z = i\sigma_x \qquad \sigma_z\sigma_x = i\sigma_y
\tag{4.4}
$$

These relations hold only for spin $j = \frac{1}{2}$. It follows from (4.4) that any product of Pauli matrices can be reduced to a linear form in these matrices.[1]

The wave function of a particle of spin $\frac{1}{2}$ is written in the form

$$
\varphi = \varphi(\mathbf{r}, \sigma) = \varphi_1(x,y,z)\,\alpha + \varphi_2(x,y,z)\,\beta = \begin{pmatrix} \varphi_1(x,y,z) \\ \varphi_2(x,y,z) \end{pmatrix} \tag{4.5}
$$

The column notation is adapted to the use of the Pauli spin matrices directly. The absolute square of $\varphi_1(x,y,z)$ is the probability density of finding the particle at the point x,y,z with spin pointing up; the absolute square of $\varphi_2(x,y,z)$ is the probability density of finding the particle at the same point with spin pointing down.

s_z is the operator associated with an infinitesimal rotation about the z direction. We get the operator for a finite rotation by multiplication of infinitesimal rotations; in particular, a rotation of the coordinate system through a finite angle ϑ about the z direction has the following effect on the spin properties of the wave function φ:

---

[1] This statement can be rephrased in algebraic language as follows: the matrices $\sigma_x, \sigma_y, \sigma_z$ together with the unit matrix form the basis of a hypercomplex number system.

$$\varphi \to U\varphi = \exp (is_z\vartheta) \ \varphi = \exp (i\tfrac{1}{2}\sigma_z\vartheta) \ \varphi$$

$$= 1 + i\frac{\vartheta}{2} \sigma_z\varphi - \frac{1}{2!}\left(\frac{\vartheta}{2}\right)^2 \varphi - \frac{i}{3!}\left(\frac{\vartheta}{2}\right)^3 \sigma_z\varphi + \cdots$$

$$= [\cos (\tfrac{1}{2}\vartheta) + i \sin (\tfrac{1}{2}\vartheta) \ \sigma_z] \ \varphi \qquad (4.6)$$

The occurrence of half-angles, $\tfrac{1}{2}\vartheta$, is characteristic of half-integral spin. In particular, (4.6) shows that a rotation of the coordinate system through the full angle 2π transforms φ into $-\varphi$, i.e., φ is double-valued. $|\varphi|^2$, the probability density, is single-valued, however.[1]

We now proceed to the composition of two spins of $\tfrac{1}{2}$, belonging to two different particles (e.g., a neutron and a proton). The spin angular momentum of the two-particle system is defined by

$$S_z = s_z(1) + s_z(2) = \tfrac{1}{2}\sigma_z(1) + \tfrac{1}{2}\sigma_z(2) \qquad (4.7)$$

with two similar equations for the x and y components, respectively.

Because of (4.4) and the fact that spin operators for the two separate particles commute with each other, the absolute square

$$S^2 = S_x{}^2 + S_y{}^2 + S_z{}^2$$

satisfies the equation

$$S^2 = \tfrac{1}{2}[3 + \mathbf{\sigma}(1)\cdot\mathbf{\sigma}(2)] \qquad (4.8)$$

A second application of the multiplication rules (4.4) gives:

$$S^2(S^2 - 2) = 0,$$

so that S^2 has only two eigenvalues: 0 and 2. There is only one eigen-function for $S^2 = 0$, namely the *singlet spin function:*

$$\chi_0 \equiv \frac{1}{\sqrt{2}} [\alpha(1) \ \beta(2) - \beta(1) \ \alpha(2)] \qquad (4.9)$$

This spin state is called the singlet state because it is non-degenerate. In the vector model of addition of angular momenta (see Section 5) this state is interpreted as the one in which the two spins $\mathbf{\sigma}_1$ and $\mathbf{\sigma}_2$ are opposite each other, so that each component of $\tfrac{1}{2}(\mathbf{\sigma}_1+\mathbf{\sigma}_2) = \mathbf{S}$ is separately zero, and hence $S^2 = 0$ also.

The eigenvalue 2 of S^2 is of the form $j(j+1)$ with $j = 1$, i.e., this state has (spin) angular momentum unity and correspondingly a degeneracy of $2j+1 = 3$. It is therefore called the *triplet spin state.* The simul-

---

[1] Since double-valued wave functions are admitted for half-integral spin, the double-valued character of $\exp (im\phi)$ with m half-integral is not a valid argument against half-integral values of the orbital angular momentum l.

taneous eigenfunctions of S^2 and S_z are denoted by $\chi_{1,m}$, where $m = 1,0,-1$ is the eigenvalue of S_z. They are

$$\chi_{1,1} \equiv \alpha(1)\,\alpha(2) \qquad \chi_{1,0} \equiv \frac{1}{\sqrt{2}}\,[\alpha(1)\,\beta(2) + \beta(1)\,\alpha(2)]$$

$$\chi_{1,-1} \equiv \beta(1)\,\beta(2)$$

(4.10)

In the vector addition model this state is interpreted as the one in which the two spins $\mathfrak{d}_1$ and $\mathfrak{d}_2$ are parallel to each other, the two spins of $\frac{1}{2}$ adding up to a total spin of 1.

Since there are three spin functions for the triplet state, and only one for the singlet state, the statistical weights of the two states for uncorrelated spins are $\frac{3}{4}$ and $\frac{1}{4}$, respectively. That is, if the spin directions of two particles (e.g., a neutron and proton in neutron-proton scattering) are random, the likelihood of finding the two particles in the triplet spin state is $\frac{3}{4}$, the likelihood of finding them in the singlet spin state is $\frac{1}{4}$.

At first this appears as a contradiction to the vector addition model: we might expect, from a naive point of view, that two spins are as often parallel as anti-parallel to each other, giving equal statistical weights to the two states. The contradiction is resolved by analyzing the quantum-mechanical meaning of "parallel" and "anti-parallel" spins in this case. Since σ_x and σ_y do not commute with σ_z, the spin direction of a particle cannot be defined uniquely as a vector in space. Rather, if σ_z is known (say the spin is up, $\sigma_z = 2m = +1$), the components σ_y and σ_x are unknown and their momentary values are either $+1$ or -1, with equal probability. Thus the statement "the spin direction is up" must be interpreted as "the spin vector points somewhere along a cone around the z direction." This is illustrated schematically in Figure 4.1a.

There are four equally probable possibilities for the relative position of the spin of the two particles as indicated in Fig. 4.1. Figures 4.1a and 4.1d correspond to a total spin $j = 1$ with $m = 1$ and -1, respectively. There are two possibilities, however, in cases (b) and (c). The two spins may combine in such a way that they are always opposed to each other; or they may combine so that both point toward the same side. In the first case they add up exactly to zero, and in the second case they add up to a total spin perpendicular to the z axis. The first case corresponds to the singlet state ($j = 0$), the second case corresponds to the triplet state $j = 1$, $m = 0$. [A straightforward geometrical consideration also shows that the scalar product $\mathfrak{d}(1) \cdot \mathfrak{d}(2)$ is -3 in the first case but equal to $1 + 1 - 1 = 1$ in the second case, in

agreement with (4.8).]   Figure 4.1 indicates that a relative probability
of three to one is obtained for the ratio of parallel to anti-parallel
alignment.   It comes from the fact that two particles, whose spins
have opposite z components, may still combine to a total spin equal
to unity.

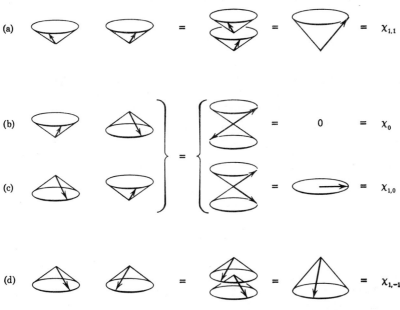

FIG. 4.1.   Two spins of $\tfrac{1}{2}$ can combine in four possible ways, three of which yield
triplet (parallel) spin states, whereas the fourth possibility corresponds to the
singlet (anti-parallel) spin state.

5. VECTOR ADDITION OF ANGULAR MOMENTA

Consider two angular momentum operators $\mathbf{J}_1$ and $\mathbf{J}_2$, each of which
separately satisfies the commutation rules (1.3) and which commute
with each other.   For example, the two angular momenta may be the
orbital angular momentum and spin angular momentum of the same
particle, or the angular momenta of two different particles.   Consider
the product of two angular momentum eigenfunctions $\mathsf{Y}_{jm}(1)\,\mathsf{Y}_{j'm'}(2)$
belonging to eigenvalues $j(j+1)$ of $J_1{}^2$, m of J_{1z}, $j'(j'+1)$ of $J_2{}^2$,
and m' of J_{2z}, respectively.   This product wave function is also an
eigenfunction of the z component of the total angular momentum

$$J_z = J_{1z} + J_{2z}$$

with eigenvalue $M = m + m'$.   In general, however, this product wave
function is not an eigenfunction of

$$J^2 = (J_{1x}+J_{2x})^2 + (J_{1y}+J_{2y})^2 + (J_{1z}+J_{2z})^2$$

However, linear combinations of products $\mathsf{Y}_{jm}(1)\,\mathsf{Y}_{j'm'}(2)$ can be formed which are simultaneous eigenfunctions of J^2, with eigenvalue $J(J+1)$, and of J_z, with eigenvalue M. These eigenfunctions of the total angular momentum will be denoted by $\mathcal{Y}^M_{Jjj'}$:

$$\mathcal{Y}^M_{Jjj'} = \sum_{m=-j}^{j} \sum_{m'=-j'}^{j'} C_{jj'}(J,M;m,m')\,\mathsf{Y}_{jm}(1)\,\mathsf{Y}_{j'm'}(2) \qquad (5.1)$$

The numerical coefficients C in this linear superposition are called Clebsch-Gordan coefficients or vector addition coefficients.[1] They are real numbers. It is apparent from the preceding considerations that $C_{jj'}(J,M;m,m')$ vanishes unless $M = m+m'$. The double sum in (5.1) is therefore only a single sum over m, with m' determined by $m' = M - m$. Nevertheless we prefer to write it as a double sum to bring out certain formal properties of the Clebsch-Gordan coefficients.

As a simple example of such Clebsch-Gordan series, consider (4.9) and (4.10) for the addition of two angular momenta of $\frac{1}{2}$. Looking at $\chi_{1,1}$, (4.10), we see that the Clebsch-Gordan coefficient

$$C_{jj'}(J,J;j,j') = 1 \qquad \text{(for } J=j+j') \qquad (5.2)$$

for $j=j'=\frac{1}{2}$ and $J=1$. This equation holds generally for the "stretched" configuration $J=j+j'$ and $J_z = M = J$. The same holds for the stretched configuration in the opposite direction, i.e., for $J=j+j'$, $C_{jj'}(J,-J;-j,-j') = 1$ also. As another example, we obtain from (4.9) the equations:

$$C_{1/2,1/2}(0,0;\tfrac{1}{2},-\tfrac{1}{2}) = -C_{1/2,1/2}(0,0;-\tfrac{1}{2},\tfrac{1}{2}) = 2^{-1/2}$$

It is apparent that the Clebsch-Gordan coefficients are not necessarily symmetric in the interchange of j,m with j',m'. Rather, they satisfy the relation

$$C_{jj'}(J,M;m,m') = (-1)^{J-j-j'}C_{j'j}(J,M;m',m) \qquad (5.3)$$

which can be checked also in connection with $\chi_{1,0}$, (4.10). Relation (5.3) is a special case of the more general symmetry relation (5.9).

The possible values of the quantum number J are

---

[1] We mention notation: Condon (35) uses the symbol $(jj'mm'|jj'JM)$ for our $C_{jj'}(J,M;m,m')$ and puts $j=j_1$, $j'=j_2$, $J=j$, $m=m_1$, $m'=m_2$, and $M=m$, so that the symbol is written $(j_1j_2m_1m_2|j_1j_2jm)$. Wigner (31) uses the symbol $S^{jj'}_{Jmm'}$. It should be emphasized, however, that the coefficients themselves are the same here as in Wigner (31) and Condon (35), i.e., the phases of the spherical harmonics as well as the normalization are chosen the same way.

$$J = j+j', j+j'-1, j+j'-2, \cdots, |j-j'| \qquad (5.4)$$

Conversely we can write the product $Y_{jm}(1)\, Y_{j'm'}(2)$ as a linear superposition of the $\mathcal{Y}^M_{Jjj'}$, as follows:

$$Y_{jm}(1)\, Y_{j'm'}(2) = \sum_{J=|j-j'|}^{j+j'} \sum_{M=-J}^{J} C_{jj'}(J,M;m,m')\, \mathcal{Y}^M_{Jjj'} \qquad (5.5)$$

The sum over M consists of only one term, $M = m+m'$.

Certain *orthogonality relations* follow from the fact that the functions Y_{jm} form an orthonormal set, and so do the $\mathcal{Y}^M_{Jjj'}$. In effect, the Clebsch-Gordan coefficients are the matrix elements of a unitary transformation, and, since they are real numbers, the transformation is actually an orthogonal transformation. We get:

$$\sum_{m=-j}^{j} \sum_{m'=-j'}^{j'} C_{jj'}(J,M;m,m')\, C_{jj'}(J',M';m,m') = \delta_{JJ'}\, \delta_{MM'} \qquad (5.6)$$

$$\sum_{J=|j-j'|}^{j+j'} \sum_{M=-J}^{J} C_{jj'}(J,M;m,m')\, C_{jj'}(J,M;m'',m''') = \delta_{mm''}\, \delta_{m'm'''} \qquad (5.7)$$

In spite of their apparently unsymmetrical definition, the Clebsch-Gordan coefficients are almost symmetrical in all three angular momenta J,j,j'. The symmetry relations can be exhibited most clearly by a method due to Racah (42a) and Eisenbud (48). We define the quantity $V(jj'J,mm'M)$ by:[1]

$$V(jj'J,mm'M) \equiv (-)^{J-M}\,(2J+1)^{-1/2}\, C_{jj'}(J,-M;m,m') \qquad (5.8)$$

V vanishes unless $m+m'+M=0$. Furthermore, it obeys the following symmetry relations:

$$V(abc,\alpha\beta\gamma) = (-)^{a+b-c}\, V(bac,\beta\alpha\gamma) = (-)^{a+b+c}\, V(acb,\alpha\gamma\beta)$$

$$= (-)^{a-b+c}\, V(cba,\gamma\beta\alpha) = (-)^{2b}\, V(cab,\gamma\alpha\beta)$$

$$= (-)^{2c}\, V(bca,\beta\gamma\alpha) = (-)^{a+b+c}\, V(abc,-\alpha-\beta-\gamma) \qquad (5.9)$$

As a particular result of these symmetry relations, we quote the modified form of the orthogonality relation (5.6):

$$\sum_{M=-J}^{J} \sum_{m''=-j''}^{j''} C_{jj''}(J,M;m,m'')\, C_{j'j''}(J,M;m',m'') = \frac{2J+1}{2j+1}\, \delta_{jj'}\delta_{mm'}$$

$$(5.10)$$

[1] Notice the $-M$ on the right-hand side!

The general formula for the Clebsch-Gordan coefficients was derived by Wigner (31), but it is very unwieldy.[1] Tables 5.1 and 5.2

TABLE 5.1

CLEBSCH-GORDAN COEFFICIENTS $C_{jj'}(J,M;m,m')$ FOR $j' = \frac{1}{2}$

	$m' = \frac{1}{2}$	$m' = -\frac{1}{2}$
$J = j + \frac{1}{2}$	$\left[\dfrac{j+M+\frac{1}{2}}{2j+1} \right]^{1/2}$	$\left[\dfrac{j-M+\frac{1}{2}}{2j+1} \right]^{1/2}$
$J = j - \frac{1}{2}$	$-\left[\dfrac{j-M+\frac{1}{2}}{2j+1} \right]^{1/2}$	$\left[\dfrac{j+M+\frac{1}{2}}{2j+1} \right]^{1/2}$

TABLE 5.2

CLEBSCH-GORDAN COEFFICIENTS $C_{jj'}(J,M;m,m')$ FOR $j' = 1$

	$m' = 1$	$m' = 0$	$m' = -1$
$J = j+1$	$\left[\dfrac{(j+M)(j+M+1)}{(2j+1)(2j+2)} \right]^{1/2}$	$\left[\dfrac{(j-M+1)(j+M+1)}{(2j+1)(j+1)} \right]^{1/2}$	$\left[\dfrac{(j-M)(j-M+1)}{(2j+1)(2j+2)} \right]^{1/2}$
$J = j$	$-\left[\dfrac{(j+M)(j-M+1)}{2j(j+1)} \right]^{1/2}$	$\dfrac{M}{[j(j+1)]^{1/2}}$	$\left[\dfrac{(j-M)(j+M+1)}{2j(j+1)} \right]^{1/2}$
$J = j-1$	$\left[\dfrac{(j-M)(j-M+1)}{2j(2j+1)} \right]^{1/2}$	$-\left[\dfrac{(j-M)(j+M)}{j(2j+1)} \right]^{1/2}$	$\left[\dfrac{(j+M+1)(j+M)}{2j(2j+1)} \right]^{1/2}$

are short tables of the Clebsch-Gordan coefficients, taken from Condon (35). We restrict ourselves to the case where j' is either $\frac{1}{2}$ or 1. Condon (35) also tabulates the cases $j' = \frac{3}{2}$ and $j' = 2$. Tables 5.1 and 5.2 can be used not only when j' is either $\frac{1}{2}$ or 1, but whenever any one of j, j', or J is $\frac{1}{2}$ or 1, by exploiting the symmetry relations (5.9). The tables given here suffice for neutron-proton scattering with tensor forces (for which $j' = S = 1$, triplet state), for the analysis of magnetic moments by either the Schmidt model ($j' = \frac{1}{2}$) or by the Wigner-Margenau approach, and for many nuclear reaction experiments. If all of j, j', and J exceed 1, the tables of Condon (35) should be consulted.

In the analysis of angular distributions in nuclear reactions, or of angular correlations in two successive radioactive decays, the product of two spherical harmonics of the *same* angle variables must be expressed as a linear combination of spherical harmonics. The relevant formula is

[1] For a derivation of Wigner's general formula without the explicit use of group theoretical methods, see Racah (42a).

$Y_{lm}(\theta,\phi) \ Y_{l'm'}(\theta,\phi)$

$$= \sum_L \sum_M \left[\frac{(2l+1)(2l'+1)}{4\pi(2L+1)} \right]^{1/2} C_{ll'}(L,0\,;0,0) \ C_{ll'}(L,M\,;m,m') \ Y_{LM}(\theta,\phi)$$

(5.11)

Frequently sums of products of three Clebsch-Gordan coefficients, summed over three of the six magnetic quantum numbers, are needed. Such sums have been evaluated by Racah (42a), and somewhat less explicitly by Myers (38). The formulas are too complicated to reproduce here, however. For applications, see Lloyd (50, 51a) and Blatt (51).

SYMBOLS

$A_l(r)$	Coefficient in the expansion of a plane wave (3.1), (3.2)
$C_{jj'}(J,M\,;m,m')$	Clebsch-Gordan coefficient (5.1)
$d\Omega$	Element of solid angle (2.6)
$g(\theta,\phi)$	An arbitrary square integrable function of θ and ϕ (Section 2)
H	Hamiltonian of the system (Section 1)
j	Quantum number for the angular momentum, defined by $J^2\varphi = j(j+1)\varphi$ (1.4)
j'	Quantum number for an angular momentum which combines with j to give the total angular momentum J (5.1)
$j_l(kr)$	Spherical Bessel function (3.2)
J	Quantum number for the total angular momentum (5.1)
$\mathbf{J}$	A general angular momentum vector (Section 1)
J^2	Absolute square of the vector $\mathbf{J}$ (Section 1)
J_x, J_y, J_z	Components of the vector $\mathbf{J}$ (Section 1)
$J_\lambda(z)$	Bessel function of z of the first kind and order λ (3.2)
k	Wave number of a plane wave (3.1)
$\mathbf{k}$	Wave vector of a plane wave (3.5)
l	Quantum number for the orbital angular momentum, defined by $L^2\varphi = l(l+1)\varphi$ (2.2)
$\mathbf{L}$	Orbital angular momentum vector (Section 1)
L_x, L_y, L_z	Components of the vector $\mathbf{L}$ (1.2), (1.3)
m	Quantum number for the z component of an angular momentum, defined by $J_z\varphi = m\varphi$ (1.4)

m'	Quantum number for the z component of the angular momentum j' (5.1)
M	Quantum number for the z component of the total angular momentum $[=m+m']$ (5.1)
$n!!$	The double factorial (2.3)
$P_l(\cos\theta)$	Legendre polynomial of order l (2.5)
r	Radial coordinate in the spherical coordinate system (3.1)
$\mathbf{s}$	Spin angular momentum vector (Section 4)
s_x, s_y, s_z	Components of the vector $\mathbf{s}$ (Section 4)
$\mathbf{S}$	Spin vector of a two-particle system (Section 4)
S^2	Absolute square of the vector $\mathbf{S}$ (4.8)
S_z	z component of the vector $\mathbf{S}$ (4.7)
U	Matrix associated with a rotation around the z axis through a finite angle ϑ (4.6)
$V(jj'J, mm'M)$	A quantity related to the Clebsch-Gordan coefficient (5.8)
Y_{jm}	Eigenfunction of the angular momentum operators J^2 and J_z with eigenvalues $j(j+1)$ and m, respectively (1.4)
$\mathcal{Y}^M_{Jjj'}$	Eigenfunction of the total angular momentum (5.1)
$Y_{lm}(\theta,\phi)$	Normalized spherical harmonic (2.4)
α	Angle between the directions (θ,ϕ) and (θ',ϕ') (2.7)
α	Spin function for a particle with spin up (4.1)
β	Spin function for a particle with spin down (4.1)
$\delta_{mm'}$	Kronecker delta (2.6)
ϑ	Angle of rotation (1.1)
θ	Polar angle (colatitude) defining the position of a particle (2.1)
Θ	Polar angle (colatitude) of the wave vector $\mathbf{k}$ (3.5)
$\sigma_x, \sigma_y, \sigma_z$	Pauli spin matrices (4.2), (4.3)
$\varphi(x,y,z)$	A wave function (1.1)
φ'	The wave function φ after a rotation of the coordinate system (1.1)
ϕ	Polar angle (longitude) defining the position of a particle (2.1)
$\varphi_1(x,y,z)$	Up-spin component of the wave function φ (4.5)

$\varphi_2(x,y,z)$ Down-spin component of the wave function φ (4.5)

Φ Polar angle (longitude) of the wave vector $\mathbf{k}$ (3.5)

χ_0 Spin function for the singlet state of two particles of spin $\frac{1}{2}$ (4.9)

$\chi_{1,m}$ Spin function for the triplet state of two particles of spin $\frac{1}{2}$, corresponding to the orientation m of the resultant spin   (4.10)

APPENDIX B

Multipole Radiation

1. VECTOR SPHERICAL HARMONICS

Let us suppose that the differential equations and boundary conditions for some classical vector field $\mathbf{A}(\mathbf{r})$ (which may or may not be an electromagnetic field) are invariant under rotations of the coordinate system and under reflection (the parity operation). If $\mathbf{A}(\mathbf{r})$ is a solution, we obtain another solution by rotating the vector field bodily through some angle ϑ about the z axis. This "rotated" field has the following components:

$$A_x'(x,y,z) = \cos\vartheta\, A_x(x\cos\vartheta+y\sin\vartheta,\, y\cos\vartheta-x\sin\vartheta,\, z)$$
$$- \sin\vartheta\, A_y(x\cos\vartheta+y\sin\vartheta,\, y\cos\vartheta-x\sin\vartheta,\, z)$$

$$A_y'(x,y,z) = \sin\vartheta\, A_x(x\cos\vartheta+y\sin\vartheta,\, y\cos\vartheta-x\sin\vartheta,\, z) \qquad (1.1)$$
$$+ \cos\vartheta\, A_y(x\cos\vartheta+y\sin\vartheta,\, y\cos\vartheta-x\sin\vartheta,\, z)$$

$$A_z'(x,y,z) = A_z(x\cos\vartheta+y\sin\vartheta,\, y\cos\vartheta-x\sin\vartheta,\, z)$$

Since the field equations are linear (by assumption), we get yet another solution by taking the difference between the rotated field $\mathbf{A}'$ and the original field $\mathbf{A}$. We let ϑ become infinitesimally small and obtain the new solution in the form

$$\mathbf{A}' - \mathbf{A} = -i\vartheta\, J_z \mathbf{A} = -i\vartheta\, (L_z + S_z)\, \mathbf{A} \qquad (1.2)$$

where L_z is the angular momentum operator defined by (A,1.2) and S_z is defined as follows:

$$S_z \begin{pmatrix} A_x \\ A_y \\ A_z \end{pmatrix} \equiv \begin{pmatrix} -iA_y \\ iA_x \\ 0 \end{pmatrix} \qquad (1.3)$$

Since $J_z\mathbf{A}$ is a solution if $\mathbf{A}$ is a solution, the infinitesimal rotation operator J_z must commute with the differential equation of the vector field $\mathbf{A}$. It is easy to verify that J_z commutes with the operation $\nabla \times \mathbf{A}$.

The form $J_z = L_z + S_z$ can be interpreted as a breakup of the angular momentum operator J_z[1] into orbital and spin angular momentum. The additional operator S_z which did not appear in (A,1.2) is needed because of the "shuffling" of components apparent in (1.1): only the z component (along the axis of rotation) transforms like a scalar field. Thus the "spin" operator S_z is a consequence of the vector nature of the field **A**. The operator identity $S_z(S_z^2 - 1) = 0$ shows that S_z can have only three eigenvalues: 1, 0, and -1. Hence the spin associated with a vector field is unity. The three eigenvectors of S_z which correspond to these three eigenvalues are

$$\chi_1 = -\frac{1}{\sqrt{2}} (\mathbf{e}_x + i\mathbf{e}_y) \qquad \chi_0 = \mathbf{e}_z \qquad \chi_{-1} = \frac{1}{\sqrt{2}} (\mathbf{e}_x - i\mathbf{e}_y) \quad (1.4)$$

where $\mathbf{e}_x$, $\mathbf{e}_y$, and $\mathbf{e}_z$ are three unit vectors along the coordinate directions. The χ_m are normalized to unit length, and the signs are chosen to agree with the general relations (A,1.4).

The operators J_x and J_y are defined analogously to J_z, (1.2), by performing rotations about the x and y axes, respectively. The three components of the vector **J** obey the commutation rules:

$$J_x J_y - J_y J_x = iJ_z, \quad \text{etc.}$$

which are characteristic of angular momentum operators.

We now define *vector spherical harmonics*[2] $\mathbf{Y}(\theta, \phi)$ as vector functions of the angles only (independent of the radial coordinate r) which are simultaneous eigenfunctions of J_z and $J^2 = J_x^2 + J_y^2 + J_z^2$. Since the operators **L** and **S** commute, we can construct these vector spherical harmonics by using the vector addition law (A,5.1). For each value of $J^2 = J(J+1)$ with $J \geq 1$, there are three kinds of vector spherical harmonics, corresponding to $l = J+1$, $l = J$, and $l = J - 1$. They are

$$\mathbf{Y}_{Jl1}^M(\theta, \phi) \equiv \sum_{m=-l}^{l} \sum_{m'=-1}^{1} C_{l1}(J, M; m, m') \, Y_{lm}(\theta, \phi) \, \chi_m \qquad (1.5)$$

We observe that only integral values of J appear, and this is necessary for a classical field since it must be single-valued. There are three different vector spherical harmonics for each value of J except for $J = 0$. In the case $J = 0$ we get only one vector spherical har-

---

[1] At this stage of the analysis it is not apparent that the infinitesimal rotation operator J_z is related to the angular momentum in the field. For the special case of the electromagnetic field a proof appears in Section 3.

[2] Vector spherical harmonics similar to those defined here have been used by various authors, e.g., Corben (40), Goertzel (46) and Berestetski (48).

monic, corresponding to a value of **L** equal to unity and directed oppositely to **S**. The corresponding vector spherical harmonic is $Y_{011}^0 = -(4\pi)^{-1/2}e_r$, where e_r is a unit vector in the radial direction.

The vector functions Y_{Jl1}^M have parity $(-1)^l$. Thus, for given values of J and M, the parity of the function with $l=J$ is $(-1)^J$, while the parity of the other two functions is $(-1)^{J+1}$. Since the scalar spherical harmonics Y_{lm} form a complete set for scalar functions, and the χ_m are a complete set of basis vectors in three dimensions, the vector spherical harmonics (1.5) are a complete set also. That is, any vector field **A(r)** can be written as a linear combination of the $Y_{Jl1}^M(\theta,\phi)$ with coefficients which depend on the radial coordinate r only.

The vector spherical harmonics which we shall use most are the ones with $l=J$. We introduce the special notation $X_{JM}(\theta,\phi)$ for $Y_{JJ1}^M(\theta,\phi)$. These functions can also be expressed in the form

$$X_{JM}(\theta,\phi) \equiv Y_{JJ1}^M(\theta,\phi) = \frac{L\,Y_{JM}(\theta,\phi)}{\sqrt{J(J+1)}} \tag{1.6}$$

where **L** is the differential operator $-i r \times \nabla$ and the Y's are the scalar spherical harmonics of Appendix A. The parity of X_{JM} is $(-1)^J$, and X_0 vanishes identically.

Since the operator $\nabla \times$ commutes with the operator **J**, the curl of an expression with some definite value of J and M must be a linear combination of vector spherical harmonics with the same J and M. In particular, we have

$$\nabla \times [f(r)\,X_{JM}(\theta,\phi)] = \nabla \times [f(r)\,Y_{JJ1}^M(\theta,\phi)]$$

$$= f_+(r)\,Y_{J,J+1,1}^M(\theta,\phi) + f_-(r)\,Y_{J,J-1,1}^M(\theta,\phi) \tag{1.7}$$

where $f(r)$ is an arbitrary function of r, and $f_+(r)$ and $f_-(r)$ can be deduced from $f(r)$. The vector spherical harmonics on the right side of (1.7) have parity $-(-1)^J$, in agreement with the fact that taking the curl of an expression with definite parity transforms it into an expression with opposite parity.

Since the vector spherical harmonics form a complete set, an arbitrary vector field **A(r)** can be expanded into a series:

$$A(r) = \sum_{J=0}^{\infty} \sum_{M=-J}^{J} A(J,M;r) \tag{1.8a}$$

with

$$\mathbf{A}(J,M;\mathbf{r}) = r^{-1}[f(J,M;r)\,\mathbf{X}_{JM} + g(J,M;r)\,\mathbf{Y}^{M}_{J,J+1,1}$$
$$+ h(J,M;r)\,\mathbf{Y}^{M}_{J,J-1,1}] \quad (1.8b)$$

where f, g, and h are functions of the radial coordinate r only. Each term $\mathbf{A}(J,M;\mathbf{r})$ is called a "pure multipole field" and is an eigenfunction of the operators J^{2} and J_{z}:

$$J^{2}\,\mathbf{A}(J,M;\mathbf{r}) = J(J+1)\,\mathbf{A}(J,M;\mathbf{r})$$
$$J_{z}\,\mathbf{A}(J,M;\mathbf{r}) = M\,\mathbf{A}(J,M;\mathbf{r}) \tag{1.9}$$

Furthermore the first term in (1.8b) has parity $(-1)^{J}$, while the remaining two terms have parity $-(-1)^{J}$.

The vector spherical harmonics satisfy the orthogonality and normalization relations

$$\int [\mathbf{Y}^{M}_{Jl1}(\theta,\phi)]^{*} \cdot [\mathbf{Y}^{M'}_{J'l'1}(\theta,\phi)]\,d\Omega = \delta_{JJ'}\delta_{MM'}\delta_{ll'} \tag{1.10}$$

These relations can be used to obtain explicit expressions for the functions f, g, and h in (1.8b). We form the dot product of the general vector field $\mathbf{A}(\mathbf{r})$ with the quantity $[\mathbf{Y}^{M}_{Jl1}(\theta,\phi)]^{*}$ and integrate over all angles, but not over r. This gives the results

$$r^{-1}f(J,M;r) = \int [\mathbf{X}_{JM}(\theta,\phi)]^{*}\cdot\mathbf{A}(r,\theta,\phi)\,d\Omega$$
$$r^{-1}g(J,M;r) = \int [\mathbf{Y}^{M}_{J,J+1,1}(\theta,\phi)]^{*}\cdot\mathbf{A}(r,\theta,\phi)\,d\Omega \tag{1.11}$$
$$r^{-1}h(J,M;r) = \int [\mathbf{Y}^{M}_{J,J-1,1}(\theta,\phi)]^{*}\cdot\mathbf{A}(r,\theta,\phi)\,d\Omega$$

2. ELECTRIC AND MAGNETIC MULTIPOLE EXPANSION IN FREE SPACE

We now apply the expansion (1.8) to the electromagnetic field in free space. We restrict ourselves to fields varying periodically in time:

$$\mathbf{\mathcal{E}}(\mathbf{r},t) = \mathbf{\mathcal{E}}(\mathbf{r})\,e^{-i\omega t} + \mathbf{\mathcal{E}}^{*}(\mathbf{r})\,e^{+i\omega t} \tag{2.1}$$

with a similar equation for the magnetic field $\mathcal{H}$. The Maxwell equations in free space (using mixed Gaussian units) are then[1]

$$c\,\boldsymbol{\nabla}\times\mathcal{H} = -i\omega\mathbf{\mathcal{E}} \qquad c\,\boldsymbol{\nabla}\times\mathbf{\mathcal{E}} = i\omega\mathcal{H} \tag{2.2}$$

It is a consequence of these equations that the divergence of $\mathbf{\mathcal{E}}$ and $\mathcal{H}$ is zero.

Evidently, both vector fields $\mathbf{\mathcal{E}}$ and $\mathcal{H}$ can be expanded in the form (1.8). From now on, we shall use the quantum numbers l,m instead

---

[1] From here on the symbols $\mathbf{\mathcal{E}}$ and $\mathcal{H}$ stand for the functions $\mathbf{\mathcal{E}}(\mathbf{r})$ and $\mathcal{H}(\mathbf{r})$ defined by (2.1), i.e., $\mathbf{\mathcal{E}}$ and $\mathcal{H}$ are independent of time.

of J,M in the multipole expansions (1.8). The electromagnetic multipole fields are furthermore subdivided into *electric* and *magnetic* multipoles. This division is made on account of the parity of the field. According to the definitions of Chapter XII, Section 2, the relations are as follows: In the *electric* multipole radiation of order l,m, the electric field has the parity $-(-1)^l$, and the magnetic field has the parity $(-1)^l$. In the *magnetic* multipole radiation of order l,m the parities are exactly opposite.

The parity properties of the field strengths make it possible to determine directly the angular dependence of the field strengths. Consider first the *electric* multipole radiation of order l,m. Its magnetic field must have the parity $(-1)^l$, and hence in the expansion (1.8) of this field the functions $g(l,m;r)$ and $h(l,m;r)$ must vanish since the $Y^m_{l,l\pm1,1}$ have the wrong parity:

$$\mathfrak{IC} = r^{-1} f_E(l,m;r) \, \mathbf{X}_{lm}(\theta,\phi) \qquad \text{(electric radiation)} \qquad (2.3)$$

The function $f_E(l,m;r)$ can be determined from the free-space wave equation $(\kappa \equiv \omega/c)$

$$\nabla \times \nabla \times \mathfrak{IC} - \kappa^2 \mathfrak{IC} = 0 \qquad (2.4)$$

which follows from (2.2). Substituting (2.3) into (2.4) leads to the well-known radial equation for f in free space:

$$\left[\frac{d^2}{dr^2} - \frac{l(l+1)}{r^2} + \kappa^2 \right] f(l,m;r) = 0 \qquad (2.5)$$

Since we are interested in radiation emitted by a source at the origin, we look for a solution of (2.5) which represents an outgoing wave. This is the function $u_l^{(+)}(r)$ which was defined in Chapter VIII, (VIII,2.41). It is normalized by the condition that

$$u_l^{(+)}(r) \cong \exp\left[i(\kappa r - \tfrac{1}{2}l\pi)\right] \qquad \text{(for } r \to \infty)$$

Hence we can write for the magnetic field of the *electric multipole radiation of order l,m*

$$\left.\begin{aligned} \mathfrak{IC}(\mathbf{r}) &= a_E(l,m) \, \mathfrak{IC}_E(l,m;\mathbf{r}) \\[4pt] \mathfrak{IC}_E(l,m;\mathbf{r}) &= \frac{u_l^{(+)}(r)}{\kappa r} \, \mathbf{X}_{lm}(\theta,\phi) \end{aligned}\right\} \text{(outside the source)} \qquad (2.6)$$

In this form the field appears as an amplitude $a_E(l,m)$ times a standard space dependence which is non-dimensional. Thus the amplitude $a_E(l,m)$ has the dimension of a field $(= \text{charge}/r^2)$.

The corresponding electric field of the *electric multipole radiation of order l,m* can be calculated by applying the first Maxwell equation (2.2) to (2.6):

$$\left.\begin{aligned} \mathcal{E}(\mathbf{r}) &= a_E(l,m)\ \mathcal{E}_E(l,m;\mathbf{r}) \\ \mathcal{E}_E(l,m;\mathbf{r}) &= \frac{i}{\kappa}\ \boldsymbol{\nabla}\times\mathcal{H}_E(l,m;\mathbf{r}) \end{aligned}\right\} \text{(outside the source)} \qquad (2.7)$$

It is seen from relation (1.7) that the electric field $\mathcal{E}$ belongs to the same eigenvalues of J_z and J^2 as $\mathcal{H}$ but, if written in the form (1.8), would give rise to $f(l,m;r)=0$, $g(l,m;r)\neq0$, $h(l,m;r)\neq0$.

The electric and magnetic fields of the *magnetic* multipole radiation can be derived in a similar way by exchanging the roles of $\mathcal{E}$ and $\mathcal{H}$. We get the following expressions, which are analogous to (2.6) and (2.7), for *magnetic radiation of order l,m* outside the source:

$$\left.\begin{aligned} \mathcal{E}(\mathbf{r}) &= a_M(l,m)\ \mathcal{E}_M(l,m;\mathbf{r}) \\ \mathcal{E}_M(l,m;\mathbf{r}) &= \frac{u_l^{(+)}(r)}{\kappa r}\ \mathbf{X}_{lm}(\theta,\phi) \end{aligned}\right\} \text{(outside the source)} \qquad (2.8)$$

and

$$\left.\begin{aligned} \mathcal{H}(\mathbf{r}) &= a_M(l,m)\ \mathcal{H}_M(l,m;\mathbf{r}) \\ \mathcal{H}_M(l,m;\mathbf{r}) &= -\frac{i}{\kappa}\ \boldsymbol{\nabla}\times\mathcal{E}_M(l,m;\mathbf{r}) \end{aligned}\right\} \text{(outside the source)} \qquad (2.9)$$

Hence expressions (XII,2.7) and (XII,2.8) are justified.[1]

The vector spherical harmonic $\mathbf{X}_{lm}(\theta,\phi)$ is easily shown to be a transverse vector, i.e., perpendicular to the radial vector $\mathbf{r}$ at all points of the sphere. Hence the magnetic field in electric multipole radiation has no radial component, and this radiation is therefore sometimes called "transverse magnetic" or *TM* radiation. It seems more appropriate to call it electric radiation, since we shall see that the electric charge density in the source determines the major part of that radiation, whereas the current density determines the magnetic (or *TE*) radiation.

It should be noted that $\mathbf{X}_{lm}=0$ for $l=0$. Hence no multipole radiation exists of order $l=0$.

---

[1] Expressions for the electric and magnetic fields in pure multipole radiation have been derived by many authors, e.g., Heitler (36), Hansen (35), Dancoff (39a), Corben (40), Goertzel (46), Franz (50).

3. ENERGY AND ANGULAR MOMENTUM OF THE MULTIPOLE
RADIATION

We now study the energy and the angular momentum of the multi-pole radiation. Consider a region of space, such as a large spherical box around the origin. The energy of the electromagnetic field in this sphere is given by

$$\text{Energy in field} = \frac{1}{4\pi} \int (\boldsymbol{\mathcal{E}}^* \cdot \boldsymbol{\mathcal{E}} + \boldsymbol{\mathcal{H}}^* \cdot \boldsymbol{\mathcal{H}}) \, dV \qquad (3.1)$$

Here only the time-independent terms are included because the others do not contribute to the average value. The density of linear momentum in the field is $1/c^2$ of the Poynting vector (which gives the energy flow), i.e., the linear momentum density is $(4\pi c)^{-1}(\boldsymbol{\mathcal{E}} \times \boldsymbol{\mathcal{H}})$. The density of angular momentum is the cross product of the radius vector $\mathbf{r}$ and the linear momentum density. Hence we get for the time average of the total angular momentum in the field

$$\mathbf{G} = (4\pi c)^{-1} \int \mathbf{r} \times (\boldsymbol{\mathcal{E}}^* \times \boldsymbol{\mathcal{H}} + \boldsymbol{\mathcal{E}} \times \boldsymbol{\mathcal{H}}^*) \, dV \qquad (3.2)$$

We wish to relate the angular momentum in the radiation field to the infinitesimal rotation operator of the previous section.[1] It is possible to prove the equality

$$\kappa^{-1} \int [\boldsymbol{\mathcal{E}}^* \cdot (J_z \boldsymbol{\mathcal{E}}) + \boldsymbol{\mathcal{H}}^* \cdot (J_z \boldsymbol{\mathcal{H}})] \, dV$$
$$= z \text{ component of } \int \mathbf{r} \times (\boldsymbol{\mathcal{E}}^* \times \boldsymbol{\mathcal{H}} + \boldsymbol{\mathcal{E}} \times \boldsymbol{\mathcal{H}}^*) \, dV \qquad (3.3)$$

by the use of the Maxwell equations (2.2) and a number of vector relations. It is necessary for the validity of (3.3) that all surface integrals vanish, i.e., the fields must be zero at the boundary of the large volume into which the fields are included. We can imagine, for example, that the field was switched on some finite time T ago, and the volume is chosen such that its radius exceeds cT.

Let us consider in particular a pure multipole field l,m. In this case $J_z \boldsymbol{\mathcal{E}} = m\boldsymbol{\mathcal{E}}$, $J_z \boldsymbol{\mathcal{H}} = m\boldsymbol{\mathcal{H}}$, and we get directly from (3.1), (3.2) and (3.3)

$$G_z = \frac{m}{\omega} \frac{1}{4\pi} \int (|\boldsymbol{\mathcal{E}}|^2 + |\boldsymbol{\mathcal{H}}|^2) \, dV = \left(\frac{m}{\omega}\right) \times (\text{energy in field}) \qquad (3.4)$$

---

[1] The following proof, as well as much of the rest of this appendix is based on the work of Franz (50). Indeed, the only additions to Franz's work are at the very beginning and end of this appendix: the derivation of the operator $\mathbf{J}$ from infinitesimal rotations, and the relation of the multipole fields to the source of the radiation (the multipole moments).

Hence, if there is only one quantum of this multipole radiation in the field, the energy is $\hbar\omega$ and the z component of the angular momentum is $\hbar m$. A more detailed investigation (J. H. D. Jensen, private communication) shows that, in this case, the square of the angular momentum is $l(l+1)\hbar^2$. This constitutes the proof that the angular momentum of each quantum of a multipole radiation field, is determined by its order l,m just as the angular momentum of a particle is determined by the quantum numbers l and m.[1]

4. THE SOURCES OF MULTIPOLE RADIATION; MULTIPOLE MOMENTS

We now connect the radiation with its sources and we determine the amplitudes $a_E(l,m)$ in (2.6) and (2.7) as functions of the current density and magnetization of the source. In view of the later applications to nuclei, we shall assume that the source contains not only a distribution of currents $\mathbf{j}(\mathbf{r})$ and charges $\rho(\mathbf{r})$, but also a distribution of magnetization $\mathbf{M}(\mathbf{r})$. The Maxwell equations for a periodically varying field then are[2]

$$c \, \nabla \times \mathfrak{IC} = -i\omega\mathcal{E} + 4\pi\mathbf{j} \tag{4.1a}$$

$$c \, \nabla \times \mathcal{E} = i\omega \, (\mathfrak{IC} + 4\pi\mathbf{M}) \tag{4.1b}$$

$$\text{div } \mathbf{j} = i\omega\rho \tag{4.1c}$$

Equations (4.1) reduce to (2.2) outside the source. We shall also need the equations for $\mathcal{E}$ or $\mathfrak{IC}$ alone, obtained by eliminating one or the other of the fields from (4.1). These equations are, with $\kappa \equiv \omega/c$,

---

[1] It follows from this derivation that the angular momentum is contained everywhere in the field, not merely in the near zone, as asserted by Heitler (36). This can be seen most simply by imagining that the field was emitted during a short time Δt. The field then spreads out like a spherical shell, and the angular momentum contained in the field initially has to stay within that expanding shell.
We can write (3.2) in the form

$$\mathbf{G} = (4\pi c)^{-1}\int[(\mathbf{r}\cdot\mathfrak{IC})\mathcal{E}^* - (\mathbf{r}\cdot\mathcal{E}^*)\mathfrak{IC}] \, dV + \text{complex conjugate}$$

Heitler's argument is based on the fact that the fields are transverse in the wave zone. However, this transversality is not complete. Either $\mathcal{E}$ or $\mathfrak{IC}$ or both have radial components proportional to r^{-2}, so that either $(\mathbf{r}\cdot\mathcal{E})$ or $(\mathbf{r}\cdot\mathfrak{IC})$ or both are proportional to r^{-1}, giving a finite contribution to the integral even in the wave zone.

[2] The continuity equation (4.1c) is independent of the preceding two. The three equations (4.1) imply that $\text{div}\,\mathcal{E} = 4\pi\rho$ and $\text{div}(\mathfrak{IC}+4\pi\mathbf{M}) = \text{div}(\mathbf{B}) = 0$, which are the remaining Maxwell equations. This derivation of the remaining two Maxwell equations from the three equations (4.1) depends upon the assumption $\omega \neq 0$, and consequently fails for static fields (which are of no interest here).

$$\nabla \times \nabla \times \mathfrak{IC} - \kappa^2 \mathfrak{IC} = \frac{4\pi}{c} (\nabla \times \mathbf{j} + c\kappa^2 \mathbf{M}) \qquad (4.2a)$$

$$\nabla \times \nabla \times \mathcal{E} - \kappa^2 \mathcal{E} = \frac{4\pi i \kappa}{c} (\mathbf{j} + c\nabla \times \mathbf{M}) \qquad (4.2b)$$

Evidently these equations are the generalizations of (2.4) in the presence of the sources.

We shall determine the solutions of (4.2) which have the character of pure multipole radiations. We begin with the electric radiation of order l,m. It was shown in Section 2 that the magnetic field must have the form (2.3). The need for this special form arises from symmetry considerations (correct angular momentum and parity) and is therefore not affected by the presence of sources of the field. On the other hand, the function $f_E(l,m;r)$ defined by (2.3) no longer satisfies the differential equation (2.5). We find the correct differential equation by substituting (2.3) into (4.2a), taking the scalar product of $\mathbf{X}_{lm}{}^*(\theta,\phi)$ with the differential equation (4.2a), and integrating over all angles (but not over r). The result is

$$\left[-\frac{d^2}{dr^2} + \frac{l(l+1)}{r^2} - \kappa^2 \right] f_E(l,m;r) = K_E(l,m;r) \qquad (4.3)$$

where the source term K_E is given by

$$K_E(l,m;r) = \frac{4\pi r}{c} \int [\mathbf{X}_{lm}{}^*(\theta,\phi)] \cdot [\nabla \times \mathbf{j} + c\kappa^2 \mathbf{M}] \, d\Omega \qquad (4.4)$$

The integration in (4.4) is over the angles only, not over r. Outside the source itself, the source term K vanishes, and we obtain (2.5) whose solution is (2.6).

We get similar expressions for the *magnetic* radiation of order l,m. In this case the electric field is given by an expression of the form (2.3):

$$\mathcal{E} = r^{-1} f_M(l,m;r) \, \mathbf{X}_{lm}(\theta,\phi) \qquad \text{(magnetic radiation)} \qquad (4.5)$$

where $f_M(l,m;r)$ satisfies a differential equation equal to (4.3) except for the source term, which becomes

$$K_M(l,m;r) = \frac{4\pi i \kappa r}{c} \int [\mathbf{X}_{lm}{}^*(\theta,\phi)] \cdot [\mathbf{j} + c\nabla \times \mathbf{M}] \, d\Omega \qquad (4.6)$$

As in (4.4), the integration is over the angles only, not over r. Outside the source itself, the source term again vanishes, so that the electric field in the magnetic radiation is given by (2.8).

Equation (4.3) with the source terms (4.4) and (4.6) enables us to determine the values of the amplitudes $a_E(l,m)$ and $a_M(l,m)$ of the fields outside the source. We simply solve (4.3) with the sources (4.4) and (4.6) for all r and find the asymptotic form of f_E and f_M for large r. Comparison of the asymptotic form of f_E with (2.6) determines the amplitude $a_E(l,m)$, while a comparison of the asymptotic form of f_M with (2.8) determines the amplitude $a_M(l,m)$.

The Green's function for (4.3) can be written in terms of the solutions of the homogeneous differential equation. We need the regular solution $F_l(r)$, (VIII,2.39), in addition to the outgoing wave solution $u_l^{(+)}(r)$, (VIII,2.41), employed so far. Let $r_<$ denote the smaller of r and r', $r_>$ denote the larger of r and r'. Then the Green's function for (4.3) which leads to outgoing radiation is

$$G(r,r') = \kappa^{-1} F_l(r_<) \, u_l^{(+)}(r_>) \qquad (4.7)$$

The solution of (4.3) for arbitrary values of r is

$$f_E(l,m;r) = \int_0^\infty G(r,r') \, K_E(r') \, dr' \qquad (4.8)$$

We are interested only in the asymptotic behavior of this solution for large r, outside the source. Then the values of r' which contribute to the integral (4.8) are smaller than r, so that we can identify $r_<$ in (4.7) with r', $r_>$ with r, giving

$$f_E(l,m;r) = \kappa^{-1} \left[\int_0^\infty F_l(r') \, K_E(r') \, dr' \right] u_l^{(+)}(r)$$
$$\text{(outside the source)} \quad (4.9)$$

Comparison of (4.9) with (2.3) and (2.6) gives the following value for the amplitude of the electric radiation:

$$a_E(l,m) = \int_0^\infty F_l(r) \, K_E(r) \, dr$$
$$= \frac{4\pi}{c} \int r^{-1} F_l(r) \, \mathbf{X}_{lm}^* \cdot (\boldsymbol{\nabla} \times \mathbf{j} + c\kappa^2 \mathbf{M}) \, dV \qquad (4.10)$$

An entirely analogous derivation gives, for the amplitude of the magnetic radiation,

$$a_M(l,m) = \int_0^\infty F_l(r) \, K_M(r) \, dr$$
$$= \frac{4\pi i \kappa}{c} \int r^{-1} F_l(r) \, \mathbf{X}_{lm}^* \cdot (\mathbf{j} + c\boldsymbol{\nabla} \times \mathbf{M}) \, dV \qquad (4.11)$$

The last integrals in (4.10) and (4.11) extend over the entire volume of the source distribution. We emphasize that expressions (4.10) and (4.11) are exact. We have not made any approximations (such as wavelength long compared to the dimensions of the source) and have identified the multipole fields and the contributing parts of the source by their symmetry properties under rotation and inversion, properties which are independent of the wavelength and follow directly from the basic invariance of the Maxwell equations. These relations were derived independently by Wallace (51) by a somewhat different method.

At this stage of the analysis, however, it becomes preferable to assume that the wavelength of the light is large compared to the dimensions of the source, i.e., that $\kappa r \ll 1$ for all values of r which contribute to the integrals in (4.10) and (4.11). In that case we can replace the regular solution $F_l(r)$ by its asymptotic form for small values of r, $(\kappa r)^{l+1}/(2l+1)!!$. We also use the explicit form (1.6) for $\mathbf{X}_{lm}$ and the Hermitean property of the operator $\mathbf{L}$ to get instead of (4.10) the approximate form

$$a_E(l,m) \cong \frac{4\pi}{c} \frac{\kappa^{l+1}}{(2l+1)!!\sqrt{l(l+1)}} \int r^l \, Y_{lm}{}^*(\theta,\phi) \, (\mathbf{L}\cdot\nabla\times\mathbf{j} + c\kappa^2\mathbf{L}\cdot\mathbf{M}) \, dV$$

$$(4.12)$$

We now use the vector identities:

$$\mathbf{L}\cdot\nabla\times\mathbf{j} = -i\left[(\mathbf{r}\cdot\nabla + 2)(\nabla\cdot\mathbf{j}) - \nabla^2(\mathbf{r}\cdot\mathbf{j})\right]$$

$$\mathbf{L}\cdot\mathbf{M} = i\nabla\cdot(\mathbf{r}\times\mathbf{M})$$

$$(4.13)$$

The divergence of $\mathbf{j}$ can be expressed in terms of the charge density ρ by means of the continuity equation, (4.1c). The integral in (4.12) then assumes the form

$$\int r^l \, Y_{lm}{}^*(\theta,\phi) \, [\omega(\mathbf{r}\cdot\nabla)\rho + 2\omega\rho + i\nabla^2(\mathbf{r}\cdot\mathbf{j}) + ic\kappa^2\nabla\cdot(\mathbf{r}\times\mathbf{M})] \, dV$$

We now perform integrations by parts. The operator $(\mathbf{r}\cdot\nabla) = r\partial/\partial r$ then gives a factor $-(l+3)$, while the Laplacian operator ∇^2 gives zero when applied to the function $r^l Y_{lm}{}^*$. Thus the final result is[1]

---

[1] It may appear surprising that this final result depends on the current density $\mathbf{j}$ only through $\nabla\cdot\mathbf{j}$ (i.e., through ρ), whereas the exact expression (4.12) contains $\mathbf{j}$ only through $\nabla\times\mathbf{j}$. (This difficulty was pointed out to us by Dr. B. French, in a private communication.) However, if the divergence and curl of a vector field are assigned arbitrary independent values, the field decreases for large distances only very slowly, like r^{-2}. Conversely, if we know that $\mathbf{j}$ vanishes identically outside some source radius R, $\nabla\cdot\mathbf{j}$ and $\nabla\times\mathbf{j}$ are no longer independent of each other.

$$a_E(l,m) \cong - \frac{4\pi}{(2l+1)!!} \left(\frac{l+1}{l} \right)^{1/2} \kappa^{l+2} \, (Q_{lm} + Q'_{lm}) \qquad (4.14)$$

where

$$Q_{lm} = \int r^l \, Y_{lm}^*(\theta,\phi) \, \rho(\mathbf{r}) \, dV \qquad (4.15)$$

$$Q'_{lm} = - \frac{i\kappa}{l+1} \int r^l \, Y_{lm}^*(\theta,\phi) \, \mathrm{div} \, (\mathbf{r} \times \mathbf{M}) \, dV \qquad (4.16)$$

An entirely similar derivation reduces (4.11) to the approximate form[1]

$$.a_M(l,m) \cong + \frac{4\pi}{(2l+1)!!} \left(\frac{l+1}{l} \right)^{1/2} \kappa^{l+2} \, (M_{lm} + M'_{lm}) \qquad (4.17)$$

where

$$M_{lm} = - \frac{1}{c(l+1)} \int r^l \, Y_{lm}^*(\theta,\phi) \, \mathrm{div} \, (\mathbf{r} \times \mathbf{j}) \, dV \qquad (4.18)$$

$$M'_{lm} = - \int r^l \, Y_{lm}^*(\theta,\phi) \, \mathrm{div} \, \mathbf{M} \, dV \qquad (4.19)$$

Unlike equations (4.10) and (4.11), equations (4.14) to (4.19) are only approximate and depend for their validity on the assumption that the wavelength of the emitted light is large compared to the dimensions of the source.

5. EXPANSION OF A PLANE WAVE INTO MULTIPOLE FIELDS

It is convenient to consider circularly polarized light. For right and left circularly polarized light waves moving in the z direction, the electric vector is given by

$$\mathcal{E}(\mathbf{r}) = \frac{1}{\sqrt{2}} (\mathbf{e}_x \pm i\mathbf{e}_y) \exp(i\kappa z) = \mp \exp(i\kappa z) \, \chi_{\pm 1} \qquad (5.1)$$

where the upper sign refers to right circular polarization, the lower one to left circular polarization. The magnetic field is determined from the free-space Maxwell equations (2.2) to be

$$\mathcal{H}(\mathbf{r}) = \mathbf{e}_z \times \mathcal{E}(\mathbf{r}) = i \exp(i\kappa z) \, \chi_{\pm 1} \qquad (5.2)$$

We now use the expansion, (A.3.1) and (A.3.2), for the exponential, and we express the product $Y_{l,0}(\theta) \, \chi_m$ in terms of the vector spherical harmonics $\mathbf{Y}_{Jl1}^M$ by the use of (A.5.5). The result is[2]

---

[1] The choice of opposite signs in (4.14) and (4.17) was made in order to get physically reasonable signs for the multipole moments Q and M.

[2] The term $J = 0$ is absent since $M = m_l + m_s$ is never zero.

$$\mathbf{\mathcal{E}(r)} = \mp \sum_{J=1}^{\infty} \sum_{l=J-1}^{J+1} i^l \sqrt{4\pi(2l+1)} \; C_{l1}(J, \pm 1;0, \pm 1) \; j_l(\kappa r) \; \mathbf{Y}_{Jl1}^{\pm 1}(\theta, \phi)$$

$$(5.3a)$$

$$\mathbf{\mathcal{H}(r)} = \sum_{J=1}^{\infty} \sum_{l=J-1}^{J+1} i^{l+1} \sqrt{4\pi(2l+1)} \; C_{l1}(J, \pm 1;0, \pm 1) \; j_l(\kappa r) \; \mathbf{Y}_{Jl1}^{\pm 1}(\theta, \phi)$$

$$(5.3b)$$

We observe that the only multipole fields which occur are those with $M = \pm 1$. This is a consequence of the fact that we are quantizing angular momenta in the direction of the beam, so that the orbital angular momentum has $m_l = 0$, and the spin of the photon, though unity, can have the z components $m_s = \pm 1$ only, because the electromagnetic field is transverse, whereas the vector $\chi_0 = \mathbf{e}_z$ for $m_s = 0$ is longitudinal. Furthermore only the regular spherical Bessel function $j_l(\kappa r) = (\kappa r)^{-1} F_l(r)$ occurs in this expansion because the plane wave (5.1) is regular everywhere, including the point $r = 0$.

In order to bring the expansion (5.3) into a more familiar form, we concentrate our attention on the terms involving the vector spherical harmonics $\mathbf{Y}_{JJ1}^{M}$ with $l = J$, i.e., the $\mathbf{X}_{JM}$ defined by (1.6). From Table 5.2 of Appendix A we obtain for the relevant Clebsch-Gordan coefficients

$$C_{l1}(J = l, \pm 1;0, \pm 1) = \mp \sqrt{\tfrac{1}{2}}$$

We identify the terms in $\mathbf{\mathcal{E}(r)}$, (5.3a), which are proportional to $\mathbf{X}_{JM}$ as magnetic radiation, the terms in $\mathbf{\mathcal{H}(r)}$ proportional to $\mathbf{X}_{JM}$ as electric radiation, according to the arguments of Section 2. The magnetic field in magnetic radiation and the electric field in electric radiation are then found from the free-space Maxwell equations (2.2). The result is (writing l instead of J)

$$\mathbf{\mathcal{E}(r)} = \sum_{l=1}^{\infty} i^l \sqrt{2\pi(2l+1)} \; \{ \pm \kappa^{-1} \, \text{curl} \, [j_l(\kappa r) \, \mathbf{X}_{l,\pm 1}] + j_l(\kappa r) \, \mathbf{X}_{l,\pm 1} \}$$

$$(5.4a)$$

$$\mathbf{\mathcal{H}(r)} = \sum_{l=1}^{\infty} i^l \sqrt{2\pi(2l+1)} \; \left\{ \mp i \, j_l(\kappa r) \, \mathbf{X}_{l,\pm 1} - \frac{i}{\kappa} \, \text{curl} \, [j_l(\kappa r) \, \mathbf{X}_{l,\pm 1}] \right\}$$

$$(5.4b)$$

This is the desired expansion of the plane wave, (5.1) and (5.2). In each brace the first term represents electric radiation, the second magnetic radiation.

6. THE ABSORPTION PROBABILITY OF A LIGHT QUANTUM

We determine the probability that a system is excited from a lower state a to a higher state b by the absorption of a light quantum from an unpolarized incident beam. The beam is parallel to the z axis and is not monochromatic. It contains all frequencies near the resonance frequency $\omega_{ab} = (E_b - E_a)/\hbar$, and the number of quanta incident per square centimeter per second with frequencies between ω and $\omega + d\omega$ is $S(\omega)\, d\omega$. We also assume that the parity and angular momentum of states a and b are such that the transition can be performed only by the absorption of an electric multipole quantum of order l.[1]

We connect the absorption probability $A_E(l)$ with the spontaneous emission probabilities $T_E(l,m)$ which were determined in Chapter XII, Section 3, and are given by (XII,3.21). The incident plane wave contains multipole radiation with the quantum numbers $m = \pm 1$ only; hence the absorption is the reverse process of the emission of a multipole l with $m = \pm 1$. Thus the absorption probability $A_E(l)$ is proportional to the sum of the emission probabilities $T_E(l, m=1)$ and $T_E(l, m=-1)$; it is also proportional to the flux in the incident light beam at the absorption frequency ω_{ab}, i.e., to $S(\omega_{ab})$. We can therefore write

$$A_E(l) = q_l\, S(\omega_{ab})\, [T_E(l,1) + T_E(l,-1)] \qquad (6.1)$$

where q_l is a constant factor which we must now determine.

In order to find q_l we make use of the fact that the probabilities of the two inverse processes, the absorption and the spontaneous emission, are equal if the intensity of the incident light in the case of absorption is such that there is one light quantum in each proper vibration of the radiation field. Under this condition the statistical weight of the end states in the two inverse processes is equal: every proper vibration *into* which a quantum may be emitted corresponds to one proper vibration *from* which a light quantum may be absorbed. Let $S_{0l}(\omega_{ab})$ be the light flux corresponding to this condition for the multipole radiation of order l. Then we get

$$A_E(l) = T_E(l,1) + T_E(l,-1) = q_l\, S_{0l}(\omega_{ab})\, [T_E(l,1) + T_E(l,-1)] \quad (6.2)$$

so that the coefficient q_l in (6.1) is given by

$$q_l = [S_{0l}(\omega_{ab})]^{-1} \qquad (6.3)$$

Thus the problem is reduced to the determination of the particular flux $S_{0l}(\omega)$, which corresponds to one light quantum in each proper

[1] This assumption is made for the sake of simplicity and can be removed without difficulty.

vibration of the radiation field with multipole order l. In order to define the proper vibrations we include the radiation field in a large sphere of radius R with perfectly reflecting walls (at which the tangential component of the electric field must vanish). The proper vibrations (normal modes) of the radiation field in this box are standing waves of definite multipole type. The electric modes have the form

$$\mathcal{E}_E(l,m;\mathbf{r}) = \frac{i}{\kappa} \nabla \times [j_l(\kappa r)\, \mathbf{X}_{lm}]$$

$$\mathcal{K}_E(l,m;\mathbf{r}) = j_l(\kappa r)\, \mathbf{X}_{lm}$$

(6.4)

where $j_l(\kappa r)$ is the spherical Bessel function used in Appendix A, Section 3. The magnetic multipole modes are obtained by the replacement $\mathcal{K} \rightarrow \mathcal{E}$, $\mathcal{E} \rightarrow -\mathcal{K}$. In either case the boundary condition at $r = R$ restricts the possible values of the wave number κ. We need the number of normal modes of given multipole type l,m with wave numbers κ between κ and $\kappa + d\kappa$. Let us call this number $z(\kappa)\, d\kappa$ (it is independent of l and m). Then the use of the asymptotic form (A,3.4) for the spherical Bessel functions together with the boundary condition at the walls of the sphere gives

$$z(\kappa)\, d\kappa = \frac{R}{\pi} d\kappa = \frac{R}{\pi}\left(\frac{d\omega}{c}\right)$$

(6.5)

We shall now construct a plane wave which corresponds to an incident continuous spectrum of frequencies. This wave is an incoherent superposition of waves of type (5.1) having frequencies ω within some finite frequency interval. The amplitudes of the waves (5.1) of frequency ω we shall call $A_{0l}^{+}(\omega)$ and $A_{0l}^{-}(\omega)$ for the right-hand and left-hand circularly polarized parts, respectively. $|A_{0l}^{+}(\omega)|^2\, d\omega$ is the intensity of the right-hand circularly polarized wave in the frequency interval $d\omega$. We shall choose the amplitudes A_{0l} such that the number of quanta of type l,m within the frequency interval ω, $\omega + d\omega$ is given by (6.5). Then the quantum flux (number of quanta per square centimeter per second) in this wave in the frequency interval $d\omega$ is $S_{0l}(\omega)\, d\omega$.

We start by determining the amplitudes A_{0l}^{+} and A_{0l}^{-}. The energy of the electromagnetic field in this plane wave associated with a given multipole type (say electric, with definite l and m) can be found by taking the relevant term from (5.4a) and substituting this field into (3.1). Since the various frequencies which make up this beam are by assumption incoherent, the cross terms drop out, and the energy dE

contained in the frequency interval ω, $\omega+d\omega$ and of multipole type $l, m = +1$ is

$$dE(l,\ m=+1)\ =\ (2l+1)\int_0^R j_l{}^2(\kappa r)\ r^2\ dr\ |A_{0l}^+(\omega)|^2\ d\omega$$

$$=\ (2l+1)\frac{R}{2\kappa^2}\ |A_{0l}^+(\omega)|^2\ d\omega \tag{6.6}$$

where we have used the asymptotic form (A,3.4) of $j_l(\kappa r)$ to evaluate the integral. A similar expression holds for $dE(l, m = -1)$.

The number of quanta of definite multipole type in the frequency range in question is given by $dE/(\hbar\omega)$. Equating this to (6.5), we get

$$|A_{0l}^+(\omega)|^2\ =\ |A_{0l}^-(\omega)|^2\ =\ \frac{2}{\pi}\left(\frac{\hbar\omega}{c}\right)\kappa^2\ (2l+1)^{-1} \tag{6.7}$$

Now that we know the amplitudes, we merely have to determine the flux of quanta associated with this plane wave. The *energy* flux is given by the average value of the Poynting vector, i.e., by (XII,3.13) and (XII,3.14). The energy flux associated with the frequency interval $d\omega$ is therefore

$$\text{Energy flux in } d\omega\ =\ \frac{c}{2\pi}\left[|A_{0l}^+(\omega)|^2 + |A_{0l}^-(\omega)|^2\right]d\omega \tag{6.8}$$

The flux of quanta is obtained from (6.8) by division by the quantum energy $\hbar\omega$, and this flux must be equated to $S_{0l}(\omega)\ d\omega$. We then get the final result for the proportionality coefficient q_l in (6.1):

$$q_l\ =\ [S_{0l}(\omega)]^{-1}\ =\ (2l+1)\frac{\pi^2}{2\kappa^2} \tag{6.9}$$

Equations (6.1) and (6.9), together with (XII,3.21) for the transition probability $T_E(l,m)$, give the absorption probability (XII,3.25).

SYMBOLS

a	Quantum state of a material system before absorption of radiation (Section 6)
$a_E(l,m)$	Amplitude of the electric multipole radiation of order l,m (2.6)
$a_M(l,m)$	Amplitude of the magnetic multipole radiation of order l,m (2.8)
$\mathbf{A}(\mathbf{r})$	A general vector field (Section 1)
$\mathbf{A'}$	The vector field $\mathbf{A}$ after a rotation of the coordinate system (11.)

$A_E(l)$ — Probability per unit time for the transition $a \rightarrow b$ with absorption of a quantum of electric multipole radiation of order l (Section 6)

$\mathbf{A}(J,M;\mathbf{r})$ — The part of the general vector field $\mathbf{A}(\mathbf{r})$ with total angular momentum J and z component of total angular momentum M (1.8)

$A_{0l}^{+}(\omega)$ — Amplitude of the right-hand circularly polarized wave of frequency ω in the incident spectrum (Section 6)

$A_{0l}^{-}(\omega)$ — Amplitude of the left-hand circularly polarized wave of frequency ω in the incident spectrum (Section 6)

b — Quantum state of a material system after absorption of radiation (Section 6)

$\mathbf{B}$ — Magnetic induction vector (Section 4)

c — Speed of light (2.2)

$C_{l1}(J,M;m,m')$ — Clebsch-Gordan coefficient; for its definition and properties see Appendix A, Section 5 (1.5)

$dE(l,m)$ — Energy contained in the frequency interval ω, $\omega+d\omega$ and associated with radiation of multipole type l,m (6.6)

$d\Omega$ — Element of solid angle (1.10)

$\mathbf{e}_r$ — A unit vector in the outward radial direction (Section 1)

$\mathbf{e}_x$ — A unit vector in the x direction (1.4)

$\mathbf{e}_y$ — A unit vector in the y direction (1.4)

$\mathbf{e}_z$ — A unit vector in the z direction (1.4)

E_a — Energy of the system in quantum state a (Section 6)

E_b — Energy of the system in quantum state b (Section 6)

$\boldsymbol{\varepsilon} = \boldsymbol{\varepsilon}(\mathbf{r})$ — Electric field vector of a periodically varying field (2.1)

$\boldsymbol{\varepsilon}(\mathbf{r},t)$ — Electric field vector of a field varying arbitrarily with time (2.1)

$\boldsymbol{\varepsilon}_E(l,m;\mathbf{r})$ — Standard electric field of the electric multipole radiation of order l,m (2.7)

$\boldsymbol{\varepsilon}_M(l,m;\mathbf{r})$ — Standard electric field of the magnetic multipole radiation of order l,m (2.8)

$f(r)$ — An arbitrary function of r (1.7)

$f_{+}(r)$ — A function derivable from $f(r)$ (1.7)

$f_{-}(r)$ — A function derivable from $f(r)$ (1.7)

$f(J,M;r)$	Coefficient of the vector spherical harmonic $\mathbf{X}_{JM}$ in the multipole expansion of a general vector field (1.8b)
$f_E(l,m;r)$	Radial dependence of the electric multipole field of order l,m (2.3)
$f_M(l,m;r)$	Radial dependence of the magnetic multipole field of order l,m (4.5)
$F_l(r)$	Regular solution of the radial equation for angular momentum l; for its definition, see Chapter VIII, (VIII,2.39) (4.7)
$g(J,M;r)$	Coefficient of the vector spherical harmonic $\mathbf{Y}^M_{J,J+1,1}$ in the multipole expansion of a general vector field (1.8b)
$\mathbf{G}$	Angular momentum vector for the radiation field as a whole (3.2)
$G(r,r')$	The Green's function for the radial equation (4.7)
$h(J,M;r)$	Coefficient of the vector spherical harmonic $\mathbf{Y}^M_{J,J-1,1}$ in the multipole expansion of a general vector field (1.8b)
$\mathcal{H} = \mathcal{H}(\mathbf{r})$	Magnetic field vector for a periodically varying field (2.2)
$\mathcal{H}_E(l,m;\mathbf{r})$	Standard magnetic field of the electric multipole radiation of order l,m (2.6)
$\mathcal{H}_M(l,m;\mathbf{r})$	Standard magnetic field of the magnetic multipole radiation of order l,m (2.9)
$\mathbf{j} = \mathbf{j}(\mathbf{r})$	Current density in the source of the field (4.1)
$j_l(\kappa r)$	Spherical Bessel function; for its definition and properties see Appendix A, Section 3 (5.3)
J	Quantum number for the total angular momentum, defined by $J^2\mathbf{Y}=J(J+1)\mathbf{Y}$ (1.5)
J^2	Absolute square of the vector $\mathbf{J}$ (Section 1)
J_z	z component of the vector $\mathbf{J}$ (1.2)
$\mathbf{J}$	Angular momentum vector operator for a vector field (Section 1)
$K_E(l,m;r)$	Source term for the radial wave equation of the electric multipole field of order l,m (4.3), (4.4)
$K_M(l,m;r)$	Source term for the radial wave equation of the magnetic multipole field of order l,m (4.6)
	Quantum number for the orbital angular momentum, defined by $L^2\mathbf{Y}=l(l+1)\mathbf{Y}$ (1.5)
	Quantum number for the total angular momentum (used in place of J) (Section 2 ff)

L	Orbital angular momentum vector operator $[= -i\mathbf{r} \times \nabla]$ (Section 1)
L_z	z component of the orbital angular momentum operator **L** (1.2)
m	Quantum number for the z component of the orbital angular momentum (Section 1)
m	Quantum number for the z component of the total angular momentum (used in place of M) (Sections 2 ff.)
m'	Quantum number for the z component of the spin angular momentum (Section 1)
M	Quantum number for the z component of the total angular momentum, defined by $J_z\mathbf{Y} = M\mathbf{Y}$ (1.5)
$\mathbf{M} = \mathbf{M}(\mathbf{r})$	Density of magnetization in the source of the field (4.1)
M_{lm}	Magnetic multipole moment of order l,m associated with the convection currents (4.17), (4.18)
M'_{lm}	Magnetic multipole moment of order l,m associated with the distribution of magnetization **M** (4.17), (4.19)
q_l	Proportionality factor relating the probability for emission and absorption of multipole radiation of order l (6.1)
Q_{lm}	Electric multipole moment of order l,m associated with the convection currents (4.14), (4.15)
Q'_{lm}	Electric multipole moment of order l,m associated with the distribution of magnetization **M** (4.14), (4.16)
$\mathbf{r}$	Position vector (Section 1)
$r_<$	The smaller of r,r' (4.7)
$r_>$	The larger of r,r' (4.7)
R	Radius of a large sphere with reflecting walls (Section 6)
S	Spin angular momentum vector operator for a vector field (Section 1)
S_z	z component of **S** (1.3)
$S(\omega)$	Quantum flux of the incident light beam per unit range of the circular frequency ω (Section 6)
$S_{0l}(\omega)$	Light flux corresponding to one light quantum in each proper vibration of the radiation field with multipole order l (6.2)
t	Time coordinate (2.1)

T	A large time interval (Section 3)
$T_E(l,m)$	Probability per unit time of spontaneous emission of a quantum of electric multipole radiation of order l,m, the material system dropping from state b to state a (Section 6)
$u_l^{(+)}(r)$	Radial wave function for an outgoing wave with angular momentum l; for its definition see Chapter VIII, (VIII,2.41) (2.6)
$\mathbf{X}_{JM}(\theta,\phi)$	Vector spherical harmonic with $l=J$ (1.6)
$Y_{lm}(\theta,\phi)$	Scalar spherical harmonic; for its definition see Appendix A, Section 2 (1.5)
$\mathbf{Y}_{Jl1}^{M}(\theta,\phi)$	Vector spherical harmonic (1.5)
$z(\kappa)$	Number of normal modes of multipole order l,m per unit range of the wave number κ (6.5)
$\delta_{JJ'}$	Kronecker delta (1.10)
Δt	A short time interval (Section 3)
ϑ	Angle of rotation (1.1)
θ	Polar angle (colatitude) of the position vector $\mathbf{r}$ (1.5)
κ	Wave number of the electromagnetic radiation $[=\omega/c]$ (2.4)
$\rho=\rho(\mathbf{r})$	Charge density in the source of the field (4.1)
ϕ	Polar angle (longitude) of the position vector $\mathbf{r}$ (1.5)
χ_1	Eigenfunction of a vector field with spin up (1.4)
χ_0	Eigenfunction of a vector field with horizontal spin (1.4)
χ_{-1}	Eigenfunction of a vector field with spin down (1.4)
ω	Circular frequency of a periodically varying electromagnetic field (2.1)
ω_{ab}	Resonance frequency for the absorption of light by a system going from state a to state b $[=(E_b-E_a)/\hbar]$ (Section 6)

References

Roman and Arabic numbers in parentheses at end of reference indicate chapter and section numbers in this volume.

Aamodt, L. C.   See Townes, C. H. (49a).

Abelson, P. H. (39).   Phys. Rev., **56**, 753 (1939).   (XIII,3)

Adair, R. K. (49).   (With C. K. Bockelman and R. E. Peterson.)   Phys. Rev., **76**, 308 (1949) L.   (IX,2)

—— See also Barschall, H. H. (49).

Adams, E. N., II.   See Avery, R. (49).

Akhiezer, A. (48).   (With I. Pomeranchuk.)   J. Exptl. Theoret. Phys. (U.S.S.R.), **18**, 603 (1948).   (VIII,8)

Albert, R. D. (48).   (With C. S. Wu.)   Phys. Rev., **74**, 847 (1948) L.   (XIII, 2)

Alder, K. (51).   Phys. Rev., **83**, 1266 (1951) L.   (XII,6)

Allen, J. S. (42).   Phys. Rev., **61**, 692 (1942).   (XIII,3)

—— (49).   (With H. R. Paneth and A. H. Morrish.)   Phys. Rev., **75**, 570 (1949).   (XIII,5)

—— See also Smith, P. B. (51).

Almy, G. M.   See Diven, B. C. (50).

Amaldi, E. (42).   (With D. Bocciarelli, B. Ferretti, and G. Trabacchi.)   Naturwiss., **30**, 582 (1942); Ricerca sci., **13**, 502 (1942).   (IV,2)

—— (46).   (With D. Bocciarelli, C. Cacciaputo, and G. Trabacchi.)   Nuovo cimento, **3**, 203 (1946).   (IX, 2)

Anderson, E. E.   See Sutton, R. B. (47).

Anderson, H. L. (47).   (With A. Novick.)   Phys. Rev., **71**, 372 (1947).   (V,2)

Angus, J.   See Curran, S. C. (48), (49).

Arfken, G. B.   See Breit, G. (50); Hatcher, R. D. (49).

Arnold, W. R. (47).   (With A. Roberts.)   Phys. Rev., **71**, 878 (1947).   (I,7)

—— (50).   Phys. Rev., **79**, 170 (1950); **80**, 34 (1950).   (XII,6)

Ashkin, J. (48).   (With T. Wu.)   Phys. Rev., **73**, 973 (1948).   (IV,1)

Aston, F. W. (27).   Proc. Roy. Soc., **A115**, 487 (1927).   (I,2)

Austern, N. (50).   Chicago Meeting of the Physical Society, Nov. 24, 1950, paper J6.   (XII,4)

—— (51).   (With R. G. Sachs.)   Phys. Rev., **81**, 710 (1951).   (XII,6,7)

—— See also Sachs, R. G. (51).

Avery, R. (48).   (With R. G. Sachs.)   Phys. Rev., **74**, 1320 (1948).   (I,7), (VI,5)

—— (49).   (With E. N. Adams, II.)   Phys. Rev., **75**, 1106 (1949) L.   (VI,5)

—— See also Blanchard, C. H. (51).

Axel, P. (49).   (With S. M. Dancoff.)   Phys. Rev., **76**, 892 (1949).   (XII,6)

—— (50).   Phys. Rev., **80**, 104 (1950) L.   (XIV, 2)

—— See also Mann, L. G. (50); Ovadia, J. (51).

Bacher, R. F.   See Bethe, H. A. (36a).

Bailey, C. D. (46).   (With W. E. Bennett, T. Bergstralh, R. G. Nuckolls, H. T. Richards, and J. H. Williams.)   Phys. Rev., **70**, 583 (1946).   (II,3)

Baldwin, G. C. (48).   (With G. S. Klaiber.)   Phys. Rev., **73**, 1156 (1948).   (XII,7)

818 References

Barber, W. C. (50). Phys. Rev., **80**, 332 (1950). (XII,6)
Bardeen, J. (37). Phys. Rev., **51**, 799 (1937). (VIII,6)
—— (38). (With E. Feenberg.) Phys. Rev., **54**, 809 (1938). (VIII,6)
Barkas, W. H. (39). (With M. G. White.) Phys. Rev., **56**, 288 (1939). (V,4)
—— (39a). Phys. Rev., **55**, 691 (1939). (VII,2)
Barker, E. C. See Snell, A. H. (49), (50a).
Barker, F. C. (49). (With R. E. Peierls.) Phys. Rev., **75**, 312 (1949) L. (II,3)
Barnes, C. A. (50). (With G. H. Stafford and D. H. Wilkinson.) Nature, **165**, 69 (1950). (XII,4)
Barrett, J. H. (50). Phys. Rev., **79**, 907 (1950) L. (XIII,1)
Barschall, H. H. (40). (With M. H. Kanner.) Phys. Rev., **58**, 590 (1940). (V,4)
—— (48). (With C. K. Bockelman and L. W. Seagondollar.) Phys. Rev., **73**, 659 (1948). (IX,2)
—— (49). (With C. K. Bockelman, R. E. Peterson, and R. K. Adair.) Phys. Rev., **76**, 1146 (1949). (IX,2), (XIV,1)
—— (49a). (With R. F. Taschek.) Phys. Rev., **75**, 1819 (1949). (IV,2)
—— See also Gittings, H. T. (49); Henkel, R. L. (50;) Peterson, R. E. (50).
Bartholomew, G. A. See Kinsey, B. B. (50).
Bartlett, J. H., Jr. (36). Phys. Rev., **49**, 102 (1936) L. (III,3)
Bashkin, S. (50). (With B. Petree, F. P. Mooring, and R. E. Peterson.) Phys. Rev., **77**, 748 (1950) A. (VIII,4)
Baumhoff, L. See Horning, W. (49).
Becker, R. A. See McElhinney, J. (49).
Beckerley, J. G. (45). Phys. Rev., **67**, 11 (1945). (II,4)
Becquerel, H. (96). Compt. rend., **122** (1896). (I,3)
Beeman, W. W. (47). Phys. Rev., **72**, 986 (1947). (IX,2)
Bell, P. R. (49). (With B. H. Ketelle and J. M. Cassidy.) Phys. Rev., **76**, 574 (1949). (XII,6)
Bell, R. E. (48). (With L. G. Elliott.) Phys. Rev., **74**, 1552 (1948) L. (II,2)
—— (50). (With R. L. Graham.) Phys. Rev., **78**, 490 (1950). (XII,6)
—— See also Elliott, L. G. (48), (49).
Bender, R. S. (49). (With F. C. Shoemaker, S. G. Kaufmann, and G. M. B. Bouricius.) Phys. Rev., **76**, 273 (1949). (IX,3)
Benfield, A. E. (48). Phys. Rev., **74**, 621 (1948). (XIII,1)
Bennett, W. E. (41). (With T. W. Bonner, E. Hudspeth, H. T. Richards, and B. E. Watt.) Phys. Rev., **59**, 781 (1941). (IX,6)
—— See also Bailey, C. D. (46).
Benoist, P. (49). (With R. Bouchez, P. Daudel, R. Daudel, and A. Rogozinski.) Phys. Rev., **76**, 1000 (1949) L. (XIII,3)
Berestetski, V. B. (48). J. Exptl. Theoret. Phys. (U.S.S.R.), **18**, 1057 (1948). (In Russian.) (XII,6), (B,1)
Bergstralh, T. See Bailey, C. D. (46).
Bergström, I. (50). Phys. Rev., **80**, 114 (1950) L. (XII,6)
Berthelot, A. (42). J. phys. et radium, **3**, 17, 52 (1942). (XIV,1)
—— (44). Ann. phys., **19**, 219 (1944). (XII,6)
Bethe, H. A. (33). *Handbuch der Physik*, vol. 24, 1, Chapter 3 (1933). (II,5), (XII,7), (XIII,3,5), (XIV,2), (A,1,2)
—— (34). (With R. Peierls.) Nature, **133**, 532 (1934). (XIII,1)

Bethe, H. A (35). (With R. Peierls.) Proc. Roy. Soc. (London), **A149,** 176 (1935).   (II,3)

—————(36).   Phys. Rev., **50,** 332 (1936).   (VIII,6)

————— (36a).   (With R. F. Bacher.)   Revs. Mod. Phys., **8,** 193 (1936).   (I,2), (II,2,3), (VI,2), (XIII,2)

————— (37).   Revs. Mod. Phys., **9,** 71 (1937).   (VIII,3), (X,4), (XII,6)

————— (37a).   (With G. Placzek.)   Phys. Rev., **51,** 450 (1937).   (VIII,4), (X,4)

————— (38).   Phys. Rev., **53,** 842 (1938) L.   (VII,4)

————— (38a).   Phys. Rev., **53,** 39 (1938).   (IX,6)

————— (39).   (With F. Hoyle and R. Peierls.)   Nature, **143,** 200 (1939). (XIII,4)

————— (40).   Phys. Rev., **57,** 1125 (1940).   (VIII,4)

————— (40a).   Phys. Rev., **57,** 260, 390 (1940).   (IV,2)

————— (49).   Phys. Rev., **76,** 38 (1949).   (II,3,4), (XII,4)

————— (50).   (With C. Longmire.)   Phys. Rev., **77,** 647 (1950).   (XII,4)

————— See also Camac, M. (48); Hurwitz, H., Jr. (51); Konopinski, E. J. (38); Levinger, J. S. (50); Rose, M. E. (37).

Biedenharn, L. C. (50).   Thesis, M.I.T., 1950.   (II,5), (V,5)

————— (51).   Phys. Rev., **82,** 100 (1951) L.   (X,2)

————— (51a).   (With M. E. Rose.)   Phys. Rev., **83,** 459 (1951) L.   (XIII,7)

————— See also Blatt, J. M. (51).

Bishop, G. R. (50).   (With C. H. Collie, H. Halban, A. Hedgran, K. Siegbahn, S. du Toit, and R. Wilson.)   Phys. Rev., **80,** 211 (1950).   (XII,4)

————— (51).   (With H. Halban, P. F. D. Shaw, and R. Wilson.)   Phys. Rev., **81,** 219 (1951).   (XII,4)

Biswas, S. (49).   Phys. Rev., **75,** 530 (1949) L.   (XI,3)

Blair, J. M. (50).   (With J. R. Wallace.)   Phys. Rev., **79,** 28 (1950).   (IX,2)

Blanchard, C. H. (51).   (With R. Avery.)   Phys. Rev., **81,** 35 (1951).   (III, 3)

Blaser, J. P. (51).   (With F. Boehm, P. Marmier, and D. C. Peaslee.)   Helv. Phys. Acta, **24,** 3 (1951).   (I,4)

Blatt, J. M. (48).   Phys. Rev., **74,** 92 (1948).   (II,3)

————— (49).   (With J. D. Jackson.)   Phys. Rev., **76,** 18 (1949).   (II,2,3)

————— (51).   (With L. C. Biedenharn.)   Phys. Rev., **82,** 123 (1951) L.   (X,3), (A,5)

————— See also Jackson, J. D. (50).

Bloch, F. (35).   (With C. Möller.)   Nature, **136,** 911 (1935).   (XIII,5)

————— (36).   (With G. Gamow.)   Phys. Rev., **50,** 260 (1936) L.   (XII,7)

————— (40).   Phys. Rev., **58,** 829 (1940).   (VIII,9)

————— (47).   (With A. C. Graves, M. Packard, and R. W. Spence.)   Phys. Rev., **71,** 551 (1947).   (V,2)

————— (48).   (With D. Nicodemus and H. H. Staub.)   Phys. Rev., **74,** 1025 (1948).   (I,7), (II,5)

————— (51).   Phys. Rev., **83,** 839 (1951) L.   (XIV,2)

Bloch, I. (51a).   (With M. M. Hull, Jr., A. A. Broyles, W. G. Bouricius, B. E. Freeman, and G. Breit.)   Revs. Mod. Phys., **23,** 147 (1951). (VIII,2,5)

————— See also Breit, G. (47), (48).

Bocciarelli, D.   See Amaldi, E. (42), (46).

Bockelman, C. K.   See Adair, R. K. (49); Barschall, H. H. (48), (49); Peterson, R. E. (50).

Boehm, F. See Blaser, J. P. (51).

Bohm, D. See Lewis, H. (46).

Bohr, A. (51). Phys. Rev., **81**, 134 (1951). (XIV,2)

────── (51a). Phys. Rev., **81**, 331 (1951). (XIV,2)

Bohr, N. (36). Nature, **137**, 344 (1936). (VIII,3,7)

────── (37). (With F. Kalckar.) Kgl. Danske Videnskab. Selskab, Mat-fys. Medd., **14**, 10 (1937). (VII,5), (VIII,3,6,7)

────── (39). (With J. A. Wheeler.) Phys. Rev., **56**, 426 (1939). (VI,2), (VII,5)

Bondelid, R. O. See Mather, K. B. (50).

Bonner, T. W. See Bennett, W. E. (41).

Born, M. (27). (With J. R. Oppenheimer.) Ann. Physik, **84**, 457 (1927). (VII,4)

Borst, L. M. (46). (With A. J. Ulrich, C. L. Osborne, and B. Hasbrouck.) Phys. Rev., **70**, 557 (1946). (IX,2)

Bothe, W. (39). (With W. Gentner.) Z. Physik, **112**, 45 (1939). (XII,7)

Bouchez, R. (47). (With R. Daudel, P. Daudel, and R. Muxart.) J. phys. et radium, **8**, 336 (1947). (XIII,3)

────── (49). (With R. Daudel, P. Daudel, R. Muxart, and A. Rogozinski.) J. phys. et radium, **10**, 511 (1949). (XIII,3)

────── (50). C. R. Acad. Sci. Paris, **230**, 440 (1950). (XIII,5)

────── See also Benoist, P. (49).

Bouricius, G. M. B. See Bender, R. S. (49).

Bouricius, W. G. See Bloch, I. (51a).

Bowers, W. A. (49). (With N. Rosen.) Phys. Rev., **75**, 523 (1949) L. (XIII,2)

Bradt, H. L. See Tendham, D. S. (47).

Brady, E. L. (50). (With M. Deutsch.) Phys. Rev., **78**, 558 (1950). (XII,6)

Breit, G. (35). (With E. P. Wigner.) Phys. Rev., **48**, 918 (1935) L. (III,3)

────── (35a). (With F. L. Yost.) Phys. Rev., **48**, 203 (1935). (VIII,9)

────── (36). (With E. U. Condon and R. D. Present.) Phys. Rev., **50**, 825 (1936). (II,2,4)

────── (36a). (With E. Feenberg.) Phys. Rev., **50**, 850 (1936). (II,4), (III,3)

────── (36b). (With E. P. Wigner.) Phys. Rev., **49**, 519, 642 (1936). (VIII,7), (X,4)

────── (37). (With J. R. Stehn.) Phys. Rev., **52**, 396 (1937). (II,4)

────── (37a). Phys. Rev., **51**, 248 (1937). (IV,1)

────── (38). (With E. P. Wigner.) Phys. Rev., **53**, 998 (1938). (III,4)

────── (38a). Phys. Rev., **53**, 153 (1938). (IV,1)

────── (39). (With H. M. Thaxton and L. Eisenbud.) Phys. Rev., **55**, 1018 (1939). (II,2,4), (V,3)

────── (39a). (With I. E. Hoisington, S. S. Share, and H. M. Thaxton.) Phys. Rev., **55**, 1103 (1939) L. (II,4)

────── (40). Phys. Rev., **58**, 506, 1068 (1940). (VIII,1,9)

────── (47). (With I. Bloch.) Phys. Rev., **72**, 135 (1947). (II,5)

────── (47a). Phys. Rev., **71**, 215 (1947). (II,3)

────── (47b). (With P. R. Zilsel.) Phys. Rev., **71**, 232 (1947). (II,3)

────── (47c). Phys. Rev., **71**, 400 (1947). (II,5)

────── (48). (With I. Bloch.) Phys. Rev., **74**, 397 (1948). (IX,5)

────── (50). (With G. B. Arfken, and W. W. Clendenin.) Phys. Rev., **78**, 390 (1950). (I,7)

Breit, G. (51). (With M. C. Yovits.) Phys. Rev., **81,** 416 (1951). (III,3)
—— See also Bloch, I. (51a), Hatcher, R. D. (49); Hoisington, I. E. (39); Kittel, C. (39); Share, S. S. (37); Yost, F. L. (35), (36).
Bridge, H. S. See Sutton, R. B. (47).
Brolley, J. E., Jr. (50). (With J. H. Coon and J. L. Fowler.) Phys. Rev., **79,** 227 (1950) A. (IV,2)
—— (51). (With J. H. Coon, and J. L. Fowler.) Phys. Rev., **82,** 190 (1951). (IV,2)
Brosi, A. R. See Zeldes, H. (50).
Broström, K. G. (47). (With T. Huus and R. Tangen.) Phys. Rev., **71,** 661 (1947). (IX,3)
Brown, A. B. (50). (With C. Y. Chao, W. A. Fowler, and C. C. Lauritsen.) Phys. Rev., **78,** 88 (1950). (IX,5)
Brown, F. W. (39). (With M. S. Plesset.) Phys. Rev., **56,** 841 (1939) L. (V,2,4)
—— (39a). Phys. Rev., **56,** 1107 (1939). (V,2)
Brown, H. (39b). (With D. R. Inglis.) Phys. Rev., **55,** 1182 (1939). (VII,4)
—— See also Longmire, C. (49).
Brown, R. H. (49). (With U. Camerini, P. H. Fowler, H. Heitler, D. T. King, and C. F. Powell.) Phil. Mag., **40,** 862 (1949). (IX,4)
Broyles, A. A. (50). (With B. Kivel.) Phys. Rev., **77,** 839 (1950) L. (II,5)
—— See also Bloch, I. (51a).
Brueckner, K. (49). (With W. M. Powell.) Phys. Rev., **75,** 1274 (1949). (IX,4)
—— (49a). (With W. Hartsough, E. Hayward, and W. M. Powell.) Phys. Rev., **75,** 555 (1949). (IV,3)
Bucherer, A. H. (09). Ann. Physik, **28,** 513 (1909). (XIII,1)
Buck, J. H. (38). Phys. Rev., **54,** 1025 (1938). (IX,3)
Buckingham, R. (41). (With H. S. W. Massey.) Proc. Roy. Soc. (London), **A179,** 123 (1941). (V,4)
—— See also Massey, H. S. W. (48a).
Buechner, W. W. See Van Patter, D. M. (51).
Bunker, M. E. (51). (With L. M. Langer and R. J. D. Moffat.) Phys. Rev., **81,** 30 (1951). (XIII,7)
Burg, A. B. See Gordy, W. (48).
Burgy, M. T. See Hughes, D. J. (50); Ringo, G. R. (51).
Burhop, E. H. S. (48). (With H. N. Yadav.) Nature **162,** 738 (1948). (IV,1)
—— (48a). (With H. S. W. Massey.) Proc. Roy. Soc. (London), **A192,** 156 (1948). (V,4)
—— See also Massey, H. S. W. (48).
Butler, S. T. (50). Phys. Rev., **80,** 1095 (1950) L. (IX,6)
—— (51). Proc. Roy. Soc. (London), **A208,** 559 (1951). (IX,6)
Cacciaputo, C. See Amaldi, E. (46).
Caldirola, P. (46). Phys. Rev., **69,** 608 (1946). (II,5)
Camac, M. (48). (With H. A. Bethe.) Phys. Rev., **73,** 191 (1948). (IV,1)
Camerini, U. (49). (With T. Coor, J. H. Davies, P. H. Fowler, W. O. Lock, H. Muirhead, and N. Tobin.) Phil. Mag., **40,** 1073 (1949). (IX,4)
—— See also Brown, R. H. (49).
Carroll, K. G. (40). Phys. Rev., **57,** 791 (1940). (VIII,3)
—— See also Margenau, H. (38b); Tyrrell, W. A., Jr. (39).
Carver, J. H. (51). (With D. H. Wilkinson.) Nature, **167,** 154 (1951) L. (XII,4)

Case, K. M. (50). (With A. Pais.) Phys. Rev., **80**, 203 (1950). (IV,1,4)

Casimir, H. B. G. (36). Arch. Musee Teyler, **8**, 201 (1936). (I,7)

Cassen, B. (36). (With E. U. Condon.) Phys. Rev., **50**, 846 (1936). (III,5)

Cassidy, J. M. See Bell, P. R. (49).

Chadwick, J. (32). Proc. Roy. Soc. (London), **A136**, 692 (1932). (I,1)

Chamberlain, O. (50). (With C. Wiegand.) Phys. Rev., **79**, 81 (1950). (IV,4)

———— (51). (With E. Segrè and C. Wiegand.) Phys. Rev., **81**, 284 (1951) L. (IV,4)

Chao, C. Y. (50). (With A. V. Tollestrup, W. A. Fowler, and C. C. Lauritsen.) Phys. Rev., **79**, 108 (1950). (XII,5)

———— (50a). Phys. Rev., **80**, 1035 (1950). (IX,5)

———— See also Brown, A. B. (50).

Chew, G. F. (48). (With M. L. Goldberger.) Phys. Rev., **73**, 1409 (1948). (IV,1)

———— (49). (With M. L. Goldberger.) Phys. Rev., **75**, 1637 (1949). (II,3), (XII,4)

Christian, R. S. (49). Phys. Rev., **75**, 1675 (1949). (II,5)

———— (50). (With E. W. Hart.) Phys. Rev., **77**, 441 (1950). (IV, 1,3)

———— (50a). (With H. P. Noyes.) Phys. Rev., **79**, 85 (1950). (IV,1,4)

Christy, R. F. (48). (With R. Latter.) Revs. Mod. Phys., **20**, 185 (1948). (VIII,2)

Clapp, R. E. (49). Phys. Rev., **76**, 873 (1949) L. (V,5)

Clarke, R. L. See Paul, E. B. (52).

Clendenin, W. W. See Breit, G. (50).

Cockroft, A. L. See Curran, S. C. (48), (49).

Cohen, B. L. (50). Phys. Rev., **80**, 105 (1950). (XI,2)

Cohen, V. W. (39). (With H. H. Goldsmith and J. S. Schwinger.) Phys. Rev., **55**, 106 (1939) L. (II,3)

———— (40). (With H. H. Goldsmith and M. Hamermesh.) Phys. Rev., **57**, 352 (1940). (II,3)

Collie, C. H. See Bishop, G. R. (50); Wilson, R. (49).

Condon, E. U. (29). (With R. W. Gurney.) Phys. Rev., **33**, 127 (1929). (I,3), (XI,1)

———— (35). (With G. H. Shortley.) *Theory of Atomic Spectra*, Cambridge University Press, London, 1935. (VI,6), (VII,3), (A,1,2,5)

———— See also Breit, G. (36); Cassen, B. (36); Gurney, R. W. (28).

Cook, C. S. (48). (With L. M. Langer and H. C. Price, Jr.) Phys. Rev., **73**, 1395 (1948) L. (XIII,2)

Cook, L. J. (49). (With E. M. McMillan, J. M. Peterson, and D. C. Sewell.) Phys. Rev., **75**, 7 (1949). (IX,4)

Coon, J. H. See Brolley, J. E., Jr. (50), (51).

Coor, T. See Camerini, U. (49).

Corben, H. C. (40). (With J. S. Schwinger.) Phys. Rev., **58**, 953 (1940). (B,1,2)

Cork, B. (50). (With L. Johnston and C. Richman.) Phys. Rev., **79**, 71 (1950). (IV,4)

Cork, J. M. See Lawson, J. L. (40).

Coster, D. (48). (With H. Groendijk and H. de Vries.) Physica, **14**, 1 (1948). (IX,2)

Courant, E. D. (48). Phys. Rev., **74**, 1226 (1948) A. (XII,7)

Courant, E. D. (51). Phys. Rev., **82,** 703 (1951). (XII,7)

Courant, R. (31). (With D. Hilbert.) *Methoden der mathematischen Physik,* J. Springer, Berlin, 1931. (III,4)

Crane, H. R. (48). Revs. Mod. Phys., **20,** 278 (1948). (XIII,1)

Critchfield, C. L. (41). (With E. Teller.) Phys. Rev., **60,** 10 (1941). (IX,5), (X,3)

—— (41a). (With E. P. Wigner.) Phys. Rev., **60,** 412 (1941). (XIII,5)

—— (42). Phys. Rev., **61,** 249 (1942). (XIII,5,7)

—— (43). Phys. Rev., **63,** 417 (1943). (XIII, 5,7)

—— (48). Phys. Rev., **73,** 1 (1948). (V,4)

—— (49). (With D. C. Dodder.) Phys. Rev., **76,** 602 (1949). (VII,3), (IX,3)

—— See also Gamow, G. (49).

Curie-Joliot, I. (32). (With F. Joliot.) Compt. rend., **194,** 273 (1932). (I,1)

—— (45). J. phys. et radium, **6,** 209 (1945). (VI,2)

Curran, S. C. (48). (With J. Angus and A. L. Cockroft.) Nature, **162,** 302 (1948) L. (XIII,2)

—— (49). (With J. Angus and A. L. Cockroft.) Phys. Rev., **76,** 853 (1949) L. (XIII,2)

Curtis, N. W. (50). (With J. Hornbostel, D. W. Lee, and E. O. Salant.) Phys. Rev., **77,** 290 (1950). (XII,7)

Dancoff, S. M. (36). (With D. R. Inglis.) Phys. Rev., **50,** 784 (1936) L. (VII,3)

—— (39). Phys. Rev., **56,** 384 (1939) L. (VI,5)

—— (39a). (With P. Morrison.) Phys. Rev., **55,** 122 (1939). (XII,5), (B,2)

—— (40). Phys. Rev., **58,** 326 (1940). (VI,5)

—— See also Axel, P. (49).

Daudel, P. See Benoist, P. (49); Bouchez, R. (47), (49).

Daudel, R. (47). Revue sci. (Paris), **85,** 162 (1947). (XIII,3)

—— See also Benoist, P. (49); Bouchez, R. (47), (49).

Davidson, J. P., Jr. (51). Phys. Rev., **82,** 48 (1951). (XIII,7)

Davidson, W. L. See Shull, C. G. (48).

Davies, J. H. See Camerini, U. (49).

Davis, L., Jr.(48). (With B. T. Feld, C. W. Zabel, and J. R. Zacharias.) Phys. Rev., **73,** 525 (1948). (I,7)

—— (49). (With D. E. Nagle and J. R. Zacharias.) Phys. Rev., **76,** 1068 (1949). (VI,5)

de Groot, S. R. (50). (With H. A. Tolhoek.) Physica, **16,** 456 (1950). (XIII,5,7)

De Juren, J. (50). Phys. Rev., **80,** 27 (1950). (IV,3)

Dennison, D. M. (40). Phys. Rev., **57,** 454 (1940). (VII,4)

de-Shalit, A. (51). Helv. Phys. Acta, **24,** 296 (1951). (XIV,2)

—— See also Frauenfelder, H. (50); Huber, O. (51).

Deutsch, M. (44). (With L. G. Elliott.) Phys. Rev., **65,** 211 (1944). (XIV,2)

—— See also Brady, E. L. (50); Good, W. M. (46); Metzger, F. (50); Stevenson, D. J. (50).

Devaney, J. (50). Thesis, M.I.T., 1950. (I,4), (XI,2,3)

de Vries, H. See Coster, D. (48).

De Wire, J. W. See Sutton, R. B. (47).

Dieke, G. H. (49). (With F. S. Tomkins.) Phys. Rev., **76,** 283 (1949). (V,2)

Diven, B. C. (50). (With G. M. Almy.) Phys. Rev., **80**, 407 (1950). (XII,7)
───── See also McElhinney, J. (49).
Dodder, D. C. See Critchfield, C. L. (49).
Drell, S. D. (49). Phys. Rev., **75**, 132 (1949). (XII,5)
───── (50). Phys. Rev., **81**, 656 (1951) A. (XII,5)
Duffield, R. B. See McElhinney, J. (49).
Dunning J. See Rainwater, L. J. (47).
Dunworth, J. V. (40). Rev. Sci. Instr., **11**, 167 (1940). (XII,6)
du Toit, S. See Bishop, G. R. (50).
Ebel, A. (50). Thesis, M.I.T., 1950. (XII,6)
Ehrenfest, P. (31). (With J. R. Oppenheimer.) Phys. Rev., **37**, 333 (1931). (I,1,8)
Ehrman, J. B. (51). Phys. Rev., **81**, 412 (1951). (VI,6)
Eisenbud, L. (41). (With E. P. Wigner.) Proc. Natl. Acad. Sci. U.S.A., **27**, 281 (1941). (II,5), (III,3)
───── (48). "The Formal Properties of Nuclear Collisions," Thesis, Princeton 1948. (X,1,4), (A,5)
───── (51). J. Franklin Inst., **251**, 231 (1951). (X,3), (XII,6)
───── See also Breit, G. (39); Wigner, E. P. (47).
Eisenstein, J. (48). (With F. Rohrlich.) Phys. Rev., **73**, 641 (1948). (IV,1)
───── See also Rohrlich, F. (49).
Eisner, E. (47). (With R. G. Sachs.) Phys. Rev., **72**, 680 (1947). (X,3)
Elliott, L. G. (48). (With R. E. Bell.) Phys. Rev., **74**, 1869 (1948). (XII,6)
───── (49). (With R. E. Bell.) Phys. Rev., **76**, 168 (1949). (XII,6)
───── See also Bell, R. E. (48); Deutsch, M. (44).
Elsasser, W. M. (33). J. phys. et radium, **4**, 549 (1933). (VI,2), (VII,4), (XIV,1)
───── (34). J. phys. et radium, **5**, 389, 635 (1934). (VI,2) (VII,4), (XIV,1)
Emde, F. See Jahnke, E. (33).
Everhart, G. G. See Gittings, H. T. (49).
Ewing, D. H. See Weisskopf, V. F. (40).
Falkoff, D. L. (48). Phys. Rev., **73**, 518 (1948). (XII,6)
───── (50). (With G. E. Uhlenbeck.) Phys. Rev., **79**, 323 (1950). (XII,6)
───── (50a). (With G. E. Uhlenbeck.) Phys. Rev., **79**, 334 (1950). (XII,6)
───── (51). Phys. Rev., **82**, 98 (1951) L. (XII,6)
───── See also Ling, D. S., Jr. (48).
Fano, L. See Way, K. (50).
Fano, U. (37). Naturwiss., **25**, 602 (1937). (VII,4)
Farkas, A. (34). (With L. Farkas and P. Harteck.) Proc. Roy. Soc. (London), **A144**, 481 (1934). (II,3)
Farkas, L. See Farkas, A. (34).
Feenberg, E. (35). (With J. K. Knipp.) Phys. Rev., **48**, 906 (1935). (II,2), (V,2)
───── (36). Phys. Rev., **50**, 674 (1936) L. (II,1), (V,1)
───── (36a). (With S. S. Share.) Phys. Rev., **50**, 253 (1936). (V,2)
───── (36b). Phys. Rev., **49**, 328 (1936). (XII,7)
───── (37). Phys. Rev., **51**, 777 (1937) L. (III,2,5)
───── (37a). Phys. Rev., **42**, 667 (1937) L. (III,4)
───── (37b). (With E. P. Wigner.) Phys. Rev., **51**, 95 (1937). (VII,3)
───── (37c). (With M. Phillips.) Phys. Rev., **51**, 597 (1937). (VII,3)

Feenberg, E. (39). Phys. Rev., **55**, 504 (1939) L.   (VII,5)

—— (41). Phys. Rev., **59**, 593 (1941).   (VI,1)

—— (41a). Phys. Rev., **60**, 204 (1941).   (VI,2)

—— (41b). Phys. Rev., **59**, 149 (1941).   (VII,5)

—— (42). Phys. Rev., **61**, 387 (1942) A.   (VI,1,2)

—— (46). (With G. Goertzel.) Phys. Rev., **70**, 597 (1946).   (III,4), (VI,1,2)

—— (46a). (With H. Primakoff.) Phys. Rev., **70**, 980 (1946) L.   (III,4)

—— (47). Revs. Mod. Phys., **19**, 239 (1947).   (VI,2)

—— (49). (With K. C. Hammack.) Phys. Rev., **75**, 1877 (1949).   (XIV,2)

—— (50). (With G. Trigg.) Revs. Mod. Phys., **22**, 399 (1950).   (XIII,4,7)

—— See also Bardeen, J. (38); Breit, G. (36a); Motz, L. (38); Phillips, M. (41); Shull, F. B. (49); Wigner, E. P. (41).

Feingold, A. M. (50). (With E. P. Wigner.) Phys. Rev., **79**, 221 (1950) A. (VI,6), (VII,3)

—— (51). Revs. Mod. Phys., **23**, 10 (1951).   (XIII,4,6)

Feld, B. T. (49). "Nuclear Electric Quadrupole Moments and Quadrupole Couplings in Molecules," National Research Council, Nuclear Science Series, Preliminary Report No. 2, May 1949.   (I,7)

—— (50). (With I. L. Lebow and L. S. Osborne.) Phys. Rev., **77**, 731 (1950). (IX,4)

—— See also Davis, L., Jr. (48); Goldsmith, H. H. (47).

Feldman, L. See Wu, C. S. (49), (51), (51a).

Fermi, E. (34). Z. Physik., **88**, 161 (1934).   (XIII,2,5)

—— (35). Phys. Rev., **48**, 570 (1935).   (XII,4)

—— (36). Ricerca sci., **7**, 13 (1936).   (II,3)

—— (47a). (With L. Marshall.) Phys. Rev., **71**, 666 (1947).   (II,3)

—— (47b). (With W. J. Sturm and R. G. Sachs.) Phys. Rev., **71**, 589 (1947). (II,3)

—— (49). (With L. Marshall.) Phys. Rev., **75**, 578 (1949).   (V,4)

Fernbach, S. (49). (With R. Serber and T. B. Taylor.) Phys. Rev., **75**, 1352 (1949).   (IX,4)

Ferretti, B. See Amaldi, E. (42).

Feshbach, H. (44). Phys. Rev., **65**, 307 (1944).   (VIII,8)

—— (47). (With D. C. Peaslee and V. F. Weisskopf.) Phys. Rev., **71**, 145 (1947).   (VIII,2,7)

—— (49). (With W. Rarita.) Phys. Rev., **75**, 1384 (1949).   (V,5)

—— (49a). (With V. F. Weisskopf.) Phys. Rev., **76**, 1550 (1949).   (I,4), (VIII,2,4), (IX,2)

—— (49b). (With J. S. Schwinger and J. A. Harr.) "Effect of Tensor Range in Nuclear Two Body Problems," Computation Laboratory of Harvard University, Cambridge, Massachusetts, Nov. 1949.   (II,5)

—— (51). (With J. S. Schwinger.) Phys. Rev., **84**, 194 (1951).   (XII,4)

—— See also Lax, M. (48); Morse, P. M. (45); Pease, R. L. (51).

Fierz, M. (37). Z. Physik, **104**, 553 (1937).   (XIII,5)

—— (43). Helv. Phys. Acta, **16**, 365 (1943).   (XII,6)

—— (49). Helv. Phys. Acta, **22**, 489 (1949).   (XII,6)

Fillmore, F. L. See Panofsky, W. K. H. (50).

Fireman, E. L. (49). Phys. Rev., **75**, 323 (1949) L.   (XIII,1)

Fisk, J. B. (34). Proc. Roy. Soc. (London), **A143**, 674 (1934).   (XII,5)

Fisk, J. B. (34a). (With H. M. Taylor.) Proc. Roy. Soc., (London), **A146,** 178 (1934). (XII,5)

Fluegge, S. (37). Z. Physik, **105,** 522 (1937). (V,2)

—— (46). "An Introduction to Nuclear Physics" in *Nuclear Physics Tables,* J. Mattauch and S. Fluegge, Interscience Publishers, New York, 1946. (I,8)

Fock, V. (34). Z. Physik, **89,** 744 (1934). (XII,7)

Foldy, L. L. (50). Phys. Rev., **78,** 636 (1950) L. (II,5)

—— (50a). (With F. J. Milford.) Phys. Rev., **80,** 751 (1950) L. (XIV,2)

—— See also Osborn, R. K. (50).

Foley, H. M. See Townes, C. H. (49).

Fowler, J. L. See Brolley, J. E., Jr. (50), (51).

Fowler, P. H. See Brown, R. H. (49); Camerini, U. (49).

Fowler, R. H. (30). Proc. Roy. Soc. (London), **A129,** 1 (1930). (XII,5)

Fowler, W. A. (49). (With C. C. Lauritsen.) Phys. Rev., **76,** 314 (1949). (XII,6)

—— See also Brown, A. B. (50); Chao, C. Y. (50); Hornyak, W. F. (50); Streib, J. F. (41); Tollestrup, A. V. (50).

Frank, N. H. (37). Phys. Rev., **51,** 577 (1937). (VII,3)

Frankel, S. See Stump, R. (50).

Franz, W. (50). Z. Physik, **127,** 363 (1950). (B,2,3)

Frauenfelder, H. (50). (With O. Huber, A. de-Shalit, and W. Zünti.) Phys. Rev., **79,** 1029 (1950) L. (XII,6)

Freedman, M. S. (50). (With A. H. Jaffey and F. Wagner, Jr.) Phys. Rev., **79,** 410 (1950) L. (XIII,7)

Freeman, B. E. See Bloch, I. (51a).

Freier, G. D. See Lampi, E. E. (50).

French, B. See Goldberger, M. L. (51).

Frenkel, J. (39). J. Phys. (U.S.S.R.), **1,** 125 (1939). (VII,5)

—— (39a). Phys. Rev., **55,** 987 (1939). (VII,5)

Friedlander, G. See Perlman, M. L. (48).

Frisch, D. H. (46). Phys. Rev., **70,** 589 (1946). (II,3)

—— (50). Report No. 43, Laboratory for Nuclear Science and Engineering, M.I.T., 1950. (VII,2)

Fuchs, M. (51). Thesis, University of Michigan, 1951. (XIII,7)

Fulbright, H. W. (51). (With J. C. D. Milton.) Phys. Rev., **82,** 274 (1951). (XIII,7)

Fuller, E. G. (49). Phys. Rev., **76,** 576 (1949). (XII,4)

—— (50). Phys. Rev., **79,** 303 (1950). (XII,4)

Furry, W. H. (36). Phys. Rev., **50,** 784 (1936) L. (VII,3)

—— (37). Phys. Rev., **51,** 125 (1937). (XIII,1)

—— (39). Phys. Rev., **56,** 1184 (1939). (XIII,1)

Gamow, G. (28). Z. Physik, **52,** 510 (1928). (I,3), (VIII,9), (XI,1,2,3)

—— (28a). Z. Physik, **51,** 204 (1928). (VIII,9), (XI,1,3)

—— (28b). (With F. G. Houtermans.) Z. Physik, **52,** 496 (1928). (VIII,9)

—— (34). Z. Physik, **89,** 592 (1934). (VI,2)

—— (36). (With E. Teller.) Phys. Rev., **49,** 895 (1936). (XIII,2)

—— (49). (With C. L. Critchfield.) *Theory of Atomic Nucleus and Nuclear Energy Sources,* Clarendon Press, Oxford, 1949. (III,4)

Gamow, G. See also Bloch, F. (36).

Gardner, J. H. (49). (With E. M. Purcell.) Phys. Rev., **76**, 1262 (1949). (I,7)

Gardner, J. W. (49a). Proc. Phys. Soc. (London), **62**, 763 (1949). (XII,6)

—— (51). Phys. Rev., **82**, 283 (1951) L. (XII,6)

Geiger, H. See Rutherford, E. (08).

Gellman, H. (50). (With B. A. Griffith and J. P. Stanley.) Phys. Rev., **80**, 866 (1950). (XII,5)

Gentner, W. See Bothe, W. (39).

Gerjuoy, E. (40). Phys. Rev., **58**, 503 (1940). (IX,5)

—— (42). (With J. S. Schwinger.) Phys. Rev., **61**, 138 (1942). (V,3,5)

—— (50). Phys. Rev., **77**, 568 (1950) L. (IV,3)

—— (51). Phys. Rev., **81**, 62 (1951). (VII,3), (XIII,6)

Geschwind, S. (51). (With R. Gunther-Mohr and C. H. Townes.) Phys. Rev., **81**, 288 (1951). (I,7)

—— See also Gunther-Mohr, G. R. (51).

Ghiorso, A. See Perlman, I. (50).

Ghoshal, S. N. (50). Phys. Rev., **80**, 939 (1950). (IX,3)

Gittings, H. T. (49). (With H. H. Barschall and G. G. Everhart.) Phys. Rev., **75**, 1610 (1949). (IX,2)

Glueckauf, E. (48). Proc. Phys. Soc. (London), **61**, 25 (1948). (XI,1), (XIV,1)

Goertzel, G. (46). Phys. Rev., **70**, 897 (1946). (XII,6), (B,1,2)

—— (48). Phys. Rev., **73**, 1463 (1948). (X,4)

—— See also Feenberg, E. (46); Rose, M. E. (47), (49), (51).

Goldberger, M. L. (47). (With F. Seitz.) Phys. Rev., **71**, 294 (1947). (II,3)

—— (48). Phys. Rev., **74**, 1269 (1948). (IX,4)

—— (51). (With B. French.) Phys. Rev., to be published. (IX,6)

—— (51a). Phys. Rev., **82**, 757 (1951) L. (II,3)

—— See also Chew, G. F. (48), (49).

Goldhaber, G. (51a). Phys. Rev., **81**, 930 (1951). (XII,4)

Goldhaber, M. (48). (With E. Teller.) Phys. Rev., **74**, 1046 (1948). (XII,7)

—— (48a). (With G. Scharff-Goldhaber.) Phys. Rev., **73**, 1472 (1948). (XIII,1)

—— (51). (With A. W. Sunyar.) Phys. Rev., **83**, 906 (1951). (XII,5,6), (XIV,2)

—— See also Sunyar, A. W. (49).

Goldin, I. (50). Thesis, M.I.T., 1950. (VII,2)

Goldsmith, H. H. (47). (With H. W. Ibser and B. T. Feld.) Revs. Mod. Phys., **19**, 259 (1947). (IX,1,2,5)

—— (48). (With D. R. Inglis.) "The Properties of Atomic Nuclei," I. Spins, Magnetic Moments and Quadrupole Moments, Brookhaven National Laboratory, October 1, 1948. (I,7)

—— See also Cohen, V. W. (39), (40).

Goldstein, H. (50). Phys. Rev., **79**, 740 (1950) L. (VII,3)

Goldstein, N. See Hughes, D. J. (49).

Good, R. H., Jr. (51). Thesis, University of Michigan, 1951. (XIII,2)

Good, W. M. (46). (With D. C. Peaslee and M. Deutsch.) Phys. Rev., **69**, 313 1946). (XIII,7)

Gordy, W. (48). (With H. Ring and A. B. Burg.) Phys. Rev., **74**, 1191 (1948); erratum, Phys. Rev., **75**, 208 (1949). (I,7)

—— (49). Phys. Rev., **76**, 139 (1949). (XIV,2)

Gordy, W. See also Johnson, C. M. (51).

Graham, G. A. R. (45). (With H. Halban.) Revs. Mod. Phys., **17**, 297 (1945). (XII,4)

Graham, R. L. See Bell, R. E. (50).

Graves, A. C. See Bloch, F. (47).

Greuling, E. (42). Phys. Rev., **61**, 568 (1942). (XIII,5,7)

—— (51). (With M. L. Meeks.) Phys. Rev., **82**, 531 (1951). (XIII,5,7)

Griffith, B. A. (49). (With J. P. Stanley.) Phys. Rev., **75**, 534 (1949). (XII,5)

—— See also Gellman, H. (50).

Groendijk, H. See Coster D. (48).

Grönblom, B. O. (37). Naturwiss., **25**, 526 (1937) L. (VII,3)

—— (38). Z. Physik, **110**, 37 (1938). (VII,3)

—— (39). (With R. E. Marshak.) Phys. Rev., **55**, 229 (1939) L. (VII,4)

—— (39a). Phys, Rev., **56**, 508 (1939). (XIII,6)

Gugelot, P. C. (51). Phys. Rev., **81**, 51 (1951). (VIII,6)

Guindon, W. B. (48). Phys. Rev., **74**, 145 (1948). (II,5)

Gunther-Mohr, G. R. (51). (With S. Geschwind and C. H. Townes.) Phys. Rev., **81**, 289 (1951). (I,7)

—— See also Geschwind, S. (51).

Gurney, R. W. (28). (With E. U. Condon.) Nature, **122**, 439 (1928). (XI,1)

—— See also Condon, E. U. (29).

Guth, E. (48). (With C. J. Mullin.) Phys. Rev., **74**, 832, 833 (1948) L. (XII,4)

—— (48a). (With C. J. Mullin and J. F. Marshall.) Phys. Rev., **74**, 834 (1948) L. (XII,4)

—— (49). (With C. J. Mullin.) Phys. Rev., **76**, 234 (1949). (XII,4)

—— (51). Phys. Rev., to be published. (IX,6)

—— See also Marshall, J. F. (49), (50); Mullin, C. J. (49).

Guthrie, A. (42). (With R. G. Sachs.) Phys. Rev., **62**, 8 (1942). (VI,6)

Hadley, J. (49). (With E. L. Kelly, C. Leith, E. Segrè, C. Wiegand, and H. York.) Phys. Rev., **75**, 351 (1949). (IV,3)

Hafstad, L. R. (38). (With E. Teller.) Phys. Rev., **54**, 681 (1938). (VII,4)

Halban, H. See Bishop, G. R. (50), (51); Graham, G. A. R. (45); Wilson, R. (49).

Hall, H. (50). Phys. Rev., **79**, 745 (1950) L. (XIII,2)

Hall, T. See Sutton, R. B. (47).

Halpern, I. See Woodward, W. M. (49).

Halpern, O. (41). (With M. Hamermesh and M. H. Johnson.) Phys. Rev., **59**, 981 (1941). (II,3)

Hamermesh, B. (49). (With A. Wattenberg.) Phys. Rev., **75**, 1290 (1949). (XII,4)

—— (51). Phys. Rev., **81**, 487 (1951) L. (XII,7)

Hamermesh, M. (50). Phys. Rev., **77**, 140, (1950) L. (II,3)

—— See also Cohen, V. W. (40); Halpern, O. (41).

Hamilton, D. R. (40). Phys. Rev., **58**, 122 (1940). (XII,6)

—— (47). Phys. Rev., **71**, 456 (1947) L. (XIII,5,7)

—— (48). Phys. Rev., **74**, 782 (1948). (XII,6)

Hammack, K. C. See Feenberg, E. (49).

Hanna, G. C. (49). (With B. Pontecorvo.) Phys. Rev., **75**, 983 (1949) L. (XIII,2)

Hanna, G. C.   See also Pontecorvo, B. (49).

Hansen, W. W. (35).   Phys. Rev., **47**, 139 (1935).   (B,2)

Hanson, A. O.   See McElhinney, J. (49).

Hanstein, H. B. (40).   Phys. Rev., **57**, 1045 (1940) L.   (II,3)

—— (41).   Phys. Rev., **59**, 489 (1941).   (II,3)

Hárkins, W. D. (17).   J. Am. Chem. Soc., **39**, 856 (1917).   (XIV,1)

—— (22).   Phys. Rev., **19**, 136 (1922).   (I,1), (VI,1)

Harr, J. A.   See Feshbach, H. (49b); Rose, M. E. (49), (51).

Harris, S. P. (47).   (With A. S. Langsdorf, Jr., and F. G. P. Seidl.)   Phys. Rev., **72**, 866 (1947).   (IX,2)

—— (50).   (With C. O. Muehlhause and G. E. Thomas.)   Phys. Rev., **79**, 11 (1950).   (IX,2)

Hart, E. W.   See Christian, R. S. (50).

Harteck, P.   See Farkas, A. (34).

Hartsough, W.   See Brueckner, K. (49a).

Harvey, J. A. (51).   Phys. Rev., **81**, 353 (1951).   (XIV,1)

Hasbrouck, B.   See Borst, L. M. (46).

Hatcher, R. D. (49).   (With G. B. Arfken and G. Breit.)   Phys. Rev., **75**, 1389 (1949).   (II,2,3)

Havens, W. W., Jr. (46).   (With L. J. Rainwater.)   Phys. Rev., **70**, 154 (1946).   (IX,2)

—— (47).   (With C. S. Wu, L. J. Rainwater, and C. L. Meaker.)   Phys. Rev., **71**, 165 (1947).   (IX,2)

—— See also Rainwater, L. J. (47); Wu, C. S. (47); Tittman, J. (50).

Haxel, O. (49).   (With J. H. D. Jensen, and H. E. Suess.)   Phys. Rev., **75**, 1766 (1949).   (XIV,2)

Hayward, E.   See Brueckner, K. (49a).

Hayward, R. W. (50).   Phys. Rev., **79**, 409 (1950) L.   (XIII,7)

Hebb, M. H. (38).   (With G. E. Uhlenbeck.)   Physica, **5**, 605 (1938).   (XII,5)

—— (40).   (With E. Nelson.)   Phys. Rev., **58**, 486 (1940).   (XII,5)

Hedgran, A.   See Bishop, G. R. (50).

Heisenberg, W. (32).   Z. Physik, **77**, 1 (1932).   (I,1), (III,3)

—— (43).   Z. Physik, **120**, 513, 673 (1943).   (X,1)

Heitler, H.   See Brown, R. H. (49).

Heitler, W. (29).   (With G. Herzberg.)   Naturwiss., **17**, 673 (1929).   (I,8)

—— (36).   Proc. Cambridge Phil. Soc., **32**, 112 (1936).   (B,2,3)

Helmholtz, A. C. (47).   (With E. M. McMillan and D. C. Sewell.)   Phys. Rev., **72**, 1003 (1947).   (IX,6)

—— See also Segrè, E. (49a).

Hemmendinger, A.   See Taschek, R. (48).

Henkel, R. L. (50).   (With H. H. Barschall.)   Phys. Rev., **80**, 145 (1950).   (IX,2)

Hepner, W. (42).   (With R. Peierls.)   Proc. Roy. Soc. (London), **A181**, 43 (1942).   (II,5), (XII,4)

Herring, C. (37).   Phys. Rev., **52**, 361 (1937).   (X,2)

Herzberg, G. (39).   *Molecular Spectra and Molecular Structure* Prentice-Hall, New York, 1939.   (I,8)

—— See also Heitler, W. (29).

Heydenburg, N. P. (48).   (With C. M. Hudson, D. R. Inglis, and W. D. White-head, Jr.)   Phys. Rev., **74**, 405 (1948).   (IX,5)

Hilbert, D. See Courant, R. (31).

Hill, R. D. (49). Phys. Rev., **76**, 333 (1949).	(XIV,2)

—— (49a). Phys. Rev., **76**, 998 (1949) L.	(XIV, 2)

—— (51). Phys. Rev., **81**, 470 (1951) L.	(XII,6)

—— See also Metzger, F. (51).

Hirzel, O. (47). (With H. Wäffler.) Helv. Phys. Acta, **20**, 373 (1947). (XII,7)

—— See also Wäffler, H. (48).

Höcker, H. (42). Physik. Z., **43**, 236 (1942).	(V,4)

Hoisington, I. E. (39). (With S. S. Share and G. Breit.) Phys. Rev., **56**, 884 (1939).	(II,2)

—— See also Breit, G. (39a).

Holstein, T. See Primakoff, H. (39).

Hornbostel, J. (49). (With E. O. Salant.) Phys. Rev., **76**, 859 (1949).	(IX,4)

—— See also Curtis, N. W. (50).

Horning, W. (49). (With L. Baumhoff.) Phys. Rev., **75**, 370 (1949).	(IX,4)

Hornyak, W. F. (48). (With T. Lauritsen.) Revs. Mod. Phys., **20**, 191 (1948). (IX,1,5)

—— (50). (With T. Lauritsen, P. Morrison, and W. A. Fowler.) (Revs. Mod. Phys., **22**, 291 (1950).	(VI,6), (VII,4), (IX,1,5,6), (XII,6), (XIII,4)

—— See also Rasmussen, V. K. (50).

Horton, G. K. (48). Proc. Phys. Soc. (London), **60**, 457 (1948).	(XII,5)

Hough, P. V. C. (50). Phys. Rev., **80**, 1069 (1950).	(XII,4)

Houtermans, F. G. See Gamow, G. (28b).

Hoyle, F. See Bethe, H. A. (39).

Hu, T. See Massey, H. S. W. (48).

Huang, K. See Van Patter, D. M. (51).

Huber, O. (48). (With R. M. Steffen and F. Humbel.) Helv Phys. Acta, **21**, 192, (1948).	(XII,6)

—— (51). (With F. Humbel, H. Schneider, A. de-Shalit, and W. Zünti.) Helv. Phys. Acta, **24**, 127 (1951).	(XII,6)

—— See also Frauenfelder, H. (50); Walter, M. (50).

Huber, P. See Stebler, A. (48).

Hudson, C. M. See Heydenburg, N. P. (48).

Hudspeth, E. See Bennett, W. E. (41).

Hughes, D. J. (49). (With W. D. B. Spatz and N. Goldstein.) Phys. Rev., **75**, 1781 (1949).	(IX,2)

—— (50). (With M. T. Burgy and G. R. Ringo.) Phys. Rev., **77**, 291 (1950) L. (II,3)

—— (50a). (With D. Sherman.) Phys. Rev., **78**, 632 (1950) L.	(IX,2), (XIV,1)

—— See also Ringo, G. R. (51).

Hull, M. M., Jr. See Bloch, I. (51a).

Hulme, H. R. (32). Proc. Roy. Soc. (London), **A138**, 643 (1932).	(XII,5)

—— (36). (With N. F. Mott, F. Oppenheimer, and H. M. Taylor.) Proc. Roy. Soc. (London), **A155**, 315 (1936).	(XII,5)

—— See also Jaeger, J. C. (35).

Hulthen, L. (42). Phys. Rev., **61**, 671 (1942) L.	(II,2,3)

—— (48). Arkiv Mat. Astron. Fysik, **35A**, No. 25 (1948).	(II,3)

Humbel, F. See Huber, O. (48), (51).

Humblet, J. (48).   Physica **14**, 285 (1948).   (V,2)

Hummel, H. H. (51).   (With D. R. Inglis.)   Phys. Rev., **81**, 910 (1951).
  (VII,3)

Hund, F. (37).   Z. Physik, **105**, 202 (1937).   (VI,6), (VII,3)

Hurwitz, H., Jr. (51).   (With H. A. Bethe.)   Phys. Rev., **81**, 898 (1951) L.
  (VII,2), (VIII,6), (XIV,1)

Husimi, K. (38).   Proc. Phys.-Math. Soc. Japan, **20**, 912 (1938).   (VIII,6)

Huus, T.   See Broström, K. G. (47).

Hylleraas, E. A. (30).   Z. Physik, **65**, 209 (1930).   (V,1)

Ibser, H. W.   See Goldsmith, H. H. (47).

Inglis, D. R. (36).   Phys. Rev., **50**, 783 (1936) L.   (VII,3)

―――― (37).   Phys. Rev., **51**, 531 (1937).   (V,2), (VII,3)

―――― (38).   Phys. Rev., **53**, 880 (1938).   (VII,3)

―――― (39).   Phys. Rev., **55**, 329 (1939).   (VII,4)

―――― (39a).   Phys. Rev., **56**, 1175 (1939).   (VII,4)

―――― (41).   Phys. Rev., **60**, 837 (1941).   (VII,4)

―――― (48).   Phys, Rev., **74**, 21 (1948).   (IX,5)

―――― (51).   Phys. Rev., **81**, 914 (1951).   (VII,3)

―――― See also Brown, H. (39b); Dancoff, S. M. (36); Goldsmith, H. H. (48);
  Heydenburg, N. P. (48); Hummel, H. H. (51).

Irving, J. (51).   Phil. Mag., **42**, 338 (1951).   (V,2)

Jackson, J. D. (50).   (With J. M. Blatt.)   Revs. Mod. Phys., **22**, 77 (1950).
  (II,4)

―――― See also Blatt, J. M. (49).

Jaeger, J. C. (35).   (With H. R. Hulme.)   Proc. Roy. Soc. (London), **A148**,
  708 (1935).   (XII,5)

Jaffey, A. H.   See Freedman, M. S. (50).

Jahn, H. A. (50).   Proc. Roy. Soc. (London), **A201**, 516 (1950).   (VII,3)

Jahnke E. (33).   (With F. Emde.)   *Funktionentafeln*, B. G. Teubner, Leipzig,
  1933; (reprint: Dover, New York, 1943).   (A,3)

Janossy, L. (39).   Proc. Cambridge Phil. Soc., **35**, 616 (1939).   (V,1)

Jastrow, R. (50).   Phys. Rev., **79**, 389 (1950) L.   (IV,1,3,4), (VII,5)

―――― (51).   Phys. Rev., **81**, 165 (1951).   (IV, 1,3,5)

Jean, M. (50).   (With J. Prentki.)   J. phys. et radium, **11**, 33 (1950).   (IV,1)

Jennings, B.   See Shoupp, W. E. (49).

Jensen, E. N.   See Laslett, L. J. (50).

Jensen, J. H. D. (50).   (With P. Jensen.)   Z. Naturforsch., **5a**, 343 (1950).
  (XII,7)

―――― See also Haxel, O. (49); Steinwedel, H. (50), (50a); Suess (52).

Jensen, P.   See Jensen, J. H. D. (50).

Johns, M. W.   See Petch, H. E. (50).

Johnson, C. M. (51).   (With W. Gordy and R. Livingston.)   Phys. Rev., **83**, 1249
  (1951) L.   (XIII,7)

Johnson, M. H.   See Halpern, O. (41).

Johnson, V. R. (51).   Phys. Rev., **81**, 316 (1951) A.   (VI,6)

Johnston, H.   See Murphy, G. M. (34).

Johnston, L.   See Cork, B. (50).

Joliot, F.   See Curie-Joliot, I. (32).

Jones, Wm. B. (47).   Phys. Rev., **72**, 362 (1947).   (IX,2)

―――― (48).   Phys. Rev., **74**, 364 (1948).   (II,3)

Kalckar, F. (37). (With J. R. Oppenheimer and R. Serber.) Phys. Rev., **52,** 279 (1937). (IX,5)

—— See also Bohr, N. (37).

Kan Chang Wang (42). Phys. Rev., **61,** 97 (1942) L. (XIII,3)

Kanner, M. H. See Barschall, H. H. (40).

Kaplan, I. (51). Phys. Rev., **81,** 962 (1951). (XI,3)

Kapur, P. L. (38). (With R. Peierls.) Proc. Roy. Soc. (London), **A166,** 277 (1938). (VIII,7)

Karr, H. J. See Mather, K. B. (50).

Kato, T. (50). Phys. Rev., **80,** 475 (1950) L. (II,3)

Kaufmann, S. G. See Bender, R. S. (49).

Keilson, J. (51). Phys. Rev., **82,** 759 (1951) L. (XIV, 2)

Kellog, J. M. B. (36). (With I. I. Rabi and J. R. Zacharias.) Phys. Rev., **50,** 472 (1936). (I,7)

—— (39). (With I. I. Rabi, N. F. Ramsey, Jr., and J. R. Zacharias.) Phys. Rev., **56,** 728 (1939). (II,1,5)

—— (40). (With I. I. Rabi, N. F. Ramsey, Jr., and J. R. Zacharias.) Phys. Rev., **57,** 677 (1940). (II,1,5)

—— (46). (With S. Millman.) Revs. Mod. Phys., **18,** 323 (1946). (I,7)

Kelly, E. L. (49). (With E. Segrè.) Phys. Rev., **75,** 999 (1949). (IX,3)

—— (50). (With C. Leith, E. Segrè and C. Wiegand.) Phys. Rev., **79,** 96 (1950). (IV,3)

—— See also Hadley, J. (49).

Kemmer, N. (37). Nature **140,** 192 (1937). (III,4)

Kerst, D. W. See Price, G. A. (50).

Ketelle, B. H. See Bell, P. R. (49); Zeldes, H. (50).

King, D. T. See Brown, R. H. (49)

Kinsey, B. B. (50). (With G. A. Bartholomew and W. H. Walker.) Phys. Rev., **77,** 723 (1950); **78,** 481 (1950) L; **78,** 77 (1950) L. (VIII,6), (XII,7)

Kirkwood, D. H. W. See Pontecorvo, B. (49).

Kittel, C. (39). (With G. Breit.) Phys. Rev., **56,** 744 (1939). (II,3)

—— (42). Phys. Rev., **62,** 109 (1942). (VII,4)

Kivel, B. See Broyles, A. A. (50).

Klaiber, G. S. See Baldwin, G. C. (48).

Knipp, J. K. See Feenberg, E. (35).

Kohman, T. P. (48). Phys. Rev., **73,** 16 (1948). (VI,2)

Kohn, W. (48). Phys. Rev., **74,** 1763 (1948). (II,3)

Kojima, S. (43). Proc. Imp. Acad. Tokyo, **19,** 282 (1943). (XII,5)

Kolsky, H. G. (51). (With T. E. Phipps, Jr., N. F. Ramsey, and H. B. Silsbee.) Phys. Rev., **81,** 1061 (1951) L. (II,5)

Konopinski, E. J. (35). (With G. E. Uhlenbeck.) Phys. Rev., **48,** 7 (1935). (XIII,5)

—— (38). (With H. A. Bethe.) Phys. Rev., **54,** 130 (1938). (VIII,3), (IX,6)

—— (41). (With G. E. Uhlenbeck.) Phys Rev., **60,** 308 (1941). (XIII,5,7)

—— (43). Revs. Mod. Phys., **15,** 209 (1943). (XIII,5,7)

—— (47). Phys. Rev., **72,** 518 (1947) L. (XIII,2)

—— (48). (With E. Teller.) Phys. Rev., **73,** 822 (1948). (IX,5)

Kopfermann, H. (45). *Kernmomente,* Edwards Brothers, Ann Arbor, Michigan, 1945. (I,6,8)

Korsching, H. See Schüler, H. (37a).

Kroeger, W. J. (38). Phys. Rev., **54**, 1048 (1938).   (VII,3)

Kruger, P. G. See Laughlin, J. S. (47), (48); Phillips, J. A. (50a).

Kudar, J. (29). Z. Physik, **53**, 61, 95 (1929).   (VIII,9), (XI,2)

Kurath, D. (50). Phys. Rev., **80**, 98 (1950) L.   (XIV, 2)

Kurie, F. N. D. (36). (With J. R. Richardson and H. C. Paxton.) Phys. Rev., **49**, 368 (1936).   (XIII,2)

——— (48). Phys. Rev., **73**, 1207 (1948) L.   (XIII,2)

Kusaka, S. (41). Phys. Rev., **60**, 61 (1941) L.   (XIII,1)

Kusch, P. (49). Phys. Rev., **76**, 138 (1949) L.   (VII,3)

Lamb, W. E., Jr. (38). (With L. I. Schiff.) Phys. Rev., **53**, 651 (1938).   (I,7), (VI,5)

Lampi, E. E. (50). (With G. D. Freier and J. H. Williams.) Phys. Rev., **80**, 853 (1950).   (II,3)

Landau, L. (37). Physik. Z. Sowjetunion, **11**, 556 (1937).   (VIII,6)

——— (44). (With J. Smorodinsky.) J. Phys. (U.S.S.R.), **8**, 154 (1944).   (II,3,4)

Langer, L. M. (51). (With R. J. D. Moffat.) Phys. Rev., **82**, 635 (1951).   (XIII,7)

——— See also Bunker, M. E. (51); Cook, C. S. (48).

Langsdorf, A. S., Jr. See Harris, S. P. (47).

Laslett, L. J. (50). (With E. N. Jensen and A. Pashkin.) Phys. Rev., **79**, 412 (1950) L.   (XIII,7)

Lassen, N. O. (48). Phys. Rev., **74**, 1533 (1948); erratum, Phys. Rev., **75**, 1099 (1949).   (XII,4)

Latimer, W. M. (37). Phys. Rev., **51**, 141 (1937) L.   (VII,4)

Latter, R. See Christy, R. F. (48).

Laubenstein, R. A. (50). Thesis, University of Wisconsin, 1950.   (VIII,10), (IX,3)

——— See also Mobley, R. C. (50).

Laue, M. von (28). Z. Physik, **52**, 726 (1928).   (VIII,9)

Laughlin, J. S. (47). (With P. G. Kruger.) Phys. Rev., **71**, 736 (1947).   (IV,2)

——— (48). (With P. G. Kruger.) Phys. Rev., **73**, 197 (1948).   (IV,2)

Lauritsen, C. C. See Brown, A. B. (50); Chao, C. Y. (50); Fowler, W. A. (49) Rasmussen, V. K. (50); Streib, J. F. (41); Tollestrup, A. V. (50).

Lauritsen, T. (50). (With R. G. Thomas.) Phys. Rev., **78**, 88 (1950).   (IX,5)

——— (51). "Energy Levels of Light Nuclei," 1950 Nuclear Science Review. (VI,6)

——— See also Hornyak, W. F. (48), (50); Rasmussen, V. K. (50).

Lavatelli, L. S. See Sutton, R. B. (47).

Lawson, J. L. (39). Phys. Rev., **56**, 131 (1939).   (XIII,2)

——— (40). (With J. M. Cork.) Phys. Rev., **57**, 982 (1940).   (XIII,2)

——— (48). (With M. L. Perlman.) Phys. Rev., **74**, 1190 (1948).   (XII,7)

Lawson, J. S., Jr. See Phillips, J. A. (50a).

Lax, M. (48). (With H. Feshbach.) J. Acoust. Soc. Am., **20**, 108 (1948).   (VIII,2,5)

——— (50). Phys. Rev., **78**, 306 (1950) L.   (II,3)

——— See also Morse, P. M. (45).

Lebow, I. L. See Feld, B. T. (50).

Lee, D. W. See Curtis, N. W. (50).

Lee, T. D. (49). (With M. Rosenbluth and C. N. Yang.) Phys. Rev., **75**, 905 (1949). (XIII,5)

Leininger, R. F. (49). (With E. Segrè and C. Wiegand.) Phys. Rev., **76**, 897 (1949). (XIII,3)

Leith, C. See Hadley, J. (49); Kelly, E. L. (50).

Levinger, J. S. (49). Phys. Rev., **76**, 699 (1949). (XII,4)

———— (50). (With H. A. Bethe.) Phys. Rev., **78**, 115 (1950). (XII,4,7)

Levinthal, E. C. (50). Phys. Rev., **78**, 204 (1950). (II,5)

Lewis, H. (46). (With D. Bohm.) Phys. Rev., **69**, 129 (1946) L. (XIII,5)

Lidofsky, L. I. See Macklin, P. A. (51).

Lindenfeld, P. See Perez-Mendez, V. (50).

Ling, D. S. Jr. (48). (With D. L. Falkoff.) Phys. Rev., **74**, 1224 (1948). (XII,6)

———— (48a). Thesis, University of Michigan, 1948. (XII,6)

Lippmann, B. A. (50). (With J. S. Schwinger.) Phys. Rev., **79**, 469 (1950). (II,3)

———— (50a). Phys. Rev., **79**, 481 (1950). (II,3)

Littauer, R. M. (50). Proc. Phys. Soc. (London), **A63**, 294 (1950) L. (XII,6), (XIII,4)

Livingston, R. See Johnson, C. M. (51).

Lloyd, S. P. (50). Phys. Rev., **80**, 118 (1950) L. (XII,6), (A,5)

———— (51). Phys. Rev., **81**, 161 (1951) L. (XII,6), (XIII,7)

———— (51a). Thesis, University of Illinois, 1951. (XII,6) (A,5)

———— (51b). Phys. Rev., **82**, 277 (1951) L. (XII,6)

———— (51c). Phys. Rev., **83**, 716 (1951). (XII,6)

Lock, W. O. See Camerini, U. (49).

Long, E. A. See Sutton, R. B. (47).

Longmire, C. (49). (With H. Brown.) Phys. Rev., **75**, 264 (1949); erratum, **75**, 1102 (1949) L. (XIII,2)

———— (49a). (With C. S. Wu and C. H. Townes.) Phys. Rev., **76**, 695 (1949) L. (XIII,7)

———— (51). (With A. M. L. Messiah.) Phys. Rev., **83**, 464 (1951) L. (XIII,7)

———— See also Bethe, H. A. (50).

Low, F. (48). Phys. Rev., **74**, 1885 (1948) L. (II,2)

Low, W. (50). (With C. H. Townes.) Phys. Rev., **80**, 608 (1950). (XIV, 1)

———— See also Townes, C. H. (49).

Lowan, A. N. See Morse, P. M. (45)

Lowen, I. S. (41). Phys. Rev., **59**, 835 (1941) L. (XII,6)

———— (49). (With N. Tralli.) Phys. Rev., **75**, 529 (1949) L. (XII,5)

McCord, R. V. See Snell, A. H. (50).

McDaniel, B. D. See Walker, R. L. (50).

McElhinney, J. (49). (With A. O. Hanson, R. A. Becker, R. B. Duffield, and B. C. Diven.) Phys. Rev., **75**, 542 (1949). (I,2), (XII,7)

McGinnis, C. L. (51). Phys. Rev., **81**, 734 (1951). (XII,6)

McGowan, F. K. (50). Phys. Rev., **79**, 404 (1950). (XII,6)

———— (50a). Phys. Rev., **80**, 482 (1950). (XII,6)

———— (51). Phys. Rev., **81**, 1066 (1951) L. (XII,6)

Mack, J. E. (50). Revs. Mod. Phys., **22**, 64 (1950). (I,7)

Macklin, P. A. (51). (With L. I. Lidofsky and C. S. Wu.) Phys. Rev., **82**, 334 (1951) A. (XIII,7)

McMillan, E. M. (46). J. Acoust. Soc. Am., **18**, 344 (1946). (X,2)

—— (47). J. Acoust. Soc. Am., **19**, 922 (1947) L. (X,2)

—— See also Cook, L. J. (49); Helmholtz, A. C. (47).

McPhail, M. R. (40). Phys. Rev., **57**, 669 (1940). (IX,2)

Majorana, E. (33). Z. Physik, **82**, 137 (1933). (I,1), (III,3)

—— (37). Nuovo cimento, **14**, 171, 322 (1937). (XIII,1)

Mann, L. G. (50). (With P. Axel.) Phys. Rev., **80**, 759 (1950). (XII,6)

Margenau, H. (34). Phys. Rev., **46**, 613 (1934). (VII,3)

—— (37). (With D. T. Warren.) Phys. Rev., **52**, 790 (1937). (V,2)

—— (38). (With W. A. Tyrrell, Jr.) Phys. Rev., **54**, 422 (1938). (V,2)

—— (38a). Phys. Rev., **53**, 198 (1938) L. (V,2)

—— (38b). (With K. G. Carroll.) Phys. Rev., **54**, 705 (1938). (V,2), (VII,3)

—— (39). Phys. Rev., **55**, 1173 (1939). (V,2), (VII,3)

—— (40). Phys. Rev., **57**, 383 (1940). (II,5)

—— (40a). (With E. P. Wigner.) Phys. Rev., **58**, 103 (1940). (VI,5), (XIV, 2)

—— (41). Phys. Rev., **59**, 37 (1941). (VII,4)

—— See also Tyrrell, W. A. Jr. (39).

Marmier, P. See Blaser, J. P. (51).

Marshak, R. E. (42). Phys. Rev., **61**, 431 (1942). (XIII,5,7)

—— (46). Phys. Rev., **70**, 980 (1946) L. (XIII,7)

—— (49). Phys. Rev., **75**, 513 (1949). (XIII,7)

—— See also Grönblom, B. O. (39); Snyder, H. (47).

Marshall, J. F. (49). (With E. Guth.) Phys. Rev., **76**, 1879, 1880 (1949). (XII,4)

—— (50). (With E. Guth.) Phys. Rev., **78**, 738 (1950). (XII,4)

—— See also Guth, E. (48a).

Marshall, L. See Fermi, E. (47a), (49).

Massey, H. S. W. (48). (With E. H. S. Burhop and T. Hu.) Phys. Rev., **73**, 1403 (1948). (IV,1)

—— (48a). (With R. Buckingham.) Phys. Rev., **73**, 260 (1948). (V,4)

—— See also Buckingham, R. (41); Burhop, E. (48); Mott, N. F. (33).

Mather, K. B. (50). (With H. J. Karr and R. O. Bondelid.) Phys. Rev., **78**, 292 (1950) L. (V,4)

Matricon, M. (38). Compt. rend., **206**, 651, 1809 (1938). (VII,3)

Mayer, M. G. (48). Phys. Rev., **74**, 235 (1948). (VI,2), (XIV,1)

—— (49). Phys. Rev., **75**, 1969 (1949). (XIV,2)

—— (50). Phys. Rev., **78**, 16, 22 (1950). (XIV,2)

—— (51). (With S. A. Moszkowski and L. W. Nordheim.) Revs. Mod. Phys., **23**, 315 (1951). (XIII,7), (XIV,2)

—— See also Sachs, R. G. (38).

Meaker, C. L. See Havens, W. W. (47).

Medicus, H. (50). (With P. Preiswerk and P. Scherrer.) Helv. Phys. Acta, **23**, 299 (1950). (XII,6)

Meeks, M. L. See Greuling, E. (51).

Meiners, E. P., Jr. (49). Phys. Rev., **76**, 259 (1949). (XII,4)

Melkonian, E. (49). Phys. Rev., **76**, 1744 (1949).   (II,3)

Messiah, A. M. L. See Longmire, C. (51).

Metzger, F. (50). (With M. Deutsch.) Phys. Rev., **78**, 551 (1950).   (XII,6)

—— (51). (With R. D. Hill.) Phys. Rev., **82**, 646 (1951).   (XII,6)

Milford, F. J. See Foldy, L. L. (50a).

Millman, S. See Kellogg, J. M. B. (46).

Milton, J. C. D. See Fulbright, H. W. (51).

Mitchell, A. C. G. (48). Revs. Mod. Phys., **20**, 296 (1948).   (XIII,4)

—— See also Peacock, C. L. (48a).

Mobley, R. C. (50). (With R. A. Laubenstein.) Phys. Rev., **80**, 309 (1950).
    (II,2)

Moffat, R. J. D. See Bunker, M. E. (51); Langer, L. M. (51).

Möller, C. (37). Physik. Z. Sowjetunion, **11**, 9 (1937); Phys. Rev., **51**, 84 (1937).
    (XIII,3)

—— (43). (With L. Rosenfeld.) Kgl. Danske Videnskab. Selskab, Mat.-fys.
    Medd., **20**, No. 12 (1943).   (XII,4)

—— (45). Kgl. Danske Videnskab. Selskab, Mat.-fys. Medd., **23**, 1 (1945).
    (X,1)

—— See also Bloch, F. (35).

Moon, M. L. See Waggoner, M. A. (50).

Mooring, F. P. See Bashkin, S. (50).

Morrish, A. H. See Allen, J. S. (49).

Morrison, P. (48). Phys. Rev., **74**, 1224 (1948) A.   (V,5), (VI,5)

—— See also Dancoff, S. M. (39a); Hornyak, W. F. (50).

Morse, P. M. (45). (With A. N. Lowan, H. Feshbach, and M. Lax.) U.S. Navy,
    Department of Research and Inventions, Report No. 62, 1R, 1945.   (VIII,2)

Morton, G. A. See Shull, C. G. (48).

Moshinsky, M. (51). Phys. Rev., **81**, 347 (1951).   (X,4)

Moszkowski, S. A. (51). Phys. Rev., **83**, 1071 (1951) L.   (XII,6), (XIV,2)

—— (51a). Phys. Rev., **82**, 118 (1951) L.   (XIII,6,7), (XIV,2)

—— (51b). Phys. Rev., **82**, 35 (1951).   (XIII,4)

—— See also Mayer, M. G. (51).

Mott, N. F. (33). (With H. S. W. Massey.) *The Theory of Atomic Collisions*,
    Clarendon Press, Oxford, 1933.   (II,3)

—— See also Hulme, H. R. (36); Taylor, H. M. (32), (33).

Motz, L. (38). (With E. Feenberg.) Phys. Rev., **54**, 1055 (1938).   (VIII,6)

—— (40). (With J. S. Schwinger.) Phys. Rev., **57**, 162 (1940) L.; **58**, 26
    (1940).   (V,4)

Muehlhause, C. O. (50). Phys. Rev., **79**, 277 (1950).   (XII,7)

—— See also Harris, S. P. (50).

Muether, H. R. (50). (With S. L. Ridgway.) Phys. Rev., **80**, 750 (1950) L.
    (XIII,7)

—— See also Sherr, R. (49).

Muirhead, H. See Camerini, U. (49).

Mullin, C. J. (49). (With E. Guth.) Phys. Rev., **76**, 682 (1949) L.   (XII,4)

—— See also Guth, E. (48), (48a), (49).

Murphy, G. M. (34). (With H. Johnston.) Phys. Rev., **46**, 95 (1934).   (II,3)

Muxart, R. See Bouchez, R. (47), (49).

Myers, F. E. (42). (With L. C. Van Atta.) Phys. Rev., **61**, 19 (1942).   (II,2),
    (XII,4)

Myers, R. D. (38).   Phys. Rev., **54**, 361 (1938).   (X,3), (A,5)

Nafe, J. E. (48).   (With E. B. Nelson.)   Phys. Rev., **73**, 718 (1948).   (II,3)
——— See also Nelson, E. B. (49).

Nagle, D. E.   See Davis, L., Jr. (48).

Nakabayasi, K. (37).   Sci. Repts. Tohoku Imp. Univ., **25**, 1141 (1937).   (V,2), (VII,3)

Nakano, Y. (49).   Phys. Rev., **76**, 981 (1949) L.   (IX,5)

Nedelsky, L. (33).   (With J. R. Oppenheimer.)   Phys. Rev., **44**, 948 (1933). (XII,5)

Nelson, E.   See Hebb, M. H. (40).

Nelson, E. B. (49).   (With J. E. Nafe.)   Phys. Rev., **75**, 1194 (1949).   (V,2)
——— See also Nafe, J. E. (48).

Neumann, G. (14).   Ann. Physik, **45**, 529 (1914).   (XIII,1)

Newell, G. F. (50).   Phys. Rev., **77**, 141 (1950) L.   (II,5)

Nicodemus, D.   See Bloch, F. (48).

Nordheim, L. W. (37).   (With F. L. Yost.)   Phys. Rev., **51**, 942 (1937).
(III,5), (XIII,6)
——— (49).   Phys. Rev., **75**, 1894 (1949).   (XIV,2)
——— (50).   Phys. Rev., **78**, 294 (1950) L.   (XIII,6,7), (XIV,2)
——— (51).   Revs. Mod. Phys., **23**, 322 (1951).   (XIII,7), (XIV,2)
——— See also Mayer, M. G. (51).

Nordsieck, A. (40).   Phys. Rev., **58**, 310 (1940).   (II,5)

Novey, T. B. (50).   Phys. Rev., **78**, 66 (1950).   (XIII,7)

Novick, A.   See Anderson, H. L. (47).

Noyes, H. P.   See Christian, R. S. (50a).

Nuckolls, R. G.   See Bailey, C. D. (46).

Nye, H. A.   See Rarita, W. (41b).

Occhialini, G.   See Powell, C. F. (47).

Ochiai, K. (37).   Phys. Rev., **52**, 1221 (1937).   (V,4)

Oppenheimer, F.   See Hulme, H. R. (36).

Oppenheimer, J. R. (35).   Phys. Rev., **47**, 845 (1935).   (IX,6)
——— (35a).   (With M. Phillips.)   Phys. Rev., **48**, 500 (1935).   (IX,6)
——— (38).   (With R. Serber.)   Phys. Rev., **53**, 636 (1938).   (IX,5)
——— (39).   (With J. S. Schwinger.)   Phys. Rev., **56**, 1066 (1939) L.   (XII,5)
——— See also Born, M. (27); Ehrenfest, P. (31); Kalckar, F. (37); Nedelsky, L. (33).

Osborn, R. K. (50).   (With L. L. Foldy.)   Phys. Rev., **79**, 795 (1950).   (VI,5)

Osborne, C. L.   See Borst, L. M. (46).

Osborne, L. S.   See Feld, B. T. (50).

Osoba, J. S. (49).   Phys. Rev., **76**, 345 (1949).   (XII,6)

Ovadia, J. (51).   (With P. Axel.)   Phys. Rev., **81**, 332 (1951) A.   (XII,6)
——— (51a).   Thesis, University of Illinois, 1951.   (XII,6)

Packard, M.   See Bloch, F. (47).

Padfield, D. (49).   Nature, **163**, 22 (1949).   (II,5)

Pais, A.   See Case, K. M. (50).

Paneth, H. R.   See Allen, J. S. (49).

Panofsky, W. K. H. (50).   (With F. L. Fillmore.)   Phys. Rev., **79**, 57 (1950). (IV,4)

Pashkin, A.   See Laslett, L. J. (50).

Paul, E. B. (52).   (With R. L. Clarke.)   New York Physical Society Meeting, January 1952, Abstract N8.   (VIII,6)

Pauli, W., Jr. (24). Naturwiss, **12**, 741 (1924).   (I,7)
——— (33). "Die allgemeinen Prinzipien der Wellenmechanik," *Handbuch der Physik*, vol. 24, 1, Chapter 2.   (I,8)
——— (36). Ann. inst. Henri Poincaré, **6**, 109 (1936).   (XIII,5)
——— (41). Revs. Mod. Phys., **13**, 203 (1941).   (XIII,5)
Paxton, H. C. See Kurie, F. N. D. (36).
Peacock, C. L. (48a). (With A. C. G. Mitchell.) Phys. Rev., **75**, 1272 (1948). (XII,6)
Pease, R. L. (50). Thesis, M.I.T., 1950.   (V,2,4,5)
——— (51). (With H. Feshbach.) Phys. Rev., **81**, 142 (1951) L.   (V,2,4,5)
Peaslee, D. C. (48). Phys. Rev., **74**, 1001 (1948).   (IX,6)
——— See also Blaser, J. P. (51); Feshbach, H. (47); Good, W. M. (46).
Peierls, R. See Barker, F. C. (49); Bethe, H. A. (34), (35), (39); Hepner, W. (42); Kapur, P. L. (38).
Perez-Mendez, V. (50). (With P. Lindenfeld.) Phys. Rev., **80**, 1097 (1950) L. (XIII,6)
Perlman, I. (50). (With A. Ghiorso and G. T. Seaborg.) Phys. Rev., **77**, 26 (1950).   (I,5), (XI,1,3), (XIV,1)
——— See also Seaborg, G. T. (48).
Perlman, M. L. (48). (With G. Friedlander.) Phys. Rev., **74**, 442 (1948). (XII,7)
——— See also Lawson, J. L. (48).
Petch, H. E. (50). (With M. W. Johns.) Phys. Rev., **80**, 478 (1950) L. (XII,5)
Peterson, J. M. See Cook, L. J. (49).
Peterson, R. E. (50). (With H. H. Barschall and C. K. Bockelman.) Phys. Rev., **79**, 593 (1950).   (IX,2)
——— See also Adair, R. K. (49); Barschall, H. H. (49); Bashkin, S. (50).
Petree, B. See Bashkin, S. (50).
Phillips, J. A. (50a). (With J. S. Lawson, Jr., and P. G. Kruger.) Phys. Rev., **80**, 326 (1950).   (XII,4)
Phillips, M. (40). Phys. Rev., **57**, 160 (1940) L.   (VI,5)
——— (41). (With E. Feenberg.) Phys. Rev., **59**, 400 (1941) L.   (VI,1,2)
——— See also Feenberg, E. (37c); Oppenheimer, J. R. (35a).
Phipps, T. E., Jr. See Kolsky, H. G. (51).
Placzek, G. See Bethe, H. A. (37a).
Pleasantson, F. See Snell, A. H. (50).
Plesset, M. S. (36). Phys. Rev., **49**, 551 (1936) L.   (III,3)
——— (41). Am. J. Phys., **9**, 1 (1941).   (VII,5)
——— See also Brown, F. W. (39).
Pomeranchuk, I. See Akhiezer, A. (48).
Pontecorvo, B. (49). (With D. H. W. Kirkwood and G. C. Hanna.) Phys. Rev., **75**, 982 (1949) L.   (XIII,3)
——— See also Hanna, G. C. (49).
Poss, H. L. (49). "The Properties of Atomic Nuclei," I. Spins, Magnetic Moments and Electric Quadrupole Moments, Brookhaven National Laboratory, October 1, 1949.   (I,7)
——— (50). Phys. Rev., **79**, 539 (1950) L.   (XII,7)
Powell, C. F. (47). (With G. Occhialini.) Cambridge Conference (Physical Society London 1947), p. 150.   (IV,2)
——— See also Brown, R. H. (49).

Powell, W. M.   See Brueckner, K. (49), (49a).
Preiswerk, P.   See Medicus, H. (50).
Prentki, J.   See Jean, M. (50).
Present, R. D. (41).   Phys. Rev., **60**, 28 (1941).   (VII,5)
—— (50).   Phys. Rev., **80**, 43 (1950).   (VII,3)
—— See also Breit, G. (36); Rarita, W. (37).
Price, G. A. (50).   (With D. W. Kerst.)   Phys. Rev., **77**, 806 (1950).   (XII,7)
Price, H. C., Jr.   See Cook, C. S. (48).
Primakoff, H. (37).   Phys. Rev., **52**, 1000 (1937).   (V,4)
—— (39).   (With T. Holstein.)   Phys. Rev., **55**, 1218 (1939).   (III,1), (V,1)
—— (47).   Phys. Rev., **72**, 118 (1947).   (II,5), (V,1)
—— See also Feenberg, E. (46a).
Proctor, W. G. (51).   (With F. C. Yu.)   Phys. Rev., **81**, 20 (1951).   (VI,5)
Pruett, J. R. (48).   Phys. Rev., **73**, 1219 (1948) A.   (XIII,2)
Pryce, M. H. L. (50).   Proc. Phys. Soc. (London), **A63**, 692 (1950).   (XI,1), (XIV,1)
Purcell, E. M.   See Gardner, J. H. (49).
Rabi, I. I.   See Kellogg, J. M. B. (36), (39), (40).
Racah, G. (37).   Nuovo cimento, **14**, 93 (1937).   (XIII,1)
—— (42).   Phys. Rev., **61**, 186 (1942).   (VII,3)
—— (42a).   Phys. Rev., **62**, 438 (1942).   (XII,6), (A,5)
—— (50).   Helv. Phys. Acta, **23**, Supplement III, p. 229 (1950).   (VII,3)
—— (50a).   Phys. Rev., **78**, 622 (1950).   (XIV,2)
Rae, E. R. (49).   Phil. Mag., **40**, 1155 (1949).   (XII,5)
Rainwater, L. J. (47).   (With W. W. Havens, C. S. Wu, and J. Dunning.)   Phys. Rev., **71**, 65 (1947).   (IX,2)
—— (50).   Phys. Rev., **79**, 432 (1950).   (XIV,2)
—— See also Havens, W. W., (46), (47); Wu, C. S. (47); Tittman, J. (50).
Ramsey, N. F., Jr.   See Kellogg, J. M. B. (39), (40); Kolsky, H. G. (51); Salant, E.O. (40).
Ramsey, W. H. (48).   Proc. Cambridge Phil. Soc., **44**, 87 (1948).   (II,2,3)
Rarita, W. (37).   (With R. D. Present.)   Phys. Rev., **51**, 788 (1937).   (II,2), (V,2,3)
—— (38).   (With Z. I. Slawsky.)   Phys. Rev., **54**, 1053 (1938).   (II,2)
—— (41).   (With J. S. Schwinger.)   Phys. Rev., **59**, 436 (1941).   (II,5), (V,5), (XII,4)
—— (41a).   (With J. S. Schwinger.)   Phys. Rev., **59**, 556 (1941).   (III,5), (IV,1,2), (XII,4).
—— (41b).   (With J. S. Schwinger and H. A. Nye.)   Phys. Rev., **59**, 209 (1941).   (III,5), (IV,1), (XII,4)
—— See Feshbach, H. (49).
Rasetti, F. (30).   Z. Physik, **61**, 598 (1930).   (I,8)
Rasmussen, V. K. (50).   (With W. F. Hornyak, C. C. Lauritsen, and T. Lauritsen.)   Phys. Rev., **77**, 617 (1950).   (XII,5)
Rayleigh, Lord (79).   Proc. Roy. Soc. (London), **A29**, 91 (1879).   (VII,5)
—— (82).   Phil. Mag., **14**, 184 (1882).   (VII,5)
Reitz, J. R. (50).   Phys. Rev. **77**, 10 (1950).   (XII,5), (XIII,2)
Richards, H. T.   See Bailey, C. D. (46); Bennett, W. E. (41); Smith, R. V. (48).
Richardson, J. R.   See Kurie, F. N. D. (36).
Richman, C.   See Cork, B. (50).
Ridgway, S. L.   See Muether, H. R. (50).

Ring, H. See Gordy, W. (48).

Ringo, G. R. (51). (With M. T. Burgy and D. J. Hughes.) Phys. Rev., **82,** 344 (1951) A. (II,3)

—— See also Hughes, D. J. (50).

Roberts, A. See Arnold, W. R. (47); Waggoner, M. A. (50).

Roberts, D. M. (51). (With R. M. Steffen.) Phys. Rev., **81,** 332 (1951) A. (XII,6)

Robson, J. M. (50). Phys. Rev., **78,** 311 (1950) L. (I,3), (XIII,4)

Rogers, E. H. (49). (With H. H. Staub.) Phys. Rev., **76,** 980 (1949). (I,7)

Rogozinski, A. See Benoist, P. (49); Bouchez, R. (49).

Rohrlich, F. (49). (With J. Eisenstein.) Phys. Rev., **75,** 705 (1949). (IV,1)

—— See also Eisenstein, J. (48).

Rojansky, V. (42). *Introductory Quantum Mechanics,* Prentice-Hall, New York, 1942. (A,1)

Rose, B. (50). (With A. R. W. Wilson.) Phys. Rev., **78,** 68 (1950). (XII,6), (XIII,4)

Rose, M. E. (35). (With G. E. Uhlenbeck.) Phys. Rev., **48,** 211 (1935). (XII,5)

—— (36). Phys. Rev., **49,** 727 (1936). (XIII,2)

—— (37). (With H. A. Bethe.) Phys. Rev., **51,** 205 (1937). (VII,3)

—— (40). Phys. Rev., **57,** 958 (1940). (IX,3)

—— (47). (With G. Goertzel.) Phys. Rev., **72,** 749 (1947). (XII,4)

—— (49). (With G. Goertzel, B. I. Spinrad, J. A. Harr, and P. Strong.) Phys. Rev., **76,** 1883 (1949) L. (XII,5,6)

—— (49a). Phys. Rev., **76,** 678 (1949). (XII,5)

—— (49b). Phys. Rev., **75,** 1444 (1949) L. (XIII,5)

—— (51). (With G. Goertzel, B. I. Spinrad, J. Harr, and P. Strong.) Phys. Rev., **83,** 79 (1951). (XII,5,6)

—— See also Biedenharn, L. C. (51a).

Rosen, N. See Bowers, W. A. (49).

Rosenbluth, M. See Lee, T. D. (49).

Rosenfeld, L. See Möller, C. (43).

Rossi, B. (48). Revs. Mod. Phys., **20,** 537 (1948). (IX,4)

Rutherford, E. (08). (With H. Geiger.) Proc. Roy. Soc. (London), **A81,** 141 (1908). (I,3)

—— (11). Phil. Mag., **21,** 669 (1911). (I,1)

Sachs, R. G. (38). (With M. G. Mayer.) Phys. Rev., **53,** 991 (1938). (II,2)

—— (39). Phys. Rev., **55,** 825 (1939). (VII,4)

—— (40). Phys. Rev., **57,** 159 (1940) L. (XII,5)

—— (40a). Phys. Rev., **57,** 194 (1940). (XII,5)

—— (46). Phys. Rev., **69,** 611 (1946). (VI,5)

—— (47). Phys. Rev., **72,** 91 (1947). (II,5)

—— (47a). Phys. Rev., **72,** 312 (1947). (VI,5)

—— (48). Phys. Rev., **74,** 433 (1948). (I,7), (V,5), (VI,5)

—— (51). (With N. Austern.) Phys. Rev., **81,** 705 (1951). (XII,3,4,6,7)

—— See also Austern, N. (51); Avery, R. (48); Eisner, E. (47); Fermi, E. (47b); Guthrie, A. (42); Wolfenstein, L. (48).

Sakata, S. See Yukawa, H. (35), (37).

Salant, E. O. (40). (With N. F. Ramsey.) Phys. Rev., **57,** 1075 (1940). (IV,2)

—— See also Curtis, N. W. (50); Hornbostel, J. (49).

Salpeter, E. E. (51). Phys. Rev., **82**, 60 (1951). (II,3), (XII,4)
Sargent, B. W. (33). Proc. Roy. Soc. (London), **A139**, 659 (1933). (XIII,4)
Saxon, D. (49). Phys. Rev., **76**, 986 (1949) L. (XIII,1)
Scharff-Goldhaber, G. See Goldhaber, M. (48a).
Scherrer, P. See Medicus, H. (50).
Schiff, L. I. (48). Phys. Rev., **73**, 1311 (1948). (XII,7)
—— (49). *Quantum Mechanics*, McGraw-Hill, New York, 1949. (III,4), (XIII,5)
—— (50). Phys. Rev., **78**, 83 (1950). (XII,4)
—— (50a). Phys. Rev., **78**, 733 (1950). (XII,4)
—— See also Lamb, W. E. Jr. (38).
Schmidt, T. (37). Z. Physik, **106**, 358 (1937). (I,7), (VI,5)
—— (40). Naturwiss., **28**, 565 (1940). (XIV,2)
Schneider, H. See Huber, O. (51).
Schüler, H. (37). Z. Physik, **107**, 12 (1937). (VI,5)
—— (37a). (With H. Korsching.) Z. Physik, **105**, 168 (1937). (VI,5)
Schwinger, J. S. (37a). (**With E. Teller.**) Phys. Rev., **52**, 286 (1937). (II,3)
—— (37b). Phys. Rev., **52**, 1250 (1937) L. (II,3)
—— (40). Phys. Rev., **58**, 1004 (1940) L. (II,3)
—— (41). Phys. Rev., **60**, 164 (1941) A. (II,5)
—— (47). Phys. Rev., **72**, 742 (1947) A. (II,3)
—— (50). Phys. Rev., **78**, 135 (1950). (II,4), (III,3)
—— See also Cohen, V. W. (39); Corben, H. C. (40); Feshbach, H. (49b), (51); Gerjuoy, E. (42); Lippmann, B. A. (50); Motz, L. (40); Oppenheimer, J. R. (39); Rarita, W. (41), (41a), (41b).
Scott, M. See Way, K. (50).
Seaborg, G. T. (48). (With I. Perlman.) Revs. Mod. Phys., **20**, 585 (1948). (I,3)
—— See also Perlman, I. (50).
Seagondollar, L. W. See Barschall, H. H. (48).
Seeger, R. J. (42). (With E. Teller.) Phys. Rev., **62**, 37 (1942). (II,3)
Segrè, E. (49). (With C. E. Wiegand.) Phys. Rev., **75**, 39 (1949). (XIII,3)
—— (49a). (With A. C. Helmholtz.) Revs. Mod. Phys., **21**, 271 (1949). (XII,6)
—— See also Chamberlain, O. (51); Hadley, J. (49); Kelly, E. L. (49), (50); Leininger, R. F. (49).
Seidl, F. G. P. (49). Phys. Rev., **75**, 1508 (1949). (IX,2)
—— See also Harris, S. P. (47).
Seitz, F. See Goldberger, M. L. (47); Wigner, E. P. (33).
Selove, W. (50). Phys. Rev., **77**, 557 (1950). (IX,2)
—— (50a). Private communication. (IX,2)
Serber, R. (47). Phys. Rev., **72**, 1114 (1947). (IV,1,3), (IX,6)
—— See also Fernbach, S. (49); Kalckar, F. (37); Oppenheimer, J. R. (38).
Sewell, D. C. See Cook, L. J. (49); Helmholtz, A. C. (47).
Shapiro, M. (51). Phys. Rev., to appear shortly. (VIII,2,5)
Share, S. S. (37). (With G. Breit.) Phys. Rev., **52**, 546 (1937). (II,1)
—— See also Breit, G. (39a); Feenberg, E. (36a); Hoisington, I. E. (39).
Shaw, P. F. D. See Bishop, G. R. (51).
Sheer, C. See Tittman, J. (50).
Sherman, D. See Hughes, D. J. (50a).
Sherr, R. (45). Phys. Rev., **68**, 240 (1945). (IV,2), (IX,2)

Sherr, R (49).   (With H. R. Muether and M. G. White.)   Phys. Rev., **75,** 282
   (1949).   (VI,6), (XIII,4)
Sherwin, C. W. (49).   Phys. Rev., **75,** 1799 (1949).   (XIII,7)
———— (51).   Phys. Rev., **82,** 52 (1951).   (XIII,7)
Shimose, T. (38).   Proc. Phys. Math. Soc. Japan, **20,** 83 (1938) L.   (VII,3)
Shoemaker, F. C.   See Bender, R. S. (49).
Shortley, G. H.   See Condon, E. U. (35).
Shoupp, W. E. (49).   (With B. Jennings and K. H. Sun.)   Phys. Rev., **75,** 1
   (1949).   (IX,5)
Shull, C. G. (48).   (With E. O. Wollan, G. A. Morton, and W. L. Davidson.)
   Phys. Rev., **73,** 842 (1948).   (II,3)
———— See also Wollan, E. O. (48).
Shull, F. B. (49).   (With E. Feenberg.)   Phys. Rev., **75,** 1768 (1949) L.
   (XIII,7)
Siegbahn, K.   See Bishop, G. R. (50).
Siegel, A. (51).   Phys. Rev., **82,** 194 (1951).   (IV,1)
Siegert, A. J. F. (37).   Phys. Rev., **52,** 787 (1937).   (I,7), (VI,5), (XII,7)
———— (39).   Phys. Rev., **56,** 750 (1939).   (VIII,9)
Silsbee, H. B.   See Kolsky, H. G. (51).
Simons, L. (39).   Phys. Rev., **55,** 792 (1939) L.   (II,3)
———— (40).   Kgl. Danske Videnskab. Selskab., Mat.-fys. Medd., **17,** No. 7
   (1940).   (II,3)
Slawsky, Z. I.   See Rarita, W. (38).
Sleator, W. Jr. (47).   Phys. Rev. **72,** 207 (1947).   (IV,2)
Smith, P. B. (51).   (With J. S. Allen.)   Phys. Rev., **81,** 381 (1951).   (XIII,3)
Smith, R. V. (48).   (With H. T. Richards.)   Phys. Rev., **74,** 1871 (1948) L.
   (II,2), (V,4)
Smorodinsky, J. (44).   J. Phys. (U.S.S.R.), **8,** 219 (1944).   (II,3)
———— (47).   J. Phys. (U.S.S.R.), **11,** 195 (1947).   (II,3)
———— See also Landau, L. (44).
Sneddon, I. N. (48).   (With B. F. Touschek.(Proc. Cambridge Phil. Soc.,
   44, 391 (1948).   (VIII,6)
Snell, A. H. (49).   (With E. C. Barker and R. L. Sternberg.)   Phys. Rev., **75,**
   1290 (1949).   (XII,4)
———— (50).   (With F. Pleasantson and R. V. McCord.)   Phys. Rev., **78,** 310
   (1950) L.   (I,3), (XIII,4)
———— (50a).   (With E. C. Barker and R. L. Sternberg.)   Phys. Rev., **80,** 637
   (1950).   (XII,4)
Snyder, H. (47).   (With R. E. Marshak.)   Phys. Rev., **72,** 1253 (1947) L.
   (IV,1)
Snyder, T.   See Sutton, R. B. (47).
Spatz, W. D. B.   See Hughes, D. J. (49).
Spees, A. H.   See Zahn, C. T. (37), (38).
Spence, R. W.   See Bloch, F. (47).
Sperduto, A.   See Van Patter, D. M. (51).
Spiers, J. A. (50).   Phys. Rev., **80,** 491 (1950) L.   (XII,6)
Spinrad, B. I.   See Rose, M. E. (49), (51).
Spruch, L. (50).   Phys. Rev., **80,** 372 (1950).   (V,5), (VI,5)
Stafford, G. H.   See Barnes, C. A. (50).
Stanley, J. P.   See Gellman, H. (50); Griffith, B. A. (49).
Staub, H. H.   See Bloch, F. (48); Rogers, E. H. (49).

Stearns, M. B.   See Walker, R. L. (50).

Stebler, A. (48).   (With P. Huber.)   Helv. Phys. Acta, **21,** 59, (1948).
(IX,5)

Steffen, R. M.   See Huber, O. (48); Roberts, D. M. (51).

Stehn, J. R.   See Breit, G. (37).

Steinwedel, H. (50).   (With J. H. D. Jensen.)   Phys. Rev., **79,** 1019 (1950) L.
(XII,7)

――― (50a).   (With J. H. D. Jensen.)   Z. Naturforsch., **5a,** 413 (1950).   (XII,7)

Stephens, W. E. (40).   Phys. Rev., **57,** 938 (1940) L.   (VI,2)

――― See also Toms, M. E. (51).

Sternberg, R. L.   See Snell, A. H. (49), (50a).

Sternheimer, R. (50).   Phys. Rev., **80,** 102 (1950) L.   (I,7)

Stevenson, D. J. (50).   (With M. Deutsch.)   Phys. Rev., **78,** 640 (1950).
(XIII,7)

Strait, E. N.   See Van Patter, D. M. (51).

Strauch, K. (51).   Phys. Rev., **81,** 973 (1951).   (XII,7)

Streib, J. F. (41).   (With W. A. Fowler and C. C. Lauritsen.)   Phys. Rev., **59,**
253 (1941).   (XII,5)

Strong, P.   See Rose, M. E. (49), (51).

Stump, R. (50).   (With S. Frankel.)   Phys. Rev., **79,** 243 (1950).   (XIII,7)

Sturm, W. J. (47).   Phys. Rev., **71,** 757 (1947).   (IX,2)

――― See also Fermi, E. (47b).

Suess, H. E. (52).   (With J. H. D. Jensen.)   M. Siegbahn Anniversary Volume,
Stockholm, 1952, p. 589.   (XIV,1)

――― See also Haxel, O. (49).

Sun, K. H.   See Shoupp, W. E. (49).

Sunyar, A. W. (49).   (With M. Goldhaber.)   Phys. Rev., **76,** 189 (1949)
(IX,2)

――― See also Goldhaber, M. (51).

Sutton, R. B. (47).   (With T. Hall, E. E. Anderson, H. S. Bridge, J. W. De Wire,
L. S. Lavatelli, E. A. Long, T. Snyder, and R. W. Williams.)   Phys. Rev.,
72, 1147 (1947).   (II,3)

Svartholm, N. (45).   Thesis, Lund, 1945.   (V,2,3)

――― (48).   Arkiv. Mat., Astron. Fysik, **35A,** Nos. 7 and 8 (1948).   (V,2,3)

Talmi, I. (51).   Phys. Rev., **82,** 101 (1951) L.   (XIV,2)

Tangen, R.   See Broström, K. G. (47).

Taschek, R. F. (42).   Phys. Rev., **61,** 13 (1942).   (V,4)

――― (48).   (With A. Hemmendinger.)   Phys. Rev., **74,** 373 (1948).   (IX,5)

――― See also Barschall, H. H. (49a).

Taylor, H. M. (32).   (With N. F. Mott.)   Proc. Roy. Soc. (London), **A138,** 665
(1932).   (XII,5)

――― (33).   (With N. F. Mott.)   Proc. Roy. Soc. (London), **A142,** 215 (1933).
(XII,5)

――― See also Fisk, J. B. (34a); Hulme, H. R. (36).

Taylor, T. B.   See Fernbach, S. (49).

Teichmann, T. (49).   Thesis, Princeton University, 1949.   (IX,2), (X,4)

――― (50).   Phys. Rev., **77,** 506 (1950).   (X,4)

Teller, E.   See Critchfield, C. L. (41); Gamow, G. (36); Goldhaber, M. (48);
Hafstad, L. R. (38); Konopinski, E. J. (48): Schwinger, J. S. (37a); Seeger,
R. J. (42).

Tendham, D. J. (47). (With H. L. Bradt.) Phys. Rev., **72,** 1118 (1947). (IX,3)

Thaxton, H. M. See Breit, G. (39), (39a).

Thellung, A. (48). (With F. Villars.) Phys. Rev., **73,** 924 (1948). (I,7)

Thew, K. See Way, K. (50).

Thomas, G. E. See Harris, S. P. (50).

Thomas, L. H. (35). Phys. Rev., **47,** 903 (1935). (V,1)

Thomas, R. (40). Phys. Rev., **58,** 714 (1940). (XII,5)

Thomas, R. G. (50). Phys. Rev., **80,** 138 (1950) A. (VII,3), (XII,6)

——— (51). Phys. Rev., **81,** 148 (1951) L. (VIII,7,8)

——— (51a). Private communication (1951). (XII,6)

——— See also Lauritsen, T. (50).

Thomson, J. J. (13). *Rays of Positive Electricity*, Longmans, Green, 1913. (I,1)

Tiomno, J. (49). (With J. A. Wheeler.) Revs. Mod. Phys., **21,** 144 (1949). (XIII,5)

——— See also Yang, C. N. (50).

Tittman, J. (50). (With C. Sheer, L. J. Rainwater, and W. W. Havens, Jr.) Phys. Rev., **80,** 903 (1950) L. (IX,2)

Tobin, N. See Camerini, U. (49).

Tolansky, S. (39). Proc. Roy. Soc. (London), **A170,** 205 (1939). (I,7)

Tolhoek, H. A. See de Groot, S. R. (50).

Tollestrup, A. V. (50). (With W. A. Fowler and C. C. Lauritsen.) Phys. Rev., **78,** 372 (1950). (I,3), (II,2), (V,2,4)

——— See also Chao, C. Y. (50).

Tomkins, F. S. See Dieke, G. H. (49).

Toms, M. E. (51). (With W. E. Stephens.) Phys. Rev., **82,** 709 (1951). (XII,7)

Toraldo di Francia, G. (50). Phys. Rev., **78,** 298 (1950) L. (II,3)

Touschek, B. F. See Sneddon, I. N. (48).

Townes, C. H. (47). Phys. Rev., **71,** 909 (1947). (I,7)

——— (49). (With H. M. Foley and W. Low.) Phys. Rev., **76,** 1415 (1949). (XIV,2)

——— (49a). (With L. C. Aamodt.) Phys. Rev., **76,** 691 (1949) L. (XIII,7)

——— See also Geschwind, S. (51); Gunther-Mohr, G. R. (51); Longmire, C. (49a); Low, W. (50).

Trabbacchi, G. See Amaldi, E. (42), (46).

Tralli, N. See Lowen, I. S. (49).

Trigg, G. See Feenberg, E. (50).

Tyler, A. W. (39). Phys. Rev., **56,** 125 (1939). (XIII,2)

Tyrrell, W. A., Jr. (39). (With K. G. Carroll and H. Margenau.) Phys. Rev., **55,** 790 (1939) L. (VII,3)

——— (39a). Phys. Rev., **56,** 250 (1939). (VII,3)

——— See also Margenau, H. (38).

Uhlenbeck, G. E. See Falkoff, D. L. (50), (50a); Hebb, M. H. (38); Konopinski, B. J. (35), (41); Rose, M. E. (35); Van Lier, C. (37).

Ulrich, A. J. See Borst, L. M. (46).

Van Atta, L. C. See Myers, F. E. (42).

Van Lier, C. (37). (With G. E. Uhlenbeck.) Physica, **4,** 531 (1937). (VIII,6)

Van Patter, D. M. (51). (With A. Sperduto, K. Huang, E. N. Strait, and W. W. Buechner.) Phys. Rev., **81,** 233 (1951). (VII,3)

Villars, F. (47).   Helv. Phys. Acta, **20,** 476 (1947).   (I,7), (VI,5)
———— See also Thellung, A. (48).
Volkoff, G. M. (40).   Phys. Rev., **57,** 866 (1940).   (IX,6).
———— (42).   Phys. Rev., **62,** 126 (1942).   (III,4)
———— (42a).   Phys. Rev., **62,** 134 (1942).   (III,4)
Wäffler, H. (48).   (With O. Hirzel.)   Helv. Phys. Acta, **21,** 200 (1948).
   (XII,7)
———— See also Hirzel, O. (47).
Waggoner, M. A. (50).   (With M. L. Moon and A. Roberts.)   Phys. Rev., **80,**
   420 (1950).   (XII,5)
———— (50a).   Phys. Rev., **80,** 489 (1950) L.   (XII,6)
Wagner, F., Jr.   See Freedman, M. S. (50).
Walker, R. L. (49).   Phys. Rev., **76,** 244 (1949).   (IX,5)
———— (50).   (With B. D. McDaniel, and M. B. Stearns.)   Phys. Rev., **79,** 242
   (1950) A.   (XII,7)
Walker, W. H.   See Kinsey, B. B. (50).
Wallace, J. R.   See Blair, J. M. (50).
Wallace, P. R. (51).   Phys. Rev., **82,** 297 (1951) A.
Wallace, R. (51a).   Phys. Rev., **81,** 493 (1951).   (IV,3)
Walter, M. (50).   (With O. Huber and W. Zünti.)   Helv. Phys. Acta, **23,** 697
   (1950).   (XII,6)
Warren, D. T.   See Margenau, H. (37).
Warshaw, S. D. (50).   Phys. Rev., **80,** 111 (1950) L.   (XIII,6)
Watanabe, S. (39).   Z. Physik, **112,** 159 (1939); Z. Physik, **113,** 482 (1939).
   (VII,3)
Watson, G. N.   See Whittaker, E. T. (50).
Watt, B. E.   See Bennett, W. E. (41).
Wattenberg, A.   See Hamermesh, B. (49).
Way, K. (36).   (With J. A. Wheeler.)   Phys. Rev., **50,** 675 (1936) L.   (III,3)
———— (37).   Phys. Rev., **51,** 552 (1937).   (XII,4)
———— (39).   Phys. Rev., **56,** 556 (1939).   (VII,4)
———— (48).   (With E. P. Wigner.)   Phys. Rev., **73,** 1318 (1948).   (VI,2)
———— (49).   Phys. Rev., **75,** 1448 (1949) L.   (XIV,1)
———— (50).   (With L. Fano, M. Scott, and K. Thew.)   "Nuclear Data," Natl.
   Bur. Standards (U.S.) Circ. 499, Sept. 1, 1950.   (XII,6)
Wefelmeier, W. (37).   Naturwiss., **25,** 525 (1937) L.   (VII,4)
———— (37a).   Z. Physik, **107,** 332 (1937).   (VII,4)
Weinstock, R. (44).   Phys. Rev., **65,** 1 (1944).   (II,3)
Weisskopf, V. F. (37).   Phys. Rev., **52,** 295 (1937).   (VIII,3,6)
———— (40).   (With D. H. Ewing.)   Phys. Rev., **57,** 472, 935 (1940).
   (VIII,3,6)
———— (41).   Phys. Rev., **59,** 318 (1941).   (XII,7)
———— (50).   Helv. Phys. Acta, **23,** 187 (1950).   (VIII,7), (XIV,3)
———— (51).   Science, **113,** 101 (1951).   (XIV,3)
———— See also Feshbach, H. (47), (49a).
Weizsäcker, C. F. von (35).   Z. Physik, **96,** 431 (1935).   (VI,2)
———— (36).   Naturwiss., **24,** 813 (1936).   (XII,6).
———— (38).   Naturwiss., **26,** 209, 225 (1938).   (VII,4)
———— (39).   Naturwiss., **27,** 133 (1939).   (VII,5)
Welles, S. B. (42).   Phys. Rev., **62,** 197 (1942).   (VII,3), (XIV,2)

Wergeland, H. (41). Skrifter Norske Videnskaps-Akad. Oslo, No. 1 (1941). (VII,4)

Weyl, H. (31). *The Theory of Groups and Quantum Mechanics*, London, 1931. (VI,3)

Wheeler, J. A. (36). Phys. Rev., **50**, 643 (1936). (III,3), (IV,1)

—— (37). Phys. Rev., **52**, 1083 (1937). (V,4), (VII,4)

—— (37a). Phys. Rev., **52**, 1107 (1937). (VII,4), (X,1)

—— (41). Phys. Rev., **59**, 16 (1941). (VII,4), (IX,3,5)

—— (41a). Phys. Rev., **59**, 27 (1941). (VII,4), (IX,3,5)

—— See also Bohr, N. (39); Tiomno, J. (49); Way, K. (36); Yost, F. L. (35), (36).

White, M. G. See Barkas, W. H. (39); Sherr, R. (49).

Whitehead, W. D. Jr. See Heydenburg, N. P. (48).

Whittaker, E. T. (50). (With G. N. Watson.) *Modern Analysis*, Cambridge University Press, 1950. (A,3)

Wicher, E. R. (36). J. Terr. Mag., **41**, 389 (1936). (VIII,2)

Wick, G. C. (34). Nuovo cimento, **11**, 227 (1934). (VI,2)

—— (37). Physik. Z., **38**, 403 (1937). (II,3)

Wiegand, C. See Chamberlain, O. (50), (51); Hadley, J. (49); Kelly, E. L. (50); Segrè, E. (49); Leininger, R. F. (49).

Wigner, E. P. (27). Göttinger Nachrichten 375 (1927). (I,7), (VIII,10), (X,3)

—— (31). *Gruppentheorie*, F. Vieweg and Son, Braunschweig, 1931; reprint: Edward Brothers, Ann Arbor, Michigan, 1944. (X,3), (A,1)

—— (32). Göttinger Nachrichten **31**, 546 (1932). (X,2), (XIII,5)

—— (33). (With F. Seitz.) Phys. Rev., **43**, 804 (1933). (III,3)

—— (33a). Phys. Rev., **43**, 252 (1933). (I,1), (II,1,2), (III,3), (V,1)

—— (33b). Z. Physik., **83**, 253 (1933). (I,1), (II,1), (III,3)

—— (34). Phys. Rev., **46**, 1002 (1934). (VII,3)

—— (36). Proc. Natl. Acad. Sci., **22**, 662 (1936). (III,4)

—— (37). Phys. Rev., **51**, 106 (1937). (VI,3,6)

—— (37a). Phys. Rev., **51**, 947 (1937). (VI,3,4,5), (VII,2)

—— (38). Trans Faraday Soc., **34**, 678 (1938). (VII,3)

—— (39). Phys. Rev., **56**, 519 (1939). (XIII,6)

—— (40). Bicentennial Symposium, University of Pennsylvania, 1940. (VII,2)

—— (41). (With E. Feenberg.) Reports on Progress in Physics, The Physical Society, London, **8**, 274 (1941). (VI,6)

—— (46). Proc. Natl. Acad. Sci., **32**, 302 (1946). (X,2,4)

—— (46a). Phys. Rev., **70**, 606 (1946). (X,4)

—— (46b). Phys. Rev., **70**, 15 (1946). (X,4)

—— (47). (With L. Eisenbud.) Phys. Rev., **72**, 29 (1947). (VIII,10), (X,1,2,4)

—— (48). Phys, Rev., **73**, 1002 (1948). (VIII,7), (X,4)

—— (49). Am. J. Phys., **17**, 99 (1949). (X,4)

—— (51). Proc. Cambridge Phil. Soc., **47**, 790 (1951). (VIII,2,7), (X,4)

—— See also Breit, G. (35), (36b), (38); Critchfield, L. (41a); Eisenbud, L. (41); Feenberg, E., (37b); Feingold, A. M. (50); Margenau, H. (40a); Way, K. (48).

Wilkinson, D. H. See Barnes, C. A. (50); Carver, J. H. (51).

Williams, J. H. See Bailey, C. D. (46); Lampi, E. E. (50).

Williams, R. W. See Sutton, R. B. (47).

Wilson, A. R. W.   See Rose, B. (50).
Wilson, R. (49).   (With C. H. Collie and H. Halban.)   Nature, **163,** 245 (1949). (XII,4)
―――― See also Bishop, G. R. (50), (51).
Wolfenstein, L. (48).   (With R. G. Sachs.)   Phys. Rev., **73,** 528 (1948). (X,3)
―――― (49).   Phys. Rev., **76,** 541 (1949); **75,** 1664 (1949).   (II,3)
―――― (51).   Phys. Rev., **82,** 690 (1951).   (X,3)
Wollan, E. O. (48).   (With C. G. Shull.)   Phys. Rev., **73,** 830 (1948).   (II,3)
―――― See also Shull, C. G. (48).
Woodward, W. M. (49).   (With I. Halpern.)   Phys. Rev., **76,** 107 (1949). (XII,4)
Wright, B. T. (47).   Phys. Rev., **71,** 839 (1947).   (XIII,3)
Wu, C. S. (47).   (With L. J. Rainwater and W. W. Havens.)   Phys. Rev., **71,** 174 (1947).   (IX,2)
―――― (49).   (With L. Feldman.)   Phys. Rev., **76,** 693 (1949) L.   (XIII,7)
―――― (50).   Revs. Mod. Phys., **22,** 386 (1950).   (XIII,7)
―――― (51).   (With L. Feldman.)   Phys. Rev., **82,** 457 (1951) L.   (XIII,7)
―――― (51a).   (With L. Feldman.)   Phys. Rev., **82,** 332 (1951) A.   (XIII,7)
―――― See also Albert, R. D. (48); Havens, W. W. (47); Longmire, C. (49a); Macklin, P. A. (51); Rainwater, L. J. (47).
Wu, T. (48).   Phys. Rev., **73,** 934, 1132 (1948).   (IV,1)
―――― See also Ashkin, J. (48).
Yadav, H. N.   See Burhop, E. H. S. (48).
Yamaguchi, Y. (51).   Prog. Theor. Phys., **6,** 443 (1951) L.   (XII,5)
Yang, C. N. (48).   Phys. Rev., **74,** 764 (1948).   (X,3), (XII,6), (XIII,7)
―――― (50).   (With J. Tiomno.)   Phys. Rev., **79,** 495 (1950).   (XIII,2,5)
―――― See also Lee, T. D. (49).
York, H.   See Hadley, J. (49).
Yost, F. L. (35).   (With J. A. Wheeler and G. Breit.)   J. Terr. Mag., **40,** 443 (1935).   (VIII,2)
―――― (36).   (With J. A. Wheeler and G. Breit.)   Phys. Rev., **49,** 174 (1936). (II,4), (VIII,2)
―――― See also Breit, G. (35a); Nordheim, L. W. (37).
Young, G. (39).   Phys. Rev., **55,** 1102 (1939) L.   (VII,5)
Yovits, M. C.   See Breit, G. (51).
Yu, F. C.   See Proctor, W. G. (51).
Yukawa, H. (35).   (With S. Sakata.)   Proc. Phys.-Mat. Soc. Japan, **17,** 397 (1935).   (XII,5)
―――― (35a).   Proc. Phys.-Mat. Soc. Japan, **17,** 48 (1935).   (XIII,3)
―――― (37).   (With S. Sakata.)   Proc. Phys.-Mat. Soc. Japan, **19,** 542 (1937). (V,4)
Zabel, C. W.   See Davis, L., Jr. (48).
Zacharias, J. R.   See Davis, L., Jr. (48), (49); Kellogg, J. M. B. (36), (39), (40).
Zahn, C. T. (37).   (With A. H. Spees.)   Phys. Rev., **62,** 524 (1937).   (XIII,1)
―――― (38).   (With A. H. Spees.)   Phys. Rev., **53,** 357, 365 (1938).   (XIII,1)
Zeldes, H. (50).   (With B. H. Ketelle and A. R. Brosi.)   Phys. Rev., **79,** 901 (1950) L.   (XIII,7)
Zilsel, P. R.   See Breit, G. (47b).
Zinnes, I. (50).   Phys. Rev., **80,** 386 (1950).   (XII,6)
Zünti, W.   See Frauenfelder, H. (50); Huber, O. (51); Walter, M. (50).

INDEX

Page numbers in italics indicate pages in which the subject is discussed in detail.